Gloria

MORNINGTON.
Glory be to the Father, and to the Son,
and to the Ho - ly Ghost;
As it was in the beginning
is now, and
ev - er shall be:
world with - out end. A - men.

D1438754

THE

METHODIST HYMN-BOOK

WITH TUNES

THE

METHODIST HYMN-BOOK

WITH TUNES

'Speaking one to another in psalms and hymns and spiritual songs, singing and making melody with your heart to the Lord'

LONDON

METHODIST CONFERENCE OFFICE

35th Edition, 1972

Made and printed in Great Britain by The Garden City Press Limited,
Letchworth, Hertfordshire SG6 1JS

PREFACE

METHODISM was born in song. Charles Wesley wrote the first hymns of the Evangelical Revival during the great Whitsuntide of 1738 when his brother and he were " filled with the Spirit," and from that time onwards the Methodists have never ceased to sing. Their characteristic poet is still Charles Wesley. While for half a century hymns poured continually from his pen on almost every subject within the compass of Christianity, and while no part of the New Testament escaped him, most of all he sang the " gospel according to St. Paul." He is the poet of the Evangelical faith. In consequence Methodism has always been able to sing its creed.

At the time of the consummation of Methodist Union it is appropriate to recall the principal hymn-books of our past. Wesley's first collection was made in Georgia in 1737. Of the many other hymn-books issued during his life-time the chief were the so-called " Morning Hymn-Book " of 1741, which sold for the small sum of a shilling, the " Hymns and Spiritual Songs, intended for the use of real Christians of all Denominations," which was published in 1753, and the " Large Hymn-Book " of 1780, which was Wesley's own definitive edition. The Wesleyan Methodists continued to use this book for almost a century, with some additions, particularly in 1831. In 1875 the collection was revised and a large Supplement added. Finally, in 1904, a hymn-book was issued which, while thoroughly Methodist in tone, drew upon many new sources and followed a quite new arrangement.

In the first years of Primitive Methodism a small book was used whose hymns struck a characteristically evangelistic note. In 1825 Hugh Bourne drew up a new hymn-book to which the earlier collection was added, and this " Large Hymn-Book " served the Primitive Methodist Church for almost thirty years. In 1854 the Rev. John Flesher edited a much improved book, which was used till 1886, when a new collection was made. To this a large Supplement was added in 1912.

Of the three branches of Methodism that drew together to form the United Methodist Church in 1907, the Methodist New Connexion used Wesley's book of 1780, with supplements, till 1834, when a new book was prepared which followed the old model. This was superseded in 1864 by " Hymns for Divine Worship." Representatives of the Methodist New Connexion collaborated with the Wesleyans in the production of the hymn-book of 1904, and this is one of the hymn-books used in the United Methodist Church until to-day.

The original Bible Christian Hymn-book was enlarged in 1838, slightly altered in 1862, and reached its present form in 1889. Hymn-books for the use of the United Methodist Free Churches were issued in 1860 and 1889, the latter including a selection of Psalms and Canticles.

In all the books of the several churches the classical hymns of the Methodist Revival stood side by side with hymns suited to the needs of their own day. Recent years have brought a growing demand for a book that should serve this generation in the same way. In 1929, therefore, the Conferences of the three Churches that were contemplating Union appointed a joint Committee to undertake the work. Its labours have been shared by representatives of the Wesleyan Reform Union, and a Committee in Australia has sent suggestions. The blessing of God which has rested on the sessions is, the Committee trusts, a prophecy of a wider and deeper blessing that the book will bring to all the churches of Methodism.

This hymn-book is issued for the use of *all* British Methodists, and for not a few Methodists "beyond the seas" as well. It is the first such book since Wesley's final collection of a hundred and fifty years ago. Its publication, therefore, may rightly be called an historic event in Methodism. Wesley's historic preface for its predecessor of 1780 is appended in full.

This collection, like that of 1780, is primarily evangelical. It contains a large number of hymns which have proved their power both to deepen the spiritual life of believers and to inspire saving faith in Christ. Among their writers Charles Wesley holds a dominant place. The claims of poetry have always been in mind, but those of religion have been paramount, and not a few hymns have been selected chiefly because they are dear to the people of God. For the one aim of every true hymn-book must be to "raise or quicken the spirit of devotion."

Yet while the present book is a lineal descendant of Wesley's collection, it differs from it both in arrangement and contents. Most of the differences have the same origin—the collection of 1780 was meant to serve a movement, this to serve a church. The earlier book set apart no hymns for the Sacraments, or for the great Seasons of the Christian Year—Christmas, Passion-tide, Easter, Pentecost; this book gives them a large place. Again, almost all the hymns in Wesley's book were written at the time, specially to serve the Evangelical Revival; here hymns are gathered from every age of the Church, from the Psalms of the Old Testament and the Canticles of the first Christian century to the hymns of to-day. In other words, while this hymn-book is distinctively Methodist, it is also catholic, in the true sense of that word.

In order to keep the collection within due limits a number of excellent hymns have been omitted because others are included which better express the same truths. In some instances careful editorial emendations have been made in order to restore a hymn to general use.

The selection of Psalms will be a great enrichment of public worship and the system of chanting adopted will be found both simple and effective.

In this collection there is not only a Section devoted to "Children," but in every appropriate part of the book hymns have been included for the young. These are indicated by a mark in the General Index. They have been distributed in this way both because the greatest hymns appeal to young and old alike and because it is well that the young should learn the range of the Christian life.

This hymn-book, like its predecessors, is intended for use in private devotion as well as in public worship. A few hymns have therefore been included that are especially suitable for select gatherings or for solitary communion with God. Most good hymns, however, may be used either in public or private worship, and it is confidently hoped that this book will enrich both.

In the manifold ministries of Divine worship, song is specifically the people's part, and in Methodism, in particular, the whole congregation has always been called to sing the hymns. We hope that none of our people will consent to be cut off from any part of their heritage of song. In many a hymn that may not at first attract, they will find "hid treasure" if only they will seek it.

Watts's great hymn, "I'll praise my Maker while I've breath," has found a place in every Methodist hymn-book since 1737. It was on Wesley's lips as he lay dying, and its message is one of the heirlooms of Methodism. St. Augustine described a hymn as "a song with praise of God." To praise God is the high calling of man. A hymn is only a hymn if in it men speak to the Most High and He to them. May every hymn in this book be sung always and only to the glory of God

LONDON,
December, 1933.

PREFACE TO

A COLLECTION OF HYMNS

FOR USE OF THE PEOPLE CALLED METHODISTS

For many years I have been importuned to publish such a Hymn Book as might be used in all our Congregations throughout Great Britain and Ireland. I have hitherto withstood the importunity, as I believed such a Publication was needless, considering the various Hymn Books which my Brother and I have published within these forty years last past; so that it may be doubted whether any religious Community in the world has a greater variety of them.

But it has been answered, "Such a publication is highly needful upon this very account; for the greater part of the people, being poor, are not able to purchase so many books: and those that have purchased them are, as it were, bewildered in the immense variety. A proper Collection of Hymns for general use, carefully made out of all these books, is therefore still wanting; and one comprised in so moderate a compass, as to be neither cumbersome nor expensive."

It has been replied, "You have such a collection already (entitled 'Hymns and Spiritual Songs,') which I extracted several years ago from a variety of Hymn Books." But it is objected, "This is in the other extreme; it is far too small. It does not, it cannot, in so narrow a compass, contain variety enough; not so much as we want, among whom singing makes so considerable a part of the public service. What we want is, a Collection not too large, that it may be cheap and portable; nor too small, that it may contain a sufficient variety for all ordinary occasions."

Such a Hymn Book you have now before you. It is not so large as to be either cumbersome, or expensive: and it is large enough to contain such a variety of hymns as will not soon be worn threadbare. It is large enough to contain all the important truths of our most holy religion, whether speculative or practical; yea, to illustrate them all, and to prove them both by Scripture and reason: and this is done in a regular order. The hymns are not carelessly jumbled together, but carefully ranged under proper heads, according to the experience of real Christians. So that this book is, in effect, a little body of experimental and practical divinity.

As but a small part of these hymns is of my own composing, I do not think it inconsistent with modesty to declare, that I am persuaded no such Hymn Book as this has yet been published in the English language. In what other publication of the kind have you so distinct and full an account of scriptural Christianity: such a declaration of the heights and depths of religion, speculative and practical: so strong cautions against the most plausible Errors; particularly those that are now most prevalent? and so clear directions for making your calling and election sure; for perfecting holiness in the fear of God?

May I be permitted to add a few words with regard to the *poetry?* Then I will speak to those who are judges thereof, with all freedom and unreserve.

To these I may say, without offence, 1. In these hymns there is no doggerel; no botches; nothing put in to patch up the rhyme; no feeble expletives. 2. Here is nothing turgid or bombast, on the one hand, or low and creeping on the other. 3. Here are no *cant* expressions, no words without meaning. Those who impute this to us know not what they say. We talk common sense, both in prose and verse, and use no word but in a fixed and determinate sense. 4. Here are, allow me to say, both the purity, the strength, and the elegance of the English language; and, at the same time, the utmost simplicity and plainness, suited to every capacity. Lastly, I desire men of taste to judge, (these are the only competent judges), whether there be not in some of the following hymns the true Spirit of Poetry, such as cannot be acquired by art and labour, but must be the gift of nature. By labour a man may become a tolerable imitator of Spenser, Shakespeare, or Milton; and may heap together pretty compound epithets, as *pale-eyed*, *meek-eyed*, and the like; but unless he be *born* a Poet, he will never attain the genuine spirit of Poetry.

And here I beg leave to mention a thought which has been long upon my mind, and which I should long ago have inserted in the public papers, had I not been unwilling to stir up a nest of hornets. Many Gentlemen have done my Brother and me (though without naming us) the honour to reprint many of our hymns. Now they are perfectly welcome so to do, provided they print them just as they are. But I desire they would not attempt to mend them—for they really are not able. None of them is able to mend either the sense or the verse. Therefore, I must beg of them one of these two favours: either to let them stand just as they are, to take them for better for worse; or to add the true reading in the margin, or at the bottom of the page; that we may no longer be accountable either for the nonsense or for the doggerel of other men.

But to return. That which is of infinitely more moment than the Spirit of Poetry, is the spirit of piety. And I trust, all persons of real judgment will find *this* breathing through the whole Collection. It is in this view chiefly that I would recommend it to every truly pious Reader, as a means of raising or quickening the spirit of devotion, of confirming his faith; of enlivening his hope; and of kindling and increasing his love to God and man. When Poetry thus keeps its place, as the handmaid of Piety, it shall attain, not a poor perishable wreath, but a crown that fadeth not away.

London, Oct. 20, 1779. JOHN WESLEY.

ACKNOWLEDGMENTS

Permission to insert hymns has been granted by authors, publishers, and present owners of copyright according to the following list. In a few instances it has not been possible to trace ownership. If for this reason, or through inadvertence, rights still surviving have been overlooked, it is hoped that such failure may be condoned.

Special acknowledgments are due to writers, or their representatives, who have generously placed hymns at the disposal of the committee. A blank in the second column indicates that the author is also the owner of the copyright. An asterisk denotes that permission has been obtained on payment of a fee.

AUTHOR	OWNER OF COPYRIGHT	NO. OF HYMN
Ainger, A. C.	*S.P.C.K.	812
	*Messrs. Novello & Co.	887
Alexander, Mrs. C. F.	Miss E. Alexander	392
Armitage, Mrs. E. S.	Mrs. F. P. Wilson	843

AUTHOR	OWNER OF COPYRIGHT	NO. OF HYMN
Baring-Gould, S.	*Messrs. A. W. Ridley & Co.	616, 822, 944
Batey, James R.	....	687
Bax, Clifford	*Mr. A. D. Peters	912
Benson, A. C.	*Messrs. Novello & Co.	965
Betham-Edwards, M. B.	*The Misses Horder	845
Bickersteth, Bishop ..	Messrs. Longmans Green & Co., Ltd.	501, 754, 958
Blatchford, A. N.	*Messrs. Reid Bros., Ltd.	971
Blunt, A. G. W.	Mr. R. Blunt	972
Bonar, Horatius	Miss E. M. Bonar	444
Bourne, G. H.........	Mr. A. C. Bourne Webb	731
Bowie, W. Russell ...	Dean of Liverpool	906
Brailsford, E. J.	Miss H. N. Brailsford	852
Bridges, R. S.	*Mrs. Bridges and the Oxford University Press from *The Yattendon Hymnal*	45, 70, 177, 419, 493, 882, 932, 936
Briggs, G. W.	*Oxford University Press from *Enlarged Songs of Praise*	840
	The Headmaster of Loughborough Grammar School and the Headmistress of Loughborough High School from *Songs of Praise*......	979
Bright, W.............	TheWarden of Keble College, Oxford	759, 933
Brooke, Stopford A. ..	Miss H. Brooke	123, 147, 166
Budry, E. L.	....	213
Burke, C.	The Mothers' Union	397
Burton, Henry	The Family	253, 256, 888
Butler, H. M.	Messrs. Gard, Lyell & Co.	686
Butler, Mary	*National Sunday School Union	850
Callin, R. W.	Methodist Conference	587
Carpenter, W. Boyd ..	Mrs. M. Wentworth-Shields for Executors	884
Chatfield, A. W.	Rev. J. Kyrle Chatfield	239
Codner, Mrs. E.	Mr. Trevor L. C. Wood	321
Collins, H.	The Right Rev. D. C. O'Connell ...	438
Coster, G. T.	Mr. V. B. Coster	266, 891
Cousin, Mrs. A. R. ...	Messrs. Auld & Macdonald	637
Cushing, W. O.	*Messrs. Marshall, Morgan & Scott, Ltd.	499
Dearmer, P.	*Oxford University Press from *Enlarged Songs of Praise*	279, 864
	*Oxford University Press from *The English Hymnal*	894
Dodgshun, E.	....	897
Draper, W. H.	*Messrs. J. Curwen & Sons, Ltd.	28
East, James T.	Methodist Conference	862
Ellerton, J.	Oxford University Press	189, 667, 671, 776, 782, 949, 975, 976
Farningham, M.	*Messrs. James Clarke & Co., Ltd. .	394
Felkin, Mrs..........	....	967
Fletcher, F.	Mr. F. Fletcher and Oxford University Press	241
Fullerton, W. Y.	....	809
Gabriel, C. H.	*Charles M. Alexander Copyrights Trust	336
Gill, T. H.	Mr. E. W. B. Gill	55, 71, 396, 409, 694
Gill, W. H.	*Messrs. W. H. Boosey & Co.	970
Gray, H. B...........	Miss Selina Gray	869
Greenaway, Ada R. ..	*Proprietors of *Hymns Ancient and Modern*	240
Greenwell, Dora	Messrs. H. R. Allenson, Ltd........	259, 381
Gregory, G. Osborn ..	....	757
Gurney, Mrs. D. F. ..	*Oxford University Press from *The English Hymnal*	777
Hankey, Katherine ...	Miss A. E. Rashdall	161
Hatch, Edwin	Miss B. Hatch	300, 623
Hawkins, Hester P. ..	Mr. L. M. Hawkins	614
Hensley, L.	Miss Lucy Hensley and Oxford University Press	811
Holland, H. Scott	*Oxford University Press from *The English Hymnal*	883
Hopps, J. P.	*National Sunday School Union	810, 849
Horne, C. S.	The Hon. Mrs. K. N. Horne	116, 715
Hosmer, F. L.........	*The Beacon Press from *The Hymn and Tunebook*	742, 980

AUTHOR	OWNER OF COPYRIGHT	NO. OF HYMN
Housman, L.	*Oxford University Press from *The English Hymnal*	136
How, Bishop	Mr. F. D. How	164, 209, 303, **673, 854** 886, 923
Hoyle, R. B.		213
Hull, Miss E. H., D.Litt.		632
Hunter, J.	Rev. Canon L. S. Hunter	163
Irons, Miss G. M.		345
Jenkins, W. V.	Rev. F. C. Vaughan Jenkins and Miss G. Vaughan Jenkins	577, **688, 774**
Jones, Miss E.		915
Julian, J.	Trustees per Mr. W. H. Hortin	**740**
Kipling, Rudyard	Messrs. Methuen & Co., Ltd., from *The Five Nations*, and the Author	**889**
	Messrs. Macmillan & Co., Ltd., from *Puck of Pook's Hill* and the Author	**899**
Lewis, H. Elvet		753
Luke, Mrs. J.	*National Sunday School Union	865
Macalister, Edith F. B.	*National Sunday School Union	847
MacDonald, George	Dr. Grevil e MacDonald	739, **930**
Maclagan, W. D.		825
Macnicol, N.		159
Mathams, Walter J.	Mr. Hamish H. Mathams	252, **841**
Matheson, Annie		795
	*National Sunday School Union	846
Matheson, G.	*Messrs. Novello & Co.	448
	Messrs. McClure, Naismith, Brodie & Co., for Miss Jane G. Matheson's Trust	596, 935
Mathews, B. J.		798
Matson, W. Tidd	Miss Mabel M. Matson	373, **529**
Maude, Mary F.	Miss Mary Maude	569
Merrill, W. P.	Mr. W. P. Merrill and Oxford University Press	585
Midlane, Albert	Mrs. M. E. Mill	738
	*Messrs. Reid Bros., Ltd.	839
Monod, Theodore	*Messrs. Marshall, Morgan & Scott, Ltd.	170
Moule, H. C. G.	Trustees, Bishop Moule, deceased	472, **868**
Mudie, C. E.	Miss M. Mudie	416, **451**
Myers, F. W. H.	Messrs. Macmillan & Co., Ltd.	254
Noble, James A.	*Mr. E. L. Ashcroft-Noble	**941**
Olivant, Mary R.		537
Owen, Frances M.	Mr. A. S. Owen	398
Owens, Priscilla J.	*Messrs. Marshall, Morgan & Scott, Ltd.	**634**
Parker, W. H.	*National Sunday School Union	286, **858**
Penstone, Maria M.	Mr. R. Holland	857
Piggott, W. Charter		657
Pollock, T. B.	*Rev. Dudley Clark	175, 295, **727, 741**
Pott, F.	Miss Mary F. Pott	165, 668
Rawley, F. H.	*Messrs. Marshall, Morgan & Scott, Ltd.	380
Rossetti, Miss C. G.	Messrs. Macmillan & Co., Ltd., from *Poetical Works of Christina Rossetti*	137
	*S.P.C.K.	94, 138, 435, 893
Shillito, Edward		231
Shuttleworth, H. C.	Oxford University Press	982
Skrine, John H.	Mrs. Inez E. A. Walker	593
Smith, W. Chalmers	Mr. William Galbraith and the Oxford University Press	34
Spring-Rice, Cecil	*Mr. John Murray	900
Stephenson, T. B.	National Children's Home	786
Stevenson, Miss I. S.	Oxford University Press	916
Stock, Miss S. G.	Church Missionary Society	796, **806**
Stone, S. J.	Rev. W. G. Boyd	827, **922**
Studdert-Kennedy, G.A.	*Messrs. Hodder & Stoughton, Ltd.	588
Symonds, J. A.	*Mr. John Murray	910
Tarrant, W. G.	Mrs. W. G. Tarrant	**896**
Tennyson, Alfred	Messrs. Macmillan & Co., Ltd., from *Lord Tennyson's Works*	**640**

AUTHOR	OWNER OF COPYRIGHT	NO. OF HYMN
Thring, Godfrey	*Leonard G. P. Thring	133, 271, 728, 920, 940
Van Dyke, H.	*Charles Scribner's Sons	601
Vine, A. H.	Miss Vine	285
Walker, Vera E.		819
Walmsley, Robert	Miss G. Walmsley	314
Waring, Miss A. L.	*S.P.C.K.	473, 528, 602
Waugh, Benjamin	*The Misses Horder	450
Wills, W. G.	Mrs. L. H. Wills	871

A system of metre-signatures has been introduced which shows at a glance not only the syllables but also the rhyming of the lines. For example: the three forms of metre known as "six lines eights" are expressed in the following manner, the figures indicating the number of feet, and the full-points the regularity and irregularity of the rhyming:

8 8.8 8.8 8 8.8.8.8.8 8. 8 8.8.D.

The Committee desires to place on record its very deep sense of appreciation of the services rendered by the Rev. F. Luke Wiseman, who presided over all the meetings. His unique knowledge of the Methodist Hymnology and Music, and of the Methodist People, his understanding of human nature, and his discerning and tactful handling of delicate questions, have been of inestimable service to the Committee.

LONDON,
***December*, 1933.**

PREFACE TO THE EDITION WITH TUNES

In the early days of Christianity believers spoke to one another in psalms and hymns and spiritual songs. When at Whitsuntide 1738 the Lord turned again the captivity of John and Charles Wesley so that their chains fell off and their heart was free, their mouth was filled with laughter and their tongue with singing. Their followers shared their experience. An observer in the 18th century might have written of them as Pliny wrote of the Christians of the second : " They meet at daybreak to sing an hymn to one Christ as God." Reflecting on the swift spread of the evangelical revival he might have added, concerning Wesley, what Cardinal Cajetan said of Luther : " He has conquered us by his songs."

But what were the people to sing ? Charles Wesley and Isaac Watts supplied in abundance matchless verse, but whence came the fitting melodies ? Watts, confining his songs almost entirely to the six Church metres, would find a tune to suit his words in the collections of Ravenscroft, Playford, Wilkins, and Chetham. But Charles Wesley's muse demanded greater variety of lyrical expression. John Wesley, therefore, was obliged to make his own compilation. In 1742 he made his first essay and published " A collection of Tunes, set to Music as they are commonly sung at the Foundery." This little book, of which only four copies are known to remain, contains forty-three tunes, unharmonized, in as many as twelve different metres. But while marking considerable advance in point of variety of metre and containing some striking melodies, this quaint collection still lacked tunes for several of Charles Welsey's characteristic metres.

In 1761 Wesley tried again, and published the famous " Hymns with Tunes Annext." To this compilation he writes a notable Preface not unworthy to stand beside the famous Preface to the 1780 Hymn-Book. After a laudatory reference to Butts' " Harmonia Sacra," which had been published a few years previously, as "exceeding beyond all degrees of comparison anything of the kind which has appeared in England before," he says that " it is not the thing which I want." He then proceeds in characteristic vein, " I want the people called *Methodists* to sing true, the tunes which are in *common use* among them. At the same time I want them to have in one volume, the *best Hymns* which we have printed: and that, in a *small* and *portable* volume, and one of an *easy price*. I have been endeavouring for more than twenty years to procure such a book as this. But in vain. Masters of music were above following any direction but their own. And I was determined, whoever compiled this, should follow *my* direction—not *mending* our tunes, but setting them down, neither better nor worse than they were. At length I have prevailed. The following collection contains all the tunes which are in *common use* among us. They are pricked *true*, exactly as I desire all our congregations may sing them. And here is prefixt to them a collection of those hymns which are (I think) some of *the best* we have published. The volume likewise *is small*, as well as the *price*. This, therefore, I recommend preferable to all others."

This tune book, which was called " Sacred Melody," contains seventy-six tunes so arranged that each of the one hundred and forty-nine " select hymns " has an appropriate tune. The tunes are given in melody only and are arranged in order of metre, of which there are twenty-three varieties. The hymns in the accompanying volume are grouped according to their metre and follow in the same order as the tune—a unique arrangement, showing what great importance Wesley attached to the tune. Comparison with " Harmonia Sacra " shows how readily imitation waits on admiration, and suggests that there must have been some working agreement with the publisher of the earlier collection. From "Sacred Melody" then we may learn the main sources of early Methodist song. Here we find some of the noble psalm tunes of the 16th and 17th centuries; strong German chorales learnt in intercourse with the Moravians and contained in Freylinghausen's "Gesangbuch" which Wesley brought back from Herrnhut; adaptations from the works of the great masters of music—Handel, T. A. Arne, and others; popular melodies old and new; and new tunes composed for the Wesleys chiefly by John Frederick Lampe.

Towards the end of the 18th century the popularity of singing led to the introduction of a large number of new tunes, varying in different parts of the country. These were for the most part in the lighter vein and more florid form in vogue at the time. With the avowed purpose of calling the people back to the more staid song of the earlier days, Charles Wesley, the talented musician, son of the poet, in 1821 brought out "Sacred Harmony," a revised edition of the "Sacred Harmony" of 1780, with figured bass accompaniment for harpsichord or organ. But this edition did not succeed in re-establishing the supremacy of the book. For the most part choirmasters preferred to make their own selection of tunes, providing manuscript copies for the choir. But the need for a standard tune book became more and more apparent, and in 1846 the Book Room issued the "Companion for the Wesleyan Hymn-Book"—a collection of tunes of considerable merit which was widely used and has, indeed, proved of service in compiling the present book. Other collections which may be mentioned are Booth's "Wesleyan Psalmist" which, emanating from Leeds, found much favour among the societies in the North of England, the "Westminster Tune Book," a collection of tunes of a severer type, and Samuel Sebastian Wesley's masterly "European Psalmody" which, however, did not see the light until 1872.

In 1876 the Wesleyan Conference published a new edition of the Hymn-Book with appropriate tunes, in which, for the first time since the 1761 Hymn-Book, each hymn had assigned its proper tune. This book continued to be used until 1904, when it was superseded by "The Methodist Hymn-Book with Tunes," the editor of the musical edition being Sir Frederick Bridge. On the selection committee were representatives of the United Methodist Church and also of the Wesleyan Reform Union, and this Book has been in use in many of the churches of these denominations.

Meanwhile the other branches of the Methodist Church had been equally assiduous in the cultivation of sacred song. In 1889 the Primitive Methodist Hymnal supplied that section of the Church with a wide selection of "Old and familiar melodies combined with the best modern tunes," and these received a notable addition in 1912 when a Supplement was issued so that village choirs as well as the singers in large towns might enjoy the more recent contributions to psalmody.

In 1884 the Annual Assembly of the Methodist Free Church resolved that a hymn and tune book should be prepared to replace an earlier publication of 1860 and to present their congregations with a careful selection of the psalmody of the day. The result of the committee's work appeared five years later, and since 1889 this edition has supplied the musical needs of that Church.

In anticipation of Methodist Union the Conferences of the three uniting Churches decided to appoint a representative Committee to prepare a book of tunes for the hymns selected by a similarly appointed Hymn-Book Committee. For over two years this Committee has been diligently engaged on its task. Its aim has been to provide a collection of tunes which, while giving appropriate expression to the sentiment of the several hymns, shall be true to the robust and simple Methodist spirit and thoroughly adapted for congregational singing.

For such purpose the great requisite is melody—a tune which however enriched by suitable harmony is nevertheless independent of it. A congregation is not a choral society; it is heard at its best when engaged in unison singing. Simple persuasive melody is therefore essential. To find it the Committee has conducted a wide search among tune books old and new, and has given careful examination to many hundreds of original compositions which have been submitted. It has culled many of the noble chorales of the churches of the Reformation. Following Wesley's example it has not hesitated to include some folk-songs as well as the grand old psalm tunes which are the foundation of British psalmody. As the lyrics of any period are likely to obtain their most natural musical expression in contemporary melodies, the Committee has given particular attention to tunes of the 18th and early 19th centuries. It has gladly availed itself also of the rich store of tunes of somewhat different idiom, by eminent modern composers, written specially for congregational use, which have a special attraction for the younger generation. For the same reason it has included several modal melodies based on the old ecclesiastical scales and has increased the number of tunes in the minor mode, though to nothing like the proportion in which they are found in early Methodist Tune-Books.

In assigning to each hymn its tune the Committee has sought for a melody well fitted in structure and emotional range to express the sentiment and prevailing mood of the hymn.

The selection of tunes for such a book as the present, however, cannot be determined on grounds of musical excellence alone. Considerations of traditional usage, historic interest, invariable association, exercise great weight. As far as possible the Committee has respected long association of hymn and tune. It should be remembered, however, that though a hymn has been found in all the hymnals of the uniting Churches, the tune to which it has been sung has rarely been identical. The gratification of one section, therefore, may involve the disappointment of the other two. But where the Committee has disturbed a prized alliance of words and music, it has usually been able to find another place in the book for the familiar melody, and by cross reference to make practicable the continuance of the old association. In the case of such tunes the Committee has asked: "Is it good of its kind?" In respect to evangelistic hymns, the Committee has considered that the inclusion of a popular hymn with chorus has determined, as a matter of course, the use of the familiar tune.

A few additional tunes have been appended which for various reasons were omitted from the body of the work. Among these will be found Sir Hubert Parry's sublime setting of Charles Wesley's last hymn.

As to the rendering of the tunes, the Committee after careful consideration decided not to insert expression marks. In congregational singing only broad effects of light and shade are possible. Moreover, there is no invariable standard of expression. The higher musical intelligence now prevalent will determine the manner of rendering most suitable to the sentiment and the occasion. Any attempt, again, to standardize the minim is to be deprecated. Every melody has its own tempo. In general it may be said that the chorales and psalm tunes are heard to best advantage when sung rather slowly. For the "Amen," a musical setting has been provided for every hymn to which the Hymn-Book Committee has appended it.

In the pointing of the psalms, the Committee has adopted the speech rhythm method as most effectively preserving the rhetorical flow of the words, and on the whole the easiest for a congregation to follow when once its principle is apprehended.

At the commencement of its task the Committee invited as its Musical Adviser Dr. Maurice L. Wostenholm, whose musical ability, intimate acquaintance with Methodist Psalmody and sympathy with its spirit peculiarly fitted him for the position. For more than a year he co-operated with the Committee and was in constant attendance at their meetings. Unhappily, however, a serious breakdown in health compelled his retirement, to the great regret of the Committee.

The Committee has been fortunate to secure the services of Dr. George F. Brockless, who likewise has had wide experience of Methodist service. The Committee is greatly indebted to him for deep interest shewn and valuable work done, which includes the pointing of the psalms. The selection of tunes is enriched by original compositions from both of its musical advisers.

The Committee desires to tender its thanks to all those composers who submitted new tunes for approval, and regrets that lack of space has prevented the fuller use of them. Thanks also are due to organists and choirmasters of Churches, not only in Great Britain, but also in Australia and elsewhere, for valuable suggestions which have helped to lighten the burden of a difficult task.

Every effort has been made to discover the composer of each tune included in this collection, together with the present owner of the copyright. If in any case the rights of composer or owner have not been acknowledged, the Committee desires to apologize for unintentional omission.

The Committee commends its work to our Heavenly Father in devout acknowledgment of gracious aid afforded throughout its labours, and with the prayer that the Book may prove of service to the Methodist Church, as truly expressing its spirit, quickening its devotion, and increasing the power and persuasiveness of its ministry of song.

All the compositions in the following list are copyright in Great Britain and Ireland, in the British Colonies, the Dominion of Canada, and the Australasian Commonwealth; and in many instances they are also copyright in the United States of America. An asterisk indicates the tunes for which a fee has been paid, and a blank in the second column that the composer is the owner of the copyright.

The Committee also desires to express its thanks to Mr. E. Noel Burghes for great assistance with respect to Copyrights, and to Rev. Dr. Millar Patrick for valuable historical information.

A.T. = Additional Tunes.
C. = Chants.
R. = Responses.

COMPOSER	OWNER OF COPYRIGHT	NO. OF HYMN
Agutter, B.	*Messrs. Paxton & Co., Ltd.	R.5
Anderson, J. S.	*Oxford University Press, from *The Revised Church Hymary*	159
Armes, P.	*Mr. A. H. H. Armes	781
Aylward, T. E.		398
Baker, F. G.	*The Misses Horder	46
Baker, H.	*The Misses Horder	325, 791
Baring-Gould, S.	*Messrs. A. W. Ridley & Co., Ltd.	944
Barker, Elizabeth	Lady Barker	A.T. 20
Barnby, J.	*Messrs. Novello & Co., Ltd.	105, 394 (1), 438, 474, 755, 777, 945, 961, 971, C.9 (B)
	*Proprietors of *Hymns Ancient and Modern*	212
	*Methodist Sunday School Department	425
	*Messrs. Bramall & Bramall	622, 737
Barnicott, O. R.	Methodist Conference	218
	*The Misses Horder	A.T. 18
Baskeyfield, G.		514 (1)

COMPOSER	OWNER OF COPYRIGHT	NO. OF HYMN
Beer, A.		371 (2), 375 (2), 523, 610, 668 (1)
Bell, J. M.	The Executrix	708
Bennett, G. J.	Methodist Conference	473
Benson, J. A.	Mrs. Benson	891
Birkbeck, J. B.	Mr. G. H. Birkbeck	A.T.22
Blanchard, G. F.	*Messrs. Reid Bros., Ltd.	889
Booth, J.	*Mr. Clifford Booth	850, 909
Boyd, W.	*Messrs. Novello & Co., Ltd.	817
Bridge, J. C.	*Messrs. Novello & Co., Ltd.	300
Bridge, J. F.	*Messrs. Novello & Co., Ltd.	122, R.1, 2
	Methodist Conference	179, 786
	The late Mrs. Robinson	203
	Mrs. R. F. Stainer	334 (1), 640
Briggs, G. W.	Principal of Loughborough College	443
Brockless, G. F.	Methodist Conference	127 (1), 489, 593, 789, 861, 954 (1), C.3, 10 (F)
Brown, A. H.	*Oxford University Press	302, 369, 439, 492, 631, 646, 774, 951 (1)
Buck, P. C.	*	882
Bullinger, E. W.	*Miss E. W. Dodson	A.T. 21
Caldbeck, G. T.	*Messrs. Longmans Green & Co., Ltd.	501 (2)
Calkin, J. B.	*Messrs. J. F. Shaw & Co., Ltd.	268, 533
	*Messrs. Novello & Co., Ltd.	849
Carter, E. S.		867
Challinor, F. A.	*National Sunday School Union	858
Cluley, J.	Methodist Conference	194, 773 (2)
Cooke, W. H.	*The Misses Horder	9
Cooper, A. S.	*Messrs. Novello & Co., Ltd.	416
Coward, H.	*	332
	*Messrs. J. Curwen & Sons, Ltd., from Curwen Edition, No. 28141	672
Dale, B. J.	Methodist Conference	169
Dale, R. F.	Miss Pickersgill-Cunliffe	918
David, J. W.	Methodist Conference	608
Davies, H. Walford.	*The Misses Horder	508
	*Oxford University Press, from *A Student's Hymnal, Hymns of the Kingdom*	44, 260 (1), 405
Dixon, R. W.	*Miss C. Simpson, from *The Burnley Tune Book*	843
Duckworth, F.		A.T. 15
Dunman, S. J. P.	*Methodist Sunday School Department	127 (2)
Dyer, H. A.	*Mrs. Popham	265
Earnshaw, R. H.	Mr. N. Earnshaw	910
Edwards, F. G.	*Messrs. Novello & Co., Ltd.	C.24 (B)
Elgar, E.	*Messrs. Novello & Co., Ltd.	C.5 (D)
Elliott, J. W.	*Messrs. Novello & Co., Ltd.	196, 776, 885
Ferguson, W. H.		526 (2), 743
Finlay, K. G.	*	838
Floyd, A. E.	*	907
	*Methodist Sunday School Department	174, 381, 899
Foster, M. B.	*The Misses Horder	147
	Mr. John T. Park, Stainland	482
Gabriel, C. H.	*Charles M. Alexander Copyrights Trust	116 (2), 336
Garbutt, C.	Methodist Conference	760
Garrett, G. M.	Mrs. A. M. Sylvester	649
Gatty, A. S.	The Abbot, Downside Abbey	241
Gilbert, W. B.	*Messrs. Novello & Co., Ltd.	679, 829
Gill, W. H.	*Messrs. Boosey & Co., Ltd.	970
Gladstone, W. H.	*Messrs. Novello & Co., Ltd.	562
	Mrs. Gladstone	687
Gounod, C.	*Messrs. Novello & Co., Ltd.	928
Greatorex, W.	*Oxford University Press	686 (2)
Gregory, A. S.		C.55 (A)
Gregory, S. H.		873
Gregory, T. C.		98, 468 (3)
Groves, C. T.	Methodist Conference	76, 936
Hands, J. D.	*Methodist Sunday School Department	164
Harding, H. A.	Methodist Conference	420, 788
Hart, W. H.	Mr. L. M. Hawkins	666
Harwood, B.		5
Hervey, F. A. J.	*Messrs. Novello & Co., Ltd.	A.T. 10
Holmes, H. J. E.	*	573
Holst, G.	*	30, 137
	*Messrs. J. Curwen & Sons, Ltd., from Curwen Edition, No. 71632	900

COMPOSER	OWNER OF COPYRIGHT	NO. OF HYMN
Hopkins, E. J.	*Messrs. A. Weekes & Co., Ltd.	149, 834
Hornabrook, Mrs. M.	Methodist Conference	321 (2)
Horner, E. F.	Methodist Conference	433, 447, 767
Howard, C.	*Mr. John T. Park, Stainland	A.T. 29
Hughes, J.	*Mrs. Hughes	615 (1)
Hulton, E.	*Proprietors of _Hymns Ancient and Modern_	186, 974
Hurst, W.	*Proprietors of _Hymns Ancient and Modern_	758
Hutchinson, T.		935
Ireland, J. N.	*	144, 521 (1)
Jackson, R.	Mrs. E. Taylor	297, 871, A.T. 3
James, F.	Methodist Conference	35
Jamouneau, A. F.	Methodist Conference	442
Jefferson, G.		9 (1)
Jenkins, D.	*Miss Jenkins	528, 596
Jewson, J. P.	Mr. H. G. Sanderson	614
Jones, G. H.	Mrs. Morris	645
Jordan, C. W.	Methodist Conference	669
	*Miss Jordan	A.T. 1
Jutson, C. B.	Mr. H. H. J. Jutson	857
Keeton, H.	Methodist Conference	481
Lahee, H.	*The Misses Horder	85, 401
Lamplough, E. S.	Methodist Conference	805 (2)
Langran, J.	*Messrs. Novello & Co., Ltd.	772, 830
Legge, A.	*Miss T. C. M. Legge	101
Lightwood, J. T.		27 (1), C.22 (B)
	Methodist Conference	253 (1), 636, 955
	*Methodist Sunday School Department	864
Lomas, G.	*The Misses Horder	451, 536, 913
Macfarren, G. A.	Messrs. Burns, Oates & Washbourne, Ltd.	592, 957
	*The National Church League	733
Mackenzie, A. C.	*Messrs. Novello & Co., Ltd.	61, C.5 (A)
Maclagan, W. D.	Sir Eric Maclagan	569, 621
Maker, F. C.	*Proprietors of _The Psalms and Hymns Trust_	206, 524, 967, A.T. 23
Mann, A. H.	*Mr. Bayford Stone	168, 856, 862
	*Messrs. Novello & Co., Ltd.	705, 711
Mannin, J.	Hon. Mrs. Horne	715
Martin, G. C.	Methodist Conference	31
	*Messrs. Novello & Co., Ltd.	548, 872, C.2 (4th)
Martin, G. W.	*Messrs. Novello & Co., Ltd.	542
Matthews, T. R.	*Messrs. Novello & Co., Ltd.	150, 286, 877
Maunder, J. H.	*Messrs. Novello & Co., Ltd.	52, C.34 (A)
Mendelssohn, F.	*Messrs. Novello & Co., Ltd.	117
Monk, W. H.	*Proprietors of _Hymns Ancient and Modern_	249, 258, 586, 759
Morley, H. L.	Mr. L. M. Hawkins	544 (1)
Morris, R. O.	*Oxford University Press, from _Songs of Praise_	138
Moulton, W. F.	Mrs. Moulton	396 C.21 (B)
	Methodist Conference	495,
Mountain, J.	Mrs. Mountain	170
Naylor, C. L.	*Methodist Sunday School Department	841 (2)
Naylor, E. W.	*	484
Newman, R. S.	Mrs. Newman	310, 921, 941
North, J. W. Allen	Methodist Conference	915
Northrop, A.		959
Oakeley, H. S.	*The Copyright Company	441, 942 (2)
Orchard, E. J.	Mrs. S. Williams	544 (2)
Parkyn, W.	*	119
Parratt, W.	Methodist Conference	444, 827
	The family of the late Sir W. Parratt	682 (1)
Parry, C. H. H.	*The National Society	145
	*Messrs. Novello & Co., Ltd.	252, 426
	*Proprietors of _Hymns Ancient and Modern_	911
	*Messrs. Longmans Green & Co., Ltd. for Proprietors of _The Hymnal Companion_	984
	Methodist Conference	A.T. 32
Parry, J.	*The Caniedydd Committee of the Union of Welsh Independents	195, 644
	*Messrs. Hughes & Son	726

COMPOSER	OWNER OF COPYRIGHT	NO. OF HYMN
Peace, A. L.	*Messrs. Novello & Co., Ltd.	448
	*Messrs. W. Paxton & Co., Ltd.	513
Perrot, C. H.	Mr. C. H. Perrot	399
Pitts, W.	Mr. E. E. Pither	966
Pritchard, T. C. L.	*From *The Revised Church Hymnary,* Oxford University Press	642
Rendall, E. D.	Messrs. H. E. & K. G. Rendall	660
Rhodes, Jane	*Methodist Sunday School Department	798
Roberts, R. E.	*Oxford University Press, from *Songs of Praise*	146
Sanderson, W.	Methodist Conference	253 (2)
Sankey, I. D.	*Messrs. Marshall, Morgan & Scott, Ltd.	171, 436, 517
Scholefield, C. C.	*Oxford University Press, from *The English Hymnal*	667
	*The Presbyterian Church of England	975
Selby, B. L.	*Proprietors of *Hymns Ancient and Modern*	806
Sharp, C.	Miss M. Karpeles	490 (arr.)
Shaw, G.	*	641 (arr.)
Shaw, M.	Messrs. J. Curwen & Sons, Ltd.	
	From Curwen Edition No. 6300	616 (2),
	From Curwen Edition No. 6300	815, 842 (2)
	From Curwen Edition No. 80629	851 (2)
	*Oxford University Press, from *Songs of Praise*	812 (2), 841 (1)
Smallwood, W.	Mr. S. Winder	153, 590
Smith, H. P.	*The Misses Horder	32
Smith, S.	*Messrs. Novello & Co., Ltd.	673
Somervell, A.		923
Stainer, Mrs. R. F.	Methodist Conference	309
Stainer, J.	*Messrs. Novello & Co., Ltd.	20, 183, 318 (1), 844, 980 Amen 3, 5, C.2 (4th), 8 (D), R.3, 4
	*J. F. R. Stainer	148, 522, 741, 825, 839, 937
	National Children's Home and Orphanage	888
Stanford, C. V.	*Messrs. Stainer & Bell, Ltd.	51, 392
	*Messrs. Novello & Co., Ltd.	132
Stewart, R. P.	*Christian Knowledge Society, Dublin.	354, 916
Stimpson, O. J.	Mrs. Jefferson	947
Sullivan, A. S.	*Messrs. Novello & Co., Ltd.	18, 130, 346, 506, 706, 731, 822, 848, 964 (1) 964 (2), 977
	*Messrs. J. F. Shaw & Co., Ltd.	423
Summers, J.	*Messrs. A. W. Ford & Co., Ltd.	920
Swift, J. F.	*Mr. John T. Park, Stainland	29
Terry, R. R.		254, 805 (1), 887
Thompson, R. G.		231
Thorne, E. H.	*Messrs. Novello & Co., Ltd.	R.6
Tiddeman, Miss M.	*Proprietors of *Hymns Ancient and Modern*	462
Tours, B.	*Messrs. Novello & Co., Ltd.	835, 932 (2)
Tozer, A. E.	From *Catholic Hymns,* Messrs. Cary & Co., Ltd., London	402, A.T. 7
Vincent, C.	*	243, 459, 633, 700
Vincent, G. F.	*Mrs. Vincent	782
Walker, F.	Messrs. Novello & Co., Ltd.	C.32 (A)
Wallhead, T.	Methodist Conference	409
Watson, A.	*Messrs. J. Curwen & Sons, Ltd. From Curwen Edition No. 28144	A.T. 30
White, L. M.	Methodist Conference	477
Williams, R. Vaughan	*From *The English Hymnal,* Oxford University Press	273, 832 (1), 914
Williams, T. J.	*Messrs. W. Gwenlyn Evans & Son	616 (1)
Wilson, D. F. R.	*	279, 770, 840
Wiseman, C. L.	*Methodist Sunday School Department	116 (1)
		696 (1)
Wiseman, F. L.	Methodist Conference	5, 94, 314, 429 (1), 655 (1), 697, 812 (1)
	*Methodist Sunday School Department	190, 435, 799, 863
Wolstenholme, W.	Mr. J. T. Lightwood	C.7 (E)
Wood, C.	*Oxford University Press, from *Songs of Praise*	639
Woods, B. E.	Methodist Conference	526
Wostenholm, M. L.	Methodist Conference	256. 483, 537, 890
Yoakley, J.	Mr. J. N. Yoakley	613

From *Songs of Praise* (by permission of the Oxford University Press):
25, 119 (2), 138, 146, 266, 348, 443, 639, 657, 812 (2), 841, 845, 930, 968 (1)

From *The English Hymnal* (by permission of the Oxford University Press):
53, 154 (1), 273, 395, 620, 667 (2), 804, 832 (1), 852, 854, 897, 914

From *A Student's Hymnal* (Hymns of the Kingdom) (by permission of the Oxford University Press):
44, 166, 260 (1), 405

From *The Revised Church Hymnary* (by permission of the Oxford University Press):
303 (2), 330, 577

The following tunes have been harmonized or adapted by the musical advisers:
62, 93, 102, 118, 121, 123, 131, 191, 205, 211, 230, 238, 264, 275, 282, 298, 330, 345, 361, 373, 380, 397, 409, 417, 429, 431, 437, 446, 511, 559, 565, 574, 577, 588, 589, 591, 655, 656, 666, 674, 696, 713, 724, 738, 808, 809, 814, 819, 823, 831, 866, 874, 901, 908, 954

CONTENTS

HYMNS WITH TUNES

Adoration and Worship

1

RICHMOND (*First Tune*). C.M. T. HAWEIS, 1734-1820.

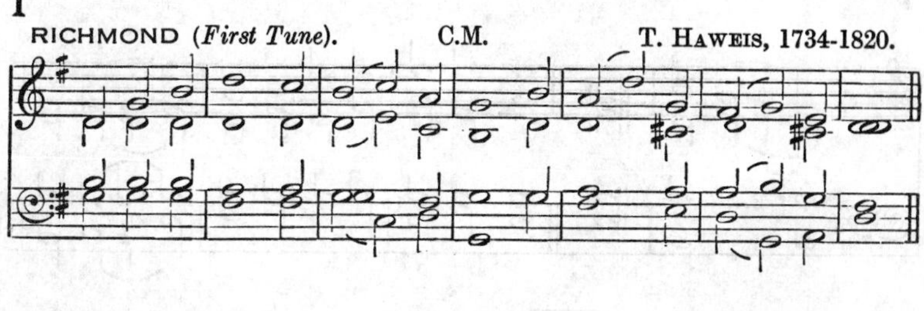

1 O FOR a thousand tongues to sing
My great Redeemer's praise,
The glories of my God and King,
The triumphs of His grace!

2 My gracious Master and my God,
Assist me to proclaim,
To spread through all the earth abroad
The honours of Thy name.

3 Jesus! the name that charms our fears,
That bids our sorrows cease;
'Tis music in the sinner's ears,
'Tis life, and health, and peace.

4 He speaks, and, listening to His voice,
New life the dead receive,
The mournful, broken hearts rejoice,
The humble poor believe.

5 He breaks the power of cancelled sin,
He sets the prisoner free;
His blood can make the foulest clean,
His blood availed for me.

6 See all your sins on Jesus laid:
The Lamb of God was slain,
His soul was once an offering made
For every soul of man.

Charles Wesley, 1707-88.

Adoration and Worship

1

LYDIA (*Second Tune*). C.M. T. PHILLIPS, 1735-1807.

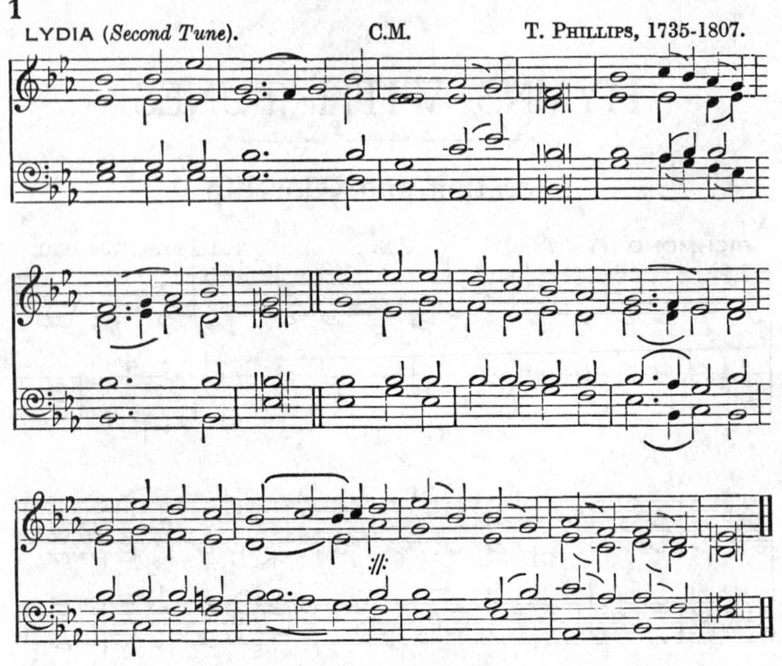

1 O FOR a thousand tongues to sing
My great Redeemer's praise,
The glories of my God and King,
The triumphs of His grace!

2 My gracious Master and my God,
Assist me to proclaim,
To spread through all the earth abroad
The honours of Thy name.

3 Jesus! the name that charms our fears,
That bids our sorrows cease;
'Tis music in the sinner's ears,
'Tis life, and health, and peace.

4 He speaks, and, listening to His voice,
New life the dead receive,
The mournful, broken hearts rejoice,
The humble poor believe.

5 He breaks the power of cancelled sin,
He sets the prisoner free;
His blood can make the foulest clean,
His blood availed for me.

6 See all your sins on Jesus laid:
The Lamb of God was slain,
His soul was once an offering made
For every soul of man.

Charles Wesley, 1707-88.

2

OLD 100TH. L.M. *French Psalter*, 1551 (Original Version).

1 All people that on earth do dwell,
Sing to the Lord with cheerful voice:
Him serve with mirth, His praise forth tell;
Come ye before Him and rejoice.

2 The Lord ye know is God indeed;
Without our aid He did us make:
We are His folk, He doth us feed;
And for His sheep He doth us take.

3 O enter then His gates with praise;
Approach with joy His courts unto;
Praise, laud, and bless His name always,
For it is seemly so to do.

4 For why? The Lord our God is good;
His mercy is for ever sure;
His truth at all times firmly stood,
And shall from age to age endure.
Amen.

William Kethe, d. 1593 (?).

3

OLD 100TH. L.M. *French Psalter*, 1551.

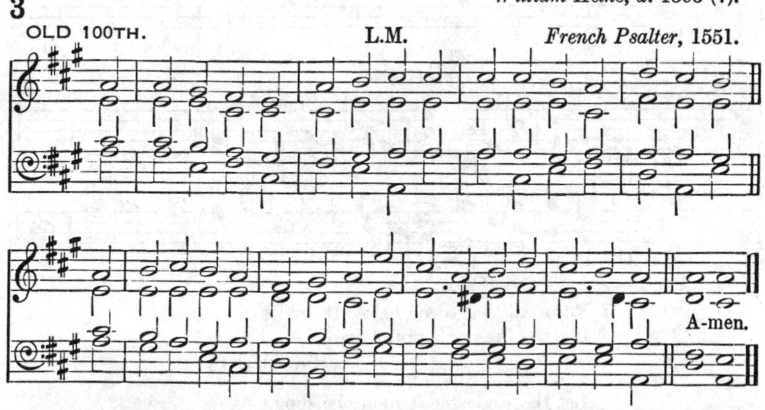

1 Before Jehovah's awful throne,
Ye nations, bow with sacred joy:
Know that the Lord is God alone;
He can create, and He destroy.

2 His sovereign power, without our aid,
Made us of clay, and formed us men;
And when like wandering sheep we strayed,
He brought us to His fold again.

3 We'll crowd Thy gates with thankful songs;
High as the heavens our voices raise;
And earth, with her ten thousand tongues,
Shall fill Thy courts with sounding praise.

4 Wide as the world is Thy command;
Vast as eternity Thy love;
Firm as a rock Thy truth shall stand,
When rolling years shall cease to move.
Amen.

Isaac Watts, 1674-1748;
alt. by John Wesley, 1703-91.

4

8 8.8 8. and Hallelujahs.

ST. FRANCIS (LASST UNS ERFREUEN). *Geistliche Kirchengesäng*, 1623.

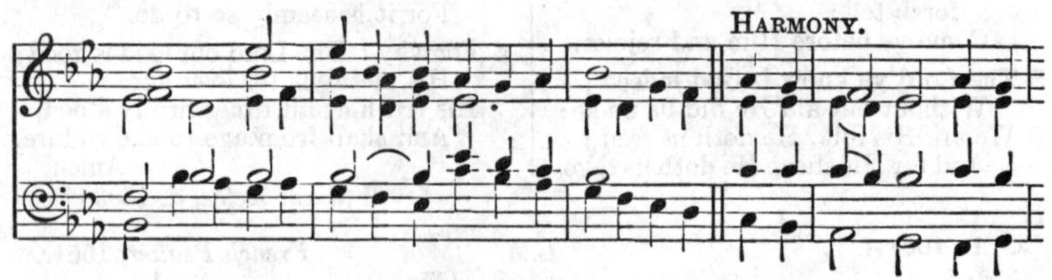

1 FROM all that dwell below the skies
Let the Creator's praise arise:
Hallelujah!

Let the Redeemer's name be sung,
Through every land, by every tongue:
Hallelujah!

2 Eternal are Thy mercies, Lord;
Eternal truth attends Thy word:
Hallelujah!

Thy praise shall sound from shore to shore,
Till suns shall rise and set no more:
Hallelujah!

Isaac Watts, 1674-1748.

5

DALLAS (*First Tune*). 10 4.6 6.6 6.10 4. F. L. Wiseman, 1858-1944

Let all the world in
ev' - - ry

1 Let all the world in every corner sing:
My God and King!
The heavens are not too high,
His praise may thither fly;
The earth is not too low,
His praises there may grow.
Let all the world in every corner sing:
My God and King!

2 Let all the world in every corner sing:
My God and King!
The Church with psalms must shout,
No door can keep them out:
But, above all, the heart
Must bear the longest part.
Let all the world in every corner sing:
My God and King!

George Herbert, 1593-1632.

5

10 4.6 6.6 6.10 4.

LUCKINGTON (*Second Tune*). B. HARWOOD, 1859-1949

1 LET all the world in every corner sing:
My God and King!
The heavens are not too high,
His praise may thither fly;
The earth is not too low,
His praises there may grow.
Let all the world in every corner sing:
My God and King!

2 Let all the world in every corner sing:
My God and King!
The Church with psalms must shout,
No door can keep them out:
But, above all, the heart
Must bear the longest part.
Let all the world in every corner sing:
My God and King!

George Herbert, 1593-1632.

6

SAUL (FERTILE PLAINS). L.M. From HANDEL's *Joshua*, 1747.

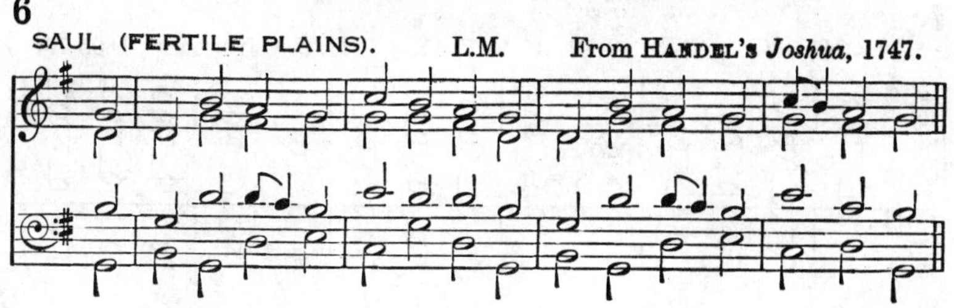

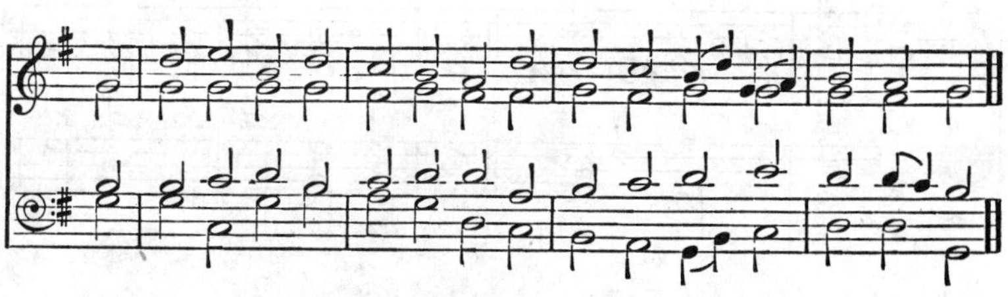

1 ETERNAL Power! whose high abode
Becomes the grandeur of a God:
Infinite lengths beyond the bounds
Where stars revolve their little rounds.

2 Thee while the first archangel sings,
He hides his face beneath his wings,
And throngs of shining thrones around
Fall worshipping, and spread the ground.

3 Lord, what shall earth and ashes do?
We would adore our Maker too;
From sin and dust to Thee we cry,
The Great, the Holy, and the High!

4 Earth from afar has heard Thy fame,
And babes have learnt to lisp Thy name;
But O the glories of Thy mind
Leave all our soaring thoughts behind!

5 God is in heaven, and men below;
Be short our tunes, our words be few;
A sacred reverence checks our songs,
And praise sits silent on our tongues.

Isaac Watts, 1674-1748.

7

HOUGHTON. 10 10.11 11. H. J. GAUNTLETT, 1805-76.

1 O HEAVENLY King, look down from above;
Assist us to sing Thy mercy and love:
So sweetly o'erflowing, so plenteous the store,
Thou still art bestowing, and giving us more.

2 O God of our life, we hallow Thy name;
Our business and strife is Thee to proclaim.
Accept our thanksgiving for creating grace;
The living, the living shall show forth Thy praise.

3 Our Father and Lord, almighty art Thou;
Preserved by Thy word, we worship Thee now;
The bountiful donor of all we enjoy,
Our tongues, to Thine honour, and lives we employ.

4 But O above all Thy kindness we praise,
From sin and from thrall which saves the lost race;
Thy Son Thou hast given the world to redeem,
And bring us to heaven whose trust is in Him.

5 Wherefore of Thy love we sing and rejoice,
With angels above we lift up our voice:
Thy love each believer shall gladly adore,
For ever and ever, when time is no more. Amen.

Charles Wesley, 1707-88.

8

HANOVER. 5.5.5.5.6.5.6.5. W. CROFT, 1678-1727.

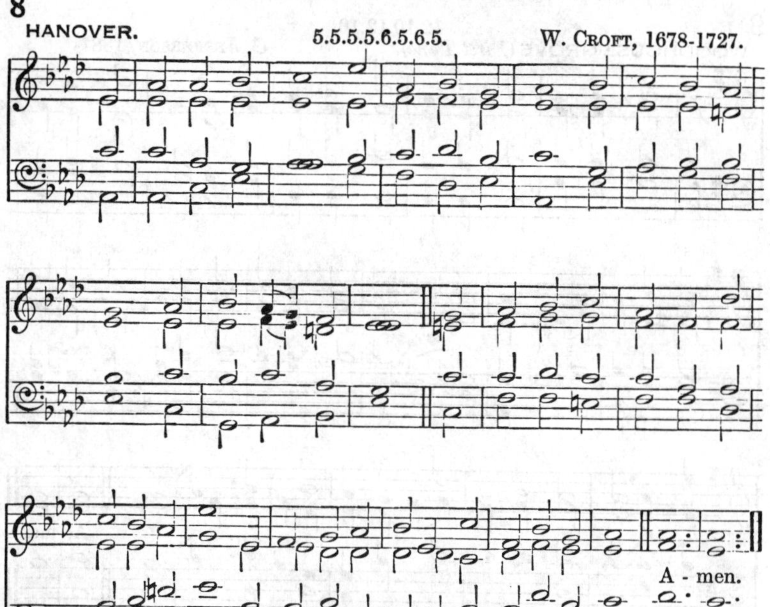

1 O WORSHIP the King,
All glorious above;
O gratefully sing
His power and His love:
Our shield and defender,
The ancient of days,
Pavilioned in splendour,
And girded with praise.

2 O tell of His might,
O sing of His grace,
Whose robe is the light,
Whose canopy space;
His chariots of wrath
The deep thunder-clouds form,
And dark is His path
On the wings of the storm.

3 The earth with its store
Of wonders untold,
Almighty! Thy power
Hath founded of old,
Hath stablished it fast
By a changeless decree,
And round it hath cast,
Like a mantle, the sea.

4 Thy bountiful care
What tongue can recite?
It breathes in the air,
It shines in the light,
It streams from the hills,
It descends to the plain,
And sweetly distils
In the dew and the rain.

5 Frail children of dust,
And feeble as frail,
In Thee do we trust,
Nor find Thee to fail;
Thy mercies how tender,
How firm to the end,
Our Maker, Defender,
Redeemer, and Friend!

6 O measureless Might!
Ineffable Love!
While angels delight
To hymn Thee above,
The humbler creation,
Though feeble their lays,
With true adoration
Shall lisp to Thy praise. Amen.

Robert Grant, 1785-1838

May also be sung to HOUGHTON, No. 7.

† This chord is for the first and last verses only.

Adoration and Worship

1.

O WORSHIP the Lord in the beauty of holiness!
Bow down before Him, His glory proclaim;
With gold of obedience and incense of lowliness,
Kneel and adore Him, the Lord is His name.

2.

Low at His feet lay thy burden of carefulness,
High on His heart He will bear it for thee,
Comfort thy sorrows, and answer thy prayerfulness,
Guiding thy steps as may best for thee be.

3.

Fear not to enter His courts in the slenderness
Of the poor wealth thou wouldst reckon as thine:
Truth in its beauty and love in its tenderness:
These are the offerings to lay on His shrine.

4.

These, though we bring them in trembling and fearfulness,
He will accept for the name that is dear;
Mornings of joy give for evenings of tearfulness,
Trust for our trembling, and hope for our fear.

5.

O worship the Lord in the beauty of holiness!
Bow down before Him, His glory proclaim;
With gold of obedience and incense of lowliness,
Kneel and adore Him, the Lord is His name. Amen.

John Samuel Bewley Monsell, 1811-75.

10

NUN DANKET. 6.7.6.7.6.6.6.6. J. Crüger, 1598-1662.

Nun danket alle Gott.

1 Now thank we all our God,
With hearts, and hands, and voices;
Who wondrous things hath done,
In whom His world rejoices;
Who, from our mothers' arms,
Hath blessed us on our way
With countless gifts of love,
And still is ours to-day.

2 O may this bounteous God
Through all our life be near us,
With ever-joyful hearts
And blessèd peace to cheer us,
And keep us in His grace,
And guide us when perplexed,
And free us from all ills
In this world and the next.

3 All praise and thanks to God
The Father now be given,
The Son, and Him who reigns
With Them in highest heaven:
The one, eternal God,
Whom earth and heaven adore;
For thus it was, is now,
And shall be evermore. Amen.

Martin Rinkart, 1586-1649;
tr. by Catherine Winkworth, 1827-78.

11

DATCHET. 11 11.11 11. G. J. Elvey, 1816-93.

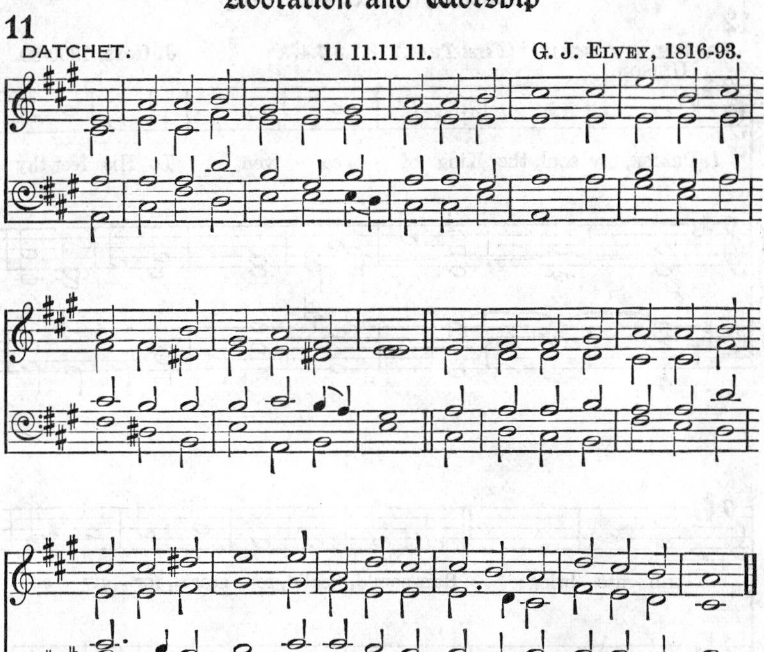

1 With gladness we worship, rejoice as we sing,
Free hearts and free voices how blessèd to bring,
The old, thankful story shall scale Thine abode,
Thou King of all glory, most bountiful God.

2 Thy right would we give Thee—true homage Thy due,
And honour eternal, the universe through,
With all Thy creation, earth, heaven and sea,
In one acclamation we celebrate Thee.

3 Renewed by Thy Spirit, redeemed by Thy Son,
Thy children revere Thee for all Thou hast done.
O Father! returning to love and to light,
Thy children are yearning to praise Thee aright.

4 We join with the angels, and so there is given
From earth Hallelujah, in answer to heaven.
Amen! Be Thou glorious below and above,
Redeeming, victorious, and infinite Love!

George Rawson, 1807-89.

12

PRAISE, MY SOUL *(*First Tune.*) 8.7.8.7.4.7. J. Goss, 1800-80.

UNISON.

1. PRAISE, my soul, the King of heaven, To His feet thy tribute bring; Ran-som'd, heal'd, re-stor'd, for-giv-en, Who like thee His praise should sing? Praise Him! Praise Him!

* The Music of verse 2 may be used throughout.

Adoration and Worship

Praise Him! Praise Him! Praise the ev - er - last - ing King.
HARMONY.
mf
2 Praise Him for His grace and fa - - - vour To our fa - thers
mf
in dis - tress; Praise Him, still the same for ev - er,
Slow to chide and swift to bless: Praise Him! Praise Him!
ff
ff
Praise Him! Praise Him! Glo - rious in His faith - ful - ness.

Slower.
SOPRANOS ONLY.
p
3. Fa-ther - like He tends and spares us; Well our fee - ble
Slower.
p
frame He knows; In His hands He gent - ly bears us,
Res - cues us from all our foes: Praise Him! Praise Him!
ff
ff
Praise Him! Praise Him! Wide - ly as His mer - cy flows.

UNISON. Tempo 1mo.
4. An-gels in the height, a-dore Him; Ye be-hold Him
Tempo 1mo.
face to face; Sun and moon, bow down be-fore Him;
Dwell-ers all in time and space, Praise Him! Praise Him!
Praise Him! Praise Him! Praise with us the God of grace.
HARMONY.
A-men.

Henry Francis Lyte, 1793-1847.

12 8.7.8.7.4.7.

REGENT SQUARE (*Second Tune*). H. SMART, 1813-79.

1 PRAISE, my soul, the King of heaven,
To His feet thy tribute bring;
Ransomed, healed, restored, forgiven,
Who like thee His praise should sing?
Praise Him! Praise Him!
Praise the everlasting King.

2 Praise Him for His grace and favour
To our fathers in distress;
Praise Him, still the same for ever,
Slow to chide and swift to bless:
Praise Him! Praise Him!
Glorious in His faithfulness.

3 Father-like He tends and spares us;
Well our feeble frame He knows;
In His hands He gently bears us,
Rescues us from all our foes:
Praise Him! Praise Him!
Widely as His mercy flows.

4 Angels in the height, adore Him;
Ye behold Him face to face;
Sun and moon, bow down before Him;
Dwellers all in time and space,
Praise Him! Praise Him!
Praise with us the God of grace. Amen.

Henry Francis Lyte, 1793-1847.

13

LAUS DEO. 8.7.8.7. R. Redhead, 1820-1901.

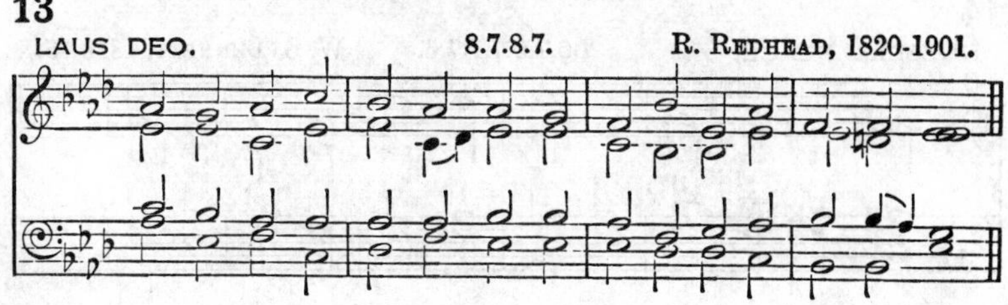

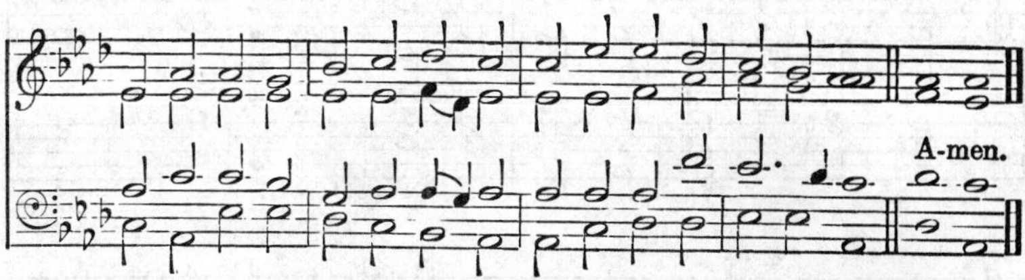

1.

Praise the Lord! Ye heavens, adore Him;
Praise Him, angels in the height;
Sun and moon, rejoice before Him;
Praise Him, all ye stars and light.

2.

Praise the Lord, for He hath spoken;
Worlds His mighty voice obeyed;
Laws, that never shall be broken,
For their guidance He hath made.

3.

Praise the Lord, for He is glorious;
Never shall His promise fail:
God hath made His saints victorious;
Sin and death shall not prevail.

4.

Praise the God of our salvation;
Hosts on high His power proclaim;
Heaven and earth, and all creation,
Laud and magnify His name. Amen.

Anonymous: Foundling Hospital Collection, 1796.

14

RUSSELL PLACE. 7.6.7.6.7.7.7.6. W. S. BENNETT, 1816-75.

1 PRAISE the Lord who reigns above,
And keeps His court below;
Praise the holy God of love,
And all His greatness show;
Praise Him for His noble deeds,
Praise Him for His matchless power:
Him from whom all good proceeds
Let earth and heaven adore.

2 Celebrate the eternal God
With harp and psaltery,
Timbrels soft and cymbals loud
In His high praise agree:
Praise Him every tuneful string;
All the reach of heavenly art,
All the powers of music bring,
The music of the heart.

3 Him, in whom they move and live,
Let every creature sing,
Glory to their Maker give,
And homage to their King:
Hallowed be His name beneath,
As in heaven on earth adored;
Praise the Lord in every breath,
Let all things praise the Lord. Amen.

Charles Wesley, 1707-88.

15

LEONI. 6.6.8.4. D. *Sacred Harmony*, 1780.

1 PRAISE to the living God!
All praisèd be His name,
Who was, and is, and is to be,
For aye the same!
The One Eternal God
Ere aught that now appears:
The First, the Last, beyond all thought
His timeless years!

2 Formless, all lovely forms
Declare His loveliness;
Holy, no holiness of earth
Can His express.
Lo, He is Lord of all!
Creation speaks His praise,
And everywhere, above, below,
His will obeys.

3 His Spirit floweth free,
High surging where it will:
In prophet's word He spake of old,
He speaketh still.
Established is His law,
And changeless it shall stand,
Deep writ upon the human heart,
On sea, on land.

4 Eternal life hath He
Implanted in the soul;
His love shall be our strength and stay,
While ages roll.
Praise to the living God!
All praisèd be His name,
Who was, and is, and is to be,
For aye the same. Amen.

Jewish Doxology (Medieval);
tr. by Max Landsberg, 1845-1928;
and *Newton Mann*, 1836-1926

16

AUSTRIA. 8.7.8.7. D. F. J. Haydn, 1732-1809.

1 Raise the psalm: let earth adoring,
Through each kindred, tribe, and tongue,
To her God His praise restoring,
Raise the new accordant song.
Bless His name, each farthest nation;
Sing His praise, His truth display:
Tell anew His high salvation
With each new return of day.

2 Tell it out beneath the heaven,
To each kindred, tribe, and tongue,
Tell it out from morn till even
In your unexhausted song:
Tell that God for ever reigneth,
He, who set the world so fast,
He, who still its state sustaineth
Till the day of doom to last.

3 Tell them that the day is coming
When that righteous doom shall be:
Then shall heaven new joys illumine,
Gladness shine o'er earth and sea.
Yea, the far-resounding ocean
Shall its thousand voices raise,
All its waves in glad commotion
Chant the fullness of His praise.

4 And earth's fields, with herbs and flowers,
Shall put on their choice array,
And in all their leafy bowers
Shall the woods keep holy-day:
When the Judge, to earth descending,
Righteous judgement shall ordain,
Fraud and wrong shall then have ending,
Truth, immortal truth, shall reign.
Amen.

Edward Churton, 1800-74.

A lower setting will be found at No. 228.

17

AMSTERDAM. 7.6.7.6.7.7.7.6. *Foundery Collection*, 1742.

1 Meet and right it is to sing,
In every time and place,
Glory to our heavenly King,
The God of truth and grace:
Join we then with sweet accord,
All in one thanksgiving join;
Holy, holy, holy Lord,
Eternal praise be Thine.

2 Thee the first-born sons of light,
In choral symphonies,
Praise by day, day without night,
And never, never cease;
Angels and archangels all
Praise the mystic Three in One,
Sing, and stop, and gaze, and fall
O'erwhelmed before Thy throne.

3 Vying with that happy choir,
Who chant Thy praise above,
We on eagles' wings aspire,
The wings of faith and love:
Thee they sing with glory crowned,
We extol the slaughtered Lamb;
Lower if our voices sound,
Our subject is the same.

4 Father, God, Thy love we praise,
Which gave Thy Son to die;
Jesus, full of truth and grace,
Alike we glorify;
Spirit, Comforter divine,
Praise by all to Thee be given;
Till we in full chorus join,
And earth is turned to heaven.
Amen.

Charles Wesley, 1707-88.

18

EVER FAITHFUL. 7 7.7 7. A. SULLIVAN, 1842-1900.

By permission of Novello and Company, Limited.

1 LET us with a gladsome mind
Praise the Lord, for He is kind:
For His mercies aye endure,
Ever faithful, ever sure.

2 Let us blaze His name abroad,
For of gods He is the God:

3 He, with all-commanding might,
Filled the new-made world with light:

4 All things living He doth feed,
His full hand supplies their need:

5 He His chosen race did bless
In the wasteful wilderness:

6 Let us then with gladsome mind
Praise the Lord, for He is kind:

John Milton, 1608-74.

19

MONKLAND. 7 7.7 7. Arr. by J. WILKES, 1785-1869.

1 PRAISE, O praise our God and King!
Hymns of adoration sing:
For His mercies still endure,
Ever faithful, ever sure.

2 Praise Him that He made the sun
Day by day his course to run:

3 And the silver moon by night,
Shining with her gentle light:

4 Praise Him that He gave the rain
To mature the swelling grain:

5 And hath bid the fruitful field
Crops of precious increase yield:

6 Praise Him for our harvest store,
He hath filled the garner floor:

7 And for richer food than this,
Pledge of everlasting bliss:

8 Glory to our bounteous King!
Glory let creation sing,
Glory to the Father, Son,
And blest Spirit, Three in One.
Amen.

Henry Williams Baker, 1821-77.

20

TE DEUM LAUDAMUS. 7 7.7 7. D. J. STAINER, 1840-1901.

UNISON.

1 COME, O come, in pious lays
Sound we God Almighty's praise;
Hither bring, in one consent,
Heart and voice and instrument:
Nor a creature dumb be found,
That hath either voice or sound.
Let those things which do not live
In still music praises give.

2 Come, ye sons of human race,
In this chorus take your place;
And amid the mortal throng
Be ye masters of the song.
Let, in praise of God, the sound
Run a never-ending round,
That our song of praise may be
Everlasting, as is He.

3 So, from heaven, on earth He shall
Let His gracious blessings fall;
And this huge wide orb we see
Shall one choir, one temple be;
That our song may over-climb
All the bounds of place and time,
And ascend from sphere to sphere
To the great Almighty's ear.

George Wither, 1588-1667.

21

LEONI. 6.6.8.4. D. *Sacred Harmony*, 1780.

THE God of Abraham praise,
Who reigns enthroned above,
Ancient of everlasting days,
And God of love.
Jehovah! Great I AM!
By earth and heaven confessed;
I bow and bless the sacred name
For ever blessed.

2 The God of Abraham praise,
At whose supreme command
From earth I rise, and seek the joys
At His right hand.
I all on earth forsake—
Its wisdom, fame, and power—
And Him my only portion make,
My shield and tower.

3 The God of Abraham praise,
Whose all-sufficient grace
Shall guide me all my happy days
In all my ways.
He calls a worm His friend,
He calls Himself my God;
And He shall save me to the end
Through Jesu's blood.

4 He by Himself hath sworn,
I on His oath depend:
I shall, on eagles' wings upborne,
To heaven ascend;
I shall behold His face,
I shall His power adore,
And sing the wonders of His grace
For evermore.

* * * *

5 Though nature's strength decay,
And earth and hell withstand,
To Canaan's bounds I urge my way
At His command.
The watery deep I pass,
With Jesus in my view;
And through the howling wilderness
My way pursue.

6 The goodly land I see,
With peace and plenty blest;
A land of sacred liberty
And endless rest:
There milk and honey flow,
And oil and wine abound,
And trees of life for ever grow,
With mercy crowned.

7 There dwells the Lord our King,
The Lord our Righteousness,
Triumphant o'er the world and sin,
The Prince of Peace;
On Zion's sacred height
His kingdom still maintains,
And glorious with His saints in light
For ever reigns.

8 He keeps His own secure,
He guards them by His side,
Arrays in garments white and pure
His spotless bride:
With streams of sacred bliss,
With groves of living joys,
With all the fruits of paradise,
He still supplies.

9 Before the great Three-One
They all exulting stand,
And tell the wonders He hath done,
Through all their land:
The listening spheres attend,
And swell the growing fame;
And sing, in songs which never end,
The wondrous name.

* * * *

10 The God who reigns on high
The great archangels sing;
And, Holy, holy, holy, cry,
Almighty King.
Who was and is the same,
And evermore shall be;
Jehovah, Father, Great I AM,
We worship Thee.

11 Before the Saviour's face
The ransomed nations bow;
O'erwhelmed at His almighty grace,
For ever new:
He shows His prints of love,
They kindle to a flame,
And sound through all the worlds above
The slaughtered Lamb.

12 The whole triumphant host
Give thanks to God on high;
Hail, Father, Son, and Holy Ghost!
They ever cry.
Hail, Abraham's God, and mine!
I join the heavenly lays;
All might and majesty are Thine,
And endless praise. Amen.

Thomas Olivers, 1725-99.

22

BETTER WORLD. 8.3.8.3.8 8 8.3. Old English Air.

1 COME, let us all unite and sing—
God is love!
While heaven and earth their praises
God is love! [bring—
Let every soul from sin awake,
Each in his heart sweet music make,
And sweetly sing for Jesu's sake—
God is love!

2 O tell to earth's remotest bound—
God is love!
In Christ is full redemption found—
God is love!
His blood can cleanse our sins away;
His Spirit turns our night to day,
And leads our souls with joy to say—
God is love!

3 How happy is our portion here—
God is love!
His promises our spirits cheer—
God is love!
He is our Sun and Shield by day,
By night He near our tents will stay,
He will be with us all the way—
God is love!

4 In Zion we shall sing again—
God is love!
Yes, this shall be our highest strain—
God is love!
Whilst endless ages roll along,
In concert with the heavenly throng,
This shall be still our sweetest song—
God is love!

Howard Kingsbury, c. 1850.

23

GWALCHMAI. 7.4.7.4. D. J. D. JONES, 1827-70.

1 KING of glory, King of peace,
I will love Thee;
And that love may never cease,
I will move Thee.
Thou hast granted my request,
Thou hast heard me;
Thou didst note my working breast,
Thou hast spared me.

2 Wherefore with my utmost art
I will sing Thee,
And the cream of all my heart
I will bring Thee.
Though my sins against me cried,
Thou didst clear me;
And alone, when they replied,
Thou didst hear me.

3 Seven whole days, not one in seven,
I will praise Thee;
In my heart, though not in heaven,
I can raise Thee.
Small it is, in this poor sort
To enrol Thee:
E'en eternity's too short
To extol Thee.

George Herbert, 1593-1632.

24

PALATINE. C.M. O. Gibbons, 1583-1625.

1 O God, my strength and fortitude,
In truth I will love Thee;
Thou art my castle and defence
In my necessity.

2 When I, beset with pain and grief,
Prayed to my God for grace,
Forthwith my God heard my complaint
Out of His holy place.

3 The Lord descended from above,
And bowed the heavens high,
And underneath His feet He cast
The darkness of the sky.

4 On cherub and on cherubim
Full royally He rode;
And on the wings of all the winds
Came flying all abroad.

5 He brought me forth in open place,
That so I might be free;
And kept me safe, because He had
A favour unto me.

6 Unspotted are the ways of God,
His word is truly tried;
He is a sure defence to such
As in His ways abide.

Thomas Sternhold, c. 1500-49.

25

WÜRZBURG 8.7.8.7. D. *Andächtige und auserlesene Gesänger,* Würzburg, 1705.

1 Round the Lord in glory seated,
  Cherubim and seraphim
Filled His temple, and repeated
  Each to each the alternate hymn:
Lord, Thy glory fills the heaven,
  Earth is with its fullness stored;
Unto Thee be glory given,
  Holy, holy, holy Lord!

2 Heaven is still with glory ringing,
  Earth takes up the angels' cry,
Holy, holy, holy, singing,
  Lord of Hosts, the Lord most High:

3 With His seraph-train before Him,
  With His holy Church below,
Thus unite we to adore Him,
  Bid we thus our anthem flow: Amen.

Richard Mant, 1776-1848.

26

CROFT'S 136TH. 6.6.6.6.4.4.4.4. W. CROFT, 1678-1727.

1 Ye holy angels bright,
Who wait at God's right hand,
Or through the realms of light
Fly at your Lord's command,
Assist our song,
Or else the theme
Too high doth seem
For mortal tongue.

2 Ye blessèd souls at rest,
Who see your Saviour's face,
Whose glory, ev'n the least
Is far above our grace.
God's praises sound,
As in His sight
With sweet delight
Ye do abound.

3 Ye saints, who toil below,
Adore your heavenly King,
And, onward as ye go,
Some joyful anthem sing;
Take what He gives,
And praise Him still
Through good and ill,
Who ever lives.

4 My soul, bear thou thy part,
Triumph in God above,
And with a well-tuned heart
Sing thou the songs of love.
Let all thy days
Till life shall end,
Whate'er He send,
Be filled with praise. Amen.

Richard Baxter, 1615-91;
alt. by John Hampden Gurney, 1802-62,
and Richard Robert Chope, 1830-1928.

27

LYTHAM ST. ANNES (*First Tune*). 4 4.7.8 8.7. J. T. LIGHTWOOD, 1856-1944

1 ANGELS holy,
High and lowly,
Sing the praises of the Lord!
Earth and sky; all living nature;
Man, the stamp of thy Creator,
Praise ye, praise ye God the Lord!

2 Sun and moon bright,
Night and noon-light,
Starry temples azure-floored;
Cloud and rain, and wild wind's madness,
Sons of God that shout for gladness,
Praise ye, praise ye God the Lord!

3 Ocean hoary,
Tell His glory;
Cliffs, where tumbling seas have roared,
Pulse of waters, blithely beating,
Wave advancing, wave retreating,
Praise ye, praise ye God the Lord!

4 Rock and highland,
Wood and island,
Crag, where eagle's pride hath soared;
Mighty mountains, purple-breasted,
Peaks cloud-cleaving, snowy-crested,
Praise ye, praise ye God the Lord!

5 Rolling river,
Praise Him ever,
From the mountain's deep vein poured;
Silver fountain, clearly gushing,
Troubled torrent, madly rushing,
Praise ye, praise ye God the Lord!

6 Praise Him ever,
Bounteous giver;
Praise Him, Father, Friend and Lord!
Each glad soul its free course winging,
Each glad voice its free song singing,
Praise the great and mighty Lord!
Amen.

John Stuart Blackie, 1809-95.

28

8 8.8 8. and refrain.

ST. FRANCIS (LASST UNS ERFREUEN). *Geistliche Kirchengesäng*, 1623.

Laudato sia Dio mio Signore.

1 ALL creatures of our God and King,
Lift up your voice and with us sing:
Alleluia, Alleluia!
Thou burning sun with golden beam,
Thou silver moon with softer gleam:
O praise Him, O praise Him,
Alleluia, Alleluia, Alleluia!

2 Thou rushing wind that art so strong,
Ye clouds that sail in heaven along,
O praise Him, Alleluia!
Thou rising morn, in praise rejoice,
Ye lights of evening, find a voice:

3 Thou flowing water, pure and clear,
Make music for thy Lord to hear,
Alleluia, Alleluia!
Thou fire so masterful and bright,
That givest man both warmth and light:

4 Dear mother earth, who day by day
Unfoldest blessings on our way,
O praise Him, Alleluia!
The flowers and fruits that in thee grow,
Let them His glory also show:

5 And all ye men of tender heart,
Forgiving others, take your part,
O sing ye, Alleluia!
Ye who long pain and sorrow bear,
Praise God and on Him cast your care:

6 And thou, most kind and gentle death,
Waiting to hush our latest breath,
O praise Him, Alleluia!
Thou leadest home the child of God,
And Christ our Lord the way hath trod:

7 Let all things their Creator bless,
And worship Him in humbleness,
O praise Him, Alleluia!
Praise, praise the Father, praise the Son,
And praise the Spirit, Three in One:

St. Francis of Assisi, 1182-1226;
tr. by William Henry Draper, 1855-1933.

29

TE LAUDANT OMNIA. 7 7.7 7.7 7. J. F. SWIFT, 1847-1931.

1 ALL things praise Thee, Lord most high;
Heaven and earth and sea and sky,
All were for Thy glory made,
That Thy greatness thus displayed
Should all worship bring to Thee;
All things praise Thee: Lord, may we.

2 All things praise Thee; night to night
Sings in silent hymns of light;
All things praise Thee; day to day
Chants Thy power, in burning ray;
Time and space are praising Thee,
All things praise Thee: Lord, may we.

3 All things praise Thee; round her zones
Earth, with her ten thousand tones,
Rolls a ceaseless choral strain;
Roaring wind and deep-voiced main,
Rustling leaf and humming bee,
All things praise Thee: Lord, may we.

4 All things praise Thee; high and low,
Rain and dew and seven-hued bow,
Crimson sunset, fleecy cloud,
Rippling stream and tempest loud;
Summer, winter, all to Thee
Glory render: Lord, may we.

5 All things praise Thee; gracious Lord,
Great Creator, powerful Word,
Omnipresent Spirit, now
At Thy feet we humbly bow,
Lift our hearts in praise to Thee;
All things praise Thee: Lord, may we. Amen.

George William Conder, 1821-74.

30

SHEEN. 14 14.14 15. G. Holst, 1874-1934

Slower.

A - men.

'Απὸ δόξης εἰς δόξαν πορευόμενοι.

1 From glory to glory advancing, we praise Thee, O Lord;
Thy name with the Father and Spirit be ever adored.
From strength unto strength we go forward on Sion's highway,
To appear before God in the city of infinite day.

2 Thanksgiving and glory and worship, and blessing and love,
One heart and one song have the saints upon earth and above.
Evermore, O Lord, to Thy servants Thy presence be nigh;
Ever fit us by service on earth for Thy service on high. Amen.

From Liturgy of St. James;
tr. by C. W. Humphreys, c. 1906.

31

COMPTON. 6.6 8. D. 3 3. 6 6. G. C. Martin, 1844-1916.

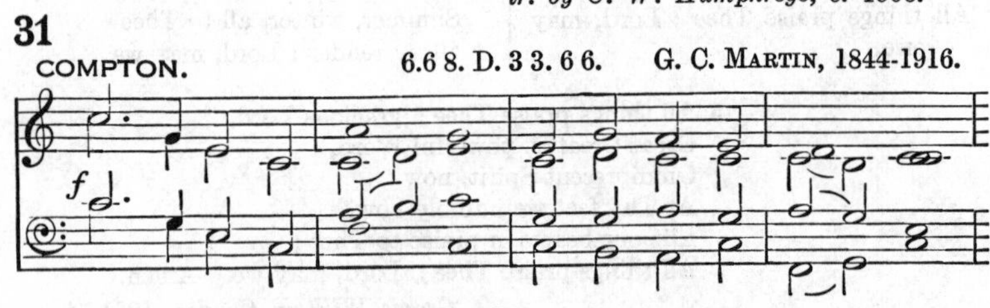

Gott ist gegenwärtig.

1 God reveals His presence:
Let us now adore Him,
And with awe appear before Him.
God is in His temple:
All within keep silence,
Prostrate lie with deepest reverence.
Him alone
God we own,
Him our God and Saviour:
Praise His name for ever.

2 God reveals His presence:
Hear the harps resounding,
See the crowds the throne surrounding!
Holy, holy, holy!
Hear the hymn ascending,
Angels, saints, their voices blending.
Bow Thine ear
To us here;
Hearken, O Lord Jesus,
To our meaner praises.

3 O Thou Fount of blessing,
Purify my spirit:
Trusting only in Thy merit,
Like the holy angels
Who behold Thy glory,
May I ceaselessly adore Thee.
Let Thy will
Ever still
Rule Thy Church terrestrial,
As the hosts celestial. Amen.

Gerhard Tersteegen, 1697-1769;
tr. by Frederick William Foster, 1760-1835;
and John Miller, 1756-90.

32

MARYTON. L.M. H. P. Smith, 1825-98.

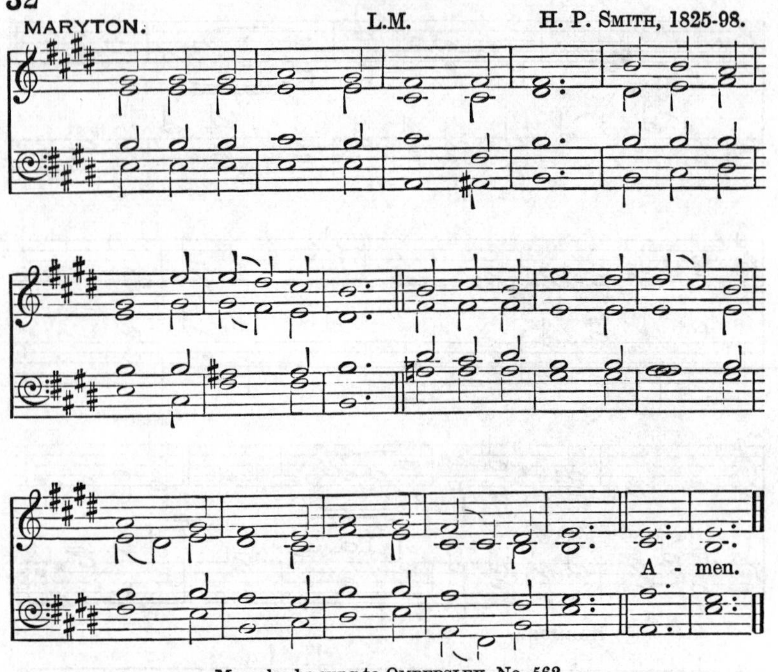

May also be sung to OMBERSLEY, No. 562.

1 Lord of all being, throned afar,
Thy glory flames from sun and star;
Centre and soul of every sphere,
Yet to each loving heart how near.

2 Sun of our life, Thy quickening ray
Sheds on our path the glow of day;
Star of our hope, Thy softened light
Cheers the long watches of the night.

3 Our midnight is Thy smile withdrawn,
Our noontide is Thy gracious dawn,
Our rainbow arch, Thy mercy's sign;
All, save the clouds of sin, are Thine.

4 Lord of all life, below, above,
Whose light is truth, whose warmth is love,
Before Thy ever-blazing throne
We ask no lustre of our own.

5 Grant us Thy truth to make us free,
And kindling hearts that burn for Thee,
Till all Thy living altars claim
One holy light, one heavenly flame. Amen.

Oliver Wendell Holmes, 1809-94.

33

STRASBURG 8 8.8 8.8 8. *Strasburg Psalter*, 1525.

Te Deum laudamus.

1 Infinite God, to Thee we raise
Our hearts in solemn songs of praise;
By all Thy works on earth adored,
We worship Thee, the common Lord;
The everlasting Father own,
And bow our souls before Thy throne.

2 Thee all the choir of angels sings,
The Lord of hosts, the King of kings;
Cherubs proclaim Thy praise aloud,
And seraphs shout the Triune God;
And: Holy, holy, holy! cry,
Thy glory fills both earth and sky!

3 God of the patriarchal race,
The ancient seers record Thy praise,
The goodly apostolic band
In highest joy and glory stand;
And all the saints and prophets join
To extol Thy majesty divine.

4 Head of the martyrs' noble host.
Of Thee they justly make their boast;
The Church, to earth's remotest bounds,
Her heavenly Founder's praise resounds;
And strives, with those around the throne,
To hymn the mystic Three in One.

5 Father of endless majesty,
All might and love they render Thee;
Thy true and only Son adore,
The same in dignity and power;
And God the Holy Ghost declare,
The saints' eternal Comforter.

Charles Wesley, 1707-88.

34

ST. DENIO 11 11.11 11. Welsh Hymn Melody.

1 IMMORTAL, invisible, God only wise,
In light inaccessible hid from our eyes,
Most blessèd, most glorious, the Ancient of Days,
Almighty, victorious, Thy great name we praise.

2 Unresting, unhasting, and silent as light,
Nor wanting, nor wasting, Thou rulest in might;
Thy justice like mountains high soaring above
Thy clouds which are fountains of goodness and love.

3 To all, life Thou givest—to both great and small;
In all life Thou livest, the true life of all;
We blossom and flourish as leaves on the tree,
And wither and perish—but nought changeth Thee.

4 Great Father of Glory, pure Father of Light,
Thine angels adore Thee, all veiling their sight;
All laud we would render; O help us to see:
'Tis only the splendour of light hideth Thee.

5 Immortal, invisible, God only wise,
In light inaccessible hid from our eyes,
Most blessèd, most glorious, the Ancient of Days,
Almighty, victorious, Thy great name we praise. Amen.

Walter Chalmers Smith, 1824-1908.

NORICUM. 7.7.7.7.7.7. F. James, 1858-1922.

May also be sung to CHARTERHOUSE, No. 416.

1 For the beauty of the earth,
  For the beauty of the skies,
For the love which from our birth
  Over and around us lies,
Gracious God, to Thee we raise
This our sacrifice of praise.

2 For the beauty of each hour
  Of the day and of the night,
Hill and vale, and tree and flower,
  Sun and moon and stars of light:

3 For the joy of ear and eye,
  For the heart and mind's delight,
For the mystic harmony
  Linking sense to sound and sight:

4 For the joy of human love,
  Brother, sister, parent, child,
Friends on earth and friends above,
  For all gentle thoughts and mild:

5 For each perfect gift of Thine
  To our race so freely given,
Graces human and divine,
  Flowers of earth and buds of heaven:

Folliott Sandford Pierpoint, 1835-1917.

Also:

39 Father, in whom we live
58 The Lord Jehovah reigns
73 My God, how wonderful Thou art
78 How shall I sing that majesty
425 My God, my King
668 Angel voices, ever singing
671 Sing Alleluia forth

God

THE HOLY TRINITY

36

NICÆA. 11 12.12 10. J. B. Dykes, 1823-76.

Amen.

1 Holy, holy, holy, Lord God Almighty!
Early in the morning our song shall rise to Thee;
Holy, holy, holy, merciful and mighty,
God in Three Persons, blessèd Trinity!

2 Holy, holy, holy; all the saints adore Thee,
Casting down their golden crowns around the glassy sea;
Cherubim and seraphim falling down before Thee,
Who wert, and art, and evermore shalt be.

3 Holy, holy, holy; though the darkness hide Thee,
Though the eye of sinful man Thy glory may not see,
Only Thou art holy; there is none beside Thee
Perfect in power, in love, and purity!

4 Holy, holy, holy, Lord God Almighty!
All Thy works shall praise Thy name in earth and sky and sea;
Holy, holy, holy, merciful and mighty,
God in Three Persons, blessèd Trinity! Amen.

Reginald Heber, 1783-1826.

37

DUNFERMLINE. C.M. *Scottish Psalter*, 1615.

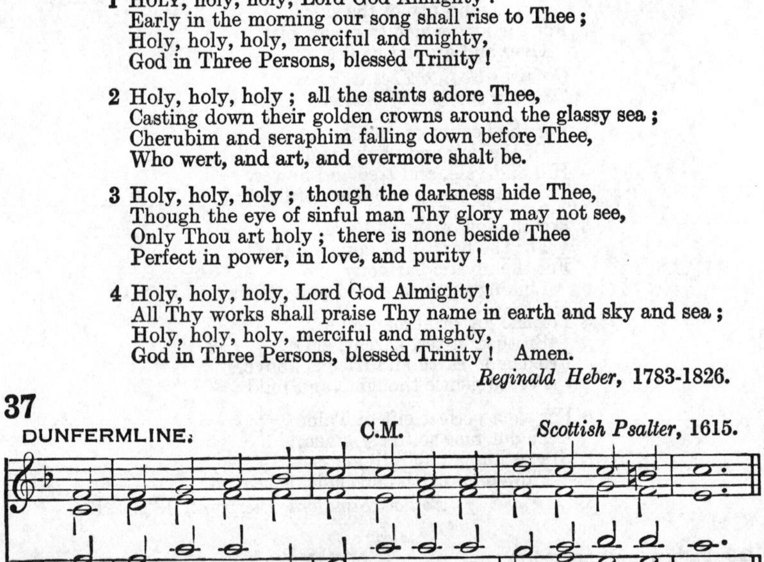

1 Hail! holy, holy, holy Lord!
Whom One in Three we know;
By all Thy heavenly host adored,
By all Thy Church below.

2 One undivided Trinity
With triumph we proclaim;
Thy universe is full of Thee,
And speaks Thy glorious name.

3 Thee, Holy Father, we confess,
Thee, Holy Son, adore,
Thee, Spirit of truth and holiness,
We worship evermore.

4 Three Persons equally divine
We magnify and love;
And both the choirs ere long shall join,
To sing Thy praise above.

5 Hail! holy, holy, holy Lord,
Our heavenly song shall be,
Supreme, essential One, adored
In co-eternal Three. Amen.

Charles Wesley, 1707-88.

38

RIVAULX L.M. J. B. Dykes, 1823-76.

1 Father of heaven, whose love profound
A ransom for our souls hath found,
Before Thy throne we sinners bend;
To us Thy pardoning love extend.

2 Almighty Son, incarnate Word,
Our Prophet, Priest, Redeemer, Lord,
Before Thy throne we sinners bend;
To us Thy saving grace extend.

3 Eternal Spirit, by whose breath
The soul is raised from sin and death,
Before Thy throne we sinners bend;
To us Thy quickening power extend.

4 Thrice holy: Father, Spirit, Son;
Mysterious Godhead, Three in One,
Before Thy throne we sinners bend;
Grace, pardon, life to us extend.
Amen.

Edward Cooper, 1770-1833.

39

FAIRFIELD. D.S.M. P. Latrobe, 1795-1863.

1 Father, in whom we live,
In whom we are, and move,
The glory, power, and praise receive
Of Thy creating love.
Let all the angel throng
Give thanks to God on high;
While earth repeats the joyful song,
And echoes to the sky.

2 Incarnate Deity,
Let all the ransomed race
Render in thanks their lives to Thee,
For Thy redeeming grace.
The grace to sinners showed
Ye heavenly choirs proclaim,
And cry: Salvation to our God,
Salvation to the Lamb!

3 Spirit of Holiness,
Let all Thy saints adore
Thy sacred energy, and bless
Thine heart-renewing power.
Not angel tongues can tell
Thy love's ecstatic height,
The glorious joy unspeakable,
The beatific sight.

4 Eternal, Triune Lord!
Let all the hosts above,
Let all the sons of men, record
And dwell upon Thy love.
When heaven and earth are fled
Before Thy glorious face,
Sing all the saints Thy love hath made
Thine everlasting praise.

Amen.

Charles Wesley, 1707-88.

The Holy Trinity

40

CROFT'S 136TH. 6.6.6.6.8 8. W. CROFT, 1678-1727.

May also be sung to TRUMPET, A. T. No. 17.

1 WE give immortal praise
To God the Father's love,
For all our comforts here,
And better hopes above.
He sent His own eternal Son,
To die for sins that man had done.

2 To God the Son belongs
Immortal glory too,
Who bought us with His blood
From everlasting woe;
And now He lives, and now He reigns,
And sees the fruit of all His pains.

3 To God the Spirit's name
Immortal worship give,
Whose new-creating power
Makes the dead sinner live.
His work completes the great design,
And fills the soul with joy divine.

4 Almighty God, to Thee
Be endless honours done,
The undivided Three,
And the mysterious One.
Where reason fails, with all her powers,
There faith prevails and love adores.

Isaac Watts, 1674-1748.

Also:

41 God is a name my soul adores

41 IN CREATION AND PROVIDENCE

BRESLAU. L.M. *As Hymnodus Sacer*, Leipzig, 1625

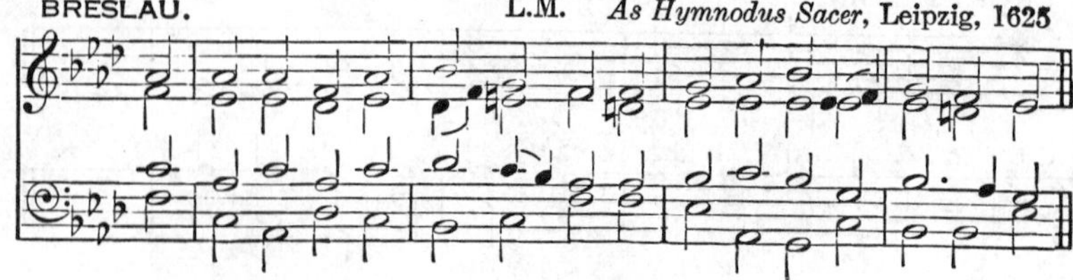

1 God is a name my soul adores,
The almighty Three, the eternal One; [powers,
Nature and grace, with all their
Confess the Infinite unknown.

2 Thy voice produced the sea and spheres, [shine;
Bade the waves roar, the planets
But nothing like Thyself appears
Through all these spacious works of Thine.

3 Still restless nature dies and grows,
From change to change the creatures run:
Thy being no succession knows,
And all Thy vast designs are one.

4 A glance of Thine runs through the globe,
Rules the bright worlds, and moves their frame; [robe,
Of light Thou form'st Thy dazzling
Thy ministers are living flame.

5 How shall polluted mortals dare
To sing Thy glory or Thy grace?
Beneath Thy feet we lie afar,
And see but shadows of Thy face.

6 Who can behold the blazing light?
Who can approach consuming flame?
None but Thy wisdom knows Thy might, [name.
None but Thy word can speak Thy

Isaac Watts, 1674-1748.

42

VOM HIMMEL HOCH (ERFURT). L.M. M. Luther, 1483-1546.

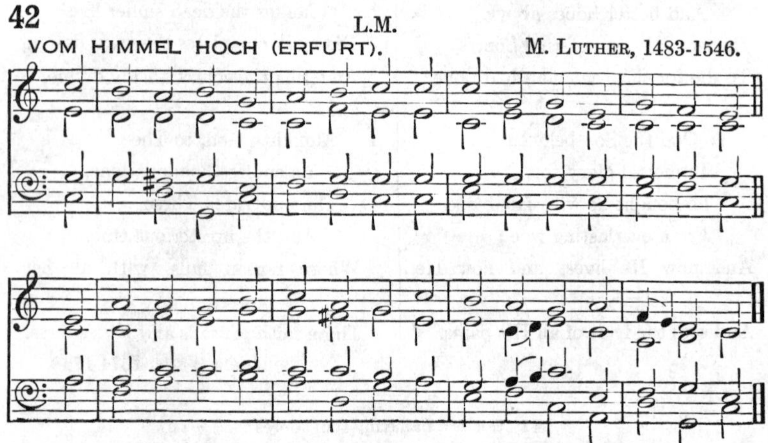

O Gott, du Tiefe sonder Grund.

1 O God, Thou bottomless abyss!
Thee to perfection who can know?
O height immense! What words suffice
Thy countless attributes to show?

2 Unfathomable depths Thou art;
O plunge me in Thy mercy's sea!
Void of true wisdom is my heart;
With love embrace and cover me.

3 Eternity Thy fountain was,
Which, like Thee, no beginning knew;
Thou wast ere time began his race,
Ere glowed with stars the ethereal blue.

4 Unchangeable, all-perfect Lord,
Essential life's unbounded sea,
What lives and moves, lives by Thy word;
It lives, and moves, and is from Thee.

5 Greatness unspeakable is Thine,
Greatness, whose undiminished ray,
When short-lived worlds are lost, shall shine
When earth and heaven are fled away.

Ernst Lange, 1650-1727;
tr. by John Wesley, 1703-91.

43

ST. FLAVIAN. C.M. Day's *Psalter*, 1562.

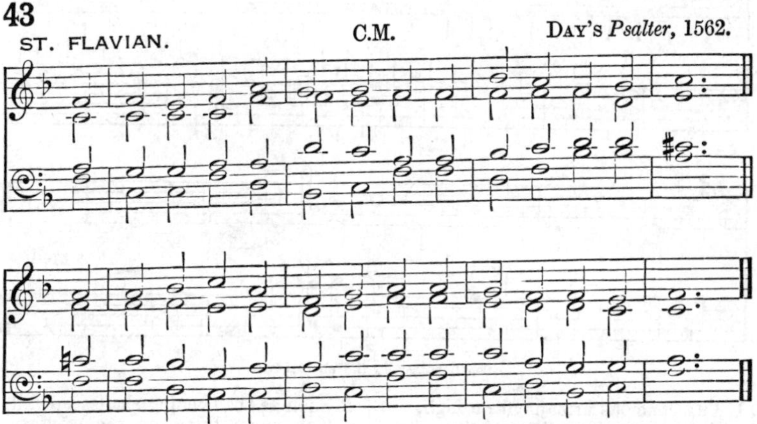

1 There is a book, who runs may read,
Which heavenly truth imparts,
And all the lore its scholars need,
Pure eyes and Christian hearts.

2 The works of God above, below,
Within us and around,
Are pages in that book, to show
How God Himself is found.

3 The glorious sky, embracing all,
Is like the Maker's love,
Wherewith encompassed, great and small
In peace and order move.

4 One Name above all glorious names,
With its ten thousand tongues
The everlasting sea proclaims,
Echoing angelic songs.

5 Two worlds are ours: 'tis only sin
Forbids us to descry
The mystic heaven and earth within,
Plain as the sea and sky.

6 Thou, who hast given me eyes to see
And love this sight so fair,
Give me a heart to find out Thee,
And read Thee everywhere.

John Keble, 1792-1866.

44

FIRMAMENT. D.L.M.

1st and 3rd Verses UNISON.
2nd Verse HARMONY.

H. WALFORD DAVIES, 1869-1941

1 THE spacious firmament on high,
With all the blue ethereal sky,
And spangled heavens, a shining frame,
Their great Original proclaim.
The unwearied sun, from day to day,
Doth his Creator's power display;
And publishes to every land
The work of an almighty hand.

2 Soon as the evening shades prevail,
The moon takes up the wondrous tale,
And nightly to the listening earth
Repeats the story of her birth:
While all the stars that round her burn,
And all the planets in their turn,
Confirm the tidings as they roll,
And spread the truth from pole to pole.

3 What though in solemn silence all
Move round this dark terrestrial ball;
What though no real voice nor sound
Amidst their radiant orbs be found:
In reason's ear they all rejoice,
And utter forth a glorious voice,
For ever singing as they shine:
The hand that made us is divine! Amen.

Joseph Addison, 1672-1719.

45

OLD 104TH. 5.5.5.5.6.5.6.5. RAVENSCROFT'S *Psalter*, 1621.

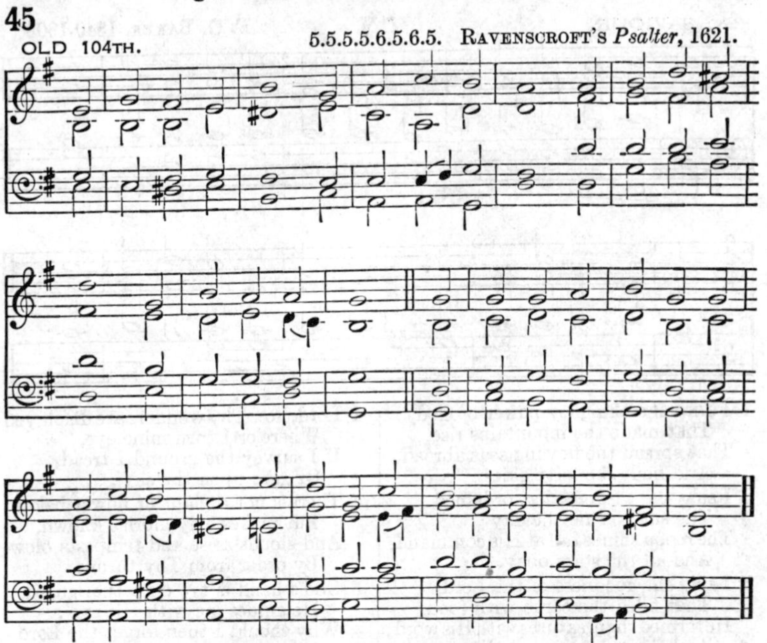

1 My soul, praise the Lord!
O God, Thou art great:
In fathomless works
Thyself Thou dost hide.
Before Thy dark wisdom
And power uncreate,
Man's mind, that dare praise Thee,
In fear must abide.

2 This earth where we dwell,
That journeys in space,
With air as a robe
Thou wrappest around:
Her countries she turneth
To greet the sun's face,
Then plungeth to slumber
In darkness profound.

3 All seemeth so sure,
Yet nought doth remain:
Unending their change
Obeys Thy decree.
The valleys of ocean
Stand up a dry plain,
Thou whelmest the mountains
Beneath the deep sea.

4 The clouds gather rain
And melt o'er the land,
Then back to the sun
Are drawn by his shine:
Whereby the corn springeth
Through toil of man's hand,
And vineyards that gladden
His heart with good wine.

5 All beasts of the field
Rejoice in their life;
Among the tall trees
Are light birds on wing;
With strains of their music
The woodlands are rife;
They nest in thick branches
And welcome sweet spring.

6 Lo, there is Thy sea,
Whose bosom below
With creatures doth teem,
Scaled fishes and finned.
Above, the ships laden
With merchandise go,
Nor fear the wild waters,
Nor rage of rude wind.

7 O God, Thou art great!
No greatness I see,
Except Thee alone,
Thy praise to record.
On all Thy works musing
My pleasure shall be;
My joy shall be singing:
My soul, praise the Lord!

William Kethe, d. 1593 (?);
alt. by Robert Seymour Bridges, 1844-1930. *Y. H.*

46

ST. SAVIOUR. C.M. F. G. BAKER, 1840-1908

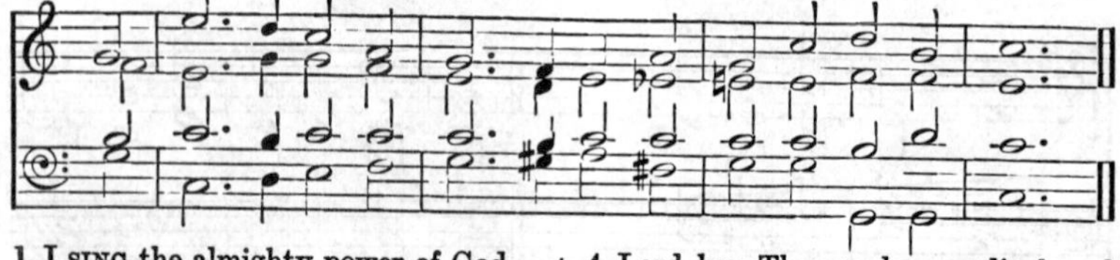

1 I SING the almighty power of God,
That made the mountains rise,
That spread the flowing seas abroad,
And built the lofty skies.

2 I sing the wisdom that ordained
The sun to rule the day;
The moon shines full at His command,
And all the stars obey.

3 I sing the goodness of the Lord,
That filled the earth with food;
He formed the creatures with His word,
And then pronounced them good.

4 Lord, how Thy wonders are displayed
Where'er I turn mine eye,
If I survey the ground I tread,
Or gaze upon the sky;

5 There's not a plant or flower below
But makes Thy glories known,
And clouds arise and tempests blow
By order from Thy throne.

6 God's hand is my perpetual guard,
He guides me with His eye;
Why should I then forget the Lord,
Whose love is ever nigh?

Isaac Watts, 1674-1748.

47

EISENACH. L.M. J. H. SCHEIN, 1586-1630
Arr. by J. S. BACH, 1685-1750

Ped.

A - men.

1 Father of all! whose powerful voice
Called forth this universal frame;
Whose mercies over all rejoice,
Through endless ages still the same:

2 Thou by Thy word upholdest all;
Thy bounteous love to all is showed,
Thou hear'st Thy every creature's call,
And fillest every mouth with good.

3 Giver and Lord of life, whose power
And guardian care for all are free,
To Thee, in fierce temptation's hour,
From sin and Satan let us flee.

4 Thine, Lord, we are, and ours Thou art;
In us be all Thy goodness showed.
Renew, enlarge, and fill our heart
With peace, and joy, and heaven, and God.

5 Father, 'tis Thine each day to yield
Thy children's wants a fresh supply;
Thou cloth'st the lilies of the field,
And hearest the young ravens cry.

6 On Thee we cast our care; we live
Through Thee, who know'st our every need:
O feed us with Thy grace, and give
Our souls this day the living bread.
Amen.

John Wesley, 1703-91

48

BERKSHIRE. L.M. C. Wesley, 1757-1834

1 High in the heavens, eternal God,
Thy goodness in full glory shines;
Thy truth shall break through every cloud
That veils and darkens Thy designs.

2 For ever firm Thy justice stands,
As mountains their foundations keep;
Wise are the wonders of Thy hands;
Thy judgements are a mighty deep.

3 Thy providence is kind and large,
Both man and beast Thy bounty share;
The whole creation is Thy charge,
But saints are Thy peculiar care.

4 My God, how excellent Thy grace,
Whence all our hope and comfort springs!
The sons of Adam in distress
Fly to the shadow of Thy wings.

5 Life, like a fountain rich and free,
Springs from the presence of the Lord;
And in Thy light our souls shall see
The glories promised in Thy word.

Isaac Watts, 1674-1748.

49

UNIVERSITY. C.M. J. RANDALL, 1715-99.

1 THY ceaseless, unexhausted love,
Unmerited and free,
Delights our evil to remove,
And help our misery.

2 Thou waitest to be gracious still;
Thou dost with sinners bear,
That, saved, we may Thy goodness feel,
And all Thy grace declare.

3 Thy goodness and Thy truth to me,
To every soul, abound,
A vast, unfathomable sea,
Where all our thoughts are drowned.

4 Its streams the whole creation reach,
So plenteous is the store,
Enough for all, enough for each,
Enough for evermore.

5 Faithful, O Lord, Thy mercies are,
A rock that cannot move:
A thousand promises declare
Thy constancy of love.

6 Throughout the universe it reigns,
Unalterably sure;
And while the truth of God remains,
The goodness must endure.

Charles Wesley, 1707-88.

50

KILMARNOCK. C.M. N. DOUGALL, 1776-1862.

May also be sung to STRACATHRO, No. 102.

1 The Lord's my Shepherd, I'll not want;
He makes me down to lie
In pastures green; He leadeth me
The quiet waters by.

2 My soul He doth restore again,
And me to walk doth make
Within the paths of righteousness,
E'en for His own name's sake.

3 Yea, though I walk in death's dark vale,
Yet will I fear no ill;
For Thou art with me, and Thy rod
And staff me comfort still.

4 My table Thou hast furnishèd
In presence of my foes;
My head Thou dost with oil anoint,
And my cup overflows.

5 Goodness and mercy all my life
Shall surely follow me,
And in God's house for evermore
My dwelling-place shall be.

William Whittingham, 1524-79;
Francis Rous, 1579-1659;
Revised by Westminster Assembly Divines, 1650.

51

St. Columba. C.M.

Irish Traditional Melody.
Arr. by C. V. Stanford, 1852-1924.

May also be sung to University, No. 49.

1 The God of love my Shepherd is,
And He that doth me feed;
While He is mine and I am His,
What can I want or need?

2 He leads me to the tender grass,
Where I both feed and rest;
Then to the streams that gently pass:
In both I have the best.

3 Or if I stray, He doth convert,
And bring my mind in frame,
And all this not for my desert,
But for His holy name.

4 Yea, in death's shady black abode
Well may I walk, not fear;
For Thou art with me, and Thy rod
To guide, Thy staff to bear.

5 Surely Thy sweet and wondrous love
Shall measure all my days;
And, as it never shall remove,
So neither shall my praise.

George Herbert, 1593-1632.

52

MARTHAM. L.M. J. H. MAUNDER, 1858-1920.

1 O LOVE of God, how strong and true;
Eternal, and yet ever new;
Uncomprehended and unbought,
Beyond all knowledge and all thought!

2 O heavenly Love, how precious still,
In days of weariness and ill,
In nights of pain and helplessness,
To heal, to comfort, and to bless.

3 O wide-embracing, wondrous Love;
We read thee in the sky above,
We read thee in the earth below,
In seas that swell and streams that flow.

4 We read thee best in Him who came
To bear for us the Cross of shame,
Sent by the Father from on high,
Our life to live, our death to die.

5 We read thy power to bless and save
E'en in the darkness of the grave;
Still more in resurrection light
We read the fullness of thy might.

6 O Love of God, our shield and stay
Through all the perils of our way;
Eternal Love, in thee we rest,
For ever safe, for ever blest.

Horatius Bonar, 1808-89.

53

SUSSEX (*First Tune*). 8.7.8.7. *English Traditional Melody.*

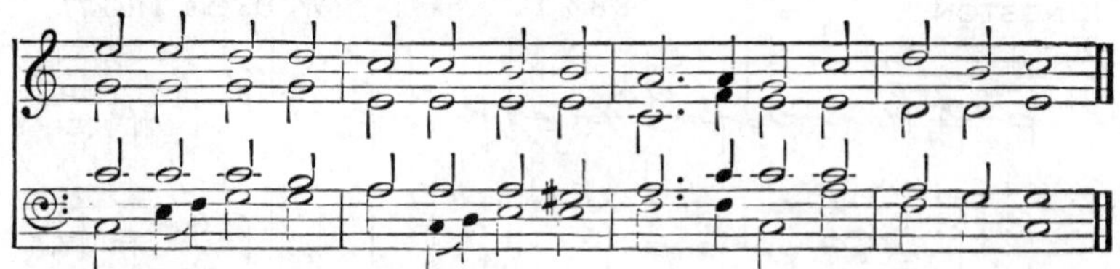

1 God is love: His mercy brightens
All the path in which we rove;
Bliss He wakes, and woe He lightens:
God is wisdom, God is love.

2 Chance and change are busy ever;
Man decays, and ages move;
But His mercy waneth never:
God is wisdom, God is love.

3 E'en the hour that darkest seemeth
Will His changeless goodness prove;
From the gloom His brightness streameth:
God is wisdom, God is love.

4 He with earthly cares entwineth
Hope and comfort from above;
Everywhere His glory shineth:
God is wisdom, God is love.

John Bowring, 1792-1872.

54

SELMA. S.M. *Traditional Scottish Melody of the Isle of Arran.*

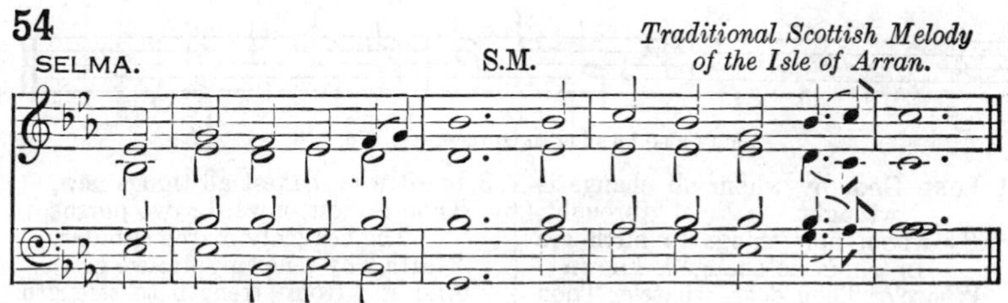

1 My soul, repeat His praise
Whose mercies are so great,
Whose anger is so slow to rise,
So ready to abate.

2 God will not always chide;
And when His strokes are felt,
His strokes are fewer than our crimes,
And lighter than our guilt.

3 High as the heavens are raised
Above the ground we tread,
So far the riches of His grace
Our highest thoughts exceed.

4 The pity of the Lord
To those that fear His name
Is such as tender parents feel;
He knows our feeble frame.

5 Our days are as the grass,
Or like the morning flower;
If one sharp blast sweep o'er the field,
It withers in an hour.

6 But Thy compassions, Lord,
To endless years endure;
And children's children ever find
Thy words of promise sure.
Amen.

Isaac Watts, 1674-1748.

55

KINGSTON. 8 8.6. D. W. HAYES, 1706-77.

May also be sung to GROSVENOR, No. 576.

1 LORD God, by whom all change is wrought,
By whom new things to birth are brought,
In whom no change is known;
Whate'er Thou dost, whate'er Thou art,
Thy people still in Thee have part,
Still, still Thou art our own.

2 Ancient of Days, we dwell in Thee;
Out of Thine own eternity
Our peace and joy are wrought;
We rest in our eternal God,
And make secure and sweet abode
With Thee, who changest not.

3 Spirit who makest all things new,
Thou leadest onward; we pursue
The heavenly march sublime.
'Neath Thy renewing fire we glow,
And still from strength to strength we go,
From height to height we climb.

4 Darkness and dread we leave behind;
New light, new glory still we find,
New realms divine possess;
New births of grace, new raptures bring;
Triumphant, the new song we sing,
The great Renewer bless.

5 To Thee we rise, in Thee we rest;
We stay at home, we go in quest,
Still Thou art our abode.
The rapture swells, the wonder grows,
As full on us new life still flows
From our unchanging God.

Thomas Hornblower Gill, 1819-1906.

56

ST. STEPHEN. C.M. W. JONES, 1726-1800.

1 Sweet is the memory of Thy grace,
My God, my heavenly King:
Let age to age Thy righteousness
In sounds of glory sing.

2 God reigns on high, but not confines
His bounty to the skies:
Through the whole earth His goodness shines,
And every want supplies.

3 With longing eyes the creatures wait
On Thee for daily food;
Thy liberal hand provides them meat,
And fills their mouths with good.

4 How kind are Thy compassions, Lord,
How slow Thine anger moves;
But soon He sends His pardoning word,
To cheer the souls He loves.

5 Creatures, with all their endless race,
Thy power and praise proclaim;
But we, who taste Thy richer grace,
Delight to bless Thy name.

Isaac Watts, 1674-1748.

57

WILTSHIRE. C.M. G. T. Smart, 1776-1867.

1 In all my vast concerns with Thee,
In vain my soul would try
To shun Thy presence, Lord, or flee
The notice of Thine eye.

2 Thy all-surrounding sight surveys
My rising and my rest,
My public walks, my private ways,
The secrets of my breast.

3 My thoughts lie open to Thee, Lord,
Before they're formed within;
And, ere my lips pronounce the word,
Thou know'st the sense I mean.

4 O wondrous knowledge, deep and high;
Where can a creature hide?
Within Thy circling arms I lie,
Beset on every side.

5 So let Thy grace surround me still,
And like a bulwark prove,
To guard my soul from every ill,
Secured by sovereign love. Amen.

Isaac Watts, 1674-1748.

58

ADORATION. 6.6.6.6.8 8. W. H. HAVERGAL, 1793-1870.

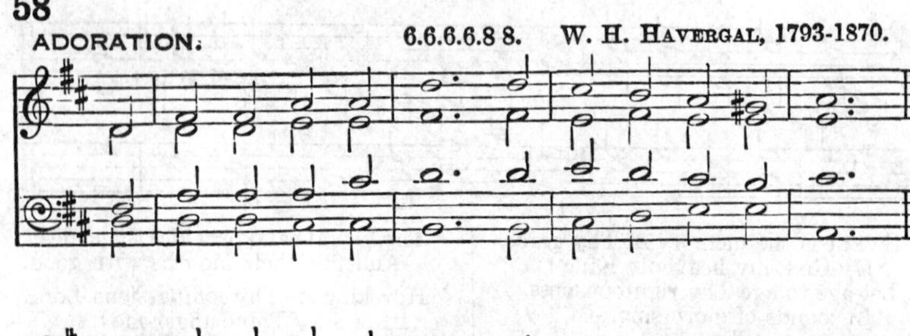

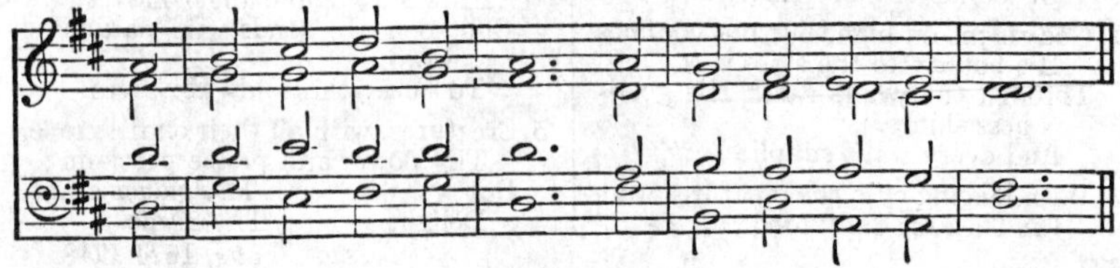

1 THE Lord Jehovah reigns;
His throne is built on high,
The garments He assumes
Are light and majesty: [bright,
His glories shine with beams so
No mortal eye can bear the sight.

2 The thunders of His hand
Keep the wide world in awe;
His wrath and justice stand
To guard His holy law;
And where His love resolves to bless,
His truth confirms and seals the grace.

3 Through all His mighty works
Amazing wisdom shines,
Confounds the powers of hell,
And breaks their dark designs;
Strong is His arm, and shall fulfil
His great decrees and sovereign will.

4 And will this sovereign King
Of Glory condescend?
And will He write His name
My Father and my Friend?
I love His name, I love His word,
Join all my powers to praise the Lord. Amen.

Isaac Watts, 1674-1748.

Also:

His Love in Redemption

59

ELEVATION. 7.6.7.6.7.8.7.6. R. MELLOR, 1816-82

1 GOOD Thou art, and good Thou dost,
Thy mercies reach to all,
Chiefly those who on Thee trust,
And for Thy mercy call;
New they every morning are;
As fathers when their children cry,
Us Thou dost in pity spare,
And all our wants supply.

2 Mercy o'er Thy works presides;
Thy providence displayed
Still preserves, and still provides
For all Thy hands have made;
Keeps with most distinguished care
The man who on Thy love depends;
Watches every numbered hair,
And all his steps attends.

3 Who can sound the depths unknown
Of Thy redeeming grace;
Grace that gave Thine only Son
To save a ruined race?
Millions of transgressors poor
Thou hast for Jesu's sake forgiven,
Made them of Thy favour sure,
And snatched from hell to heaven.

4 Millions more Thou ready art
To save, and to forgive;
Every soul and every heart
Of man Thou wouldst receive:
Father, now accept of mine,
Which now, through Christ, I offer Thee;
Tell me now, in love divine,
That Thou hast pardoned me.

Charles Wesley, 1707-88.

PEARSALL. 7.6.7.6. D. St. Gall *Gesangbuch*, 1863.

1 Ere God had built the mountains,
Or raised the fruitful hills;
Before He filled the fountains
That feed the running rills;
In me, from everlasting,
The wonderful I AM
Found pleasures never wasting,
And Wisdom is my name.

2 When, like a tent to dwell in,
He spread the skies abroad,
And swathed about the swelling
Of ocean's mighty flood,
He wrought by weight and measure,
And I was with Him then;
Myself the Father's pleasure,
And mine, the sons of men.

3 Thus Wisdom's words discover
Thy glory and Thy grace,
Thou everlasting lover
Of our unworthy race:
Thy gracious eye surveyed us
Ere stars were seen above;
In wisdom Thou hast made us,
And died for us in love.

4 And couldst Thou be delighted
With creatures such as we,
Who, when we saw Thee, slighted
And nailed Thee to a tree?
Unfathomable wonder,
And mystery divine;
The voice that speaks in thunder
Says: Sinner, I am thine!

William Cowper, 1731-1800.

61

EXULTATION. 8.7.8.7. D. A. C. MACKENZIE, 1847-1935

1 EARTH, with all thy thousand voices,
Praise in songs the eternal King;
Praise His name, whose praise rejoices
Ears that hear and tongues that sing.
Lord, from each far-peopled dwelling
Earth shall raise the glad acclaim;
All shall kneel, Thy greatness telling,
Sing Thy praise and bless Thy name.

2 Come and hear the wondrous story,
How our mighty God of old,
In the terrors of His glory,
Back the flowing billows rolled:
Walled within the threatening waters,
Free we passed the upright wave;
Then was joy to Israel's daughters,
Loud they sang His power to save.

3 Bless the Lord, who ever liveth;
Sound His praise through every land,
Who our dying souls reviveth,
By whose arm upheld we stand.
Now upon this cheerful morrow
We Thine altars will adorn,
And the gifts we vowed in sorrow
Pay on joy's returning morn.

4 Come, each faithful soul, who fearest
Him who fills the eternal throne:
Hear, rejoicing while thou hearest,
What our God for us hath done;
When we made our supplication,
When our voice in prayer was strong,
Straight we found His glad salvation;
And His mercy fills our tongue.

Edward Churton, 1800-74.

62

O AMOR QUAM EXSTATICUS. L.M. Old French Melody.

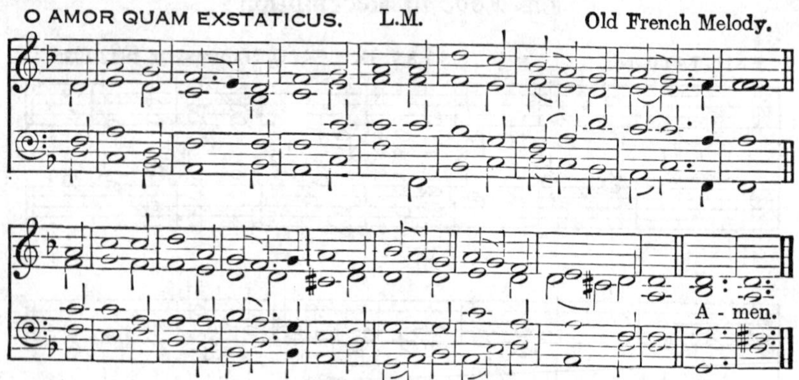

O amor quam exstaticus.

1 O LOVE, how deep, how broad, how high!
It fills the heart with ecstasy,
That God, the Son of God, should take
Our mortal form, for mortals' sake.

2 He sent no angel to our race,
Of higher or of lower place,
But wore the robe of human frame
Himself, and to this lost world came.

3 For us He was baptized and bore
His holy fast, and hungered sore;
For us temptation sharp He knew,
For us the tempter overthrew.

4 For us He prayed, for us He taught,
For us His daily works He wrought:
By words and signs and actions thus
Still seeking, not Himself, but us.

5 For us to wicked men betrayed, [rayed,
Scourged, mocked, in purple robe ar-
He bore the shameful Cross and death,
For us at length gave up His breath.

6 For us He rose from death again;
For us He went on high to reign;
For us He sent His Spirit here
To guide, to strengthen, and to cheer.

7 To Him whose boundless love has won
Salvation for us through His Son,
To God the Father, glory be,
Both now and through eternity. Amen.

Anonymous: From a 15th cent. MS.;
tr. and doxology by Benjamin Webb, 1820-85.

63

OSSETT. L.M. A. WIDDOP, *c.* 1750-1801.

Du ewiger Abgrund der seligen Liebe.

1 ETERNAL depth of love divine,
In Jesus, God with us, displayed;
How bright Thy beaming glories shine!
How wide Thy healing streams are spread!

2 With whom dost Thou delight to dwell?
Sinners, a vile and thankless race:
O God, what tongue aright can tell
How vast Thy love, how great Thy grace!

3 The dictates of Thy sovereign will
With joy our grateful hearts receive:
All Thy delight in us fulfil;
Lo! all we are to Thee we give.

4 To Thy sure love, Thy tender care,
Our flesh, soul, spirit, we resign:
O fix Thy sacred presence there,
And seal the abode for ever Thine!

5 O King of Glory, Thy rich grace
Our feeble thought surpasses far;
Yea, even our sins, though numberless,
Less numerous than Thy mercies are.

6 Still, Lord, Thy saving health display,
And arm our souls with heavenly zeal;
So fearless shall we urge our way
Through all the powers of earth and hell.

Nicolaus Ludwig von Zinzendorf, 1700-60;
tr. by John Wesley, 1703-91.

64

LOBE DEN HERREN. 14 14.4 7.8. *Stralsund Gesangbuch*, 1665.

A - men.

Lobe den Herren, den mächtigen König der Ehren.

1 PRAISE to the Lord, the Almighty, the King of creation;
O my soul, praise Him, for He is thy health and salvation;
All ye who hear,
Brothers and sisters draw near,
Praise Him in glad adoration.

2 Praise to the Lord, who doth prosper thy work and defend thee;
Surely His goodness and mercy here daily attend thee:
Ponder anew
What the Almighty can do,
If with His love He befriend thee.

3 Praise to the Lord, who, when tempests their warfare are waging,
Who, when the elements madly around thee are raging,
Biddeth them cease,
Turneth their fury to peace,
Whirlwinds and waters assuaging.

4 Praise to the Lord, who when darkness of sin is abounding,
Who, when the godless do triumph, all virtue confounding,
Sheddeth His light,
Chaseth the horrors of night,
Saints with His mercy surrounding.

5 Praise to the Lord! O let all that is in me adore Him!
All that hath life and breath, come now with praises before Him!
Let the Amen
Sound from His people again:
Gladly for aye we adore Him. Amen.

Joachim Neander, 1650-80;
tr. by Catherine Winkworth, 1827-78, *and others.*

65

TARSUS. 8 8.8. D. J. Goss, 1800-80.

A- men.

1 O God of God, in whom combine,
The heights and depths of love divine,
With thankful hearts to Thee we sing;
To Thee our longing souls aspire,
In fervent flames of strong desire:
Come, and Thy sacred unction bring.

2 O powerful Love, to Thee we bow;
Object of all our wishes Thou,
Our hearts are naked to Thine eye;
To Thee, who from the eternal throne
Cam'st emptied of Thy glory down,
For us to groan, to bleed, to die.

3 Grace we implore: when billows roll,
Grace is the anchor of the soul;
Grace every sickness knows to heal;
Grace can subdue each fond desire,
And patience in all pain inspire,
Howe'er rebellious nature swell.

4 Be heaven, e'en now, our soul's abode,
Hid be our life with Christ in God,
Our spirit, Lord, be one with Thine;
Let all our works in Thee be wrought,
And filled with Thee be all our thought,
Till in us Thy full likeness shine. Amen.

German: tr. by John Wesley, 1703-91.

66

HARWICH. 5 5 11. D. B. MILGROVE, c. 1731-1810.

1 O GOD of all grace,
Thy goodness we praise;
Thy Son Thou hast given to die in our place.
He came from above
Our curse to remove;
He hath loved, He hath loved us, because He would love.

2 Love moved Him to die,
And on this we rely;
He hath loved, He hath loved us: we cannot tell why;
But this we can tell,
He hath loved us so well
As to lay down His life to redeem us from hell.

3 He hath ransomed our race;
O how shall we praise
Or worthily sing Thy unspeakable grace?
Nothing else will we know
In our journey below,
But singing Thy grace to Thy paradise go.

4 Nay, and when we remove
To Thy presence above,
Our heaven shall be still to sing of Thy love.
We all shall commend
The love of our Friend,
For ever beginning what never shall end.

Charles Wesley, 1707-88.

DRESDEN. 8 8.8. D. J. SCHMIDLIN, 1770.

Du unvergleichlich's Gut.

1 O GOD, of good the unfathomed sea!
Who would not give his heart to Thee?
Who would not love Thee with his might?
O Jesu, Lover of mankind,
Who would not his whole soul and mind,
With all his strength, to Thee unite?

2 Thou shin'st with everlasting rays;
Before the insufferable blaze
Angels with both wings veil their eyes:
Yet free as air Thy bounty streams
On all Thy works; Thy mercy's beams
Diffusive as Thy sun's arise.

3 Astonished at Thy frowning brow,
Earth, hell, and heaven's strong pillars bow;
Terrible majesty is Thine.
Who then can that vast love express
Which bows Thee down to me, who less
Than nothing am, till Thou art mine?

4 High throned on heaven's eternal hill,
In number, weight, and measure still
Thou sweetly orderest all that is:
And yet Thou deign'st to come to me,
And guide my steps, that I, with Thee
Enthroned, may reign in endless bliss.

5 Fountain of good! All blessing flows
From Thee; no want Thy fullness knows:
What but Thyself canst Thou desire?
Yet, self-sufficient as Thou art,
Thou dost desire my worthless heart;
This, only this, dost Thou require.

6 Primeval Beauty! In Thy sight
The first-born, fairest sons of light
See all their brightest glories fade:
What then to me Thine eyes could turn—
In sin conceived, of woman born—
A worm, a leaf, a blast, a shade?

7 Hell's armies tremble at Thy nod,
And trembling own the Almighty God,
Sovereign of earth, hell, air, and sky:
But who is this that comes from far,
Whose garments rolled in blood appear?
'Tis God made Man, for man to die!

8 O God, of good the unfathomed sea!
Who would not give his heart to Thee?
Who would not love Thee with his might?
O Jesu, Lover of mankind,
Who would not his whole soul and mind,
With all his strength, to Thee unite?

Johann Scheffler, 1624-77;
tr. by John Wesley, 1703-91.

His Love in Redemption

68

JESHURUN. 7.6.7.6.7.7.7.6. H. J. GAUNTLETT, 1805-76.

1 NONE is like Jeshurun's God,
So great, so strong, so high;
Lo! He spreads His wings abroad,
He rides upon the sky:
Israel is His first-born son;
God, the almighty God, is thine;
See Him to thy help come down,
The excellence divine.

2 Thee the great Jehovah deigns
To succour and defend;
Thee the eternal God sustains,
Thy Maker and thy Friend:
Israel, what hast thou to dread?
Safe from all impending harms,
Round thee and beneath are spread
The everlasting arms.

3 God is thine; disdain to fear
The enemy within:
God shall in thy flesh appear,
And make an end of sin;
God the man of sin shall slay,
Fill thee with triumphant joy;
God shall thrust him out, and say:
Destroy them all, destroy!

4 All the struggle then is o'er,
And wars and fightings cease;
Israel then shall sin no more,
But dwell in perfect peace:
All his enemies are gone;
Sin shall have in him no part;
Israel now shall dwell alone,
With Jesus in his heart.

5 Blest, O Israel, art thou!
What people is like thee?
Saved from sin by Jesus, now
Thou art and still shalt be;
Jesus is thy sevenfold shield,
Jesus is thy flaming sword;
Earth, and hell, and sin shall yield
To God's almighty Word.

Charles Wesley, 1707-88.

69

CELESTE. 8.8.8.8. *Lancashire Sunday School Songs*, 1857.

1 This, this is the God we adore,
Our faithful, unchangeable Friend;
Whose love is as great as His power,
And neither knows measure nor end.

2 'Tis Jesus, the first and the last,
Whose Spirit shall guide us safe home;
We'll praise Him for all that is past,
And trust Him for all that's to come.

Joseph Hart, 1712-68.

70

MEINE HOFFNUNG. 8.7.8.7.3 3 7. J. Neander, 1650-80.

Meine Hoffnung stehet feste.

1 All my hope on God is founded;
He doth still my trust renew,
Me through change and chance He guideth,
Only good and only true.
God unknown,
He alone
Calls my heart to be His own.

2 Pride of man and earthly glory,
Sword and crown betray his trust:
What with care and toil he buildeth,
Tower and temple fall to dust.
But God's power,
Hour by hour,
Is my temple and my tower.

3 God's great goodness aye endureth,
Deep His wisdom passing thought:
Splendour, light, and life attend Him,
Beauty springeth out of nought.
Evermore
From His store
New-born worlds rise and adore.

4 Daily doth the Almighty Giver
Bounteous gifts on us bestow.
His desire our soul delighteth,
Pleasure leads us where we go.
Love doth stand
At His hand;
Joy doth wait on His command.

5 Still from man to God eternal
Sacrifice of praise be done,
High above all praises praising
For the gift of Christ His Son.
Christ doth call
One and all:
Ye who follow shall not fall.

Joachim Neander, 1650-80;
tr. by Robert Seymour Bridges, 1844-1930. *Y. H.*

71

LUTHER. 8.7.8.7.8 8.7. KLUG'S *Gesangbuch*, 1535.

May be sung to GOLDEN CHAIN, No. 961.

1 We come unto our fathers' God;
Their Rock is our salvation;
The eternal arms, their dear abode,
We make our habitation;
We bring Thee, Lord, the praise they brought;
We seek Thee as Thy saints have sought
In every generation.

2 The fire divine their steps that led
Still goeth bright before us;
The heavenly shield around them spread
Is still high holden o'er us;
The grace those sinners that subdued,
The strength those weaklings that renewed,
Doth vanquish, doth restore us.

3 The cleaving sins that brought them low
Are still our souls oppressing;
The tears that from their eyes did flow
Fall fast, our shame confessing;
As with Thee, Lord, prevailed their cry,
So our strong prayer ascends on high
And bringeth down Thy blessing.

4 Their joy unto their Lord we bring;
Their song to us descendeth;
The Spirit who in them did sing
To us His music lendeth;
His song in them, in us, is one;
We raise it high, we send it on,
The song that never endeth.

5 Ye saints to come, take up the strain,
The same sweet theme endeavour:
Unbroken be the golden chain;
Keep on the song for ever;
Safe in the same dear dwelling-place,
Rich with the same eternal grace,
Bless the same boundless giver.

Thomas Hornblower Gill, 1819-1906.

72

ST. MAGNUS. C.M. J. CLARKE, 1659 *or* 1670-1707

1 BEGIN, my soul, some heavenly theme;
Awake, my voice, and sing
The mighty works, or mightier name,
Of our eternal King.

2 Tell of His wondrous faithfulness,
And sound His power abroad;
Sing the sweet promise of His grace,
The quickening word of God.

3 Proclaim salvation from the Lord,
For wretched, dying men:
His hand hath writ the sacred word
With an immortal pen.

4 Engraved as in eternal brass,
The mighty promise shines
Nor can the powers of darkness rase
Those everlasting lines.

5 His every word of grace is strong
As that which built the skies;
The voice that rolls the stars along
Speaks all the promises.

6 Now shall my fainting heart rejoice
To know Thy favour sure:
I trust the all-creating voice,
And faith desires no more.

Isaac Watts, 1674-1748.

73

WESTMINSTER. C.M. J. TURLE, 1802-82.

1 MY God, how wonderful Thou art,
Thy majesty how bright!
How beautiful Thy mercy-seat,
In depths of burning light!

2 How dread are Thine eternal years,
O everlasting Lord,
By prostrate spirits day and night
Incessantly adored!

3 How beautiful, how beautiful,
The sight of Thee must be,
Thine endless wisdom, boundless power,
And awful purity!

4 O how I fear Thee, living God,
With deepest, tenderest fears,
And worship Thee with trembling hope
And penitential tears!

5 Yet I may love Thee too, O Lord,
Almighty as Thou art,
For Thou hast stooped to ask of me
The love of my poor heart.

6 No earthly father loves like Thee;
No mother, e'er so mild,
Bears and forbears as Thou hast done
With me, Thy sinful child.

7 Father of Jesus, love's reward,
What rapture will it be
Prostrate before Thy throne to lie,
And gaze, and gaze on Thee.

Frederick William Faber, 1814-63.

74

GERONTIUS. C.M. J. B. DYKES, 1823-76.

1 PRAISE to the Holiest in the height,
And in the depth be praise :
In all His words most wonderful ;
Most sure in all His ways.

2 O loving wisdom of our God !
When all was sin and shame,
A second Adam to the fight
And to the rescue came.

3 O wisest love ! that flesh and blood
Which did in Adam fail,
Should strive afresh against the foe,
Should strive and should prevail.

4 And that a higher gift than grace
Should flesh and blood refine,
God's presence, and His very self
And essence all-divine.

5 O generous love ! that He, who smote
In man for man the foe,
The double agony in man
For man should undergo.

6 And in the garden secretly,
And on the Cross on high,
Should teach His brethren, and [inspire
To suffer and to die.

7 Praise to the Holiest in the height,
And in the depth be praise :
In all His words most wonderful ;
Most sure in all His ways.

John Henry Newman, 1801-90.

75

MELCOMBE. L.M. S. WEBBE, 1740-1816.

1 FATHER, whose everlasting love
Thy only Son for sinners gave,
Whose grace to all did freely move,
And sent Him down the world to save :

2 Help us Thy mercy to extol,
Immense, unfathomed, unconfined;
To praise the Lamb who died for all,
The general Saviour of mankind.

3 Thy undistinguishing regard
Was cast on Adam's fallen race ;
For all Thou hast in Christ prepared
Sufficient, sovereign, saving grace.

4 The world He suffered to redeem ;
For all He hath the atonement made ;
For those that will not come to Him
The ransom of His life was paid.

5 Arise, O God, maintain Thy cause !
The fullness of the Gentiles call ;
Lift up the standard of Thy Cross,
And all shall own Thou diedst for all.

Charles Wesley, 1707-88.

76

HARDWICKE. (*First Tune*). 8.7.8.7. Iambic. C. T. GROVES, 1888-1955.

8.7.8.7. Iambic.

DOMINUS REGIT ME (*Second Tune*). J. B. DYKES, 1823-76.

1 THE King of love my Shepherd is,
Whose goodness faileth never;
I nothing lack if I am His
And He is mine for ever.

2 Where streams of living water flow
My ransomed soul He leadeth,
And where the verdant pastures grow
With food celestial feedeth.

3 Perverse and foolish oft I strayed;
But yet in love He sought me,
And on His shoulder gently laid,
And home rejoicing brought me.

4 In death's dark vale I fear no ill
With Thee, dear Lord, beside me;
Thy rod and staff my comfort still,
Thy Cross before to guide me.

5 Thou spread'st a table in my sight;
Thy unction grace bestoweth;
And O what transport of delight
From Thy pure chalice floweth!

6 And so through all the length of days
Thy goodness faileth never;
Good Shepherd, may I sing Thy praise
Within Thy house for ever!
Amen.

Henry Williams Baker, 1821-77.

His Love in Redemption

77

JERUSALEM. C.M. S. GROSVENOR, c. 1840.

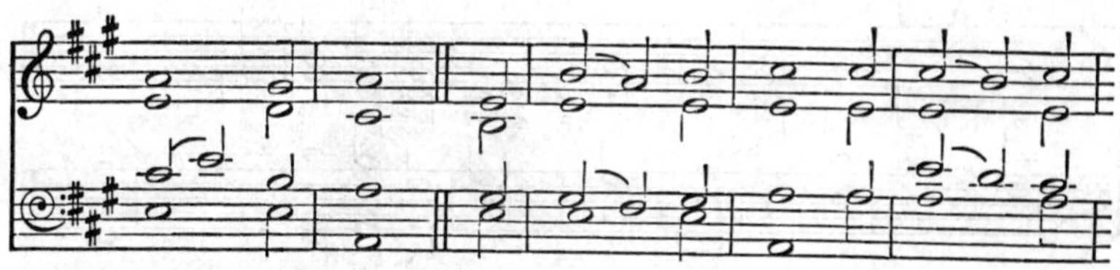

1 WHAT shall I do my God to love,
My loving God to praise?
The length, and breadth, and height to prove,
And depth of sovereign grace?

2 Thy sovereign grace to all extends,
Immense and unconfined;
From age to age it never ends;
It reaches all mankind.

3 Throughout the world its breadth is known,
Wide as infinity;
So wide it never passed by one,
Or it had passed by me.

4 My trespass was grown up to heaven;
But far above the skies,
In Christ abundantly forgiven,
I see Thy mercies rise.

5 The depth of all-redeeming love
What angel tongue can tell?
O may I to the utmost prove
The gift unspeakable.

6 Come quickly, gracious Lord, and take
Possession of Thine own;
My longing heart vouchsafe to make
Thine everlasting throne. Amen.

Charles Wesley, 1707-88.

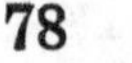

78

SOLL'S SEIN. D.C.M. CORNER'S *Gesangbuch*, 1631.

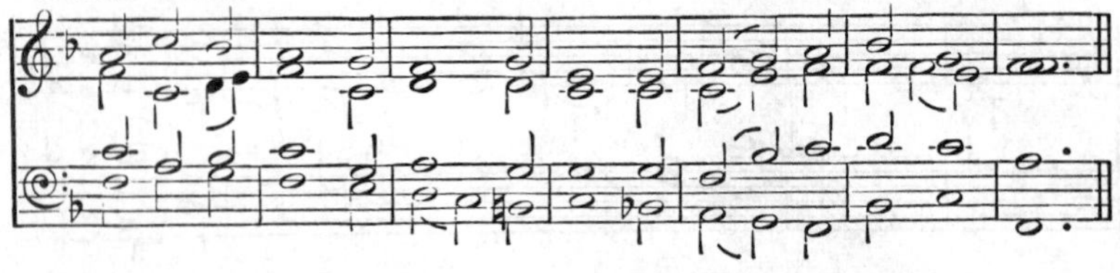

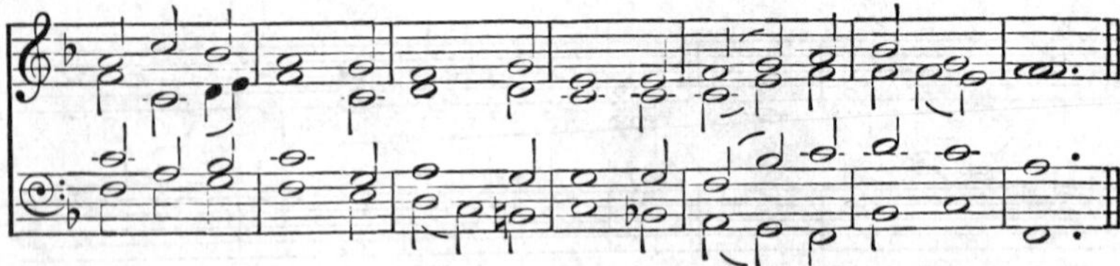

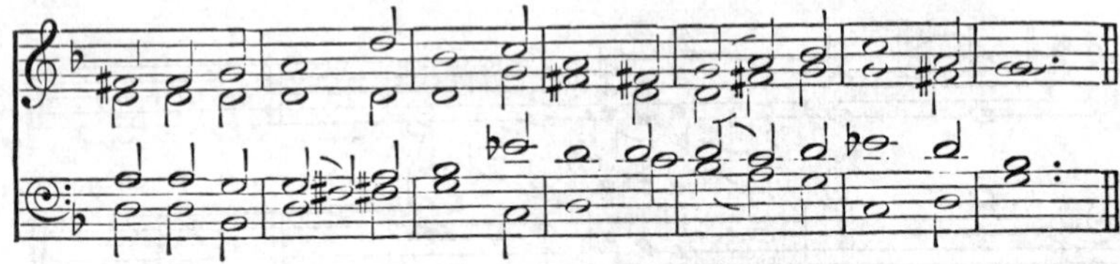

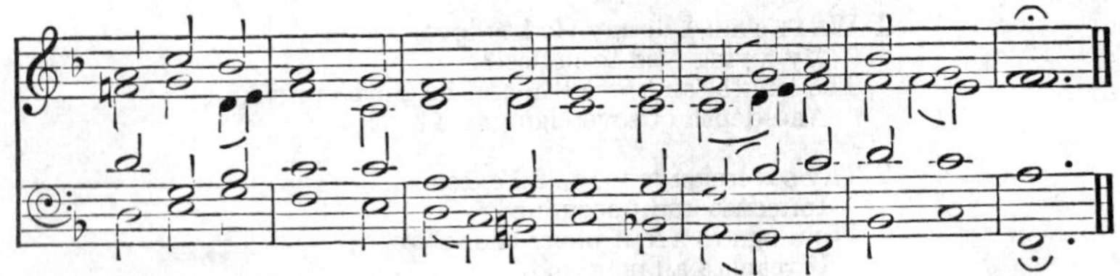

1 How shall I sing that majesty
Which angels do admire ?
Let dust in dust and silence lie ;
Sing, sing, ye heavenly choir.
Thousands of thousands stand around
Thy throne, O God most high ;
Ten thousand times ten thousand sound
Thy praise ; but who am I ?

2 Thy brightness unto them appears ;
Whilst I Thy footsteps trace
A sound of God comes to my ears,
But they behold Thy face.
They sing because Thou art their Sun ;
Lord, send a beam on me ;
For where heaven is but once begun
There alleluias be.

3 Enlighten with faith's light my heart,
Inflame it with love's fire ;
Then shall I sing and bear a part
With that celestial choir.
I shall, I fear, be dark and cold,
With all my fire and light ;
Yet when Thou dost accept their gold,
Lord, treasure up my mite.

4 How great a being, Lord, is Thine,
Which doth all beings keep !
Thy knowledge is the only line
To sound so vast a deep.
Thou art a sea without a shore,
A sun without a sphere ;
Thy time is now and evermore,
Thy place is everywhere.

John Mason, c. 1645-94.

79

JUSTIFICATION. L.M. J. EAGLETON, 1785-1832.

May also be sung to WARRINGTON, No. 389.

1 PRAISE ye the Lord! 'Tis good to raise
Your hearts and voices in His praise:
His nature and His works invite
To make this duty our delight.

2 He formed the stars, those heavenly flames,
He counts their numbers, calls their names;
His wisdom's vast, and knows no bound,
A deep where all our thoughts are drowned.

3 Sing to the Lord! Exalt Him high,
Who spreads His clouds along the sky;
There He prepares the fruitful rain,
Nor lets the drops descend in vain.

4 He makes the grass the hills adorn,
And clothes the smiling fields with corn;
The beasts with food His hands supply,
And the young ravens when they cry.

5 What is the creature's skill or force?
The sprightly man, or warlike horse?
The piercing wit, the active limb?
All are too mean delights for Him.

6 But saints are lovely in His sight,
He views His children with delight;
He sees their hope, He knows their fear,
And looks, and loves His image there.

Isaac Watts, 1674-1748.

80

DRESDEN. 8 8.8. D. J. SCHMIDLIN, 1770.

1 THEE will I praise with all my heart,
And tell mankind how good Thou art,
How marvellous Thy works of grace;
Thy name I will in songs record,
And joy and glory in my Lord,
Extolled above all thanks and praise.

2 The Lord will save His people here;
In times of need their help is near
To all by sin and hell oppressed;
And they that know Thy name will trust
In Thee, who, to Thy promise just,
Hast never left a soul distressed.

3 The Lord is by His judgements known;
He helps His poor afflicted one,
His sorrows all He bears in mind;
The mourner shall not always weep,
Who sows in tears in joy shall reap,
With grief who seeks with joy shall find.

4 A helpless soul that looks to Thee
Is sure at last Thy face to see,
And all Thy goodness to partake;
The sinner who for Thee doth grieve,
And longs, and labours to believe,
Thou never, never wilt forsake.

Charles Wesley, 1707-88.

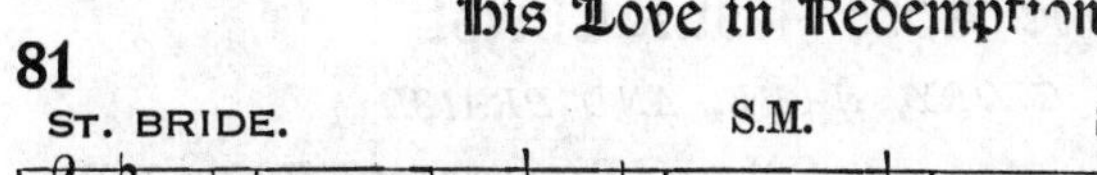

His Love in Redemption

81

ST. BRIDE. S.M. S. HOWARD, 1710-82.

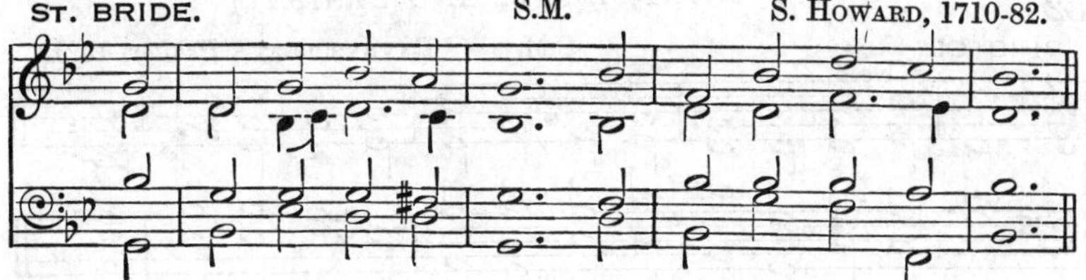

1 Not what these hands have done
Can save this guilty soul;
Not what this toiling flesh has borne
Can make my spirit whole.

2 Not what I feel or do
Can give me peace with God;
Not all my prayers, and sighs, and tears
Can bear my awful load.

3 Thy work alone, O Christ,
Can ease this weight of sin;
Thy blood alone, O Lamb of God,
Can give me peace within.

4 Thy love to me, O God,
Not mine, O Lord, to Thee,
Can rid me of this dark unrest,
And set my spirit free.

5 Thy grace alone, O God,
To me can pardon speak;
Thy power alone, O Son of God,
Can this sore bondage break.

6 I bless the Christ of God,
I rest on love divine,
And with unfaltering lip and heart,
I call this Saviour mine.

Horatius Bonar, 1808-89.

Also:

22 Come, let us all unite
24 O God, my strength
52 O Love of God, how strong
54 My soul, repeat His praise
56 Sweet is the memory
318 Souls of men
356 Great God of wonders!
424 O bless the Lord, my soul!
427 Through all the changing scenes
428 I'll praise my Maker
969 O Lord of heaven

The Lord Jesus Christ

HIS GLORY, NAME, AND PRAISE

82

BRISTOL. C.M. RAVENSCROFT'S *Psalter*, 1621.

1 HARK the glad sound! the Saviour comes,
The Saviour promised long;
Let every heart prepare a throne,
And every voice a song.

2 He comes the prisoners to release,
In Satan's bondage held;
The gates of brass before Him burst,
The iron fetters yield.

3 He comes the broken heart to bind,
The bleeding soul to cure,
And with the treasures of His grace
To enrich the humble poor.

4 Our glad hosannas, Prince of Peace,
Thy welcome shall proclaim,
And heaven's eternal arches ring
With Thy belovèd name.

Philip Doddridge, 1702-51.

83

CORDE NATUS. 8.7.8.7.8.7.7. Melody from *Piae Cantiones*, 1582.

His Glory, Name, and Praise

Corde natus ex parentis.

1 Of the Father's love begotten
Ere the worlds began to be,
He is Alpha and Omega,
He the source, the ending, He,
Of the things that are, that have been,
And that future years shall see,
Evermore and evermore.

2 By His word was all created;
He commanded and 'twas done;
Earth and sky and boundless ocean,
Universe of three in one,
All that sees the moon's soft radiance,
All that breathes beneath the sun.
Evermore and evermore.

3 This is He whom seers in old time
Chanted of with one accord,
Whom the voices of the prophets
Promised in their faithful word;
Now He shines, the long-expected;
Let creation praise its Lord,
Evermore and evermore.

4 Now let old and young uniting
Chant to Thee harmonious lays;
Maid and matron hymn Thy glory,
Infant lips their anthems raise,
Boys and girls together singing
With pure heart their song of praise.
Evermore and evermore.

5 O ye heights of heaven, adore Him;
Angel hosts, His praises sing;
All dominions, bow before Him,
And extol our God and King;
Let no tongue on earth be silent,
Every voice in concert sing,
Evermore and evermore. Amen.

Aurelius Clemens Prudentius, 348-413;
tr. by John Mason Neale, 1818-66.

84

ST. THEODULPH. 7.6.7.6. D. M. TESCHNER, *c.* 1615.

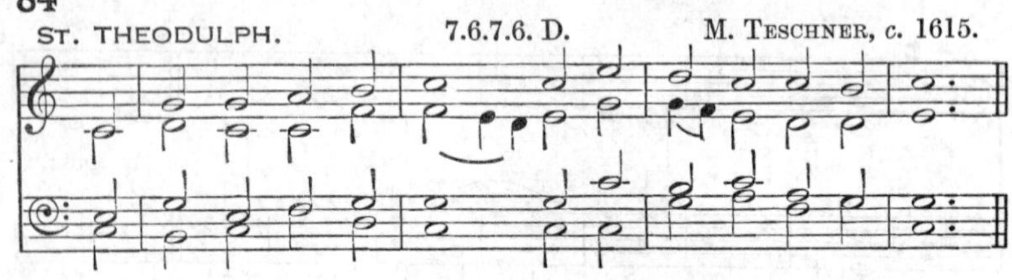

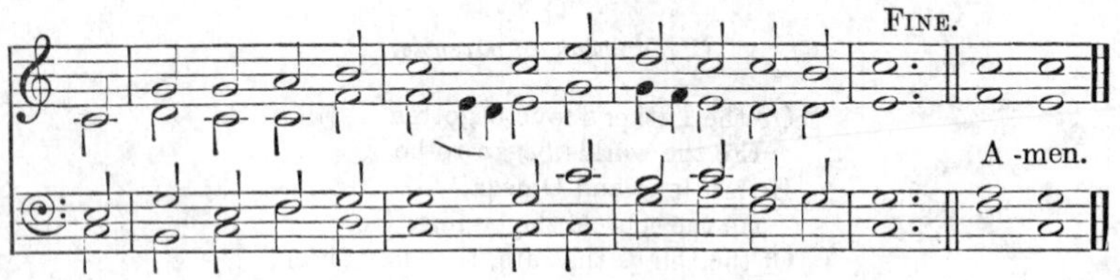

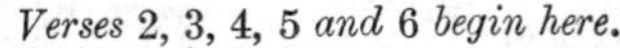

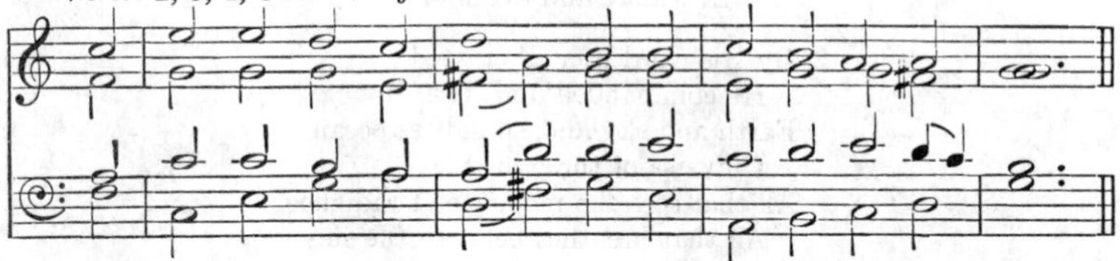

Gloria, laus et honor.

1 *All glory, laud, and honour*
To Thee, Redeemer, King,
To whom the lips of children
Made sweet hosannas ring!

2 Thou art the King of Israel,
Thou David's royal Son,
Who in the Lord's name comest,
The King and blessèd One.
All glory—

3 The company of angels
Are praising Thee on high,
And mortal men and all things
Created make reply.
All glory—

4 The people of the Hebrews
With palms before Thee went;
Our praise, and prayer, and anthems
Before Thee we present.
All glory—

5 To Thee before Thy passion
They sang their hymns of praise;
To Thee now high exalted
Our melody we raise.
All glory—

6 Thou didst accept their praises;
Accept the prayers we bring,
Who in all good delightest,
Thou good and gracious King.
All glory— Amen.

Theodulf of Orleans, c. 750-821;
tr. by John Mason Neale, 1818-66.

85

NATIVITY. C.M. H. LAHEE, 1826-1912.

May also be sung to LYDIA, No. 92.

1 COME, let us join our cheerful songs
With angels round the throne;
Ten thousand thousand are their
But all their joys are one. [tongues,

2 Worthy the Lamb that died, they cry,
To be exalted thus;
Worthy the Lamb, our hearts reply,
For He was slain for us.

3 Jesus is worthy to receive
Honour and power divine;
And blessings, more than we can give,
Be, Lord, for ever Thine.

4 The whole creation join in one
To bless the sacred name
Of Him that sits upon the throne,
And to adore the Lamb.

Isaac Watts, 1674-1748.

86

SONG 5. L.M. O. GIBBONS, 1583-1625.

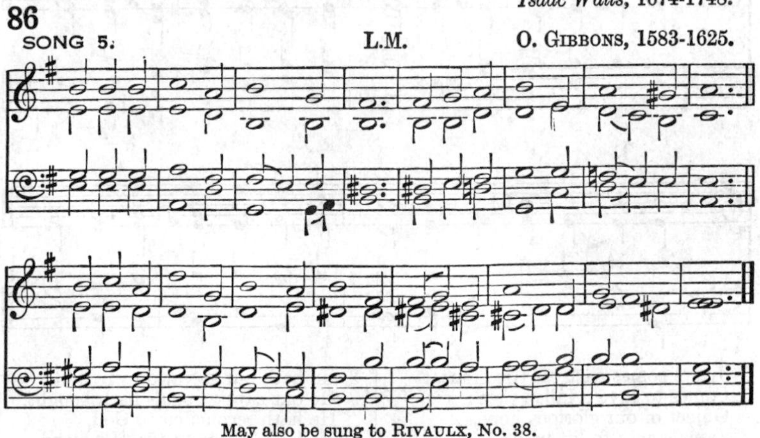

May also be sung to RIVAULX, No. 38.

1 STRONG Son of God, immortal Love,
Whom we, that have not seen Thy face,
By faith, and faith alone, embrace,
Believing where we cannot prove;

2 Thou wilt not leave us in the dust:
Thou madest man, he knows not why:
He thinks he was not made to die;
And Thou hast made him: Thou art just.

3 Thou seemest human and divine,
The highest, holiest manhood, Thou:
Our wills are ours, we know not how:
Our wills are ours, to make them Thine.

4 Our little systems have their day:
They have their day and cease to be:
They are but broken lights of Thee,
And Thou, O Lord, art more than they.

Alfred Tennyson, 1809-92.

1 Jesus comes with all His grace,
Comes to save a fallen race:
Object of our glorious hope,
Jesus comes to lift us up.

2 Let the living stones cry out;
Let the sons of Abraham shout;
Praise we all our lowly King,
Give Him thanks, rejoice, and sing.

3 He hath our salvation wrought,
He our captive souls hath bought,
He hath reconciled to God,
He hath washed us in His blood.

4 We are now His lawful right,
Walk as children of the light;
We shall soon obtain the grace,
Pure in heart, to see His face.

5 We shall gain our calling's prize;
After God we all shall rise,
Filled with joy, and love, and peace,
Perfected in holiness.

Charles Wesley, 1707-88.

88

ST. ASAPH. D.C.M. G. M. Giornivichi, 1745-1804.

1 We know, by faith we surely know,
The Son of God is come,
Is manifested here below,
And makes our hearts His home:
To us He hath, in gracious love,
An understanding given,
To recognize Him from above
The Lord of earth and heaven.

2 The self-existing God supreme,
Our Saviour we adore,
Fountain of life eternal, Him
We worship evermore:
Out of His plenitude receive
Ineffable delight,
And shall through endless ages live
Triumphant in His sight.

Charles Wesley, 1707-88.

89

7.7.7.7.

LÜBECK. FREYLINGHAUSEN'S *Gesangbuch*, 1704.

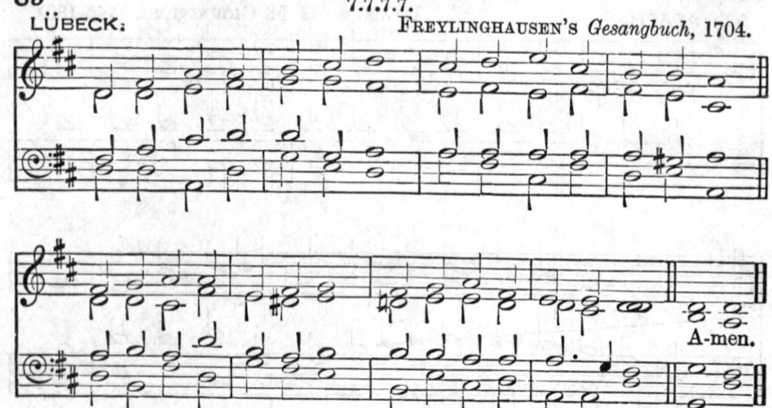

1 CHRIST, of all my hopes the ground,
Christ, the spring of all my joy,
Still in Thee may I be found,
Still for Thee my powers employ.

2 Let Thy love my heart inflame,
Keep Thy fear before my sight,
Be Thy praise my highest aim,
Be Thy smile my chief delight.

3 When affliction clouds my sky,
And the wintry tempests blow,
Let Thy mercy-beaming eye
Sweetly cheer the night of woe.

4 When new triumphs of Thy name
Swell the raptured songs above,
May I feel a kindred flame,
Full of zeal, and full of love.

5 Life's best joy, to see Thy praise
Fly on wings of gospel light,
Leading on millennial days,
Scattering all the shades of night.

6 Fountain of o'erflowing grace,
Freely from Thy fullness give;
Till I close my earthly race,
May I prove it Christ to live.

7 Firmly trusting in Thy blood,
Nothing shall my heart confound;
Safely shall I pass the flood,
Safely reach Immanuel's ground.

8 Thus, O thus, an entrance give
To the land of cloudless sky;
Having known it Christ to live,
Let me find it gain to die. Amen.

Ralph Wardlaw, 1779-1853.

90

THEODORA. 7.7.7.7. From HANDEL'S *Theodora*, 1749.

1 Object of my first desire,
Jesus, crucified for me;
All to happiness aspire,
Only to be found in Thee.

2 Thee to praise, and Thee to know,
Constitute my bliss below;
Thee to see, and Thee to love,
Constitute my bliss above.

3 Lord, it is not life to live,
If Thy presence Thou deny;
Lord, if Thou Thy presence give,
'Tis no longer death to die.

4 Source and giver of repose,
Only from Thy smile it flows,
Peace and happiness are Thine;
Mine they are, if Thou art mine.

5 Let me but Thyself possess—
Total sum of happiness—
Real bliss I then shall prove,
Heaven below and heaven above. Amen.

Augustus Montague Toplady, 1740-78.

91

MILES LANE. C.M. W. Shrubsole, 1760-1806.

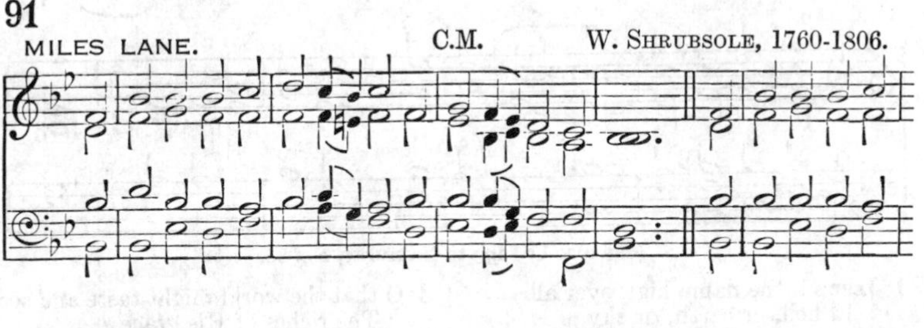

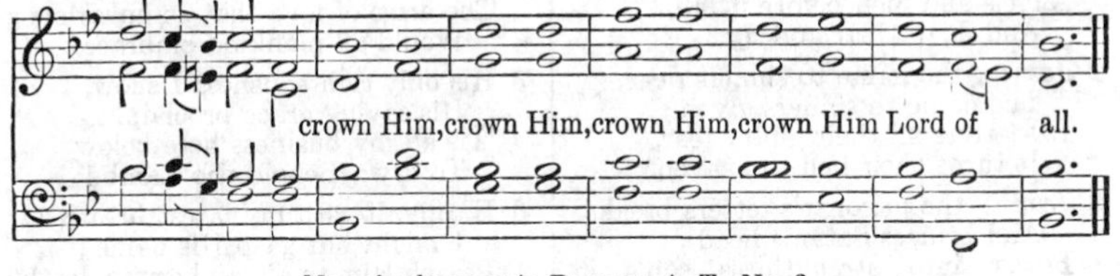
crown Him, crown Him, crown Him, crown Him Lord of all.

May also be sung to Diadem, A. T., No. 6.

1 All hail the power of Jesu's name;
Let angels prostrate fall;
Bring forth the royal diadem
To crown Him Lord of all.

2 Crown Him, ye martyrs of our God,
Who from His altar call;
Extol Him in whose path ye trod,
And crown Him Lord of all.

3 Ye seed of Israel's chosen race,
Ye ransomed from the fall,
Hail Him who saves you by His grace,
And crown Him Lord of all.

4 Sinners! whose love can ne'er forget
The wormwood and the gall;
Go spread your trophies at His feet,
And crown Him Lord of all.

5 Let every tribe and every tongue
Before Him prostrate fall,
And shout in universal song
The crownèd Lord of all.

6 O that with yonder sacred throng
We at His feet may fall,
Join in the everlasting song,
And crown Him Lord of all!

Edward Perronet, 1726-92;
John Rippon [*v.* 6], 1751-1836.

LYDIA. C.M. T. PHILLIPS, 1735-1807.

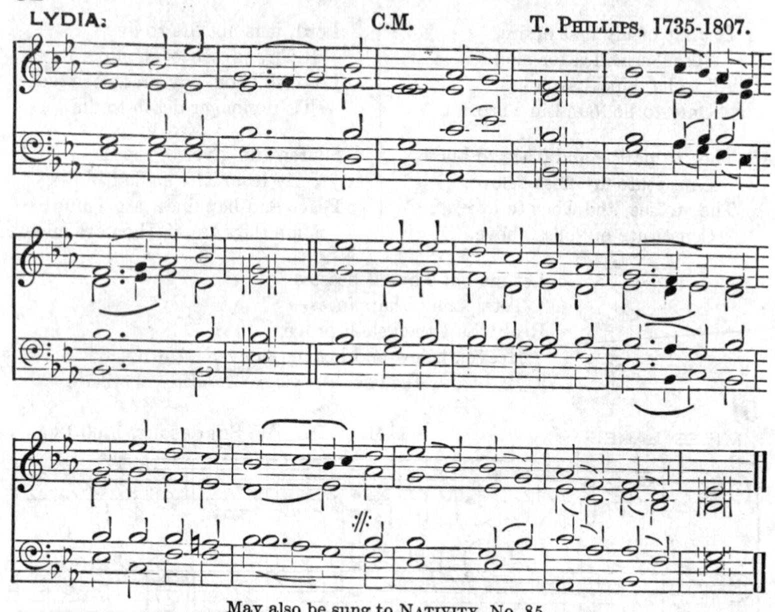

May also be sung to NATIVITY, No. 85.

1 JESUS! the name high over all,
In hell, or earth, or sky;
Angels and men before it fall,
And devils fear and fly.

2 Jesus! the name to sinners dear,
The name to sinners given;
It scatters all their guilty fear,
It turns their hell to heaven.

3 Jesus! the prisoner's fetters breaks,
And bruises Satan's head;
Power into strengthless souls it [speaks,
And life into the dead.

4 O that the world might taste and see
The riches of His grace;
The arms of love that compass me
Would all mankind embrace.

5 His only righteousness I show,
His saving grace proclaim;
'Tis all my business here below
To cry: Behold the Lamb!

6 Happy, if with my latest breath
I might but gasp His name;
Preach Him to all, and cry in death:
Behold, behold the Lamb!

Charles Wesley, 1707-88.

93

GRAFTON. 8.7.8.7.8.7. *French Church Melody.*

May also be sung to ORIEL, No. 615.

Gloriosi Salvatoris.

1 To the Name of our salvation,
Laud and honour let us pay,
Which for many a generation
Hid in God's foreknowledge lay,
But with holy exultation
We may sing aloud to-day.

2 Jesus is the Name we treasure,
Name beyond what words can tell;
Name of gladness, Name of pleasure,
Ear and heart delighting well;
Name of sweetness passing measure,
Saving us from sin and hell.

3 'Tis the Name for adoration,
Name for songs of victory,
Name for holy meditation
In this vale of misery,
Name for joyful veneration
By the citizens on high.

4 'Tis the Name that whoso preacheth
Speaks like music to the ear;
Who in prayer this Name beseecheth
Sweetest comfort findeth near;
Who its perfect wisdom reacheth,
Heavenly joy possesseth here.

5 Jesus is the Name exalted
Over every other name;
In this Name, whene'er assaulted,
We can put our foes to shame:
Strength to them who else had halted,
Eyes to blind, and feet to lame.

6 Therefore we in love adoring,
This most blessèd Name revere,
Holy Jesu, Thee imploring
So to write it in us here
That, hereafter heavenward soaring,
We may sing with Angels there.
Amen.

Anonymous, 15th cent.;
tr. by John Mason Neale, 1818-66.

94

ALL HALLOWS. 8.10.10.4. F. L. WISEMAN, 1858-1944

1 NONE other Lamb, none other Name,
None other hope in heaven or earth or sea,
None other hiding-place from guilt and shame,
None beside Thee.

2 My faith burns low, my hope burns low;
Only my heart's desire cries out in me,
By the deep thunder of its want and woe,
Cries out to Thee.

3 Lord, Thou art life, though I be dead;
Love's fire Thou art, however cold I be:
Nor heaven have I, nor place to lay my head,
Nor home, but Thee.

Christina Georgina Rossetti, 1830-94.

95

COLDREY. 7.6.7.6.7 7. H. SMART, 1813-79.

1 JESUS, Sun and Shield art Thou,
Sun and Shield for ever.
Never canst Thou cease to shine,
Cease to guard us, never.
Cheer our steps as on we go,
Come between us and the foe.

2 Jesus, Bread and Wine art Thou,
Wine and Bread for ever.
Never canst Thou cease to feed
Or refresh us, never.
Feed us still on bread divine,
Drink we still of heavenly wine.

3 Jesus, Love and Life art Thou,
Life and Love for ever.
Ne'er to quicken shalt Thou cease,
Or to love us, never.
All of life and love we need
Is in Thee, in Thee indeed.

4 Jesus, Peace and Joy art Thou,
Joy and Peace for ever.
Joy that fades not, changes not,
Peace that leaves us never.
Joy and Peace we have in Thee
Now and through eternity.

5 Jesus, Song and Strength art Thou,
Strength and Song for ever.
Strength that never can decay,
Song that ceaseth never.
Still to us this strength and song,
Through eternal days prolong.

Horatius Bonar, 1808-89.

96

SOUTHAMPTON. 6.6.6.6.8 8. ARNOLD AND CALCOTT'S *Psalms*, 1791.

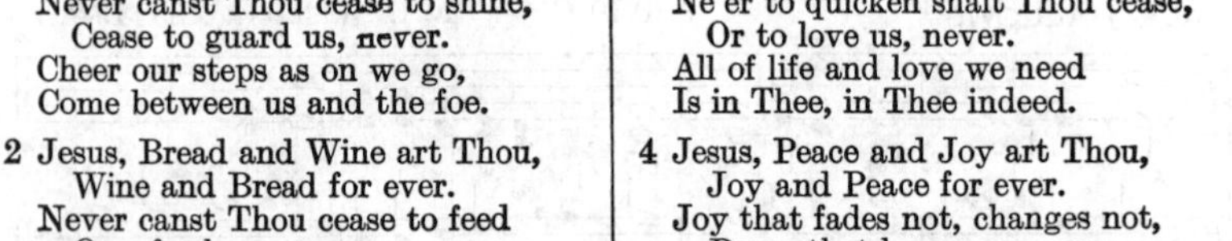

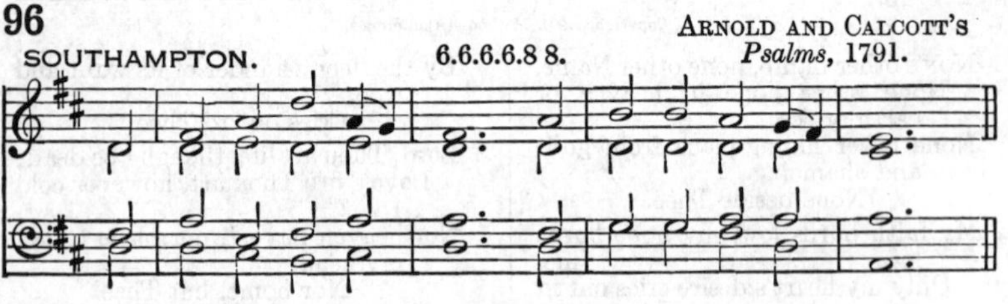

1 Join all the glorious names
Of wisdom, love, and power,
That ever mortals knew,
That angels ever bore;
All are too mean to speak His worth,
Too mean to set our Saviour forth.

2 But O what gentle means,
What condescending ways,
Doth our Redeemer use,
To teach His heavenly grace;
My soul, with joy and wonder see
What forms of love He bears for thee!

3 Arrayed in mortal flesh
The Covenant Angel stands,
And holds the promises
And pardons in His hands;
Commissioned from His Father's throne
To make His grace to mortals known.

4 Great Prophet of my God,
My tongue would bless Thy name:
By Thee the joyful news
Of our salvation came;
The joyful news of sins forgiven,
Of hell subdued, and peace with heaven.

5 Be Thou my Counsellor,
My Pattern and my Guide;
And through this desert land
Still keep me near Thy side:
O let my feet ne'er run astray,
Nor rove, nor seek the crooked way!

6 I love my Shepherd's voice;
His watchful eye shall keep
My wandering soul among
The thousands of His sheep:
He feeds His flock, He calls their names,
Bears in His arms the tender lambs.

7 Jesus, my great High-priest,
Offered His blood and died;
My guilty conscience seeks
No sacrifice beside;
His powerful blood did once atone,
And now it pleads before the throne.

8 O Thou almighty Lord,
My Conqueror and my King,
Thy sceptre and Thy sword,
Thy reign of grace, I sing;
Thine is the power: behold I sit
In willing bonds before Thy feet.

9 Now let my soul arise,
And tread the tempter down:
My Captain leads me forth
To conquest and a crown:
March on, nor fear to win the day,
Though death and hell obstruct the way.

10 Should all the hosts of death,
And powers of hell unknown,
Put their most dreadful forms
Of rage and malice on,
I shall be safe; for Christ displays
Superior power and guardian grace.

Isaac Watts, 1674-1748.

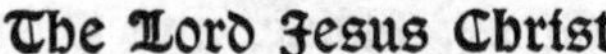

ECCLES. 6 6.7.7.7.7. R. BOGGETT, *c.* 1810-79.

1 O FILIAL Deity,
Accept my new-born cry;
See the travail of Thy soul,
Saviour, and be satisfied;
Take me now, possess me whole,
Who for me, for me, hast died.

2 Of life the Fountain Thou,
I know, I feel it now;
Faint and dead no more I droop:
Thou art in me; Thy supplies,
Every moment springing up,
Into life eternal rise.

3 Thou the good Shepherd art,
From Thee I ne'er shall part;
Thou my Keeper and my Guide,
Make me still Thy tender care;
Gently lead me by Thy side,
Sweetly in Thy bosom bear.

4 Thou art my daily Bread;
O Christ, Thou art my Head;
Motion, virtue, strength, to me,
Me Thy living member, flow;
Nourished I, and fed by Thee,
Up to Thee in all things grow.

5 Prophet, to me reveal
Thy Father's perfect will;
Never mortal spake like Thee,
Human prophet like divine;
Loud and strong their voices be,
Small, and still, and inward Thine.

6 On Thee, my Priest, I call,
Thy blood atoned for all;
Still the Lamb as slain appears,
Still Thou stand'st before the [throne,
Ever offering up my prayers,
These presenting with Thine own.

7 Jesu, Thou art my King,
From Thee my strength I bring;
Shadowed by Thy mighty hand,
Saviour, who shall pluck me thence?
Faith supports; by faith I stand,
Strong in Thy omnipotence.

Charles Wesley, 1707-88.

WARWICK GARDENS. 8.8.8.8.8.8. T. C. GREGORY, 1901-

May also be sung to ST. CHRYSOSTOM (Barnby), No. 438.

1 THOU hidden Source of calm repose,
Thou all-sufficient Love divine,
My help and refuge from my foes,
Secure I am, if Thou art mine:
And lo! from sin, and grief, and shame
I hide me, Jesus, in Thy name.

2 Thy mighty name salvation is,
And keeps my happy soul above;
Comfort it brings, and power, and peace,
And joy, and everlasting love:
To me, with Thy dear name, are given
Pardon, and holiness, and heaven.

3 Jesus, my all in all Thou art;
My rest in toil, my ease in pain,
The medicine of my broken heart,
In war my peace, in loss my gain,
My smile beneath the tyrant's frown,
In shame my glory and my crown:

4 In want my plentiful supply,
In weakness my almighty power,
In bonds my perfect liberty,
My light in Satan's darkest hour,
In grief my joy unspeakable,
My life in death, my heaven in hell.

Charles Wesley, 1707-88.

99

ST. PETER. C.M. A. R. REINAGLE, 1799-1877.

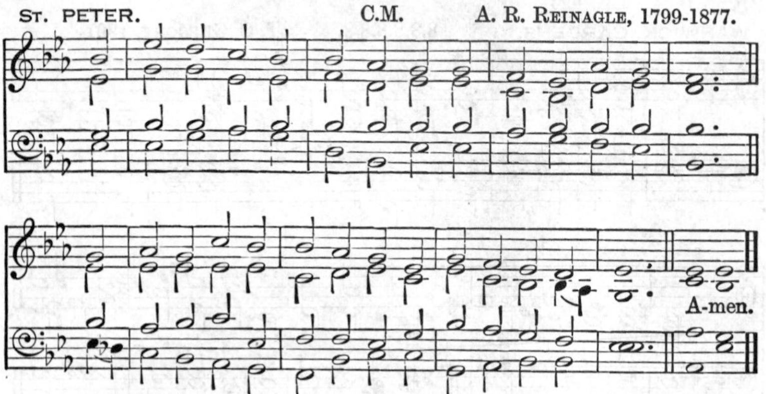

1 How sweet the name of Jesus sounds
In a believer's ear! [wounds,
It soothes his sorrows, heals his
And drives away his fear.

2 It makes the wounded spirit whole,
And calms the troubled breast;
'Tis manna to the hungry soul,
And to the weary rest.

3 Dear name! the Rock on which I build,
My shield, and hiding-place,
My never-failing treasury, filled
With boundless stores of grace!

4 Jesus, my Shepherd, Brother, Friend,
My Prophet, Priest, and King,
My Lord, my Life, my Way, my End,
Accept the praise I bring.

5 Weak is the effort of my heart,
And cold my warmest thought;
But when I see Thee as Thou art
I'll praise Thee as I ought.

6 Till then I would Thy love proclaim
With every fleeting breath;
And may the music of Thy name
Refresh my soul in death. Amen.

John Newton, 1725-1807.

100

ALL SAINTS. 8.7.8.7.7 7. *Darmstadt Gesangbuch*, 1698.

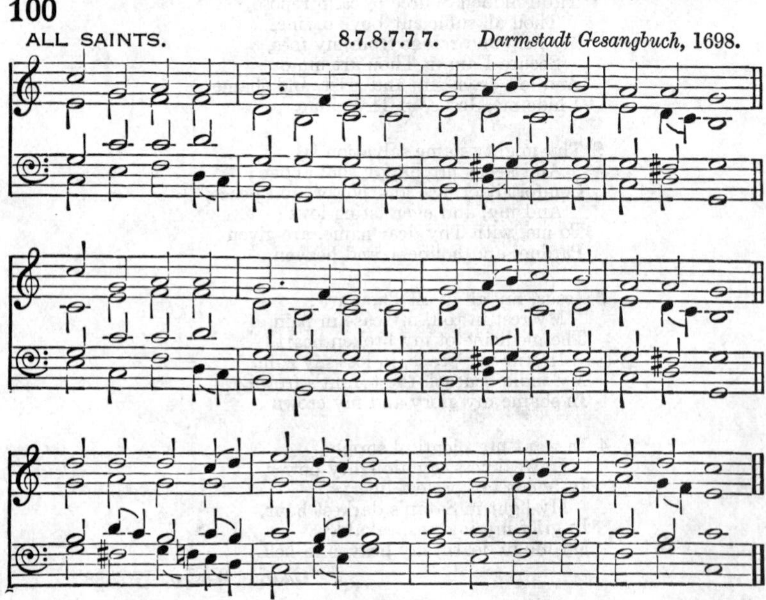

1 One there is above all others
Well deserves the name of friend;
His is love beyond a brother's,
Costly, free, and knows no end:
They who once His kindness prove,
Find it everlasting love.

2 Which of all our friends, to save us,
Could or would have shed his blood?
But our Jesus died to have us
Reconciled in Him to God:
This was boundless love indeed;
Jesus is a friend in need.

3 When He lived on earth abasèd
Friend of sinners was His name;
Now above all glories raisèd,
He rejoices in the same; [friends,
Still He calls them brethren,
And to all their wants attends.

4 O for grace our hearts to soften!
Teach us, Lord, at length to love;
We, alas! forget too often
What a friend we have above;
But when home our souls are brought,
We shall love Thee as we ought.

John Newton, 1725-1807.

101

THEODORA. 5.4.5.4. D. A. Legge, 1843-1919.

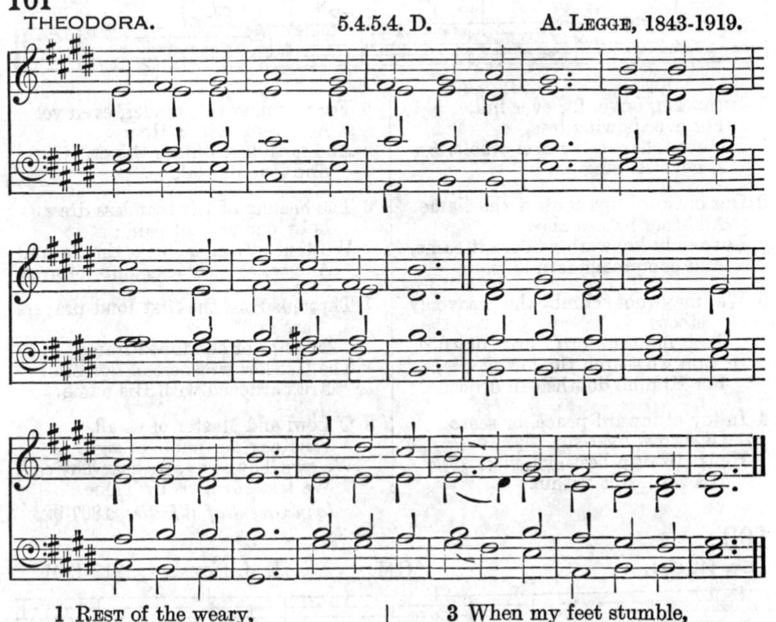

1 Rest of the weary,
Joy of the sad,
Hope of the dreary,
Light of the glad,
Home of the stranger,
Strength to the end,
Refuge from danger,
Saviour and Friend.

2 Pillow where, lying,
Love rests its head,
Peace of the dying,
Life of the dead,
Path of the lowly,
Prize at the end,
Breath of the holy,
Saviour and Friend.

3 When my feet stumble,
I'll to Thee cry:
Crown of the humble,
Cross of the high.
When my steps wander,
Over me bend,
Truer and fonder,
Saviour and Friend.

4 Ever confessing
Thee, I will raise
Unto Thee blessing,
Glory, and praise;
All my endeavour,
World without end,
Thine to be ever,
Saviour and Friend.

John Samuel Bewley Monsell, 1811-75.

102

STRACATHRO. C.M. C. HUTCHESON, 1792-1860.

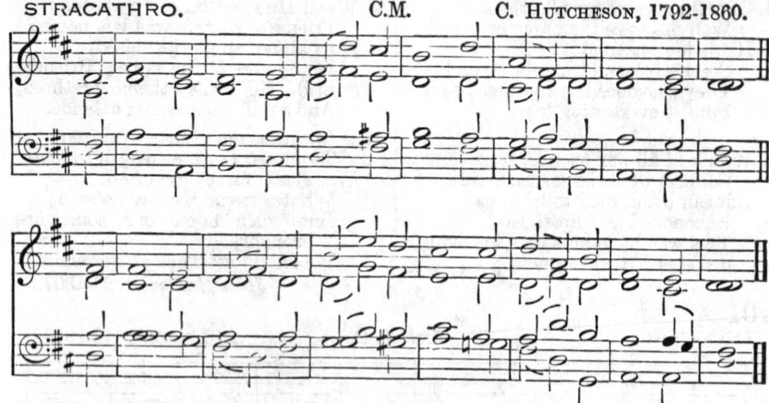

1 IMMORTAL Love, for ever full,
For ever flowing free,
For ever shared, for ever whole,
A never-ebbing sea:

2 Our outward lips confess the Name
All other names above;
Love only knoweth whence it came,
And comprehendeth love.

3 We may not climb the heavenly steeps
To bring the Lord Christ down:
In vain we search the lowest deeps,
For Him no depths can drown.

4 In joy of inward peace, or sense
Of sorrow over sin,
He is His own best evidence,
His witness is within.

5 For warm, sweet, tender, even yet
A present help is He;
And faith has still its Olivet,
And love its Galilee.

6 The healing of His seamless dress
Is by our beds of pain;
We touch Him in life's throng and press,
And we are whole again.

7 Through Him the first fond prayers are said
Our lips of childhood frame,
The last low whispers of our dead
Are burdened with His name.

8 O Lord and Master of us all,
Whate'er our name or sign,
We own Thy sway, we hear Thy call,
We test our lives by Thine.

John Greenleaf Whittier, 1807-92.

103

ST. HUGH. C.M. E. J. HOPKINS, 1818-1901.

1 O Lord and Master of us all,
Whate'er our name or sign,
We own Thy sway, we hear Thy call,
We test our lives by Thine.

2 Thou judgest us: Thy purity
Doth all our lusts condemn;
The love that draws us nearer Thee
Is hot with wrath to them.

3 Our thoughts lie open to Thy sight;
And, naked to Thy glance,
Our secret sins are in the light
Of Thy pure countenance.

4 Yet, weak and blinded though we be,
Thou dost our service own;
We bring our varying gifts to Thee,
And Thou rejectest none.

5 Apart from Thee all gain is loss,
All labour vainly done;
The solemn shadow of Thy Cross
Is better than the sun.

6 Our Friend, our Brother, and our [Lord,
What may Thy service be?
Nor name, nor form, nor ritual word,
But simply following Thee.

7 We faintly hear, we dimly see,
In differing phrase we pray;
But, dim or clear, we own in Thee
The Light, the Truth, the Way.

John Greenleaf Whittier, 1807-92.

104

HENSBURY. C.M. R. Bennett, 1788-1819.

1 Thou great Redeemer, dying Lamb,
We love to hear of Thee;
No music's like Thy charming name,
Nor half so sweet can be.

2 Our Jesus shall be still our theme
While in this world we stay:
We'll sing our Jesu's lovely name
When all things else decay.

3 When we appear in yonder cloud,
With all that favoured throng,
Then will we sing more sweet, more loud,
And Christ shall be our song.

John Cennick, 1718-55.

105

ST. OLAVE. 6 6.6 6.6 6. J. BARNBY, 1838-96.

By permission of Novello and Company, Limited.

1 JESUS, the First and Last,
On Thee my soul is cast:
Thou didst Thy work begin
By blotting out my sin;
Thou wilt the root remove,
And perfect me in love.

2 Yet when the work is done,
The work is but begun:
Partaker of Thy grace,
I long to see Thy face;
The first I prove below,
The last I die to know.

Charles Wesley, 1707-88.

106

PAVIA. L.M. German, 13th Century.

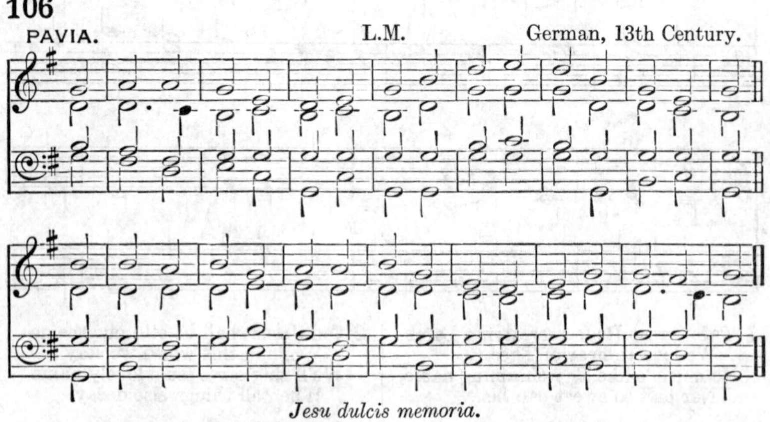

Jesu dulcis memoria.

1 JESU! The very thought is sweet,
In that dear name all heart-joys meet;
But sweeter than the honey far
The glimpses of His presence are.

2 No word is sung more sweet than this,
No name is heard more full of bliss,
No thought brings sweeter comfort nigh
Than Jesus, Son of God most high.

3 I seek for Jesus in repose,
When round my heart its chambers close;
Abroad, and when I shut the door,
I long for Jesus evermore.

4 With Mary in the morning gloom
I seek for Jesus at the tomb;
For Him, with love's most earnest cry,
I seek with heart and not with eye.

5 Jesus, to God the Father gone,
Is seated on the heavenly throne:
My heart hath also passed from me,
That where He is there it may be.

6 We follow Jesus now, and raise
The voice of prayer, the hymn of praise
That He at last may make us meet
With Him to gain the heavenly seat.

Attributed to Bernard of Clairvaux, 1091-1153;
tr. by John Mason Neale, 1818-66.

107

BISHOPTHORPE. C.M. J. CLARKE, 1659 *or* 1670-1707

Jesu, Rex admirabilis.

1 O JESUS, King most wonderful!
Thou Conqueror renowned;
Thou Sweetness most ineffable,
In whom all joys are found!

2 When once Thou visitest the heart,
Then truth begins to shine,
Then earthly vanities depart,
Then kindles love divine.

3 O Jesus, Light of all below!
Thou Fount of living fire,
Surpassing all the joys we know,
And all we can desire:

4 Jesus, may all confess Thy name,
Thy wondrous love adore; [flame
And, seeking Thee, themselves in-
To seek Thee more and more.

5 Thee may our tongues for ever bless,
Thee may we love alone,
And ever in our lives express
The image of Thine own.

6 Abide with us, and let Thy light
Shine, Lord, on every heart;
Dispel the darkness of our night,
And joy to all impart.

7 Jesus, our Love and Joy, to Thee,
The Father's holy Son,
All might, and praise, and glory be,
While endless ages run. Amen.

Attributed to Bernard of Clairvaux, 1091-1153;
tr. by Edward Caswall, 1814-78.

108

KILMARNOCK. C.M. N. DOUGALL, 1776-1862.

May also be sung to STRACATHRO, No. 102.

Jesu dulcis memoria.

1 JESU, the very thought of Thee
With sweetness fills my breast;
But sweeter far Thy face to see,
And in Thy presence rest.

2 Nor voice can sing, nor heart can [frame,
Nor can the memory find
A sweeter sound than Thy blest [name,
O Saviour of mankind!

3 O Hope of every contrite heart,
O Joy of all the meek,
To those who fall how kind Thou art!
How good to those who seek!

4 But what to those who find? Ah! this
Nor tongue nor pen can show:
The love of Jesus, what it is
None but His loved ones know.

5 Jesu, our only joy be Thou,
As Thou our prize wilt be;
Jesu, be Thou our glory now,
And through eternity. Amen.

Attributed to Bernard of Clairvaux, 1091-1153;
tr. by Edward Caswall, 1814-78.

109

WAREHAM. L.M. W. KNAPP, c. 1688-1768.

May also be sung to ST. LUKE, No. 156.

Jesu, Dulcedo cordium.

1 Jesu, Thou Joy of loving hearts,
Thou Fount of life, Thou Light of men,
From the best bliss that earth imparts
We turn unfilled to Thee again.

2 Thy truth unchanged hath ever stood;
Thou savest those that on Thee call;
To them that seek Thee Thou art good,
To them that find Thee, all in all.

3 We taste Thee, O Thou living Bread,
And long to feast upon Thee still;
We drink of Thee, the fountain-head,
And thirst our souls from Thee to fill.

4 Our restless spirits yearn for Thee,
Where'er our changeful lot is cast;
Glad when Thy gracious smile we see,
Blest when our faith can hold Thee fast.

5 O Jesus, ever with us stay;
Make all our moments calm and bright;
Chase the dark night of sin away;
Shed o'er the world Thy holy light.
Amen.

Attributed to Bernard of Clairvaux, 1091-1153;
tr. by Ray Palmer, 1808-87.

110

HOLLINGSIDE. 7.7.7.7. D. J. B. Dykes, 1823-76.

May also be sung to Aberystwyth, No. 726, and Hotham, No. 479.

1 Jesu, Lover of my soul,
Let me to Thy bosom fly,
While the nearer waters roll,
While the tempest still is high:
Hide me, O my Saviour, hide,
Till the storm of life be past;
Safe into the haven guide,
O receive my soul at last.

2 Other refuge have I none,
Hangs my helpless soul on Thee;
Leave, ah! leave me not alone,
Still support and comfort me:
All my trust on Thee is stayed,
All my help from Thee I bring;
Cover my defenceless head
With the shadow of Thy wing.

3 Thou, O Christ, art all I want,
More than all in Thee I find.
Raise the fallen, cheer the faint,
Heal the sick, and lead the blind:
Just and holy is Thy name,
I am all unrighteousness;
False and full of sin I am,
Thou art full of truth and grace.

4 Plenteous grace with Thee is found,
Grace to cover all my sin;
Let the healing streams abound,
Make and keep me pure within:
Thou of life the fountain art,
Freely let me take of Thee,
Spring Thou up within my heart,
Rise to all eternity. Amen.

Charles Wesley, 1707-88.

111

SOUTHWELL. C.M. H. S. IRONS, 1834-1905.

1 JESUS, these eyes have never seen
That radiant form of Thine;
The veil of sense hangs dark between
Thy blessèd face and mine.

2 I see Thee not, I hear Thee not,
Yet art Thou oft with me;
And earth hath ne'er so dear a spot,
As where I meet with Thee.

3 Like some bright dream that comes unsought,
When slumbers o'er me roll,
Thy image ever fills my thought,
And charms my ravished soul.

4 Yet, though I have not seen, and still
Must rest in faith alone;
I love Thee, dearest Lord, and will,
Unseen but not unknown.

5 When death these mortal eyes shall seal,
And still this throbbing heart,
The rending veil shall Thee reveal
All glorious as Thou art.

Ray Palmer, 1808-87.

112

NARENZA. S.M. Leisentritt's *Hymnologium*, 1584.

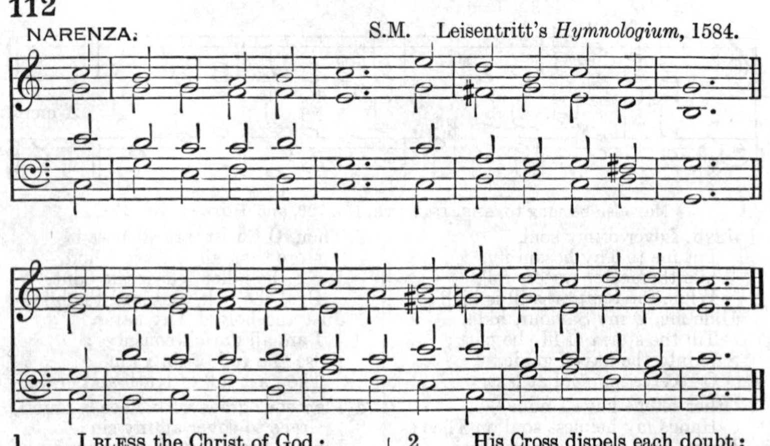

1 I BLESS the Christ of God;
I rest on love divine;
And with unfaltering lip and heart,
I call the Saviour mine.

2 His Cross dispels each doubt:
I bury in His tomb
Each thought of unbelief and fear,
Each lingering shade of gloom.

3 I praise the God of grace;
I trust His truth and might;
He calls me His, I call Him mine,
My God, my joy, my light.

4 In Him is only good,
In me is only ill;
My ill but draws His goodness forth,
And me He loveth still.

5 'Tis He who saveth me,
And freely pardon gives;
I love because He loveth me,
I live because He lives.

6 My life with Him is hid,
My death has passed away,
My clouds have melted into light,
My midnight into day.

Horatius Bonar, 1808-89.

113

LAUDES DOMINI. 6 6.6. D. J. BARNBY, 1838-96.

A-men.

Beim frühen Morgenlicht.

1 WHEN morning gilds the skies,
My heart awaking cries:
May Jesus Christ be praised!
Alike at work and prayer
To Jesus I repair:
May Jesus Christ be praised!

2 Does sadness fill my mind?
A solace here I find—
May Jesus Christ be praised!
When evil thoughts molest,
With this I shield my breast—
May Jesus Christ be praised!

3 Be this, when day is past,
Of all my thoughts the last,
May Jesus Christ be praised!
The night becomes as day,
When from the heart we say:
May Jesus Christ be praised!

4 To God, the Word, on high
The hosts of angels cry,
May Jesus Christ be praised!
Let mortals, too, upraise
Their voice in hymns of praise:
May Jesus Christ be praised!

5 Let earth's wide circle round
In joyful notes resound:
May Jesus Christ be praised!
Let air, and sea, and sky,
From depth to height, reply:
May Jesus Christ be praised!

6 Be this while life is mine,
My canticle divine,
May Jesus Christ be praised!
Be this the eternal song
Through all the ages long,
May Jesus Christ be praised!

Amen.

Anonymous;
tr. by Edward Caswall, 1814-78.

MILLENNIUM. 6.6.6.6.8 8. Source unknown.

1 Let earth and heaven agree,
Angels and men be joined,
To celebrate with me
The Saviour of mankind;
To adore the all-atoning Lamb,
And bless the sound of Jesu's name.

2 Jesus, transporting sound!
The joy of earth and heaven;
No other help is found,
No other name is given,
By which we can salvation have;
But Jesus came the world to save.

3 Jesus, harmonious name!
It charms the hosts above;
They evermore proclaim
And wonder at His love;
'Tis all their happiness to gaze,
'Tis heaven to see our Jesu's face.

4 His name the sinner hears,
And is from sin set free;
'Tis music in his ears,
'Tis life and victory;
New songs do now his lips employ,
And dances his glad heart for joy.

5 Stung by the scorpion sin,
My poor expiring soul
The healing sound drinks in,
And is at once made whole:
See there my Lord upon the tree!
I hear, I feel, He died for me.

6 O unexampled love!
O all-redeeming grace!
How swiftly didst Thou move
To save a fallen race:
What shall I do to make it known
What Thou for all mankind hast done?

7 O for a trumpet voice,
On all the world to call!
To bid their hearts rejoice
In Him who died for all;
For all my Lord was crucified,
For all, for all my Saviour died.

Charles Wesley, 1707-88.

115

ASCALON. 6 6.8.D. Hoffman & Richter's *Silesian Folk-Songs*, 1842.

1 My heart and voice I raise,
To spread Messiah's praise;
Messiah's praise let all repeat;
The universal Lord,
By whose almighty word
Creation rose in form complete.

2 A servant's form He wore,
And in His body bore
Our dreadful curse on Calvary:
He like a victim stood,
And poured His sacred blood,
To set the guilty captives free.

3 But soon the Victor rose
Triumphant o'er His foes,
And led the vanquished host in chains:
He threw their empire down,
His foes compelled to own
O'er all the great Messiah reigns.

4 With mercy's mildest grace,
He governs all our race
In wisdom, righteousness, and love:
Who to Messiah fly
Shall find redemption nigh,
And all His great salvation prove.

5 Hail, Saviour, Prince of Peace!
Thy kingdom shall increase,
Till all the world Thy glory see,
And righteousness abound
As the great deep profound,
And fill the earth with purity.

Benjamin Rhodes, 1743-1815.

116 10 10.10 10. and refrain.

SING WE THE KING (*First Tune*). C. L. WISEMAN, 1893-

His Glory, Name, and Praise

1.

SING we the King who is coming to reign,
Glory to Jesus, the Lamb that was slain,
Life and salvation His empire shall bring,
Joy to the nations when Jesus is King.

Come let us sing : Praise to our King,
Jesus our King, Jesus our King :
This is our song, who to Jesus belong :
Glory to Jesus, to Jesus our King.

2.

All men shall dwell in His marvellous light,
Races long severed His love shall unite,
Justice and truth from His sceptre shall spring,
Wrong shall be ended when Jesus is King.

3.

All shall be well in His kingdom of peace,
Freedom shall flourish and wisdom increase,
Foe shall be friend when His triumph we sing,
Sword shall be sickle when Jesus is King.

4.

Souls shall be saved from the burden of sin,
Doubt shall not darken His witness within,
Hell hath no terrors, and death hath no sting;
Love is victorious when Jesus is King.

5.

Kingdom of Christ, for thy coming we pray,
Hasten, O Father, the dawn of the day
When this new song Thy creation shall sing,
Satan is vanquished and Jesus is King.

Charles Silvester Horne, 1865-1914.

116

10 10.10 10. and refrain.

THE GLORY SONG (*Second Tune*). C. H. GABRIEL, 1856-1932.

REFRAIN.
Come let us sing: Praise to our King, Je - sus our
Come . . let us sing: Praise to our King,
Come let us sing: Praise to our King, . . Je - sus our
King, Je - sus our King: This is our song, who to
Je - sus our King: This is our song, . . who to
King, . . Je - sus our King: This is our song, who to

Je - sus be - long: Glo-ry to Je - sus, to Je - sus our King.

1 Sing we the King who is coming to reign,
Glory to Jesus, the Lamb that was slain,
Life and salvation His empire shall bring,
Joy to the nations when Jesus is King.

Come let us sing: Praise to our King,
Jesus our King, Jesus our King:
This is our song, who to Jesus belong:
Glory to Jesus, to Jesus our King.

2 All men shall dwell in His marvellous light,
Races long severed His love shall unite,
Justice and truth from His sceptre shall spring,
Wrong shall be ended when Jesus is King.

3 All shall be well in His kingdom of peace,
Freedom shall flourish and wisdom increase,
Foe shall be friend when His triumph we sing,
Sword shall be sickle when Jesus is King.

4 Souls shall be saved from the burden of sin,
Doubt shall not darken His witness within,
Hell hath no terrors, and death hath no sting;
Love is victorious when Jesus is King.

5 Kingdom of Christ, for thy coming we pray,
Hasten, O Father, the dawn of the day
When this new song Thy creation shall sing,
Satan is vanquished and Jesus is King.

Charles Silvester Horne, 1865-1914.

Also:

1 O for a thousand tongues to sing
142 Let earth and heaven combine
144 My song is love unknown
171 Jesus, I will trust Thee
201 There is a fountain
225 Christ, above all glory seated
411 Head of Thy Church triumphant
412 Worship, and thanks, and blessing
672 Saviour, blessèd Saviour
924 Christ, whose glory

The Lord Jesus Christ

117 HIS INCARNATION

BERLIN. 7 7.7 7. D. and refrain. MENDELSSOHN, 1809-47.

By permission of Novello and Company, Limited.

1 HARK! the herald-angels sing
Glory to the new-born King,
Peace on earth, and mercy mild,
God and sinners reconciled.
Joyful, all ye nations, rise,
Join the triumph of the skies;
With the angelic host proclaim,
Christ is born in Bethlehem.

Hark! the herald-angels sing
Glory to the new-born King.

2 Christ, by highest heaven adored,
Christ, the everlasting Lord,
Late in time behold Him come,
Offspring of a virgin's womb!
Veiled in flesh the Godhead see;
Hail the incarnate Deity!
Pleased as man with men to dwell,
Jesus, our Immanuel.

3 Mild He lays His glory by,
Born that man no more may die,
Born to raise the sons of earth,
Born to give them second birth.
Hail the heaven-born Prince of Peace!
Hail the Sun of Righteousness!
Light and life to all He brings,
Risen with healing in His wings.

Charles Wesley, 1707-88.

118 J. F. WADE'S MS. Book, 1751 (Stonyhurst).

ADESTE FIDELES. Irregular.

Adeste fideles laeti triumphantes.

1 O COME, all ye faithful,
Joyful and triumphant,
Come ye, O come ye to Bethlehem;
Come and behold Him
Born the King of angels:
O come, let us adore Him, Christ the Lord.

2 True God of true God,
Light of Light eternal,
Lo! He abhors not the Virgin's womb,
Son of the Father,
Begotten, not created:
O come, let us adore Him, Christ the Lord.

3 Sing, choirs of angels,
Sing in exultation,
Sing, all ye citizens of heaven above,
Glory to God
In the highest:
O come, let us adore Him, Christ the Lord.

4 Yea, Lord, we greet Thee,
Born this happy morning;
Jesus, to Thee be glory given,
Word of the Father,
Now in flesh appearing:
O come, let us adore Him, Christ the Lord.

J. F. WADE, *c.* 1710-86;
tr. by Frederick Oakeley, 1802-80.

119 8.7.8.7.4.7.

WOODFORD GREEN (*First Tune*). W. PARKYN, 1881-

1 ANGELS from the realms of glory,
Wing your flight o'er all the earth;
Ye, who sang creation's story,
Now proclaim Messiah's birth;
Come and worship,
Worship Christ, the new-born King.

2 Shepherds in the field abiding,
Watching o'er your flocks by night,
God with man is now residing,
Yonder shines the infant light;
Come and worship,
Worship Christ, the new-born King.

3 Sages, leave your contemplations;
Brighter visions beam afar;
Seek the great Desire of nations;
Ye have seen His natal star;
Come and worship,
Worship Christ, the new-born King.

4 Saints, before the altar bending,
Watching long with hope and fear,
Suddenly the Lord, descending,
In His temple shall appear;
Come and worship,
Worship Christ, the new-born King.

James Montgomery, 1771-1854.

IRIS (*Second Tune*). 8.7.8.7.4.7. French Carol Melody.

120

YORKSHIRE. 10 10.10 10.10 10. J. WAINWRIGHT, 1723-68.

1 CHRISTIANS, awake, salute the happy morn,
Whereon the Saviour of the world was born;
Rise to adore the mystery of love,
Which hosts of angels chanted from above;
With them the joyful tidings first begun
Of God incarnate and the Virgin's Son.

2 Then to the watchful shepherds it was told,
Who heard the angelic herald's voice: Behold,
I bring good tidings of a Saviour's birth
To you and all the nations upon earth;
This day hath God fulfilled His promised word,
This day is born a Saviour, Christ the Lord.

3 He spake; and straightway the celestial choir
In hymns of joy, unknown before, conspire.
The praises of redeeming love they sang,
And heaven's whole orb with hallelujahs rang;
God's highest glory was their anthem still,
Peace upon earth, and unto men good-will.

4 To Bethlehem straight the enlightened shepherds ran,
To see the wonder God had wrought for man:
Then to their flocks, still praising God, return,
And their glad hearts with holy rapture burn;
Amazed, the wondrous tidings they proclaim,
The first apostles of His infant fame.

5 O may we keep and ponder in our mind
God's wondrous love in saving lost mankind;
Trace we the Babe, who hath retrieved our loss,
From the poor manger to the bitter Cross;
Tread in His steps, assisted by His grace,
Till man's first heavenly state again takes place.

6 Then may we hope, the angelic hosts among,
To sing, redeemed, a glad triumphal song;
He that was born upon this joyful day
Around us all His glory shall display;
Saved by His love, incessant we shall sing
Eternal praise to heaven's almighty King.

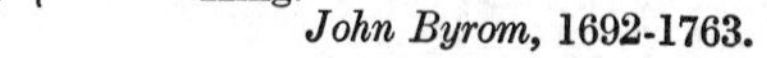

John Byrom, 1692-1763.

121

BONN. 8.6.6. D. J. G. EBELING, 1637-76.

Fröhlich soll mein Herze springen.

1 ALL my heart this night rejoices,
As I hear, far and near,
Sweetest angel voices:
Christ is born! their choirs are singing,
Till the air, everywhere,
Now with joy is ringing.

2 Hark! a voice from yonder manger,
Soft and sweet, doth entreat:
Flee from woe and danger;
Brethren, come; from all doth grieve you,
You are freed; all you need
I will surely give you.

3 Come then, let us hasten yonder;
Here let all, great and small,
Kneel in awe and wonder.
Love Him who with love is yearning;
Hail the Star, that from far
Bright with hope is burning.

4 Thee, O Lord, with heed I'll cherish,
Live to Thee, and with Thee
Dying, shall not perish,
But shall dwell with Thee for ever
Far on high, in the joy
That can alter never.

Paulus Gerhardt, 1607-76;
tr. by Catherine Winkworth, 1827-78.

122

SPEAN (*First Tune*). 11.10.11.10. Dactylic. J. F. Bridge, 1844-1924

By permission of Novello and Company, Limited.

11.10.11.10. Dactylic.

EPIPHANY HYMN (*Second Tune*). J. F. Thrupp, 1827-67.

1 Brightest and best of the sons of the
morning, [us thine aid ;
Dawn on our darkness, and lend
Star of the East, the horizon adorning,
Guide where our infant Redeemer
is laid.

2 Cold on His cradle the dew-drops are
shining ; [of the stall ;
Low lies His head with the beasts
Angels adore Him in slumber
reclining, [of all.
Maker, and Monarch, and Saviour

3 Say, shall we yield Him, in costly
devotion, [divine,
Odours of Edom, and offerings
Gems of the mountain and pearls of
the ocean, [the mine ?
Myrrh from the forest or gold from

4 Vainly we offer each ample oblation ;
Vainly with gifts would His favour
secure ;
Richer by far is the heart's adoration ;
Dearer to God are the prayers of
the poor.

5 Brightest and best of the sons of the
morning, [thine aid ;
Dawn on our darkness, and lend us
Star of the East, the horizon adorning,
Guide where our infant Redeemer
is laid.

Reginald Heber, 1783-1826.

123

STILLE NACHT. Irregular. F. Gruber, 1787-1863.

Stille Nacht, heilige Nacht.

1 Still the night, holy the night !
Sleeps the world ; hid from sight,
Mary and Joseph in stable bare
Watch o'er the Child beloved and fair,
Sleeping in heavenly rest.

2 Still the night, holy the night !
Shepherds first saw the light,
Heard resounding clear and long,
Far and near, the angel-song,
Christ the Redeemer is here !

3 Still the night, holy the night !
Son of God, O how bright
Love is smiling from Thy face !
Strikes for us now the hour of grace,
Saviour, since Thou art born !

Joseph Mohr, 1792-1848 ;
tr. by Stopford Augustus Brooke, 1832-1916.

124

OXFORD. 7 7.7 7. and refrain. J. Goss, 1800-80.

SOLO OR UNISON.

REFRAIN. HARMONY.

1 SEE, amid the winter's snow,
Born for us on earth below,
See, the Lamb of God appears,
Promised from eternal years.
Hail, thou ever-blessèd morn!
Hail, redemption's happy dawn!
Sing through all Jerusalem:
Christ is born in Bethlehem!

2 Lo, within a manger lies
He who built the starry skies,
He who, throned in height sublime,
Sits amid the cherubim.

3 Say, ye holy shepherds, say,
What your joyful news to-day;
Wherefore have ye left your sheep
On the lonely mountain steep?

4 As we watched at dead of night,
Lo, we saw a wondrous light:
Angels, singing peace on earth,
Told us of the Saviour's birth.

5 Sacred Infant, all divine,
What a tender love was Thine,
Thus to come from highest bliss
Down to such a world as this!

6 Teach, O teach us, holy Child,
By Thy face so meek and mild,
Teach us to resemble Thee
In Thy sweet humility.

Edward Caswall, 1814-78.

125

BETHLEHEM. 8.6.8.6.7.6.8.6. J. BARNBY, 1838-96.

May also be sung to FOREST GREEN, No. 897.

1 O LITTLE town of Bethlehem,
How still we see thee lie!
Above thy deep and dreamless sleep
The silent stars go by:
Yet in thy dark street shineth
The everlasting Light;
The hopes and fears of all the years
Are met in thee to-night.

2 O morning stars, together
Proclaim the holy birth,
And praises sing to God the King,
And peace to men on earth;
For Christ is born of Mary;
And, gathered all above,
While mortals sleep, the angels keep
Their watch of wondering love.

3 How silently, how silently
The wondrous gift is given!
So God imparts to human hearts
The blessings of His heaven.
No ear may hear His coming;
But in this world of sin,
Where meek souls will receive Him, still
The dear Christ enters in.

4 O holy Child of Bethlehem,
Descend to us, we pray;
Cast out our sin, and enter in;
Be born in us to-day.
We hear the Christmas angels
The great glad tidings tell;
O come to us, abide with us,
Our Lord Immanuel. Amen.

Phillips Brooks, 1835-93.

126

VOM HIMMEL HOCH (ERFURT). L.M. M. LUTHER, 1483-1546, Arr. by J. S. BACH, 1685-1750.

Vom Himmel hoch da Komm ich her.

1 GIVE heed, my heart, lift up thine eyes:
Who is it in yon manger lies?
Who is this child so young and fair?
The blessèd Christ Child lieth there.

2 Ah, Lord, who hast created all,
How hast Thou made Thee weak and small,
That Thou must choose Thy infant bed
Where ass and ox but lately fed?

3 Were earth a thousand times as fair,
Beset with gold and jewels rare,
She yet were far too poor to be
A narrow cradle, Lord, for Thee.

4 Ah, dearest Jesus, holy child,
Make Thee a bed, soft, undefiled,
Within my heart, that it may be
A quiet chamber kept for Thee.

5 My heart for very joy doth leap,
My lips no more their silence keep;
I too must sing with joyful tongue
That sweetest ancient cradle-song:

6 Glory to God in highest heaven,
Who unto man His Son hath given;
While angels sing with pious mirth
A glad new year to all the earth.

Martin Luther, 1483-1546;
tr. by Catherine Winkworth, 1827-78.

127

ÒRAN NA PRASAICH (*The Song of the Manger*).
(*First Tune*). 8.7.8.7. D. G. F. Brockless, 1887-1957.

1 Cradled in a manger, meanly
Laid the Son of Man His head;
Sleeping His first earthly slumber
Where the oxen had been fed.
Happy were those shepherds listening
To the holy angel's word;
Happy they within that stable,
Worshipping their infant Lord.

2 Happy all who hear the message
Of His coming from above;
Happier still who hail His coming,
And with praises greet His love.
Blessèd Saviour, Christ most holy,
In a manger Thou didst rest;
Canst Thou stoop again, yet lower,
And abide within my breast?

3 Evil things are there before Thee;
In the heart, where they have fed,
Wilt Thou pitifully enter,
Son of Man, and lay Thy head?
Enter, then, O Christ most holy;
Make a Christmas in my heart;
Make a heaven of my manger:
It is heaven where Thou art.

4 And to those who never listened
To the message of Thy birth,
Who have winter, but no Christmas
Bringing them Thy peace on earth,
Send to these the joyful tidings;
By all people, in each home,
Be there heard the Christmas anthem:
Praise to God, the Christ has come!

George Stringer Rowe, 1830-1913.

127

8.7.8.7. D.

ST. WINIFRED (*Second Tune*). S. J. P. DUNMAN, 1843-1913.

1 CRADLED in a manger, meanly
  Laid the Son of Man His head;
Sleeping His first earthly slumber
  Where the oxen had been fed.
Happy were those shepherds listening
  To the holy angel's word;
Happy they within that stable,
  Worshipping their infant Lord.

2 Happy all who hear the message
  Of His coming from above;
Happier still who hail His coming,
  And with praises greet His love.
Blessèd Saviour, Christ most holy,
  In a manger Thou didst rest;
Canst Thou stoop again, yet lower,
  And abide within my breast?

3 Evil things are there before Thee;
  In the heart, where they have fed,
Wilt Thou pitifully enter,
  Son of Man, and lay Thy head?
Enter, then, O Christ most holy;
  Make a Christmas in my heart;
Make a heaven of my manger:
  It is heaven where Thou art.

4 And to those who never listened
  To the message of Thy birth,
Who have winter, but no Christmas
  Bringing them Thy peace on earth,
Send to these the joyful tidings;
  By all people, in each home,
Be there heard the Christmas anthem:
  Praise to God, the Christ has come!

George Stringer Rowe, 1830-1913.

11 11.11 11. and refrain.

A VIRGIN MOST PURE. SANDYS' Collection, 1833.

REFRAIN.

1 A VIRGIN most pure, as the prophets do tell,
Hath brought forth a Baby, as it hath befel,
To be our Redeemer from death, hell, and sin,
Which Adam's transgression hath wrappèd us in.

And therefore be merry, set sorrow aside;
Christ Jesus our Saviour was born on this tide.

2 In Bethlehem in Jewry, a city there was,
Where Joseph and Mary together did pass,
All for to be taxèd with many one moe,
For Cæsar commanded the same should be so.

3 But when they had entered the city so fair,
A number of people so mighty was there,
That Joseph and Mary, whose substance was small,
Could find in the inn there no lodging at all.

4 Then were they constrained in a stable to lie,
Where horses and asses they used for to tie:
Their lodging so simple they took it no scorn,
But against the next morning our Saviour was born.

5 The King of all kings to this world being brought,
Small store of fine linen to wrap Him was sought,
But when she had swaddled her young son so sweet,
Within an ox-manger she laid Him to sleep.

6 Then God sent an angel from heaven so high,
To certain poor shepherds in fields where they lie,
And bade them no longer in sorrow to stay,
Because that our Saviour was born on this day.

7 Then presently after the shepherds did spy
A number of angels that stood in the sky;
They joyfully talkèd and sweetly did sing,
To God be all glory, our heavenly King.

Traditional.

129

WINCHESTER OLD. C.M. G. KIRBYE, ?-1634.

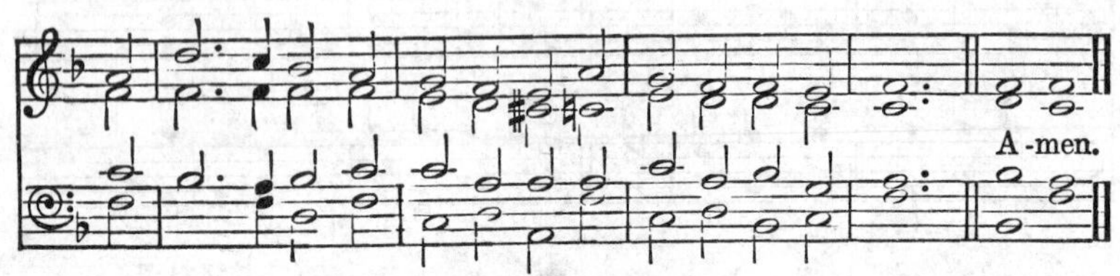

May also be sung to LYNGHAM, A.T. No. 8.

1 WHILE shepherds watched their flocks by night,
All seated on the ground,
The angel of the Lord came down,
And glory shone around.

2 Fear not! said he; for mighty dread
Had seized their troubled mind:
Glad tidings of great joy I bring
To you and all mankind.

3 To you, in David's town, this day
Is born, of David's line,
A Saviour, who is Christ the Lord;
And this shall be the sign:

4 The heavenly Babe you there shall find
To human view displayed,
All meanly wrapped in swaddling bands
And in a manger laid.

5 Thus spake the seraph; and forthwith
Appeared a shining throng
Of angels praising God, and thus
Addressed their joyful song:

6 All glory be to God on high,
And to the earth be peace;
Good will henceforth from heaven to men
Begin and never cease! Amen.

Nahum Tate, 1652-1715.

NOEL. D.C.M. Arr. by A. Sullivan, 1842-1900.

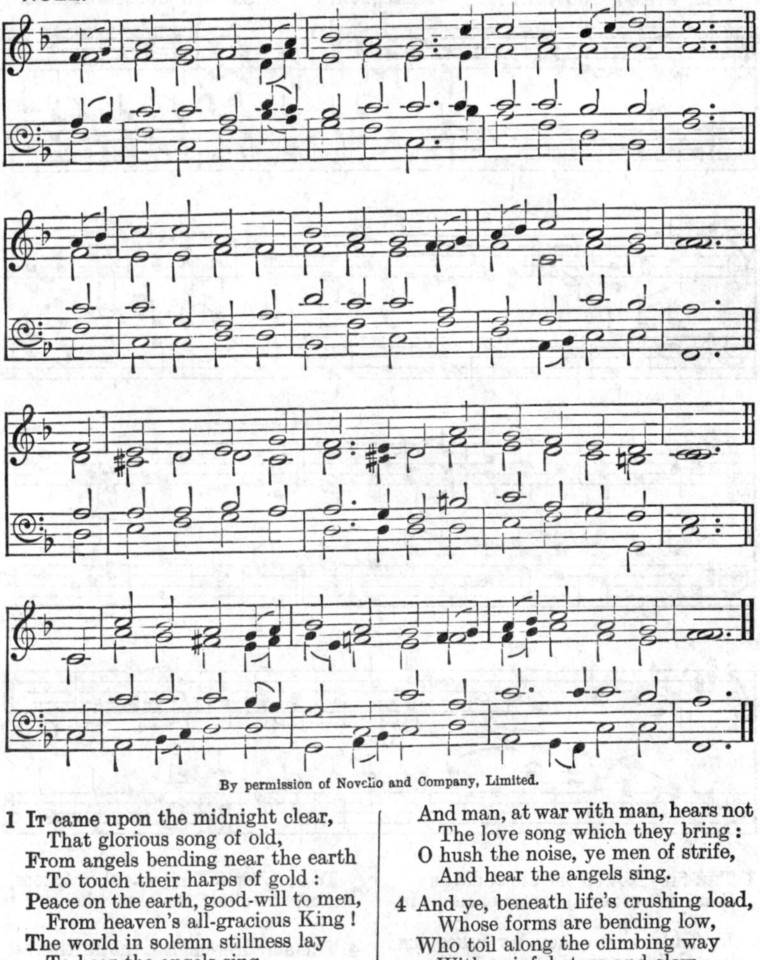

By permission of Novello and Company, Limited.

1 It came upon the midnight clear,
That glorious song of old,
From angels bending near the earth
To touch their harps of gold:
Peace on the earth, good-will to men,
From heaven's all-gracious King!
The world in solemn stillness lay
To hear the angels sing.

2 Still through the cloven skies they come
With peaceful wings unfurled;
And still their heavenly music floats
O'er all the weary world;
Above its sad and lowly plains
They bend on hovering wing,
And ever o'er its Babel sounds
The blessèd angels sing.

3 But with the woes of sin and strife
The world has suffered long;
Beneath the angel strain have rolled
Two thousand years of wrong;
And man, at war with man, hears not
The love song which they bring:
O hush the noise, ye men of strife,
And hear the angels sing.

4 And ye, beneath life's crushing load,
Whose forms are bending low,
Who toil along the climbing way
With painful steps and slow—
Look now! for glad and golden hours
Come swiftly on the wing:
O rest beside the weary road,
And hear the angels sing.

5 For lo! the days are hastening on,
By prophet bards foretold,
When with the ever-circling years
Comes round the age of gold.
When peace shall over all the earth
Its ancient splendours fling,
And the whole world give back the song
Which now the angels sing.

Edmund Hamilton Sears, 1810-76.

THE FIRST NOWELL. Irregular. SANDYS' Collection, 1833.

REFRAIN.

1 THE first Nowell the angel did say
Was to certain poor shepherds in fields as they lay:
In fields where they lay a-keeping their sheep
On a cold winter's night that was so deep.
Nowell, Nowell, Nowell, Nowell,
Born is the King of Israel.

2 They lookèd up and saw a star,
Shining in the east, beyond them far,
And to the earth it gave great light,
And so it continued both day and night.

3 And by the light of that same star,
Three wise men came from country far;
To seek for a King was their intent,
And to follow the star wherever it went.

4 This star drew nigh to the north-west,
O'er Bethlehem it took its rest,
And there it did both stop and stay
Right over the place where Jesus lay.

5 Then entered in those wise men three,
Full reverently upon their knee,
And offered there in His presence
Their gold and myrrh and frankincense.

6 Then let us all with one accord
Sing praises to our Heavenly Lord,
That hath made heaven and earth of nought,
And with His blood mankind hath bought.

Anonymous.

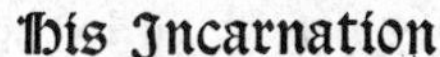

132

ORIENT. 7 7.7 7.7 7. C. V. Stanford, 1852-1924.

vv. 1-4.

Ev-ermore, ev-ermore be led . . . to Thee.

v. 5.

Hal - le - lu - jahs, Hal - le - lu - jahs to . . our . . King. A - men.

May also be sung to Dix, No. 681.

1 As with gladness men of old
Did the guiding star behold,
As with joy they hailed its light,
Leading onward, beaming bright;
So, most gracious Lord, may we
Evermore be led to Thee.

2 As with joyful steps they sped,
Saviour, to Thy lowly bed,
There to bend the knee before
Thee, whom heaven and earth adore;
So may we with willing feet
Ever seek the mercy-seat.

3 As they offered gifts most rare
At Thy cradle rude and bare;
So may we with holy joy,
Pure, and free from sin's alloy,
All our costliest treasures bring,
Christ, to Thee, our heavenly King.

4 Holy Jesus, every day
Keep us in the narrow way;
And, when earthly things are past,
Bring our ransomed souls at last
Where they need no star to guide,
Where no clouds Thy glory hide.

5 In the heavenly country bright
Need they no created light;
Thou its light, its joy, its crown,
Thou its sun which goes not down;
There for ever may we sing
Hallelujahs to our King. Amen.

William Chatterton Dix, 1837-98.

133

KIRKBRADDAN (*First Tune*). 6.5.6.5. D. E. C. WALKER, 1848-72.

FOUNDATION (*Second Tune*). 6.5.6.5. D. From HAYDN, 1732-1809.

His Incarnation

1 From the eastern mountains
Pressing on they come,
Wise men in their wisdom,
To His humble home,
Stirred by deep devotion,
Hasting from afar,
Ever journeying onward,
Guided by a star.

2 There their Lord and Saviour
Meek and lowly lay,
Wondrous light that led them
Onward on their way,
Ever now to lighten
Nations from afar,
As they journey homeward
By that guiding star.

3 Thou who in a manger
Once hast lowly lain,
Who dost now in glory
O'er all kingdoms reign,
Gather in the heathen,
Who in lands afar
Ne'er have seen the brightness
Of Thy guiding star.

4 Gather in the outcasts,
All who have gone astray,
Throw Thy radiance o'er them,
Guide them on their way,
Those who never knew Thee,
Those who have wandered far,
Guide them by the brightness
Of Thy guiding star.

5 Onward through the darkness
Of the lonely night,
Shining still before them
With Thy kindly light,
Guide them, Jew and Gentile,
Homeward from afar,
Young and old together,
By Thy guiding star.

Godfrey Thring, 1823-1903

134

HATFIELD. 7.6.7.6.7.7.7.6. *French Psalter*, 1565.

1 Glory be to God on high,
And peace on earth descend:
God comes down, He bows the sky,
And shows Himself our Friend:
God the invisible appears:
God, the blest, the great I AM,
Sojourns in this vale of tears,
And Jesus is His name.

2 Him the angels all adored,
Their Maker and their King;
Tidings of their humbled Lord
They now to mortals bring.
Emptied of His majesty,
Of His dazzling glories shorn,
Being's source begins to be,
And God Himself is born!

3 See the eternal Son of God
A mortal Son of Man;
Dwelling in an earthly clod,
Whom heaven cannot contain.
Stand amazed, ye heavens, at this:
See the Lord of earth and skies;
Humbled to the dust He is,
And in a manger lies.

4 We, the sons of men, rejoice,
The Prince of Peace proclaim;
With heaven's host lift up our voice,
And shout Immanuel's name:
Knees and hearts to Him we bow;
Of our flesh and of our bone,
Jesus is our Brother now,
And God is all our own.

Charles Wesley, 1707-88.

135

DURA. 8.8.8.8.8.8 8. H. J. GAUNTLETT, 1805-76.

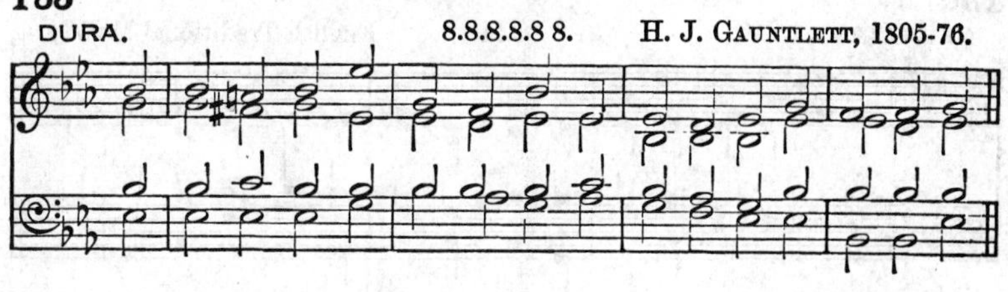

1 STUPENDOUS height of heavenly love,
   Of pitying tenderness divine;
It brought the Saviour from above,
   It caused the springing day to shine;
The sun of righteousness to appear,
And gild our gloomy hemisphere.

2 God did in Christ Himself reveal,
   To chase our darkness by His light,
Our sin and ignorance dispel,
   Direct our wandering feet aright;
And bring our souls, with pardon blest,
To realms of everlasting rest.

3 Come then, O Lord, Thy light impart,
   The faith that bids our terrors cease;
Into Thy love direct our heart,
   Into Thy way of perfect peace;
And cheer the souls of death afraid,
And guide them through the dreadful shade.

4 Answer Thy mercy's whole design,
   My God incarnated for me;
My spirit make Thy radiant shrine,
   My light and full salvation be;
And through the shades of death unknown
Conduct me to Thy dazzling throne. Amen.

Charles Wesley, 1707-88.

136

NEWBURY. C.M. English Traditional Melody.

1 The Maker of the sun and moon,
The Maker of our earth,
Lo! late in time, a fairer boon,
Himself is brought to birth.

2 How blest was all creation then,
When God so gave increase;
And Christ, to heal the hearts of men,
Brought righteousness and peace.

3 No star in all the heights of heaven
But burned to see Him go;
Yet unto earth alone was given
His human form to know.

4 His human form, by man denied,
Took death for human sin:
His endless love, through faith descried,
Still lives the world to win.

5 O perfect Love, outpassing sight,
O Light beyond our ken,
Come down through all the world to-night,
And heal the hearts of men! Amen.

Laurence Housman, 1865-

137

CRANHAM. Irregular. G. Holst, 1874-1934

The metre of this hymn is irregular. The music as printed is that of the first verse, and it can easily be adapted to the others.

Verse 2

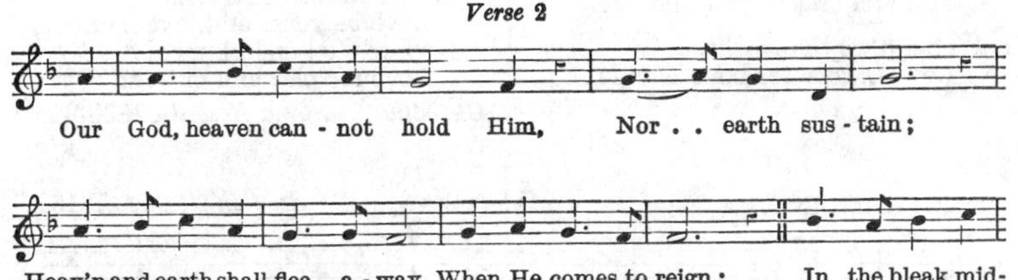
Our God, heaven can - not hold Him, Nor . . earth sus - tain;
Heav'n and earth shall flee a - way When He comes to reign: In the bleak mid-
&c.

1 In the bleak mid-winter,
  Frosty wind made moan,
Earth stood hard as iron,
  Water like a stone;
Snow had fallen, snow on snow,
  Snow on snow,
In the bleak mid-winter,
  Long ago.

2 Our God, heaven cannot hold Him,
  Nor earth sustain;
Heaven and earth shall flee away
  When He comes to reign:
In the bleak mid-winter
  A stable-place sufficed
The Lord God Almighty,
  Jesus Christ.

3 Angels and archangels
  May have gathered there,
Cherubim and seraphim
  Throngèd the air;
But His mother only,
  In her maiden bliss,
Worshipped the Belovèd
  With a kiss.

4 What can I give Him,
  Poor as I am?
If I were a shepherd,
  I would bring a lamb;
If I were a wise man,
  I would do my part;
Yet what I can I give Him—
  Give my heart.

Christina Georgina Rossetti, 1830-94.

138

HERMITAGE.

UNISON. 6.7.6.7. R. O. MORRIS, 1886-

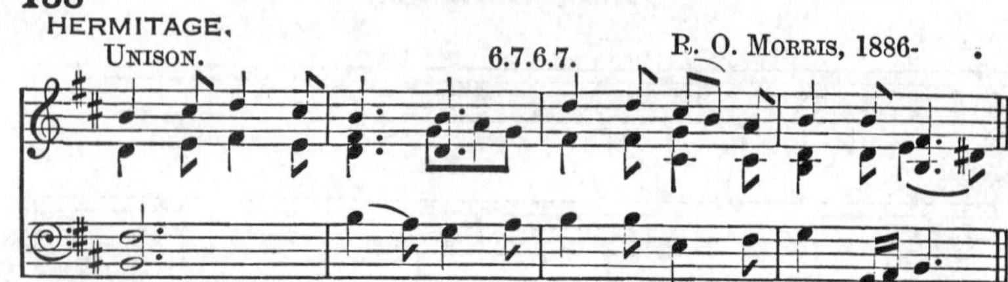

1 LOVE came down at Christmas,
Love all lovely, Love Divine;
Love was born at Christmas,
Star and angels gave the sign.

2 Worship we the Godhead,
Love Incarnate, Love Divine;
Worship we our Jesus:
But wherewith for sacred sign?

3 Love shall be our token,
Love be yours and love be mine,
Love to God and all men,
Love for plea and gift and sign.

Christina Georgina Rossetti, 1830-94.

139

DUNFERMLINE. C.M. *Scottish Psalter*, 1615.

1 THE race that long in darkness pined
Has seen a glorious Light;
The people dwell in day, who dwelt
In death's surrounding night.

2 To hail Thy rise, Thou better Sun,
The gathering nations come,
Joyous as when the reapers bear
The harvest-treasures home.

3 To us a Child of Hope is born,
To us a Son is given;
Him shall the tribes of earth obey,
Him all the hosts of heaven.

4 His name shall be the Prince of Peace,
For evermore adored,
The Wonderful, the Counsellor,
The great and mighty Lord.

5 His power increasing still shall spread,
His reign no end shall know:
Justice shall guard His throne above,
And peace abound below.

John Morison, 1750-98.

140

ST. CECILIA. 6.6.6.6. L. G. HAYNE, 1836-83.

Jam desinant suspiria.

1 GOD from on high hath heard;
Let sighs and sorrows cease;
The skies unfold, and lo!
Descends the gift of peace.

2 Hark! on the midnight air
Celestial voices swell;
The hosts of heaven proclaim
God comes on earth to dwell.

3 Haste with the shepherds; see
The mystery of grace:
A manger-bed, a Child,
Is all the eye can trace.

4 Is this the Eternal Son,
Who on the starry throne
Before the worlds begun
Was with the Father One?

5 Yes, faith can pierce the cloud
Which shrouds His glory now,
And hail Him God and Lord,
To whom all creatures bow.

6 Faith sees the sapphire throne,
Where angels evermore
Adoring tremble still,
And trembling still adore.

7 O Child! Thy silence speaks,
And bids us not refuse
To bear what flesh would shun,
To spurn what flesh would choose.

8 Fill us with holy love,
Heal Thou our earthly pride;
Born in each lowly heart,
For ever there abide. Amen.

Charles Coffin, 1676-1749;
tr. by James Russell Woodford, 1820-85.

141

BERKSHIRE. L.M. C. WESLEY, 1757-1834.

1 To us a child of royal birth,
Heir of the promises, is given;
The invisible appears on earth,
The Son of man, the God of heaven.

2 A Saviour born, in love supreme
He comes our fallen souls to raise;
He comes His people to redeem
With all His plenitude of grace.

3 The Christ, by raptured seers foretold,
Filled with the eternal Spirit's power,
Prophet, and Priest, and King behold,
And Lord of all the worlds adore.

4 The Lord of hosts, the God most high,
Who quits His throne on earth to live,
With joy we welcome from the sky,
With faith into our hearts receive.

Charles Wesley, 1707-88.

142

ADORATION. 6.6.6.6.8 8. W. H. HAVERGAL, 1793-1870.

1 LET earth and heaven combine,
Angels and men agree,
To praise in songs divine
The incarnate Deity,
Our God contracted to a span,
Incomprehensibly made man.

2 He laid His glory by,
He wrapped Him in our clay;
Unmarked by human eye,
The latent Godhead lay;
Infant of days He here became,
And bore the mild Immanuel's name.

3 Unsearchable the love
That hath the Saviour brought;
The grace is far above
Or man or angel's thought:
Suffice for us that God, we know,
Our God, is manifest below.

4 He deigns in flesh to appear,
Widest extremes to join;
To bring our vileness near,
And make us all divine:
And we the life of God shall know,
For God is manifest below.

5 Made perfect first in love,
And sanctified by grace,
We shall from earth remove,
And see His glorious face:
Then shall His love be fully showed,
And man shall then be lost in God.

Charles Wesley, 1707-88.

143

IN DULCI JUBILO. Irregular. Weihnachtslied, 14th Century.

1 Good Christian men, rejoice
With heart and soul and voice!
Give ye heed to what we say:
News! News!
Jesus Christ is born to-day.
Ox and ass before Him bow,
And He is in the manger now:
Christ is born to-day.

2 Good Christian men, rejoice
With heart and soul and voice!
Now ye hear of endless bliss:
Joy! Joy!
Jesus Christ was born for this.
He hath oped the heavenly door,
And man is blest for evermore.
Christ was born for this.

3 Good Christian men, rejoice
With heart and soul and voice!
Now ye need not fear the grave:
Peace! Peace!
Jesus Christ was born to save;
Calls you one, and calls you all,
To gain His everlasting hall.
Christ was born to save.

John Mason Neale, 1818-66.

Also:

82 Hark the glad sound
242 Come, Thou long-expected
257 O come, O come
259 And art Thou come
902 All glory to God

144 HIS LIFE, TEACHING, AND EXAMPLE

LOVE UNKNOWN.
UNISON. 6.6.6.6.4.4 4.4. J. N. IRELAND, 1879- .

1 My song is love unknown;
My Saviour's love to me;
Love to the loveless shown,
That they might lovely be.
O who am I,
That for my sake,
My Lord should take
Frail flesh, and die?

2 He came from His blest Throne,
Salvation to bestow:
But men made strange, and none
The longed-for Christ would know.
But O my Friend!
My Friend indeed,
Who at my need
His life did spend.

3 Sometimes they strew His way,
And His sweet praises sing;
Resounding all the day,
Hosannas to their King.
Then: Crucify!
Is all their breath,
And for His death
They thirst and cry.

4 Why, what hath my Lord done?
What makes this rage and spite?
He made the lame to run,
He gave the blind their sight.
Sweet injuries!
Yet they at these
Themselves displease,
And 'gainst Him rise.

5 They rise and needs will have
My dear Lord made away;
A murderer they save;
The Prince of life they slay.
Yet cheerful He
To suffering goes,
That He His foes
From thence might free.

6 In life, no house, no home
My Lord on earth might have;
In death, no friendly tomb
But what a stranger gave.
What may I say?
Heav'n was His home;
But mine the tomb
Wherein He lay.

7 Here might I stay and sing,
No story so divine;
Never was love, dear King,
Never was grief like Thine.
This is my Friend,
In whose sweet praise
I all my days
Could gladly spend.

Samuel Crossman, c. 1624-83.

145

CLINTON. C.M. C. H. H. Parry, 1848-1918.

1 What grace, O Lord, and beauty
Around Thy steps below ; [shone
What patient love was seen in all
Thy life and death of woe !

2 For ever on Thy burdened heart
A weight of sorrow hung,
Yet no ungentle, murmuring word
Escaped Thy silent tongue.

3 Thy foes might hate, despise, revile,
Thy friends unfaithful prove :
Unwearied in forgiveness still,
Thy heart could only love.

4 O give us hearts to love like Thee,
Like Thee, O Lord, to grieve
Far more for others' sins, than all
The wrongs that we receive.

5 One with Thyself, may every eye
In us, Thy brethren, see
The gentleness and grace that spring
From union, Lord, with Thee.

Edward Denny, 1796-1889.

146

PHILIPPINE. L.M. R. E. Roberts, 1925.

1 Jesus, who lived above the sky,
Came down to be a man and die ;
And in the Bible we may see
How very good He used to be.

2 He went about—He was so kind—
To cure poor people who were blind ;
And many who were sick and lame,
He pitied them and did the same.

3 And more than that, He told them, too,
The things that God would have them do ;
And was so gentle and so mild,
He would have listened to a child.

4 But such a cruel death He died !
He was hung up and crucified ;
And those kind hands that did such good,
They nailed them to a cross of wood.

5 And so He died—and this is why
He came to be a man and die ;
The Bible says He came from heaven,
That we might have our sins forgiven.

Ann Gilbert, 1782-1866.

147

SALVATOR. 7 7.5. D. M. B. FOSTER, 1851-1922.

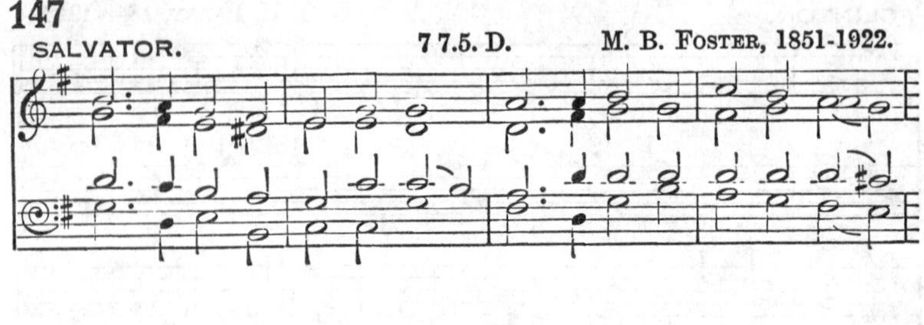

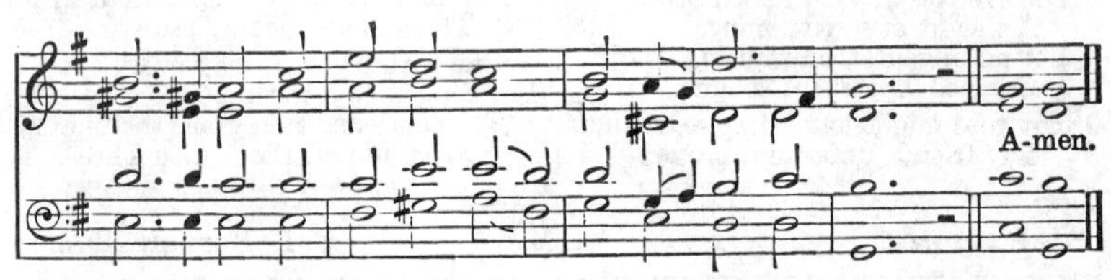

1 WHEN the Lord of Love was here,
Happy hearts to Him were dear,
Though His heart was sad;
Worn and lonely for our sake,
Yet He turned aside to make
All the weary glad.

2 Meek and lowly were His ways;
From His loving, grew His praise,
From His giving, prayer:
All the outcasts thronged to hear;
All the sorrowful drew near
To enjoy His care.

3 When He walked the fields, He drew
From the flowers, and birds, and dew,
Parables of God;
For within His heart of love
All the soul of man did move,
God had His abode.

4 Fill us, Lord, with Thy desire
All the sinful to inspire
With the Father's life;
Free us from the cares that press
On the heart of worldliness,
From the fret and strife.

5 Lord, be ours Thy power to keep,
In the very heart of grief
And in trial, love;
In our meekness to be wise,
And through sorrow to arise
To our God above. Amen.

Stopford Augustus Brooke, 1832-1916.

148

CREDO. 8.8.8.8.8.8 8. J. STAINER, 1840-1901.

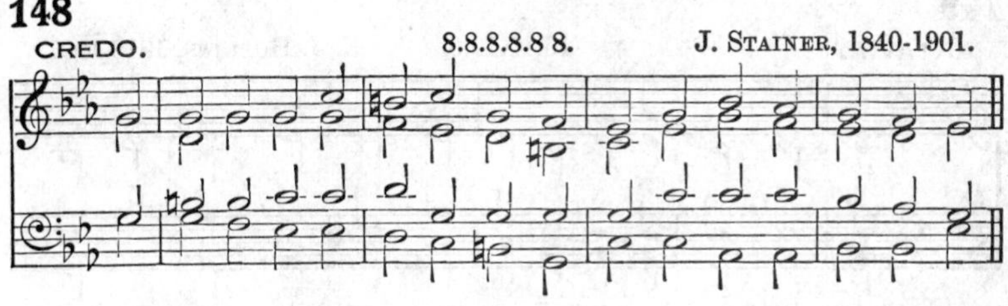

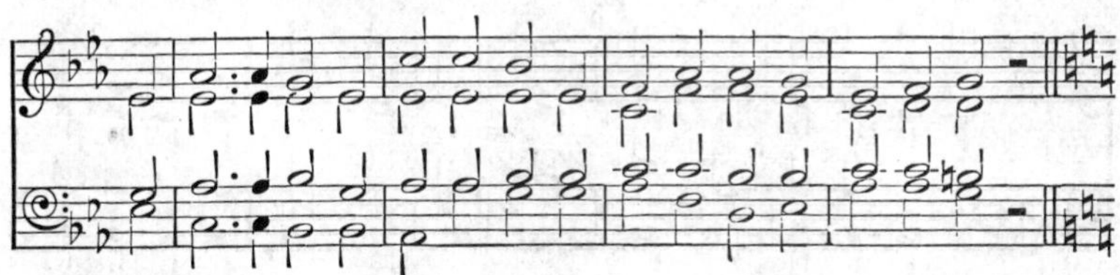

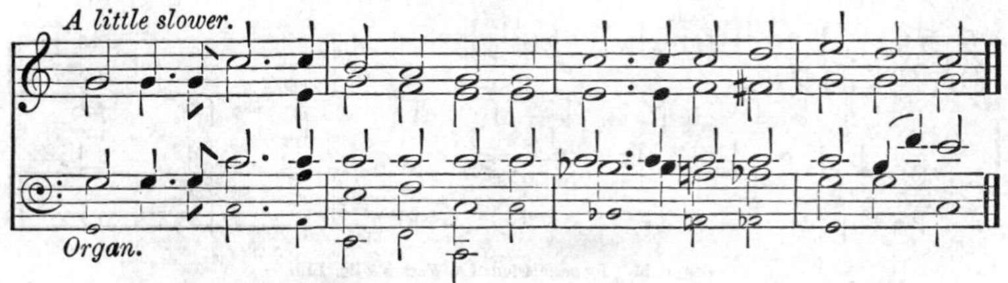

1 We saw Thee not when Thou didst come
To this poor world of sin and [death,
Nor e'er beheld Thy cottage home
In that despisèd Nazareth;
But we believe Thy footsteps trod
Its streets and plains, Thou Son of God.

2 We did not see Thee lifted high
Amid that wild and savage crew,
Nor heard Thy meek, imploring cry:
Forgive, they know not what they do!
Yet we believe the deed was done,
Which shook the earth and veiled the sun.

3 We stood not by the empty tomb
Where late Thy sacred body lay,
Nor sat within that upper room,
Nor met Thee in the open way;
But we believe that angels said:
Why seek the living with the dead?

4 We did not mark the chosen few,
When Thou didst through the clouds ascend,
First lift to heaven their wondering view,
Then to the earth all prostrate bend;
Yet we believe that mortal eyes
Beheld that journey to the skies.

5 And now that Thou dost reign on high,
And thence Thy waiting people bless,
No ray of glory from the sky
Doth shine upon our wilderness;
But we believe Thy faithful word,
And trust in our redeeming Lord.

John Hampden Gurney, 1802-62.

F

ARTAVIA. 10.10.10.6. E. J. HOPKINS, 1818-1901.

1 AND didst Thou love the race that loved not Thee ?
And didst Thou take to heaven a human brow ?
Dost plead with man's voice by the marvellous sea ?
Art Thou his kinsman now ?

2 O God, O kinsman, loved, but not enough !
O Man, with eyes majestic after death !
Whose feet have toiled along our pathways rough,
Whose lips drawn human breath !

3 By that one likeness which is ours and Thine,
By that one nature which doth hold us kin,
By that high heaven where, sinless, Thou dost shine,
To draw us sinners in ;

4 By Thy last silence in the judgement hall,
By long foreknowledge of the deadly tree,
By darkness, by the wormwood and the gall,
I pray Thee visit me.

5 Come, lest this heart should, cold and cast away,
Die e'er the Guest adored she entertain—
Lest eyes that never saw Thine earthly day
Should miss Thy heavenly reign.

Jean Ingelow, 1820-97.

150

MARGARET. Irregular. T. R. Matthews, 1826-1910.

By permission of Novello and Company, Limited.

1 Thou didst leave Thy throne
And Thy kingly crown,
When Thou camest to earth for me;
But in Bethlehem's home
Was there found no room
For Thy holy nativity:
O come to my heart, Lord Jesus;
There is room in my heart for Thee.

2 Heaven's arches rang
When the angels sang,
Proclaiming Thy royal degree;
But of lowly birth
Cam'st Thou, Lord, on earth,
And in great humility:
O come to my heart, Lord Jesus;
There is room in my heart for Thee.

3 The foxes found rest,
And the birds their nest,
In the shade of the cedar-tree;
But Thy couch was the sod,
O Thou Son of God,
In the deserts of Galilee:
O come to my heart, Lord Jesus;
There is room in my heart for Thee.

4 Thou camest, O Lord,
With the living word
That should set Thy people free;
But, with mocking scorn
And with crown of thorn,
They bore Thee to Calvary:
O come to my heart, Lord Jesus;
Thy Cross is my only plea.

5 When heaven's arches ring,
And her choirs shall sing,
At Thy coming to victory,
Let Thy voice call me home,
Saying: Yet there is room,
There is room at My side for thee!
And my heart shall rejoice, Lord Jesus,
When Thou comest and callest for me.

Emily Elizabeth Steele Elliott, 1836-97.

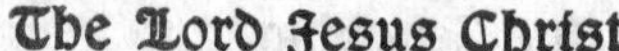

151

WHO IS HE? 7 7. and refrain. B. R. HANBY, 1833-67.

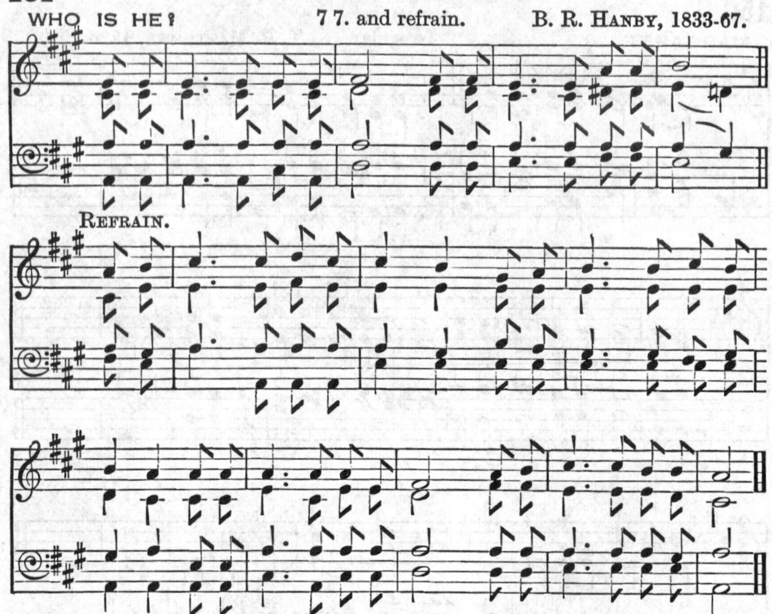

1 WHO is He, in yonder stall,
At whose feet the shepherds fall?
'Tis the Lord! O wondrous story!
'Tis the Lord, the King of Glory!
At His feet we humbly fall;
Crown Him, crown Him Lord of all.

2 Who is He, in yonder cot,
Bending to His toilsome lot?

3 Who is He, in deep distress,
Fasting in the wilderness?

4 Who is He that stands and weeps
At the grave where Lazarus sleeps?

5 Lo, at midnight, who is He
Prays in dark Gethsemane?

6 Who is He, in Calvary's throes,
Asks for blessings on His foes?

7 Who is He that from the grave
Comes to heal and help and save?

8 Who is He that from His throne
Rules through all the worlds alone?

Benjamin Russell Hanby, 1833-67.

152

NAZARETH. 8 8.8 8.8 9. T. E. PERKINS, 1831-1912.

1 WHAT means this eager, anxious throng,
Which moves with busy haste along,
These wondrous gatherings day by day?
What means this strange commotion, [pray?
In accents hushed the throng reply:
Jesus of Nazareth passeth by.

2 Who is this Jesus? Why should He
The city move so mightily?
A passing stranger, has He skill
To move the multitude at will?
Again the stirring tones reply:
Jesus of Nazareth passeth by.

3 Jesus! 'tis He who once below
Man's pathway trod 'mid pain and woe;
And burdened ones, where'er He [came,
Brought out their sick, and deaf, and lame:
The blind rejoiced to hear the cry:
Jesus of Nazareth passeth by.

4 Again He comes! From place to place
His holy footprints we can trace,
He pauseth at our threshold—nay,
He enters—condescends to stay;
Shall we not gladly raise the cry?
Jesus of Nazareth passeth by.

5 Ho! all ye heavy laden, come,
Here's pardon, comfort, rest, and home;
Ye wanderers from a Father's face,
Return, accept His proffered grace;
Ye tempted ones, there's refuge nigh—
Jesus of Nazareth passeth by.

Etta Campbell, c. 1863.

153

ANTWERP. L.M. W. SMALLWOOD, 1831-97.

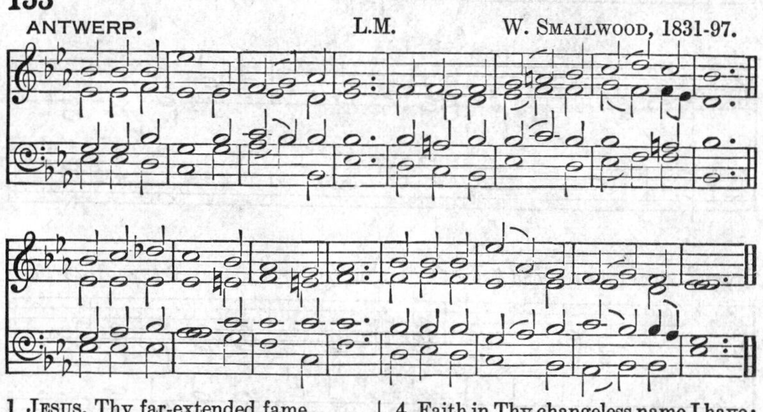

1 JESUS, Thy far-extended fame
My drooping soul exults to hear;
Thy name, Thy all-restoring name,
Is music in a sinner's ear.

2 Sinners of old Thou didst receive
With comfortable words and kind,
Their sorrows cheer, their wants relieve,
Heal the diseased, and cure the blind.

3 And art Thou not the Saviour still,
In every place and age the same?
Hast Thou forgot Thy gracious skill,
Or lost the virtue of Thy name?

4 Faith in Thy changeless name I have;
The good, the kind physician, Thou
Art able now our souls to save,
Art willing to restore them now.

5 Wouldst Thou the body's health restore,
And not regard the sin-sick soul?
The sin-sick soul Thou lov'st much more,
And surely Thou shalt make it [whole.

6 All my disease, my every sin,
To Thee, O Jesus, I confess;
In pardon, Lord, my cure begin,
And perfect it in holiness.

Charles Wesley, 1707-88.

154
KINGSFOLD (*First Tune*).
D.C.M.
English Traditional Melody.
Arr. by H. P. Allen, 1869-1946
Unison.
VOX DILECTI (*Second Tune*).
D.C.M.
J. B. Dykes, 1823-76.

p

* *In verses 2 and 3, for music of lines 5 and 6, substitute the following.*

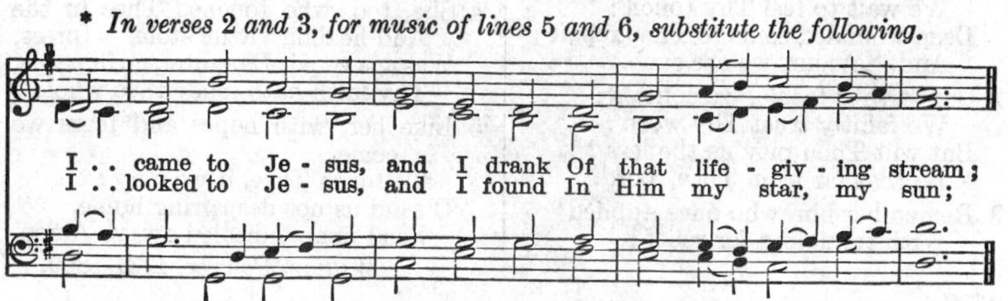
I .. came to Je - sus, and I drank Of that life - giv - ing stream;
I .. looked to Je - sus, and I found In Him my star, my sun;

1 I HEARD the voice of Jesus say:
Come unto Me and rest;
Lay down, thou weary one, lay down
Thy head upon My breast!
I came to Jesus as I was,
Weary, and worn, and sad;
I found in Him a resting-place,
And He has made me glad.

2 I heard the voice of Jesus say:
Behold, I freely give
The living water; thirsty one,
Stoop down and drink, and live!
I came to Jesus, and I drank
Of that life-giving stream;
My thirst was quenched, my soul revived,
And now I live in Him.

3 I heard the voice of Jesus say:
I am this dark world's Light;
Look unto Me, thy morn shall rise,
And all thy day be bright!
I looked to Jesus, and I found
In Him my star, my sun;
And in that light of life I'll walk
Till travelling days are done.

Horatius Bonar, 1808-89.

155

BEDFORD. C.M. W. WEALE, c. 1686-1727.

1 HEAL us, Immanuel; hear our prayer;
We wait to feel Thy touch:
Deep-wounded souls to Thee repair;
And, Saviour, we are such.

2 Our faith is feeble, we confess;
We faintly trust Thy word:
But wilt Thou pity us the less?
Be that far from Thee, Lord.

3 Remember him who once applied
With trembling for relief;
Lord, I believe! with tears he cried,
O help my unbelief!

4 She, too, who touched Thee in the press,
And healing virtue stole,
Was answered: Daughter, go in peace,
Thy faith hath made thee whole.

5 Like her, with hopes and fears we come,
To touch Thee, if we may:
O send us not despairing home,
Send none unhealed away. Amen.

William Cowper, 1731-1800.

156

ST. LUKE. L.M. *Collection of Easy Litanies*, 1852.

A - men.

1 O Thou, whom once they flocked to hear,
Thy words to hear, Thy power to feel;
Suffer the sinners to draw near,
And graciously receive us still.

2 They that be whole, Thyself hast said,
No need of a physician have;
But I am sick, and want Thine aid,
And want Thine utmost power to save.

3 Thy power, and truth, and love divine,
The same from age to age endure;
A word, a gracious word of Thine,
The most inveterate plague can cure.

4 Helpless howe'er my spirit lies,
And long hath languished at the pool,
A word of Thine shall make me rise,
And speak me in a moment whole.

5 Make this the acceptable hour;
Come, O my soul's physician Thou!
Display Thy sanctifying power,
And show me Thy salvation now. Amen.

Charles Wesley, 1707-88.

157

ST. CATHERINE. 8.7.8.7. S. Flood Jones, 1827-95.

1 Jesus calls us! O'er the tumult
Of our life's wild restless sea,
Day by day His sweet voice soundeth,
Saying: Christian, follow Me—

2 As, of old, apostles heard it
By the Galilean lake,
Turned from home and toil and kindred,
Leaving all for His dear sake.

3 Jesus calls us from the worship
Of the vain world's golden store,
From each idol that would keep us,
Saying: Christian, love Me more!

4 In our joys and in our sorrows,
Days of toil and hours of ease,
Still He calls, in cares and pleasures,
That we love Him more than these.

5 Jesus calls us! By Thy mercies,
Saviour, make us hear Thy call,
Give our hearts to Thine obedience,
Serve and love Thee best of all.

Cecil Frances Alexander, 1823-95.

158

SUBMISSION. S.M. E. GILDING, ? - 1782.

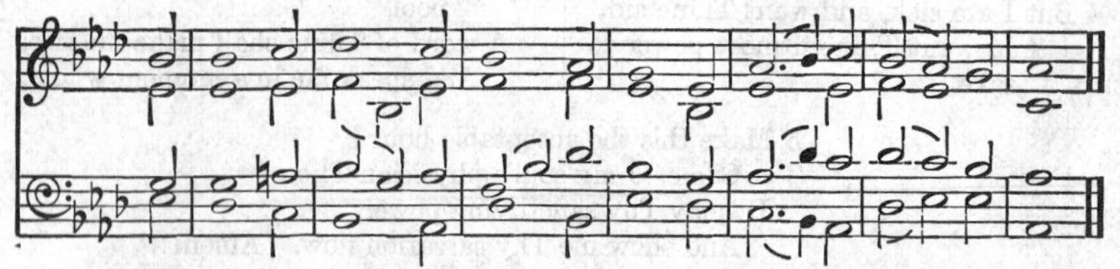

1 THOU say'st: Take up thy cross,
O man, and follow Me.
The night is black, the feet are slack;
Yet we would follow Thee.

2 But, O dear Lord, we cry,
That we Thy face could see:
Thy blessèd face one moment's space—
Then might we follow Thee.

3 Dim tracts of time divide
Those golden days from me;
Thy voice comes strange o'er years of change;
How can we follow Thee?

4 Comes faint and far Thy voice
From vales of Galilee;
Thy vision fades in ancient shades;
How should we follow Thee?

5 O heavy cross—of faith
In what we cannot see:
As once of yore Thyself restore,
And help to follow Thee.

6 If not as once Thou cam'st
In true humanity,
Come yet as Guest within the breast
That burns to follow Thee.

7 Within our heart of hearts
In nearest nearness be;
Set up Thy throne within Thine own;
Go, Lord—we follow Thee.

Francis Turner Palgrave, 1824-97.

159

FINGAL. C.M. J. S. ANDERSON, 1853- .

May also be sung to ST. MARY, No. 175.

Śiṣyahī gaṇāyā n̄ahī yogya ǰo tayālā.

1 One who is all unfit to count
As scholar in Thy school,
Thou of Thy love hast named a
O kindness wonderful! [friend—

2 So weak am I, O gracious Lord,
So all unworthy Thee,
That e'en the dust upon Thy feet
Outweighs me utterly.

3 Thou dwellest in unshadowed light,
All sin and shame above—
That Thou shouldst bear our sin and
shame,
How can I tell such love?

4 Ah, did not He the heavenly throne
A little thing esteem,
And not unworthy for my sake
A mortal body deem?

5 When in His flesh they drove the
nails,
Did He not all endure?
What name is there to fit a life
So patient and so pure?

6 So, Love itself in human form,
For love of me He came;
I cannot look upon His face
For shame, for bitter shame.

7 If there is aught of worth in me,
It comes from Thee alone;
Then keep me safe, for so, O Lord,
Thou keepest but Thine own.

Narayan Vaman Tilak, 1861-1919;
tr. by Nicol Macnicol, 1870- .

160

REDHEAD No. 66. C.M. R. Redhead, 1820-1901.

1 Thou art the Way: to Thee alone
From sin and death we flee:
And he who would the Father seek
Must seek Him, Lord, by Thee.

2 Thou art the Truth: Thy word alone
True wisdom can impart;
Thou only canst inform the mind,
And purify the heart.

3 Thou art the Life: the rending tomb
Proclaims Thy conquering arm;
And those who put their trust in Thee
Nor death nor hell shall harm.

4 Thou art the Way, the Truth, the Life:
Grant us that Way to know,
That Truth to keep, that Life to win,
Whose joys eternal flow. Amen.

George Washington Doane, 1799-1859.

161 The Lord Jesus Christ

TELL ME. 7.6.7.6. D. and refrain. W. H. DOANE, 1832-1916.

REFRAIN.
Tell me the old, old sto - ry, tell me the old, old sto - ry,
tell me the old, old sto - ry, Of Je - sus and His love.

1 Tell me the old, old story
Of unseen things above,
Of Jesus and His glory,
Of Jesus and His love.
Tell me the story simply,
As to a little child;
For I am weak, and weary,
And helpless, and defiled.
Tell me the old, old story,
Of Jesus and His love.

2 Tell me the story slowly,
That I may take it in—
That wonderful redemption,
God's remedy for sin.
Tell me the story often,
For I forget so soon;
The early dew of morning
Has passed away at noon.

3 Tell me the story softly,
With earnest tones and grave;
Remember, I'm the sinner
Whom Jesus came to save.
Tell me the story always,
If you would really be
In any time of trouble
A comforter to me.

4 Tell me the same old story
When you have cause to fear
That this world's empty glory
Is costing me too dear.
Yes, and, when that world's glory
Shall dawn upon my soul,
Tell me the old, old story—
Christ Jesus makes thee whole!

Katherine Hankey, 1834-1911.

162

LÖWENSTERN. 10 10 10. M. Von Löwenstern, 1594-1648.

1 Thou art my life; if Thou but turn away,
My life 's a thousand deaths: Thou art my way;
Without Thee, Lord, I travel not, but stray.

2 My light Thou art; without Thy glorious sight
My eyes are darkened with perpetual night:
My God, Thou art my way, my life, my light.

3 Thou art my way; I wander, if Thou fly:
Thou art my light; if hid, how blind am I!
Thou art my life; if Thou withdraw, I die.

4 Disclose Thy sunbeams; close Thy wings and stay;
See, see how I am blind, and dead, and stray,
O Thou that art my light, my life, my way!

Francis Quarles, 1592-1644.

163

GILLINGHAM. L.M. J. CLARKE, 1659 *or* 1670-1707

1 DEAR Master, in whose life I see
All that I would, but fail to be,
Let Thy clear light for ever shine,
To shame and guide this life of mine.

2 Though what I dream and what I do
In my weak days are always two,
Help me, oppressed by things undone,
O Thou, whose deeds and dreams were one!

John Hunter, 1848-1917.

164

SHEBBEAR COLLEGE. 6.6.6.6.8 8. J. D. HANDS, 1878- .

A - men.

May also be sung to LOVE UNKNOWN, No. 144.

1 Behold a little Child,
Laid in a manger bed;
The wintry blasts blow wild
Around His infant head.
But who is this, so lowly laid?
'Tis He by whom the worlds were made.

2 Alas! in what poor state
The Son of God is seen;
Why doth the Lord so great
Choose out a home so mean?
That we may learn from pride to flee,
And follow His humility.

3 Where Joseph plies his trade,
Lo! Jesus labours too;
The hands that all things made
An earthly craft pursue,
That weary men in Him may rest,
And faithful toil through Him be blest.

4 Among the doctors see
The Boy so full of grace;
Say, wherefore taketh He
The scholar's lowly place?
That Christian boys, with reverence meet,
May sit and learn at Jesus' feet.

5 Christ, once Thyself a boy,
Our boyhood guard and guide
Be Thou its light and joy,
And still with us abide,
That Thy dear love, so great and free,
May draw us evermore to Thee. Amen.

William Walsham How, 1823-97.

165

HEINLEIN. 7.7.7.7. M. Herbst, *c.* 1654-81.

1 Forty days and forty nights
Thou wast fasting in the wild,
Forty days and forty nights
Tempted, and yet undefiled:

2 Sunbeams scorching all the day,
Chilly dewdrops nightly shed,
Prowling beasts about Thy way,
Stones Thy pillow, earth Thy bed.

3 Let us Thy endurance share
And from earthly greed abstain;
With Thee watching unto prayer,
With Thee strong to suffer pain.

4 And if Satan, vexing sore,
Flesh or spirit should assail,
Thou, his vanquisher before,
Grant we may not faint nor fail.

5 So shall we have peace divine;
Hoiier gladness ours shall be;
Round us too shall angels shine,
Such as ministered to Thee.

George Hunt Smyttan, 1822-70;
Francis Pott, 1832-1909.

166

CHILDHOOD. 8.8.8.6. 'University of Wales' (*Students' Hymnal*), 1923.

1 It fell upon a summer day,
When Jesus walked in Galilee,
The mothers from a village brought
Their children to His knee.

2 He took them in His arms, and laid
His hands on each remembered head;
Suffer these little ones to come
To Me, He gently said.

3 Forbid them not; unless ye bear
The childlike heart your hearts within,
Unto My kingdom ye may come
But may not enter in.

4 Master, I fain would enter there;
O let me follow Thee, and share
Thy meek and lowly heart, and be
Freed from all worldly care.

5 Of innocence, and love, and trust,
Of quiet work, and simple word,
Of joy, and thoughtlessness of self,
Build up my life, good Lord.

6 All happy thoughts, and gentle ways,
And loving-kindness daily given,
And freedom through obedience gained,
Make in my heart Thy heaven.

7 O happy thus to live and move!
And sweet this world, where I shall find
God's beauty everywhere, His love,
His good in all mankind.

8 Then, Father, grant this childlike heart,
That I may come to Christ, and feel
His hands on me in blessing laid,
Love-giving, strong to heal.
Amen.

Stopford Augustus Brooke, 1832-1916.

167

ST. AËLRED. 888.3. J. B. Dykes, 1823-76.

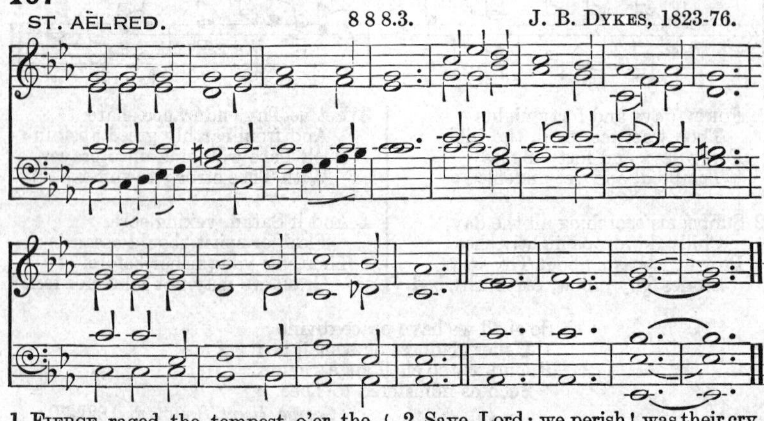

1 Fierce raged the tempest o'er the deep,
Watch did Thine anxious servants keep,
But Thou wast wrapped in guileless sleep,
Calm and still.

2 Save, Lord; we perish! was their cry.
O save us in our agony!
Thy word above the storm rose high—
Peace, be still!

3 The wild winds hushed, the angry deep
Sank like a little child to sleep,
The sullen billows ceased to leap,
At Thy will.

4 So, when our life is clouded o'er,
And storm-winds drift us from the shore,
Say, lest we sink to rise no more:
Peace, be still!

Godfrey Thring, 1823-1903.

168

STANLEY. D.L.M. A. H. MANN, 1850-1930.

1 LORD! it is good for us to be
High on the mountain here with Thee:
Here in an ampler, purer air,
Above the stir of toil and care
Of hearts oppressed with doubt and grief,
Believing in their unbelief,
Calling Thy servants all in vain
To ease them of their bitter pain.

2 Lord! it is good for us to be
With Thee, and with Thy faithful three:
Here, where the apostle's heart of rock
Is nerved against temptation's shock;
Here, where the son of thunder learns
The thought that breathes, the word that burns;
Here, where on eagles' wings we move
With him whose last, best word is love.

3 Lord! it is good for us to be
Entranced, enwrapped, alone with Thee,
Watching the glistening raiment glow
Whiter than Hermon's whitest snow,
The human lineaments which shine
Irradiant with a light divine,
Till we, too, change from grace to grace,
Gazing on that transfigured face.

4 Lord! it is good for us to be
Here on the holy mount with Thee,
When darkling in the depths of night,
When dazzled with excess of light,
We bow before the heavenly voice
Which bids bewildered souls rejoice:
Though love wax cold, and faith grow dim,
This is My Son: O hear ye Him!

Arthur Penrhyn Stanley, 1815-81.

169

SIDMOUTH. 8.8.8.8.8.8. B. J. DALE, 1885-1943

May also be sung to EATON, No. 750.

O Jesu Christ, mein schönstes Licht.

1 MY Saviour, Thou Thy love to me
   In shame, in want, in pain hast showed;
For me, on the accursèd tree,
   Thou pourèdst forth Thy guiltless blood;
Thy wounds upon my heart impress,
Nor aught shall the loved stamp efface.

2 More hard than marble is my heart,
   And foul with sins of deepest stain;
But Thou the mighty Saviour art,
   Nor flowed Thy cleansing blood in vain:
Ah, soften, melt this rock, and may
Thy blood wash all these stains away!

3 O that I, as a little child,
   May follow Thee, and never rest
Till sweetly Thou hast breathed Thy mild
   And lowly mind into my breast!
Nor ever may we parted be,
Till I become one spirit with Thee.

4 Still let Thy love point out my way;
   How wondrous things Thy love hath wrought!
Still lead me, lest I go astray;
   Direct my word, inspire my thought;
And if I fall, soon may I hear
Thy voice, and know that love is near.

5 In suffering be Thy love my peace,
   In weakness be Thy love my power;
And when the storms of life shall cease,
   Jesus, in that important hour,
In death as life be Thou my Guide,
And save me, who for me hast died. Amen.

Paulus Gerhardt, 1607-76;
tr. by John Wesley, 1703-91.

170

ALL OF THEE. 8.7.8.8.7. J. MOUNTAIN, 1843-1933.

1 O THE bitter shame and sorrow,
That a time could ever be
When I let the Saviour's pity
Plead in vain, and proudly answered:
All of self, and none of Thee!

2 Yet He found me. I beheld Him
Bleeding on the accursèd tree,
Heard Him pray: Forgive them, Father!
And my wistful heart said faintly:
Some of self, and some of Thee!

3 Day by day His tender mercy,
Healing, helping, full and free,
Sweet and strong, and, ah! so patient,
Brought me lower, while I whispered:
Less of self, and more of Thee!

4 Higher than the highest heaven,
Deeper than the deepest sea,
Lord, Thy love at last hath conquered;
Grant me now my supplication:
None of self, and all of Thee!
Amen.

Theodore Monod, 1836-1921.

171

11 11.11 11. and refrain.

JESUS, I WILL TRUST THEE (RELIANCE). I. D. SANKEY, 1840-1908.

REFRAIN.
In Thy love con - fi - ding, I will seek Thy face,

Wor-ship and a - dore Thee For Thy won-drous grace.
Je - sus, I will trust Thee, trust Thee with my soul;
Guilt - y, lost, and help - less, Thou canst make me whole.

By permission. From *Sacred Songs and Solos.*

1 Jesus, I will trust Thee, trust Thee with my soul;
Guilty, lost, and helpless, Thou canst make me whole,
There is none in heaven or on earth like Thee;
Thou hast died for sinners, therefore, Lord, for me.
In Thy love confiding, I will seek Thy face,
Worship and adore Thee for Thy wondrous grace.
Jesus, I will trust Thee, trust Thee with my soul,
Guilty, lost, and helpless, Thou canst make me whole.

2 Jesus, I will trust Thee, trust Thy written Word;
Since Thy voice of mercy I have often heard.
When Thy Spirit teacheth, to my taste how sweet,
Only may I hearken, sitting at Thy feet.

3 Jesus, I will trust Thee, pondering Thy ways,
Full of love and mercy all Thine earthly days:
Sinners gathered round Thee, lepers sought Thy face,
None too vile or loathsome for a Saviour's grace.

4 Jesus, I will trust Thee, trust Thee without doubt;
Whosoever cometh Thou wilt not cast out:
Faithful is Thy promise, precious is Thy blood—
These my soul's salvation, Thou my Saviour God.

Mary Jane Walker, 1816-78.

Also:

62 O Love, how deep
102 Immortal Love, for ever full
190 O perfect life of love!
600 O Master, let me walk
669 Dear Lord and Father
780 Master, speak!

HIS SUFFERINGS AND DEATH

172

MANCHESTER. C.M. ROBERT WAINWRIGHT, 1748-82.

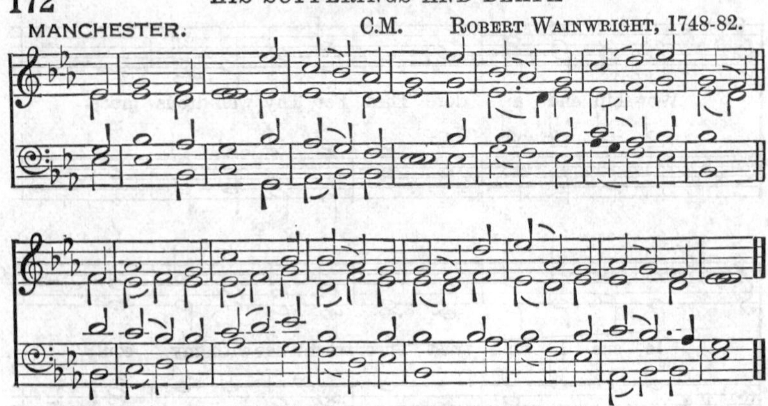

May also be sung to IRISH, No. 503.

1 WITH glorious clouds encompassed [round,
Whom angels dimly see,
Will the Unsearchable be found,
Or God appear to me ?

2 Will He forsake His throne above,
Himself to me impart ?
Answer, Thou Man of grief and love,
And speak it to my heart !

3 In manifested love explain
Thy wonderful design ;
What meant the suffering Son of Man,
The streaming blood divine ?

4 Didst Thou not in our flesh appear,
And live and die below,
That I may now perceive Thee near,
And my Redeemer know ?

5 Come then, and to my soul reveal
The heights and depths of grace,
The wounds which all my sorrows [heal,
That dear disfigured face.

6 I view the Lamb in His own light,
Whom angels dimly see,
And gaze, transported at the sight,
Through all eternity.

Charles Wesley, 1707-88.

173

EUPHONY. 8.8.8.8.8.8. H. DENNIS, 1818-87.

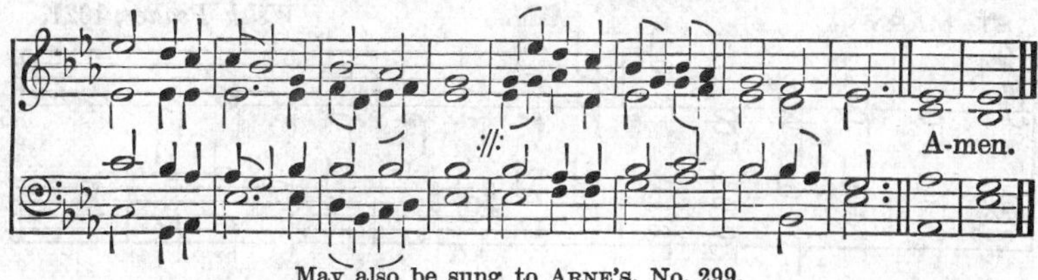

May also be sung to ARNE'S, No. 299.

1 WOULD Jesus have the sinner die ?
Why hangs He then on yonder tree ?
What means that strange expiring cry ?
Sinners, He prays for you and me :
Forgive them, Father, O forgive !
They know not that by Me they live.

2 Thou loving, all-atoning Lamb,
Thee—by Thy painful agony,
Thy sweat of blood, Thy grief and shame,
Thy Cross and passion on the tree,
Thy precious death and life—I pray :
Take all, take all my sins away !

3 O let me kiss Thy bleeding feet,
And bathe and wash them with my tears !
The story of Thy love repeat
In every drooping sinner's ears,
That all may hear the quickening sound,
Since I, even I, have mercy found.

4 O let Thy love my heart constrain !
Thy love for every sinner free,
That every fallen soul of man
May taste the grace that found out me ;
That all mankind with me may prove
Thy sovereign everlasting love.
Amen.

Charles Wesley, 1707-88.

174

ST. WILFRID. UNISON. 6.5.6.5.D. A. E. FLOYD, 1877-

1 I MET the good Shepherd
But now on the plain,
As homeward He carried
His lost one again.
I marvelled how gently
His burden He bore ;
And, as He passed by me,
I knelt to adore.

2 O Shepherd, good Shepherd,
Thy wounds they are deep ;
The wolves have sore hurt Thee,
In saving Thy sheep ;
Thy raiment all over
With crimson is dyed ;
And what is this rent
They have made in Thy side ?

3 Ah me ! How the thorns
Have entangled Thy hair,
And cruelly riven
That forehead so fair ;
How feebly Thou drawest
Thy faltering breath ;
And lo, on Thy face
Is the shadow of death.

4 O Shepherd, good Shepherd !
And is it for me
This grievous affliction
Has fallen on Thee ?
Ah, then let me strive,
For the love Thou hast borne,
To give Thee no longer
Occasion to mourn !

Edward Caswall, 1814-78.

175

ST. MARY C.M. *Welsh Psalter*, 1621.

1 Weep not for Him who onward bears
His Cross to Calvary;
He does not ask man's pitying tears,
Who wills for man to die.

2 The awful sorrow of His face,
The bowing of His frame,
Come not from torture nor disgrace:
He fears not Cross nor shame.

3 There is a deeper pang of grief,
An agony unknown,
In which His love finds no relief—
He bears it all alone.

4 He sees the souls for whom He dies
Yet clinging to their sin,
And heirs of mansions in the skies
Who will not enter in.

5 O may I in Thy sorrow share,
And mourn that sins of mine
Should ever wound with grief or care
That loving heart of Thine. Amen.

Thomas Benson Pollock, 1836-96.

176

GETHSEMANE. 7 7 7.8. P. Bliss, 1838-76.

1 Man of Sorrows! What a name
For the Son of God, who came
Ruined sinners to reclaim!
Hallelujah! what a Saviour!

2 Bearing shame and scoffing rude,
In my place condemned He stood;
Sealed my pardon with His blood:
Hallelujah! what a Saviour!

3 Guilty, vile, and helpless we;
Spotless Lamb of God was He:
Full atonement—can it be?
Hallelujah! what a Saviour!

4 Lifted up was He to die.
It is finished! was His cry;
Now in heaven exalted high:
Hallelujah! what a Saviour!

5 When He comes, our glorious King,
All His ransomed home to bring,
Then anew this song we'll sing:
Hallelujah! what a Saviour!

Philipp Bliss, 1838-76.

177

HERZLIEBSTER JESU. 11 11.11 5. J. CRÜGER, 1598-1662.

Herzliebster Jesu, was hast du verbrochen.

1 AH, holy Jesu, how hast Thou offended,
That man to judge Thee hath in hate pretended?
By foes derided, by Thine own rejected,
O most afflicted.

2 Who was the guilty? Who brought this upon Thee?
Alas, my treason, Jesu, hath undone Thee;
'Twas I, Lord Jesu, I it was denied Thee:
I crucified Thee.

3 Lo, the good Shepherd for the sheep is offered;
The slave hath sinnèd, and the Son hath suffered;
For man's atonement, while he nothing heedeth,
God intercedeth.

4 For me, kind Jesu, was Thy incarnation,
Thy mortal sorrow, and Thy life's oblation;
Thy death of anguish and Thy bitter passion,
For my salvation.

5 Therefore, kind Jesu, since I cannot pay Thee,
I do adore Thee, and will ever pray Thee,
Think on Thy pity and Thy love unswerving,
Not my deserving. Amen.

Johann Heermann, 1585-1647;
tr. by Robert Seymour Bridges, 1844-1930. *Y.H.*

178

SIMPLICITY. 7 7.7 7. O. GIBBONS, 1583-1625.

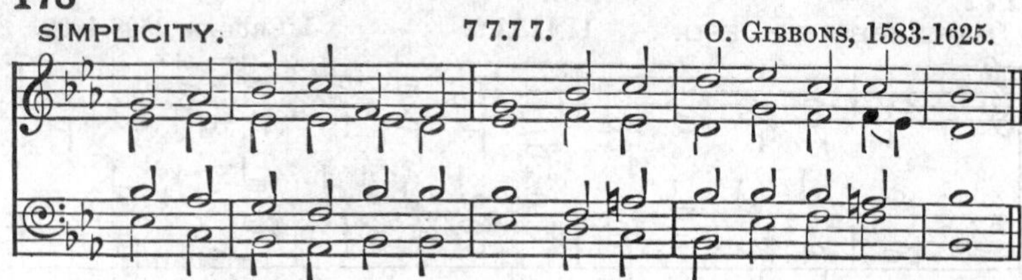

May also be sung to REDHEAD No. 47, No. 358.

1 WHEN my love to Christ grows weak,
When for deeper faith I seek,
Then in thought I go to thee,
Garden of Gethsemane!

2 There I walk amid the shades,
While the lingering twilight fades,
See that suffering, friendless One,
Weeping, praying there alone.

3 When my love for man grows weak,
When for stronger faith I seek,
Hill of Calvary! I go
To thy scenes of fear and woe.

4 There behold His agony,
Suffered on the bitter Tree;
See His anguish, see His faith,
Love triumphant still in death.

5 Then to life I turn again,
Learning all the worth of pain,
Learning all the might that lies
In a full self-sacrifice.

6 And I praise with firmer faith
Christ who vanquished pain and death;
And to Christ enthroned above
Raise my song of selfless love.

John Reynell Wreford, 1800-81. (*alt.*)

179

OLDBURY. C.M. J. F. BRIDGE, 1844-1924
Verses 1-3.

Verses 4 *and* 5.

May also be sung to ST. BERNARD, No. 408.

1 PLUNGED in a gulf of dark despair
We wretched sinners lay,
Without one cheerful beam of hope,
Or spark of glimmering day.

2 With pitying eyes the Prince of Peace
Beheld our helpless grief;
He saw, and—O amazing love!
He flew to our relief.

3 Down from the shining seats above
With joyful haste He sped,
Entered the grave in mortal flesh,
And dwelt among the dead.

4 O for this love let rocks and hills
Their lasting silence break,
And all harmonious human tongues
The Saviour's praises speak!

5 Angels, assist our mighty joys,
Strike all your harps of gold;
But when you raise your highest notes,
His love can ne'er be told.

Isaac Watts, 1674-1748.

180

HORSLEY. C.M. W. HORSLEY, 1774-1858.

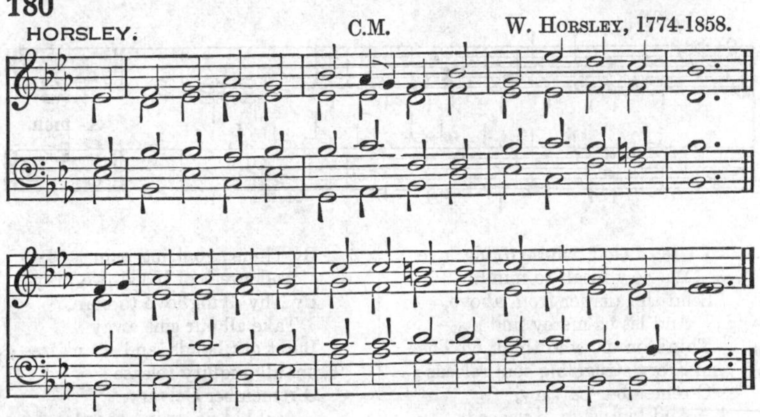

1 THERE is a green hill far away,
Without a city wall,
Where the dear Lord was crucified
Who died to save us all.

2 We may not know, we cannot tell
What pains He had to bear;
But we believe it was for us
He hung and suffered there.

3 He died that we might be forgiven,
He died to make us good,
That we might go at last to heaven,
Saved by His precious blood.

4 There was no other good enough
To pay the price of sin;
He only could unlock the gate
Of heaven, and let us in.

5 O dearly, dearly has He loved,
And we must love Him too,
And trust in His redeeming blood,
And try His works to do.

Cecil Frances Alexander, 1823-95.

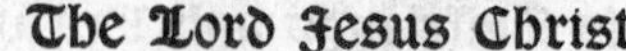

181

ATONEMENT. 7.6.7.6.7.8.7.6.

Bohemian Brethren.
Kirchengesänge, 1566.
Arr. by J. Turle, 1802-82.

A- men.

1 Lamb of God, whose dying love
  We now recall to mind,
Send the answer from above,
  And let us mercy find;
Think on us, who think on Thee;
And every struggling soul release;
O remember Calvary,
  And bid us go in peace!

2 By Thine agonizing pain
  And sweat of blood, we pray,
By Thy dying love to man,
  Take all our sins away:
Burst our bonds, and set us free;
From all iniquity release;
O remember Calvary,
  And bid us go in peace!

3 Let Thy blood, by faith applied,
  The sinner's pardon seal;
Speak us freely justified,
  And all our sickness heal;
By Thy passion on the tree,
Let all our griefs and troubles cease;
O remember Calvary,
  And bid us go in peace! Amen.

Charles Wesley, 1707-88.

ROCKINGHAM. L.M. Adapted by E. Miller, 1731-1807.

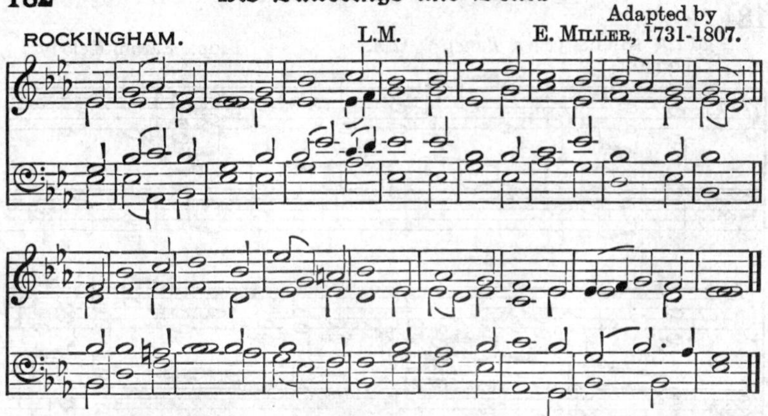

1 When I survey the wondrous Cross
On which the Prince of Glory died,
My richest gain I count but loss,
And pour contempt on all my pride.

2 Forbid it, Lord, that I should boast,
Save in the death of Christ, my God:
All the vain things that charm me most,
I sacrifice them to His blood.

3 See, from His head, His hands, His feet,
Sorrow and love flow mingled down:
Did e'er such love and sorrow meet,
Or thorns compose so rich a crown?

4 Were the whole realm of nature mine,
That were an offering far too small;
Love so amazing, so divine,
Demands my soul, my life, my all.

Isaac Watts, 1674-1748.

183

LOVE DIVINE. 8.7.8.7. J. Stainer, 1840-1901.

By permission of Novello and Company, Limited.

May also be sung to Stuttgart, No. 242.

1 In the Cross of Christ I glory:
Towering o'er the wrecks of time,
All the light of sacred story
Gathers round its head sublime.

2 When the woes of life o'ertake me,
Hopes deceive, and fears annoy,
Never shall the Cross forsake me:
Lo! it glows with peace and joy.

3 When the sun of bliss is beaming
Light and love upon my way:
From the Cross the radiance streaming
Adds more lustre to the day.

4 Bane and blessing, pain and pleasure,
By the Cross are sanctified;
Peace is there that knows no measure,
Joys that through all time abide.

5 In the Cross of Christ I glory:
Towering o'er the wrecks of time,
All the light of sacred story
Gathers round its head sublime.

John Bowring, 1792-1872.

184

VEXILLA REGIS (*First Tune*). L.M. Proper Sarum Melody.

UNISON.

A - men.

BRESLAU (*Second Tune*). L.M. *As Hymnodus Sacer*, Leipzig, 1625

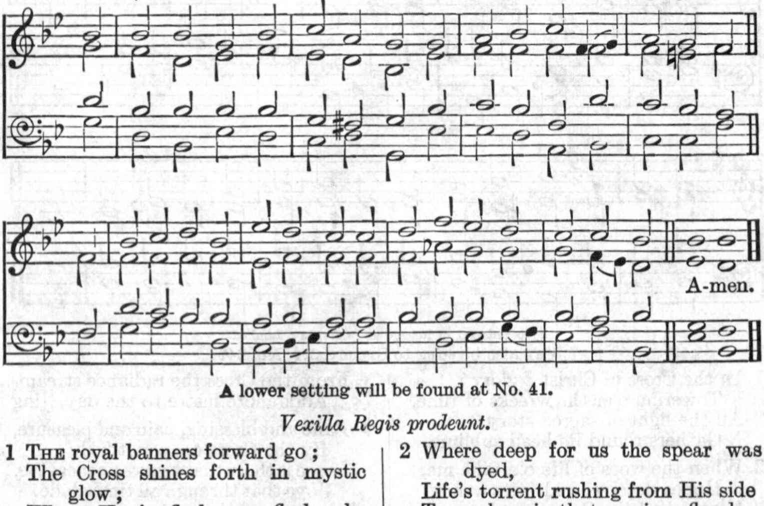

A-men.

A lower setting will be found at No. 41.

Vexilla Regis prodeunt.

1 THE royal banners forward go;
The Cross shines forth in mystic glow;
Where He in flesh, our flesh who made,
Our sentence bore, our ransom paid:

2 Where deep for us the spear was dyed,
Life's torrent rushing from His side
To wash us in that precious flood,
Where mingled water flowed, and blood.

3 Fulfilled is all that David told
In true prophetic song of old:
Amidst the nations, God, saith he,
Hath reigned and triumphed from the tree.

4 O Tree of beauty, Tree of light!
O Tree with royal purple dight!
Elect on whose triumphal breast
Those holy limbs should find their rest:

5 On whose dear arms, so widely flung,
The weight of this world's ransom hung:
The price of humankind to pay,
And spoil the spoiler of his prey.

6 To Thee, eternal Three in One,
Let homage meet by all be done:
Whom by the Cross Thou dost restore,
Preserve and govern evermore.
Amen.

Venantius Fortunatus, c. 530-609;
tr. by John Mason Neale, 1818-66.

185

8 8.7. D.

STABAT MATER. Evening Office of the Church, 1748.

Stabat Mater dolorosa.

1 At the Cross, her station keeping,
Stood the mournful mother weeping,
Where He hung, the dying Lord;
For her soul, of joy bereavèd,
Bowed with anguish, deeply grievèd,
Felt the sharp and piercing sword.

2 O how sad and sore distressèd
Now was she, that mother blessèd
Of the sole-begotten One;
Deep the woe of her affliction,
When she saw the crucifixion
Of her ever-glorious Son.

3 For His people's sins chastisèd,
She beheld her Son despisèd,
Scourged, and crowned with thorns entwined;
Saw Him then from judgement taken,
And in death by all forsaken
Till His spirit He resigned.

4 Jesus, may her deep devotion
Stir in me the same emotion,
Fount of love, Redeemer kind,
That my heart, fresh ardour gaining,
And a purer love attaining,
May with Thee acceptance find.
Amen.

Anonymous, 13th cent.;
tr. by Edward Caswall, 1814-78, *and others.*

186

GOD OF THE LIVING. 8.8.8.8.8.8. E. W. HULTON, 1845-1922

UNISON.

May also be sung to ST. CHRYSOSTOM (Barnby), No. 438.

1 O LOVE divine! what hast Thou done?
The immortal God hath died for me!
The Father's co-eternal Son
Bore all my sins upon the tree;
The immortal God for me hath died!
My Lord, my Love is crucified.

2 Behold Him, all ye that pass by,
The bleeding Prince of life and peace!
Come, sinners, see your Maker die,
And say, was ever grief like His?
Come, feel with me His blood applied:
My Lord, my Love is crucified:

3 Is crucified for me and you,
To bring us rebels back to God:
Believe, believe the record true,
Ye all are bought with Jesu's blood,
Pardon for all flows from His side:
My Lord, my Love is crucified.

4 Then let us sit beneath His Cross,
And gladly catch the healing stream,
All things for Him account but loss,
And give up all our hearts to Him;
Of nothing think or speak beside:
My Lord, my Love is crucified.

Charles Wesley, 1707-88.

187

ST. CROSS. L.M. J. B. DYKES, 1823-76.

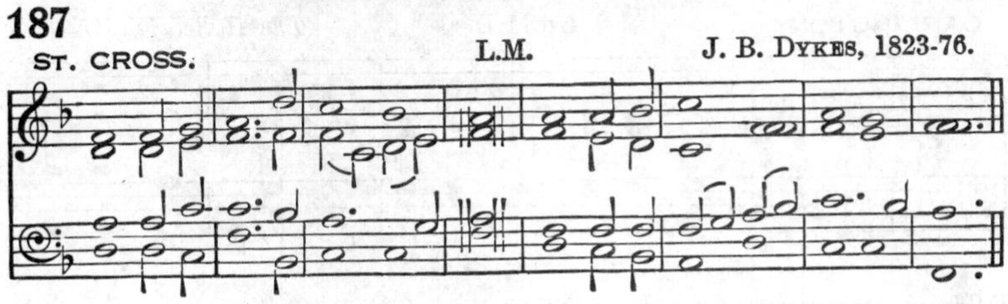

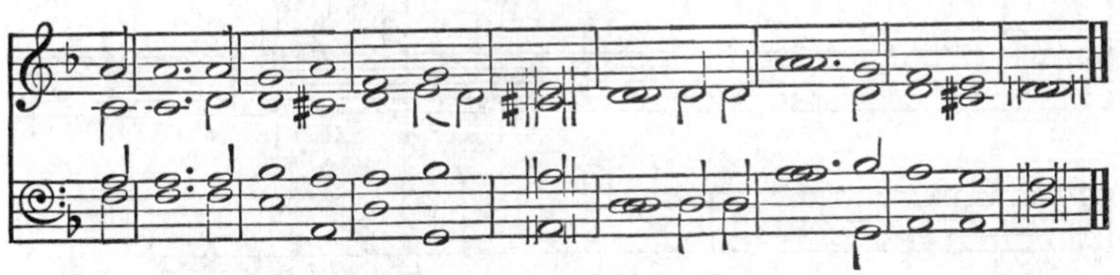

1 O COME and mourn with me awhile;
O come ye to the Saviour's side;
O come, together let us mourn:
Jesus, our Lord, is crucified.

2 Have we no tears to shed for Him,
While soldiers scoff and Jews deride?
Ah! look how patiently He hangs:
Jesus, our Lord, is crucified.

3 How fast His hands and feet are nailed,
His throat with parching thirst is dried!
His failing eyes are dim with woe:
Jesus, our Lord, is crucified.

4 Seven times He spoke, seven words of love;
And all three hours His silence cried
For mercy on the souls of men:
Jesus, our Lord, is crucified.

5 Come, let us stand beneath the Cross;
The fountain opened in His side
Shall purge our deepest stains away:
Jesus, our Lord, is crucified.

6 A broken heart, a fount of tears,
Ask, and they will not be denied;
A broken heart love's cradle is:
Jesus, our Lord, is crucified.

7 O love of God! O sin of man!
In this dread act your strength is tried;
And victory remains with love:
For He, our Lord, is crucified.

Frederick William Faber, 1814-63.

188

DARLINGTON. 5 5 11.D. *The Hallelujah*, 1849.

1 All ye that pass by,
To Jesus draw nigh :
To you is it nothing that Jesus should die ?
Your ransom and peace,
Your surety He is:
Come, see if there ever was sorrow like His.

2 He dies to atone
For sins not His own ;
Your debt He hath paid, and your work He hath done.
Ye all may receive
The peace He did leave,
Who made intercession : My Father, forgive !

3 For you and for me
He prayed on the tree :
The prayer is accepted, the sinner is free.
That sinner am I,
Who on Jesus rely,
And come for the pardon God cannot deny.

4 My pardon I claim ;
For a sinner I am,
A sinner believing in Jesus's name.
He purchased the grace
Which now I embrace :
O Father, Thou know'st He hath died in my place.

Charles Wesley, 1707-88.

189

NICHT SO TRAURIG. 7 7.7 7.7 7. J. S. Bach, 1685-1750.

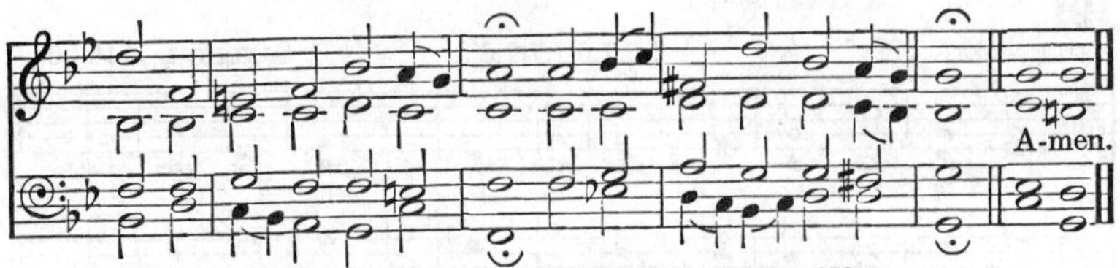

May also be sung to REDHEAD No. 76, No. 498.

1 THRONED upon the awful Tree,
King of grief, I watch with Thee;
Darkness veils Thine anguished face,
None its lines of woe can trace,
None can tell what pangs unknown
Hold Thee silent and alone;

2 Silent through those three dread hours,
Wrestling with the evil powers;
Left alone with human sin,
Gloom around Thee and within,
Till the appointed time is nigh,
Till the Lamb of God may die.

3 Hark that cry that peals aloud
Upward through the whelming cloud!
Thou, the Father's only Son,
Thou, His own Anointed One,
Thou dost ask Him—can it be:
Why hast Thou forsaken Me?

4 Lord, should fear and anguish roll
Darkly o'er my sinful soul,
Thou, who once was thus bereft
That Thine own might ne'er be left,
Teach me by that bitter cry
In the gloom to know Thee nigh.
Amen.

John Ellerton, 1826-93.

190

FONS AMORIS. S.M. F. L. WISEMAN, 1858-1944

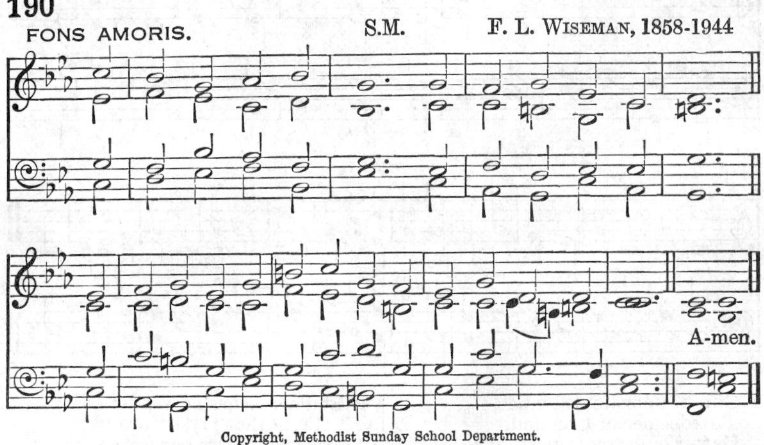

May also be sung to SOUTHWELL, No. 239.

1 O PERFECT life of love!
All, all is finished now,
All that He left His throne above
To do for us below.

2 No work is left undone
Of all the Father willed;
His toils and sorrows, one by one,
The Scriptures have fulfilled.

3 No pain that we can share
But He has felt its smart;
All forms of human grief and care
Have pierced that tender heart.

4 And on His thorn-crowned head,
And on His sinless soul,
Our sins in all their guilt were laid,
That He might make us whole.

5 In perfect love He dies;
For me He dies, for me!
O all-atoning Sacrifice,
I cling by faith to Thee.

6 In every time of need,
Before the judgement throne,
Thy work, O Lamb of God, I'll plead,
Thy merits, not my own.

7 Yet work, O Lord, in me,
As Thou for me hast wrought;
And let my love the answer be
To grace Thy love has brought.
Amen.

Henry Williams Baker, 1821-77.

The Lord Jesus Christ

191

PELHAM. 7.6.7.6.7.7.7.6. F. GIARDINI, 1716-96.

1 God of unexampled grace,
Redeemer of mankind,
Matter of eternal praise
We in Thy passion find:
Still our choicest strains we bring,
Still the joyful theme pursue,
Thee the Friend of Sinners sing,
Whose love is ever new.

2 Endless scenes of wonder rise
From that mysterious tree,
Crucified before our eyes,
Where we our Maker see:
Jesus, Lord, what hast Thou done?
Publish we the death divine,
Stop, and gaze, and fall, and own
Was never love like Thine!

3 Never love nor sorrow was
Like that my Saviour showed:
See Him stretched on yonder Cross,
And crushed beneath our load!
Now discern the Deity,
Now His heavenly birth declare!
Faith cries out: 'Tis He, 'tis He,
My God, that suffers there!

Charles Wesley, 1707-88.

192

ST. DROSTANE. L.M. J. B. DYKES, 1823-76.

May also be sung to WINCHESTER NEW, No. 274.

1 RIDE on, ride on in majesty!
Hark! All the tribes Hosanna! cry;
O Saviour meek, pursue Thy road
With palms and scattered garments strowed.

2 Ride on, ride on in majesty!
In lowly pomp ride on to die;
O Christ, Thy triumphs now begin
O'er captive death and conquered sin.

3 Ride on, ride on in majesty!
The wingèd squadrons of the sky
Look down with sad and wondering eyes
To see the approaching sacrifice.

4 Ride on, ride on in majesty!
Thy last and fiercest strife is nigh;
The Father on His sapphire throne
Expects His own anointed Son.

5 Ride on, ride on in majesty!
In lowly pomp ride on to die;
Bow Thy meek head to mortal pain,
Then take, O God, Thy power, and reign.

Henry Hart Milman, 1791-1868.

193

BURFORD. C.M. CHETHAM'S *Psalmody*, 1718.

1 BEHOLD the Saviour of mankind
Nailed to the shameful tree!
How vast the love that Him inclined
To bleed and die for thee!

2 Hark, how He groans! while nature shakes,
And earth's strong pillars bend;
The temple's veil in sunder breaks,
The solid marbles rend.

3 'Tis done! the precious ransom's paid;
Receive My soul! He cries:
See where He bows His sacred head!
He bows His head, and dies!

4 But soon He'll break death's envious chain,
And in full glory shine:
O Lamb of God, was ever pain,
Was ever love, like Thine?

Samuel Wesley, 1662-1735.

194

LLYFNANT. 7.7.7.7.7.7. J. CLULEY, 1856-1940

May also be sung to PRESSBURG, No. 643.

1 Go to dark Gethsemane,
  Ye that feel the tempter's power;
Your Redeemer's conflict see;
  Watch with Him one bitter hour;
Turn not from His griefs away:
Learn of Jesus Christ to pray.

2 Follow to the judgement-hall;
  View the Lord of Life arraigned.
O the wormwood and the gall!
  O the pangs His soul sustained!
Shun not suffering, shame, or loss:
Learn of Him to bear the cross.

3 Calvary's mournful mountain climb;
  There, adoring at His feet,
Mark that miracle of time,
  God's own sacrifice complete.
It is finished! Hear the cry:
Learn of Jesus Christ to die.

4 Early to the tomb repair
  Where they laid His breathless clay:
Angels kept their vigils there;
  Who hath taken Him away?
Christ is risen! He seeks the skies;
Saviour, teach us so to rise.

James Montgomery, 1771-1854.

195

MERTHYR TYDFIL. D.L.M. J. PARRY, 1841-1903.

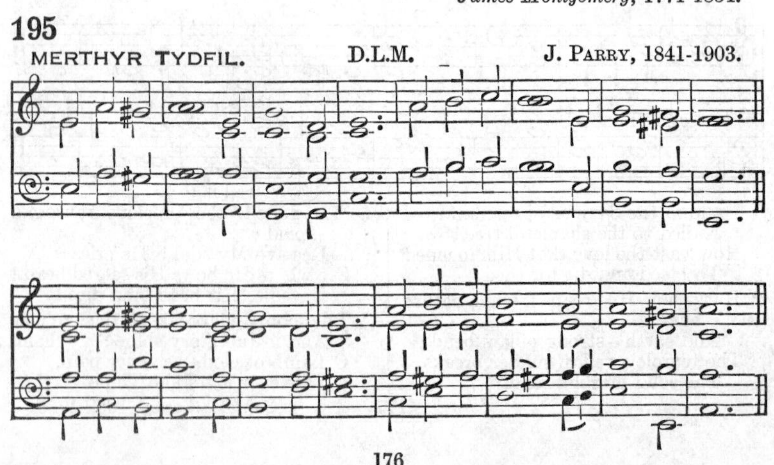

1 He dies! the Friend of Sinners dies!
Lo! Salem's daughters weep around!
A solemn darkness veils the skies,
A sudden trembling shakes the ground:
Come, saints, and with your tears bedew
The Sufferer, bruised beneath your load;
He poured out cries and tears for you,
He shed for you His precious blood.

2 Here's love and grief beyond degree:
The Lord of Glory dies for man!
But lo! what sudden joys I see:
Jesus, the dead, revives again!
The rising God forsakes the tomb;
The tomb in vain forbids His rise!
Cherubic legions guard Him home,
And shout Him welcome to the skies!

3 Break off your tears, ye saints, and tell
How high your great Deliverer reigns;
Sing how He spoiled the hosts of hell,
And led the monster death in chains.
Say: Live for ever, wondrous King!
Born to redeem, and strong to save!
Then ask the monster: Where's thy sting?
And: Where's thy victory, boasting grave?

Isaac Watts, 1674-1748;
alt. by Martin Madan, 1726-90.

196

CHURCH TRIUMPHANT. L.M. J. W. Elliott, 1833-1915.

By permission of Novello and Company, Limited.

1 We sing the praise of Him who died,
Of Him who died upon the Cross:
The sinner's hope let men deride:
For this we count the world but loss.

2 Inscribed upon the Cross we see
In shining letters: God is love.
He bears our sins upon the tree:
He brings us mercy from above.

3 The Cross—it takes our guilt away;
It holds the fainting spirit up;
It cheers with hope the gloomy day,
And sweetens every bitter cup.

4 It makes the coward spirit brave,
And nerves the feeble arm for fight;
It takes its terror from the grave,
And gilds the bed of death with light.

5 The balm of life, the cure of woe,
The measure and the pledge of love,
The sinner's refuge here below,
The angels' theme in heaven above.

Thomas Kelly, 1769-1854.

197

7.6.8.6.8.6.8.6.

BENEATH THE CROSS OF JESUS. I. D. SANKEY, 1840-1908.

1 BENEATH the Cross of Jesus
I fain would take my stand—
The shadow of a mighty rock
Within a weary land;
A home within a wilderness,
A rest upon the way,
From the burning of the noontide heat
And the burden of the day.

2 Upon that Cross of Jesus
Mine eye at times can see
The very dying form of One
Who suffered there for me.
And from my stricken heart, with tears,
Two wonders I confess—
The wonders of redeeming love,
And my own worthlessness.

3 I take, O Cross, thy shadow,
For my abiding-place!
I ask no other sunshine than
The sunshine of His face;
Content to let the world go by,
To know no gain nor loss—
My sinful self my only shame,
My glory all—the Cross.

Elizabeth Cecilia Clephane, 1830-69.

198

CROSS. 7.7.7.7. Old Melody.

1 Never further than Thy Cross,
Never higher than Thy feet;
Here earth's precious things seem dross,
Here earth's bitter things grow sweet.

2 Gazing thus our sin we see,
Learn Thy love while gazing thus;
Sin which laid the Cross on Thee,
Love which bore the Cross for us.

3 Here we learn to serve and give,
And, rejoicing, self deny;
Here we gather love to live,
Here we gather faith to die.

4 Symbols of our liberty
And our service here unite;
Captives, by Thy Cross set free,
Soldiers of Thy Cross, we fight.

5 Pressing onwards as we can,
Still to this our hearts must tend;
Where our earliest hopes began,
There our last aspirings end.

6 Till amid the Hosts of Light
We, in Thee redeemed, complete,
Through Thy Cross made pure and white,
Cast our crowns before Thy feet.

Elizabeth Rundle Charles, 1828-96.

NEAR THE CROSS. 7.6.7.6. and refrain. W. H. DOANE, 1832-1916.

REFRAIN.

1 JESUS, keep me near the Cross;
There a precious fountain,
Free to all, a healing stream,
Flows from Calvary's mountain.

In the Cross, in the Cross,
Be my glory ever;
Till my raptured soul shall find
Rest beyond the river.

2 Near the Cross, a trembling soul,
Love and mercy found me;
There the bright and morning star
Shed its beams around me.

3 Near the Cross: O Lamb of God,
Bring its scenes before me;
Help me walk from day to day,
With its shadow o'er me.

4 Near the Cross I'll watch and wait,
Hoping, trusting ever,
Till I reach the golden strand,
Just beyond the river.

Frances Jane van Alstyne, 1820-1915.

200

OLD GERMAN. 5 5 12.D. *Sacred Melody*, 1761.

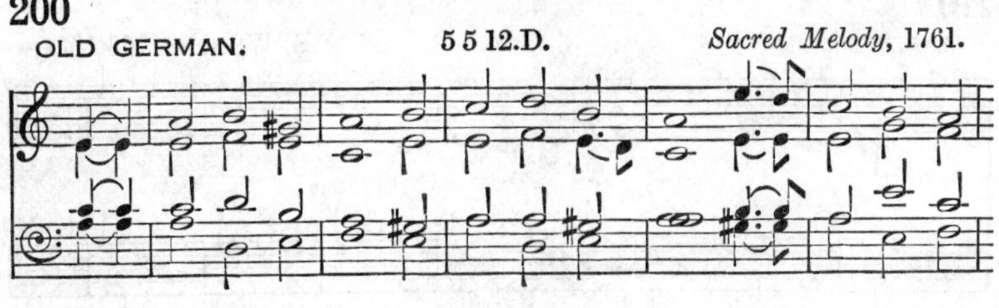

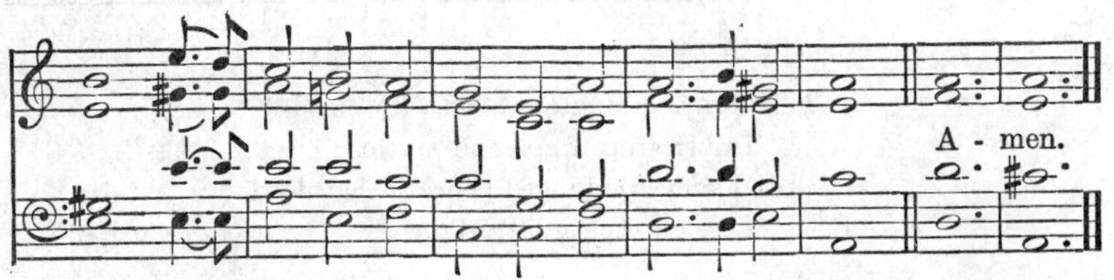

1 O JESUS, my hope,
For me offered up,
Who with clamour pursued Thee to Calvary's top,
The blood Thou hast shed,
For me let it plead,
And declare Thou hast died in Thy murderer's stead.

2 Come then from above,
Its hardness remove,
And vanquish my heart with the sense of Thy love;
Thy love on the tree
Display unto me,
And the servant of sin in a moment is free.

3 Neither passion nor pride
Thy Cross can abide,
But melt in the fountain that streams from Thy side:
Let Thy life-giving blood
Remove all my load,
And purge my foul conscience, and bring me to God.

4 Now, now let me know
Its virtue below,
Let it wash me, and I shall be whiter than snow;
Let it hallow my heart,
And throughly convert,
And make me, O Lord, in the world as Thou art.

5 Each moment applied
My weakness to hide,
Thy blood be upon me, and always abide:
My Advocate prove
With the Father above,
And speak me at last to the throne of Thy love. Amen.

Charles Wesley, 1707-88.

201

MARTYRDOM. C.M. H. WILSON, 1766-1824.

1 THERE is a fountain filled with blood
Drawn from Immanuel's veins;
And sinners, plunged beneath that flood,
Lose all their guilty stains.

2 The dying thief rejoiced to see
That fountain in his day;
And there may I, though vile as he,
Wash all my sins away.

3 O dying Lamb, Thy precious blood
Shall never lose its power,
Till all the ransomed church of God
Be saved to sin no more.

4 E'er since, by faith, I saw the stream
Thy flowing wounds supply,
Redeeming love has been my theme
And shall be till I die.

5 Then in a nobler, sweeter song
I'll sing Thy power to save,
When this poor lisping, stammering tongue
Lies silent in the grave.

William Cowper, 1731-1800.

202

PASSION CHORALE. 7.6.7.6.D. H. L. HASSLER, 1564-1612.

A-men.

O Haupt voll Blut und Wunden.

1 O SACRED Head once wounded,
With grief and pain weighed down,
How scornfully surrounded
With thorns, Thine only crown!
How pale art Thou with anguish,
With sore abuse and scorn!
How does that visage languish
Which once was bright as morn!

2 O Lord of Life and Glory,
What bliss till now was Thine!
I read the wondrous story,
I joy to call Thee mine.
Thy grief and Thy compassion
Were all for sinners' gain;
Mine, mine was the transgression,
But Thine the deadly pain.

3 What language shall I borrow
To praise Thee, heavenly Friend,
For this Thy dying sorrow,
Thy pity without end?
Lord, make me Thine for ever,
Nor let me faithless prove;
O let me never, never
Abuse such dying love!

4 Be near me, Lord, when dying;
O show Thyself to me;
And, for my succour flying,
Come, Lord, to set me free:
These eyes, new faith receiving,
From Jesus shall not move;
For he who dies believing
Dies safely through Thy love.
Amen.

Paulus Gerhardt, 1607-76 (*from Salve caput cruentatum, attributed to Bernard of Clairvaux*, 1091-1153); *tr. by James Waddell Alexander*, 1804-59.

203

SHAFTESBURY. 6 6.7.7.7.7. J. F. BRIDGE, 1844-1924.

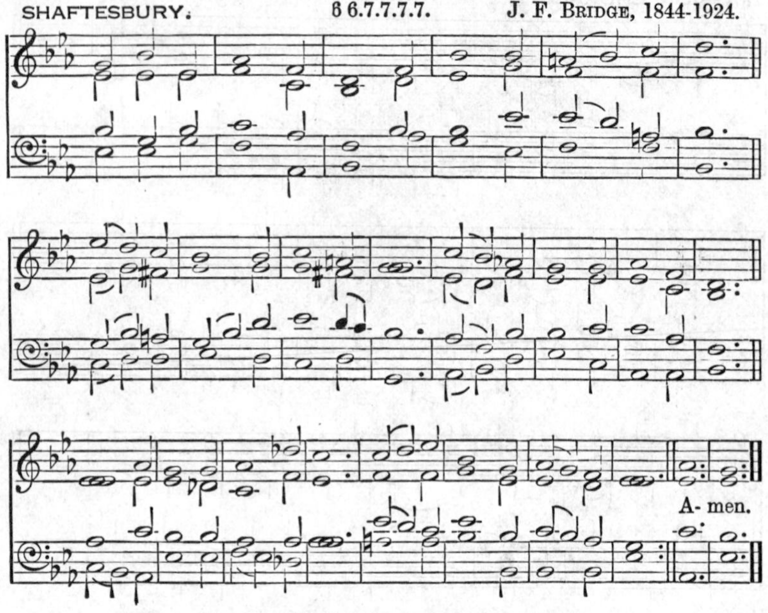

1 How shall a sinner find
The Saviour of mankind?
Canst Thou not accept my prayer?
Not bestow the grace I claim?
Where are Thy old mercies? Where
All the powers of Jesu's name?

2 I will not let Thee go
Till I Thy mercy know;
Let me hear the welcome sound,
Speak, if still Thou canst forgive:
Speak, and let the lost be found;
Speak, and let the dying live.

3 Thy love is all my plea,
Thy passion speaks for me;
By Thy pangs and bloody sweat,
By Thy depths of grief unknown,
Save me, gasping at Thy feet,
Save, O save Thy ransomed one.

4 What hast Thou done for me?
O think on Calvary!
By Thy mortal groans and sighs,
By Thy precious death I pray,
Hear my dying spirit's cries,
Take, O take my sins away! Amen.

Charles Wesley, 1707-88.

Also:

66 O God of all grace
74 Praise to the Holiest
144 My song is love
228 Hail, Thou once despisèd Jesus
446 My God, I love Thee

204

EASTER MORN. 7 7.7 7. and Hallelujahs. *Lyra Davidica*, 1708.

1 CHRIST the Lord is risen to-day;
Hallelujah!
Sons of men and angels say:
Hallelujah!
Raise your joys and triumphs high:
Hallelujah!
Sing, ye heavens; thou earth, reply:
Hallelujah!

2 Love's redeeming work is done;
Fought the fight, the battle won:
Vain the stone, the watch, the seal;
Christ hath burst the gates of hell:

3 Lives again our glorious King;
Where, O death, is now thy sting?
Once He died our souls to save:
Where's thy victory, boasting grave?

4 Soar we now where Christ hath led,
Following our exalted Head:
Made like Him, like Him we rise;
Ours the cross, the grave, the skies:

5 King of glory! Soul of bliss!
Everlasting life is this,
Thee to know, Thy power to prove,
Thus to sing, and thus to love:

Charles Wesley, 1707-88.

205

LLANFAIR. 7 7.7 7. and Hallelujahs. R. WILLIAMS, 1781-1821.

May also be sung to ASCENSION, No. 221.

Surrexit Christus hodie.

1 JESUS CHRIST is risen to-day,
Hallelujah!
Our triumphant holy day,
Hallelujah!
Who did once upon the Cross,
Hallelujah!
Suffer to redeem our loss,
Hallelujah!

2 Hymns of praises let us sing,
Unto Christ our heavenly King,
Who endured the Cross and grave,
Sinners to redeem and save:

3 But the pain, which He endured,
Our salvation hath procured;
Now above the sky He's King,
Where the angels ever sing:

4 Sing we to our God above,
Praise eternal as His love,
Praise Him, all ye heavenly host,
Father, Son, and Holy Ghost!

Anonymous: Lyra Davidica, 1708;
tr. from 14*th cent. MS.*

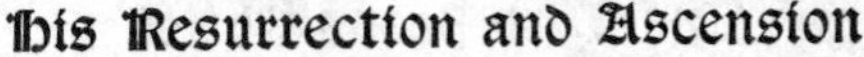

206

MORGENLIED. 8.7.8.7.D. and refrain. F. C. Maker, 1844-1927.

Refrain.

A higher setting will be found at No. 967

1 Christ is risen! Hallelujah!
Risen our victorious Head.
Sing His praises! Hallelujah!
Christ is risen from the dead.
Gratefully our hearts adore Him,
As His light once more appears,
Bowing down in joy before Him,
Rising up from grief and tears.

Christ is risen! Hallelujah!
Risen our victorious Head.
Sing His praises! Hallelujah!
Christ is risen from the dead.

2 Christ is risen! All the sadness
Of His earthly life is o'er,
Through the open gates of gladness
He returns to life once more;
Death and hell before Him bending,
He doth rise, the Victor now,
Angels on His steps attending,
Glory round His wounded brow.

3 Christ is risen! Henceforth never
Death or hell shall us enthral,
We are Christ's, in Him for ever
We have triumphed over all;
All the doubting and dejection
Of our trembling hearts have ceased:
'Tis His day of resurrection,
Let us rise and keep the feast.

John Samuel Bewley Monsell, 1811-75.

207

WÜRTEMBERG. 7 7.7 7.4. J. ROSENMÜLLER, 1619-84.

Christus ist erstanden.

1 CHRIST the Lord is risen again;
Christ hath broken every chain:
Hark! the angels shout for joy,
Singing evermore on high:
Hallelujah!

2 He who gave for us His life,
Who for us endured the strife,
Is our Paschal Lamb to-day;
We too sing for joy, and say:
Hallelujah!

3 He who bore all pain and loss
Comfortless upon the Cross,
Lives in glory now on high,
Pleads for us, and hears our cry:
Hallelujah!

4 He whose path no records tell,
Who descended into hell,
Who the strong man armed hath bound,
Now in highest heaven is crowned.
Hallelujah!

5 He who slumbered in the grave
Is exalted now to save;
Now through Christendom it rings
That the Lamb is King of kings.
Hallelujah!

6 Now He bids us tell abroad
How the lost may be restored,
How the penitent forgiven,
How we too may enter heaven:
Hallelujah!

7 Thou our Paschal Lamb indeed,
Christ, to-day Thy people feed;
Take our sins and guilt away,
That we all may sing for aye:
Hallelujah!

Michael Weisse, 1480-1534;
tr. by Catherine Winkworth, 1827-78.

208

ELLACOMBE. 7.6.7.6. D. MAINZ *Gesangbuch*, 1833.

'Αναστάσεως ἡμέρα

1 THE day of resurrection !
Earth, tell it out abroad ;
The passover of gladness,
The passover of God !
From death to life eternal,
From earth unto the sky,
Our Christ hath brought us over
With hymns of victory.

2 Our hearts be pure from evil,
That we may see aright
The Lord in rays eternal
Of resurrection light,
And, listening to His accents,
May hear, so calm and plain,
His own All hail ! and hearing,
May raise the victor-strain.

3 Now let the heavens be joyful ;
Let earth her song begin ;
The round world keep high triumph,
And all that is therein ;
Let all things seen and unseen,
Their notes of gladness blend :
For Christ the Lord hath risen,
Our joy that hath no end.

John of Damascus, 8th cent. ;
tr. by John Mason Neale, 1818-66.

209

GRATITUDE. 6.6.6.6.8 8. G. W. Martin, 1828-81.

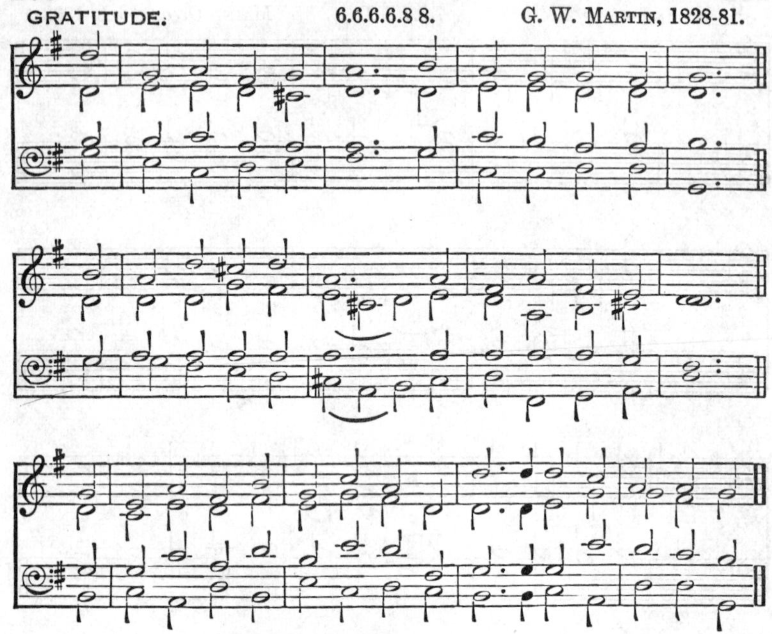

1 On wings of living light,
At earliest dawn of day,
Came down the angel bright,
And rolled the stone away.
Your voices raise with one accord,
To bless and praise your risen Lord.

2 The keepers, watching near,
At that dread sight and sound
Fell down with sudden fear
Like dead men to the ground:

3 Then rose from death's dark gloom,
Unseen by mortal eye,
Triumphant o'er the tomb,
The Lord of earth and sky!

4 Ye children of the light,
Arise with Him, arise!
See how the Daystar bright
Is burning in the skies!

5 Leave in the grave beneath
The old things passed away;
Buried with Him in death,
O live with Him to-day!

6 We sing Thee, Lord Divine,
With all our hearts and powers,
For we are ever Thine,
And Thou art ever ours.

William Walsham How, 1823-97.

210

8.7.8.7.7.8.7.4.

CHRIST LAG IN TODESBANDEN. Adapted by M. LUTHER, 1483-1546.

Christ lag in Todesbanden.

1 CHRIST JESUS lay in death's strong bands
For our offences given;
But now at God's right hand He stands,
And brings us life from heaven:
Wherefore let us joyful be,
And sing to God right thankfully
Loud songs of Hallelujah!
Hallelujah!

2 It was a strange and dreadful strife,
When Life and Death contended;
The victory remained with Life,
The reign of Death was ended:
Stript of power, no more he reigns;
An empty form alone remains;
His sting is lost for ever.
Hallelujah!

3 So let us keep the festival
Whereto the Lord invites us;
Christ is Himself the joy of all,
The Sun that warms and lights us;
By His grace He doth impart
Eternal sunshine to the heart;
The night of sin is ended.
Hallelujah!

4 Then let us feast this Easter day
On the true Bread of heaven.
The word of grace hath purged away
The old and wicked leaven;
Christ alone our souls will feed,
He is our meat and drink indeed,
Faith lives upon no other.
Hallelujah!

Martin Luther, 1483-1546;
tr. by Richard Massie, 1800-87.

211

CHRIST AROSE. 6.5.6.4. and refrain. R. Lowry, 1826-99.

Refrain.

1 Low in the grave He lay,
Jesus, my Saviour;
Waiting the coming day,
Jesus, my Lord.
Up from the grave He arose,
With a mighty triumph o'er His foes;
He arose a Victor from the dark domain,
And He lives for ever with His saints to reign:
He arose! Hallelujah! Christ arose!

2 Vainly they watch His bed,
Jesus, my Saviour;
Vainly they seal the dead,
Jesus, my Lord.

3 Death cannot keep his prey,
Jesus, my Saviour;
He tore the bars away,
Jesus, my Lord.

Robert Lowry, 1826-99.

212

SALVE, FESTA DIES. 11 11.11 11. and refrain. J. BARNBY, 1838-96.

Salve, fesia dies.

1 WELCOME, happy morning! Age to age shall say:
Hell to-day is vanquished; Heaven is won to-day!
Lo! the dead is living, God for evermore!
Him, their true Creator, all His works adore.
Welcome, happy morning! Age to age shall say.

2 Earth with joy confesses, clothing her for spring,
All good gifts returned with her returning King;
Bloom in every meadow, leaves on every bough,
Speak His sorrows ended, hail His triumph now.

3 Thou, of life the Author, death didst undergo,
Tread the path of darkness, saving strength to show;
Come, then, True and Faithful, now fulfil Thy word;
'Tis Thine own third morning: Rise, O buried Lord!

4 Loose the souls long prisoned, bound with Satan's chain;
All that now is fallen raise to life again;
Show Thy face in brightness, bid the nations see;
Bring again our daylight; day returns with Thee.

Venantius Fortunatus, c. 530-609;
tr. by John Ellerton, 1826-93.

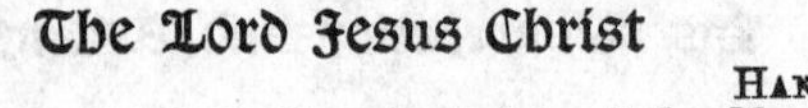

213

MACCABÆUS. 10 11.11 11. and refrain. HANDEL'S *Judas Maccabæus*, 1746.

REFRAIN.

A toi la gloire, O Ressuscite.

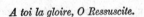

1 THINE be the glory, risen, conquering Son,
Endless is the victory Thou o'er death hast won;
Angels in bright raiment rolled the stone away,
Kept the folded grave-clothes, where Thy body lay.

Thine be the glory, risen, conquering Son,
Endless is the victory Thou o'er death hast won.

2 Lo! Jesus meets us, risen from the tomb;
Lovingly He greets us, scatters fear and gloom;
Let the Church with gladness, hymns of triumph sing,
For her Lord now liveth, death hath lost its sting.

3 No more we doubt Thee, glorious Prince of life;
Life is nought without Thee: aid us in our strife;
Make us more than conquerors, through Thy deathless love:
Bring us safe through Jordan to Thy home above.

Edmond Louis Budry, 1854-1932;
tr. by Richard Birch Hoyle, 1875-1939

214

BELGRAVE. C.M. W. HORSLEY, 1774-1858.

1 AWAKE, glad soul, awake, awake!
Thy Lord hath risen long;
Go to His grave, and with thee take
Both tuneful heart and song.

2 Where life is waking all around,
Where love's sweet voices sing,
The first bright blossom may be found
Of an eternal spring.

3 The shade and gloom of life are fled
This resurrection day;
Henceforth in Christ are no more dead,
The grave hath no more prey.

4 In Christ we live, in Christ we sleep,
In Christ we wake and rise;
And the sad tears death makes us weep,
He wipes from all our eyes.

5 Then wake, glad heart, awake, awake!
And seek thy risen Lord;
Joy in His resurrection take,
And comfort in His word.

6 And let thy life through all its ways
One long thanksgiving be;
Its theme of joy, its song of praise—
Christ died and rose for me.

John Samuel Bewley Monsell, 1811-75.

215

First three lines adapted from a *Gloria Patri*
by G. P. DA PALESTRINA, 1525-94.

VICTORY. 8 8 8.4. Alleluia by W. H. MONK.

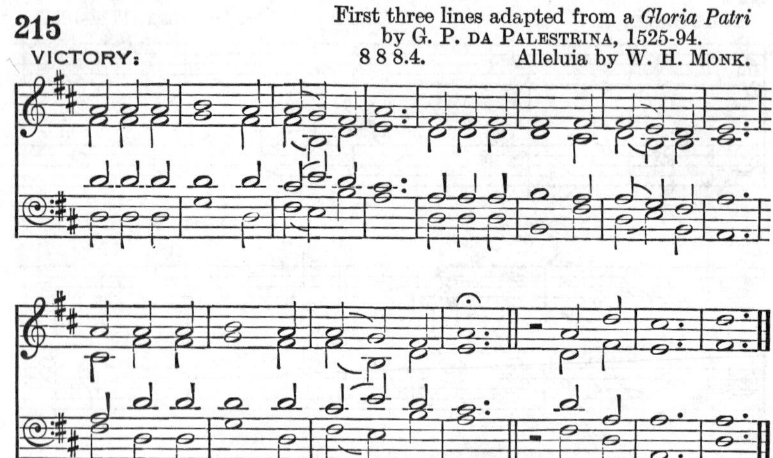

Finita jam sunt praelia.

1 THE strife is o'er, the battle done;
Now is the Victor's triumph won;
Now be the song of praise begun:
Alleluia!

2 The powers of death have done their worst,
But Christ their legions hath dispersed;
Let shouts of holy joy outburst:
Alleluia!

3 The three sad days have quickly sped;
He rises glorious from the dead;
All glory to our risen Head:
Alleluia!

4 Lord, by the stripes which wounded Thee,
From death's dread sting Thy servants free,
That we may live and sing to Thee:
Alleluia!

Anonymous, c. 12th cent.;
tr. from Symphonia Sirenum, Cologne, 1695,
by Francis Pott, 1832-1909.

216

ST. ALBINUS. 7.8.7.8.4. H. J. GAUNTLETT, 1805-76.

Jesus lebt, mit ihm auch ich.

1 Jesus lives! thy terrors now
Can, O death, no more appal us;
Jesus lives! by this we know
Thou, O grave, canst not enthral us. Hallelujah!

2 Jesus lives! to Him the throne
High o'er heaven and earth is given;
We may go where He is gone,
Live and reign with Him in heaven. Hallelujah!

3 Jesus lives! for us He died;
Hence may we, to Jesus living,
Pure in heart and act abide,
Praise to Him and glory giving.
Hallelujah!

4 Jesus lives! our hearts know well
Nought from us His love shall sever;
Life, nor death, nor powers of hell,
Part us now from Christ for ever.
Hallelujah!

5 Jesus lives! henceforth is death
Entrance-gate of life immortal;
This shall calm our trembling breath
When we pass its gloomy portal. Hallelujah!

Christian Fürchtegott Gellert, 1715-69;
tr. by Frances Elizabeth Cox, 1812-97.

217

WETHERBY. C.M. S. S. Wesley, 1810-76.

1 Ye humble souls that seek the Lord,
Chase all your fears away;
And bow with rapture down to see
The place where Jesus lay.

2 Thus low the Lord of Life was brought,
Such wonders love can do;
Thus cold in death that bosom lay,
Which throbbed and bled for you.

3 But raise your eyes and tune your songs;
The Saviour lives again:
Not all the bolts and bars of death
The Conqueror could detain.

4 High o'er the angelic bands He rears
His once dishonoured head;
And through unnumbered years He reigns,
Who dwelt among the dead.

5 With joy like His shall every saint
His vacant tomb survey;
Then rise with his ascending Lord
To realms of endless day.

Philip Doddridge, 1702-51.

218

THE FOE BEHIND. Irregular. O. R. BARNICOTT, c. 1852-1908.

1. The foe behind, the deep before, Our hosts have dared and passed the sea; And
2. Lift up, lift up your voi-ces now! The whole wide world re-joi-ces now! The
Phara-oh's war-riors strew the shore, And Is-rael's ransomed tribes are free.
Lord hath tri-umph'd glor-ious-ly! The Lord shall reign vic-tor-ious-ly!
3. Hap-py mor-row, Turning sor-row In-to peace and mirth! Bondage ending,
Love de-scending O'er the earth! 4. Seals as-sur-ing, Guards se-cur-ing,
Watch His earthly prison: Seals are shattered, Guards are scattered; Christ hath risen!

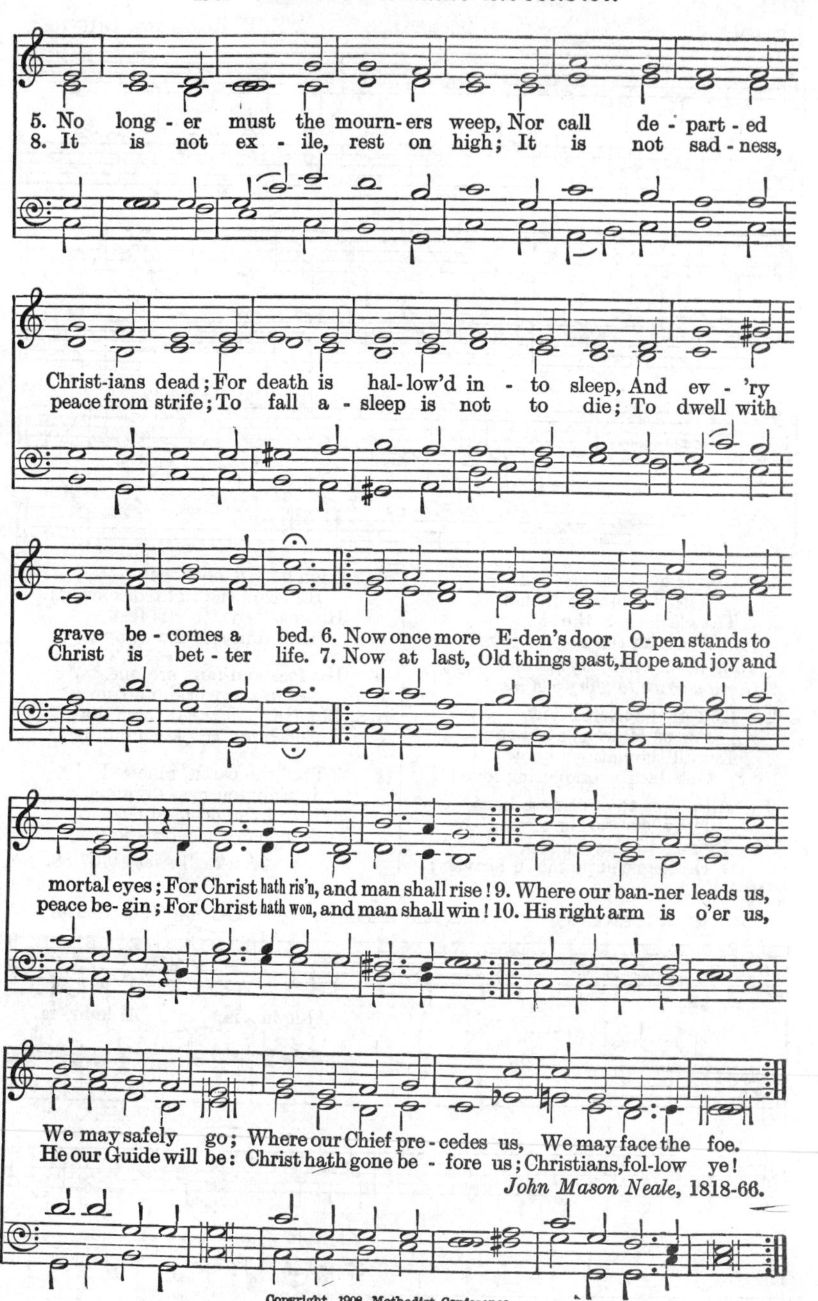
5. No longer must the mourn-ers weep, Nor call de-part-ed
8. It is not ex-ile, rest on high; It is not sad-ness,
Christ-ians dead; For death is hal-low'd in-to sleep, And ev-'ry
peace from strife; To fall a-sleep is not to die; To dwell with
grave be-comes a bed. 6. Now once more E-den's door O-pen stands to
Christ is bet-ter life. 7. Now at last, Old things past, Hope and joy and
mortal eyes; For Christ hath ris'n, and man shall rise! 9. Where our ban-ner leads us,
peace be-gin; For Christ hath won, and man shall win! 10. His right arm is o'er us,
We may safely go; Where our Chief pre-cedes us, We may face the foe.
He our Guide will be: Christ hath gone be-fore us; Christians, fol-low ye!
John Mason Neale, 1818-66.

219

DUDLEY. 6.6.6.6.6.8 8. E. F. Rimbault, 1816-76.

1 God is gone up on high,
With a triumphant noise;
The clarions of the sky
Proclaim the angelic joys!
Join all on earth, rejoice and sing;
Glory ascribe to glory's King.

2 God in the flesh below,
For us He reigns above:
Let all the nations know
Our Jesu's conquering love!

3 All power to our great Lord
Is by the Father given;
By angel hosts adored,
He reigns supreme in heaven:

4 High on His holy seat
He bears the righteous sway;
His foes beneath His feet
Shall sink and die away:

5 His foes and ours are one,
Satan, the world, and sin;
But He shall tread them down,
And bring His kingdom in:

6 Till all the earth, renewed
In righteousness divine,
With all the hosts of God
In one great chorus join.

Charles Wesley, 1707-88.

220

GOD IS ASCENDED. L.M. and Alleluias. German 16th Century.

Al-le-lu - ia, . . . Al-le-lu - ia.
Al-le-lu - ia . . . Al-le-lu - ia.

1 God is ascended up on high,
Alleluia.
With merry noise of trumpet's sound,
Alleluia.
And princely seated in the sky,
Alleluia.
Rules over all the world around.
Alleluia.

2 In human shape and flesh He went,
Adornèd with His passion's scars,
Which in heaven's sight He did present
More glorious than the glittering stars.

3 Lord, raise our sinking minds therefore
Up to our proper country dear,
And purify us evermore,
To fit us for those regions clear.

Henry More, 1614-87.

221

ASCENSION. 7 7.7 7. and Alleluias. W. H. Monk, 1823-89.

1 Hail the day that sees Him rise,
Alleluia!
Ravished from our wistful eyes!
Alleluia!
Christ, awhile to mortals given,
Alleluia!
Reascends His native heaven.
Alleluia!

2 There the pompous triumph waits:
Lift your heads, eternal gates;
Wide unfold the radiant scene;
Take the King of Glory in!

3 Him though highest heaven receives,
Still He loves the earth He leaves;
Though returning to His throne,
Still He calls mankind His own.

4 See! He lifts His hands above;
See! He shows the prints of love;
Hark! His gracious lips bestow
Blessings on His Church below.

5 Master, parted from our sight
High above yon azure height,
Grant our hearts may thither rise,
Following Thee beyond the skies.

Charles Wesley, 1707-88.

HERMANN. L.M. and Hallelujah. N. HERMANN, 1485-1561.

UNISON.

1 OUR Lord is risen from the dead!
Our Jesus is gone up on high!
The powers of hell are captive led,
Dragged to the portals of the sky.
Hallelujah.

2 There His triumphal chariot waits,
And angels chant the solemn lay:
Lift up your heads, ye heavenly gates;
Ye everlasting doors, give way;
Hallelujah.

3 Loose all your bars of massy light,
And wide unfold the ethereal scene:
He claims these mansions as His right;
Receive the King of Glory in!
Hallelujah.

4 Who is this King of Glory? Who?
The Lord that all our foes o'ercame,
The world, sin, death, and hell o'erthrew;
And Jesus is the Conqueror's name.
Hallelujah.

5 Lo! His triumphal chariot waits,
And angels chant the solemn lay:
Lift up your heads, ye heavenly gates;
Ye everlasting doors, give way!
Hallelujah.

6 Who is this King of Glory? Who?
The Lord, of glorious power possest;
The King of saints, and angels too,
God over all, for ever blest!
Hallelujah.

Charles Wesley, 1707-88.

223

REX GLORIAE. 8.7.8.7. D. H. SMART, 1813-79.

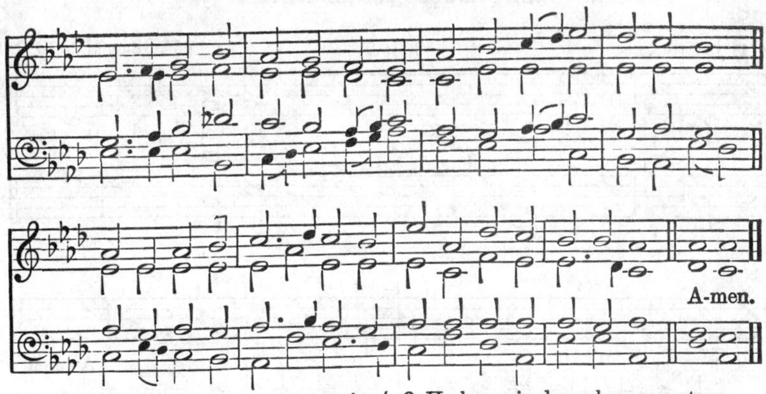

1 See the Conqueror mounts in triumph,
See the King in royal state
Riding on the clouds His chariot
To His heavenly palace gate;
Hark! the choirs of angel voices
Joyful hallelujahs sing,
And the portals high are lifted
To receive their heavenly King.

2 Who is this that comes in glory,
With the trump of jubilee?
Lord of battles, God of armies,
He has gained the victory;
He who on the Cross did suffer,
He who from the grave arose,
He has vanquished sin and Satan,
He by death has spoiled His foes.

3 He has raised our human nature
In the clouds to God's right hand;
There we sit in heavenly places,
There with Him in glory stand:
Jesus reigns, adored by angels;
Man with God is on the throne;
Mighty Lord, in Thine ascension
We by faith behold our own.

4 Glory be to God the Father;
Glory be to God the Son,
Dying, risen, ascending for us,
Who the heavenly realm has won;
Glory to the Holy Spirit;
To One God in Persons Three
Glory both in earth and heaven,
Glory, endless glory be! Amen.

Christopher Wordsworth, 1807-85.

224

LONDON NEW. C.M. *Scottish Psalter*, 1635.

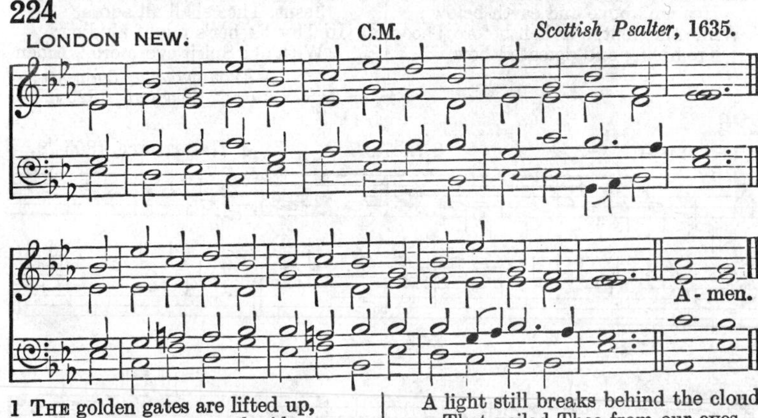

1 The golden gates are lifted up,
The doors are opened wide;
The King of Glory is gone in
Unto His Father's side.

2 Thou art gone up before us, Lord,
To make for us a place,
That we may be where now Thou art,
And look upon God's face.

3 And ever on our earthly path
A gleam of glory lies;
A light still breaks behind the cloud
That veiled Thee from our eyes.

4 Lift up our hearts, lift up our minds:
Let Thy dear grace be given,
That, while we wander here below,
Our treasure be in heaven:

5 That where Thou art at God's right hand,
Our hope, our love, may be.
Dwell Thou in us, that we may dwell
For evermore in Thee. Amen.

Cecil Frances Alexander, 1823-95.

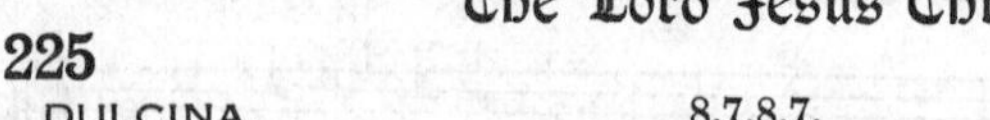

225

DULCINA. 8.7.8.7. Old English Melody.

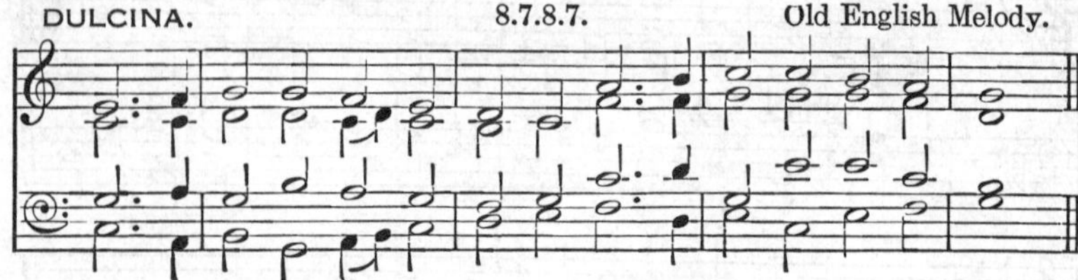

May also be sung to STUTTGART, No. 242.

Aeterne Rex altissime.

1 CHRIST, above all glory seated!
  King triumphant, strong to save!
Dying, Thou hast death defeated;
  Buried, Thou hast spoiled the grave.

2 Thou art gone where now is given,
  What no mortal might could gain,
On the eternal throne of heaven,
  In Thy Father's power to reign.

3 There Thy kingdoms all adore Thee,
  Heaven above and earth below;
While the depths of hell before Thee
  Trembling and defeated bow.

4 We, O Lord, with hearts adoring,
  Follow Thee above the sky;
Hear our prayers Thy grace imploring,
  Lift our souls to Thee on high.

5 So when Thou again in glory
  On the clouds of heaven shalt shine,
We Thy flock may stand before Thee,
  Owned for evermore as Thine.

6 Hail! all hail! In Thee confiding,
  Jesus, Thee shall all adore,
In Thy Father's might abiding
  With one Spirit evermore! Amen.

Anonymous, c. 5th cent.;
tr. by James Russell Woodford, 1820-85.

226

TRIUMPH. 8.7.8.7.8.7. H. J. GAUNTLETT, 1805-76.

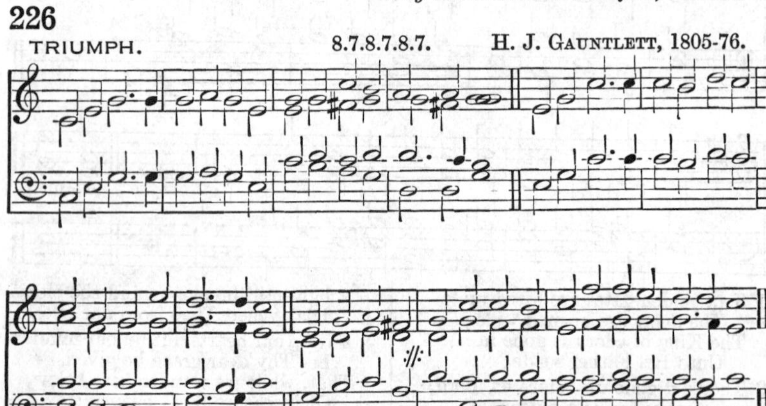

May also be sung to GRAFTON, No. 93.

1 Look, ye saints! The sight is glorious,
See the Man of Sorrows now,
From the fight returned victorious;
Every knee to Him shall bow.
Crown Him! Crown Him!
Crowns become the Victor's brow.

2 Crown the Saviour, angels crown Him:
Rich the trophies Jesus brings;
In the seat of power enthrone Him,
While the vault of heaven rings.
Crown Him! Crown Him!
Crown the Saviour, King of kings.

3 Sinners in derision crowned Him,
Mocking thus the Saviour's claim;
Saints and angels crowd around Him,
Own His title, praise His name.
Crown Him! Crown Him!
Spread abroad the Victor's fame.

4 Hark, those bursts of acclamation;
Hark, those loud triumphant chords;
Jesus takes the highest station:
O what joy the sight affords!
Crown Him! Crown Him!
King of kings, and Lord of lords!

Thomas Kelly, 1769-1854.

227

SALZBURG. 8.7.8.7.7 7.7 7. J. Hintze, 1622-1702.

Siegesfürste, Ehrenkönig.

1 Conquering Prince and Lord of glory,
Majesty enthroned in light;
All the heavens are bowed before Thee,
Far beyond them spreads Thy might;
Shall not I fall at Thy feet,
And my heart with rapture beat,
Now Thy glory is displayed,
Thine ere yet the worlds were made?

2 As I watch Thee far ascending
To the right hand of the throne,
See the host before Thee bending,
Praising Thee in sweetest tone;
Shall not I too at Thy feet
Here the angels' strain repeat,
And rejoice that heaven doth ring
With the triumph of my King?

3 Power and Spirit are o'erflowing,
On me also be they poured;
Every hindrance overthrowing,
Make Thy foes Thy footstool, Lord!
Yea, let earth's remotest end
To Thy righteous sceptre bend,
Make Thy way before Thee plain,
O'er all hearts and spirits reign.

4 Lo! Thy presence now is filling
All Thy Church in every place;
Fill my heart too; make me willing
In this season of Thy grace;
Come, Thou King of glory, come,
Deign to make my heart Thy home,
There abide and rule alone,
As upon Thy heavenly throne! Amen.

Gerhard Tersteegen, 1697-1769;
tr. by Catherine Winkworth, 1827-78.

AUSTRIA. 8.7.8.7. D. F. J. HAYDN, 1732-1809.

1 HAIL, Thou once despisèd Jesus!
Hail, Thou Galilean King!
Thou didst suffer to release us;
Thou didst free salvation bring.
Hail, Thou agonizing Saviour,
Bearer of our sin and shame!
By Thy merits we find favour;
Life is given through Thy name.

2 Paschal Lamb by God appointed,
All our sins on Thee were laid;
By almighty love anointed,
Thou hast full atonement made:
All Thy people are forgiven
Through the virtue of Thy blood;
Opened is the gate of heaven;
Peace is made 'twixt man and God.

3 Jesus, hail! enthroned in glory,
There for ever to abide;
All the heavenly host adore Thee,
Seated at Thy Father's side:
There for sinners Thou art pleading,
There Thou dost our place prepare,
Ever for us interceding,
Till in glory we appear.

4 Worship, honour, power, and blessing,
Thou art worthy to receive;
Loudest praises without ceasing,
Meet it is for us to give.
Help, ye bright, angelic spirits!
Bring your sweetest, noblest lays;
Help to sing our Saviour's merits,
Help to chant Immanuel's praise!

John Bakewell, 1721-1819.

229

FESTUS. L.M. FREYLINGHAUSEN'S *Gesangbuch*, 1714.

1 Ye faithful souls who Jesus know,
If risen indeed with Him ye are,
Superior to the joys below,
His resurrection's power declare.

2 Your faith by holy tempers prove,
By actions show your sins forgiven,
And seek the glorious things above,
And follow Christ, your Head, to heaven.

3 There your exalted Saviour see,
Seated at God's right hand again,
In all His Father's majesty,
In everlasting pomp to reign.

4 To Him continually aspire,
Contending for your native place;
And emulate the angel choir,
And only live to love and praise.

5 For who by faith your Lord receive,
Ye nothing seek or want beside;
Dead to the world and sin ye live,
Your creature-love is crucified.

6 Your real life, with Christ concealed,
Deep in the Father's bosom lies;
And, glorious as your Head revealed,
Ye soon shall meet Him in the skies.

Charles Wesley, 1707-88.

230

REJOICE AND BE GLAD. Irregular. *Revival Tune Book*, 1864.

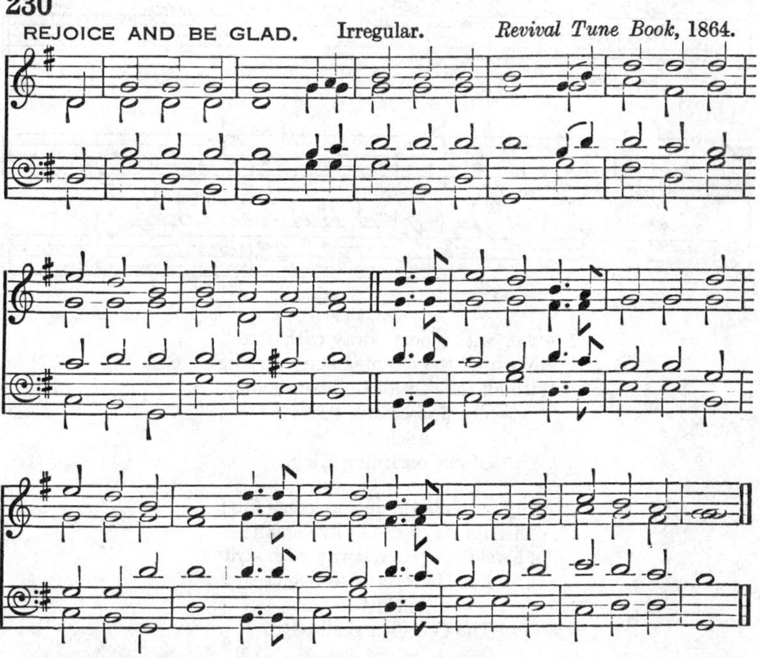

1 Rejoice and be glad! the Redeemer hath come:
Go, look on His cradle, His cross, and His tomb.
Sound His praises, tell the story of Him who was slain;
Sound His praises, tell with gladness He liveth again.

2 Rejoice and be glad! it is sunshine at last;
The clouds have departed, the shadows are past.

3 Rejoice and be glad! for the blood hath been shed;
Redemption is finished, the price hath been paid.

4 Rejoice and be glad! now the pardon is free;
The just for the unjust hath died on the tree.

5 Rejoice and be glad! for the Lamb that was slain,
O'er death is triumphant, and liveth again.

6 Rejoice and be glad! for our King is on high;
He pleadeth for us on His throne in the sky.

7 Rejoice and be glad! for He cometh again;
He cometh in glory, the Lamb that was slain.

Horatius Bonar, 1808-89.

BLAIRGOWRIE. 8.8.8.6.4.6. R. G. THOMPSON, 1862-1934.

1 AWAY with gloom, away with doubt !
With all the morning stars we sing ;
With all the sons of God we shout
The praises of a King,
Alleluia !
Of our returning King.

2 Away with death, and welcome life ;
In Him we died and live again ;
And welcome peace, away with strife !
For He returns to reign.
Alleluia !
The Crucified shall reign.

3 Then welcome beauty, He is fair ;
And welcome youth, for He is young ;
And welcome spring ; and everywhere
Let merry songs be sung !
Alleluia !
For such a King be sung !

Edward Shillito, 1872-1948

Also :

194 Go to dark Gethsemane
195 He dies ! the Friend of Sinners dies
235 I know that my Redeemer lives
661 Come, let us with our Lord arise

232

ADAM. 8.8.8.8.8.8. Anonymous.

1 ENTERED the holy place above,
Covered with meritorious scars,
The tokens of His dying love
Our great High-priest in glory bears;
He pleads His passion on the tree,
He shows Himself to God for me.

2 Before the throne my Saviour stands,
My Friend and Advocate appears;
My name is graven on His hands,
And Him the Father always hears;
While low at Jesu's Cross I bow,
He hears the blood of sprinkling now.

3 This instant now I may receive
The answer of His powerful prayer;
This instant now by Him I live,
His prevalence with God declare;
And soon my spirit, in His hands,
Shall stand where my Forerunner stands.

Charles Wesley, 1707-88.

233

IRENE. 6 6.7.7.7.7. FREYLINGHAUSEN'S *Gesangbuch*, 1704.

1 Jesus, to Thee we fly,
On Thee for help rely;
Thou our only refuge art,
Thou dost all our fears control,
Rest of every troubled heart,
Life of every dying soul.

2 We lift our joyful eyes,
And see the dazzling prize,
See the purchase of Thy blood,
Freely now to sinners given;
Thou the living way hast showed,
Thou to us hast opened heaven.

3 We now, divinely bold,
Of Thy reward lay hold;
All Thy glorious joy is ours,
All the treasures of Thy love;
Now we taste the heavenly powers,
Now we reign with Thee above.

4 Our anchor sure and fast
Within the veil is cast;
Stands our never-failing hope
Grounded in the holy place;
We shall after Thee mount up,
See the Godhead face to face.

Charles Wesley, 1707-88.

234

CAMBRIDGE. S.M. R. HARRISON, 1748-1810.

1 Not all the blood of beasts
On Jewish altars slain
Could give the guilty conscience peace
Or wash away our stain.

2 But Christ, the heavenly Lamb,
Takes all our sins away;
A sacrifice of nobler name,
And richer blood, than they.

3 My faith would lay her hand
On that meek head of Thine,
While as a penitent I stand,
And here confess my sin.

4 My soul looks back to see
The burden Thou didst bear
When hanging on the accursèd tree,
And knows her guilt was there.

5 Believing, we rejoice
To feel the curse remove;
We bless the Lamb with cheerful voice,
And trust His bleeding love.

Isaac Watts, 1674-1748.

235

TORQUAY. L.M. W. Youens, 1834-1911

1 I know that my Redeemer lives—
What joy the blest assurance gives!
He lives, He lives, who once was dead;
He lives, my everlasting Head.

2 He lives, to bless me with His love;
He lives, to plead for me above;
He lives, my hungry soul to feed;
He lives, to help in time of need.

3 He lives, and grants me daily breath;
He lives, and I shall conquer death;
He lives, my mansion to prepare;
He lives, to lead me safely there.

4 He lives, all glory to His name;
He lives, my Saviour, still the same;
What joy the blest assurance gives,
I know that my Redeemer lives!

Samuel Medley, 1738-99.

236

OLDHAM STREET. C.M. J. HOWGATE'S *Collection*, c. 1820.

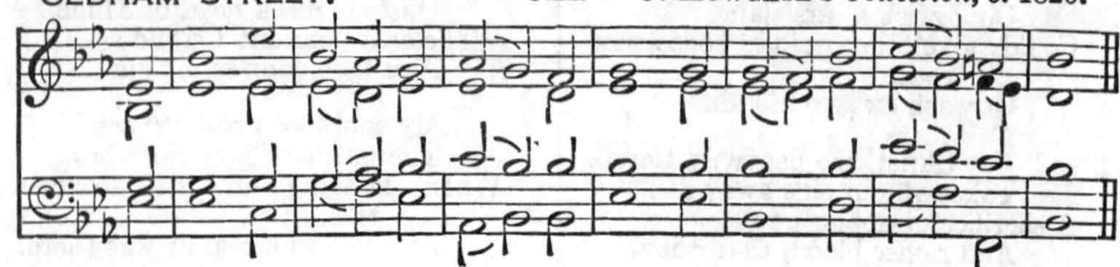

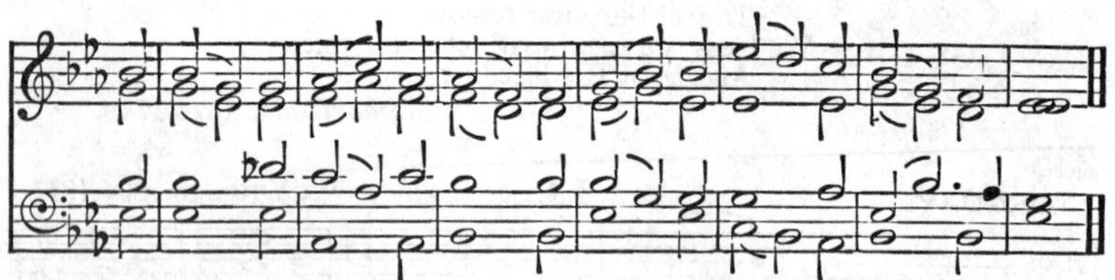

1 WITH joy we meditate the grace
Of our High-priest above;
His heart is made of tenderness,
And ever yearns with love.

2 Touched with a sympathy within,
He knows our feeble frame;
He knows what sore temptations mean,
For He hath felt the same.

3 He in the days of feeble flesh
Poured out His cries and tears;
And, though exalted, feels afresh
What every member bears.

4 He'll never quench the smoking flax,
But raise it to a flame;
The bruisèd reed He never breaks,
Nor scorns the meanest name.

5 Then let our humble faith address
His mercy and His power:
We shall obtain delivering grace
In the distressing hour.

Isaac Watts, 1674-1748.

237

WINDSOR. C.M. DAMON'S *Psalmes*, 1591.

1 There is no sorrow, Lord, too light
To bring in prayer to Thee;
Nor is there any care too slight
To wake Thy sympathy.

2 Thou who hast trod the thorny road
Wilt share each small distress;
The love which bore the greater load
Will not refuse the less.

3 There is no secret sigh we breathe
But meets the ear divine;
And every cross grows light beneath
The shadow, Lord, of Thine.

4 Life's ills without, sin's strife within:
The heart would overflow,
But for that love which died for sin,
That love which wept with woe.

Jane Crewdson, 1809-63.

238

HARLAN. 6 6.4.6 6 6.4. L. Mason, 1792-1872.

1 My faith looks up to Thee,
Thou Lamb of Calvary,
Saviour divine:
Now hear me while I pray;
Take all my guilt away;
O let me from this day
Be wholly Thine.

2 May Thy rich grace impart
Strength to my fainting heart,
My zeal inspire;
As Thou hast died for me,
O may my love to Thee
Pure, warm, and changeless be,
A living fire.

3 While life's dark maze I tread,
And griefs around me spread,
Be Thou my guide;
Bid darkness turn to day,
Wipe sorrow's tears away,
Nor let me ever stray
From Thee aside.

4 When ends life's transient dream,
When death's cold, sullen stream
Shall o'er me roll,
Blest Saviour, then, in love,
Fear and distrust remove;
O bear me safe above,
A ransomed soul. Amen.

Ray Palmer, 1808-87.

239

SOUTHWELL. S.M. DAMON'S *Psalmes*, 1579.

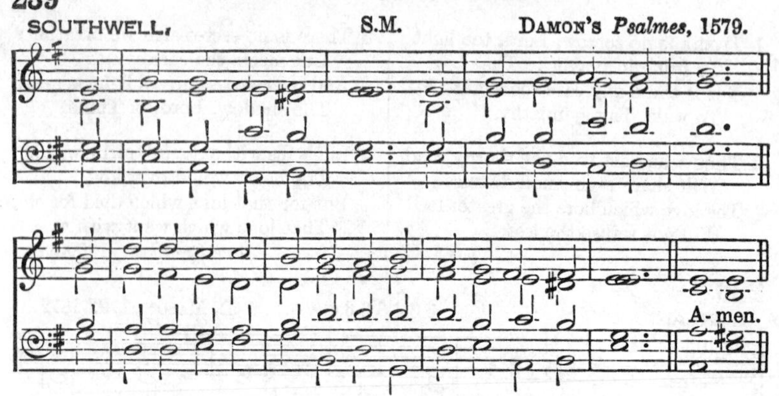

Μνώεο Χριστέ.

1 LORD Jesus, think on me,
And purge away my sin;
From earthborn passions set me free,
And make me pure within.

2 Lord Jesus, think on me,
With care and woe opprest;
Let me Thy loving servant be,
And taste Thy promised rest.

3 Lord Jesus, think on me,
Amid the battle's strife;
In all my pain and misery
Be Thou my health and life.

4 Lord Jesus, think on me,
Nor let me go astray;
Through darkness and perplexity
Point Thou the heavenly way.

5 Lord Jesus, think on me,
When flows the tempest high:
When on doth rush the enemy,
O Saviour, be Thou nigh.

6 Lord Jesus, think on me,
That, when the flood is past,
I may the eternal brightness see,
And share Thy joy at last. Amen.

Synesius, 375-430;
tr. by Allen William Chatfield, 1808-96.

240

L'OMNIPOTENT. 11.10.11.10. *Genevan Psalter*, 1551.

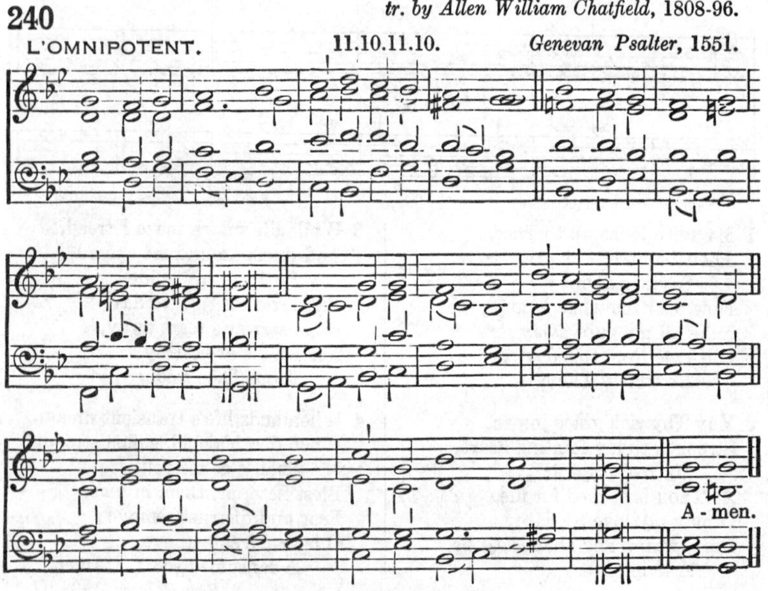

May also be sung to INTERCESSOR, No. 911.

1 O WORD of pity, for our pardon pleading,
Breathed in the hour of loneliness and pain;
O voice, which, through the ages interceding,
Calls us to fellowship with God again.

2 O word of comfort, through the silence stealing,
As the dread act of sacrifice began;
O infinite compassion, still revealing
The infinite forgiveness won for man.

3 O word of hope, to raise us nearer heaven,
When courage fails us, and when faith is dim;
The souls for whom Christ prays to Christ are given,
To find their pardon and their joy in Him.

4 O Intercessor, who art ever living
To plead for dying souls that they may live,
Teach us to know our sin which needs forgiving,
Teach us to know the love which can forgive. Amen.

Ada Rundall Greenaway, 1861- .

241

WELWYN. 11.10.11.10. A. S. GATTY, 1847-1918.

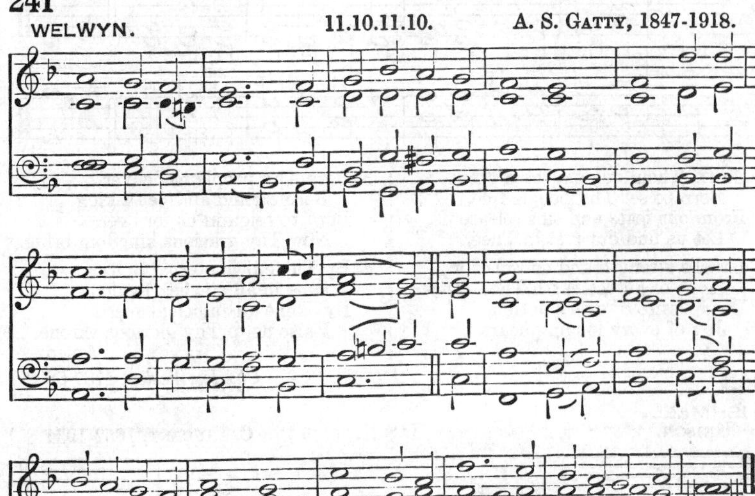

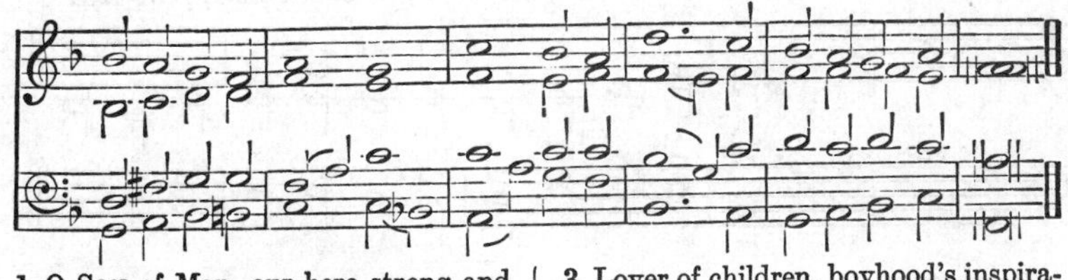

1 O SON of Man, our hero strong and tender,
Whose servants are the brave in all the earth,
Our living sacrifice to Thee we render,
Who sharest all our sorrows, all our mirth.

2 O feet so strong to climb the path of duty,
O lips divine that taught the words of truth,
Kind eyes that marked the lilies in their beauty,
And heart that kindled at the zeal of youth.

3 Lover of children, boyhood's inspiration,
Of all mankind the Servant and the King;
O Lord of joy and hope and consolation,
To Thee our fears and joys and hopes we bring.

4 Not in our failures only and our sadness
We seek Thy presence, Comforter and Friend;
O rich man's Guest, be with us in our gladness,
O poor man's Mate, our lowliest tasks attend.

Frank Fletcher, 1870- .

Also:

94 None other Lamb
110 Jesu, Lover of my soul
200 O Jesus, my hope
220 God is ascended
277 Granted is the Saviour's prayer
368 Arise, my soul, arise
771 Victim Divine, Thy grace we claim

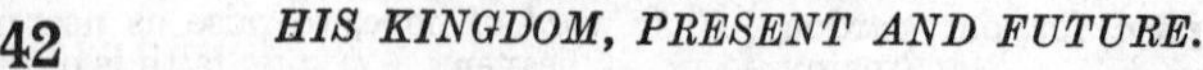
The Lord Jesus Christ

242 HIS KINGDOM, PRESENT AND FUTURE.

STUTTGART. 8.7.8.7. C. F. WITT, *c.* 1660-1716.

A-men.

1 COME, Thou long-expected Jesus,
Born to set Thy people free,
From our fears and sins release us,
Let us find our rest in Thee.

2 Israel's strength and consolation,
Hope of all the earth Thou art;
Dear Desire of every nation,
Joy of every longing heart.

3 Born Thy people to deliver,
Born a child and yet a king,
Born to reign in us for ever,
Now Thy gracious kingdom bring.

4 By Thine own eternal Spirit
Rule in all our hearts alone;
By Thine all-sufficient merit
Raise us to Thy glorious throne.
Amen.

Charles Wesley, 1707-88.

243

ISHMAEL.
UNISON. D.S.M. C. VINCENT, 1852-1934

HARMONY.

1 Jesus, the Conqueror, reigns,
In glorious strength arrayed,
His kingdom over all maintains,
And bids the earth be glad.
Ye sons of men, rejoice
In Jesu's mighty love;
Lift up your heart, lift up your voice,
To Him who rules above.

2 Extol His kingly power,
Kiss the exalted Son,
Who died; and lives, to die no more,
High on His Father's throne;
Our Advocate with God,
He undertakes our cause,
And spreads through all the earth abroad
The victory of His Cross.

3 Courage! your Captain cries,
Who all your toil foreknew:
Toil ye shall have; yet all despise,
I have o'ercome for you.
This is the victory!
Before our faith they fall;
Jesus hath died for you and me;
Believe, and conquer all!

Charles Wesley, 1707-88.

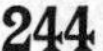

244

ST. MAGNUS. C.M. J. Clarke, 1659 *or* 1670-1707

1 The head that once was crowned with thorns
Is crowned with glory now;
A royal diadem adorns
The mighty Victor's brow.

2 The highest place that heaven affords
Is His, is His by right,
The King of kings and Lord of lords,
And heaven's eternal light.

3 The joy of all who dwell above,
The joy of all below
To whom He manifests His love,
And grants His name to know.

4 To them the cross, with all its shame,
With all its grace, is given,
Their name an everlasting name,
Their joy the joy of heaven.

5 They suffer with their Lord below,
They reign with Him above,
Their profit and their joy to know
The mystery of His love.

6 The Cross He bore is life and health,
Though shame and death to Him;
His people's hope, His people's wealth,
Their everlasting theme.

Thomas Kelly, 1769-1854.

245

LANCASHIRE (*First Tune*). 7.6.7.6. D. H. SMART, 1813-79.

HERRNHUT (*Second Tune*). 7.6.7.6. D. J. CRÜGER, 1598-1662.

His Kingdom, Present and Future

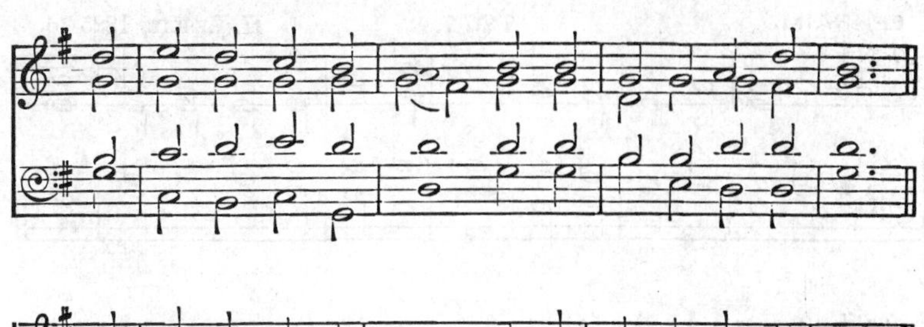

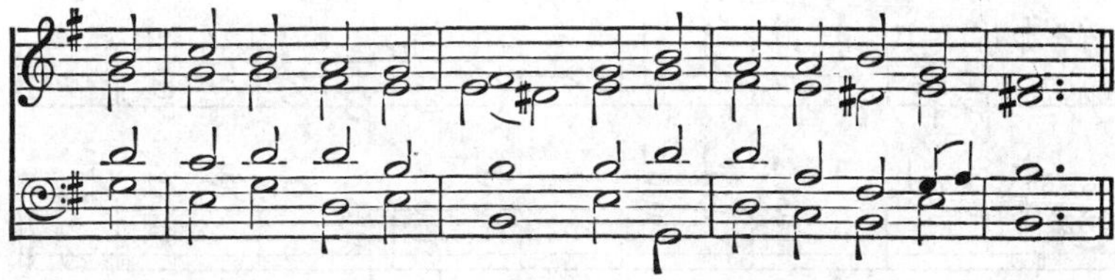

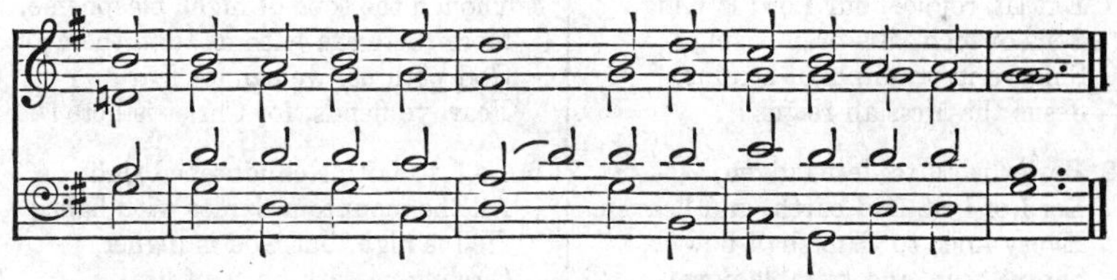

1 Hail to the Lord's Anointed;
  Great David's greater Son!
Hail, in the time appointed,
  His reign on earth begun!
He comes to break oppression,
  To set the captive free,
To take away transgression,
  And rule in equity.

2 He comes, with succour speedy,
  To those who suffer wrong;
To help the poor and needy,
  And bid the weak be strong:
To give them songs for sighing,
  Their darkness turn to light,
Whose souls, condemned and dying,
  Were precious in His sight.

3 He shall come down like showers
  Upon the fruitful earth:
Love, joy, and hope, like flowers,
  Spring in His path to birth:
Before Him, on the mountains,
  Shall peace the herald go;
And righteousness in fountains,
  From hill to valley flow.

4 Kings shall fall down before Him,
  And gold and incense bring;
All nations shall adore Him,
  His praise all people sing;
To Him shall prayer unceasing
  And daily vows ascend;
His kingdom still increasing,
  A kingdom without end.

5 O'er every foe victorious,
  He on His throne shall rest;
From age to age more glorious,
  All-blessing and all-blest.
The tide of time shall never
  His covenant remove;
His name shall stand for ever
  His changeless name of Love.

James Montgomery, 1771-1854.

246

EPHRAIM. 7 7.7 7. H. LESLIE, 1825-76.

1 EARTH, rejoice, our Lord is King!
Sons of men, His praises sing;
Sing ye in triumphant strains,
Jesus the Messiah reigns!

2 Power is all to Jesus given,
Lord of hell, and earth, and heaven,
Every knee to Him shall bow;
Satan, hear, and tremble now!

3 Angels and archangels join,
All triumphantly combine,
All in Jesu's praise agree,
Carrying on His victory.

4 Though the sons of night blaspheme,
More there are with us than them;
God with us, we cannot fear;
Fear, ye fiends, for Christ is here!

5 Lo! to faith's enlightened sight,
All the mountain flames with light;
Hell is nigh, but God is nigher,
Circling us with hosts of fire.

6 Christ the Saviour is come down,
Points us to the victor's crown,
Bids us take our seats above,
More than conquerors in His love.

Charles Wesley, 1707-88.

247

GOPSAL. 6.6.6.6.8 8. HANDEL, 1685-1759.
(Composed for this hymn.)

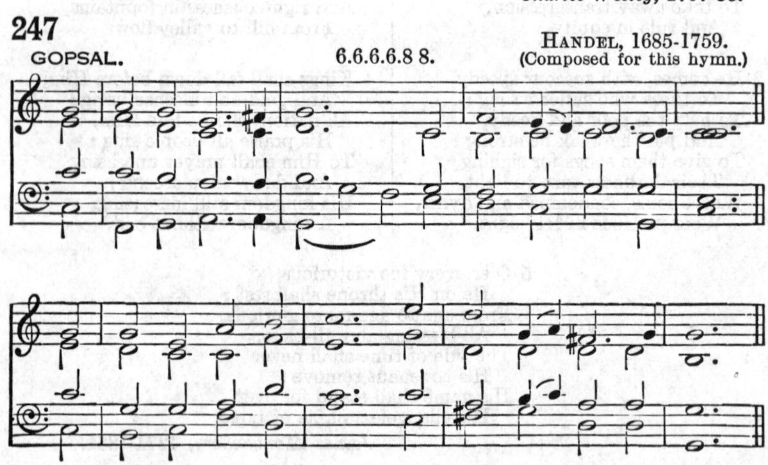

1 Rejoice, the Lord is King!
Your Lord and King adore;
Mortals, give thanks, and sing,
And triumph evermore:

Lift up your heart, lift up your voice;
Rejoice; again I say, Rejoice.

2 Jesus the Saviour reigns,
The God of truth and love;
When He had purged our stains,
He took His seat above:

3 His kingdom cannot fail,
He rules o'er earth and heaven;
The keys of death and hell
Are to our Jesus given:

4 He sits at God's right hand,
Till all His foes submit,
And bow to His command,
And fall beneath His feet:

5 He all His foes shall quell,
Shall all our sins destroy,
And every bosom swell
With pure seraphic joy:

6 Rejoice in glorious hope;
Jesus the Judge shall come,
And take His servants up
To their eternal home:

We soon shall hear the archangel's voice;
The trump of God shall sound, [*Rejoice!*

Charles Wesley, 1707-88.

248

ST. GEORGE. S.M. H. J. Gauntlett, 1805-76.

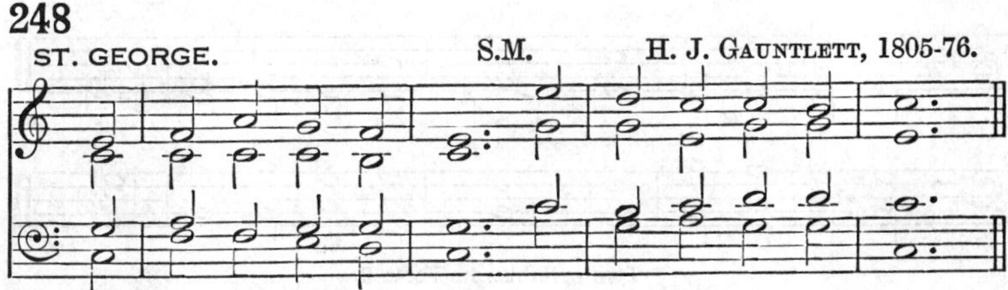

1 Jesu, the word bestow,
The true immortal seed;
Thy gospel then shall greatly grow,
And all our land o'erspread;

2 Through earth extended wide
Shall mightily prevail,
Destroy the works of self and pride,
And shake the gates of hell.

3 Its energy exert
In the believing soul;
Diffuse Thy grace through every part,
And sanctify the whole;

4 Its utmost virtue show
In pure consummate love,
And fill with all Thy life below,
And give us thrones above.
Amen.

Charles Wesley, 1707-88.

249 The Lord Jesus Christ

EVELYNS. 6.5.6.5. D. W. H. Monk, 1823-89.

* Two syllables in Verse 3.

1 In the Name of Jesus
Every knee shall bow,
Every tongue confess Him
King of Glory now.
'Tis the Father's pleasure
We should call Him Lord,
Who from the beginning
Was the mighty Word.

2 Humbled for a season,
To receive a name
From the lips of sinners
Unto whom He came,
Faithfully He bore it
Spotless to the last,
Brought it back victorious
When from death He passed.

3 Name Him, brothers, name Him,
With love strong as death,
But with awe and wonder,
And with bated breath;
He is God the Saviour,
He is Christ the Lord,
Ever to be worshipped,
Trusted, and adored.

4 In your hearts enthrone Him;
There let Him subdue
All that is not holy,
All that is not true;
Crown Him as your Captain
In temptation's hour;
Let His will enfold you
In its light and power.

5 Brothers, this Lord Jesus
Shall return again
With His Father's glory,
With His angel train;
For all wreaths of empire
Meet upon His brow,
And our hearts confess Him
King of Glory now.

Caroline Maria Noel, 1817-77.

His Kingdom, Present and Future

250

ASHLEY. C.M. and refrain. *Gospel Magazine*, 1774.

REFRAIN. *A little faster.*
Hal-le-lu-jah! Hal-le-lu-jah! Hal-le-lu-jah! Praise the Lord.

1 Salvation! O the joyful sound!
What music to our ears!
A sovereign balm for every wound,
A cordial for our fears.

Glory, honour, praise, and power,
Be unto the Lamb for ever!
Jesus Christ is our Redeemer:
Hallelujah! Praise the Lord.

2 Salvation! O Thou bleeding Lamb,
To Thee the praise belongs;
Salvation shall inspire our hearts,
And dwell upon our tongues.

3 Salvation! Let the echo fly
The spacious earth around;
While all the armies of the sky
Conspire to raise the sound.

Isaac Watts, 1674-1748;
William Walter Shirley, 1725-86.

251

WORSHIP. 7.7.4 4.7. D. J. M. HAYDN, 1737-1806

May also be sung to DELIVERANCE, No. 412.

1 OMNIPOTENT Redeemer,
Our ransomed souls adore Thee;
Whate'er is done
Thy work we own,
And give Thee all the glory;
With thankfulness acknowledge
Our time of visitation;
Thine hand confess,
And gladly bless
The God of our salvation.

2 Thou hast employed Thy servants,
And blessed their weak endeavours,
And lo, in Thee
We myriads see
Of justified believers;
The church of pardoned sinners,
Exulting in their Saviour,
Sing all day long
The gospel song,
And triumph in Thy favour.

3 Thy wonders wrought already
Require our ceaseless praises;
But show Thy power,
And myriads more
Endue with heavenly graces.
But fill our earth with glory,
And, known by every nation,
God of all grace
Receive the praise
Of all Thy new creation. Amen.

Charles Wesley, 1707-88.

His Kingdom, Present and Future

252

PILGRIM BROTHERS. 8.7.8.7. D. C. H. H. Parry, 1848-1918.

May also be sung to Austria, No. 228.

1 God is with us, God is with us,
So our brave forefathers sang,
Far across the field of battle
Loud their holy war-cry rang;
Never once they feared nor faltered,
Never once they ceased to sing:
God is with us, God is with us,
Christ our Lord shall reign as King!

2 Great the heritage they left us,
Great the conquests to be won,
Armèd hosts to meet and scatter,
Larger duties to be done.
Raise the song they nobly taught us,
Round the wide world let it ring:

3 Speed the Cross through all the nations,
Speed the victories of love,
Preach the gospel of redemption
Wheresoever men may move;
Make the future in the present,
Strong of heart, toil on and sing:

4 Soon the struggle will be over,
Soon the flags of strife be furled;
Downward from his place, defeated,
Shall the enemy be hurled;
Onward, then, with ranks unbroken,
Sure of triumph, shout and sing:

Walter John Mathams, 1853-1931.

253

BURTON (*First Tune*). 6.6.6.6.8 8. J. T. LIGHTWOOD, 1856-1944

ARNCLIFFE (*Second Tune.*) 6.6.6.6.8 8. W. SANDERSON, 1878-1935

1 **Break**, day of God, O break,
Sweet light of heavenly skies!
I all for thee forsake,
And from my dead self rise:
O Lamb of God, whose love is light,
Shine on my soul, and all is bright.

2 Break, day of God, O break!
The night has lingered long;
Our hearts with sighing wake,
We weep for sin and wrong:
O Bright and Morning Star, draw near;
O Sun of Righteousness, appear.

3 Break, day of God, O break!
The earth with strife is worn;
The hills with thunder shake,
Hearts of the people mourn:
Break, day of God, sweet day of peace,
And bid the shout of warriors cease!

4 Break, day of God, O break,
Like to the days above!
Let purity awake,
And faith, and hope, and love:
But lo, we see the brightening sky;
The golden morn is drawing nigh.

Henry Burton, 1840-1930.

254

HIGHWOOD. 11.10.11.10. R. R. Terry, 1865-1938

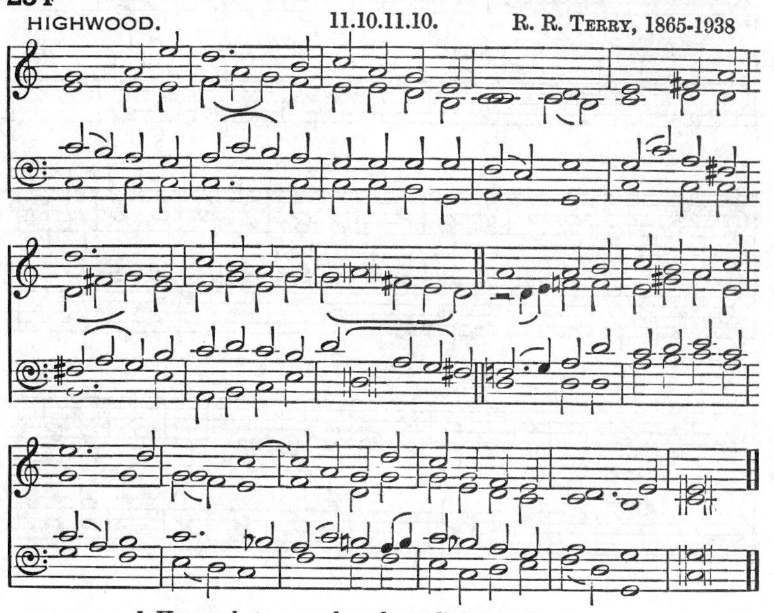

1 **Hark** what a sound, and too divine for hearing,
Stirs on the earth and trembles in the air!
Is it the thunder of the Lord's appearing?
Is it the music of His people's prayer?

2 Surely He cometh, and a thousand voices
Shout to the saints, and to the deaf are dumb;
Surely He cometh, and the earth rejoices,
Glad in His coming who hath sworn: I come!

3 This hath He done, and shall we not adore Him?
This shall He do, and can we still despair?
Come, let us quickly fling ourselves before Him,
Cast at His feet the burden of our care.

4 Yea, through life, death, through sorrow and through sinning
He shall suffice me, for He hath sufficed:
Christ is the end, for Christ was the beginning,
Christ the beginning, for the end is Christ.

Frederic William Henry Myers, 1843-1901.

The Lord Jesus Christ

255

SLEEPERS, WAKE. 8 9.8. D. 6 6.4.8 8. P. NICOLAI, 1556-1608.

Wachet auf! ruft uns die Stimme.

1 WAKE, awake, for night is flying!
The watchmen on the heights are crying:
Awake, Jerusalem, at last!
Midnight hears the welcome voices,
And at the thrilling cry rejoices:
Come forth, ye virgins, night is past!
The Bridegroom comes; awake,
Your lamps with gladness take;
Hallelujah!
And for His marriage feast prepare,
For ye must go to meet Him there.

2 Zion hears the watchmen singing,
And all her heart with joy is springing;
She wakes, she rises from her gloom;
For her Lord comes down all-glorious,
The strong in grace, in truth victorious;
Her Star is risen, her Light is come!
Ah come, Thou blessèd One,
God's own belovèd Son;
Hallelujah!
We follow till the halls we see
Where Thou hast bid us sup with Thee.

3 Now let all the heavens adore Thee,
And men and angels sing before Thee,
With harp and cymbal's clearest tone;
Of one pearl each shining portal,
Where we are with the choir immortal
Of angels round Thy dazzling throne;
Nor eye hath seen, nor ear
Hath yet attained to hear
What there is ours;
But we rejoice, and sing to Thee
Our hymn of joy eternally.

Philipp Nicolai, 1556-1608;
tr. by Catherine Winkworth, 1827-78.

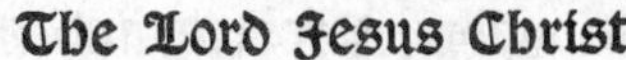

256

15 15.15 15.

M. L. WOSTENHOLM, 1887-

THERE'S A LIGHT UPON THE MOUNTAINS.

Copyright, 1908, Methodist Conference.

1 THERE'S a light upon the mountains, and the day is at the spring,
When our eyes shall see the beauty and the glory of the King;
Weary was our heart with waiting, and the night-watch seemed so long;
But His triumph-day is breaking, and we hail it with a song.

2 In the fading of the starlight we can see the coming morn;
And the lights of men are paling in the splendours of the dawn:
For the eastern skies are glowing as with light of hidden fire,
And the hearts of men are stirring with the throbs of deep desire.

3 There's a hush of expectation, and a quiet in the air;
And the breath of God is moving in the fervent breath of prayer:
For the suffering, dying Jesus is the Christ upon the throne,
And the travail of our spirit is the travail of His own.

4 He is breaking down the barriers, He is casting up the way;
He is calling for His angels to build up the gates of day:
But His angels here are human, not the shining hosts above;
For the drum-beats of His army are the heart-beats of our love.

5 Hark! we hear a distant music, and it comes with fuller swell;
'Tis the triumph-song of Jesus, of our King, Immanuel:
Zion, go ye forth to meet Him; and, my soul, be swift to bring
All thy sweetest and thy dearest for the triumph of our King!

Henry Burton, 1840-1930.

257

8 8.8 8. and refrain.

VENI IMMANUEL (EPHRATAH).

In free rhythm. UNISON. *Hymnal Noted,* 1854.

Veni, veni, Immanuel.

1 O COME, O come, Immanuel,
And ransom captive Israel,
That mourns in lonely exile here
Until the Son of God appear.

Rejoice! Rejoice! Immanuel
Shall come to thee, O Israel.

2 O come, O come, Thou Lord of might,
Who to Thy tribes, on Sinai's height,
In ancient times didst give the law
In cloud, and majesty, and awe.

3 O come, Thou Rod of Jesse, free
Thine own from Satan's tyranny;
From depths of hell Thy people save,
And give them victory o'er the grave.

4 O come, Thou Day-spring, come and cheer
Our spirits by Thine advent here;
Disperse the gloomy clouds of night,
And death's dark shadows put to flight.

5 O come, Thou Key of David, come,
And open wide our heavenly home;
Make safe the way that leads on high,
And close the path to misery.

From Antiphons in Latin Breviary, 12*th cent.;*
tr. by John Mason Neale, 1818-66.

258

BEVERLEY. 8.7.8 8.7.7.7.7.7. W. H. MONK, 1823-89.

1 THOU art coming, O my Saviour,
Thou art coming, O my King,
In Thy beauty, all-resplendent,
In Thy glory all-transcendent;
Well may we rejoice and sing;
Coming! In the opening east
Herald brightness slowly swells;
Coming! O my glorious Priest,
Hear we not Thy golden bells?

2 Thou art coming, Thou art coming;
We shall meet Thee on Thy way,
We shall see Thee, we shall know Thee,
We shall bless Thee, we shall show Thee
All our hearts could never say;
What an anthem that will be,
Ringing out our love to Thee,
Pouring out our rapture sweet,
At Thine own all-glorious feet.

3 O the joy to see Thee reigning,
Thee, our own belovèd Lord!
Every tongue Thy name confessing,
Worship, honour, glory, blessing
Brought to Thee with one accord;
Thee, our Master and our Friend,
Vindicated and enthroned,
Unto earth's remotest end
Glorified, adored, and owned!

Frances Ridley Havergal, 1836-79.

259

ST. SEPULCHRE. L.M. G. COOPER, 1820-76.

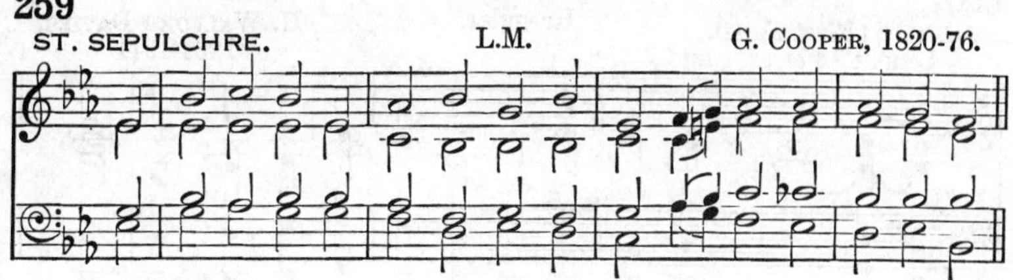

1 AND art Thou come with us to dwell,
Our Prince, our Guide, our Love, our Lord ?
And is Thy name Emmanuel,
God present with His world restored ?

2 The world is glad for Thee ! The rude
Wild moor, the city's crowded pen ;
Each waste, each peopled solitude,
Becomes a home for happy men.

3 Thou bringest all again ; with Thee
Is light, is space, is breadth and room
For each thing fair, beloved, and free,
To have its hour of life and bloom.

4 Each heart's deep instinct unconfessed ;
Each lowly wish, each daring claim ;
All, all that life hath long repressed,
Unfolds, not fearing blight or blame.

5 Thy reign eternal will not cease ;
Thy years are sure, and glad, and slow ;
Within Thy mighty world of peace
The humblest flower hath leave to blow.

6 Then come to heal Thy people's smart,
And with Thee bring Thy captive train ;
Come, Saviour of the world and heart,
Come, mighty Victor over pain. Amen.

Dora Greenwell, 1821-82.

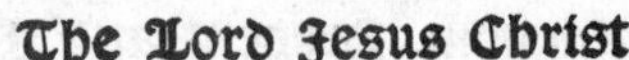

The Lord Jesus Christ

260

VISION (*First Tune*). Irregular. H. WALFORD DAVIES, 1869-1941

UNISON. *Verses 1 and 2*

HARMONY. *Verse 3*

His Kingdom, Present and Future

1.

MINE eyes have seen the glory of the coming of the Lord:
He is trampling out the vintage where the grapes of wrath are stored;
He hath loosed the fateful lightning of His terrible swift sword:
His truth is marching on.

2.

He hath sounded forth the trumpet that shall never call retreat;
He is sifting out the hearts of men before His judgement-seat:
O be swift, my soul, to answer Him; be jubilant, my feet!
Our God is marching on.

3.

In the beauty of the lilies Christ was born across the sea,
With a glory in His bosom that transfigures you and me:
As He died to make men holy, let us live to make men free,
While God is marching on.

Julia Ward Howe, 1819-1910.

1

260

BATTLE HYMN (*Second Tune*). Irregular. American

UNISON.

1 MINE eyes have seen the glory of the coming of the Lord:
He is trampling out the vintage where the grapes of wrath are stored;
He hath loosed the fateful lightning of His terrible swift sword:
His truth is marching on.

2 He hath sounded forth the trumpet that shall never call retreat;
He is sifting out the hearts of men before His judgement-seat:
O be swift, my soul, to answer Him; be jubilant, my feet!
Our God is marching on.

3 In the beauty of the lilies Christ was born across the sea,
With a glory in His bosom that transfigures you and me:
As He died to make men holy, let us live to make men free,
While God is marching on.

Julia Ward Howe, 1819-1910.

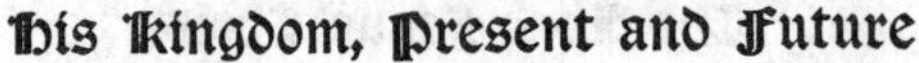

261 SALTASH. 8.7.8.7. D. *Plymouth Collection* (U.S.A.), 1855.

A-men.

1 LIGHT of those whose dreary dwelling
Borders on the shades of death,
Come, and by Thy love's revealing
Dissipate the clouds beneath;
The new heaven and earth's Creator,
In our deepest darkness rise,
Scattering all the night of nature,
Pouring eyesight on our eyes.

2 Still we wait for Thine appearing;
Life and joy Thy beams impart,
Chasing all our fears, and cheering
Every poor benighted heart:
Come, and manifest the favour
God hath for our ransomed race;
Come, Thou universal Saviour,
Come, and bring the gospel grace.

3 Save us in Thy great compassion,
O Thou mild, pacific Prince;
Give the knowledge of salvation,
Give the pardon of our sins:
By Thy all-restoring merit
Every burdened soul release;
Every weary, wandering spirit
Guide into Thy perfect peace.
Amen.

Charles Wesley, 1707-88.

262

DERBE. 5 5.5 11. D. *Sacred Harmony*, 1780.

May also be sung to ARDWICK, No. 278.

1 ALL thanks be to God,
Who scatters abroad,
Throughout every place,
By the least of His servants, His savour of grace.
Who the victory gave,
The praise let Him have,
For the work He hath done:
All honour and glory to Jesus alone!

2 Our conquering Lord
Hath prospered His word,
Hath made it prevail, [hell.
And mightily shaken the kingdom of
His arm He hath bared,
And a people prepared
His glory to show, [below.
And witness the power of His passion

3 He hath opened a door
To the penitent poor,
And rescued from sin,
And admitted the harlots and publicans in;
They have heard the glad sound,
They have liberty found
Through the blood of the Lamb, [name.
And plentiful pardon in Jesus's

4 And shall we not sing
Our Saviour and King?
Thy witnesses, we
With rapture ascribe our salvation to Thee.
Thou, Jesus, hast blessed,
And believers increased,
Who thankfully own
We are freely forgiven through mercy alone.

5 His Spirit revives
His work in our lives,
His wonders of grace, [days.
So mightily wrought in the primitive
O that all men might know
His tokens below,
Our Saviour confess,
And embrace the glad tidings of pardon and peace!

6 Thou Saviour of all,
Effectually call
The sinners that stray;
And O let a nation be born in a day!
Then, then let it spread
Thy knowledge and dread,
Till the earth is o'erflowed,
And the universe filled with the glory of God. Amen.

Charles Wesley, 1707-88.

263

ST. GEORGE'S, WINDSOR. 7.7.7.7. D. G. J. ELVEY, 1816-93.

1 SEE how great a flame aspires,
Kindled by a spark of grace!
Jesu's love the nations fires,
Sets the kingdoms on a blaze.
To bring fire on earth He came;
Kindled in some hearts it is:
O that all might catch the flame,
All partake the glorious bliss!

2 When He first the work begun,
Small and feeble was His day:
Now the word doth swiftly run,
Now it wins its widening way;
More and more it spreads and grows
Ever mighty to prevail;
Sin's strongholds it now o'erthrows,
Shakes the trembling gates of hell.

3 Sons of God, your Saviour praise!
He the door hath opened wide;
He hath given the word of grace,
Jesu's word is glorified;
Jesus, mighty to redeem,
He alone the work hath wrought;
Worthy is the work of Him,
Him who spake a world from nought.

4 Saw ye not the cloud arise,
Little as a human hand?
Now it spreads along the skies,
Hangs o'er all the thirsty land:
Lo! the promise of a shower
Drops already from above;
But the Lord will shortly pour
All the Spirit of His love!

Charles Wesley, 1707-88.

264

HELMSLEY. 8.7.8.7.4.7. *Select Hymns with Tunes Annext*, 1765.

1 Lo! He comes with clouds descending,
Once for favoured sinners slain;
Thousand thousand saints attending,
Swell the triumph of His train:
Hallelujah!
God appears on earth to reign.

2 Every eye shall now behold Him
Robed in dreadful majesty;
Those who set at nought and sold Him,
Pierced and nailed Him to the tree,
Deeply wailing,
Shall the true Messiah see.

3 The dear tokens of His passion
Still His dazzling body bears;
Cause of endless exultation
To His ransomed worshippers:
With what rapture
Gaze we on those glorious scars!

4 Yea, Amen! Let all adore Thee,
High on Thy eternal throne;
Saviour, take the power and glory,
Claim the kingdom for Thine own;
Hallelujah!
Everlasting God, come down!

Charles Wesley, 1707-88.

265

BROMSGROVE. C.M. H. A. DYER, 1878-1918.

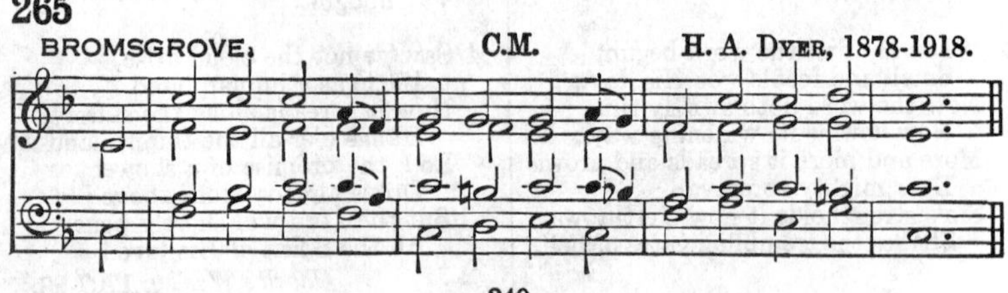

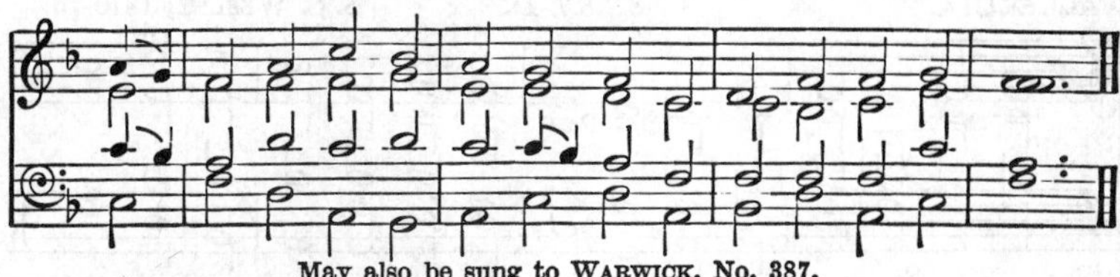

May also be sung to WARWICK, No. 387.

1 LIFT up your heads, ye gates of brass,
Ye bars of iron, yield,
And let the King of Glory pass;
The Cross is in the field.

2 Ye armies of the living God,
His sacramental host,
Where hallowed footstep never trod,
Take your appointed post.

3 Though few and small and weak your bands,
Strong in your Captain's strength,
Go to the conquest of all lands;
All must be His at length.

4 O fear not, faint not, halt not now;
Quit you like men, be strong;
To Christ shall every nation bow,
And sing with you this song:

5 Uplifted are the gates of brass;
The bars of iron yield;
Behold the King of Glory pass!
The Cross hath won the field.

James Montgomery, 1771-1854.

266

MEYER (ES IST KEIN TAG). 8 8 8.4. MEYER'S *Seelenfreud*, 1692.

1 FROM north and south and east and west,
When shall the peoples, long unblest,
All find their everlasting rest,
O Christ, in Thee?

2 When shall the climes of ageless snow
Be with the Gospel light aglow,
And all men their Redeemer know,
O Christ, in Thee?

3 When on each southern balmy coast,
Shall ransomed men, in countless host,
Rise, heart and voice, to make sweet boast,
O Christ, in Thee?

4 O when in all the orient lands,
From cities white and flaming sands,
Shall men lift dedicated hands,
O Christ, to Thee?

5 O when shall heathen darkness roll
Away in light, from pole to pole,
And endless day by every soul
Be found in Thee?

6 Bring, Lord, the long-predicted hour,
The ages' diadem and flower,
When all shall find their refuge-tower
And home in Thee. Amen.

George Thomas Coster, 1835-1912.

267 The Lord Jesus Christ

ALLELUIA. 8.7.8.7. D. S. S. WESLEY, 1810-76.

A-men.

1 LORD, her watch Thy Church is keeping;
When shall earth Thy rule obey?
When shall end the night of weeping?
When shall break the promised day?
See the whitening harvest languish,
Waiting still the labourers' toil;
Was it vain, Thy Son's deep anguish?
Shall the strong retain the spoil?

2 Tidings, sent to every creature,
Millions yet have never heard;
Can they hear without a preacher?
Lord Almighty, give the word:
Give the word; in every nation
Let the gospel trumpet sound,
Witnessing a world's salvation
To the earth's remotest bound.

3 Then the end: Thy Church completed,
All Thy chosen gathered in,
With their King in glory seated,
Satan bound, and banished sin;
Gone for ever parting, weeping,
Hunger, sorrow, death, and pain:
Lo! her watch Thy Church is keeping;
Come, Lord Jesus, come to reign!
Amen.

Henry Downton, 1818-85.

268

NOX PRÆCESSIT. C.M. J. B. CALKIN, 1827-1905.

1 Light of the lonely pilgrim's heart,
Star of the coming day,
Arise, and with Thy morning beams
Chase all our griefs away.

2 Come, blessèd Lord, bid every shore
And answering island sing
The praises of Thy royal name,
And own Thee as their King.

3 Bid the whole earth, responsive now
To the bright world above,
Break forth in rapturous strains of joy
In memory of Thy love.

4 Jesus, Thy fair creation groans—
The air, the earth, the sea—
In unison with all our hearts,
And calls aloud for Thee.

5 Thine was the Cross, with all its fruits
Of grace and peace divine;
Be Thine the crown of glory now,
The palm of victory Thine. Amen.

Edward Denny, 1796-1889.

269

ST. GODRIC. 6.6.6.6.8 8. J. B. Dykes, 1823-76.

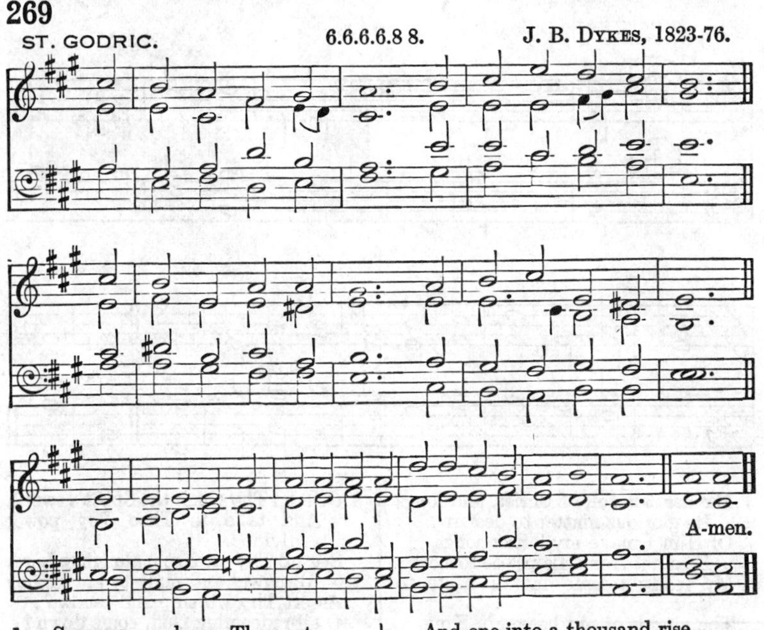

1 Saviour, we know Thou art
In every age the same:
Now, Lord, in ours exert
The virtue of Thy name;
And daily, through Thy word, increase
Thy blood-besprinkled witnesses.

2 Thy people, saved below
From every sinful stain,
Shall multiply and grow,
If Thy command ordain;
And one into a thousand rise,
And spread Thy praise through earth and skies.

3 In many a soul, and mine,
Thou hast displayed Thy power;
But to Thy people join
Ten thousand thousand more,
Saved from the guilt and strength of sin,
In life and heart entirely clean.
Amen.

Charles Wesley, 1707-88.

270

WORSLEY. 8.8.8.8.8.8 8. J. HOWGATE'S *Collection*, c. 1820.

1 My heart is full of Christ, and longs
Its glorious matter to declare!
Of Him I make my loftier songs,
I cannot from His praise forbear;
My ready tongue makes haste to sing
The glories of my heavenly King.

2 Fairer than all the earth-born race,
Perfect in comeliness Thou art;
Replenished are Thy lips with grace,
And full of love Thy tender heart:
God ever blest! we bow the knee,
And own all fullness dwells in Thee.

3 Gird on Thy thigh the Spirit's sword,
And take to Thee Thy power divine;
Stir up Thy strength, almighty Lord,
All power and majesty are Thine:
Assert Thy worship and renown;
O all-redeeming God, come down!

4 Come, and maintain Thy righteous cause,
And let Thy glorious toil succeed;
Dispread the victory of Thy Cross,
Ride on, and prosper in Thy deed;
Through earth triumphantly ride on,
And reign in every heart alone.
Amen.

Charles Wesley, 1707-88.

271

DIADEMATA. D.S.M. G. J. ELVEY, 1816-93.

May also be sung to ICH HALTE TREULICH STILL, No. 363.

1 CROWN Him with many crowns,
The Lamb upon His throne;
Hark! how the heavenly anthem drowns
All music but its own:
Awake, my soul, and sing
Of Him who died for thee,
And hail Him as thy matchless King
Through all eternity.

2 Crown Him the Lord of life,
Who triumphed o'er the grave,
And rose victorious in the strife
For those He came to save;
His glories now we sing
Who died, and rose on high,
Who died—eternal life to bring,
And lives, that death may die.

3 Crown Him the Lord of peace,
Whose power a sceptre sways
From pole to pole, that wars may cease,
And all be prayer and praise:
His reign shall know no end,
And round His piercèd feet
Fair flowers of paradise extend
Their fragrance ever sweet.

4 Crown Him the Lord of love;
Behold His hands and side,
Those wounds, yet visible above,
In beauty glorified:
All hail, Redeemer, hail!
For Thou hast died for me:
Thy praise and glory shall not fail
Throughout eternity. Amen.

Matthew Bridges, 1800-94;
Godfrey Thring, 1823-1903.

272

TRURO. L.M. C. Burney, 1726-1814.

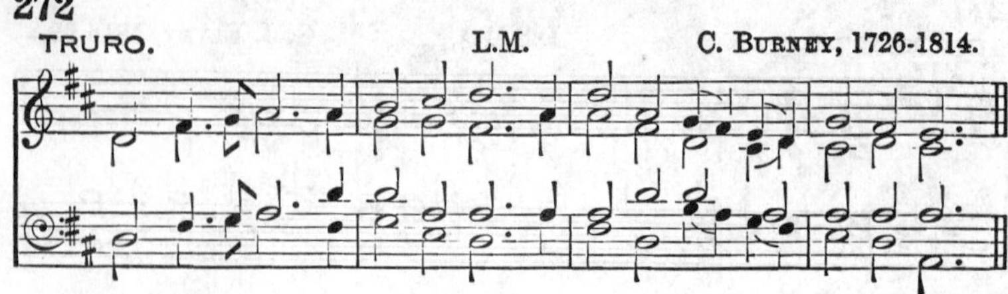

1 Jesus shall reign where'er the sun
Doth his successive journeys run;
His kingdom stretch from shore to shore,
Till suns shall rise and set no more.

2 For Him shall endless prayer be made,
And praises throng to crown His head;
His name like sweet perfume shall rise
With every morning sacrifice.

3 People and realms of every tongue
Dwell on His love with sweetest song;
And infant voices shall proclaim
Their young hosannas to His name.

4 Blessings abound where'er He reigns;
The prisoner leaps to lose his chains;
The weary find eternal rest;
And all the sons of want are blest.

5 Where He displays His healing power,
Death and the curse are known no more;
In Him the tribes of Adam boast
More blessings than their father lost.

6 Let every creature rise, and bring
Its grateful honours to our King;
Angels descend with songs again,
And earth prolong the joyful strain. Amen.

Isaac Watts, 1674-1748.

Also:

115 My heart and voice I raise
116 Sing we the King
133 From the eastern
219 God is gone up
222 Our Lord is risen
223 See the Conqueror
224 The golden gates
225 Christ, above all glory
226 Look, ye saints!
431 Love divine, all loves excelling
742 Thy kingdom come
806 Let the song go round the earth
902 All glory to God

273

HIS PERSON, MISSION AND WORK

DOWN AMPNEY. 6 6.11. D. R. VAUGHAN WILLIAMS, 1872-

Discendi, Amor santo.

1 Come down, O Love Divine,
Seek Thou this soul of mine,
And visit it with Thine own ardour glowing;
O Comforter, draw near,
Within my heart appear,
And kindle it, Thy holy flame bestowing.

2 O let it freely burn,
Till earthly passions turn
To dust and ashes, in its heat consuming;
And let Thy glorious light
Shine ever on my sight,
And clothe me round, the while my path illuming.

3 Let holy charity
Mine outward vesture be,
And lowliness become mine inner clothing;
True lowliness of heart,
Which takes the humbler part,
And o'er its own shortcomings weeps with loathing.

4 And so the yearning strong,
With which the soul will long,
Shall far outpass the power of human telling;
For none can guess its grace,
Till he become the place
Wherein the Holy Spirit makes His dwelling.

Bianco da Siena, d. 1434;
tr. by Richard Frederick Littledale, 1833-90.

274

WINCHESTER NEW. L.M. FREYLINGHAUSEN'S *Gesangbuch*, 1704.

1 LORD, we believe to us and ours
The apostolic promise given;
We wait the pentecostal powers,
The Holy Ghost sent down from heaven.

2 To every one whom God shall call
The promise is securely made;
To you far off—He calls you all;
Believe the word which Christ hath said:

3 The Holy Ghost, if I depart,
The Comforter, shall surely come,
Shall make the contrite sinner's heart
His loved, His everlasting home.

4 Assembled here with one accord,
Calmly we wait the promised grace,
The purchase of our dying Lord:
Come, Holy Ghost, and fill the place.

5 If every one that asks may find,
If still Thou dost on sinners fall,
Come as a mighty rushing wind;
Great grace be now upon us all.

6 Behold, to Thee our souls aspire,
And languish Thy descent to meet:
Kindle in each the living fire,
And fix in every heart Thy seat.
Amen.

Charles Wesley, 1707-88.

275

NEWHAVEN (LUTON). L.M. G. BURDER, 1752-1832.

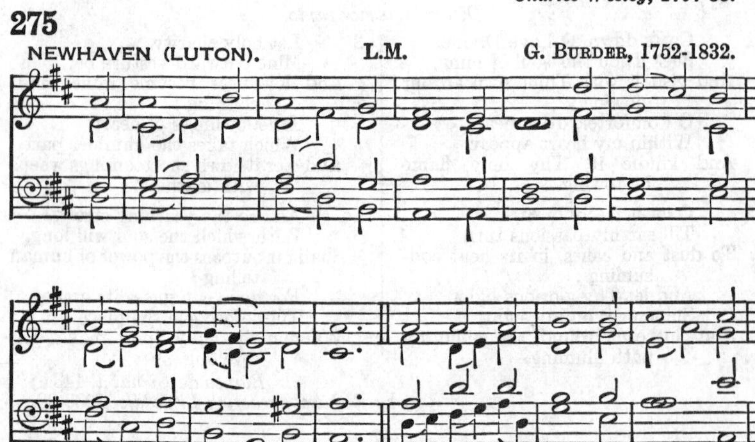

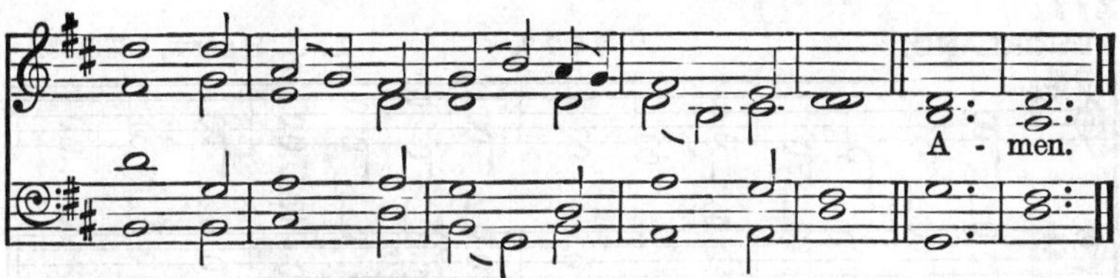

1 Jesus, we on the word depend
Spoken by Thee while present here:
The Father in My name shall send
The Holy Ghost, the Comforter.

2 That promise made to Adam's race,
Now, Lord, in us, even us, fulfil;
And give the Spirit of Thy grace,
To teach us all Thy perfect will.

3 That heavenly Teacher of mankind,
That Guide infallible impart,
To bring Thy sayings to our mind,
And write them on our faithful heart.

4 He only can the words apply
Through which we endless life possess;
And deal to each his legacy,
His Lord's unutterable peace.

5 That peace of God, that peace of Thine,
O might He now to us bring in,
And fill our souls with power divine,
And make an end of fear and sin.

6 The length and breadth of love reveal,
The height and depth of Deity;
And all the sons of glory seal,
And change, and make us all like Thee. Amen.

Charles Wesley, 1707-88.

276

WINCHESTER OLD. C.M. G. Kirbye, ? -1634.

1 When God of old came down from heaven,
In power and wrath He came;
Before His feet the clouds were riven,
Half darkness and half flame.

2 But when He came the second time,
He came in power and love;
Softer than gale at morning prime
Hovered His holy Dove.

3 The fires that rushed on Sinai down
In sudden torrents dread
Now gently light, a glorious crown,
On every sainted head.

4 And as on Israel's awe-struck ear
The voice exceeding loud,
The trump that angels quake to hear,
Thrilled from the deep, dark cloud:

5 So, when the Spirit of our God
Came down His flock to find,
A voice from heaven was heard abroad,
A rushing mighty wind.

6 It fills the Church of God; it fills
The sinful world around;
Only in stubborn hearts and wills
No place for it is found.

7 Come, Lord; come, Wisdom, Love, and Power;
Open our ears to hear;
Let us not miss the accepted hour;
Save, Lord, by love or fear. Amen.

John Keble, 1792-1866.

277

BUCKLAND. 7 7.7 7. L. G. Hayne, 1836-83.

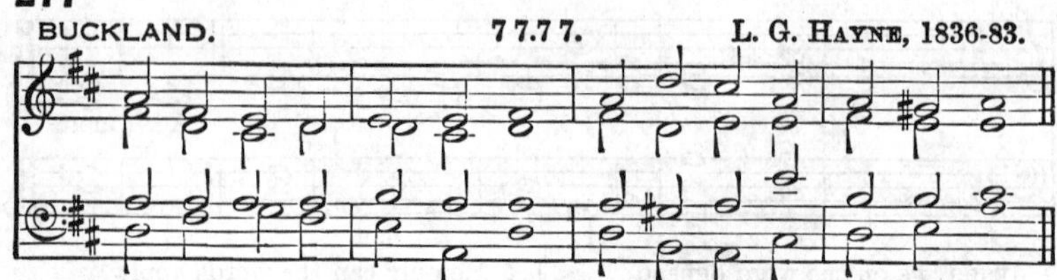

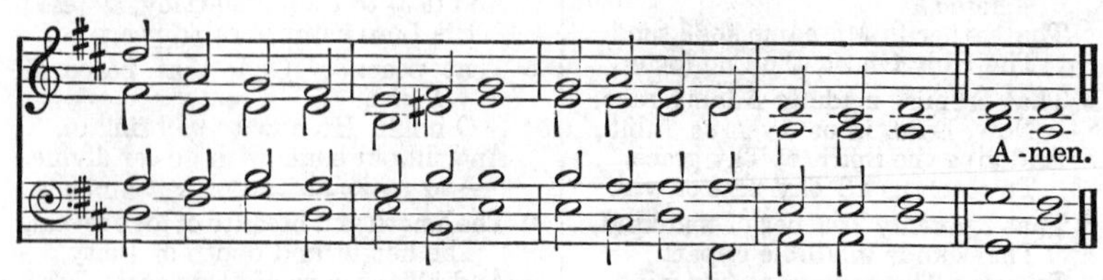

1 Granted is the Saviour's prayer,
Sent the gracious Comforter;
Promise of our parting Lord,
Jesus now to heaven restored.

2 Christ, who now gone up on high
Captive leads captivity;
While His foes from Him receive
Grace that God with man may live.

3 God, the everlasting God,
Makes with mortals His abode;
Whom the heavens cannot contain,
He vouchsafes to dwell in man.

4 Never will He thence depart,
Inmate of a humble heart;
Carrying on His work within,
Striving till He casts out sin.

5 There He helps our feeble moans,
Deepens our imperfect groans,
Intercedes in silence there,
Sighs the unutterable prayer.

6 Come, divine and peaceful Guest,
Enter our devoted breast;
Life divine in us renew,
Thou the Gift, and Giver too! Amen.

Charles Wesley, 1707-88.

278

ARDWICK. 5 5.5 11. H. J. Gauntlett, 1805-76.

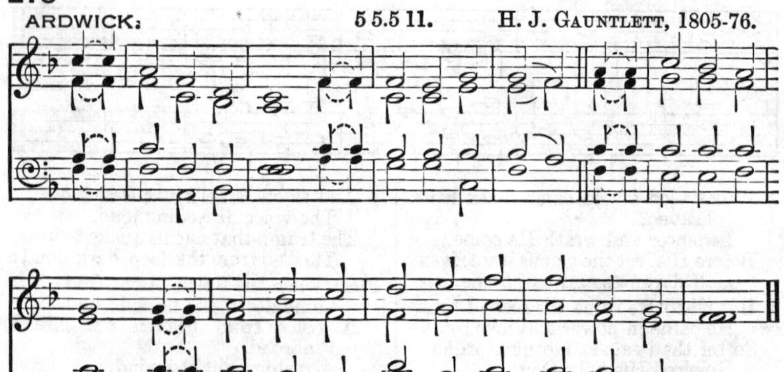

1 Away with our fears,
Our troubles and tears:
The Spirit is come,
The witness of Jesus returned to His home.

2 The pledge of our Lord
To His heaven restored
Is sent from the sky,
And tells us our Head is exalted on high.

3 Our Advocate there
By His blood and His prayer
The gift hath obtained,
For us He hath prayed, and the Comforter gained.

4 Our glorified Head
His Spirit hath shed,
With His people to stay,
And never again will He take Him away.

5 Our heavenly Guide
With us shall abide,
His comforts impart,
And set up His kingdom of love in the heart.

6 The heart that believes
His kingdom receives,
His power and His peace,
His life, and His joy's everlasting increase.

7 Then let us rejoice
In heart and in voice,
Our Leader pursue,
And shout as we travel the wilderness through:

8 With the Spirit remove
To Zion above,
Triumphant arise,
And walk with our God, till we fly to the skies.

Charles Wesley, 1707-88.

279

DRUMCONDRA. S.M. D. F. R. Wilson, 1871-1957.

May also be sung to Swabia, No. 599.

1 O Holy Spirit, God,
All loveliness is Thine;
Great things and small are both in Thee,
The star-world is Thy shrine.

2 The sunshine Thou of God,
The life of man and flower,
The wisdom and the energy
That fills the world with power.

3 Thou art the stream of love,
The unity divine;
Good men and true are one in Thee,
And in Thy radiance shine.

4 The heroes and the saints
Thy messengers became;
And all the lamps that guide the world
Were kindled at Thy flame.

5 The calls that come to us
Upon Thy winds are brought;
The light that gleams beyond our dreams
Is something Thou hast thought.

6 Give fellowship, we pray,
In love and joy and peace,
That we in counsel, knowledge, might,
And wisdom, may increase.
Amen.

Percy Dearmer, 1867-1938

280

LUSATIA. 8.8.8.8.8.8. FREYLINGHAUSEN'S *Gesangbuch*, 1704.

1 I WANT the Spirit of power within,
  Of love, and of a healthful mind:
Of power, to conquer inbred sin;
  Of love, to Thee and all mankind;
Of health, that pain and death defies,
Most vigorous when the body dies.

2 When shall I hear the inward voice
  Which only faithful souls can hear?
Pardon, and peace, and heavenly joys
  Attend the promised Comforter:
O come! and righteousness divine,
And Christ, and all with Christ, are mine.

3 O that the Comforter would come!
  Nor visit as a transient guest,
But fix in me His constant home,
  And take possession of my breast,
And fix in me His loved abode,
The temple of indwelling God.

4 Come, Holy Ghost, my heart inspire!
  Attest that I am born again;
Come, and baptize me now with fire,
  Nor let Thy former gifts be vain:
I cannot rest in sins forgiven;
Where is the earnest of my heaven?

5 Where the indubitable seal
  That ascertains the kingdom mine?
The powerful stamp I long to feel,
  The signature of love divine:
O shed it in my heart abroad,
Fullness of love, of heaven, of God.
Amen.

Charles Wesley, 1707-88.

281

WALSALL. C.M. ANCHOR'S *Collection*, c. 1721.

1 Go not, my soul, in search of Him,
Thou wilt not find Him there,
Or in the depths of shadow dim,
Or heights of upper air.

2 For not in far-off realms of space
The Spirit hath His throne;
In every heart He findeth place,
And waiteth to be known.

3 Thought answereth alone to thought,
And soul with soul hath kin;
The outward God he findeth not,
Who finds not God within.

4 And if the vision come to thee
Revealed by inward sign,
Earth will be full of Deity,
And with His glory shine.

5 Thou shalt not want for company,
Nor pitch thy tent alone;
The indwelling God will go with thee,
And show thee of His own.

6 O gift of gifts! O grace of grace,
That God should condescend
To make thy heart His dwelling-place
And be thy daily Friend!

Frederick Lucian Hosmer, 1840-1929.

282

PEMBROKE. 8 8.6. D. J. FOSTER, 1807-85.

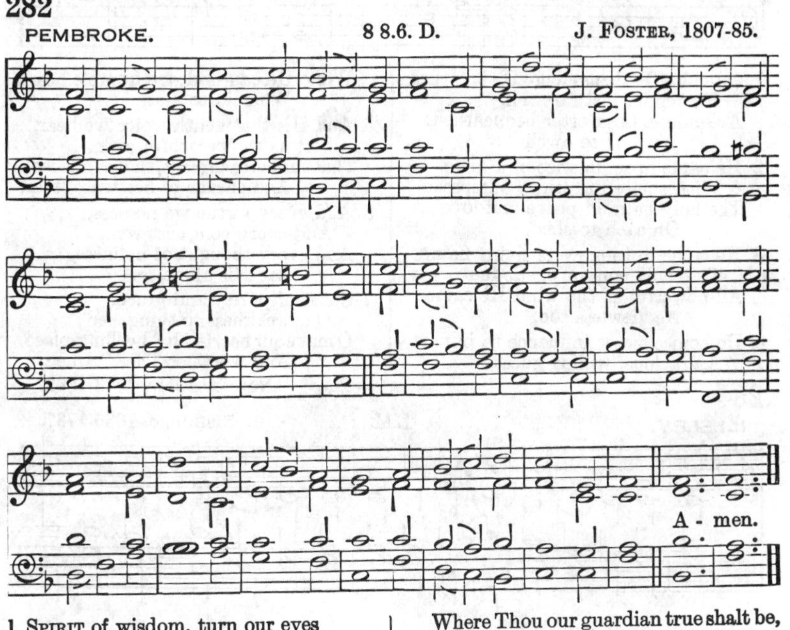

1 SPIRIT of wisdom, turn our eyes
From earth and earthly vanities
To heavenly truth and love;
Spirit of understanding true,
Our souls with heavenly light endue
To seek the things above.

2 Spirit of counsel, be our guide;
Teach us, by earthly struggles tried,
Our heavenly crown to win:
Spirit of fortitude, Thy power
Be with us in temptation's hour,
To keep us pure from sin.

3 Spirit of knowledge, lead our feet
In Thine own paths, so safe and sweet,
By angel footsteps trod;
Where Thou our guardian true shalt be,
Spirit of gentle piety,
To keep us close to God.

4 Through all our life be ever near,
Spirit of God's most holy fear,
In our heart's inmost shrine;
Our souls with awful reverence fill,
To worship His most holy will,
All-righteous and divine.

5 So lead us, Lord, through peace or strife,
Onward to everlasting life,
To win our high reward:
So may we fight our lifelong fight,
Strong in Thine own unearthly might,
And reign with Christ our Lord.
Amen.

Frederick William Faber, 1814-63.

ST. CUTHBERT. 8.6.8.4. J. B. DYKES, 1823-76.

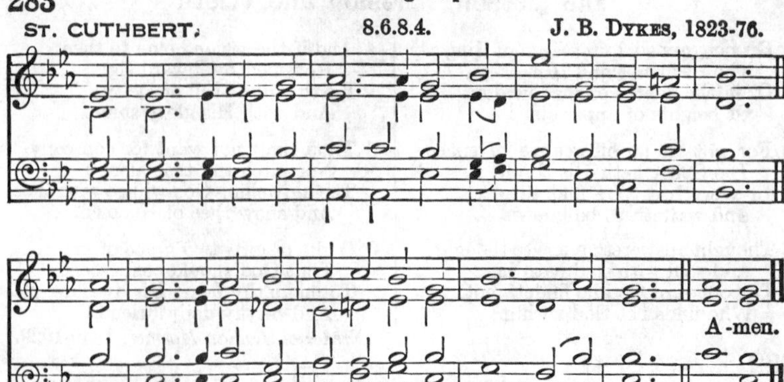

1 OUR blest Redeemer, ere He breathed
His tender last farewell,
A Guide, a Comforter bequeathed,
With us to dwell.

2 He came in semblance of a dove,
With sheltering wings outspread,
The holy balm of peace and love
On each to shed.

3 He came in tongues of living flame,
To teach, convince, subdue;
All-powerful as the wind He came,
As viewless too.

4 He comes sweet influence to impart,
A gracious, willing guest,
While He can find one humble heart
Wherein to rest.

5 And His that gentle voice we hear,
Soft as the breath of even,
That checks each fault, that calms each fear,
And speaks of heaven.

6 And every virtue we possess,
And every conquest won,
And every thought of holiness,
Are His alone.

7 Spirit of purity and grace,
Our weakness, pitying, see;
O make our hearts Thy dwelling-place,
And worthier Thee. Amen.

Harriet Auber, 1773-1862.

284

ILLSLEY. L.M. J. BISHOP, c. 1665-1737.

May also be sung to WINCHESTER NEW, No. 274.

1 FATHER, if justly still we claim
To us and ours the promise made,
To us be graciously the same,
And crown with living fire our head.

2 Our claim admit, and from above
Of holiness the Spirit shower,
Of wise discernment, humble love,
And zeal, and unity, and power.

3 The Spirit of convincing speech,
Of power demonstrative, impart,
Such as may every conscience reach,
And sound the unbelieving heart.

4 The Spirit of refining fire,
Searching the inmost of the mind,
To purge all fierce and foul desire,
And kindle life more pure and kind.

5 The Spirit of faith, in this Thy day,
To break the power of cancelled sin,
Tread down its strength, o'erturn its sway,
And still the conquest more than win.

6 The Spirit breathe of inward life,
Which in our hearts Thy laws may write;
Then grief expires, and pain, and strife:
'Tis nature all, and all delight.
Amen.

Henry More, 1614-87;
alt. by John Wesley, 1703-91.

285

CALM. L.M. J. B. DYKES, 1823-76.

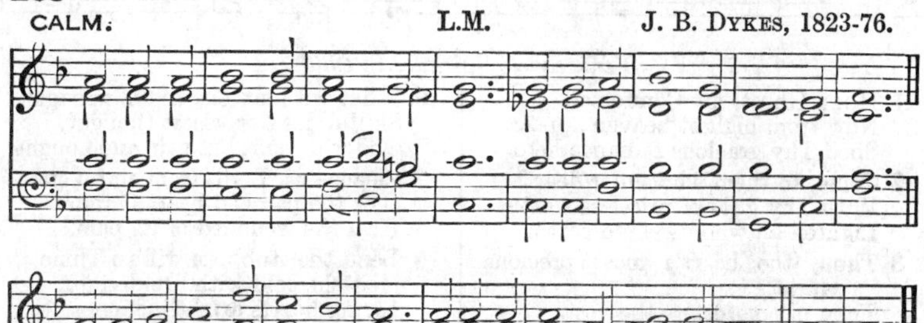

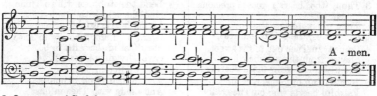

1 O BREATH of God, breathe on us now,
And move within us while we pray;
The spring of our new life art Thou,
The very light of our new day.

2 O strangely art Thou with us, Lord,
Neither in height nor depth to seek:
In nearness shall Thy voice be heard;
Spirit to spirit Thou dost speak.

3 Christ is our Advocate on high;
Thou art our Advocate within:
O plead the truth, and make reply
To every argument of sin.

4 But ah, this faithless heart of mine!
The way I know; I know my guide:
Forgive me, O my Friend divine,
That I so often turn aside.

5 Be with me when no other friend
The mystery of my heart can share;
And be Thou known, when fears transcend,
By Thy best name of Comforter.
Amen.

Alfred Henry Vine, 1845-1917.

286

NORTH COATES. 6.5.6.5. T. R. MATTHEWS, 1826-1910.

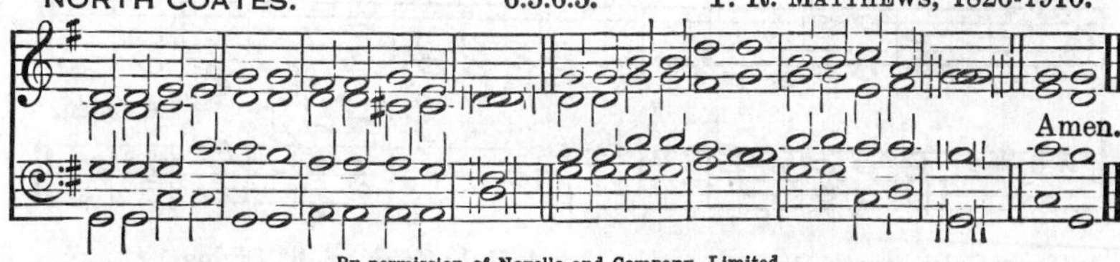

By permission of Novello and Company, Limited.

1 HOLY Spirit, hear us;
Help us while we sing;
Breathe into the music
Of the praise we bring.

2 Holy Spirit, prompt us
When we kneel to pray;
Nearer come, and teach us
What we ought to say.

3 Holy Spirit, shine Thou
On the Book we read;
Gild its holy pages
With the light we need.

4 Holy Spirit, give us
Each a lowly mind;
Make us more like Jesus,
Gentle, pure, and kind.

5 Holy Spirit, brighten
Little deeds of toil;
And our playful pastimes
Let no anger spoil.

6 Holy Spirit, help us
Daily by Thy might,
What is wrong to conquer,
And to choose the right. Amen.

William Henry Parker, 1845-1929.

287

STABAT MATER. 777. *Evening Office of the Church*, 1748.

Amen.

Veni, sancte Spiritus, Et emitte.

1 Holy Ghost, my Comforter,
Now from highest heaven appear,
Shed Thy gracious radiance here.

2 Come, to them who suffer dearth,
With Thy gifts of priceless worth,
Lighten all who dwell on earth.

3 Thou, the heart's most precious Guest,
Thou of comforters the best,
Give to us, the o'er-laden, rest.

4 Come! In Thee our toil is sweet,
Shelter from the noonday heat,
From whom sorrow flieth fleet.

5 Blessèd Sun of grace, o'er all
Faithful hearts who on Thee call
Let Thy light and solace fall.

6 What without Thy aid is wrought,
Skilful deed or wisest thought,
God will count but vain and nought.

7 Cleanse us, Lord, from sinful stain,
O'er the parchèd heart O rain!
Heal the wounded of its pain.

8 Bend the stubborn will to Thine,
Melt the cold with fire divine,
Erring hearts aright incline.

9 Grant us, Lord, who cry to Thee,
Steadfast in the faith to be,
Give Thy gift of charity.

10 May we live in holiness,
And in death find happiness,
And abide with Thee in bliss.
Amen.

Anonymous, 13th cent.;
tr. by Catherine Winkworth, 1827-78.

288

CHRISTUS. 77 77. W. Blow, c. 1826-87.

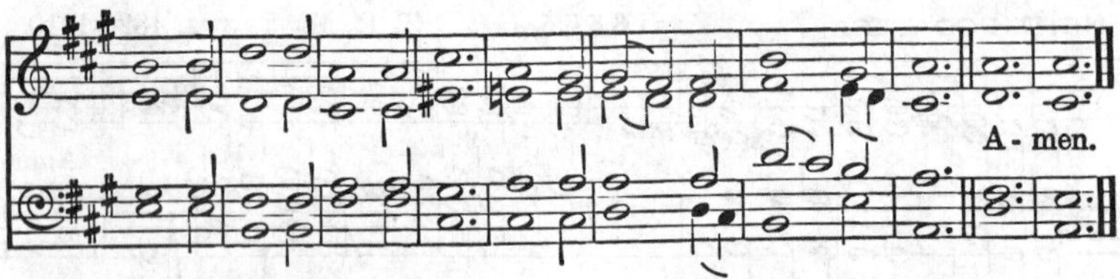

1 Holy Spirit, truth Divine,
Dawn upon this soul of mine;
Word of God, and inward light,
Wake my spirit, clear my sight.

2 Holy Spirit, love Divine,
Glow within this heart of mine,
Kindle every high desire,
Perish self in Thy pure fire.

3 Holy Spirit, power Divine,
Fill and nerve this will of mine;
By Thee may I strongly live,
Bravely bear, and nobly strive.

4 Holy Spirit, right Divine,
King within my conscience reign;
Be my Lord, and I shall be
Firmly bound, for ever free.

5 Holy Spirit, peace Divine,
Still this restless heart of mine,
Speak to calm this tossing sea,
Stayed in Thy tranquillity.

6 Holy Spirit, joy Divine,
Gladden Thou this heart of mine;
In the desert ways I'll sing:
Spring, O Well, for ever spring!
Amen.

Samuel Longfellow, 1819-92.

289

ST. AGNES. C.M. J. B. Dykes, 1823-76.

1 Spirit divine, attend our prayers
And make this house Thy home;
Descend with all Thy gracious powers;
O come, great Spirit, come!

2 Come as the light: to us reveal
Our emptiness and woe;
And lead us in those paths of life
Where all the righteous go.

3 Come as the fire, and purge our hearts
Like sacrificial flame;
Let our whole soul an offering be
To our Redeemer's name.

4 Come as the dew, and sweetly bless
This consecrated hour;
May barrenness rejoice to own
Thy fertilizing power.

5 Come as the dove, and spread Thy wings,
The wings of peaceful love;
And let Thy Church on earth become
Blest as the Church above.

6 Come as the wind, with rushing sound
And pentecostal grace,
That all of woman born may see
The glory of Thy face.

7 Spirit divine, attend our prayers;
Make a lost world Thy home;
Descend with all Thy gracious powers;
O come, great Spirit, come. Amen.

Andrew Reed, 1787-1862.

290

CHARITY. 7 7 7.5. J. Stainer, 1840-1901.

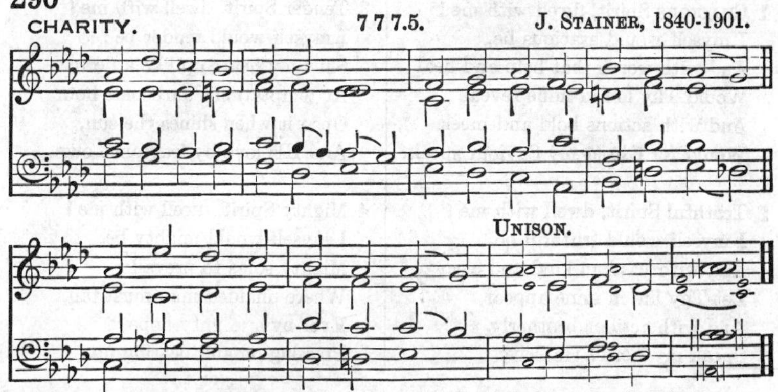

1 Gracious Spirit, Holy Ghost,
Taught by Thee, we covet most,
Of Thy gifts at Pentecost,
Holy, heavenly love.

2 Faith that mountains could remove,
Tongues of earth or heaven above,
Knowledge, all things, empty prove
Without heavenly love.

3 Though I as a martyr bleed,
Give my goods the poor to feed,
All is vain if love I need;
Therefore give me love.

4 Love is kind, and suffers long,
Love is meek, and thinks no wrong,
Love than death itself more strong:
Therefore give us love.

5 Prophecy will fade away,
Melting in the light of day;
Love will ever with us stay:
Therefore give us love.

6 Faith, and hope, and love we see,
Joining hand in hand, agree;
But the greatest of the three,
And the best, is love.

Christopher Wordsworth, 1807-85.

291

CASSEL. 7 7.7 7.7 7. THOMMEN'S *Gesangbuch*, 1745.

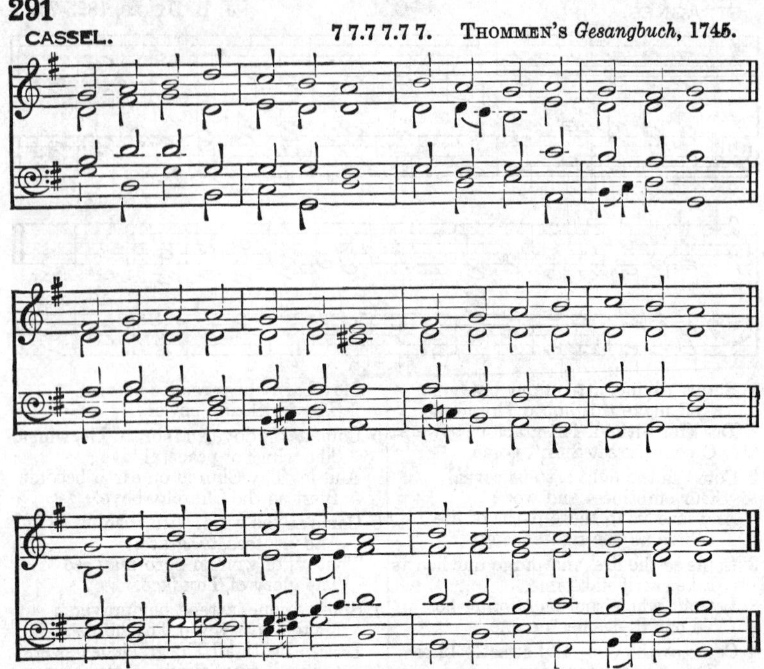

May also be sung to PARACLETE, A.T. No. 20.

1 GRACIOUS Spirit, dwell with me!
I myself would gracious be,
And with words that help and heal
Would Thy life in mine reveal,
And with actions bold and meek
Would for Christ my Saviour speak.

2 Truthful Spirit, dwell with me!
I myself would truthful be,
And with wisdom kind and clear
Let Thy life in mine appear,
And with actions brotherly
Speak my Lord's sincerity.

3 Tender Spirit, dwell with me!
I myself would tender be:
Shut my heart up like a flower
At temptation's darksome hour;
Open it when shines the sun,
And His love by fragrance own.

4 Mighty Spirit, dwell with me!
I myself would mighty be,
Mighty so as to prevail
Where unaided man must fail,
Ever by a mighty hope
Pressing on and bearing up.

5 Holy Spirit, dwell with me!
I myself would holy be;
Separate from sin, I would
Choose and cherish all things good,
And, whatever I can be,
Give to Him who gave me Thee.

Thomas Toke Lynch, 1818-71.

292

MANCHESTER. C.M. ROBERT WAINWRIGHT, 1748-82.

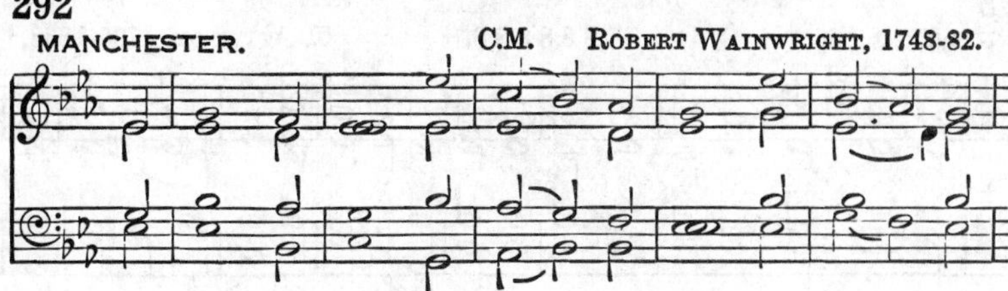

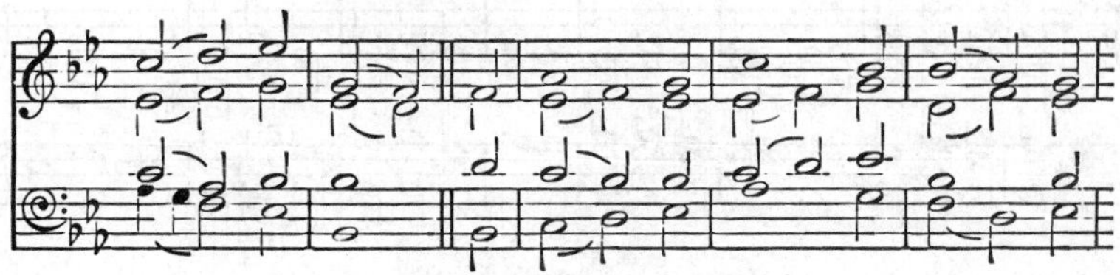

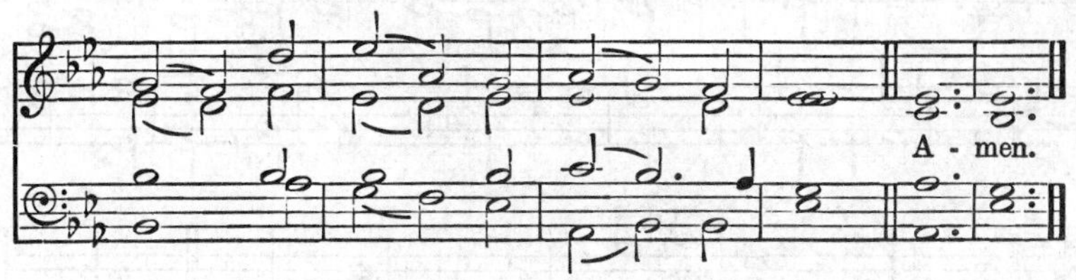

1 COME, Holy Spirit, heavenly Dove,
With all Thy quickening powers;
Kindle a flame of sacred love
In these cold hearts of ours.

2 In vain we tune our formal songs,
In vain we strive to rise;
Hosannas languish on our tongues
And our devotion dies.

3 And shall we then for ever live
At this poor dying rate?
Our love so faint, so cold to Thee,
And Thine to us so great!

4 Come, Holy Spirit, heavenly Dove,
With all Thy quickening powers;
Come, shed abroad the Saviour's love,
And that shall kindle ours. Amen

Isaac Watts, 1674-1748.

293

ATTWOOD. 8 8.8 8.8 8. T. ATTWOOD, 1765-1838.

Veni, Creator Spiritus.

1 CREATOR Spirit; by whose aid
The world's foundations first were laid;
Come, visit every waiting mind,
Come, pour Thy joys on human kind;
From sin and sorrow set us free,
And make Thy temples worthy Thee.

2 O Source of uncreated heat,
The Father's promised Paraclete,
Thrice holy Fount, thrice holy Fire,
Our hearts with heavenly love inspire;
Come, and Thy sacred unction bring
To sanctify us while we sing.

3 Plenteous of grace, descend from high,
Rich in Thy sevenfold energy;
Thou strength of His almighty hand
Whose power does heaven and earth command,
Refine and purge our earthly parts,
And stamp Thine image on our hearts.

4 Create all new; our wills control,
Subdue the rebel in our soul;
Make us eternal truths receive,
And practise all that we believe;
Give us Thyself, that we may see
The Father and the Son by Thee.

5 Immortal honour, endless fame,
Attend the almighty Father's name;
The Saviour Son be glorified,
Who for lost man's redemption died;
And equal adoration be,
Eternal Comforter, to Thee. Amen.

Anonymous, c. 10th cent.,
tr. by John Dryden, 1631-1700.

294

SION. 8.8.8.8. D. B. Milgrove, c. 1731-1810.

1 Come, holy celestial Dove,
To visit a sorrowful breast,
My burden of guilt to remove,
And bring me assurance and rest!
Thou only hast power to relieve
A sinner o'erwhelmed with his load,
The sense of acceptance to give,
And sprinkle his heart with the blood.

2 With me if of old Thou hast strove,
And strangely withheld from my sin,
And tried, by the lure of Thy love,
My worthless affections to win;
The work of Thy mercy revive,
Thy uttermost mercy exert,
And kindly continue to strive,
And hold, till I yield Thee my heart.

3 Thy call if I ever have known,
And sighed from myself to get free,
And groaned the unspeakable groan,
And longed to be happy in Thee;
Fulfil the imperfect desire,
Thy peace to my conscience reveal,
The sense of Thy favour inspire,
And give me my pardon to feel.

4 If when I had put Thee to grief,
And madly to folly returned,
Thy pity hath been my relief,
And lifted me up as I mourned;
Most pitiful Spirit of grace,
Relieve me again, and restore,
My spirit in holiness raise,
To fall and to suffer no more.
Amen.

Charles Wesley, 1707-88.

295

JOSEPH. 777.6. SCHEFFLER'S *Heilige Seelenlust*, 1657.

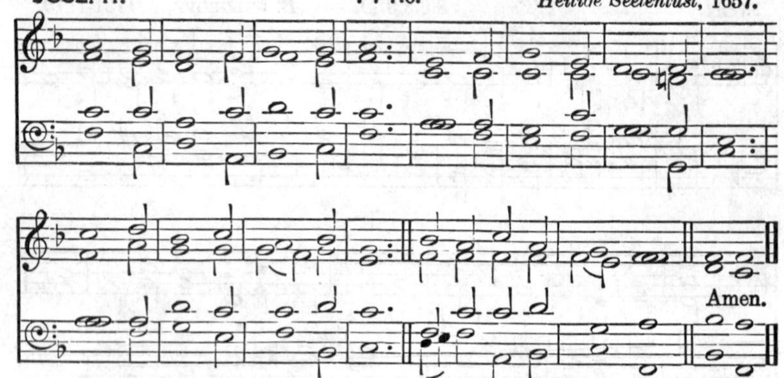

1 Spirit blest, who art adored
With the Father and the Word
One eternal God and Lord:
Hear us, Holy Spirit.

2 Holy Spirit, heavenly Dove,
Dew descending from above,
Breath of life and fire of love:
Hear us, Holy Spirit.

3 Spirit, guiding us aright,
Spirit, making darkness light,
Spirit of resistless might:
Hear us, Holy Spirit.

4 Thou whom Jesus from His throne
Gave to cheer and help His own,
That they might not be alone:
Hear us, Holy Spirit.

5 All our evil passions kill;
Bend aright our stubborn will;
Though we grieve Thee, patient [still:
Hear us, Holy Spirit.

6 Come, to raise us when we fall;
And, when snares our souls enthral,
Lead us back with gentle call:
Hear us, Holy Spirit.

7 Come, to strengthen all the weak;
Give Thy courage to the meek;
Teach our faltering tongues to [speak:
Hear us, Holy Spirit.

8 Come, to aid the souls who yearn
More of truth divine to learn,
And with deeper love to burn:
Hear us, Holy Spirit.

9 Keep us in the narrow way;
Warn us when we go astray;
Plead within us when we pray:
Hear us, Holy Spirit.

10 Holy, loving, as Thou art,
All Thy sevenfold gifts impart;
Nevermore from us depart:
Hear us, Holy Spirit. Amen.

Thomas Benson Pollock, 1836-96;
Richard Frederick Littledale (*v.* 2), 1833-90;

296

HEINLEIN. 7 7.7 7. M. HERBST, *c.* 1654-81.

1 Holy Spirit, pity me,
Pierced with grief for grieving Thee;
Present, though I mourn apart,
Listen to a wailing heart.

2 Sins unnumbered I confess,
Of exceeding sinfulness;
Sins against Thyself alone,
Only to Omniscience known:

3 Deafness to Thy whispered calls,
Rashness midst remembered falls,
Transient fears beneath the rod,
Treacherous trifling with my God;

4 Tasting that the Lord is good,
Pining then for poisoned food;
At the fountains of the skies
Craving creaturely supplies;

5 Worldly cares at worship-time;
Grovelling aims in works sublime;
Pride, when God is passing by;
Sloth, when souls in darkness die;

6 Chilled devotions, changed desires,
Quenched corruption's earlier fires:
Sins like these my heart deceive,
Thee, who only know'st them, grieve.

7 O how lightly have I slept
With Thy daily wrongs unwept,
Sought Thy chidings to defer,
Shunned the wounded Comforter:

8 Woke to holy labours fresh
With the plague-spot in my flesh;
Angel seemed to human sight,
Stood a leper in Thy light.

9 Still Thy comforts do not fail,
Still Thy healing aids avail;
Patient inmate of my breast,
Thou art grieved, yet I am blest.

10 O be merciful to me,
Now in bitterness for Thee.
Father, pardon through Thy Son
Sins against Thy Spirit done.
Amen.

William Maclardie Bunting, 1805-66.

297

ANGELUS. 7 7 7.5. R. Jackson, 1842-1914.

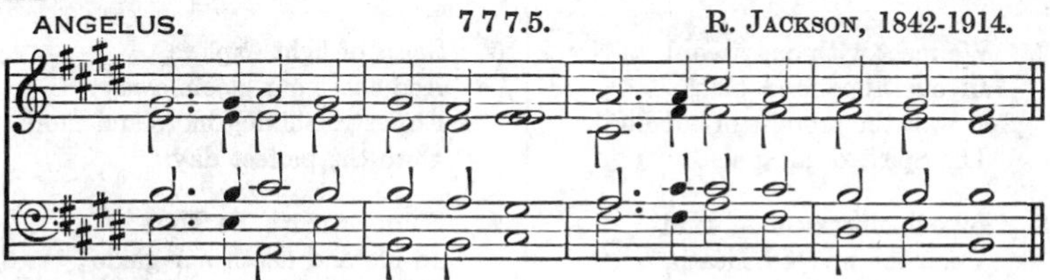

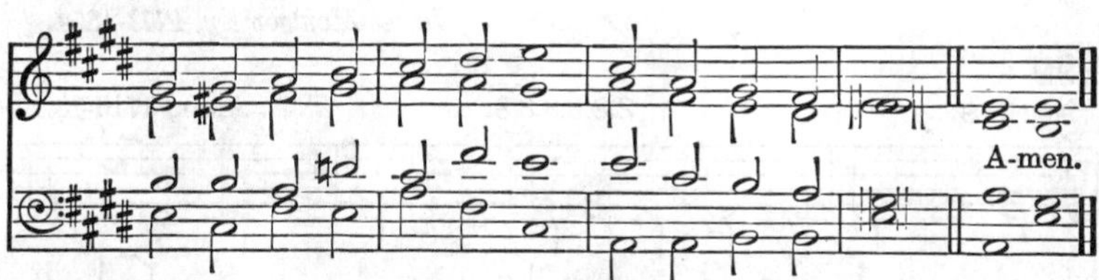

1 Come to our poor nature's night
With Thy blessèd inward light,
Holy Ghost the Infinite,
Comforter divine.

2 We are sinful—cleanse us, Lord;
Sick and faint—Thy strength afford;
Lost, until by Thee restored,
Comforter divine.

3 Like the dew Thy peace distil;
Guide, subdue our wayward will,
Things of Christ unfolding still,
Comforter divine.

4 Gentle, awful, holy Guest,
Make Thy temple in each breast;
There Thy presence be confessed,
Comforter divine.

5 With us, for us, intercede,
And, with voiceless groanings, plead
Our unutterable need,
Comforter divine.

6 In us Abba, Father! cry,
Earnest of the bliss on high,
Seal of immortality,
Comforter divine. Amen.

George Rawson, 1807-89.

298

BOWDEN. S.M. S. S. Wesley, 1810-76.

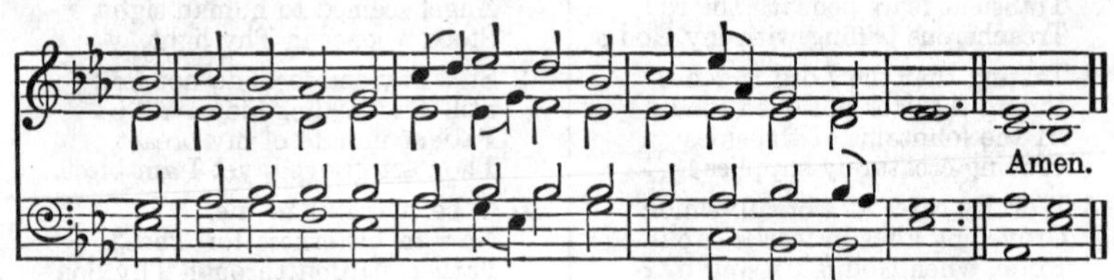

1 Lord God the Holy Ghost,
In this accepted hour,
As on the day of Pentecost,
Descend in all Thy power.

2 We meet with one accord
In our appointed place,
And wait the promise of our Lord,
The Spirit of all grace.

3 Like mighty rushing wind
Upon the waves beneath,
Move with one impulse every mind,
One soul, one feeling breathe.

4 The young, the old, inspire
With wisdom from above;
And give us hearts and tongues of
To pray and praise and love. [fire,

5 Spirit of light explore,
And chase our gloom away—
With lustre shining more and more,
Unto the perfect day.

6 Spirit of truth, be Thou
In life and death our guide;
O Spirit of adoption, now
May we be sanctified. Amen.

James Montgomery, 1771-1854.

299

ARNE'S. 8.8.8.8.8.8 8. T. A. Arne, 1710-78.

1 Come, Holy Ghost, all-quickening fire,
Come, and in me delight to rest;
Drawn by the lure of strong desire,
O come and consecrate my breast;
The temple of my soul prepare,
And fix Thy sacred presence there.

2 Eager for Thee I ask and pant;
So strong, the principle divine
Carries me out, with sweet constraint,
Till all my hallowed soul is Thine;
Plunged in the Godhead's deepest sea,
And lost in Thine immensity.

3 My peace, my life, my comfort Thou,
My treasure and my all Thou art;
True witness of my sonship, now
Engraving pardon on my heart,
Seal of my sins in Christ forgiven,
Earnest of love, and pledge of heaven.

4 Come then, my God, mark out Thine heir,
Of heaven a larger earnest give;
With clearer light Thy witness bear,
More sensibly within me live;
Let all my powers Thine entrance feel,
And deeper stamp Thyself the seal.
Amen.

Charles Wesley, 1707-88.

300

ST. BEUNO. S.M. J. C. Bridge, 1853-1929.

1 Breathe on me, Breath of God;
Fill me with life anew,
That I may love what Thou dost love,
And do what Thou wouldst do.

2 Breathe on me, Breath of God,
Until my heart is pure,
Until with Thee I will one will,
To do and to endure.

3 Breathe on me, Breath of God,
Till I am wholly Thine,
Until this earthly part of me
Glows with Thy fire divine.

4 Breathe on me, Breath of God;
So shall I never die,
But live with Thee the perfect life
Of Thine eternity. Amen.

Edwin Hatch, 1835-89.

301

SIMEON. L.M. S. STANLEY, 1767-1822.

1 On all the earth Thy Spirit shower;
The earth in righteousness renew;
Thy kingdom come, and hell's o'erpower,
And to Thy sceptre all subdue.

2 Like mighty winds, or torrents fierce,
Let it opposers all o'errun;
And every law of sin reverse,
That faith and love may make all one.

3 Yea, let Thy Spirit in every place
Its richer energy declare;
While lovely tempers, fruits of grace,
The kingdom of Thy Christ prepare.

4 Grant this, O holy God and true!
The ancient seers Thou didst inspire;
To us perform the promise due;
Descend, and crown us now with fire. Amen.

Henry More, 1614-87;
alt. by John Wesley, 1703-91.

Also:

33 Infinite God, to Thee
305 Come, Holy Ghost, our hearts inspire
377 How can a sinner know
553 Come, Holy Ghost, all-quickening fire
554 O come and dwell
730 Father of everlasting grace
765 Come, Thou everlasting Spirit
779 Come, Holy Ghost, our souls inspire

302

TILTEY ABBEY. C.M. A. H. Brown, 1830-1926.

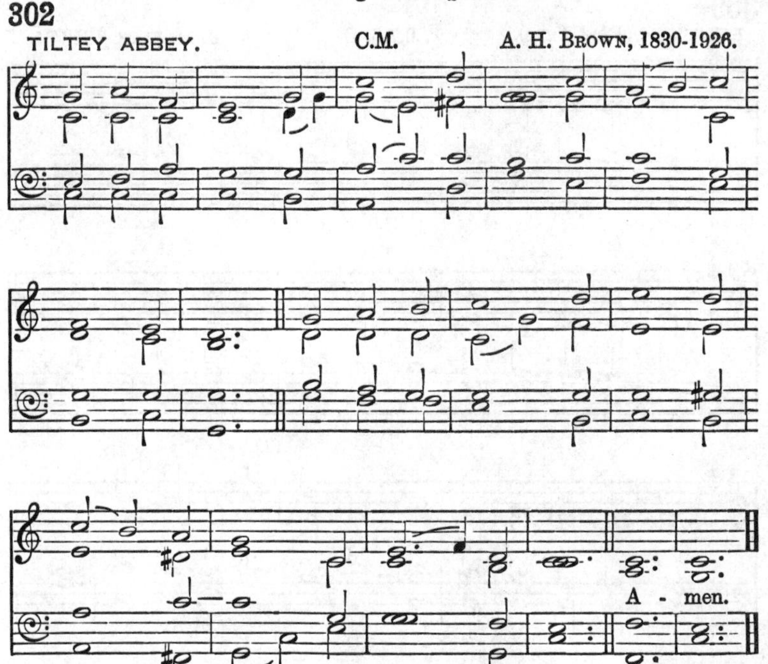

1 Father of mercies, in Thy word
What endless glory shines!
For ever be Thy name adored
For these celestial lines.

2 Here may the wretched sons of want
Exhaustless riches find;
Riches, above what earth can grant,
And lasting as the mind.

3 Here the fair tree of knowledge grows,
And yields a free repast;
Sublimer sweets than nature knows
Invite the longing taste.

4 Here the Redeemer's welcome voice
Spreads heavenly peace around;
And life and everlasting joys
Attend the blissful sound.

5 Divine instructor, gracious Lord,
Be Thou for ever near;
Teach me to love Thy sacred word,
And view my Saviour there. Amen.

Anne Steele, 1716-78.

303

BENTLEY (*First Tune*). 7.6.7.6. D. J. HULLAH, 1812-84.

NYLAND (*Second Tune*). 7.6.7.6. D. Finnish Hymn Melody.

1 O Word of God incarnate,
O Wisdom from on high,
O Truth unchanged, unchanging,
O Light of our dark sky,
We praise Thee for the radiance
That from the hallowed page,
A lantern to our footsteps,
Shines on from age to age.

2 The Church from her dear Master
Received the gift divine,
And still that light she lifteth,
O'er all the earth to shine;
It is the golden casket
Where gems of truth are stored;
It is the heaven-drawn picture
Of Christ, the living Word;

3 It floateth like a banner
Before God's host unfurled;
It shineth like a beacon
Above the darkling world;
It is the chart and compass
That, o'er life's surging sea,
'Mid mists, and rocks, and quicksands,
Still guides, O Christ, to Thee.

4 O make Thy Church, dear Saviour,
A lamp of burnished gold,
To bear before the nations
Thy true light, as of old;
O teach Thy wandering pilgrims
By this their path to trace,
Till, clouds and darkness ended,
They see Thee face to face.

William Walsham How, 1823-97.

304

TALLIS' ORDINAL. C.M. T. Tallis, c. 1510-85.

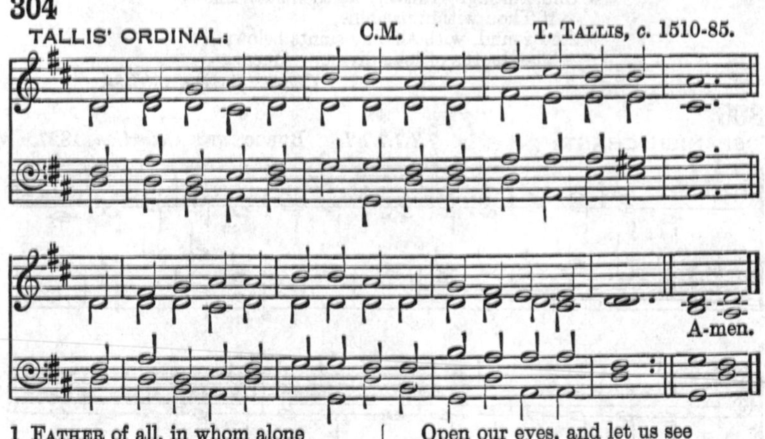

1 Father of all, in whom alone
We live, and move, and breathe,
One bright celestial ray dart down,
And cheer Thy sons beneath.

2 While in Thy word we search for Thee—
We search with trembling awe—
Open our eyes, and let us see
The wonders of Thy law.

3 Now let our darkness comprehend
The light that shines so clear;
Now the revealing Spirit send,
And give us ears to hear. Amen.

Charles Wesley, 1707-88.

305

RICHMOND. C.M. T. HAWEIS, 1734-1820.

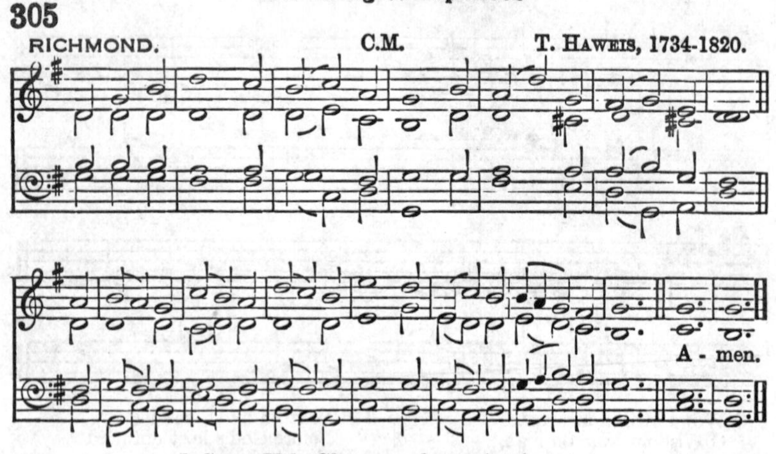

1 COME, Holy Ghost, our hearts inspire,
Let us Thine influence prove,
Source of the old prophetic fire,
Fountain of light and love.

2 Come, Holy Ghost, for moved by Thee
The prophets wrote and spoke;
Unlock the truth, Thyself the key,
Unseal the sacred Book.

3 Expand Thy wings, celestial Dove,
Brood o'er our nature's night;
On our disordered spirits move,
And let there now be light.

4 God, through Himself, we then shall know,
If Thou within us shine,
And sound, with all Thy saints below,
The depths of love divine. Amen.

Charles Wesley, 1707-88.

306

SPANISH CHANT. 7.7.7.7.7.7. BURGOYNE'S *Collection*, 1827.

1 Come, divine Interpreter,
Bring us eyes Thy Book to read,
Ears the mystic words to hear,
Words which did from Thee proceed,
Words that endless bliss impart,
Kept in an obedient heart.

2 All who read, or hear, are blessed,
If Thy plain commands we do;
Of Thy kingdom here possessed,
Thee we shall in glory view;
When Thou com'st on earth to abide,
Reign triumphant at Thy side.

Charles Wesley, 1707-88.

307

ST. JAMES. C.M. R. Courteville, *d.* 1772

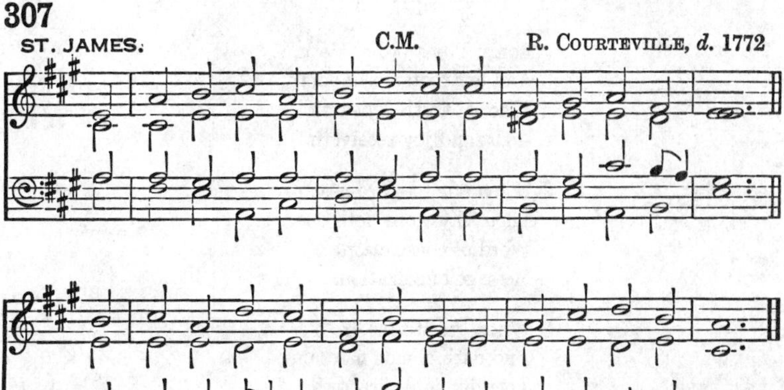

1 The Spirit breathes upon the word,
And brings the truth to sight;
Precepts and promises afford
A sanctifying light.

2 A glory gilds the sacred page,
Majestic, like the sun:
It gives a light to every age;
It gives, but borrows none.

3 The hand that gave it still supplies
The gracious light and heat;
His truths upon the nations rise;
They rise, but never set.

4 Let everlasting thanks be Thine
For such a bright display
As makes a world of darkness shine
With beams of heavenly day.

5 My soul rejoices to pursue
The steps of Him I love,
Till glory breaks upon my view
In brighter worlds above.

William Cowper, 1731-1800.

308

RAVENSHAW. 6 6.6 6. WEISSE'S *Gesangbuch*, 1531.

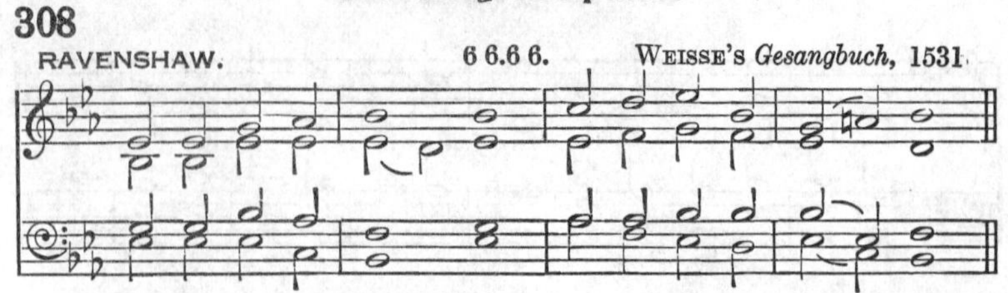

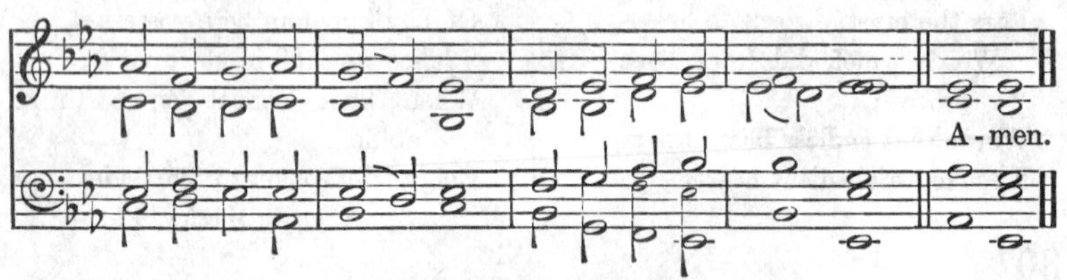

1 LORD, Thy word abideth,
And our footsteps guideth,
Who its truth believeth
Light and joy receiveth.

2 When our foes are near us,
Then Thy word doth cheer us,
Word of consolation,
Message of salvation.

3 When the storms are o'er us,
And dark clouds before us,
Then its light directeth,
And our way protecteth.

4 Who can tell the pleasure,
Who recount the treasure,
By Thy word imparted
To the simple-hearted ?

5 Word of mercy, giving
Succour to the living;
Word of life, supplying
Comfort to the dying!

6 O that we, discerning
Its most holy learning,
Lord, may love and fear Thee,
Evermore be near Thee! Amen.

Henry Williams Baker, 1821-77.

BETHSAIDA. 6.4.6.4. D. ROSALIND F. STAINER, 1884-

1 BREAK Thou the bread of life,
O Lord, to me,
As Thou didst break the loaves
Beside the sea:
Beyond the sacred page
I seek Thee, Lord;
My spirit pants for Thee,
O living Word!

2 Thou art the Bread of Life,
O Lord, to me,
Thy holy word the truth
That saveth me:
Give me to eat and live
With Thee above;
Teach me to love Thy truth,
For Thou art love.

3 O send Thy Spirit, Lord,
Now unto me,
That He may touch my eyes,
And make me see:
Show me the truth concealed
Within Thy word,
And in Thy Book revealed
I see the Lord.

Mary Artemisia Lathbury [*v.* 1], 1841-1913;
Alexander Groves [*vv.* 2, 3], 1843-1909.

310

COMPANION. 8.8.8.8.8.8. R. S. Newman, 1850-1927.

May also be sung to Marienlyst, No. 608.

1 When quiet in my house I sit,
  Thy Book be my companion still,
My joy Thy sayings to repeat,
  Talk o'er the records of Thy will,
And search the oracles divine,
Till every heartfelt word be mine.

2 O may the gracious words divine
  Subject of all my converse be!
So will the Lord His follower join,
  And walk and talk Himself with me;
So shall my heart His presence prove,
And burn with everlasting love.

3 Oft as I lay me down to rest,
  O may the reconciling word
Sweetly compose my weary breast!
  While, on the bosom of my Lord,
I sink in blissful dreams away,
And visions of eternal day.

4 Rising to sing my Saviour's praise,
  Thee may I publish all day long;
And let Thy precious word of grace
  Flow from my heart, and fill my tongue;
Fill all my life with purest love,
And join me to the Church above. Amen.

Charles Wesley, 1707-88.

Also:

782 Shine Thou upon us, Lord

The Gospel Call

311

MONTGOMERY. 10 10. 11 11. T. Call's *Tunes*, 1762.

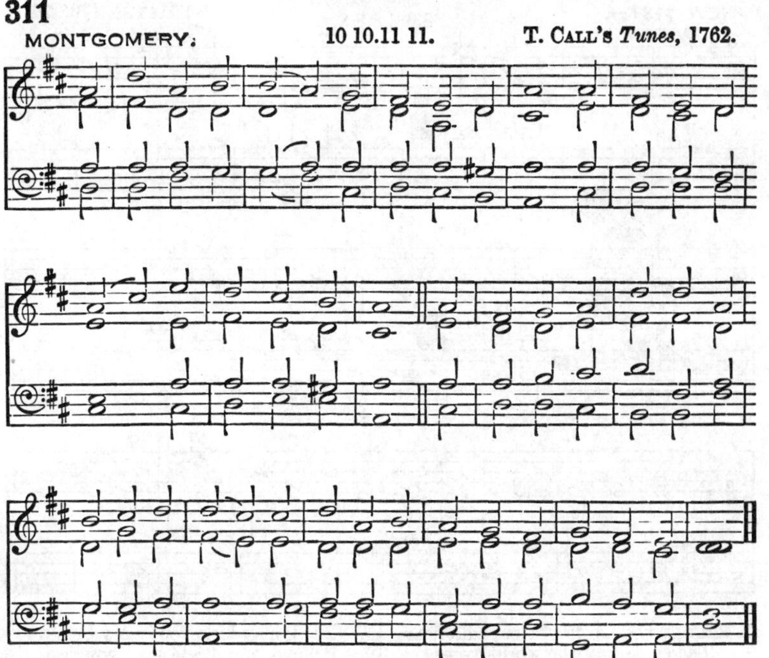

1 Thy faithfulness, Lord, each moment we find,
So true to Thy word, so loving and kind;
Thy mercy so tender to all the lost race,
The vilest offender may turn and find grace.

2 O let me commend my Saviour to you,
I set to my seal that Jesus is true:
Ye all may find favour who come at His call;
O come to my Saviour! His grace is for all.

3 To save what was lost, from heaven He came:
Come, sinners, and trust in Jesus's name;
He offers you pardon, He bids you be free:
If sin be your burden, O come unto Me!

4 Then let us submit His grace to receive,
Fall down at His feet and gladly believe:
We all are forgiven for Jesus's sake;
Our title to heaven His merits we take.

Charles Wesley, 1707-88.

312 The Gospel Call

NEW 113TH. 8.8.8.8.8 8. W. HAYES, 1706-77.

1 BEHOLD the Lamb of God, who bears
The sins of all the world away!
A servant's form He meekly wears,
He sojourns in a house of clay;
His glory is no longer seen,
But God with God is man with men.

2 See where the God incarnate stands'
And calls His wandering creatures home!
He all day long spreads out His hands,
Come, weary souls, to Jesus come!
Ye all may hide you in My breast;
Believe, and I will give you rest.

3 Sinners, believe the gospel word,
Jesus is come your souls to save!
Jesus is come, your common Lord;
Pardon ye all through Him may have,
May now be saved, whoever will;
This Man receiveth sinners still.

Charles Wesley, 1707-88.

313

11 11.11 11. and refrain.

TO GOD BE THE GLORY. W. H. DOANE, 1832-1916.

The Gospel Call

1 To God be the glory! great things He hath done!
So loved He the world that He gave us His Son;
Who yielded His life an atonement for sin,
And opened the Life gate that all may go in.

Praise the Lord! praise the Lord! Let the earth hear His voice!
Praise the Lord! praise the Lord! Let the people rejoice!
O come to the Father, through Jesus the Son:
And give Him the glory! great things He hath done!

2 O perfect redemption, the purchase of blood!
To every believer the promise of God;
The vilest offender who truly believes,
That moment from Jesus a pardon receives.

3 Great things He hath taught us, great things He hath done,
And great our rejoicing through Jesus the Son;
But purer, and higher, and greater will be
Our wonder, our rapture, when Jesus we see.

Frances Jane van Alstyne, 1820-1915.

WONDERFUL LOVE. (1) 10.4.10.7.4 10. F. L. Wiseman, 1858-1944

1 Come let us sing of a wonderful love,
Tender and true;
Out of the heart of the Father above,
Streaming to me and to you:
Wonderful love
Dwells in the heart of the Father above.

2 Jesus, the Saviour, this gospel to tell,
Joyfully came;
Came with the helpless and hopeless to dwell,
Sharing their sorrow and shame;
Seeking the lost,
Saving, redeeming at measureless cost.

3 Jesus is seeking the wanderers yet;
Why do they roam?
Love only waits to forgive and forget;
Home! weary wanderer, home!
Wonderful love
Dwells in the heart of the Father above.

4 Come to my heart, O Thou wonderful love,
Come and abide,
Lifting my life till it rises above
Envy and falsehood and pride;
Seeking to be
Lowly and humble, a learner of Thee.

Robert Walmsley, 1831-1905.

The Gospel Call

315

ST. RAPHAEL. 8.7.8.7.4.7. E. J. Hopkins, 1818-1901.

1 Hark! the gospel news is sounding:
   Christ hath suffered on the tree;
Streams of mercy are abounding;
   Grace for all is rich and free.
      Now, poor sinner,
   Look to Him who died for thee.

2 O escape to yonder mountain!
   Now begin to watch and pray;
Christ invites you to the fountain,
   Come, and wash your sins away:
      Do not tarry,
   Come to Jesus while you may.

3 Grace is flowing like a river;
   Millions there have been supplied;
Still it flows as fresh as ever
   From the Saviour's wounded side:
      None need perish;
   All may live, for Christ hath died.

4 Christ alone shall be our portion;
   Soon we hope to meet above,
Then we'll bathe in the full ocean
   Of the great Redeemer's love;
      All His fullness,
   We shall then for ever prove.

William Sanders, b. 1799-

316

JESUS SAVES. 7.3.7.3.7.7.7.3.

W. J. KIRKPATRICK, 1838-1921.

1 We have heard a joyful sound:
Jesus saves!
Spread the gladness all around:
Jesus saves!
Bear the news to every land,
Climb the steeps and cross the waves;
Onward! 'tis our Lord's command:
Jesus saves!

2 Sing above the battle's strife:
Jesus saves!
By His death and endless life,
Jesus saves!
Sing it softly through the gloom,
When the heart for mercy craves;
Sing in triumph o'er the tomb:
Jesus saves!

3 Give the winds a mighty voice:
Jesus saves!
Let the nations now rejoice:
Jesus saves!
Shout salvation full and free
To every strand that ocean laves—
This our song of victory:
Jesus saves!

Priscilla Jane Owens, 1829-99.

317

WHOSOEVER WILL. 10 11 11.7. and refrain. P. BLISS, 1838-76.

1 WHOSOEVER heareth! Shout, shout the sound;
Send the blessed tidings all the world around;
Spread the joyful news wherever man is found:
Whosoever will may come.
Whosoever will! Whosoever will!
Send the proclamation over vale and hill;
'Tis the loving Father calls the wanderer home;
Whosoever will may come.

2 Whosoever cometh need not delay;
Now the door is open, enter while you may;
Jesus is the true and only living Way:
Whosoever will may come.

3 Whosoever will, the promise is secure;
Whosoever will, for ever shall endure;
Whosoever will, 'tis life for evermore;
Whosoever will may come.

Philipp Bliss, 1838-76.

318

CROSS OF JESUS (*First Tune*). 8.7.8.7. J. STAINER, 1840-1901.

By permission of Novello and Company, Limited.

OMNI DIE (*Second Tune*). 8.7.8.7. CORNER'S *Gesangbuch*, 1631.

1 SOULS of men, why will ye scatter
Like a crowd of frightened sheep?
Foolish hearts, why will ye wander
From a love so true and deep?

2 Was there ever kindest shepherd
Half so gentle, half so sweet,
As the Saviour who would have us
Come and gather round His feet?

3 There's a wideness in God's mercy
Like the wideness of the sea;
There's a kindness in His justice
Which is more than liberty.

4 There is welcome for the sinner,
And more graces for the good;
There is mercy with the Saviour;
There is healing in His blood.

5 There is plentiful redemption
In the blood that has been shed;
There is joy for all the members
In the sorrows of the Head.

6 For the love of God is broader
Than the measures of man's mind,
And the heart of the Eternal
Is most wonderfully kind.

7 If our love were but more simple,
We should take Him at His word,
And our lives would be all sunshine
In the sweetness of our Lord.

Frederick William Faber, 1814-63.

The Gospel Call

319

WELLSPRING. 7.7.7.7.7.7. D. S. Bortniansky, 1752-1825.

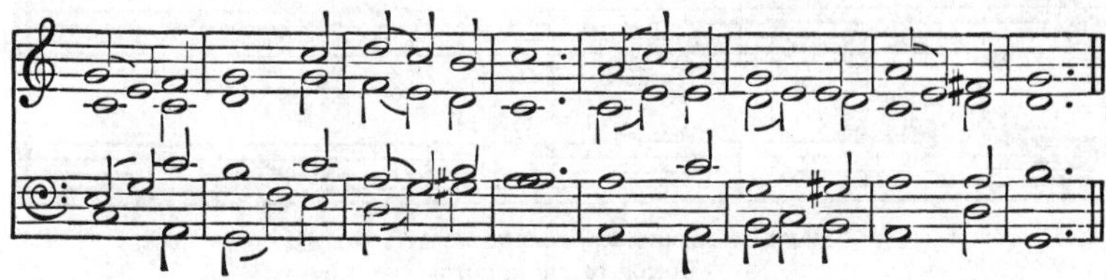

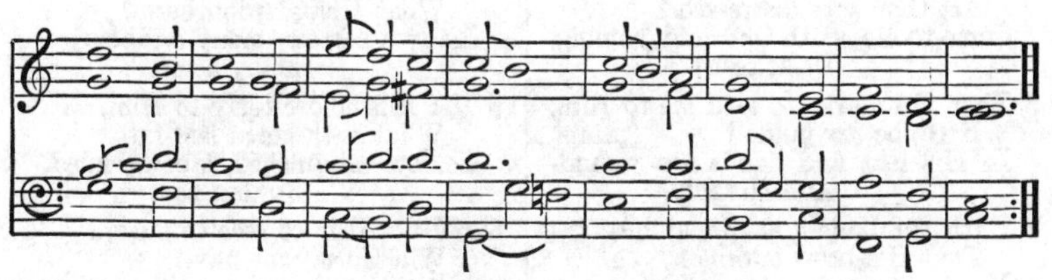

1 Weary souls that wander wide
  From the central point of bliss,
Turn to Jesus crucified,
  Fly to those dear wounds of His:
Sink into the cleansing flood;
Rise into the life of God.

2 Find in Christ the way of peace,
  Peace unspeakable, unknown;
By His pain He gives you ease,
  Life by His expiring groan:
Rise, exalted by His fall;
Find in Christ your all in all.

3 O believe the record true:
  God to you His Son hath given.
Ye may now be happy too,
  Find on earth the life of heaven,
Live the life of heaven above,
All the life of glorious love.

Charles Wesley, 1707-88.

STEPHANOS. 8.5.8.3. H. W. Baker, 1821-77.

May also be sung to Bullinger, A.T. No. 21.

Κόπον τε καὶ κάματον.

1 Art thou weary, art thou languid,
Art thou sore distressed?
Come to Me, saith One, and, coming,
Be at rest!

2 Hath He marks to lead me to Him,
If He be my guide? [prints,
In His feet and hands are wound-
And His side.

3 Hath He diadem as Monarch
That His brow adorns?
Yea, a crown in very surety,
But of thorns!

4 If I find Him, if I follow,
What His guerdon here?
Many a sorrow, many a labour,
Many a tear.

5 If I still hold closely to Him,
What hath He at last?
Sorrow vanquished, labour ended,
Jordan past.

6 If I ask Him to receive me,
Will He say me nay?
Not till earth and not till heaven
Pass away.

7 Finding, following, keeping, struggling
Is He sure to bless?
Saints, apostles, prophets, martyrs,
Answer: Yes!

St. Stephen the Sabaite, 725-794;
free tr. by John Mason Neale, 1818-66.

EVEN ME. (*First Tune*). 8.7.8.7. and refrain. W. B. Bradbury, 1816-68.

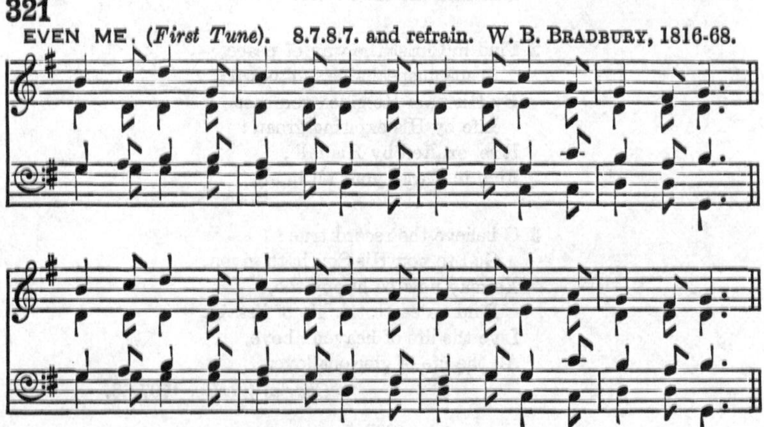

REFRAIN.

E - ven me, e - ven me, Let some drops now fall on me.

EVEN ME. (*Second Tune*). 8.7.8.7. and refrain. M. HORNABROOK, 1850-1930.

REFRAIN.

E - ven me, e - ven me, e - - - ven me!

1 LORD, I hear of showers of blessing
Thou art scattering, full and free;
Showers, the thirsty land refreshing;
Let some drops now fall on me,
Even me.

2 Pass me not, O gracious Father,
Sinful though my heart may be;
Thou might'st leave me, but the rather
Let Thy mercy light on me.

3 Pass me not, O tender Saviour;
Let me love and cling to Thee;
I am longing for Thy favour;
Whilst Thou'rt calling, O call me.

4 Pass me not, O mighty Spirit,
Thou canst make the blind to see;
Witness of the Saviour's merit,
Speak the word of power to me.

5 Love of God so pure and changeless,
Blood of Christ so rich, so free,
Grace of God so strong and boundless,
Magnify it all in me.

Elizabeth Codner, 1824-1919.

CHRIST RECEIVETH.
7.7.7.7. and refrain.
J. McGranahan, 1840-1907.
Refrain.
Sing it o'er . . . . and o'er a - gain:
Sing it o'er a - gain, sing it o'er a - gain:
Christ re - ceiv - - - eth sin - ful men; . . . . .
Christ re - ceiv - eth sin - ful men, Christ re - ceiv - eth sin - ful men;
Make the mes - - - sage clear and plain: . . . Christ re - ceiv - eth sin - ful . . men. . .
Make the mes - sage plain, Make the message plain: Christ re - ceiv - eth sin - ful men. . .

The Gospel Call

Jesus nimmt die Sünder an.

1 SINNERS Jesus will receive;
Sound His word of grace to all
Who the heavenly pathway leave,
All who linger, all who fall.

Sing it o'er and o'er again:
Christ receiveth sinful men;
Make the message clear and plain:
Christ receiveth sinful men.

2 Come, and He will give you rest;
Trust Him, for His word is plain;
He will take the sinfulest:
Christ receiveth sinful men.

3 Now my heart condemns me not,
Pure before the law I stand;
He who cleansed me from all spot
Satisfied its last demand.

4 Christ receiveth sinful men,
Even me with all my sin;
Purged from every spot and stain,
Heaven with Him I enter in.

Erdmann Neumeister, 1671-1756;
tr. by Emma Frances Bevan, 1827-1909.

323

FULDA. L.M. GARDINER'S *Sacred Melodies*, 1812.

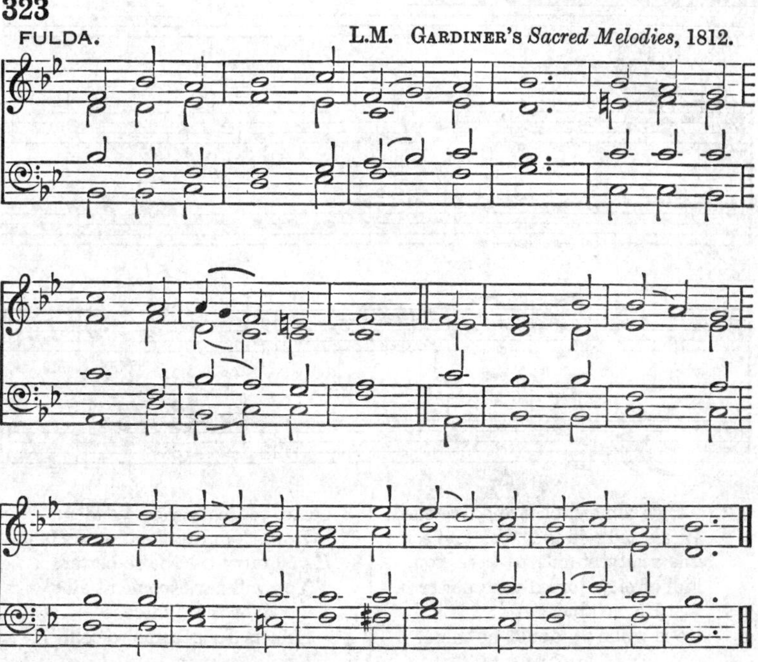

1 COME, sinners, to the gospel feast,
Let every soul be Jesu's guest;
Ye need not one be left behind,
For God hath bidden all mankind.

2 Sent by my Lord, on you I call;
The invitation is to all:
Come, all the world; come, sinner, thou!
All things in Christ are ready now.

3 Come, all ye souls by sin oppressed,
Ye restless wanderers after rest,
Ye poor, and maimed, and halt, and blind,
In Christ a hearty welcome find.

4 His love is mighty to compel;
His conquering love consent to feel,
Yield to His love's resistless power,
And fight against your God no more.

5 This is the time; no more delay!
This is the Lord's accepted day;
Come in, this moment, at His call,
And live for Him who died for all.

Charles Wesley, 1707-88.

324

BRYN CALFARIA. 8.7.8.7.4.7. W. OWEN, 1814-93.

1 COME, ye sinners, poor and wretched,
Weak and wounded, sick and sore;
Jesus ready stands to save you,
Full of pity, joined with power:
He is able,
He is willing; doubt no more.

2 Come, ye needy, come, and welcome;
God's free bounty glorify;
True belief and true repentance,
Every grace that brings us nigh,
Without money
Come to Jesus Christ and buy.

3 Come, ye weary, heavy-laden,
Bruised and broken by the fall;
If you tarry till you're better,
You will never come at all:
Not the righteous—
Sinners Jesus came to call.

4 Let not conscience make you linger,
Nor of fitness fondly dream;
All the fitness He requireth
Is to feel your need of Him:
This He gives you;
'Tis the Spirit's rising beam.

5 Lo! the incarnate God, ascended,
Pleads the merit of His blood;
Venture on Him, venture wholly;
Let no other trust intrude:
None but Jesus
Can do helpless sinners good.

Joseph Hart, 1712-68.

325

ELIM (HESPERUS). L.M. H. BAKER, 1835-1910.

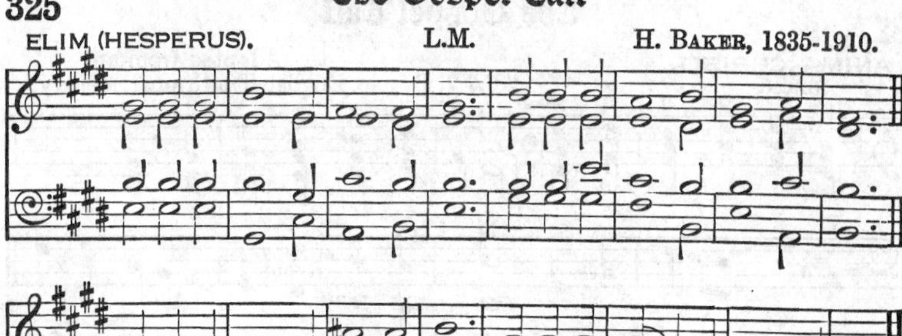

1 O COME, ye sinners, to your Lord,
In Christ to paradise restored;
His proffered benefits embrace,
The plenitude of gospel grace:

2 A pardon written with His blood,
The favour and the peace of God,
The seeing eye, the feeling sense,
The mystic joys of penitence;

3 The godly grief, the pleasing smart,
The meltings of a broken heart,
The tears that tell your sins forgiven,
The sighs that waft your souls to heaven;

4 The guiltless shame, the sweet distress,
The unutterable tenderness,
The genuine, meek humility,
The wonder—Why such love to me?

5 The o'erwhelming power of saving grace,
The sight that veils the seraph's face;
The speechless awe that dares not move,
And all the silent heaven of love.

Charles Wesley, 1707-88.

326

LIVERPOOL (NEWMARKET). L.M. RICHARD WAINWRIGHT, 1758-1825.

1 SINNERS, obey the gospel word;
Haste to the supper of my Lord!
Be wise to know your gracious day;
All things are ready, come away!

2 Ready the Father is to own
And kiss His late-returning son;
Ready your loving Saviour stands,
And spreads for you His bleeding hands.

3 Ready the Spirit of His love
Just now the hardness to remove,
To apply, and witness with the blood,
And wash and seal the sons of God.

4 Ready for you the angels wait,
To triumph in your blest estate;
Tuning their harps, they long to praise
The wonders of redeeming grace.

5 The Father, Son, and Holy Ghost
Is ready, with the shining host;
All heaven is ready to resound:
The dead's alive, the lost is found!

Charles Wesley, 1707-88.

327

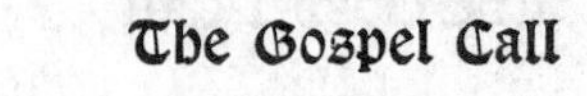

ANIMA CHRISTI. UNISON. 77 77. D. Adapted from an English Traditional Melody.

1 SINNERS, turn; why will ye die?
God, your Maker, asks you why:
God, who did your being give,
Made you with Himself to live;
He the fatal cause demands,
Asks the work of His own hands:
Why, ye thankless creatures, why
Will you cross His love, and die?

2 Sinners, turn; why will ye die?
God, your Saviour, asks you why:
God, who did your souls retrieve,
Died Himself, that you might live;
Will you let Him die in vain?
Crucify your Lord again?
Why, ye ransomed sinners, why
Will you slight His grace, and die?

3 Sinners, turn; why will ye die?
God, the Spirit, asks you why:
He who all your lives hath strove,
Wooed you to embrace His love;
Will you not His grace receive?
Will you still refuse to live?
Why, ye long-sought sinners, why
Will you grieve your God, and die?

Charles Wesley, 1707-88.

328

COME UNTO ME. 7.6.7.6. D. J. B. DYKES, 1823-76.

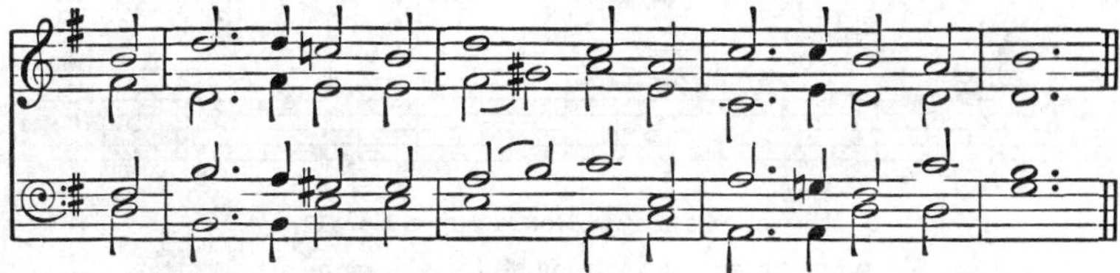

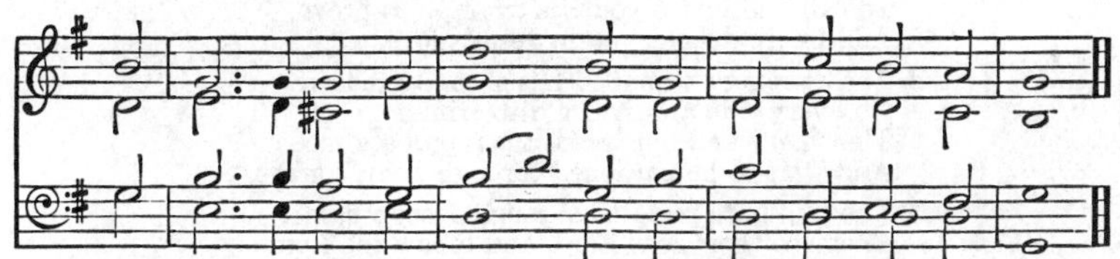

1 COME unto Me, ye weary,
And I will give you rest!
O blessèd voice of Jesus,
Which comes to hearts oppressed!
It tells of benediction,
Of pardon, grace, and peace,
Of joy that hath no ending,
Of love that cannot cease.

2 Come unto Me, ye wanderers,
And I will give you light!
O loving voice of Jesus,
Which comes to cheer the night!
Our hearts were filled with sadness,
And we had lost our way;
But Thou hast brought us gladness,
And songs at break of day.

3 Come unto Me, ye fainting,
And I will give you life!
O quickening voice of Jesus,
Which comes to aid our strife!
The foe is stern and eager;
The fight is fierce and long;
But Thou hast made us mighty,
And stronger than the strong.

4 And whosoever cometh
I will not cast him out!
O welcome voice of Jesus,
Which drives away our doubt,
Which calls us, very sinners,
Unworthy though we be
Of love so free and boundless,
To come, dear Lord, to Thee.

William Chatterton Dix, 1837-98.

329

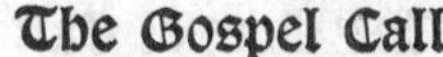

The Gospel Call

OLD 104TH. 10 10.11 11. RAVENSCROFT'S *Psalter*, 1621.

A - men.

May also be sung to MONTGOMERY, No. 311.

1 YE neighbours and friends of Jesus draw near:
His love condescends by titles so dear
To call and invite you His triumph to prove,
And freely delight you in Jesus's love.

2 The Shepherd who died His sheep to redeem;
On every side are gathered to Him
The weary and burdened, the reprobate race;
And wait to be pardoned through Jesus's grace.

3 The blind are restored through Jesus's name,
They see their dear Lord, and follow the Lamb;
The halt they are walking, and running their race;
The dumb they are talking of Jesus's grace.

4 The deaf hear His voice and comforting word,
It bids them rejoice in Jesus their Lord:
Thy sins are forgiven, accepted thou art;
They listen, and heaven springs up in their heart.

5 The lepers from all their spots are made clean,
The dead by His call are raised from their sin;
In Jesu's compassion the sick find a cure,
And gospel salvation is preached to the poor.

6 They seek Him and find: they ask and receive
The Friend of mankind, who bids them believe:
On Jesus they venture, His gift they embrace,
And forcibly enter His kingdom of grace.

7 O Jesus, ride on till all are subdued,
Thy mercy make known, and sprinkle Thy blood;
Display Thy salvation, and teach the new song
To every nation, and people, and tongue. Amen.

Charles Wesley, 1707-88.

LLANGLOFFAN. 7.6.7.6. D. Welsh Hymn Melody.

A- men.

May also be sung to DAY OF REST, No. 776.

1 O JESUS, Thou art standing
Outside the fast-closed door,
In lowly patience waiting
To pass the threshold o'er.
Shame on us, Christian brothers,
His name and sign who bear,
O shame, thrice shame upon us,
To keep Him standing there!

2 O Jesus, Thou art knocking;
And lo, that hand is scarred,
And thorns Thy brow encircle,
And tears Thy face have marred.
O love that passeth knowledge,
So patiently to wait!
O sin that hath no equal,
So fast to bar the gate!

3 O Jesus, Thou art pleading
In accents meek and low,
I died for you, My children,
And will ye treat Me so?
O Lord, with shame and sorrow
We open now the door;
Dear Saviour, enter, enter,
And leave us nevermore. Amen.

William Walsham How, 1823-97.

331

BEHOLD ME STANDING. L.M. and refrain. Mrs. J. F. Knapp, 1837-1908.

1 Behold Me standing at the door,
And hear Me pleading evermore,
With gentle voice: O heart of sin,
May I come in? May I come in?

Behold Me standing at the door,
And hear Me pleading evermore:
Say, weary heart, oppressed with sin,
May I come in? May I come in?

2 I bore the cruel thorns for thee,
I waited long and patiently:
Say, weary heart, oppressed with sin,
May I come in? May I come in?

3 I would not plead with thee in vain;
Remember all My grief and pain!
I died to ransom thee from sin,
May I come in? May I come in?

4 I bring thee joy from heaven above,
I bring thee pardon, peace, and love:
Say, weary heart, oppressed with sin,
May I come in? May I come in?

Frances Jane van Alstyne, 1820-1915.

332

ENTREATY. L.M. H. COWARD, 1849-1944

1 BEHOLD ! a Stranger at the door !
He gently knocks, has knocked before :
Has waited long, is waiting still :
You treat no other friend so ill.

2 But will He prove a friend indeed ?
He will ; the very Friend you need :
The Man of Nazareth, 'tis He,
With garments dyed at Calvary.

3 Admit Him, for the human breast
Ne'er entertained so kind a guest ;
No mortal tongue their joys can tell
With whom He condescends to dwell.

4 Yet know, nor of the terms complain,
Where Jesus comes, He comes to reign ;
To reign, and with no partial sway ;
Thoughts must be slain that disobey.

5 Sovereign of souls ! Thou Prince of Peace
O may Thy gentle reign increase !
Throw wide the door each willing mind ;
And be His empire all mankind.

Joseph Grigg, c. 1728-68.

333

ATTERCLIFFE. C.M. W. MATHER, 1756-1808.

1 COME let us, who in Christ believe,
Our common Saviour praise,
To Him with joyful voices give
The glory of His grace.

2 He now stands knocking at the door
Of every sinner's heart ;
The worst need keep Him out no [more,
Of force Him to depart.

3 Through grace we hearken to Thy [voice,
Yield to be saved from sin ;
In sure and certain hope rejoice,
That Thou wilt enter in.

4 Come quickly in, Thou heavenly [Guest,
Nor ever hence remove ;
But sup with us, and let the feast
Be everlasting love. Amen.

Charles Wesley, 1707-88.

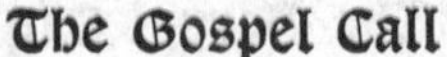

The Gospel Call

334

Irregular.

GOOD SHEPHERD (*First Tune*). J. F. BRIDGE, 1844-1924.

* Omit for v. 3.

Irregular.

THE NINETY AND NINE (*Second Tune*). I. D. SANKEY, 1840-1908.

The Gospel Call

* Omit for v. 3.

1 THERE were ninety and nine that safely lay
In the shelter of the fold;
But one was out on the hills away,
Far off from the gates of gold,
Away on the mountains wild and bare,
Away from the tender Shepherd's care.

2 Lord, Thou hast here Thy ninety and nine;
Are they not enough for Thee?
But the Shepherd made answer: This of Mine
Has wandered away from Me;
And although the road be rough and steep,
I go to the desert to find My sheep.

3 But none of the ransomed ever knew
How deep were the waters crossed,
Nor how dark was the night that the Lord passed through,
Ere He found His sheep that was lost.
Out in the desert He heard its cry,
Sick and helpless and ready to die.

4 Lord, whence are those blood-drops all the way
That mark out the mountain's track?
They were shed for one who had gone astray,
Ere the Shepherd could bring him back.
Lord, whence are Thy hands so rent and torn?
They are pierced to-night by many a thorn.

5 And all through the mountains, thunder-riven,
And up from the rocky steep,
There rose a cry to the gate of heaven:
Rejoice, I have found My sheep.
And the angels echoed around the throne:
Rejoice, for the Lord brings back His own.

Elizabeth Cecilia Clephane, 1830-69.

PASS ME NOT. 8.5.8.5. and refrain. W. H. DOANE, 1832-1916.

REFRAIN.

1 PASS me not, O gentle Saviour,
Hear my humble cry;
While on others Thou art calling,
Do not pass me by.

Saviour! Saviour!
Hear my humble cry,
And while others Thou art calling,
Do not pass me by.

2 Let me at a throne of mercy
Find a sweet relief;
Kneeling there in deep contrition,
Help my unbelief.

3 Trusting only in Thy merit,
Would I seek Thy face;
Heal my wounded, broken spirit,
Save me by Thy grace.

4 Thou the spring of all my comfort,
More than life to me,
Whom have I on earth beside Thee?
Whom in heaven but Thee?

Frances Jane van Alstyne, 1820-1915.

336

HE LIFTED ME. 8 8 8.6. and refrain. C. H. GABRIEL, 1856-1932.

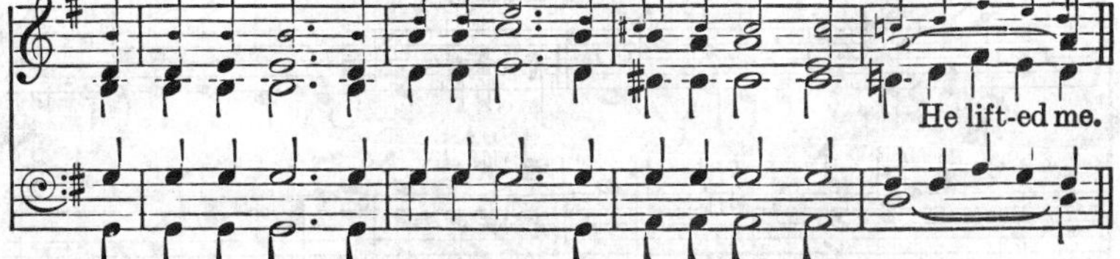

1 IN loving-kindness Jesus came,
My soul in mercy to reclaim, [shame
And from the depths of sin and
Through grace He lifted me.

From sinking sand He lifted me;
With tender hand He lifted me;
From shades of night to plains of light,
O praise His name, He lifted me!

2 He called me long before I heard,
Before my sinful heart was stirred;
But when I took Him at His word,
Forgiven He lifted me.

3 His brow was pierced with many a thorn,
His hands by cruel nails were torn,
When from my guilt and grief,
In love He lifted me. [forlorn,

4 Now on a higher plane I dwell,
And with my soul I know 'tis well;
Yet how or why, I cannot tell,
He should have lifted me.

Charles Homer Gabriel, 1856-1932.

WONDROUS LOVE. C.M. and refrain. W. G. Fischer, 1835-1912.

Refrain.

1 God loved the world of sinners lost
And ruined by the fall ;
Salvation full, at highest cost,
He offers free to all.
O 'twas love, 'twas wondrous love !
The love of God to me ;
It brought my Saviour from above,
To die on Calvary.

2 E'en now by faith I claim Him mine,
The risen Son of God ;
Redemption by His death I find,
And cleansing through the blood.

3 Love brings the glorious fullness in,
And to His saints makes known
The blessed rest from inbred sin,
Through faith in Christ alone.

4 Believing souls, rejoicing go ;
There shall to you be given
A glorious foretaste, here below,
Of endless life in heaven.

5 Of victory now o'er Satan's power
Let all the ransomed sing,
And triumph in the dying hour
Through Christ, the Lord, our King.

Martha Matilda Stockton, 1821-85.

RESCUE. 11.10.11.10. and refrain. W. H. Doane, 1832-1916.

1 Rescue the perishing, care for the dying,
 Snatch them in pity from sin and the grave;
Weep o'er the erring one, lift up the fallen,
 Tell them of Jesus, the mighty to save.
 Rescue the perishing, care for the dying;
 Jesus is merciful, Jesus will save.

2 Though they are slighting Him, still He is waiting,
 Waiting the penitent child to receive.
Plead with them earnestly, plead with them gently:
 He will forgive if they only believe.

3 Down in the human heart, crushed by the tempter,
 Feelings lie buried that grace can restore;
Touched by a loving hand, wakened by kindness,
 Chords that were broken will vibrate once more.

4 Rescue the perishing—duty demands it;
 Strength for thy labour the Lord will provide;
Back to the narrow way patiently win them;
 Tell the poor wanderer a Saviour has died.

Frances Jane van Alstyne, 1820-1915.

Also:

114 Let earth and heaven
152 What means this eager
154 I heard the voice of Jesus say
158 Thou say'st: Take up
188 All ye that pass by
262 All thanks be to God
361 Where shall my wondering soul

REPENTANCE AND FORGIVENESS

339

WRESTLING JACOB. 8.8.8.8.8.8 8. S. S. Wesley, 1810-76.

1 Come, O Thou Traveller unknown,
Whom still I hold, but cannot see!
My company before is gone,
And I am left alone with Thee;
With Thee all night I mean to stay,
And wrestle till the break of day.

2 I need not tell Thee who I am,
My misery and sin declare;
Thyself hast called me by my name;
Look on Thy hands, and read it there:
But who, I ask Thee, who art Thou?
Tell me Thy name, and tell me now.

3 In vain Thou strugglest to get free;
I never will unloose my hold!
Art Thou the Man that died for me?
The secret of Thy love unfold:
Wrestling, I will not let Thee go,
Till I Thy name, Thy nature know.

4 Wilt Thou not yet to me reveal
Thy new, unutterable name?
Tell me, I still beseech Thee, tell;
To know it now resolved I am:
Wrestling, I will not let Thee go,
Till I Thy name, Thy nature know.

5 What though my shrinking flesh complain,
  And murmur to contend so long?
I rise superior to my pain,
  When I am weak, then I am strong;
And when my all of strength shall fail,
I shall with the God-Man prevail.

* * * * * *

6 Yield to me now; for I am weak,
  But confident in self-despair;
Speak to my heart, in blessings speak,
  Be conquered by my instant prayer;
Speak, or Thou never hence shalt move,
And tell me if Thy name is Love.

7 'Tis Love! 'tis Love! Thou diedst for me!
  I hear Thy whisper in my heart;
The morning breaks, the shadows flee,
  Pure, universal Love Thou art;
To me, to all, Thy mercies move:
Thy nature and Thy name is Love.

8 My prayer hath power with God; the grace
  Unspeakable I now receive;
Through faith I see Thee face to face,
  I see Thee face to face, and live!
In vain I have not wept and strove:
Thy nature and Thy name is Love.

9 I know Thee, Saviour, who Thou art,
  Jesus, the feeble sinner's Friend;
Nor wilt Thou with the night depart,
  But stay and love me to the end;
Thy mercies never shall remove:
Thy nature and Thy name is Love.

10 The Sun of Righteousness on me
  Hath risen with healing in His wings;
Withered my nature's strength, from Thee
  My soul its life and succour brings;
My help is all laid up above:
Thy nature and Thy name is Love.

11 Contented now upon my thigh
  I halt, till life's short journey end;
All helplessness, all weakness, I
  On Thee alone for strength depend;
Nor have I power from Thee to move:
Thy nature and Thy name is Love.

12 Lame as I am, I take the prey,
  Hell, earth, and sin with ease o'ercome;
I leap for joy, pursue my way,
  And as a bounding hart fly home,
Through all eternity to prove
Thy nature and Thy name is Love.

Charles Wesley, 1707-88.

DAVID'S HARP. 8.8.8.8.8.8 8. R. KING, *c.* 1684-1711.

Abbreviated Version.

1 COME, O Thou Traveller unknown,
Whom still I hold, but cannot see!
My company before is gone,
And I am left alone with Thee;
With Thee all night I mean to stay,
And wrestle till the break of day.

2 In vain Thou strugglest to get free;
I never will unloose my hold!
Art Thou the Man that died for me?
The secret of Thy love unfold:
Wrestling, I will not let Thee go,
Till I Thy name, Thy nature know.

3 Yield to me now; for I am weak,
But confident in self-despair;
Speak to my heart, in blessings speak,
Be conquered by my instant prayer;
Speak, or Thou never hence shalt move,
And tell me if Thy name is Love.

4 'Tis Love! 'tis Love! Thou diedst for me!
I hear Thy whisper in my heart;
The morning breaks, the shadows flee,
Pure, universal Love Thou art;
To me, to all, Thy mercies move:
Thy nature and Thy name is Love.

Charles Wesley, 1707-88.

341

SHIRLAND. S.M. S. STANLEY, 1767-1822.

1 When shall Thy love constrain,
And force me to Thy breast?
When shall my soul return again
To her eternal rest?

2 Thy condescending grace
To me did freely move;
It calls me still to seek Thy face,
And stoops to ask my love.

3 Lord, at Thy feet I fall!
I long to be set free;
I fain would now obey the call,
And give up all for Thee.

4 To rescue me from woe,
Thou didst with all things part;
Didst lead a suffering life below,
To gain my worthless heart.

5 My worthless heart to gain,
The God of all that breathe
Was found in fashion as a man,
And died a cursèd death.

6 And can I yet delay
My little all to give?
To tear my soul from earth away,
For Jesus to receive?

7 Nay, but I yield, I yield!
I can hold out no more,
I sink, by dying love compelled,
And own Thee conqueror.

Charles Wesley, 1707-88.

342

BYZANTIUM. C.M. T. Jackson, 1715-81.

1 Come, let us to the Lord our God
With contrite hearts return;
Our God is gracious, nor will leave
The desolate to mourn.

2 His voice commands the tempest forth,
And stills the stormy wave;
And though His arm be strong to smite,
'Tis also strong to save.

3 Long hath the night of sorrow reigned;
The dawn shall bring us light;
God shall appear, and we shall rise
With gladness in His sight.

4 Our hearts, if God we seek to know,
Shall know Him and rejoice;
His coming like the morn shall be,
Like morning songs His voice.

5 As dew upon the tender herb,
Diffusing fragrance round;
As showers that usher in the spring,
And cheer the thirsty ground.

6 So shall His presence bless our souls,
And shed a joyful light;
That hallowed morn shall chase away
The sorrows of the night.

John Morison, 1750-98.

JENA. L.M. Vulpius' *Gesangbuch*, 1609.

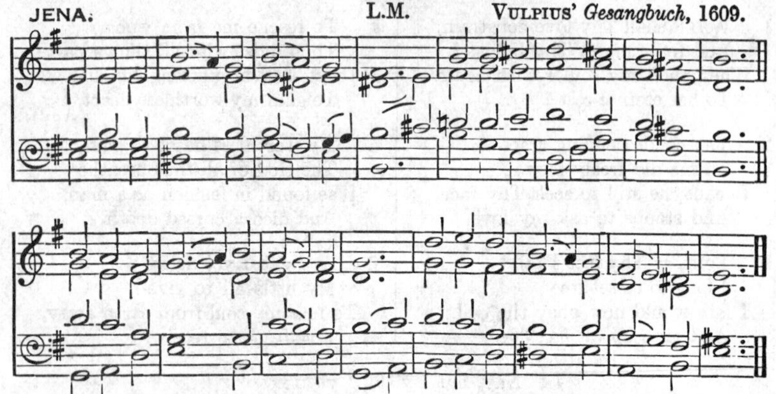

1 Wherewith, O God, shall I draw near,
And bow myself before Thy face?
How in Thy purer eyes appear?
What shall I bring to gain Thy grace?

2 Whoe'er to Thee themselves approve
Must take the path Thy Word hath showed,
Justice pursue, and mercy love,
And humbly walk by faith with God.

3 But though my life henceforth be Thine,
Present for past can ne'er atone;
Though I to Thee the whole resign,
I only give Thee back Thine own.

4 What have I then wherein to trust?
I nothing have, I nothing am;
Excluded is my every boast,
My glory swallowed up in shame.

5 Guilty I stand before Thy face,
On me I feel Thy wrath abide;
'Tis just the sentence should take place;
'Tis just—but O Thy Son hath died!

6 Jesus, the Lamb of God, hath bled,
He bore our sins upon the tree;
Beneath our curse He bowed His head;
'Tis finished! He hath died for me!

7 See where before the throne He stands,
And pours the all-prevailing prayer,
Points to His side, and lifts His hands,
And shows that I am graven there.

8 He ever lives for me to pray;
He prays that I with Him may reign:
Amen to what my Lord doth say!
Jesus, Thou canst not pray in vain.

Charles Wesley, 1707-88.

344

DORCHESTER. L.M. B. Rogers, 1614-98.

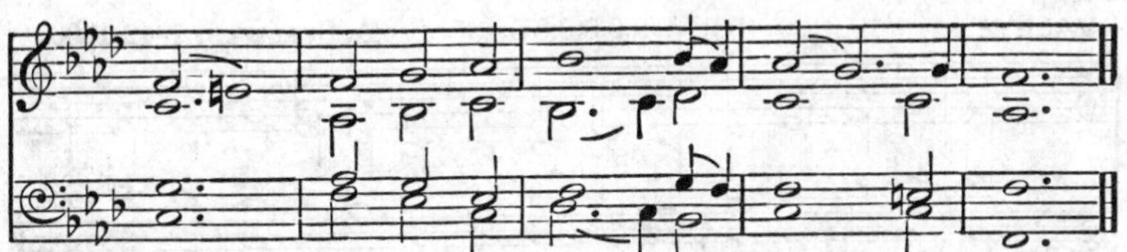

1 Jesus, the sinner's Friend, to Thee,
Lost and undone, for aid I flee,
Weary of earth, myself, and sin;
Open Thine arms, and take me in!

2 Pity, and heal my sin-sick soul;
'Tis Thou alone canst make me whole;
Fall'n, till in me Thine image shine,
And cursed I am, till Thou art mine.

3 At last I own it cannot be
That I should fit myself for Thee:
Here then to Thee I all resign;
Thine is the work, and only Thine.

4 The mansion for Thyself prepare,
Dispose my heart by entering there;
'Tis this alone can make me clean,
'Tis this alone can cast out sin.

Charles Wesley, 1707-88.

345

ISLEWORTH. 8 8 8.6. S. Howard, 1710-82.

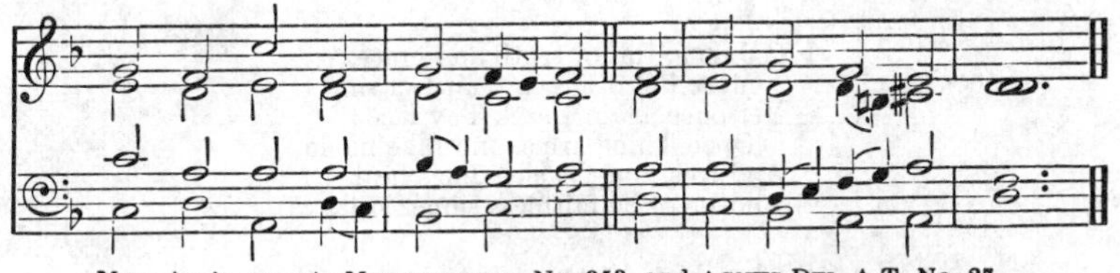

May also be sung to Misericordia, No. 353, and Agnus Dei, A.T. No. 27.

1 Drawn to the Cross which Thou hast blessed
With healing gifts for souls distressed,
To find in Thee my life, my rest:
Christ crucified, I come!

2 Stained with the sins which I have wrought
In word and deed and secret thought,
For pardon which Thy blood hath bought:
Christ crucified, I come!

3 Weary of selfishness and pride,
False pleasures gone, vain hopes denied,
Deep in Thy wounds my shame to hide:
Christ crucified, I come!

4 Thou knowest all my griefs and fears,
Thy grace abused, my misspent years;
Yet now to Thee, for cleansing tears:
Christ crucified, I come!

5 I would not, if I could, conceal
The ills which only Thou canst heal,
So to the Cross, where sinners kneel:
Christ crucified, I come!

6 Wash me, and take away each stain,
Let nothing of my sin remain;
For cleansing, though it be through pain:
Christ crucified, I come!

7 To be what Thou wouldst have me be,
Accepted, sanctified in Thee,
Through what Thy grace shall work in me:
Christ crucified, I come!

Genevieve Mary Irons, b. 1855

346

VALETE. 8.8.8.8.8 8. A. SULLIVAN, 1842-1900.

By permission of Novello and Company, Limited.

1 O JESUS, full of truth and grace,
  More full of grace than I of sin,
Yet once again I seek Thy face;
  Open Thine arms, and take me in,
And freely my backslidings heal,
And love the faithless sinner still.

2 Thou know'st the way to bring me back,
  My fallen spirit to restore:
O for Thy truth and mercy's sake,
  Forgive, and bid me sin no more;
The ruins of my soul repair,
And make my heart a house of prayer.

3 The stone to flesh again convert,
  The veil of sin again remove;
Sprinkle Thy blood upon my heart,
  And melt it by Thy dying love;
This rebel heart by love subdue,
And make it soft, and make it new.

4 Ah! give me, Lord, the tender heart
  That trembles at the approach of sin;
A godly fear of sin impart,
  Implant, and root it deep within,
That I may dread Thy gracious power,
And never dare to offend Thee more. Amen.

Charles Wesley, 1707-88.

347

YORK. C.M. *Scottish Psalter*, 1615.

1 Come, O Thou all-victorious Lord,
  Thy power to us make known;
Strike with the hammer of Thy word,
  And break these hearts of stone.

2 O that we all might now begin
  Our foolishness to mourn,
And turn at once from every sin,
  And to our Saviour turn!

3 Give us ourselves and Thee to know,
  In this our gracious day;
Repentance unto life bestow,
  And take our sins away.

4 Conclude us first in unbelief,
  And freely then release;
Fill every soul with sacred grief,
  And then with sacred peace.

5 Impoverish, Lord, and then relieve,
  And then enrich the poor;
The knowledge of our sickness give,
  The knowledge of our cure.

6 That blessèd sense of guilt impart,
  And then remove the load;
Trouble, and wash the troubled heart
  In the atoning blood.

7 Our desperate state through sin declare,
  And speak our sins forgiven;
By perfect holiness prepare,
  And take us up to heaven. Amen.

Charles Wesley, 1707-88.

CHRISTOPHER. 7.7.7.7.7.7. C. PETER, 1626-69.

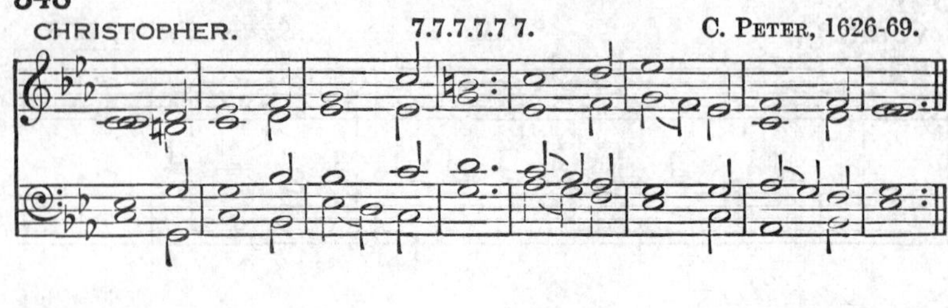

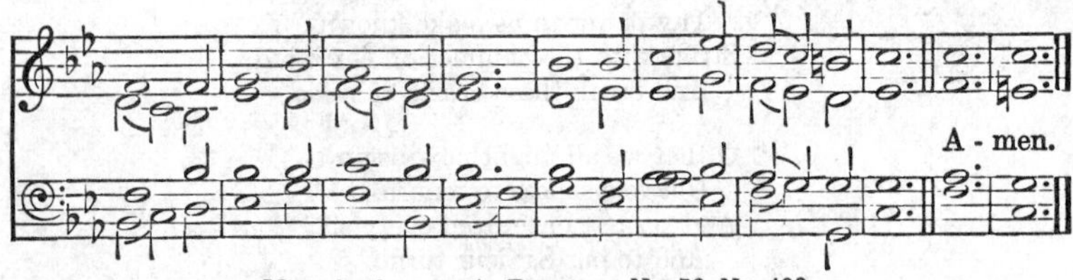

May also be sung to REDHEAD No. 76, No. 498.

1 SAVIOUR, Prince of Israel's race,
See me from Thy lofty throne;
Give the sweet relenting grace,
Soften this obdurate stone;
Stone to flesh, O God, convert;
Cast a look, and break my heart.

2 By Thy Spirit, Lord, reprove,
All my inmost sins reveal,
Sins against Thy light and love
Let me see, and let me feel;
Sins that crucified my God,
Spilt again Thy precious blood.

3 Jesu, seek Thy wandering sheep,
Make me restless to return;
Bid me look on Thee and weep,
Bitterly as Peter mourn,
Till I say, by grace restored,
Now Thou know'st I love Thee, Lord!

4 Might I in Thy sight appear
As the publican distressed,
Stand, not daring to draw near,
Smite on my unworthy breast,
Groan the sinner's only plea:
God, be merciful to me!

5 O remember me for good,
Passing through the mortal vale;
Show me the atoning blood,
When my strength and spirit fail;
Give my gasping soul to see
Jesus crucified for me! Amen.

Charles Wesley, 1707-88.

349

CAREY'S. 8.8.8.8.8.8 8. H. CAREY, 1692-1743.

1 JESUS, if still the same Thou art,
If all Thy promises are sure,
Set up Thy kingdom in my heart,
And make me rich, for I am poor;
To me be all Thy treasures given,
The kingdom of an inward heaven.

2 Thou hast pronounced the mourners blest;
And lo, for Thee I ever mourn:
I cannot: No! I will not rest,
Till Thou, my only rest, return;
Till Thou, the Prince of Peace, appear,
And I receive the Comforter.

3 Where is the blessedness bestowed
On all that hunger after Thee?
I hunger now, I thirst for God;
See the poor fainting sinner, see,
And satisfy with endless peace,
And fill me with Thy righteousness.

4 Ah, Lord! if Thou art in that sigh,
Then hear Thyself within me pray;
Hear in my heart Thy Spirit's cry,
Mark what my labouring soul would say;
Answer the deep unuttered groan,
And show that Thou and I are one.

5 Shine on Thy work, disperse the gloom,
Light in Thy light I then shall see;
Say to my soul: Thy light is come,
Glory divine is risen on thee,
Thy warfare's past, thy mourning's o'er;
Look up, for thou shalt weep no more!

Charles Wesley, 1707-88.

350

PLAISTOW. L.M. *Magdalen Chapel Hymns*, ? -1760.

1 WITH broken heart and contrite sigh,
A trembling sinner, Lord, I cry;
Thy pardoning grace is rich and free:
O God, be merciful to me!

2 I smite upon my troubled breast,
With deep and conscious guilt oppressed;
Christ and His Cross my only plea:
O God, be merciful to me!

3 Far off I stand with tearful eyes,
Nor dare uplift them to the skies;
But Thou dost all my anguish see:
O God, be merciful to me!

4 Nor alms, nor deeds that I have done,
Can for a single sin atone:
To Calvary alone I flee;
O God, be merciful to me!

5 And when, redeemed from sin and hell,
With all the ransomed throng I dwell,
My raptured song shall ever be:
God has been merciful to me!

Cornelius Elven, 1797-1873.

351

CALVARY. S.M. and refrain. L. HARTSOUGH, 1828-1919.

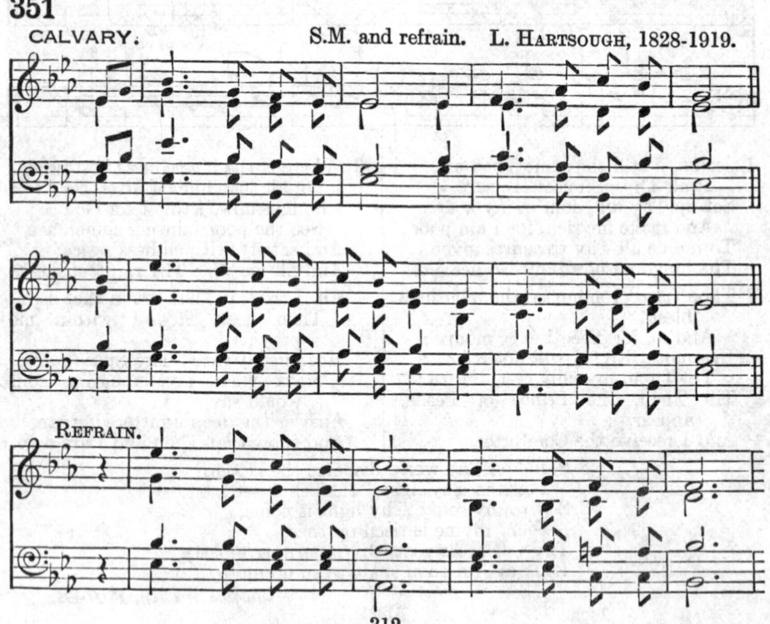

1 I HEAR Thy welcome voice
That calls me, Lord, to Thee,
For cleansing in Thy precious blood
That flowed on Calvary.

I am coming, Lord,
Coming now to Thee:
Wash me, cleanse me, by the blood
That flowed on Calvary.

2 Though coming weak and vile,
Thou dost my strength assure;
Thou dost my vileness fully cleanse,
Till spotless all and pure.

3 'Tis Jesus calls me on
To perfect faith and love,
To perfect hope, and peace, and trust,
For earth and heaven above.

4 'Tis Jesus who confirms
The blessèd work within,
By adding grace to welcomed grace,
Where reigned the power of sin.

5 All hail, atoning blood!
All hail, redeeming grace!
All hail, the gift of Christ our Lord,
Our Strength and Righteousness!

Lewis Hartsough, 1828-1919.

352

ST. BRIDE. S.M. S. HOWARD, 1710-82.

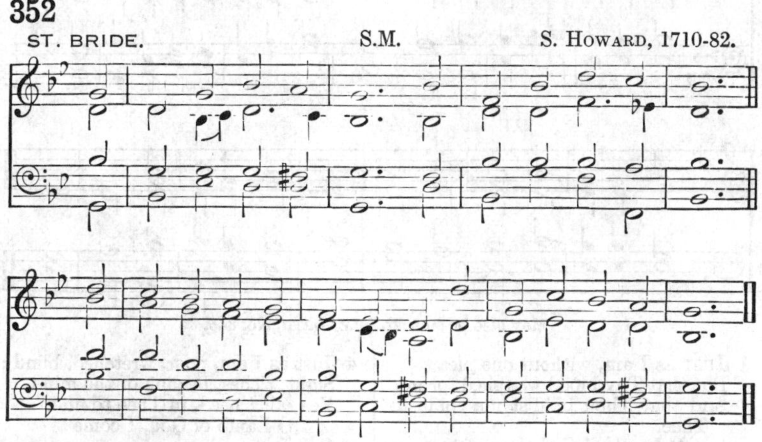

1 OPPRESSED with sin and woe,
A burdened heart I bear;
Opposed by many a mighty foe,
Yet will I not despair.

2 With this polluted heart,
I dare to come to Thee—
Holy and mighty as Thou art—
For Thou wilt pardon me.

3 I feel that I am weak,
And prone to every sin;
But Thou who giv'st to those who seek,
Wilt give me strength within.

4 I need not fear my foes;
I need not yield to care;
I need not sink beneath my woes,
For Thou wilt answer prayer.

5 In my Redeemer's name,
I give myself to Thee;
And, all unworthy as I am,
My God will welcome me.

Anne Brontë, 1820-49.

353

MISERICORDIA (*First Tune*). 8 8 8.6. H. SMART, 1813-79.

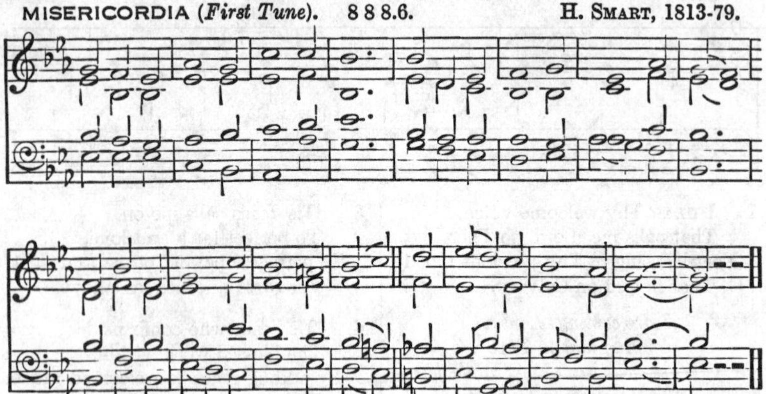

GAINSWORTH (*Second Tune*). 8 8 8.6. C. H. PURDAY, 1799-1885.

May also be sung to ISLEWORTH, No. 345.

1 JUST as I am, without one plea
But that Thy blood was shed for me,
And that Thou bidd'st me come to Thee,
O Lamb of God, I come!

2 Just as I am, and waiting not
To rid my soul of one dark blot,
To Thee, whose blood can cleanse each spot,
O Lamb of God, I come!

3 Just as I am, though tossed about
With many a conflict, many a doubt,
Fighting and fears within, without,
O Lamb of God, I come!

4 Just as I am, poor, wretched, blind;
Sight, riches, healing of the mind,
Yea, all I need, in Thee to find,
O Lamb of God, I come!

5 Just as I am, Thou wilt receive,
Wilt welcome, pardon, cleanse, relieve;
Because Thy promise I believe,
O Lamb of God, I come!

6 Just as I am—Thy love unknown
Has broken every barrier down—
Now to be Thine, yea, Thine alone,
O Lamb of God, I come!

7 Just as I am, of that free love
The breadth, length, depth, and height to prove,
Here for a season, then above,
O Lamb of God, I come!

Charlotte Elliott, 1789-1871.

354

ST. WERBURGH. 6.4.6.4.6 6.4. R. P. STEWART, 1825-94.

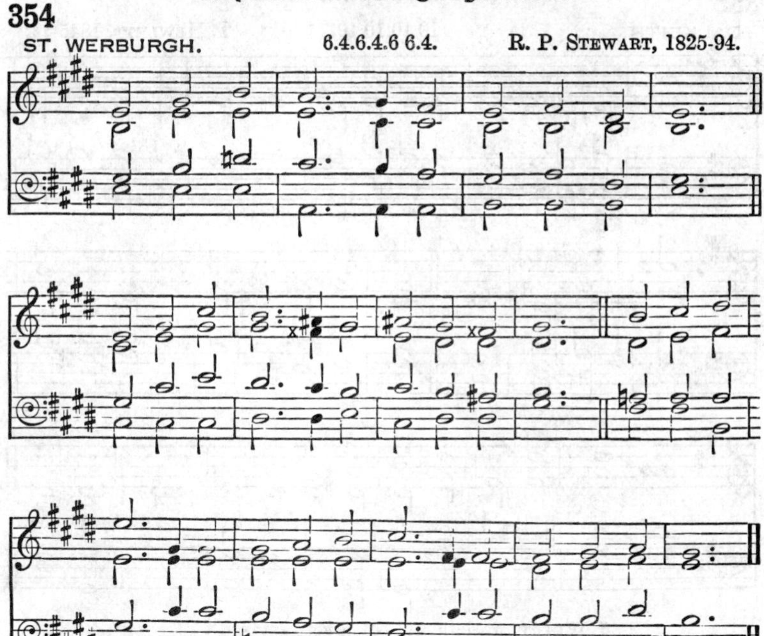

1 No, not despairingly
Come I to Thee;
No, not distrustingly
Bend I the knee:
Sin hath gone over me,
Yet is this still my plea:
Jesus hath died.

2 Ah! mine iniquity
Crimson has been,
Infinite, infinite,
Sin upon sin;
Sin of not loving Thee,
Sin of not trusting Thee,
Infinite sin.

3 Lord, I confess to Thee
Sadly my sin;
All I am tell I Thee,
All I have been:
Purge Thou my sin away,
Wash Thou my soul this day;
Lord, make me clean.

4 Faithful and just art Thou,
Forgiving all;
Loving and kind art Thou
When poor ones call:
Lord, let the cleansing blood,
Blood of the Lamb of God,
Pass o'er my soul.

5 Then all is peace and light
This soul within;
Thus shall I walk with Thee,
The loved Unseen;
Leaning on Thee, my God,
Guided along the road,
Nothing between.

Horatius Bonar, 1808-89.

DALKEITH. 10 10.10 10. T. HEWLETT, 1845-74.

1 WEARY of earth and laden with my sin,
I look at heaven and long to enter in;
But there no evil thing may find a home,
And yet I hear a voice that bids me: Come!

2 So vile I am, how dare I hope to stand
In the pure glory of that holy land,
Before the whiteness of that throne appear?
Yet there are hands stretched out to draw me near.

3 The while I fain would tread the heavenly way,
Evil is ever with me day by day;
Yet on mine ears the gracious tidings fall:
Repent, believe; thou shalt be loosed from all!

4 It is the voice of Jesus that I hear,
His are the hands stretched out to draw me near,
And His the blood that can for all atone,
And set me faultless there before the throne.

5 'Twas He who found me on the deathly wild,
And made me heir of heaven, the Father's child,
And day by day, whereby my soul may live,
Gives me His grace of pardon, and will give.

6 O great Absolver, grant my soul may wear
The lowliest garb of penitence and prayer,
That in the Father's courts my glorious dress
May be the garment of Thy righteousness.

7 Yea, Thou wilt answer for me, righteous Lord:
Thine all the merits, mine the great reward;
Thine the sharp thorns, and mine the golden crown;
Mine the life won, and Thine the life laid down.

8 Nought can I bring Thee, Lord, for all I owe;
Yet let my full heart what it can bestow:
Like Mary's gift, let my devotion prove,
Forgiven greatly, how I greatly love. Amen.

Samuel John Stone, 1839-1900.

356

SOVEREIGNTY. 8.8.8.8.8.8 8. J. NEWTON, 1802-86.

May also be sung to CREDO, No. 148.

1 GREAT God of wonders! all Thy ways
Display the attributes divine;
But countless acts of pardoning grace
Beyond Thine other wonders shine:
Who is a pardoning God like Thee?
Or who has grace so rich and free?

2 In wonder lost, with trembling joy
We take the pardon of our God;
Pardon for crimes of deepest dye,
A pardon bought with Jesu's blood:

3 Pardon—from an offended God!
Pardon—for sins of deepest dye!
Pardon—bestowed through Jesu's blood!
Pardon—that brings the rebel nigh!

4 O may this strange, this matchless grace,
This God-like miracle of love,
Fill the wide earth with grateful praise,
As now it fills the choirs above!

Samuel Davies, 1723-61.

357

MARIENBOURN. 8.8.8.8.8.8 8. *Foundery Collection*, 1742.

1 Jesus, in whom the weary find
  Their late, but permanent repose,
Physician of the sin-sick mind,
  Relieve my wants, assuage my woes;
And let my soul on Thee be cast,
Till life's fierce tyranny be past.

2 Loosed from my God, and far removed,
  Long have I wandered to and fro,
O'er earth in endless circles roved,
  Nor found whereon to rest below:
Back to my God at last I fly,
For O the waters still are high.

3 Selfish pursuits, and nature's maze,
  The things of earth, for Thee I leave;
Put forth Thy hand, Thy hand of grace,
  Into the ark of love receive,
Take this poor fluttering soul to rest,
And lodge it, Saviour, in Thy breast.

4 Fill with inviolable peace,
  Stablish and keep my settled heart;
In Thee may all my wanderings cease,
  From Thee no more may I depart;
Thy utmost goodness called to prove,
Loved with an everlasting love.

Charles Wesley, 1707-88.

358

REDHEAD No. 47. 7 7.7 7. R. Redhead, 1820-1901.

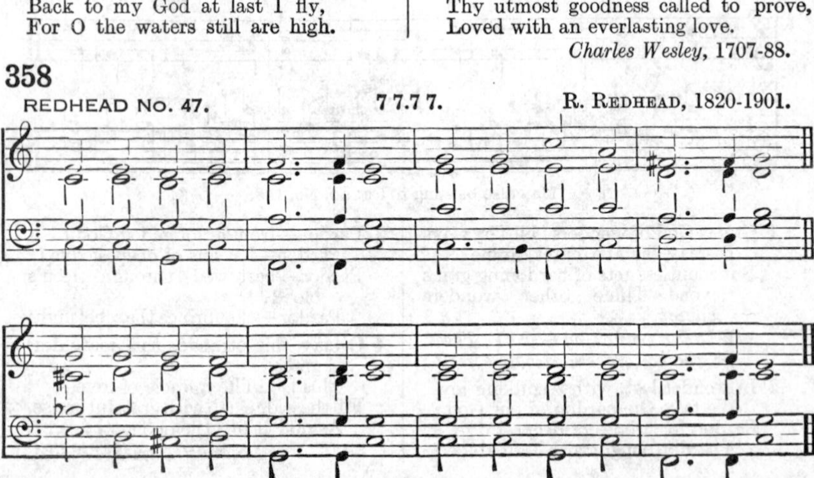

1 Depth of mercy! can there be
Mercy still reserved for me?
Can my God His wrath forbear?
Me, the chief of sinners, spare?

2 I have long withstood His grace,
Long provoked Him to His face,
Would not hearken to His calls,
Grieved Him by a thousand falls.

3 Whence to me this waste of love?
Ask my Advocate above!
See the cause in Jesu's face,
Now before the throne of grace.

4 There for me the Saviour stands;
Shows His wounds and spreads His
God is love; I know, I feel; [hands.
Jesus lives, and loves me still.

5 Jesus, answer from above:
Is not all Thy nature love?
Wilt Thou not the wrong forget?
Suffer me to kiss Thy feet?

6 Pity from Thine eye let fall;
By a look my soul recall;
Now the stone to flesh convert,
Cast a look, and break my heart.

Charles Wesley, 1707-88.

359

ST. MARTIN. 8.6.8.6.8 8.7. J. H. Sheppard, 1835-79.

Aus tiefer Noth schrei ich zu dir.

1 Out of the depths I cry to Thee,
Lord God. O hear my prayer!
Incline a gracious ear to me,
And bid me not despair:
If Thou rememberest each misdeed,
If each should have its rightful meed,
Lord, who shall stand before Thee?

2 'Tis through Thy love alone we gain
The pardon of our sin;
The strictest life is but in vain,
Our works can nothing win;
That none should boast himself of
aught, [wrought
But own in fear Thy grace hath
What in him seemeth righteous.

3 Wherefore my hope is in the Lord,
My works I count but dust,
I build not there, but on His word,
And in His goodness trust.
Up to His care myself I yield,
He is my tower, my rock, my shield,
And for His help I tarry.

4 And though it linger till the night,
And round again till morn,
My heart shall ne'er mistrust Thy
might,
Nor count itself forlorn.
Do thus, O ye of Israel's seed,
Ye of the Spirit born indeed,
Wait for your God's appearing.

5 Though great our sins and sore our
wounds,
And deep and dark our fall,
His helping mercy hath no bounds,
His love surpasseth all.
Our trusty loving Shepherd, He
Who shall at last set Israel free
From all their sin and sorrow.

Martin Luther, 1483-1546;
tr. by Catherine Winkworth, 1827-78.

360

BLOCKLEY. L.M. T. Blockley, 1800-82.

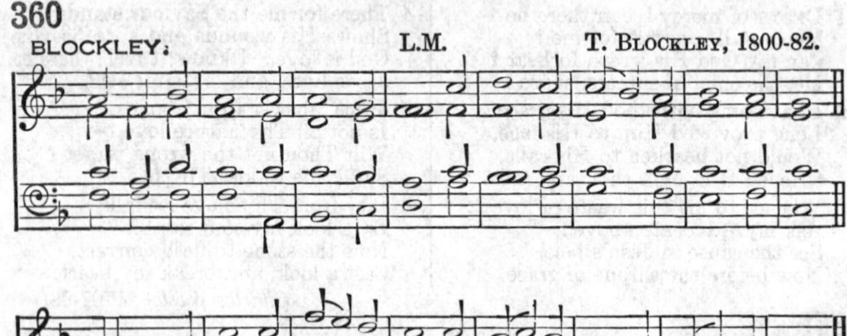

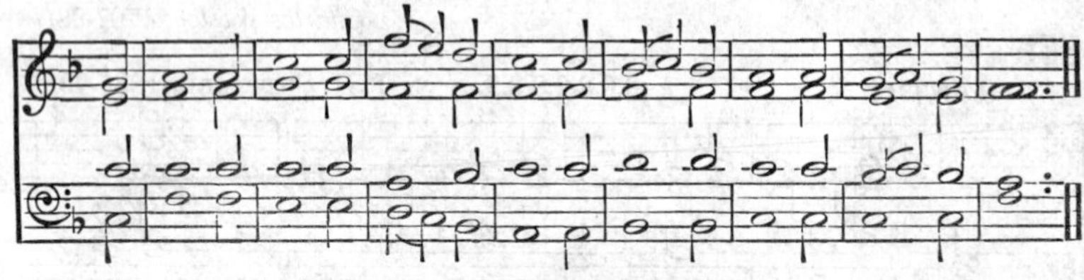

1 Happy the man that finds the grace,
The blessing of God's chosen race,
The wisdom coming from above,
The faith that sweetly works by love.

2 Happy beyond description he
Who knows: The Saviour died for me!
The gift unspeakable obtains,
And heavenly understanding gains.

3 Wisdom divine! Who tells the price
Of wisdom's costly merchandise?
Wisdom to silver we prefer,
And gold is dross compared to her.

4 Her hands are filled with length of days,
True riches, and immortal praise,
Riches of Christ, on all bestowed,
And honour that descends from God.

5 To purest joys she all invites,
Chaste, holy, spiritual delights;
Her ways are ways of pleasantness,
And all her flowery paths are peace.

6 Happy the man who wisdom gains,
Thrice happy who his guest retains;
He owns, and shall for ever own:
Wisdom, and Christ, and Heaven are one.

Charles Wesley, 1707-88.

Also:

38 Father of heaven
73 My God, how wonderful
80 Thee will I praise
159 One who is all unfit
173 Would Jesus have the sinner die?
175 Weep not for Him
187 O come and mourn
188 All ye that pass by
200 O Jesus, my hope
203 How shall a sinner find
361 Where shall my wondering soul
498 Rock of Ages, cleft for me
543 Hear Thou my prayer

OLD 23RD. 8.8.8.8.8.8. RONER'S *Melopeia Sacra*, 1720.

May also be sung to CRUCIFIXION, A.T. No. 28.

The Wesleys' Conversion Hymn. Whitsuntide, 1738.

1 WHERE shall my wondering soul begin?
How shall I all to heaven aspire?
A slave redeemed from death and sin,
A brand plucked from eternal fire,
How shall I equal triumphs raise,
Or sing my great Deliverer's praise?

2 O how shall I the goodness tell,
Father, which Thou to me hast showed?
That I, a child of wrath and hell,
I should be called a child of God,
Should know, should feel my sins forgiven,
Blest with this antepast of heaven!

3 And shall I slight my Father's love?
Or basely fear His gifts to own?
Unmindful of His favours prove?
Shall I, the hallowed Cross to shun,
Refuse His righteousness to impart,
By hiding it within my heart?

4 Outcasts of men, to you I call,
Harlots, and publicans, and thieves!
He spreads His arms to embrace you all;
Sinners alone His grace receives:
No need of Him the righteous have;
He came the lost to seek and save.

5 Come, O my guilty brethren, come,
Groaning beneath your load of sin!
His bleeding heart shall make you room,
His open side shall take you in;
He calls you now, invites you home:
Come, O my guilty brethren, come!

Charles Wesley, 1707-88.

362

MAINZER. L.M. J. MAINZER, 1801-51.

1 AUTHOR of faith, eternal Word,
Whose Spirit breathes the active flame;
Faith, like its Finisher and Lord,
To-day as yesterday the same:

2 To Thee our humble hearts aspire,
And ask the gift unspeakable;
Increase in us the kindled fire,
In us the work of faith fulfil.

3 By faith we know Thee strong to save;
Save us, a present Saviour Thou!
Whate'er we hope, by faith we have,
Future and past subsisting now.

4 To him that in Thy name believes
Eternal life with Thee is given;
Into himself he all receives,
Pardon, and holiness, and heaven.

5 The things unknown to feeble sense,
Unseen by reason's glimmering ray,
With strong, commanding evidence
Their heavenly origin display.

6 Faith lends its realizing light,
The clouds disperse, the shadows fly;
The Invisible appears in sight,
And God is seen by mortal eye.

Charles Wesley, 1707-88.

363

ICH HALTE TREULICH STILL. D.S.M. J. S. BACH, 1685-1750.

May also be sung to Ascension, No. 410.

1 Spirit of faith, come down,
Reveal the things of God;
And make to us the Godhead known,
And witness with the blood.
'Tis thine the blood to apply,
And give us eyes to see
Who did for every sinner die
Hath surely died for me.

2 No man can truly say
That Jesus is the Lord,
Unless Thou take the veil away,
And breathe the living word;
Then, only then, we feel
Our interest in His blood,
And cry, with joy unspeakable:
Thou art my Lord, my God!

3 O that the world might know
The all-atoning Lamb!
Spirit of faith, descend, and show
The virtue of His name;
The grace which all may find,
The saving power impart;
And testify to all mankind,
And speak in every heart.

4 Inspire the living faith,
Which whosoe'er receives,
The witness in himself he hath,
And consciously believes;
That faith that conquers all,
And doth the mountain move,
And saves whoe'er on Jesus call,
And perfects them in love. Amen.

Charles Wesley, 1707-88.

364

WIRKSWORTH. S.M. Green's *Psalmody*, 1724.

1 Ah! whither should I go,
Burdened, and sick, and faint?
To whom should I my troubles show,
And pour out my complaint?

2 My Saviour bids me come;
Ah! why do I delay?
He calls the weary sinner home,
And yet from Him I stay.

3 What is it keeps me back,
From which I cannot part,
Which will not let my Saviour take
Possession of my heart?

4 Some cursèd thing unknown
Must surely lurk within,
Some idol, which I will not own,
Some secret bosom-sin.

5 Jesus, the hindrance show,
Which I have feared to see;
Yet let me now consent to know
What keeps me out of Thee.

6 Searcher of hearts, in mine
Thy trying power display;
Into its darkest corners shine,
And take the veil away.

7 I now believe in Thee
Compassion reigns alone;
According to my faith to me
O let it, Lord, be done! Amen.

Charles Wesley, 1707-88.

365

FAITH. 7.6.7.6.7.8.7.6. S. S. WESLEY, 1810-76.

1 God of my salvation, hear,
And help me to believe;
Simply do I now draw near,
Thy blessing to receive:
Full of sin, alas! I am,
But to Thy wounds for refuge flee:
Friend of sinners, spotless Lamb,
Thy blood was shed for me.

2 Standing now as newly slain,
To Thee I lift mine eye;
Balm of all my grief and pain,
Thy grace is always nigh:
Now as yesterday the same
Thou art, and wilt for ever be:

3 Nothing have I, Lord, to pay,
Nor can Thy grace procure;
Empty send me not away,
For I, Thou know'st, am poor:
Dust and ashes is my name,
My all is sin and misery:

4 No good word, or work, or thought
Bring I to gain Thy grace;
Pardon I accept unbought,
Thine offer I embrace,
Coming, as at first I came,
To take, and not bestow on Thee:

5 Saviour, from Thy wounded side
I never will depart;
Here will I my spirit hide
When I am pure in heart:
Till my place above I claim,
This only shall be all my plea:

Charles Wesley, 1707-88.

366

EPWORTH. C.M. C. Wesley, 1757-1834.

1 Jesus! Redeemer, Saviour, Lord,
The weary sinner's Friend,
Come to my help, pronounce the word,
And bid my troubles end.

2 Deliverance to my soul proclaim,
And life, and liberty;
Shed forth the virtue of Thy name,
And Jesus prove to me.

3 Faith to be healed Thou know'st I have,
For Thou that faith hast given;
Thou canst, Thou wilt the sinner save,
And make me meet for heaven.

4 Thou canst o'ercome this heart of mine,
Thou wilt victorious prove;
For everlasting strength is Thine,
And everlasting love.

5 Thy powerful Spirit shall subdue
Unconquerable sin,
Cleanse this foul heart, and make it new,
And write Thy law within.

6 Bound down with twice ten thousand ties,
Yet let me hear Thy call,
My soul in confidence shall rise,
Shall rise and break through all.

Charles Wesley, 1707-88.

367

LINCOLN. C.M. Ravenscroft's *Psalter*, 1621.

1 Day after day I sought the Lord,
And waited patiently;
Until He bent down from His throne,
And hearkened to my cry.

2 He drew me from the fearful pit,
And from the miry clay;
He placed my feet upon a rock,
And led me in His way.

3 He taught my soul a new-made song,
A song of holy praise;
All they who see these things, with fear
Their hopes to God shall raise.

4 Most blessèd is the man whose hope
Upon the Lord relies;
Who follows not the proud, nor those
That turn aside to lies.

5 O Lord, what wonders hast Thou wrought,
All number far above:
Thy thoughts to us-ward overflow
With mercy, grace, and love.

Julius Charles Hare, 1796-1855.

ST. SWITHIN. 6.6.6.6.8 8. E. JESSER, c. 1770.

1 ARISE, my soul, arise,
Shake off thy guilty fears;
The bleeding Sacrifice
In my behalf appears:
Before the throne my Surety stands;
My name is written on His hands.

2 He ever lives above,
For me to intercede,
His all redeeming love,
His precious blood, to plead;
His blood atoned for all our race,
And sprinkles now the throne of grace.

3 Five bleeding wounds He bears,
Received on Calvary;
They pour effectual prayers,
They strongly speak for me:
Forgive him, O forgive! they cry,
Nor let that ransomed sinner die!

4 The Father hears Him pray,
His dear Anointed One;
He cannot turn away
The presence of His Son:
His Spirit answers to the blood,
And tells me I am born of God.

5 My God is reconciled,
His pardoning voice I hear;
He owns me for His child,
I can no longer fear;
With confidence I now draw nigh,
And Father, Abba, Father! cry.

Charles Wesley, 1707-88.

369

PURLEIGH. 8 8.6. D. A. H. BROWN, 1830-1926.

1 Thee, Jesus, Thee, the sinner's Friend,
I follow on to apprehend,
Renew the glorious strife;
Divinely confident and bold,
With faith's strong arm on Thee lay hold,
Thee, my eternal life.

2 Prisoner of hope, to Thee I turn,
And, calmly confident, I mourn,
And pray, and weep for Thee;
Tell me Thy love, Thy secret tell,
Thy mystic name in me reveal,
Reveal Thyself in me.

3 Descend, pass by me, and proclaim,
O Lord of hosts, Thy glorious name—
The Lord, the gracious Lord,
Longsuffering, merciful, and kind;
The God who always bears in mind
His everlasting word.

4 Plenteous He is in truth and grace;
He wills that all the fallen race
Should turn, repent, and live;
His pardoning grace for all is free;
Transgression, sin, iniquity,
He freely doth forgive.

5 Mercy He doth for thousands keep;
He goes and seeks the one lost sheep,
And brings His wanderer home;
And every soul that sheep might be:
Come then, my Lord, and gather me,
My Jesus, quickly come! Amen.

Charles Wesley, 1707-88.

370

CONFIDENCE. L.M. W. Moore, 1811-80.

May also be sung to Fulda, No. 323.

Christi Blut und Gerechtigkeit.

1 Jesu, Thy blood and righteousness
My beauty are, my glorious dress;
Midst flaming worlds, in these arrayed,
With joy shall I lift up my head.

2 Bold shall I stand in Thy great day;
For who aught to my charge shall lay?
Fully absolved through these I am,
From sin and fear, from guilt and shame.

3 The holy, meek, unspotted Lamb,
Who from the Father's bosom came,
Who died for me, even me, to atone,
Now for my Lord and God I own.

4 Lord, I believe Thy precious blood,
Which at the mercy-seat of God
For ever doth for sinners plead,
For me, even for my soul, was shed.

5 When from the dust of death I rise
To claim my mansion in the skies,
Even then this shall be all my plea—
Jesus hath lived, hath died for me!

* * * *

6 Jesu, be endless praise to Thee,
Whose boundless mercy hath for me,
For me and all Thy hands have made,
An everlasting ransom paid.

7 Lord, I believe, were sinners more
Than sands upon the ocean shore,
Thou hast for all a ransom paid,
For all a full atonement made.

8 Ah! give to all Thy servants, Lord,
With power to speak Thy gracious word,
That all who to Thy wounds will flee,
May find eternal life in Thee.

9 Thou God of power, Thou God of love,
Let the whole world Thy mercy prove!
Now let Thy word o'er all prevail;
Now take the spoils of death and hell.

10 O let the dead now hear Thy voice,
Now bid Thy banished ones rejoice,
Their beauty this, their glorious dress,
Jesu, Thy blood and righteousness!

Nicolaus Ludwig von Zinzendorf, 1700-60;
tr. by John Wesley, 1703-91.

371

SAGINA (First Tune). 8.8.8.8.8.8 8. T. CAMPBELL, c. 1800.
(Repeat lines 5 and 6.)
LANSDOWN (Second Tune). 8.8.8.8.8 8. A. BEER, 1874-

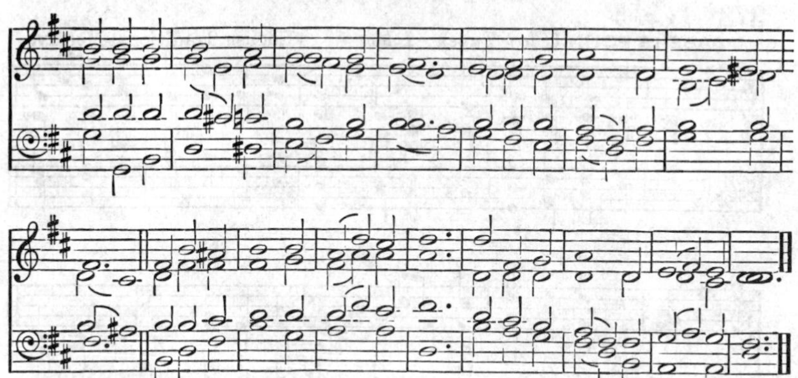

1 And can it be that I should gain
An interest in the Saviour's blood?
Died He for me, who caused His pain?
For me, who Him to death pursued?
Amazing love! how can it be
That Thou, my God, shouldst die for me!

2 'Tis mystery all! The Immortal dies:
Who can explore His strange design?
In vain the first-born seraph tries
To sound the depths of love divine.
'Tis mercy all! let earth adore,
Let angel minds inquire no more.

3 He left His Father's throne above—
So free, so infinite His grace—
Emptied Himself of all but love,
And bled for Adam's helpless race.
'Tis mercy all, immense and free;
For, O my God, it found out me!

4 Long my imprisoned spirit lay
Fast bound in sin and nature's night;
Thine eye diffused a quickening ray—
I woke, the dungeon flamed with light;
My chains fell off, my heart was free,
I rose, went forth, and followed Thee.

5 No condemnation now I dread;
Jesus, and all in Him, is mine!
Alive in Him, my living Head,
And clothed in righteousness divine,
Bold I approach the eternal throne,
And claim the crown, through Christ, my own.

Charles Wesley, 1707-88.

372

ARLINGTON. C.M. From T. A. Arne's *Artaxerxes*, 1762.

1 The God of love, to earth He came,
That you might come to heaven;
Believe, believe in Jesu's name,
And all your sin's forgiven.

2 Believe in Him that died for thee,
And, sure as He hath died,
Thy debt is paid, thy soul is free,
And thou art justified.

Charles Wesley, 1707-88.

373

A BABE IS BORN (*First Tune*). L.M. English Traditional Melody.

ELY (*Second Tune*). L.M. T. Turton, 1780-1864.

1 Lord, I was blind! I could not see
In Thy marred visage any grace;
But now the beauty of Thy face
In radiant vision dawns on me.

2 Lord, I was deaf! I could not hear
The thrilling music of Thy voice;
But now I hear Thee and rejoice,
And all Thine uttered words are dear.

3 Lord, I was dumb! I could not speak
The grace and glory of Thy name;
But now, as touched with living flame,
My lips Thine eager praises wake.

4 Lord, I was dead! I could not stir
My lifeless soul to come to Thee;
But now, since Thou hast quickened me,
I rise from sin's dark sepulchre.

5 For Thou hast made the blind to see,
The deaf to hear, the dumb to speak,
The dead to live; and lo, I break
The chains of my captivity!

William Tidd Matson, 1833-99.

374

JESUS SAVES ME NOW. 10.7.10.5. and refrain. Unknown.

1 JESUS hath died and hath risen again,
Pardon and peace to bestow;
Fully I trust Him; from sin's guilty stain
Jesus saves me now.

Jesus saves me now!
Jesus saves me now!
Yes, Jesus saves me all the time,
Jesus saves me now!

2 Sin's condemnation is over and gone,
Jesus alone knoweth how;
Life and salvation my soul hath put on;
Jesus saves me now.

3 Jesus is stronger than Satan and sin,
Satan to Jesus must bow,
Therefore I triumph without and within;
Jesus saves me now.

4 Sorrow and pain may beset me about,
Nothing can darken my brow;
Battling in faith I can joyfully shout:
Jesus saves me now.

Anonymous.

MADRID (*First Tune*). 8.8.8.8.8.8 8. W. MATTHEWS, 1759-1830.

ANCHOR (*Second Tune*). 8.8.8.8.8 8. A. BEER, 1874-

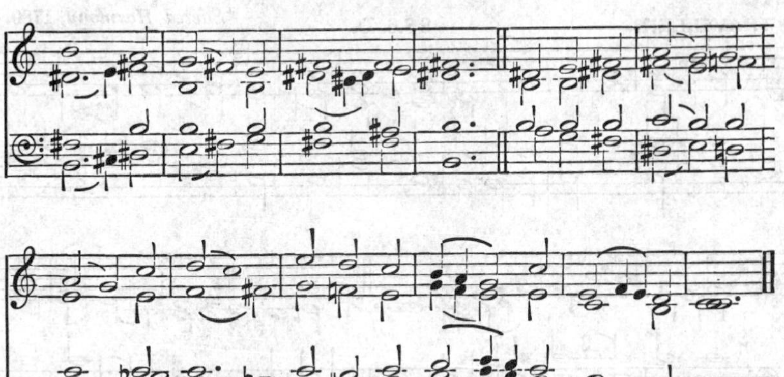

Ich habe nun den Grund gefunden.

1 Now I have found the ground wherein
  Sure my soul's anchor may remain—
The wounds of Jesus, for my sin
  Before the world's foundation slain;
Whose mercy shall unshaken stay,
When heaven and earth are fled away.

2 Father, Thine everlasting grace
  Our scanty thought surpasses far,
Thy heart still melts with tenderness,
  Thy arms of love still open are
Returning sinners to receive,
That mercy they may taste and live.

3 O Love, Thou bottomless abyss,
  My sins are swallowed up in Thee!
Covered is my unrighteousness,
  Nor spot of guilt remains on me,
While Jesu's blood through earth and skies
Mercy, free, boundless mercy! cries.

4 With faith I plunge me in this sea,
  Here is my hope, my joy, my rest;
Hither, when hell assails, I flee,
  I look into my Saviour's breast:
Away, sad doubt and anxious fear!
Mercy is all that's written there.

5 Though waves and storms go o'er my head,
  Though strength, and health, and friends be gone,
Though joys be withered all and dead,
  Though every comfort be withdrawn,
On this my steadfast soul relies—
Father, Thy mercy never dies!

6 Fixed on this ground will I remain,
  Though my heart fail and flesh decay;
This anchor shall my soul sustain,
  When earth's foundations melt away:
Mercy's full power I then shall prove,
Loved with an everlasting love.

Johann Andreas Rothe, 1688-1758;
tr. by John Wesley, 1703-91.

376

TRAVELLER. 8 8.6. D. *Sacred Harmony*, 1780.

A - men.

1 Thou great mysterious God unknown,
Whose love hath gently led me on,
Even from my infant days,
Mine inmost soul expose to view,
And tell me if I ever knew
Thy justifying grace.

2 If I have only known Thy fear,
And followed with a heart sincere
Thy drawings from above,
Now, now the further grace bestow,
And let my sprinkled conscience know
Thy sweet forgiving love.

3 Short of Thy love I would not stop,
A stranger to the gospel hope,
The sense of sin forgiven;
I would not, Lord, my soul deceive,
Without the inward witness live,
That antepast of heaven.

4 If now the witness were in me,
Would He not testify of Thee
In Jesus reconciled?
And should I not with faith draw nigh,
And boldly Abba, Father! cry,
And know myself Thy child?

5 Whate'er obstructs Thy pardoning [love,
Or sin or righteousness, remove,
Thy glory to display;
Mine heart of unbelief convince,
And now absolve me from my sins,
And take them all away.

6 Father, in me reveal Thy Son,
And to my inmost soul make known
How merciful Thou art:
The secret of Thy love reveal,
And by Thine hallowing Spirit dwell
For ever in my heart. Amen.

Charles Wesley, 1707-88.

377

ST. MICHAEL. S.M. Day's *Psalter*, 1562.

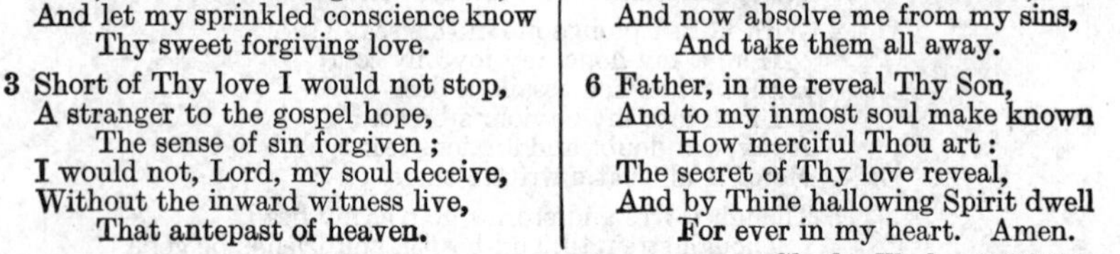

1 How can a sinner know
His sins on earth forgiven ?
How can my gracious Saviour show
My name inscribed in heaven ?

2 What we have felt and seen
With confidence we tell,
And publish to the sons of men
The signs infallible.

3 We who in Christ believe
That He for us hath died,
We all His unknown peace receive
And feel His blood applied.

4 Exults our rising soul,
Disburdened of her load,
And swells unutterably full
Of glory and of God.

5 His love, surpassing far
The love of all beneath,
We find within our hearts, and dare
The pointless darts of death.

6 Stronger than death and hell
The mystic power we prove ;
And conquerors of the world, we dwell
In heaven, who dwell in love.

7 His Spirit to us He gave,
And dwells in us we know ;
The witness in ourselves we have,
And all its fruits we show.

8 Whate'er our pardoning Lord
Commands, we gladly do ;
And guided by His sacred word,
We all His steps pursue.

Charles Wesley, 1707-88.

378

DUBLIN. C.M. J. A. Stevenson, 1762-1833.

1 Eternal Sun of Righteousness,
Display Thy beams divine,
And cause the glories of Thy face
Upon my heart to shine.

2 Light in Thy light O may I see,
Thy grace and mercy prove,
Revived and cheered and blessed by
Thee,
The God of pardoning love.

3 Lift up Thy countenance serene,
And let Thy happy child
Behold, without a cloud between,
The Godhead reconciled.

4 That all-comprising peace bestow
On me, through grace forgiven ;
The joys of holiness below,
And then the joys of heaven.
Amen.

Charles Wesley, 1707-88.

379

NUNHEAD. L.M. D. VETTES, c. 1713

1 THE people that in darkness lay,
In sin and error's deadly shade,
Have seen a glorious gospel day
In Jesu's lovely face displayed.

2 Thou only, Lord, the work hast done,
And bared Thine arm in all our sight;
Hast made the reprobates Thine own,
And claimed the outcasts as Thy right.

3 Thine arm alone, almighty Lord,
To us the great salvation brought,
Thy Word, Thy all-creating Word,
That spake at first the world from nought.

4 For this the saints lift up their voice,
And ceaseless praise to Thee is given;
For this the hosts above rejoice;
We raise the happiness of heaven.

Charles Wesley, 1707-88.

380

HYFRYDOL. 8.7.8.7. and refrain. R. H. PRITCHARD, 1811-87.

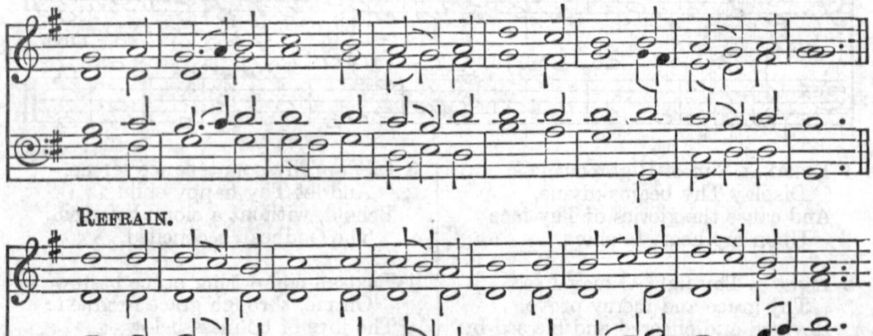

REFRAIN.

1 I WILL sing the wondrous story
Of the Christ who died for me;
How He left His home in glory,
For the Cross on Calvary.
Yes, I'll sing the wondrous story
Of the Christ who died for me—
Sing it with the saints in glory,
Gathered by the crystal sea.

2 I was lost; but Jesus found me—
Found the sheep that went astray;
Raised me up and gently led me
Back into the narrow way.

3 I was bruised; but Jesus healed me:
Faint was I from many a fall;
Sight was gone, and fears possessed me:
But He freed me from them all.

4 Days of darkness still come o'er me;
Sorrow's paths I often tread:
But the Saviour still is with me,
By His hand I'm safely led.

5 He will keep me till the river
Rolls its waters at my feet;
Then He'll bear me safely over,
Where the loved ones I shall meet.

Francis Harold Rawley, 1854-

381

KESTON. 8 8 8 7. A. E. FLOYD, 1877-

1 I AM not skilled to understand
What God hath willed, what God hath planned;
I only know at His right hand
Stands One who is my Saviour.

2 I take God at His word and deed:
Christ died to save me, this I read;
And in my heart I find a need
Of Him to be my Saviour.

3 And was there then no other way
For God to take? I cannot say;
I only bless Him, day by day,
Who saved me through my Saviour.

4 That He should leave His place on high
And come for sinful man to die,
You count it strange? So do not I,
Since I have known my Saviour.

5 And O that He fulfilled may see
The travail of His soul in me,
And with His work contented be,
As I with my dear Saviour!

6 Yea, living, dying, let me bring
My strength, my solace, from this spring,
That He who lives to be my King
Once died to be my Saviour.

Dora Greenwell, 1821-82.

Also:

81 Not what these hands have done
155 Heal us, Immanuel
171 Jesus, I will trust Thee
201 There is a fountain
233 Jesus, to Thee we fly
234 Not all the blood of beasts
345 Drawn to the Cross
478 Jesus, my Saviour
564 Father, I dare believe
760 Saviour and can it be

382

DEDICATION

BYZANTIUM. C.M. T. Jackson, 1715-81.

1 Let Him to whom we now belong
His sovereign right assert,
And take up every thankful song
And every loving heart.

2 He justly claims us for His own,
Who bought us with a price;
The Christian lives to Christ alone,
To Christ alone he dies.

3 Jesus, Thine own at last receive,
Fulfil our hearts' desire,
And let us to Thy glory live
And in Thy cause expire.

4 Our souls and bodies we resign;
With joy we render Thee
Our all, no longer ours, but Thine
To all eternity. Amen.

Charles Wesley, 1707-88.

383

TOTTENHAM. C.M. T. Greatorex, 1758-1831.

1 Being of beings, God of love,
To Thee our hearts we raise:
Thy all-sustaining power we prove,
And gladly sing Thy praise.

2 Thine, wholly Thine, we long to be:
Our sacrifice receive:
Made, and preserved, and saved by Thee,
To Thee ourselves we give.

3 Heavenward our every wish aspires;
For all Thy mercies' store,
The sole return Thy love requires
Is that we ask for more.

4 For more we ask; we open then
Our hearts to embrace Thy will;
Turn, and revive us, Lord, again,
With all Thy fullness fill.

5 Come, Holy Ghost, the Saviour's love
Shed in our hearts abroad;
So shall we ever live, and move,
And be, with Christ, in God.

Charles Wesley, 1707-88.

384

ANGELS' SONG. L.M. O. Gibbons, 1585-1625.

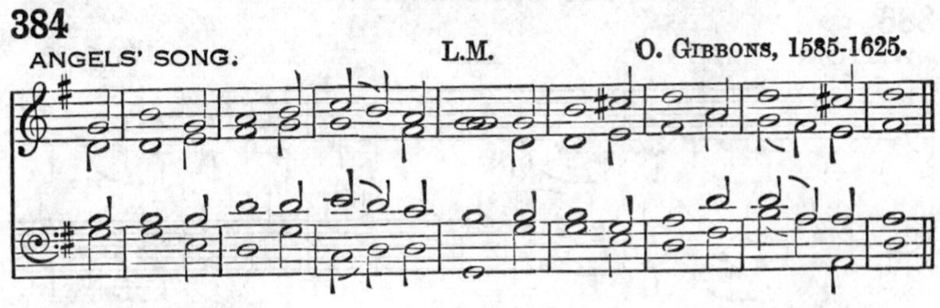

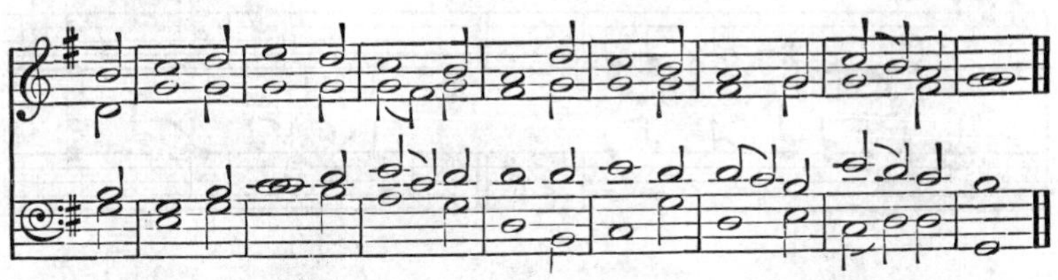

1 My soul, through my Redeemer's care,
Saved from the second death I feel,
My eyes from tears of dark despair,
My feet from falling into hell.

2 Wherefore to Him my feet shall run,
My eyes on His perfections gaze,
My soul shall live for God alone,
And all within me shout His praise.

Charles Wesley, 1707-88.

385

TYTHERTON. S.M. L. R. West, 1753-1826.

1 Jesus, I fain would find
Thy zeal for God in me,
Thy yearning pity for mankind,
Thy burning charity.

2 In me Thy Spirit dwell;
In me Thy mercies move:
So shall the fervour of my zeal
Be the pure flame of love.

Charles Wesley, 1707-88.

386

WILTON. L.M. S. Stanley, 1767-1822.

A - men.

1 O Thou who camest from above
The pure celestial fire to impart,
Kindle a flame of sacred love
On the mean altar of my heart!

2 There let it for Thy glory burn
With inextinguishable blaze;
And trembling to its source return,
In humble prayer and fervent praise.

3 Jesus, confirm my heart's desire
To work, and speak, and think for Thee;
Still let me guard the holy fire,
And still stir up Thy gift in me.

4 Ready for all Thy perfect will,
My acts of faith and love repeat,
Till death Thy endless mercies seal,
And make the sacrifice complete. Amen.

Charles Wesley, 1707-88.

387

WARWICK. C.M. S. Stanley, 1767-1822.

1 My God! I know, I feel Thee mine,
And will not quit my claim,
Till all I have is lost in Thine
And all renewed I am.

2 I hold Thee with a trembling hand,
But will not let Thee go,
Till steadfastly by faith I stand
And all Thy goodness know.

3 Jesus, Thine all-victorious love
Shed in my heart abroad;
Then shall my feet no longer rove,
Rooted and fixed in God.

4 O that in me the sacred fire
Might now begin to glow,
Burn up the dross of base desire,
And make the mountains flow!

5 O that it now from heaven might fall,
And all my sins consume!
Come, Holy Ghost, for Thee I call,
Spirit of burning, come!

6 Refining Fire, go through my heart,
Illuminate my soul;
Scatter Thy life through every part,
And sanctify the whole. Amen.

Charles Wesley, 1707-88.

388

ANGELS' SONG. L.M. O. Gibbons, 1583-1625.

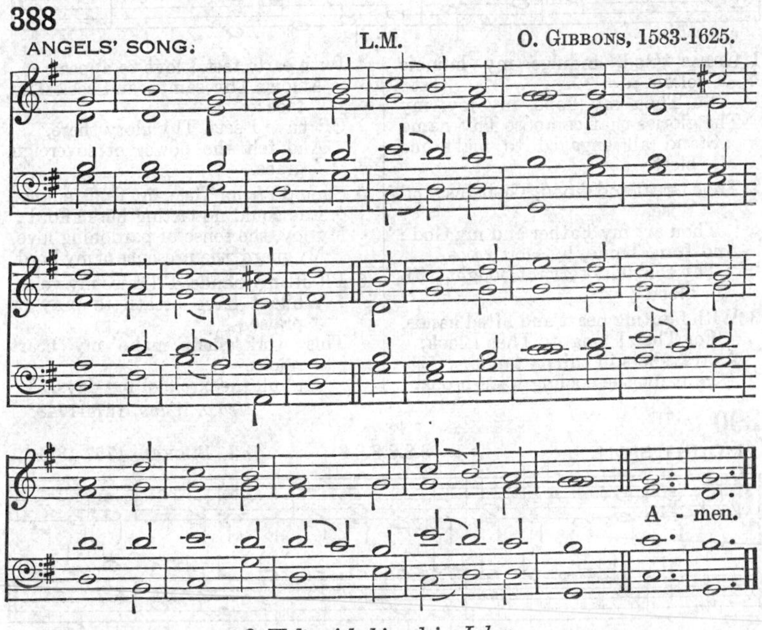

O Welt, sieh hier dein Leben.

1 My Saviour! how shall I proclaim,
How pay the mighty debt I owe?
Let all I have, and all I am,
Ceaseless to all Thy glory show.

2 Too much to Thee I cannot give;
Too much I cannot do for Thee;
Let all Thy love, and all Thy grief,
Graven on my heart for ever be.
Amen.

Paulus Gerhardt, 1607-76;
tr. by John Wesley, 1703-91.

389

WARRINGTON. L.M. R. Harrison, 1748-1810.

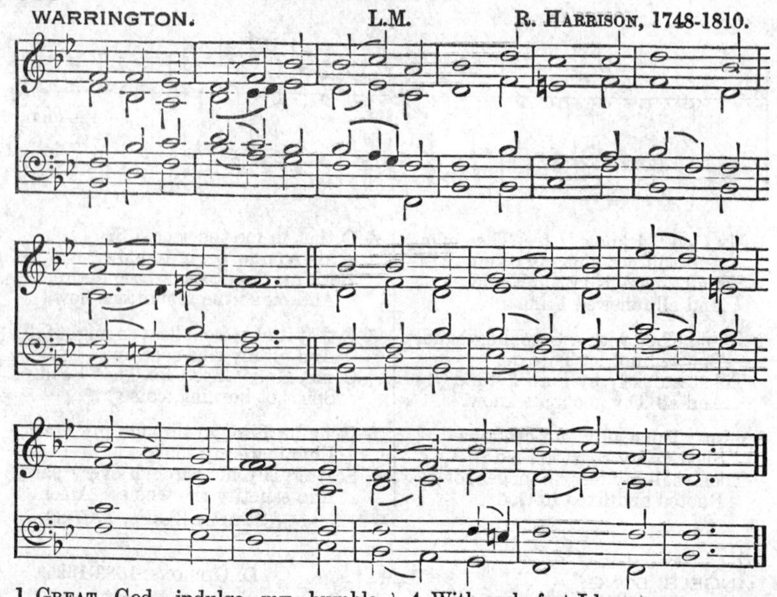

1 Great God, indulge my humble claim;
Be Thou my hope, my joy, my [rest:
The glories that compose Thy name
Stand all engaged to make me blest.

2 Thou Great and Good, Thou Just and Wise,
Thou art my Father and my God;
And I am Thine, by sacred ties,
Thy son, Thy servant bought with blood.

3 With fainting heart and lifted hands,
For Thee I long, to Thee I look,
As travellers in thirsty lands
Pant for the cooling waterbrook.

4 With early feet I love to appear
Among Thy saints, and seek Thy face;
Oft have I seen Thy glory there,
And felt the power of sovereign grace.

5 Should I from Thee, my God, remove,
Life could no lasting bliss afford;
My joy, the sense of pardoning love,
My guard, the presence of my Lord.

6 I'll lift my hands, I'll raise my voice,
While I have breath to pray or praise;
This work shall make my heart rejoice,
And fill the circle of my days.

Isaac Watts, 1674-1748.

390

MOUNT SION. 8.8.8.8.8.8. I. J. Pleyel, 1757-1831.

1 Give me the faith which can remove
And sink the mountain to a plain;
Give me the child-like praying love,
Which longs to build Thy house again;
Thy love, let it my heart o'erpower
And all my simple soul devour.

2 I would the precious time redeem,
And longer live for this alone,
To spend, and to be spent, for them
Who have not yet my Saviour known;
Fully on these my mission prove,
And only breathe, to breathe Thy love.

3 My talents, gifts, and graces, Lord,
Into Thy blessèd hands receive;
And let me live to preach Thy word,
And let me to Thy glory live;
My every sacred moment spend
In publishing the sinners' Friend.

4 Enlarge, inflame, and fill my heart
With boundless charity divine:
So shall I all my strength exert,
And love them with a zeal like Thine;
And lead them to Thy open side,
The sheep for whom their Shepherd died.

Charles Wesley, 1707-88.

391

BACA. 6.6.6.6.6 6. W. H. Havergal, 1793-1870.

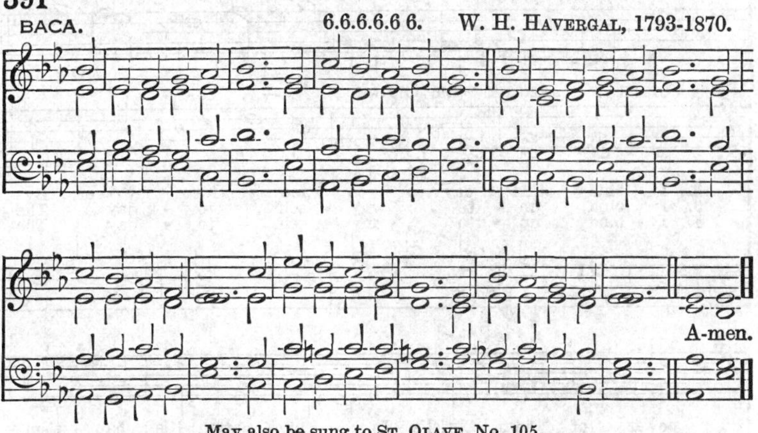

May also be sung to St. Olave, No. 105.

1 Thy life was given for me,
Thy blood, O Lord, was shed,
That I might ransomed be,
And quickened from the dead:
Thy life was given for me;
What have I given for Thee?

2 Thy Father's home of light,
Thy rainbow-circled throne,
Were left for earthly night,
For wanderings sad and lone:
Yea, all was left for me;
Have I left aught for Thee?

3 Thou, Lord, hast borne for me
More than my tongue can tell
Of bitterest agony,
To rescue me from hell:
Thou suffer'dst all for me;
What have I borne for Thee?

4 And Thou hast brought to me
Down from Thy home above
Salvation full and free,
Thy pardon and Thy love:
Great gifts Thou broughtest me;
What have I brought to Thee?

5 O let my life be given,
My years for Thee be spent,
World-fetters all be riven,
And joy with suffering blent:
Thou gav'st Thyself for me;
I give myself to Thee. Amen.

Frances Ridley Havergal, 1836-79.

The Christian Life

ST. PATRICK. Irregular.

Traditional Irish Hymn Melody.
Arr. by C. V. STANFORD, 1852-1924.

Atomriug indiu niurt tren.

UNISON.
1. I bind unto myself to-day The strong Name of the Trinity, By invocation of the same, The Three in One, and One in Three.
VOICES IN HARMONY WITH ORGAN.
2. I bind this day to me for ever, By power of faith, Christ's Incarnation; His baptism in the Jordan river; His death on Cross for
3. I bind unto myself to-day The virtues of the star-lit heaven, The glorious sun's life-giving ray, The whiteness of the
4. I bind unto myself to-day The power of God to hold and lead, His eye to watch, His might to stay, His ear to hearken

Dedication

Organ.
my . . sal - va - tion; His burst - ing
moon at e - ven, The flash - ing
to . . my need, . . The wis - dom
from the spi - ced tomb; His ri - ding up the
of the light - ning free, The whirl - ing wind's tem -
of my God to teach, His hand to guide, His
heaven - ly way; His com - ing at . . the day of
- pest - uous shocks, The sta - ble earth, the deep salt
shield to ward, The word of God to give me
doom: I bind un - to . . my - self . . to - day.
sea . . A - round the old . . e - ter - nal rocks.
speech, His heaven - ly host to be . . my guard.
DEIRDRE.
HARMONY.
8 8.8 8 D. Trochaic.
Adapted from an Ancient Irish Melody.
5. Christ be with me, Christ within me, Christ behind me, Christ before me, Christ be-

- side me, Christ to win me, Christ to com-fort and re - store me, Christ be-
- neath me, Christ a - bove me, Christ in qui - et, Christ in dan - ger, Christ in
hearts of all that love me, Christ in mouth of friend and stran-ger.
6. I bind un - to . . my - self the Name, The strong Name of . . the
Tri - ni - ty, By in - vo - ca - tion of the same, The Three in

* The accompaniment for Verse 1 may be used.

Dedication

One, and One in Three, . . Of whom all na - ture hath cre -
- a - tion, E - ter - nal Fa - ther, Spi - rit, Word. Praise to . . the
Lord of my sal - va - tion: Sal - va - tion is . . of Christ the
rall.
Lord. . . . . A - - - - men.
St. Patrick, c. 372-466;
tr. by Cecil Frances Alexander, 1823-95.
rall.

ICH HALTE TREULICH STILL. D.S.M. J. S. BACH, 1685-1750.

Cor meum Tibi dedo.

1 I GIVE my heart to Thee,
O Jesus most desired!
And heart for heart the gift shall be,
For Thou my soul hast fired:
Thou hearts alone wouldst move,
Thou only hearts dost love;
I would love Thee, as Thou lov'st me,
O Jesus most desired!

2 What offering can I make,
Dear Lord, to love like Thine?
That Thou, the Word, didst stoop to take
A human form like mine!
Give Me thy heart, My son:
Lord, Thou my heart hast won:

3 Here finds my heart its rest,
Repose that knows no shock,
The strength of love that keeps it blest
In Thee, the riven Rock:
My soul, as girt around,
Her citadel hath found:

Anonymous;
tr. by Ray Palmer, 1808-87.

394

JUST AS I AM (*First Tune*). 888.6. J. BARNBY, 1838-96.

By permission of Novello and Company, Limited.

HOWCROFT (*Second Tune*). 888.6. G. TROTTER, 1866-

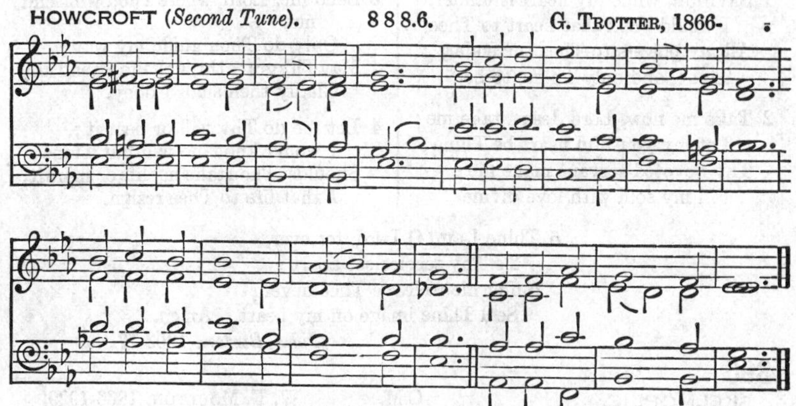

1 JUST as I am, Thine own to be,
Friend of the young, who lovest me,
To consecrate myself to Thee,
O Jesus Christ, I come.

2 In the glad morning of my day,
My life to give, my vows to pay,
With no reserve and no delay,
With all my heart I come.

3 I would live ever in the light,
I would work ever for the right,
I would serve Thee with all my might,
Therefore to Thee I come.

4 Just as I am, young, strong and free
To be the best that I can be
For truth, and righteousness, and Thee,
Lord of my life, I come.

Marianne Farningham, 1834-1909.

SHIPSTON. 8.7.8.7. English Traditional Melody.

1 Saviour, while my heart is tender,
I would yield that heart to Thee,
All my powers to Thee surrender,
Thine, and only Thine, to be.

2 Take me now, Lord Jesus, take me;
Let my youthful heart be Thine;
Thy devoted servant make me;
Fill my soul with love divine.

3 Send me, Lord, where Thou wilt send me,
Only do Thou guide my way;
May Thy grace through life attend me,
Gladly then shall I obey.

4 Let me do Thy will or bear it;
I would know no will but Thine:
Shouldst Thou take my life or spare it,
I that life to Thee resign.

5 Thine I am, O Lord, for ever,
To Thy service set apart;
Suffer me to leave Thee never;
Seal Thine image on my heart. Amen.

John Burton, 1803-77.

396

SKELMORLIE. C.M. W. F. Moulton, 1866-1929.

1 Lord, in the fullness of my might,
I would for Thee be strong:
While runneth o'er each dear delight,
To Thee should soar my song.

2 I would not give the world my heart,
And then profess Thy love;
I would not feel my strength depart,
And then Thy service prove.

3 I would not with swift-wingèd zeal
On the world's errands go,
And labour up the heavenly hill
With weary feet and slow.

4 O not for Thee my weak desires,
My poorer, baser part!
O not for Thee my fading fires,
The ashes of my heart!

5 O choose me in my golden time,
In my dear joys have part!
For Thee the glory of my prime,
The fullness of my heart!

6 I cannot, Lord, too early take
The covenant divine;
O ne'er the happy heart may break
Whose earliest love was Thine!

Thomas Hornblower Gill, 1819-1906.

397

CALVARY. 8.7.8.7.8.7. S. Stanley, 1767-1822.

1 Lord of Life and King of Glory,
Who didst deign a child to be,
Cradled on a mother's bosom,
Throned upon a mother's knee:
For the children Thou hast given
We must answer unto Thee.

2 Since the day the blessèd mother
Thee, the world's Redeemer, bore,
Thou hast crowned us with an honour
Women never knew before;
And, that we may bear it meetly,
We must seek Thine aid the more.

3 Grant us, then, pure hearts and patient,
That, in all we do or say,
Little souls our deeds may copy,
And be never led astray;
Little feet our steps may follow
In a safe and narrow way.

4 When our growing sons and daughters
Look on life with eager eyes,
Grant us then a deeper insight,
And new powers of sacrifice:
Hope to trust them, faith to guide them,
Love that nothing good denies.

5 May we keep our holy calling
Stainless in its fair renown,
That, when all the work is over,
And we lay the burden down,
Then the children Thou hast given
Still may be our joy and crown.

Christian Burke, 1859-

NUTBOURNE. 7 7.7 7.7 7. T. E. AYLWARD, 1844-1933.

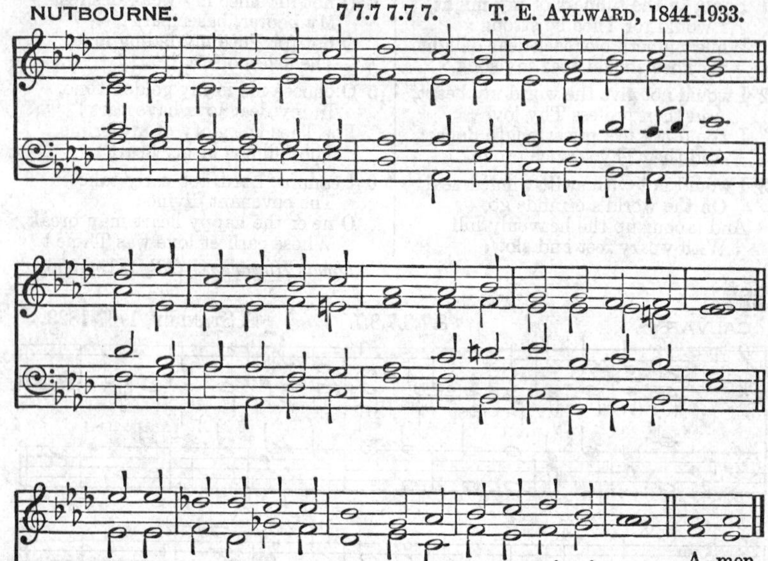

1 WHEN Thy soldiers take their swords,
When they speak the solemn words,
When they kneel before Thee here,
Feeling Thee, their Father, near:
These Thy children, Lord, defend,
To their help Thy Spirit send.

2 When the world's sharp strife is nigh,
When they hear the battle-cry,
When they rush into the fight,
Knowing not temptation's might:
These Thy children, Lord, defend,
To their zeal Thy wisdom lend.

3 When their hearts are lifted high
With success or victory,
When they feel the conqueror's pride—
Lest they grow self-satisfied—
These Thy children, Lord, defend,
Teach their souls to Thee to bend.

4 When the vows that they have made,
When the prayers that they have prayed,
Shall be fading from their hearts,
When their first warm faith departs:
These Thy children, Lord, defend,
Keep them faithful to the end.
Amen.

Frances Mary Owen, 1842-83.

399

MORNA. C.M. C. H. PERROT, 1842-1910.

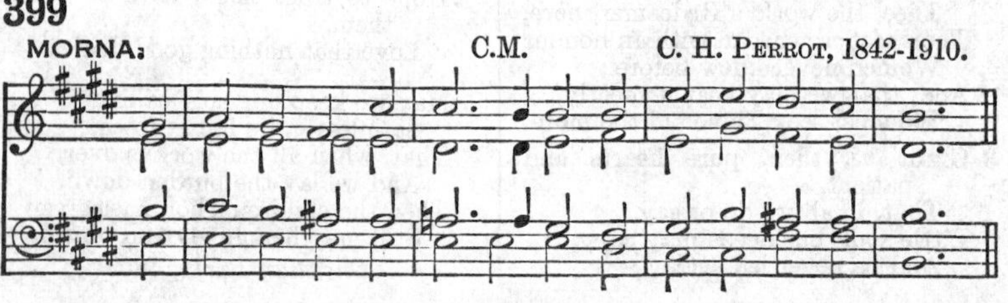

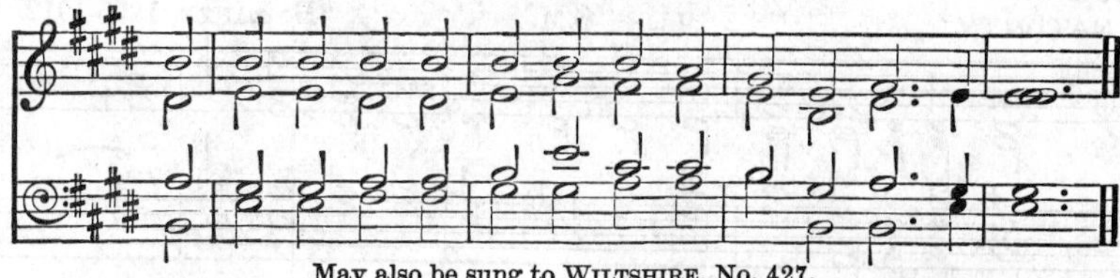

May also be sung to WILTSHIRE, No. 427.

1 WHAT shall I render to my God
For all His mercy's store ?
I'll take the gifts He hath bestowed,
And humbly ask for more.

2 The sacred cup of saving grace
I will with thanks receive,
And all His promises embrace,
And to His glory live.

3 My vows I will to His great name
Before His people pay,
And all I have, and all I am,
Upon His altar lay.

4 Thy lawful servant, Lord, I owe
To Thee whate'er is mine,
Born in Thy family below,
And by redemption Thine.

5 Thy hands created me, Thy hands
From sin have set me free,
The mercy that hath loosed my bands
Hath bound me fast to Thee.

6 The God of all-redeeming grace
My God I will proclaim,
Offer the sacrifice of praise,
And call upon His name.

7 Praise Him, ye saints, the God of love,
Who hath my sins forgiven,
Till, gathered to the church above,
We sing the songs of heaven.

Charles Wesley, 1707-88.

400

CONSECRATION. 77.77. W. H. HAVERGAL, 1793-1870.

May also be sung to NOTTINGHAM, A. T. No. 19.

1 TAKE my life, and let it be
Consecrated, Lord, to Thee.
Take my moments and my days;
Let them flow in ceaseless praise.

2 Take my hands, and let them move
At the impulse of Thy love.
Take my feet, and let them be
Swift and beautiful for Thee.

3 Take my voice, and let me sing
Always, only for my King.
Take my lips, and let them be
Filled with messages from Thee.

4 Take my silver and my gold;
Not a mite would I withhold.
Take my intellect, and use
Every power as Thou shalt choose.

5 Take my will, and make it Thine;
It shall be no longer mine.
Take my heart—it is Thine own;
It shall be Thy royal throne.

6 Take my love; my Lord, I pour
At Thy feet its treasure-store.
Take myself, and I will be
Ever, only, all for Thee!

Frances Ridley Havergal, 1836-79.

401

NATIVITY. C.M. H. Lahee, 1826-1912.

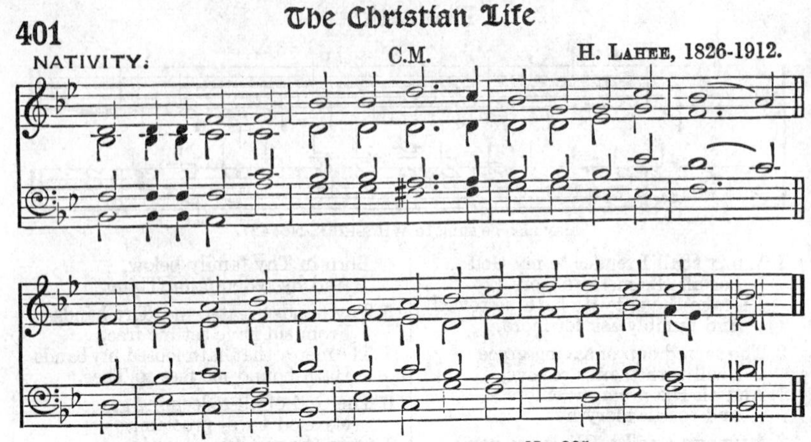

May also be sung to Bromsgrove, No. 265.

1 God's trumpet wakes the slumbering world:
Now each man to his post!
The red cross banner is unfurled:
Who joins the glorious host?

2 He who, in fealty to the truth,
And counting all the cost,
Doth consecrate his generous youth—
He joins the noble host.

3 He who, no anger on his tongue,
Nor any idle boast,
Bears steadfast witness against wrong—
He joins the sacred host.

4 He who, with calm undaunted will,
Ne'er counts the battle lost,
But, though defeated, battles still—
He joins the faithful host.

5 He who is ready for the cross,
The cause despised loves most,
And shuns not pain or shame or loss—
He joins the martyr host.

Samuel Longfellow, 1819-92.

402

FAITH OF OUR FATHERS. 8.8.8.8. and refrain. A. E. Tozer, 1857-1910.

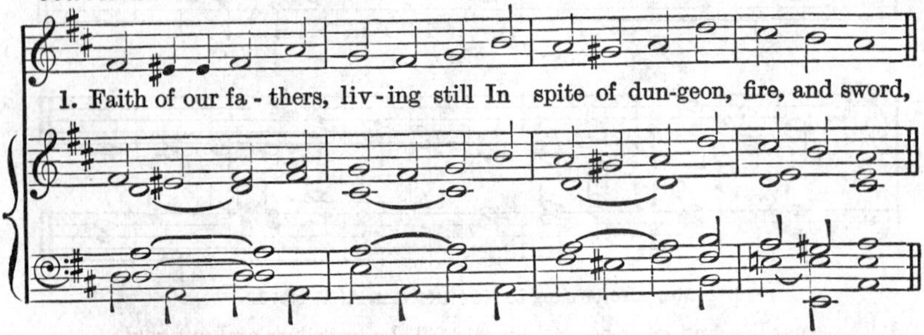

1. Faith of our fa - thers, liv - ing still In spite of dun-geon, fire, and sword,

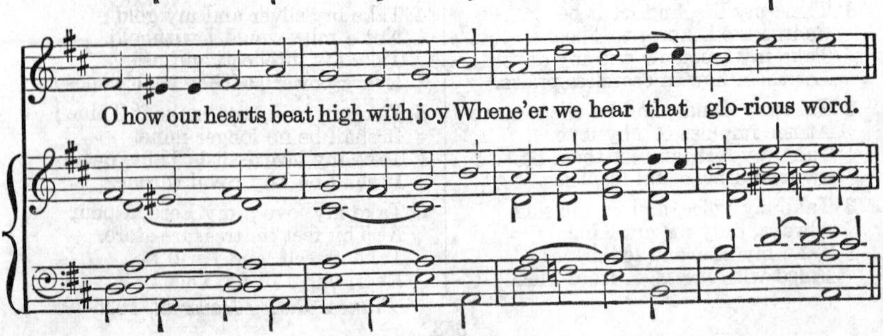

O how our hearts beat high with joy Whene'er we hear that glo-rious word.

Dedication

REFRAIN.
Faith of our fa-thers! Ho-ly faith! We will be true to thee till death;

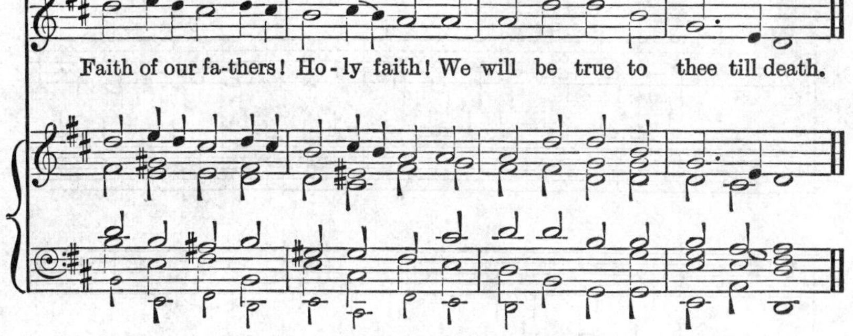

Faith of our fa-thers! Ho-ly faith! We will be true to thee till death.

May also be sung to HOLY FAITH, No. 548.

1 FAITH of our fathers, living still
In spite of dungeon, fire, and sword,
O how our hearts beat high with joy
Whene'er we hear that glorious word.

Faith of our fathers! Holy faith!
We will be true to thee till death.

2 Our fathers, chained in prisons dark,
Were still in heart and conscience free;
And blest would be their children's fate,
Though they, like them, should die for thee.

3 Faith of our fathers! God's great power
Shall soon all nations win for thee;
And through the truth that comes from God
Mankind shall then indeed be free.

4 Faith of our fathers! We will love
Both friend and foe in all our strife,
And preach thee, too, as love knows how,
By kindly words and virtuous life:

Frederick William Faber (*v. 3 alt.*), 1814-63.

403

CHRIST FOR ME. 8.3.8.3.8 8 8.3. Unknown.

May also be sung to BETTER WORLD, No. 22.

1 My heart is fixed, eternal God,
Fixed on Thee:
And my immortal choice is made:
Christ for me.
He is my Prophet, Priest, and King,
Who did for me salvation bring;
And while I've breath I mean to sing:
Christ for me.

2 In Him I see the Godhead shine;
Christ for me.
He is the Majesty Divine;
Christ for me.
The Father's well-belovèd Son,
Co-partner of His royal throne,
Who did for human guilt atone;
Christ for me.

3 In pining sickness or in health,
Christ for me,
In deepest poverty or wealth,
Christ for me.
And in that all-important day,
When I the summons must obey,
And pass from this dark world away,
Christ for me.

Richard Jukes, 1804-67.

404

DAVID'S HARP. L.M. J. DANIEL, 1842

1 How blest is life if lived for Thee,
My loving Saviour and my Lord:
No pleasures that the world can give
Such perfect gladness can afford.

2 To know I am Thy ransomed child,
Bought by Thine own most precious blood,
And from Thy loving hand to take
With grateful heart each gift of good;

3 All day to walk beneath Thy smile,
Watching Thine eye to guide me still,
To rest at night beneath Thy care,
Guarded by Thee from every ill;

4 To feel that though I journey on
By stony paths and rugged ways,
Thy blessèd feet have gone before,
And strength is given for weary days.

5 Such love shall ever make me glad,
Strong in Thy strength to work or rest,
Until I see Thee face to face,
And in Thy light am fully blest.

Anonymous:
Prust's Supplementary Hymn Book, 1869.

405

GOD BE IN MY HEAD. Irregular. H. WALFORD DAVIES, 1869-1941.

Organ.
God be in my head,
And in my un-derstanding; God be in mine eyes, And in my looking;
God be in my mouth, And in my speak - ing;
God be in my heart, And in my think - ing;
God be at mine end, And at my de - part - ing. A - men.

Anonymous: from a Sarum Primer, 1558.

Also:

157 Jesus calls us
182 When I survey
451 I lift my heart
526 O Jesus, I have promised
567 In full and glad surrender
573 O God, what offering
594 Lord, in the strength
744 O happy day

406

HARWICH. 5 5 11. D. B. MILGROVE, c. 1731-1810.

1 My God, I am Thine;
What a comfort divine,
What a blessing to know that my Jesus is mine!
In the heavenly Lamb
Thrice happy I am,
And my heart it doth dance at the sound of His name.

2 True pleasures abound
In the rapturous sound;
And whoever hath found it hath paradise found.
My Jesus to know,
And feel His blood flow,
'Tis life everlasting, 'tis heaven below.

3 Yet onward I haste
To the heavenly feast:
That, that is the fullness; but this is the taste;
And this I shall prove,
Till with joy I remove
To the heaven of heavens in Jesus's love.

Charles Wesley, 1707-88.

407

HUNGERFORD. 5 6.9.6 6.9. From *The Hallelujah*, 1849.

1 How happy are they
Who the Saviour obey,
And have laid up their treasure [above.
Tongue cannot express
The sweet comfort and peace
Of a soul in its earliest love.

2 That comfort was mine,
When the favour divine
I first found in the blood of the Lamb;
When my heart it believed,
What a joy it received,
What a heaven in Jesus's name!

3 Jesus all the day long
Was my joy and my song;
O that all His salvation may see!
He hath loved me, I cried,
He hath suffered, and died,
To redeem such a rebel as me.

4 O the rapturous height
Of the holy delight
Which I felt in the life-giving blood!
Of my Saviour possessed
I was perfectly blessed
As if filled with the fullness of God.

Charles Wesley, 1707-88.

408

ST. BERNARD. C.M. Adapted by J. RICHARDSON, 1816-79.

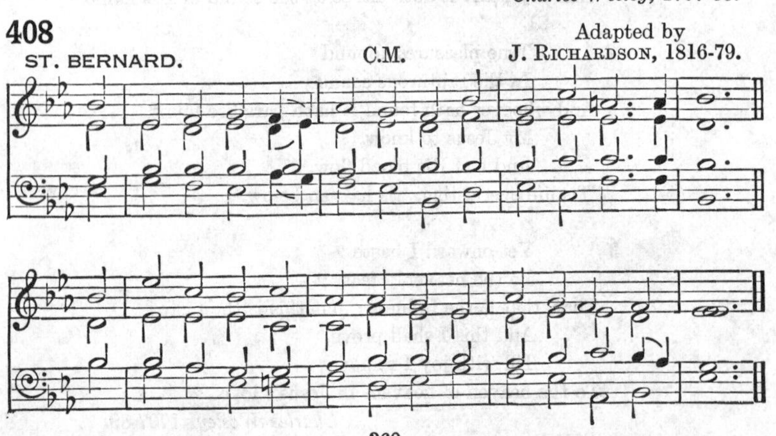

1 My God, the spring of all my joys,
The life of my delights,
The glory of my brightest days,
And comfort of my nights.

2 In darkest shades, if Thou appear,
My dawning is begun;
Thou art my soul's bright morning star,
And Thou my rising sun.

3 The opening heavens around me shine
With beams of sacred bliss,
If Jesus shows His mercy mine
And whispers I am His.

4 My soul would leave this heavy clay
At that transporting word,
Run up with joy the shining way
To see and praise my Lord.

5 Fearless of hell and ghastly death,
I'd break through every foe;
The wings of love and arms of faith
Would bear me conqueror through.

Isaac Watts, 1674-1748.

409

SHARON. C.M. T. Wallhead, 1846-1928.

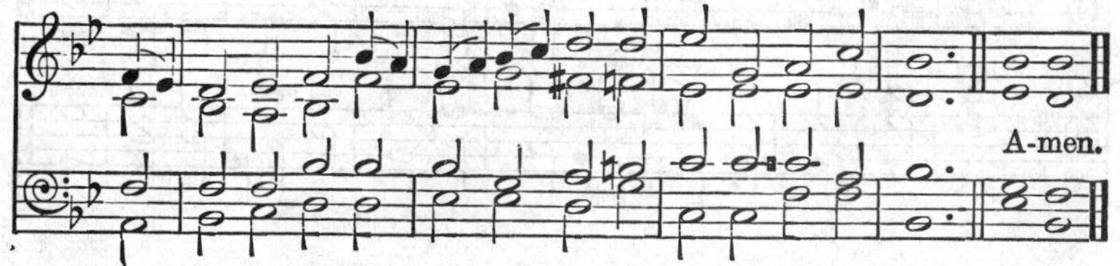

1 The glory of the spring how sweet,
The new-born life how glad;
What joy the happy earth to greet
In new, bright raiment clad.

2 Divine Renewer, Thee I bless;
I greet Thy going forth:
I love Thee in the loveliness
Of Thy renewèd earth.

3 But O these wonders of Thy grace,
These nobler works of Thine,
These marvels sweeter far to trace,
These new births more divine!

4 This new-born glow of faith so strong,
This bloom of love so fair,
This new-born ecstasy of song,
And fragrancy of prayer.

5 Creator Spirit, work in me
These wonders sweet of Thine;
Divine Renewer, graciously
Renew this heart of mine. Amen.

Thomas Hornblower Gill, 1819-1906.

410

RIDGE (First Tune). D.S.M. S. Wesley, 1766-1837.
ASCENSION (Second Tune). D.S.M. H. J. Gauntlett, 1805-76.
Unison.
Harmony.

Joy and Thanksgiving

1 Come, ye that love the Lord,
And let your joys be known;
Join in a song with sweet accord,
While ye surround His throne:
Let those refuse to sing
Who never knew our God;
But servants of the heavenly King
May speak their joys abroad.

2 The God that rules on high,
That all the earth surveys,
That rides upon the stormy sky,
And calms the roaring seas:
This awful God is ours,
Our Father and our love;
He will send down His heavenly powers,
To carry us above.

3 There we shall see His face,
And never, never sin;
There, from the rivers of His grace,
Drink endless pleasures in:
Yea, and before we rise
To that immortal state,
The thoughts of such amazing bliss
Should constant joys create.

4 The men of grace have found
Glory begun below;
Celestial fruit on earthly ground
From faith and hope may grow:
Then let our songs abound,
And every tear be dry;
We are marching through Immanuel's ground,
To fairer worlds on high.

N *Isaac Watts*, 1674-1748.

411, 412

7.7.4 4.7. D.

DYING STEPHEN (*First Tune*). J. F. LAMPE, 1703-51.

7.7.4 4.7. D.

DELIVERANCE (*Second Tune*). H. J. GAUNTLETT, 1805-76.

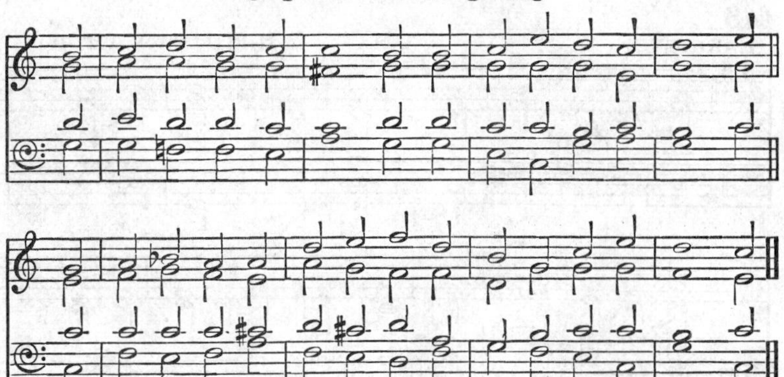

411

1 Head of Thy Church triumphant,
We joyfully adore Thee,
Till Thou appear,
Thy members here
Shall sing like those in glory.
We lift our hearts and voices
With blest anticipation,
And cry aloud,
And give to God
The praise of our salvation.

2 The name we still acknowledge
That burst our bonds in sunder,
And loudly sing
Our conquering King,
In songs of joy and wonder.
In every day's deliverance
Our Jesus we discover;
'Tis He, 'tis He
That smote the sea,
And led us safely over!

3 While in affliction's furnace,
And passing through the fire,
Thy love we praise,
Which knows our days
And ever brings us nigher.
We clap our hands exulting
In Thine almighty favour;
The love divine
Which made us Thine
Shall keep us Thine for ever.

4 By faith we see the glory
To which Thou shalt restore us;
The Cross despise
For that high prize
Which Thou hast set before us.
And if Thou count us worthy,
We each, as dying Stephen,
Shall see Thee stand
At God's right hand
To take us up to heaven.

Charles Wesley, 1707-88.

412

1 Worship, and thanks, and blessing,
And strength ascribe to Jesus!
Jesus alone
Defends His own,
When earth and hell oppress us.
Jesus with joy we witness
Almighty to deliver;
Our seals set to,
That God is true,
And reigns a King for ever.

2 Omnipotent Redeemer,
Our ransomed souls adore Thee:
Our Saviour Thou,
We find it now,
And give Thee all the glory.
We sing Thine arm unshortened,
Brought through our sore temptation;
With heart and voice
In Thee rejoice,
The God of our salvation.

3 Thine arm hath safely brought us
A way no more expected,
Than when Thy sheep
Passed through the deep,
By crystal walls protected.
Thy glory was our rearward,
Thine hand our lives did cover,
And we, even we,
Have passed the sea,
And marched triumphant over.

4 The world and Satan's malice
Thou, Jesus, hast confounded;
And, by Thy grace,
With songs of praise
Our happy souls resounded.
Accepting our deliverance,
We triumph in Thy favour,
And for the love
Which now we prove
Shall praise Thy name for ever.

Charles Wesley, 1707-88.

413

HARINGTON. C.M. H. HARINGTON, 1727-1816.

1 WHEN all Thy mercies, O my God,
My rising soul surveys,
Transported with the view, I'm lost
In wonder, love and praise.

2 Unnumbered comforts on my soul
Thy tender care bestowed,
Before my infant heart conceived
From whom those comforts flowed.

3 Through hidden dangers, toils, and deaths,
It gently cleared my way;
And through the pleasing snares of vice,
More to be feared than they.

4 Ten thousand thousand precious gifts
My daily thanks employ;
Nor is the least a thankful heart,
That takes those gifts with joy.

5 Through every period of my life
Thy goodness I'll pursue;
And after death, in distant worlds,
The glorious theme renew.

6 Through all eternity, to Thee
A grateful song I'll raise;
But O eternity's too short
To utter all Thy praise!

Joseph Addison, 1672-1719.

414

HOLLY. L.M. G. HEWS, 1806-73.

1 We thank Thee, Lord, for this fair earth,
The glittering sky, the silver sea;
For all their beauty, all their worth,
Their light and glory, come from Thee.

2 Thanks for the flowers that clothe the ground,
The trees that wave their arms above,
The hills that gird our dwellings round,
As Thou dost gird Thine own with love.

3 Yet teach us still how far more fair,
More glorious, Father, in Thy sight,
Is one pure deed, one holy prayer,
One heart that owns Thy Spirit's might.

4 So, while we gaze with thoughtful eye
On all the gifts Thy love has given,
Help us in Thee to live and die,
By Thee to rise from earth to heaven. Amen.

George Edward Lynch Cotton, 1813-66.

415

MIT FREUDEN ZART. 8.7.8.7.8 8.7.
Bohemian Brethren, *Kirchengesänge*, 1566.

UNISON.

May also be sung to LUTHER, No. 71.

Sei Lob und Ehr dem höchsten Gut.

1 Sing praise to God who reigns above,
The God of all creation,
The God of power, the God of love,
The God of our salvation;
With healing balm my soul He fills,
And every faithless murmur stills:
To God all praise and glory.

2 What God's almighty power hath made,
His gracious mercy keepeth;
By morning glow or evening shade
His watchful eye ne'er sleepeth;
Within the kingdom of His might,
Lo! all is just and all is right:
To God all praise and glory.

3 The Lord is never far away,
But, through all grief distressing,
An ever-present help and stay,
Our peace, and joy, and blessing;
As with a mother's tender hand,
He leads His own, His chosen band:
To God all praise and glory.

4 Thus, all my toilsome way along,
I sing aloud Thy praises,
That men may hear the grateful song
My voice unwearied raises;
Be joyful in the Lord, my heart,
Both soul and body bear your part:
To God all praise and glory. Amen.

Johann Jakob Schültz, 1640-90;
tr. by Frances Elizabeth Cox, 1812-97.

416

CHARTERHOUSE. 7.7.7.7.7.7. A. S. COOPER, 1835-1900.

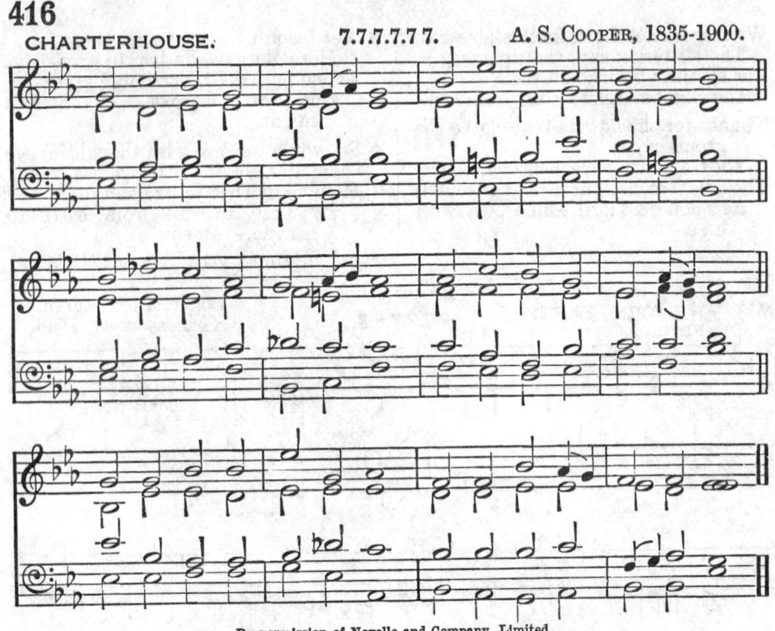

By permission of Novello and Company, Limited.

1 LIFE and light and joy are found
In the presence of the Lord;
Life with richest blessing crowned,
Light from many fountains poured;
Life and light and holy joy,
None can darken or destroy.

2 Bring to Him life's brightest hours,
He will make them still more bright;
Give to Him your noblest powers,
He will hallow all your might;
Come to Him with eager quest,
You shall hear His high behest.

3 All your questions large and deep,
All the open thoughts of youth,
Bring to Him and you shall reap
All the harvest of His truth;
You shall find in that great store
Largest love and wisest lore.

4 Then when comes life's wider sphere
And its busier enterprise,
You shall find Him ever near,
Looking with approving eyes,
On all honest work and true
His dear servants' hands can do.

Charles Edward Mudie, 1818-90.

417

NORMANDY. 8.7.8.7. D. C. BOST, 1790-1874.

May also be sung to Lux Eoi, No. 706.

1 Come, Thou Fount of every blessing,
Tune my heart to sing Thy grace;
Streams of mercy never ceasing
Call for songs of loudest praise.
Teach me some melodious measure
Sung by flaming tongues above;
O the vast, the boundless treasure
Of my Lord's unchanging love!

2 Here I raise my Ebenezer;
Hither by Thy help I'm come;
And I hope, by Thy good pleasure,
Safely to arrive at home.
Jesus sought me when a stranger,
Wandering from the fold of God;
He, to rescue me from danger,
Interposed His precious blood.

3 O to grace how great a debtor
Daily I'm constrained to be!
Let that grace, Lord, like a fetter,
Bind my wandering heart to Thee:
Prone to wander, Lord, I feel it,
Prone to leave the God I love;
Take my heart, O take and seal it,
Seal it from Thy courts above!
Amen.

Robert Robinson, 1735-90.

418

SAMSON. L.M. From Handel's *Samson*, 1742.

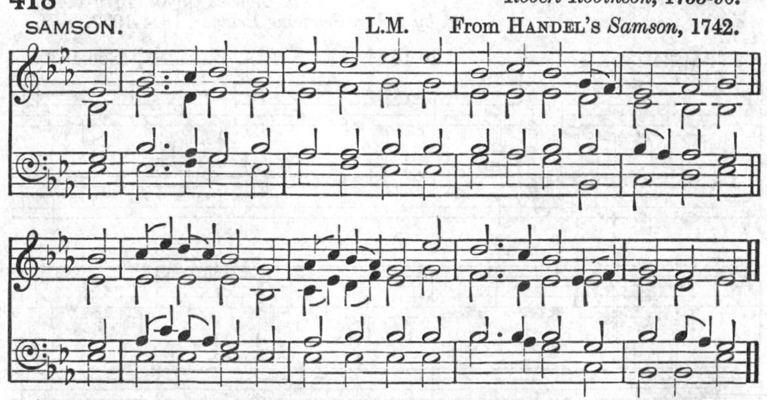

1 Awake, our souls! Away, our fears!
Let every trembling thought be gone!
Awake, and run the heavenly race,
And put a cheerful courage on.

2 True, 'tis a strait and thorny road,
And mortal spirits tire and faint;
But they forget the mighty God
That feeds the strength of every saint.

3 O mighty God, Thy matchless power
Is ever new and ever young,
And firm endures, while endless years
Their everlasting circles run.

4 From Thee, the ever flowing spring,
Our souls shall drink a fresh supply;
While such as trust their native strength
Shall melt away, and droop, and die.

5 Swift as the eagle cuts the air,
We'll mount aloft to Thine abode;
On wings of love our souls shall fly,
Nor tire along the heavenly road.

Isaac Watts, 1674-1748.

419

BINCHESTER. C.M. W. CROFT, 1678-1727.

O quam juvat, fratres, Deus.

1 HAPPY are they, they that love God,
Whose hearts have Christ confest,
Who by His Cross have found their life,
And 'neath His yoke their rest.

2 Glad is the praise, sweet are the songs,
When they together sing;
And strong the prayers that bow the ear
Of heaven's eternal King.

3 Christ to their homes giveth His peace,
And makes their loves His own;
But ah, what tares the evil one
Hath in His garden sown.

4 Sad were our lot, evil this earth,
Did not its sorrows prove
The path whereby the sheep may find
The fold of Jesus' love.

5 Then shall they know, they that love Him,
How all their pain is good;
And death itself cannot unbind
Their happy brotherhood.

Charles Coffin, 1676-1749;
tr. by Robert Seymour Bridges, 1844-1930, *Y.H.*

420

ST. MERRYN. 10 10.11 11. H. A. HARDING, 1856-1930.

1 O WHAT shall I do my Saviour to praise,
So faithful and true, so plenteous in grace,
So strong to deliver, so good to redeem
The weakest believer that hangs upon Him.

2 How happy the man whose heart is set free,
The people that can be joyful in Thee;
Their joy is to walk in the light of Thy face,
And still they are talking of Jesus's grace.

3 Their daily delight shall be in Thy name;
They shall as their right Thy righteousness claim;
Thy righteousness wearing, and cleansed by Thy blood,
Bold shall they appear in the presence of God.

4 For Jesus, my Lord, is now my defence;
I trust in His word, none plucks me from thence;
Since I have found favour, He all things will do;
My King and my Saviour shall make me anew.

Charles Wesley, 1707-88.

421

I AM SO GLAD. 10 10.10 10. and refrain. P. BLISS, 1838-76.

REFRAIN.
I am so glad that Jesus loves me,
Jesus loves me, Jesus loves me, I am so glad that Jesus loves me, Jesus loves e-ven me. . .

1 I AM so glad that our Father in heaven
Tells of His love in the Book He has given:
Wonderful things in the Bible I see;
This is the dearest, that Jesus loves me.
I am so glad that Jesus loves me,
Jesus loves even me.

2 Though I forget Him, and wander away,
Still He doth love me wherever I stray;
Back to His dear loving arms do I flee,
When I remember that Jesus loves me.

3 O if there's only one song I can sing,
When in His beauty I see the great King,
This shall my song in eternity be,
O what a wonder that Jesus loves me.

4 If one should ask of me: How can I tell?
Glory to Jesus, I know very well;
God's Holy Spirit with mine doth agree,
Constantly witnessing: Jesus loves me.

Philipp Bliss, 1838-76.

BLESSÈD ASSURANCE. Irregular. Mrs. J. F. KNAPP, 1839-1908.

REFRAIN.

This is my sto - ry, this is my song, .. Praising my Sa - viour all the day long; .. This is my sto - ry, this is my song, .. Praising my Sa - viour all the day long. . .

1 BLESSÈD assurance, Jesus is mine:
O what a foretaste of glory divine!
Heir of salvation, purchase of God;
Born of His Spirit, washed in His blood.

This is my story, this is my song,
Praising my Saviour all the day long.

2 Perfect submission, perfect delight,
Visions of rapture burst on my sight;
Angels descending, bring from above
Echoes of mercy, whispers of love.

3 Perfect submission, all is at rest,
I in my Saviour am happy and blest;
Watching and waiting, looking above,
Filled with His goodness, lost in His love.

Frances Jane van Alstyne, 1820-1915.

423

CONSTANCE. 8.7.8.7. D. Iambic. A. SULLIVAN, 1842-1900.

1 I've found a Friend; O such a Friend!
He loved me ere I knew Him;
He drew me with the cords of love,
And thus He bound me to Him;
And round my heart still closely twine
Those ties which nought can sever;
For I am His, and He is mine,
For ever and for ever.

2 I've found a Friend; O such a Friend!
He bled, He died to save me;
And not alone the gift of life,
But His own self He gave me.
Nought that I have mine own I call,
I hold it for the Giver:
My heart, my strength, my life, my all
Are His, and His for ever.

3 I've found a Friend; O such a Friend!
All power to Him is given,
To guard me on my onward course
And bring me safe to heaven.
Eternal glories gleam afar,
To nerve my faint endeavour;
So now to watch, to work, to war,
And then to rest for ever.

4 I've found a Friend; O such a Friend,
So kind, and true, and tender!
So wise a Counsellor and Guide,
So mighty a Defender!
From Him who loves me now so well
What power my soul shall sever?
Shall life or death? shall earth or hell?
No! I am His for ever.

James Grindlay Small, 1817-88.

424

MOUNT EPHRAIM. S.M. B. MILGROVE, *c.* 1731-1810.

1 O BLESS the Lord, my soul!
Let all within me join,
And aid my tongue to bless His name
Whose favours are divine.

2 O bless the Lord, my soul!
Nor let His mercies lie
Forgotten in unthankfulness,
And without praises die.

3 'Tis He forgives thy sins,
'Tis He relieves thy pain,
'Tis He that heals thy sicknesses,
And makes thee young again.

4 He fills the poor with good,
He gives the sufferers rest;
The Lord hath judgements for the proud,
And justice for the oppressed.

5 His wondrous works and ways
He made by Moses known;
But sent the world His truth and grace
By His belovèd Son.

Isaac Watts, 1674-1748.

425

SPRINGTIDE HOUR. 4 4.6. D. J. BARNBY, 1838-96.

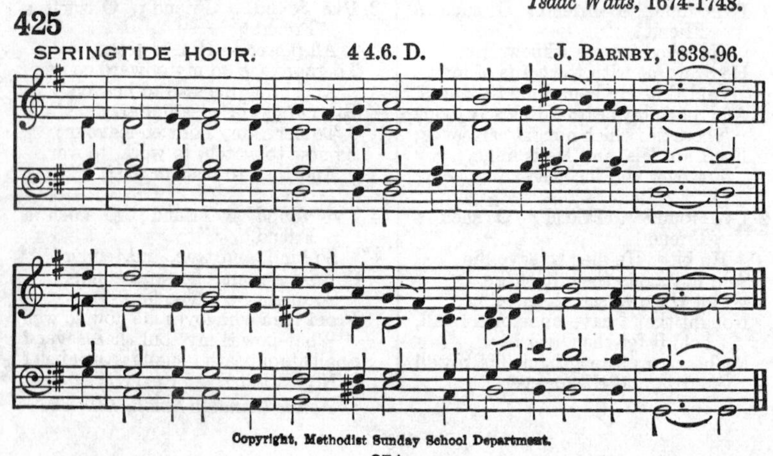

1 My God, my King,
Thy praise I sing,
My heart is all Thine own;
My highest powers,
My choicest hours,
I yield to Thee alone.

2 My voice awake,
Thy part to take;
My soul the concert join;
Till all around
Shall catch the sound,
And mix their hymns with mine.

3 But man is weak
Thy praise to speak,
Your God, ye angels, sing;
'Tis yours to see,
More near than we,
The glories of our King.

4 His truth and grace
Fill time and space;
As large His honours be,
Till all that live
Their homage give,
And praise my God with me.

Henry Francis Lyte, 1793-1847.

426

LAUDATE DOMINUM. 5.5.5.5.6.5.6.5. C. H. H. PARRY, 1848-1918.

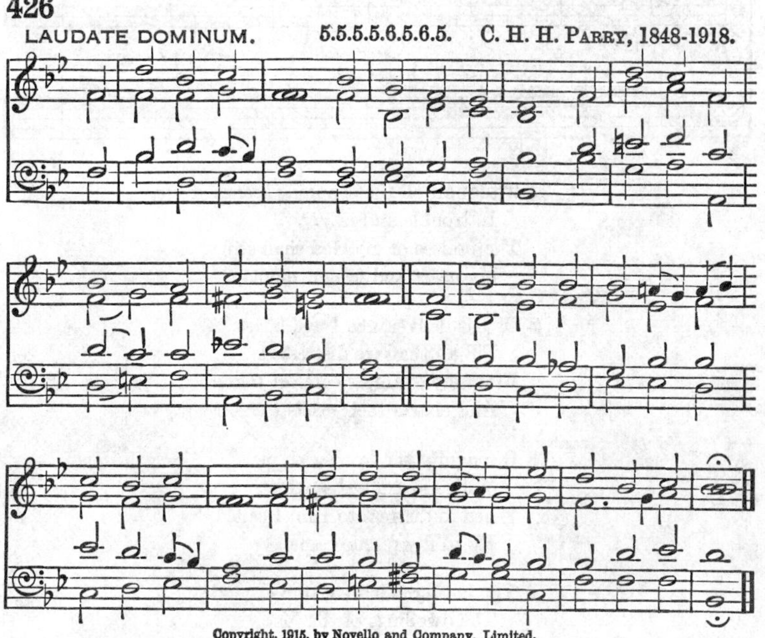

1 YE servants of God,
Your Master proclaim,
And publish abroad
His wonderful name;
The name all-victorious
Of Jesus extol;
His kingdom is glorious,
And rules over all.

2 God ruleth on high,
Almighty to save;
And still He is nigh,
His presence we have;
The great congregation
His triumph shall sing,
Ascribing salvation
To Jesus our King.

3 Salvation to God,
Who sits on the throne!
Let all cry aloud,
And honour the Son:
The praises of Jesus,
The angels proclaim,
Fall down on their faces,
And worship the Lamb.

4 Then let us adore,
And give Him His right,
All glory and power,
All wisdom and might,
All honour and blessing,
With angels above,
And thanks never-ceasing,
And infinite love.

Charles Wesley, 1707-88.

427

WILTSHIRE. C.M. G. T. SMART, 1776-1867.

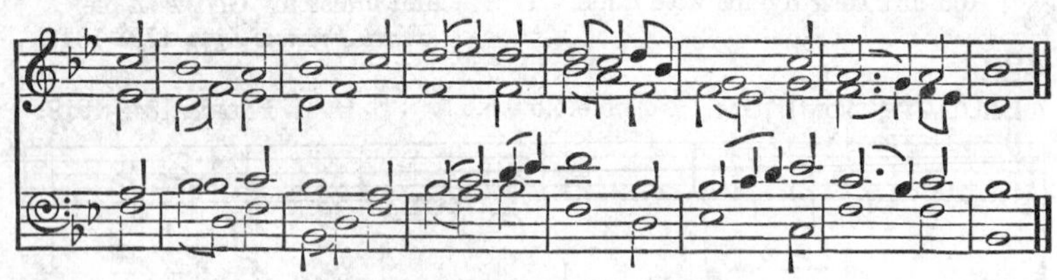

1 THROUGH all the changing scenes of life,
In trouble and in joy,
The praises of my God shall still
My heart and tongue employ.

2 Of His deliverance I will boast,
Till all that are distressed
From my example comfort take,
And charm their griefs to rest.

3 O magnify the Lord with me,
With me exalt His name;
When in distress to Him I called,
He to my rescue came.

4 The hosts of God encamp around
The dwellings of the just;
Deliverance He affords to all
Who on His succour trust.

5 O make but trial of His love;
Experience will decide
How blest they are, and only they,
Who in His truth confide.

6 Fear Him, ye saints, and you will then
Have nothing else to fear;
Make you His service your delight,
He'll make your wants His care.

Nahum Tate, 1652-1715;
Nicholas Brady, 1639-1726.

428

MONMOUTH. 8 8.8. D. G. DAVIS, *c.* 1768-1824.

May also be sung to DRESDEN, No. 80.

1 I'LL praise my Maker while I've
breath;
And when my voice is lost in death,
Praise shall employ my nobler
powers:
My days of praise shall ne'er be past,
While life, and thought, and being last,
Or immortality endures.

2 Happy the man whose hopes rely
On Israel's God! He made the sky,
And earth, and sea, with all their
train:
His truth for ever stands secure;
He saves the oppressed, He feeds the
poor, [vain.
And none shall find His promise

3 The Lord pours eyesight on the blind;
The Lord supports the fainting mind;
He sends the labouring conscience
peace;
He helps the stranger in distress,
The widow, and the fatherless,
And grants the prisoner sweet
release.

4 I'll praise Him while He lends me
breath;
And when my voice is lost in death,
Praise shall employ my nobler
powers:
My days of praise shall ne'er be past,
While life, and thought, and being last,
Or immortality endures.

Isaac Watts, 1674-1748.

GOD OF MY LIFE (*First Tune*). L.M. F. L. WISEMAN, 1858-1944

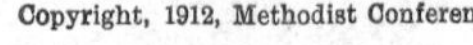

Copyright, 1912, Methodist Conference.

HEATON NORRIS (*Second Tune*). L.M. J. GRIMSHAW, ?-1818.

1 GOD of my life, through all my days
My grateful powers shall sound Thy praise;
My song shall wake with opening light,
And cheer the dark and silent night.

2 When anxious cares would break my rest,
And griefs would tear my throbbing breast,
Thy tuneful praises, raised on high,
Shall check the murmur and the sigh.

3 When death o'er nature shall prevail,
And all the powers of language fail,
Joy through my swimming eyes shall break,
And mean the thanks I cannot speak.

4 But O when that last conflict's o'er,
And I am chained to earth no more,
With what glad accents shall I rise
To join the music of the skies!

5 Soon shall I learn the exalted strains
Which echo through the heavenly plains;
And emulate, with joy unknown,
The glowing seraphs round the throne.

6 The cheerful tribute will I give
Long as a deathless soul shall live;
A work so sweet, a theme so high,
Demands and crowns eternity.

Philip Doddridge, 1702-51.

Also:

56 Sweet is the memory of Thy grace
69 This, this is the God we adore
70 All my hope on God is founded
108 Jesu, the very thought of Thee
207 Christ the Lord is risen again
214 Awake, glad soul
231 Away with gloom
235 I know that my Redeemer lives
278 Away with our fears
367 Day after day
368 Arise, my soul, arise
371 And can it be
399 What shall I render
524 My God, I thank Thee who hast made
525 Through the love of God our Saviour
744 O happy day

430

GIESSEN. 8.8.8.8.8.8. Unknown.

May also be sung to St. Matthias, No. 692.

O Jesu Christ, mein schönstes Licht.

1 Jesu, Thy boundless love to me
No thought can reach, no tongue declare;
O knit my thankful heart to Thee,
And reign without a rival there:
Thine wholly, Thine alone, I am,
Be Thou alone my constant flame.

2 O grant that nothing in my soul
May dwell but Thy pure love alone;
O may Thy love possess me whole,
My joy, my treasure, and my crown:
Strange flames far from my heart remove;
My every act, word, thought, be love.

3 O Love, how cheering is Thy ray;
All pain before Thy presence flies,
Care, anguish, sorrow, melt away,
Where'er Thy healing beams arise:
O Jesu, nothing may I see,
Nothing desire, or seek, but Thee.

4 Unwearied may I this pursue,
Dauntless to the high prize aspire;
Hourly within my soul renew
This holy flame, this heavenly fire;
And day and night be all my care
To guard the sacred treasure there.

Paulus Gerhardt, 1607-76;
tr. by John Wesley, 1703-91.

LOVE DIVINE (*First Tune*). 8.7.8.7. D. J. ZUNDEL, 1815-82.

BITHYNIA (*Second Tune*). 8.7.8.7. D. S. WEBBE, 1740-1816.

1 Love divine, all loves excelling,
Joy of heaven, to earth come down;
Fix in us Thy humble dwelling,
All Thy faithful mercies crown:
Jesu, Thou art all compassion,
Pure, unbounded love Thou art;
Visit us with Thy salvation,
Enter every trembling heart.

2 Come, almighty to deliver,
Let us all Thy grace receive;
Suddenly return, and never,
Never more Thy temples leave:
Thee we would be always blessing,
Serve Thee as Thy hosts above,
Pray, and praise Thee, without ceasing,
Glory in Thy perfect love.

3 Finish then Thy new creation,
Pure and spotless let us be;
Let us see Thy great salvation,
Perfectly restored in Thee;
Changed from glory into glory,
Till in heaven we take our place,
Till we cast our crowns before Thee,
Lost in wonder, love, and praise.

Charles Wesley, 1707-88.

432

ST. BEES. 7 7.7 7. J. B. Dykes, 1823-76.

May be sung to Christ Chapel, No. 540.

1 Hark, my soul! it is the Lord;
'Tis thy Saviour, hear His word;
Jesus speaks, and speaks to thee:
Say, poor sinner, lov'st thou Me?

2 I delivered thee when bound,
And, when bleeding, healed thy wound;
Sought thee wandering, set thee right;
Turned thy darkness into light.

3 Can a woman's tender care
Cease toward the child she bare?
Yes, she may forgetful be;
Yet will I remember thee.

4 Mine is an unchanging love,
Higher than the heights above,
Deeper than the depths beneath,
Free and faithful, strong as death.

5 Thou shalt see My glory soon,
When the work of grace is done;
Partner of My throne shalt be;
Say, poor sinner, lov'st thou Me?

6 Lord, it is my chief complaint
That my love is weak and faint;
Yet I love Thee, and adore;
O for grace to love Thee more. Amen.

William Cowper, 1731-1800.

433

ALDERSGATE STREET. 8.8.8.8.8.8. E. F. HORNER, 1864-1928.

May also be sung to EUPHONY, No. 173.

Verborgne Gottesliebe du.

1 THOU hidden love of God, whose height,
Whose depth unfathomed, no man knows,
I see from far Thy beauteous light,
Inly I sigh for Thy repose;
My heart is pained, nor can it be
At rest, till it finds rest in Thee.

2 Thy secret voice invites me still
The sweetness of Thy yoke to prove;
And fain I would: but though my will
Seems fixed, yet wide my passions rove;
Yet hindrances strew all the way;
I aim at Thee, yet from Thee stray.

3 'Tis mercy all, that Thou hast brought
My mind to seek her peace in Thee;
Yet, while I seek but find Thee not,
No peace my wandering soul shall see:
O when shall all my wanderings end,
And all my steps to Thee-ward tend!

4 Is there a thing beneath the sun
That strives with Thee my heart to share?
Ah, tear it thence, and reign alone,
The Lord of every motion there!
Then shall my heart from earth be free,
When it hath found repose in Thee.

5 O hide this self from me, that I
No more, but Christ in me, may live!
My vile affections crucify,
Nor let one darling lust survive!
In all things nothing may I see,
Nothing desire or seek, but Thee!

6 Each moment draw from earth away
My heart, that lowly waits Thy call;
Speak to my inmost soul, and say,
I am thy Love, thy God, thy All!
To feel Thy power, to hear Thy voice,
To taste Thy love, be all my choice.
Amen.

Gerhard Tersteegen, 1697-1769;
tr. by John Wesley, 1703-91.

434

ALLGÜTIGER, MEIN PREISGESANG 8 8.6. D. G. P. WEIMAR, 1734-1800.

May also be sung to PRAISE, No. 487.

1 O LOVE divine, how sweet Thou art!
When shall I find my willing heart
All taken up by Thee?
I thirst, I faint, I die to prove
The greatness of redeeming love,
The love of Christ to me.

2 Stronger His love than death or hell;
Its riches are unsearchable;
The first-born sons of light
Desire in vain its depths to see,
They cannot reach the mystery,
The length, the breadth, and height.

3 God only knows the love of God;
O that it now were shed abroad
In this poor stony heart!
For love I sigh, for love I pine:
This only portion, Lord, be mine,
Be mine this better part!

4 O that I could for ever sit
Like Mary at the Master's feet!
Be this my happy choice:
My only care, delight, and bliss,
My joy, my heaven on earth, be this—
To hear the Bridegroom's voice!

Charles Wesley, 1707-88.

435

LOVEST THOU ME. 8.8.8.4. F. L. WISEMAN, 1858-1944

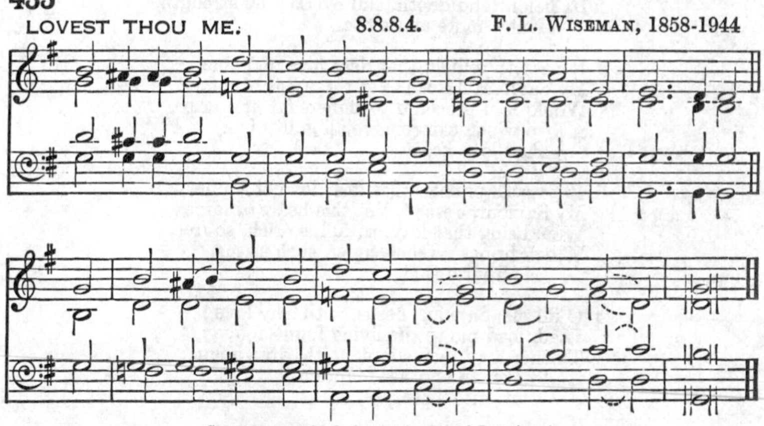

1 LOVE is the key of life and death,
Of hidden heavenly mystery:
Of all Christ is, of all He saith,
Love is the key.

2 As three times to His saint He saith,
He saith to me, He saith to thee,
Breathing His grace-conferring breath:
Lovest thou Me?

3 Ah, Lord, I have such feeble faith,
Such feeble hope to comfort me:
But love it is, is strong as death;
And I love Thee.

Christina Georgina Rossetti, 1830-94.

436

IT PASSETH KNOWLEDGE. 10 10.10 10.4. I. D. SANKEY, 1840-1908.

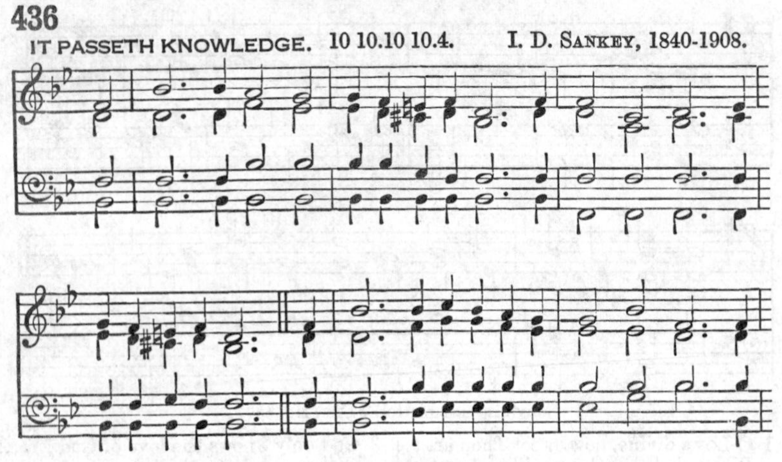

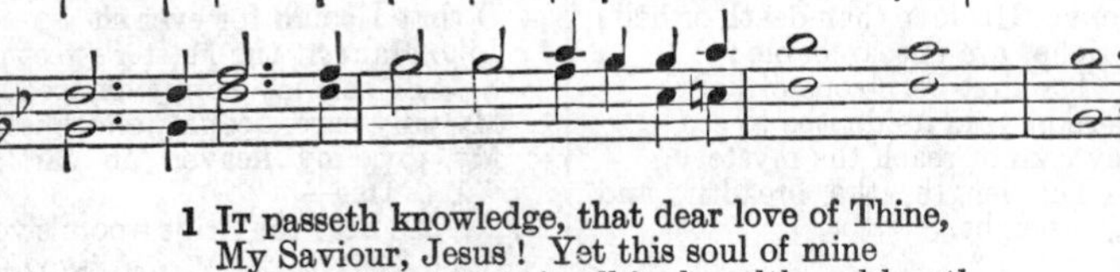

1 It passeth knowledge, that dear love of Thine,
My Saviour, Jesus! Yet this soul of mine
Would of Thy love, in all its breadth and length,
Its height and depth, and everlasting strength,
Know more and more.

2 It passeth telling, that dear love of Thine,
My Saviour, Jesus! Yet these lips of mine
Would fain proclaim to sinners far and near
A love which can remove all guilty fear,
And love beget.

3 It passeth praises, that dear love of Thine,
My Saviour, Jesus! Yet this heart of mine
Would sing that love, so full, so rich, so free,
Which brings a rebel sinner, such as me,
Nigh unto God.

4 O fill me, Saviour, Jesus, with Thy love!
Lead, lead me to the living fount above;
Thither may I, in simple faith, draw nigh,
And never to another fountain fly,
But unto Thee.

5 And then, when Jesus face to face I see,
When at His lofty throne I bow the knee,
Then of His love, in all its breadth and length,
Its height and depth, its everlasting strength,
My soul shall sing.

Mary Shekleton, 1827-83.

MY JESUS, I LOVE THEE. 11 11.11 11. Unknown.

1 My Jesus, I love Thee, I know Thou art mine,
For Thee all the pleasures of sin I resign;
My gracious Redeemer, my Saviour art Thou,
If ever I loved Thee, my Jesus, 'tis now.

2 I love Thee because Thou hast first lovèd me,
And purchased my pardon on Calvary's tree;
I love Thee for wearing the thorns on Thy brow,
If ever I loved Thee, my Jesus, 'tis now.

3 I will love Thee in life, I will love Thee in death,
And praise Thee as long as Thou lendest me breath;
And say, when the death-dew lies cold on my brow,
If ever I loved Thee, my Jesus, 'tis now.

4 In mansions of glory and endless delight,
I'll ever adore Thee and dwell in Thy sight;
I'll sing with the glittering crown on my brow,
If ever I loved Thee, my Jesus, 'tis now.

J. H. Duffell:
The London Hymn Book, 1864

438

8 8.8 8.8 8.

ST. CHRYSOSTOM (BARNBY). J. BARNBY, 1838-96.

A - men.

By permission of Novello and Company, Limited.

1 JESU, my Lord, my God, my All,
Hear me, blest Saviour, when I call;
Hear me, and from Thy dwelling-place
Pour down the riches of Thy grace:

Jesu, my Lord, I Thee adore;
O make me love Thee more and more.

2 Jesu, too late I Thee have sought;
How can I love Thee as I ought?
And how extol Thy matchless fame,
The glorious beauty of Thy name?

3 Jesu, what didst Thou find in me,
That Thou hast dealt so lovingly?
How great the joy that Thou hast brought,
So far exceeding hope or thought!

4 Jesu, of Thee shall be my song;
To Thee my heart and soul belong;
All that I have or am is Thine,
And Thou, blest Saviour, Thou art mine: Amen.

Henry Collins, 1827-1919.

439

SAFFRON WALDEN. 8.8.8.6. A. H. BROWN, 1830-1926.

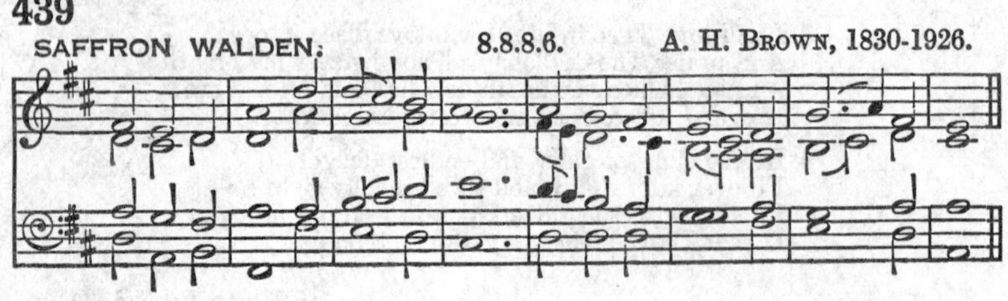

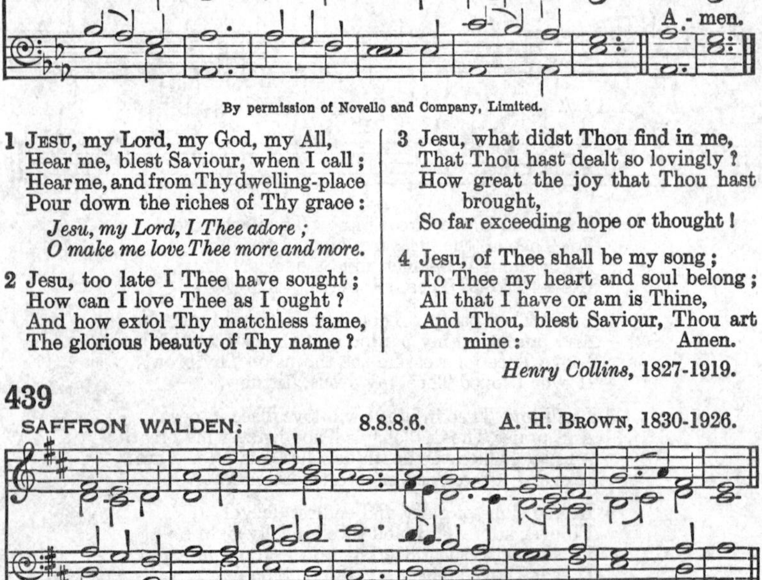

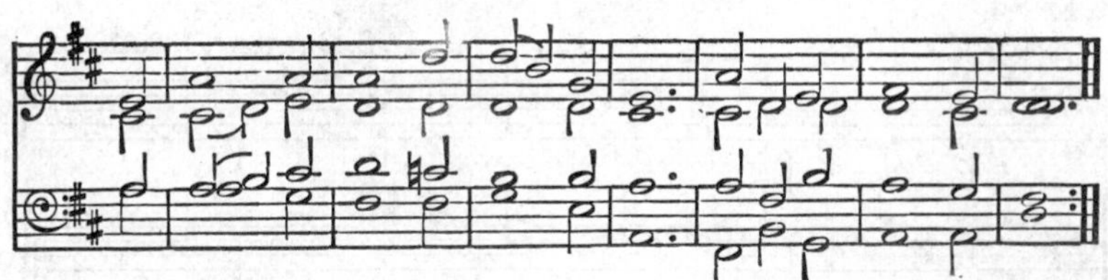

1 O Saviour, I have nought to plead,
In earth beneath or heaven above,
But just my own exceeding need,
And Thy exceeding love.

2 The need will soon be past and gone,
Exceeding great, but quickly o'er;
The love unbought is all Thine own,
And lasts for evermore.

Jane Crewdson, 1809-63.

440

FULNECK. 6 6.7.7.7.7. C. Latrobe, 1758-1836.

1 Far off we need not rove
To find the God of love;
In His providential care,
Ever intimately near,
All His various works declare,
God, the bounteous God is here.

2 We live, and move, and are,
Through His preserving care;
He doth still in life maintain
Every soul that moves and lives;
Gives us back our breath again,
Being every moment gives.

3 Who live O God in Thee,
Entirely Thine should be:
Thine we are, a heaven-born race,
Only to Thy glory move,
Thee with all our powers we praise,
Thee with all our being love.

Charles Wesley, 1707-88.

441

DOMINICA. S.M. H. S. OAKELEY, 1830-1903.

1 RICHES unsearchable
In Jesu's love we know;
And pleasures, springing from the well
Of life, our souls o'erflow.

2 The spirit we receive
Of wisdom, grace, and power;
And always sorrowful we live,
Rejoicing evermore.

3 Angels our servants are,
And keep in all our ways,
And in their watchful hands they bear
The sacred sons of grace:

4 Unto that heavenly bliss
They all our steps attend;
And God Himself our Father is,
And Jesus is our Friend.

Charles Wesley, 1707-88.

442

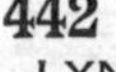

LYNTON. C.M. A. J. JAMOUNEAU, 1865-1927

1 HAPPY the heart where graces reign,
Where love inspires the breast;
Love is the brightest of the train,
And perfects all the rest.

2 Knowledge, alas, 'tis all in vain,
And all in vain our fear;
Our stubborn sins will fight and reign,
If love be absent there.

3 'Tis love that makes our cheerful feet
In swift obedience move:
The devils know, and tremble too;
But Satan cannot love.

4 This is the grace that lives and sings
When faith and hope shall cease;
'Tis this shall strike our joyful strings
In the sweet realm of bliss.

5 Before we quite forsake our clay,
Or leave this dark abode,
The wings of love bear us away
To see our gracious God.

Isaac Watts, 1674-1748.

443

7.7.7.7. D.

LOUGHBOROUGH COLLEGE. G. W. BRIGGS, 1875-

1 LOVED with everlasting love,
Led by grace that love to know;
Spirit, breathing from above,
Thou hast taught me it is so.
O this full and perfect peace!
O this transport all divine!
In a love which cannot cease
I am His, and He is mine.

2 Heaven above is softer blue,
Earth around is sweeter green;
Something lives in every hue,
Christless eyes have never seen:
Birds with gladder songs o'erflow,
Flowers with deeper beauties shine,
Since I know, as now I know,
I am His, and He is mine.

3 His for ever, only His:
Who the Lord and me shall part?
Ah, with what a rest of bliss
Christ can fill the loving heart!
Heaven and earth may fade and flee,
First-born light in gloom decline;
But, while God and I shall be,
I am His, and He is mine.

George Wade Robinson, 1838-77.

444

FROGMORE. 6.4.6.4. W. PARRATT, 1841-1924.

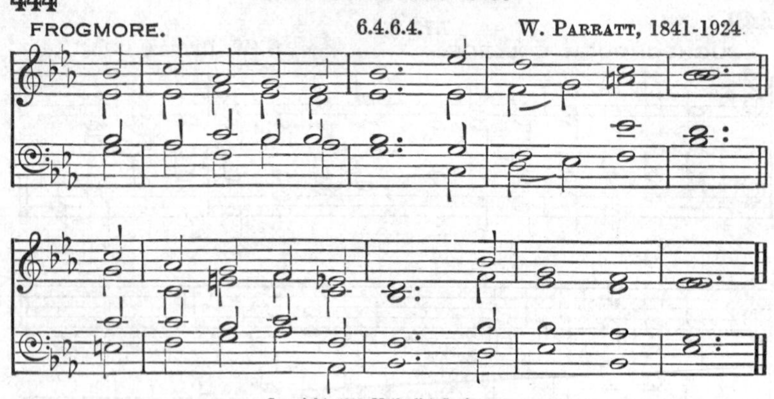

1 BELOVÈD, let us love:
Love is of God;
In God alone hath love
Its true abode.

2 Belovèd, let us love:
For they who love,
They only are His sons,
Born from above.

3 Belovèd, let us love:
For love is rest,
And he who loveth not,
Abides unblest.

4 Belovèd, let us love:
In love is light,
And he who loveth not,
Dwelleth in night.

5 Belovèd, let us love:
For only thus
Shall we behold that God
Who loveth us.

Horatius Bonar, 1808-89.

445

NEW 113TH. 8.8.8.8.8 8. W. HAYES, 1706-77.

May also be sung to COMPANION, No. 310.

Ich will dich lieben, meine Stärke.

1 Thee will I love, my strength, my tower,
Thee will I love, my joy, my crown,
Thee will I love with all my power,
In all Thy works, and Thee alone;
Thee will I love, till the pure fire
Fill my whole soul with chaste desire.

2 Ah, why did I so late Thee know,
Thee, lovelier than the sons of men!
Ah, why did I no sooner go
To Thee, the only ease in pain!
Ashamed, I sigh, and inly mourn,
That I so late to Thee did turn.

3 In darkness willingly I strayed,
I sought Thee, yet from Thee I roved,
Far wide my wandering thoughts were spread,
Thy creatures more than Thee I loved;
And now if more at length I see,
'Tis through Thy light, and comes from Thee.

4 I thank Thee, uncreated Sun,
That Thy bright beams on me have shined;
I thank Thee, who hast overthrown
My foes, and healed my wounded mind;
I thank Thee, whose enlivening voice
Bids my freed heart in Thee rejoice.

5 Give to mine eyes refreshing tears,
Give to my heart chaste, hallowed fires,
Give to my soul, with filial fears,
The love that all heaven's host inspires;
That all my powers, with all their might,
In Thy sole glory may unite.

6 Thee will I love, my joy, my crown,
Thee will I love, my Lord, my God;
Thee will I love, beneath Thy frown,
Or smile, Thy sceptre, or Thy rod;
What though my flesh and heart decay?
Thee shall I love in endless day!

Johann Scheffler, 1624-77;
tr. by John Wesley, 1703-91.

446

CULROSS. C.M. *Scottish Psalter*, 1634.

May also be sung to Westminster, No. 73.

O Deus ego amo Te.

1 My God, I love Thee—not because
I hope for heaven thereby,
Nor yet because who love Thee not
Are lost eternally.

2 Thou, O my Jesus, Thou didst me
Upon the Cross embrace;
For me didst bear the nails and spear,
And manifold disgrace,

3 And griefs and torments numberless,
And sweat of agony,
And death itself—and all for me,
Who was Thine enemy.

4 Then why, O blessèd Jesus Christ,
Should I not love Thee well?
Not for the sake of winning heaven,
Or of escaping hell;

5 Not with the hope of gaining aught;
Not seeking a reward;
But as Thyself hast lovèd me,
O ever-loving Lord.

6 E'en so I love Thee, and will love,
And in Thy praise will sing;
Because Thou art my loving God
And my eternal King.

Attributed to Francis Xavier, c. 1506-52;
tr. by Edward Caswall, 1814-78.

447

ALDERSGATE STREET. 8.8.8.8.8.8 8. E. F. HORNER, 1864-1928.

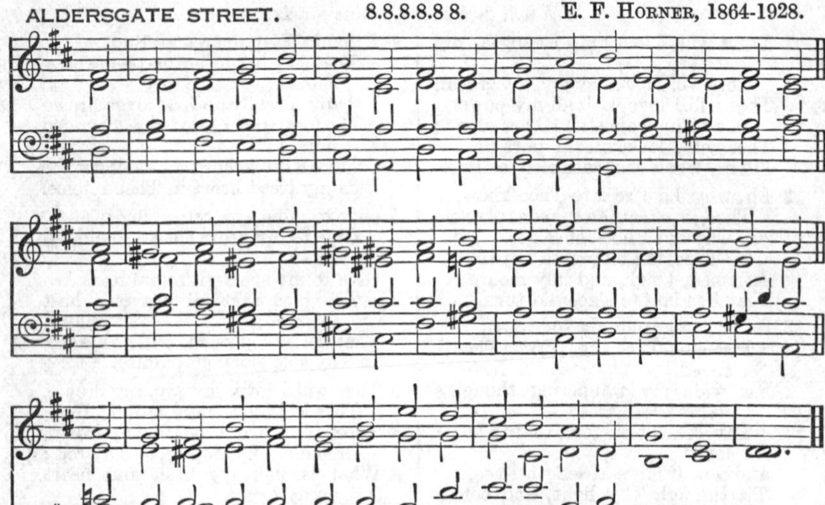

May also be sung to MELITA, No. 917.

Liebe die du mich zum Bilde.

1 O LOVE, who formedst me to wear
The image of Thy Godhead here;
Who soughtest me with tender care
Through all my wanderings wild and drear:
O Love, I give myself to Thee,
Thine ever, only Thine to be.

2 O Love, of whom is truth and light,
The Word and Spirit, life and power,
Whose heart was bared to them that smite,
To shield us in our trial hour:

3 O Love, who thus hast bound me fast,
Beneath that gentle yoke of Thine;
Love, who hast conquered me at last,
And rapt away this heart of mine:

4 O Love, who once shalt bid me rise
From out this dying life of ours;
O Love, who once above yon skies
Shalt set me in the fadeless bowers:

Johann Scheffler, 1624-77;
tr. by Catherine Winkworth, 1827-78.

448

ST. MARGARET. 8.8.8 8.6. A. L. PEACE, 1844-1912.

1 O Love that wilt not let me go,
I rest my weary soul in Thee:
I give Thee back the life I owe,
That in Thine ocean depths its flow
May richer, fuller be.

2 O Light that followest all my way,
I yield my flickering torch to Thee:
My heart restores its borrowed ray,
That in Thy sunshine's blaze its day
May brighter, fairer be.

3 O Joy that seekest me through pain,
I cannot close my heart to Thee:
I trace the rainbow through the rain
And feel the promise is not vain,
That morn shall tearless be.

4 O Cross that liftest up my head,
I dare not ask to fly from Thee:
I lay in dust life's glory dead,
And from the ground there blossoms [red
Life that shall endless be.

George Matheson, 1842-1906.

449

EDEN. L.M. T. B. Mason, 1801-61

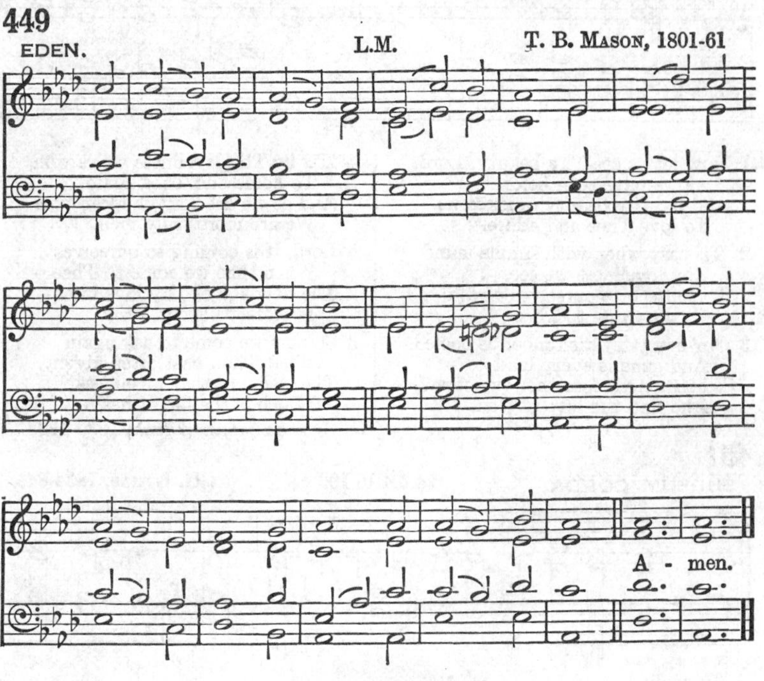

Der Gott von unserm Bunde.

1 O Lord, enlarge our scanty thought
To know the wonders Thou hast wrought; [tell
Unloose our stammering tongues, to
Thy love immense, unsearchable.

2 What are our works but sin and death, [breathe;
Till Thou Thy quickening Spirit
Thou giv'st the power Thy grace to move:
O wondrous grace! O boundless love!

3 How can it be, Thou heavenly King,
That Thou shouldst us to glory bring; [throne,
Make slaves the partners of Thy
Decked with a never-fading crown?

4 Hence our hearts melt, our eyes o'erflow,
Our words are lost; nor will we know,
Nor will we think of aught beside,
My Lord, my Love is crucified!

5 First-born of many brethren Thou;
To Thee, lo! all our souls we bow;
To Thee our hearts and hands we give:
Thine may we die, Thine may we live! Amen.

Nicolaus Ludwig von Zinzendorf, 1700-60, *v.* 1;
Johann Nitschmann, 1712-83, *vv.* 2-4;
Anna Nitschmann, 1715-60, *v.* 5;
tr. by John Wesley, 1703-91.

450

EDGWARE. C.M. Unknown.

1 Now let us see Thy beauty, Lord,
As we have seen before;
And by Thy beauty quicken us
To love Thee and adore.

2 'Tis easy when with simple mind
Thy loveliness we see,
To consecrate ourselves afresh
To duty and to Thee.

3 Our every feverish mood is cooled,
And gone is every load,
When we can lose the love of self,
And find the love of God.

4 'Tis by Thy loveliness we're won
To home and Thee again,
And as we are Thy children true
We are more truly men.

5 Lord, it is coming to ourselves
When thus we come to Thee;
The bondage of Thy loveliness
Is perfect liberty.

6 So now we come to ask again
What Thou hast often given,
The vision of that loveliness
Which is the life of heaven.

Benjamin Waugh, 1839-1908.

451

SURSUM CORDA. 6.4.6.4.10 10. G. LOMAS, 1834-84.

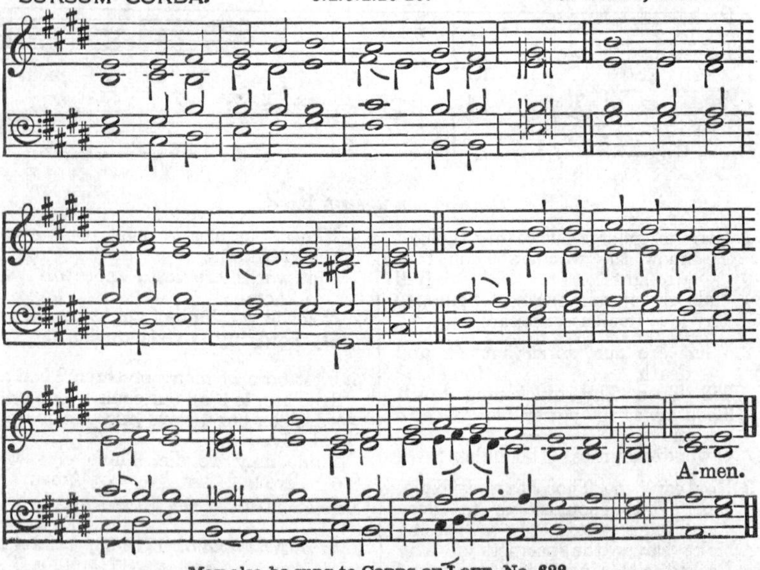

A-men.

May also be sung to CORDS OF LOVE, No. 622.

1 I LIFT my heart to Thee,
Saviour divine;
For Thou art all to me,
And I am Thine.
Is there on earth a closer bond than this:
That my Belovèd's mine, and I am His?

2 Thine am I by all ties;
But chiefly Thine,
That through Thy sacrifice
Thou, Lord, art mine.
By Thine own cords of love, so sweetly wound
Around me, I to Thee am closely bound.

3 To Thee, Thou dying Lamb,
I all things owe;
All that I have, and am,
And all I know.
All that I have is now no longer mine,
And I am not my own; Lord, I am Thine.

4 How can I, Lord, withhold
Life's brightest hour
From Thee; or gathered gold,
Or any power?
Why should I keep one precious thing from Thee,
When Thou hast given Thine own dear self for me?

5 I pray Thee, Saviour, keep
Me in Thy love,
Until death's holy sleep
Shall me remove
To that fair realm where, sin and sorrow o'er,
Thou and Thine own are one for evermore. Amen.

Charles Edward Mudie, 1818-90.

452

STELLA. 8.8.8.8.8.8. Old English Melody.

1 WHAT shall I do my God to love,
My Saviour, and the world's, to praise?
Whose tenderest compassions move
To me and all the fallen race,
Whose mercy is divinely free
For all the fallen race and—me.

2 I long to know, and to make known,
The heights and depths of love divine,
The kindness Thou to me hast shown,
Whose every sin was counted Thine:
My God for me resigned His breath;
He died to save my soul from death.

3 How shall I thank Thee for the grace
On me and all mankind bestowed?
O that my every breath were praise!
O that my heart were filled with God!
My heart would then with love o'erflow,
And all my life Thy glory show.

Charles Wesley, 1707-88.

O

453

6.5.6.5.7 7.6.5.

O MY SAVIOUR, HEAR ME. H. P. MAIN, 1839-1925.

1 O MY Saviour, hear me,
Draw me close to Thee;
Thou hast paid my ransom,
Thou hast died for me:
Now by simple faith I claim
Pardon through Thy gracious name;
Thou my Ark of safety,
Let me fly to Thee.

2 O my Saviour, bless me,
Bless me, while I pray;
Grant Thy grace to help me
Take my fear away:
I believe Thy promise, Lord,
I will trust Thy holy Word;
Thou my soul's Redeemer,
Bless me while I pray.

3 O my Saviour, love me,
Make me all Thine own;
Leave me not to wander
In this world alone:
Bless my way with light divine,
Let Thy glory round me shine;
Thou my Rock, my Refuge,
Make me all Thine own.

4 O my Saviour, guard me,
Keep me evermore;
Bless me, love me, guide me,
Till my work is o'er:
May I then with glad surprise
Chant Thy praise beyond the skies;
There with Thee, my Saviour,
Dwell for evermore.

Frances Jane van Alstyne, 1820-1915.

454

ST. FRANCES. C.M. G. A. LÖHR, 1821-97.

May also be sung to OLDHAM STREET, No. 236.

1 I WOULD commune with Thee, my God;
E'en to Thy seat I come;
I leave my joys, I leave my sins,
And seek in Thee my home.

2 I stand upon the mount of God,
With sunlight in my soul;
I hear the storms in vales beneath,
I hear the thunders roll.

3 But I am calm with Thee, my God,
Beneath these glorious skies;
And to the height on which I stand,
Nor storms nor clouds can rise.

4 O this is life! O this is joy!
My God to find Thee so!
Thy face to see, Thy voice to hear,
And all Thy love to know.

George Burden Bubier, 1823-69.

455, 456

MARTYRDOM. C.M. H. WILSON, 1766-1824.

455

1 As pants the hart for cooling streams,
When heated in the chase,
So longs my soul, O God, for Thee,
And Thy refreshing grace.

2 For Thee, my God, the living God,
My thirsty soul doth pine;
O when shall I behold Thy face,
Thou Majesty divine!

3 God of my strength, how long shall I,
Like one forgotten, mourn?
Forlorn, forsaken, and exposed
To my oppressor's scorn.

4 Why restless, why cast down, my soul?
Hope still, and thou shalt sing
The praise of Him who is thy God,
Thy health's eternal spring.

Nahum Tate, 1652-1715;
Nicholas Brady, 1659-1726.

456

1 FOR ever here my rest shall be,
Close to Thy bleeding side;
This all my hope, and all my plea,
For me the Saviour died.

2 My dying Saviour, and my God,
Fountain for guilt and sin,
Sprinkle me ever with Thy blood,
And cleanse, and keep me clean.

3 Wash me, and make me thus Thine own,
Wash me, and mine Thou art,
Wash me, but not my feet alone,
My hands, my head, my heart.

4 The atonement of Thy blood apply,
Till faith to sight improve,
Till hope in full fruition die,
And all my soul be love.

Charles Wesley, 1707-88.

457

ARABIA. 8.8.8.8. D. W. J. WHITE, c. 1820.

1 THOU Shepherd of Israel, and mine,
The joy and desire of my heart,
For closer communion I pine,
I long to reside where Thou art:
The pasture I languish to find
Where all, who their Shepherd obey,
Are fed, on Thy bosom reclined,
And screened from the heat of the day.

2 Ah! show me that happiest place,
The place of Thy people's abode,
Where saints in an ecstasy gaze,
And hang on a crucified God;
Thy love for a sinner declare,
Thy passion and death on the tree;
My spirit to Calvary bear,
To suffer and triumph with Thee.

3 'Tis there, with the lambs of Thy flock,
There only, I covet to rest,
To lie at the foot of the rock,
Or rise to be hid in Thy breast;
'Tis there I would always abide,
And never a moment depart,
Concealed in the cleft of Thy side,
Eternally held in Thy heart.

Charles Wesley, 1707-88.

SONG 1: 10.10.10.10.10 10. O. GIBBONS, 1583-1625.

1 LONG did I toil, and knew no earthly rest;
Far did I rove, and found no certain home;
At last I sought them in His sheltering breast,
Who opes His arms, and bids the weary come:
With Him I found a home, a rest divine;
And I since then am His, and He is mine.

2 The good I have is from His stores supplied;
The ill is only what He deems the best;
With Him as Friend I'm rich, with nought beside,
And poor without Him, though of all possest:
Changes may come—I take, or I resign,
Content while I am His, while He is mine.

3 Whate'er may change, in Him no change is seen;
A glorious Sun, that wanes not, nor declines;
Above the clouds and storms He walks serene,
And on His people's inward darkness shines:
All may depart—I fret not nor repine,
While I my Saviour's am, while He is mine.

4 While here, alas! I know but half His love,
But half discern Him, and but half adore;
But when I meet Him in the realms above,
I hope to love Him better, praise Him more,
And feel, and tell, amid the choir divine,
How fully I am His, and He is mine.

John Quarles, 1624-65;
Henry Francis Lyte, 1793-1847.

459

ST DOROTHEA. 7.6.7.6.7.8.7.6. C. VINCENT, 1852-1934

1 To the haven of Thy breast,
O Son of Man, I fly;
Be my refuge and my rest,
For O the storm is high!
Save me from the furious blast,
A covert from the tempest be;
Hide me, Jesus, till o'erpast
The storm of sin I see.

2 Welcome as the water-spring
To a dry, barren place,
O descend on me, and bring
Thy sweet refreshing grace!
O'er a parched and weary land
As a great rock extends its shade,
Hide me, Saviour, with Thine hand,
And screen my naked head.

3 In the time of my distress
Thou hast my succour been,
In my utter helplessness
Restraining me from sin;
O how swiftly didst Thou move
To save me in the trying hour!
Still protect me with Thy love,
And shield me with Thy power.

4 First and last in me perform
The work Thou hast begun;
Be my shelter from the storm,
My shadow from the sun;
Weary, parched with thirst, and faint,
Till Thou the abiding Spirit breathe,
Every moment, Lord, I want
The merit of Thy death.

Charles Wesley, 1707-88.

460

TIVERTON. C.M. J. Griggs, ? -1768.

1 Talk with us, Lord, Thyself reveal,
While here o'er earth we rove;
Speak to our hearts, and let us feel
The kindling of Thy love.

2 With Thee conversing, we forget
All time, and toil, and care;
Labour is rest, and pain is sweet,
If Thou, my God, art here.

3 Here then, my God, vouchsafe to stay,
And bid my heart rejoice;
My bounding heart shall own Thy
And echo to Thy voice. [sway,

4 Thou callest me to seek Thy face;
'Tis all I wish to seek;
To attend the whispers of Thy grace,
And hear Thee inly speak.

5 Let this my every hour employ,
Till I Thy glory see:
Enter into my Master's joy,
And find my heaven in Thee. Amen.

Charles Wesley, 1707-88.

461

CHESHIRE. C.M. Este's *Psalter*, 1592.

May also be sung to Belmont, No. 766.

1 O for a closer walk with God,
A calm and heavenly frame,
A light to shine upon the road
That leads me to the Lamb.

2 Where is the blessedness I knew
When first I saw the Lord?
Where is that soul-refreshing view
Of Jesus and His word?

3 What peaceful hours I once enjoyed!
How sweet their memory still!
But they have left an aching void
The world can never fill.

4 Return, O holy Dove! return,
Sweet messenger of rest! [mourn,
I hate the sins that made Thee
And drove Thee from my breast.

5 The dearest idol I have known,
Whate'er that idol be,
Help me to tear it from Thy throne,
And worship only Thee.

6 So shall my walk be close with God,
Calm and serene my frame;
So purer light shall mark the road
That leads me to the Lamb.

William Cowper, 1731-1800.

462

IBSTONE. 6.6.6.6. M. TIDDEMAN, 1837-1913

1 I HUNGER and I thirst;
Jesus, my manna be:
Ye living waters, burst
Out of the rock for me.

2 Thou bruised and broken Bread,
My life-long wants supply;
As living souls are fed,
O feed me, or I die.

3 Thou true life-giving Vine,
Let me Thy sweetness prove;
Renew my life with Thine,
Refresh my soul with love.

4 Rough paths my feet have trod,
Since first their course began;
Feed me, Thou Bread of God;
Help me, Thou Son of Man.

5 For still the desert lies
My thirsting soul before;
O living waters rise
Within me evermore. Amen.

John Samuel Bewley Monsell, 1811-75.

463

WESTMINSTER NEW. C.M. J. NARES, 1715-83.

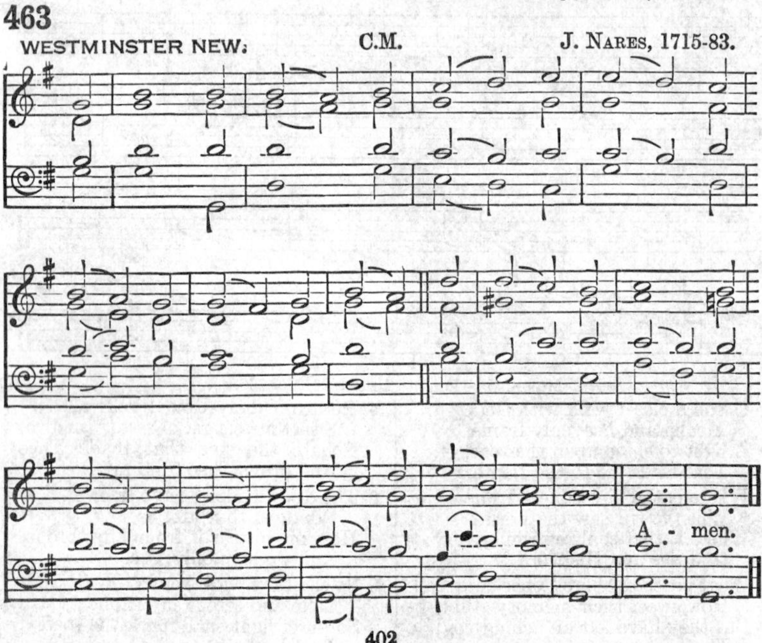

O Jesus Christus, wachs' in mir.

1 O Jesus Christ, grow Thou in me,
And all things else recede:
My heart be daily nearer Thee
From sin be daily freed.

2 Each day let Thy supporting might
My weakness still embrace;
My darkness vanish in Thy light,
Thy life my death efface.

3 In Thy bright beams which on me fall,
Fade every evil thought;
That I am nothing, Thou art all,
I would be daily taught.

4 More of Thy glory let me see,
Thou Holy, Wise, and True!
I would Thy living image be,
In joy and sorrow too.

5 Fill me with gladness from above,
Hold me by strength divine!
Lord, let the glow of Thy great love
Through my whole being shine.

6 Make this poor self grow less and less,
Be Thou my life and aim;
O make me daily, through Thy grace,
More meet to bear Thy name!
Amen.

Johann Caspar Lavater, 1741-1801;
tr. by Elizabeth Lee Smith, 1817-98.

464

COLESHILL. C.M. Barton's *Psalmes*, 1706.

1 Jesus, the all-restoring Word,
My fallen spirit's hope,
After Thy lovely likeness, Lord,
Ah, when shall I wake up?

2 Thou, O my God, Thou only art
The Life, the Truth, the Way;
Quicken my soul, instruct my heart,
My sinking footsteps stay.

3 Of all Thou hast in earth below,
In heaven above, to give,
Give me Thy love alone to know,
In Thee to walk and live.

4 Fill me with all the life of love;
In mystic union join
Me to Thyself, and let me prove
The fellowship divine.

5 Open the intercourse between
My longing soul and Thee,
Never to be broke off again
To all eternity. Amen.

Charles Wesley, 1707-88.

465

LEAMINGTON. 7.6.7.6.7.7.7.6. S. ARNOLD, 1740-1802.

A - men.

1 OPEN, Lord, my inward ear,
And bid my heart rejoice;
Bid my quiet spirit hear
Thy comfortable voice;
Never in the whirlwind found,
Or where earthquakes rock the place,
Still and silent is the sound,
The whisper of Thy grace.

2 From the world of sin, and noise,
And hurry I withdraw;
For the small and inward voice
I wait with humble awe;
Silent am I now and still,
Dare not in Thy presence move;
To my waiting soul reveal
The secret of Thy love.

3 Thou didst undertake for me,
For me to death wast sold;
Wisdom in a mystery
Of bleeding love unfold;
Teach the lesson of Thy Cross,
Let me die with Thee to reign;
All things let me count but loss,
So I may Thee regain.

4 Show me, as my soul can bear,
The depth of inbred sin;
All the unbelief declare,
The pride that lurks within;
Take me, whom Thyself hast bought,
Bring into captivity
Every high aspiring thought
That would not stoop to Thee.

5 Lord, my time is in Thy hand,
My soul to Thee convert;
Thou canst make me understand,
Though I am slow of heart;
Thine in whom I live and move,
Thine the work, the praise is Thine;
Thou art wisdom, power, and love,
And all Thou art is mine. Amen.

Charles Wesley, 1707-88.

466

PASTOR. 7.6.7.6. M. Vulpius, 1560-1616.

1 My soul, there is a country
Afar beyond the stars,
Where stands a wingèd sentry
All skilful in the wars.

2 There, above noise, and danger,
Sweet peace sits, crowned with [smiles,
And One born in a manger
Commands the beauteous files.

3 He is thy gracious friend,
And—O my soul, awake!
Did in pure love descend,
To die here for thy sake.

4 If thou canst get but thither,
There grows the flower of peace,
The rose that cannot wither,
Thy fortress, and thy ease.

5 Leave then thy foolish ranges;
For none can thee secure,
But One, who never changes,
Thy God, thy Life, thy Cure.

Henry Vaughan, 1621-95.

467

PSALM 32. 6.6.6.6. H. Lawes, 1596-1662.

May also be sung to St. Cecilia, No. 140.

1 My spirit longs for Thee
Within my troubled breast,
Unworthy though I be
Of so divine a guest.

2 Of so divine a guest
Unworthy though I be,
Yet has my heart no rest
Unless it come from Thee.

3 Unless it come from Thee,
In vain I look around;
In all that I can see
No rest is to be found.

4 No rest is to be found
But in Thy blessèd love;
O let my wish be crowned,
And send it from above! Amen.

John Byrom, 1692-1763.

468
HORBURY (*First Tune*). 6.4.6.4.6 6 4. J. B. Dykes, 1823-76.
6.4.6.4.6 6 4.
NEARER TO THEE (*Second Tune*). American.

NEARER, MY GOD, TO THEE

(Third Tune). 6.4.6.4.6 6 4. T. C. Gregory, 1901-

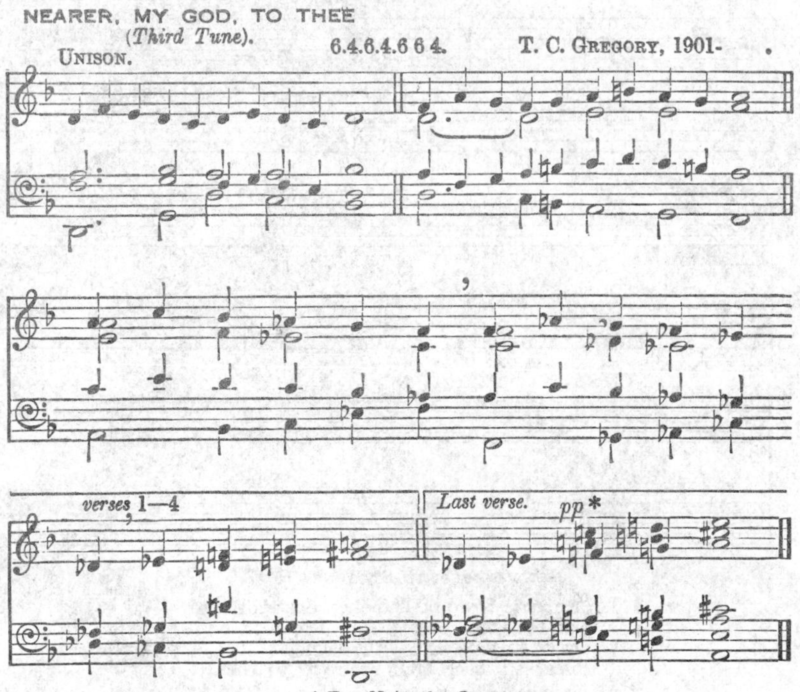

* Top Notes for Organ.

1 Nearer, my God, to Thee,
Nearer to Thee!
E'en though it be a cross
That raiseth me,
Still all my song shall be,
Nearer, my God, to Thee,
Nearer to Thee!

2 Though, like the wanderer,
The sun gone down,
Darkness be over me,
My rest a stone,
Yet in my dreams I'd be
Nearer, my God, to Thee,
Nearer to Thee!

3 There let the way appear
Steps unto heaven;
All that Thou send'st to me
In mercy given;
Angels to beckon me
Nearer, my God, to Thee,
Nearer to Thee!

4 Then, with my waking thoughts
Bright with Thy praise,
Out of my stony griefs
Bethel I'll raise;
So by my woes to be
Nearer, my God, to Thee,
Nearer to Thee!

5 Or if on joyful wing
Cleaving the sky,
Sun, moon, and stars forgot,
Upwards I fly,
Still all my song shall be,
Nearer, my God, to Thee,
Nearer to Thee!

Sarah Flower Adams, 1805-48.

469

SONG 24. 10.10.10.10. O. GIBBONS, 1583-1625.

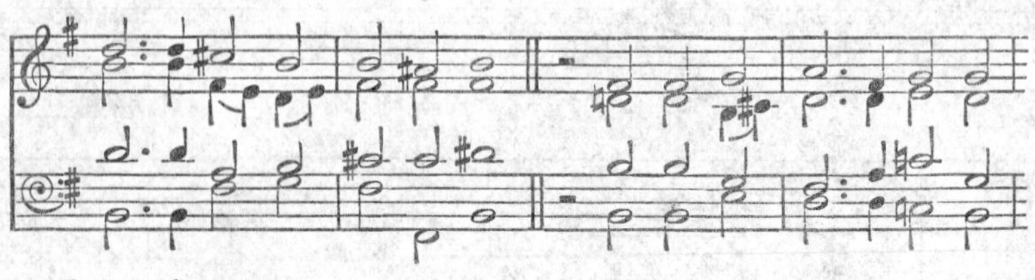

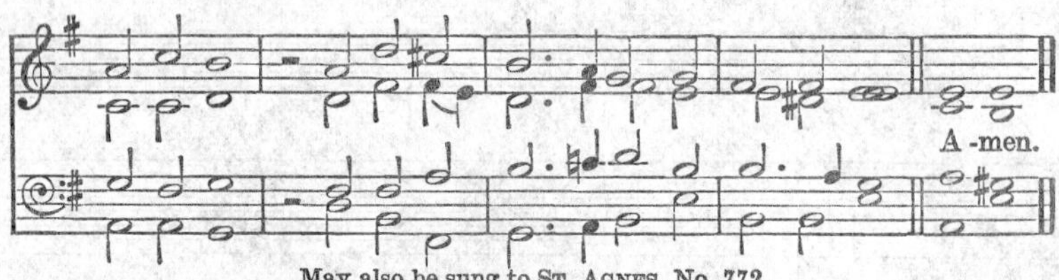

May also be sung to ST. AGNES, No. 772.

1 THAT mystic Word of Thine, O sovereign Lord,
Is all too pure, too high, too deep for me;
Weary of striving, and with longing faint,
I breathe it back again in prayer to Thee.

2 Abide in me, I pray, and I in Thee;
From this good hour, O leave me nevermore!
Then shall the discord cease, the wound be healed,
The life-long bleeding of the soul be o'er.

3 Abide in me; o'ershadow by Thy love
Each half-formed purpose and dark thought of sin;
Quench, ere it rise, each selfish, low desire;
And keep my soul as Thine, calm and divine.

4 As some rare perfume in a vase of clay
Pervades it with a fragrance not its own,
So, when Thou dwellest in a mortal soul,
All heaven's own sweetness seems around it thrown.

5 Abide in me: there have been moments blest
When I have heard Thy voice and felt Thy power:
Then evil lost its grasp, and passion, hushed,
Owned the Divine enchantment of the hour.

6 These were but seasons beautiful and rare;
Abide in me, and they shall ever be;
Fulfil at once Thy precept and my prayer:
Come and abide in me, and I in Thee. Amen.

Harriet Beecher Stowe, 1812-96.

470

SELMA. S.M. *Traditional Scottish Melody of the Isle of Arran.*

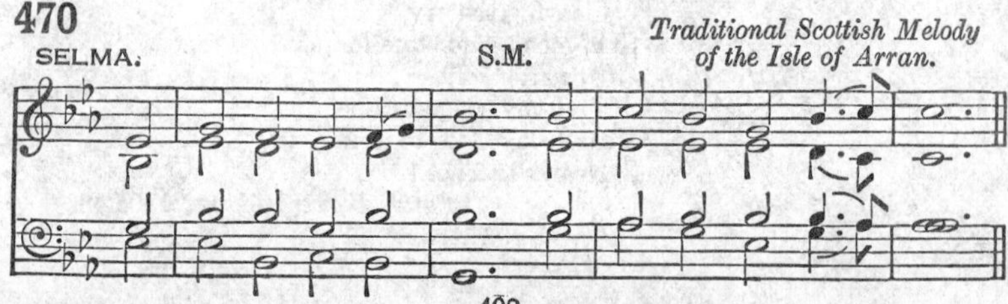

1 Still with Thee, O my God,
I would desire to be;
By day, by night, at home, abroad,
I would be still with Thee.

2 With Thee, when dawn comes in,
And calls me back to care;
Each day returning, to begin
With Thee, my God, in prayer.

3 With Thee, amid the crowd
That throngs the busy mart;
To hear Thy voice 'mid clamour loud,
Speak softly to my heart.

4 With Thee, when day is done,
And evening calms the mind;
The setting, as the rising sun,
With Thee my heart would find.

5 With Thee, when darkness brings
The signal of repose;
Calm in the shadow of Thy wings,
Mine eyelids I would close.

6 With Thee, in Thee, by faith
Abiding I would be;
By day, by night, in life, in death,
I would be still with Thee. Amen.

James Drummond Burns, 1823-64.

471

BERKSHIRE. L.M. C. Wesley, 1757-1834.

May also be sung to Eden, No. 449.

1 O God, my God, my all Thou art:
Ere shines the dawn of rising day,
Thy sovereign light within my heart,
Thy all-enlivening power display.

2 For Thee my thirsty soul doth pant,
While in this desert land I live;
And hungry as I am, and faint,
Thy love alone can comfort give.

3 In a dry land, behold, I place
My whole desire on Thee, O Lord;
And more I joy to gain Thy grace,
Than all earth's treasures can afford.

4 More dear than life itself, Thy love
My heart and tongue shall still employ;
And to declare Thy praise will prove
My peace, my glory, and my joy.

5 In blessing Thee, with grateful songs
My happy life shall glide away;
The praise that to Thy name belongs
Hourly with lifted hands I'll pay.

6 Thy name, O God, upon my bed
Dwells on my lips, and fires my thought;
With trembling awe, in midnight shade,
I muse on all Thy hands have [wrought.

7 In all I do I feel Thine aid;
Therefore Thy greatness will I sing,
O God, who bidd'st my heart be glad
Beneath the shadow of Thy wing.

8 My soul draws nigh and cleaves to Thee:
Then let or earth or hell assail,
Thy mighty hand shall set me free;
For whom Thou sav'st, he ne'er shall fail.

From unknown Spanish source;
tr. by John Wesley, 1703-91.

472

BATTLE. 10 10.10 10. H. LAWES, 1596-1662.

1 COME in, O come! The door stands open now;
I knew Thy voice; Lord Jesus, it was Thou.
The sun has set long since; the storms begin:
'Tis time for Thee, my Saviour; O come in!

2 I seek no more to alter things, or mend,
Before the coming of so great a Friend:
All were at best unseemly; and 'twere ill,
Beyond all else, to keep Thee waiting still.

3 Then, as Thou art, all holiness and bliss,
Come in, and see my chamber as it is;
I bid Thee welcome boldly, in the name
Of Thy great glory and my want and shame.

4 Come, not to find, but make, this troubled heart
A dwelling worthy of Thee as Thou art;
To chase the gloom, the terror, and the sin,
Come, all Thyself, yea come, Lord Jesus, in! Amen.

Handley Carr Glyn Moule, 1841-1920.

NETTLEHAM. Irregular. G. J. BENNETT, 1863-1930.

1 My heart is resting, O my God,
I will give thanks and sing:
My heart is at the secret source
Of every precious thing.
Now the frail vessel Thou hast made
No hand but Thine shall fill;
For the waters of the earth have failed,
And I am thirsty still.

2 I thirst for springs of heavenly life,
And here all day they rise;
I seek the treasure of Thy love,
And close at hand it lies;
And a new song is in my mouth,
To long-loved music set—
Glory to Thee for all the grace
I have not tasted yet;

3 Glory to Thee for strength withheld,
For want and weakness known,
And the fear that sends me to Thy breast
For what is most my own.
I have a heritage of joy,
That yet I must not see;
But the hand that bled to make it mine
Is keeping it for me.

4 My heart is resting, O my God,
My heart is in Thy care;
I hear the voice of joy and health
Resounding everywhere.
Thou art my portion! saith my soul,
Ten thousand voices say,
And the music of their glad Amen
Will never die away.

Anna Laetitia Waring, 1820-1910.

ALVERSTOKE. 11.10.11.10. J. BARNBY, 1838-96.

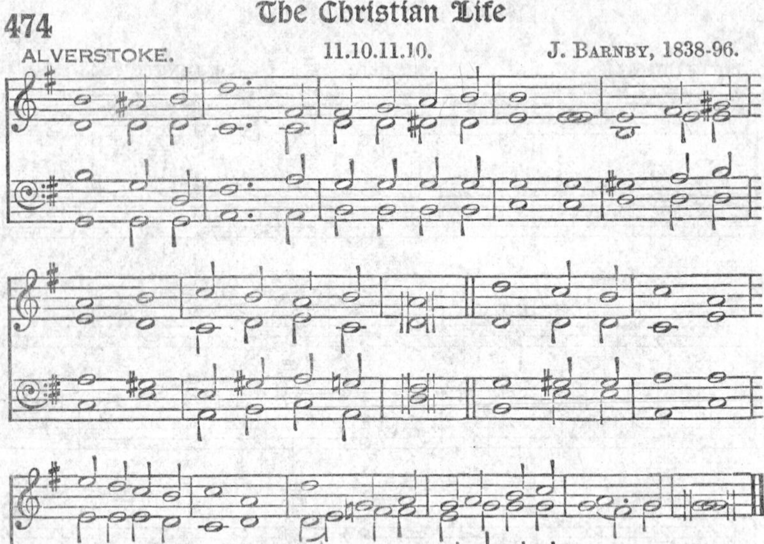

By permission of Novello and Company, Limited.

1 STILL, still with Thee, when purple morning breaketh,
When the bird waketh, and the shadows flee;
Fairer than morning, lovelier than daylight,
Dawns the sweet consciousness, I am with Thee.

2 Alone with Thee, amid the mystic shadows,
The solemn hush of nature newly born;
Alone with Thee in breathless adoration,
In the calm dew and freshness of the morn.

3 As in the dawning, o'er the waveless ocean,
The image of the morning star doth rest;
So in this stillness, Thou beholdest only
Thine image in the waters of my breast.

4 Still, still with Thee! As to each newborn morning
A fresh and solemn splendour still is given;
So does this blessèd consciousness, awaking,
Breathe each day nearness unto Thee and heaven.

5 When sinks the soul, subdued by toil to slumber,
Its closing eye looks up to Thee in prayer;
Sweet the repose beneath Thy wings o'ershading,
But sweeter still, to wake and find Thee there.

6 So shall it be at last, in that bright morning,
When the soul waketh, and life's shadows flee;
O in that hour, fairer than daylight dawning,
Shall rise the glorious thought—I am with Thee!

Harriet Beecher Stowe, 1812-96.

Also:

109 Jesu, Thou Joy
110 Jesu, Lover of my soul
111 Jesus, these eyes
273 Come down, O Love
383 Being of beings
508 As helpless as a child
550 O for a heart
605 Jesus, the gift divine

475

I NEED THEE. 6.4.6.4. and refrain. R. LOWRY, 1826-99.

1 I NEED Thee every hour,
Most gracious Lord;
No tender voice like Thine
Can peace afford.

I need Thee, O I need Thee,
Every hour I need Thee;
O bless me now, my Saviour;
I come to Thee.

2 I need Thee every hour;
Stay Thou near by:
Temptations lose their power
When Thou art nigh.

3 I need Thee every hour,
In joy or pain;
Come quickly and abide,
Or life is vain.

4 I need Thee every hour;
Teach me Thy will,
And Thy rich promises
In me fulfil.

Annie Sherwood Hawks, 1835-1918.

476

GREENLAND. 7.6.7.6. D. Adapted from J. M. Haydn, 1737-1806

1 From trials unexempted
Thy dearest children are;
But let us not be tempted
Above what we can bear;
Exposed to no temptation
That may our souls o'erpower,
Be Thou our strong salvation
Through every fiery hour.

2 Ah! leave us not to venture
Within the verge of sin;
Or if the snare we enter,
Thy timely help bring in;
And if Thy wisdom try us,
Till pain and woe are past,
Almighty Love, stand by us,
And save from first to last.

3 Fain would we cease from sinning
In thought, and word, and deed;
From sin in its beginning
We languish to be freed;
From every base desire,
Our fallen nature's shame,
Jesus, we dare require
Deliverance in Thy name.

4 For every sinful action
Thou hast atonement made,
The perfect satisfaction
Thy precious blood has paid:
But take entire possession;
To make an end of sin,
To finish the transgression,
Most holy God, come in! Amen.

Charles Wesley, 1707-88.

477

GERSAU. 7.6.7.6.7.8.7.6. L. M. White, 1860-1950

1 Son of God, if Thy free grace
Again hath raised me up,
Called me still to seek Thy face,
And given me back my hope;
Still Thy timely help afford,
And all Thy loving-kindness show:
Keep me, keep me, gracious Lord,
And never let me go!

2 By me, O my Saviour, stand
In sore temptation's hour;
Save me with Thine outstretched hand,
And show forth all Thy power;
O be mindful of Thy word,
Thy all-sufficient grace bestow:
Keep me, keep me, gracious Lord,
And never let me go!

3 Give me, Lord, a holy fear,
And fix it in my heart,
That I may from evil near
With timely care depart;
Sin be more than hell abhorred;
Till Thou destroy the tyrant foe,
Keep me, keep me, gracious Lord,
And never let me go!

4 Never let me leave Thy breast,
From Thee, my Saviour, stray;
Thou art my Support and Rest,
My true and living Way;
My exceeding great Reward,
In heaven above and earth below:
Keep me, keep me, gracious Lord,
And never let me go! Amen.

Charles Wesley, 1707-88.

478

ANGELS' SONG. L.M. O. GIBBONS, 1583-1625.

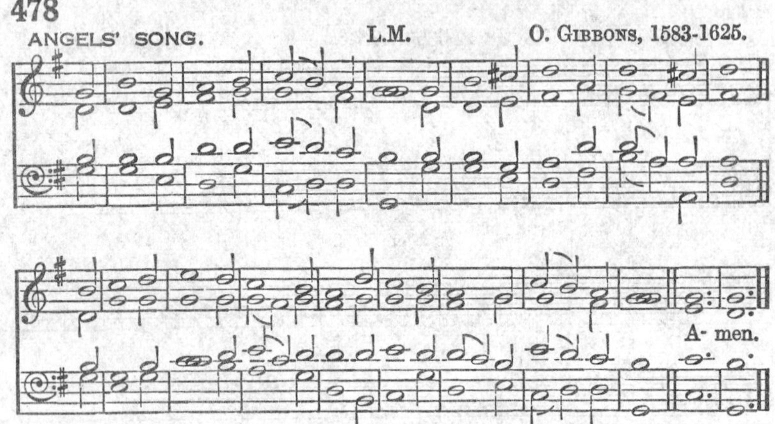

1 JESUS, my Saviour, Brother, Friend,
On whom I cast my every care,
On whom for all things I depend,
Inspire, and then accept, my prayer.

2 If I have tasted of Thy grace,
The grace that sure salvation brings;
If with me now Thy Spirit stays,
And hovering hides me in His wings:

3 Still let Him with my weakness stay,
Nor for a moment's space depart,
Evil and danger turn away,
And keep till He renews my heart.

4 When to the right or left I stray,
His voice behind me may I hear:
Return, and walk in Christ thy way;
Fly back to Christ, for sin is near.

5 His sacred unction from above
Be still my Comforter and Guide;
Till all the hardness He remove,
And in my loving heart reside.

6 Jesus, I fain would walk in Thee,
From nature's every path retreat;
Thou art my Way, my Leader be,
And set upon the rock my feet.

7 Uphold me, Saviour, or I fall,
O reach me out Thy gracious hand!
Only on Thee for help I call,
Only by faith in Thee I stand. Amen.

Charles Wesley, 1707-88.

479

HOTHAM. 7.7.7.7. D. *Sacred Melody*, 1765.

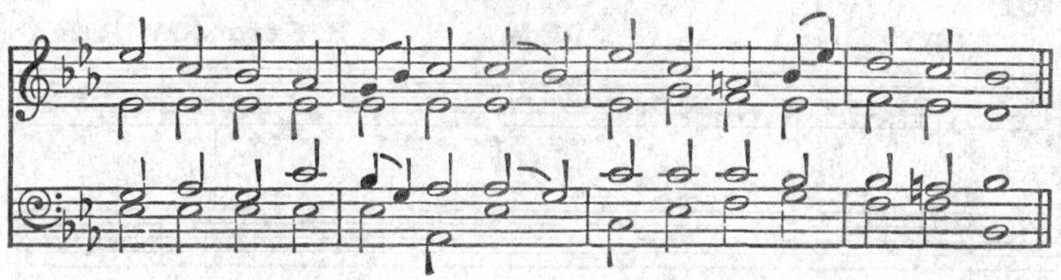

1 Fainting soul, be bold, be strong,
  Wait the leisure of thy Lord;
Though it seem to tarry long,
  True and faithful is His word:
On His word my soul I cast—
  He cannot Himself deny;
Surely it shall speak at last;
  It shall speak, and shall not lie.

2 Every one that seeks shall find,
  Every one that asks shall have,
Christ, the Saviour of mankind,
  Willing, able, all to save;
I shall His salvation see,
  I in faith on Jesus call,
I from sin shall be set free,
  Perfectly set free from all.

3 Lord, my time is in Thine hand;
  Weak and helpless as I am,
Surely Thou canst make me stand;
  I believe in Jesu's name:
Saviour in temptation Thou;
  Thou hast saved me heretofore,
Thou from sin dost save me now,
  Thou shalt save me evermore.

Charles Wesley, 1707-88.

480

BABYLON'S STREAMS. L.M. T. Campion, *c.* 1575-1619.

1 Ah! Lord, with trembling I confess,
A gracious soul may fall from grace;
The salt may lose its seasoning power,
And never, never find it more.

2 Lest that my fearful case should be,
Each moment knit my soul to Thee;
And lead me to the mount above,
Through the low vale of humble love.

Charles Wesley, 1707-88.

481

VICTORY. D.S.M. H. KEETON, 1847-1921.

May also be sung to ISHMAEL, No. 243.

1 HARK, how the watchmen cry!
Attend the trumpet's sound!
Stand to your arms, the foe is nigh,
The powers of hell surround:
Who bow to Christ's command,
Your arms and hearts prepare!
The day of battle is at hand!
Go forth to glorious war!

2 Go up with Christ your Head,
Your Captain's footsteps see;
Follow your Captain, and be led
To certain victory.
All power to Him is given,
He ever reigns the same;
Salvation, happiness, and heaven
Are all in Jesu's name.

3 Jesu's tremendous name
Puts all our foes to flight:
Jesus, the meek, the angry Lamb,
A Lion is in fight.
By all hell's host withstood,
We all hell's host o'erthrow;
And conquering them, through Jesu's blood,
We still to conquer go.

4 Our Captain leads us on;
He beckons from the skies,
And reaches out a starry crown,
And bids us take the prize:
Be faithful unto death,
Partake My victory;
And thou shalt wear this glorious wreath,
And thou shalt reign with Me!

Charles Wesley, 1707-88.

482

CLARION. 6.4.6.4.6 7 6.4. M. B. Foster, 1851-1922.

1 Hark, 'tis the watchman's cry:
Wake, brethren, wake!
Jesus Himself is nigh;
Wake, brethren, wake!
Sleep is for sons of night;
Ye are children of the light;
Yours is the glory bright;
Wake, brethren, wake!

2 Call to each wakening band:
Watch, brethren, watch!
Clear is our Lord's command:
Watch, brethren, watch!
Be ye as men that wait
Always at their Master's gate,
E'en though He tarry late;
Watch, brethren, watch!

3 Heed we the Master's call:
Work, brethren, work!
There's room enough for all,
Work, brethren, work!
This vineyard of the Lord
Constant labour will afford;
He will your work reward:
Work, brethren, work!

4 Hear we the Saviour's voice:
Pray, brethren, pray!
Would ye His heart rejoice,
Pray, brethren, pray!
Sin calls for ceaseless fear,
Weakness needs the Strong One near;
Long as ye struggle here,
Pray, brethren, pray!

5 Sound now the final chord,
Praise, brethren, praise!
Thrice holy is the Lord,
Praise, brethren, praise!
What more befits the tongues
Soon to join the angels' songs?
Whilst heaven the note prolongs,
Praise, brethren, praise!

Anonymous: from The Revival, 1859.

483
DEFIANCE.
8.8.8.8.8.8.
M. L. WOSTENHOLM, 1887-
TENORS AND BASSES.
Maestoso.
mf Sw. reeds.
sf
sf
senza Ped.
1. SUR-
- ROUND-ED by a host of foes, Stormed by a host of foes within, Nor
Ped.
swift to flee, nor strong to oppose, Sin- gle, against hell, earth, and
sin,
Sin- gle, yet un - dismay'd, I
sf
mf

boldly.
f
am: I dare believe in Je - su's name.
2. What tho' a thou - sand hosts engage, A thou-sand worlds, my
soul to shake? I have a shield shall quell their rage, And

drive the a - lien ar - - - mies back;
Slower, and with great expression.
rall.
p
Por - tray'd it bears a bleed - ing
Slower.
rall.
sf
tempo I
f
Lamb: I dare be-lieve in Je - su's name.
tempo I.

3. Me to re-trieve from Sa - tan's hands, Me from this e - vil
world to free, To purge my sins, and loose my bands, And
save from all in - i - - qui - ty,

My Lord and God from heav'n He came: I dare be-lieve in Je - su's name.
Sal - va - tion in His name there is, Sal - va - tion from sin,
f
sf

death, and hell, Sal - va-tion in - to glo-rious bliss, How great sal-va-tion,
who can tell? But all He hath for mine I claim: I
cresc. poco a poco.
cresc. poco a poco.
cresc. poco a poco.
ff rall.
dare be - lieve in Je - - su's name. A - men.
Charles Wesley, 1707-88.
ff
rall.
ff

May also be sung to MOUNT SION, No. 390.

484

D.S.M.

FROM STRENGTH TO STRENGTH. E. W. NAYLOR, 1867-1934

UNISON.

1 SOLDIERS of Christ, arise,
And put your armour on,
Strong in the strength which God supplies
Through His eternal Son;
Strong in the Lord of Hosts,
And in His mighty power,
Who in the strength of Jesus trusts
Is more than conqueror.

2 Stand then in His great might,
With all His strength endued;
But take, to arm you for the fight,
The panoply of God;
That, having all things done,
And all your conflicts passed,
Ye may o'ercome through Christ alone,
And stand entire at last.

3 Stand then against your foes,
In close and firm array;
Legions of wily fiends oppose
Throughout the evil day:
But meet the sons of night;
But mock their vain design,
Armed in the arms of heavenly light,
Of righteousness divine.

4 Leave no unguarded place,
No weakness of the soul;
Take every virtue, every grace,
And fortify the whole:
Indissolubly joined,
To battle all proceed;
But arm yourselves with all the mind
That was in Christ, your Head.

Charles Wesley, 1707-88.

485

AZMON. C.M. C. G. GLASER, 1784-1829.

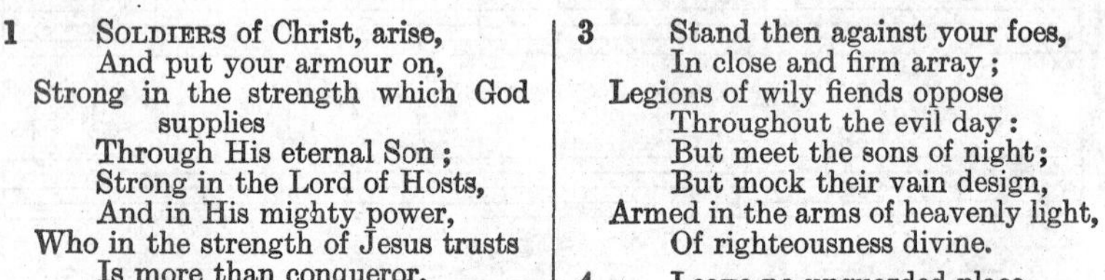

May also be sung to RICHMOND, No. 305.

1 I'M not ashamed to own my Lord,
Or to defend His cause,
Maintain the honour of His word,
The glory of His Cross.

2 Jesus, my God! I know His name,
His name is all my trust;
Nor will He put my soul to shame,
Nor let my hope be lost.

3 Firm as His throne His promise stands,
And He can well secure
What I've committed to His hands
Till the decisive hour.

4 Then will He own my worthless name
Before His Father's face,
And in the new Jerusalem
Appoint my soul a place.

Isaac Watts, 1674-1748.

486

JUSTIFICATION. L.M. J. EAGLETON, 1785-1832.

1 ARM of the Lord, awake, awake!
Thine own immortal strength put on;
With terror clothed, hell's kingdom shake,
And cast Thy foes with fury down.

2 As in the ancient days appear;
The sacred annals speak Thy fame:
Be now omnipotently near,
To endless ages still the same.

3 Thy arm, Lord, is not shortened now,
It wants not now the power to save;
Still present with Thy people, Thou
Bear'st them through life's disparted wave.

4 By death and hell pursued in vain,
To Thee the ransomed seed shall come;
Shouting, their heavenly Zion gain,
And pass through death triumphant home.

Charles Wesley, 1707-88.

487

PRAISE. 8 8.6. D. A. Radiger, 1749-1817.

1 Come on, my partners in distress,
My comrades through the wilderness,
Who still your bodies feel;
Awhile forget your griefs and fears,
And look beyond this vale of tears
To that celestial hill.

2 Beyond the bounds of time and space,
Look forward to that heavenly place,
The saints' secure abode:
On faith's strong eagle-pinions rise,
And force your passage to the skies,
And scale the mount of God.

3 Who suffer with our Master here,
We shall before His face appear,
And by His side sit down;
To patient faith the prize is sure,
And all that to the end endure
The cross, shall wear the crown.

4 Thrice blessèd, bliss-inspiring hope!
It lifts the fainting spirits up,
It brings to life the dead;
Our conflicts here shall soon be past,
And you and I ascend at last,
Triumphant with our Head.

5 That great mysterious Deity
We soon with open face shall see;
The beatific sight
Shall fill heaven's sounding courts with praise,
And wide diffuse the golden blaze
Of everlasting light.

6 The Father shining on His throne,
The glorious co-eternal Son,
The Spirit, one and seven,
Conspire our rapture to complete;
And lo! we fall before His feet,
And silence heightens heaven.

7 In hope of that ecstatic pause,
Jesus, we now sustain the cross,
And at Thy footstool fall;
Till Thou our hidden life reveal,
Till Thou our ravished spirits fill,
And God is all in all.

Charles Wesley, 1707-88.

488

UNIVERSITY COLLEGE. 7 7.7 7. H. J. GAUNTLETT, 1805-76.

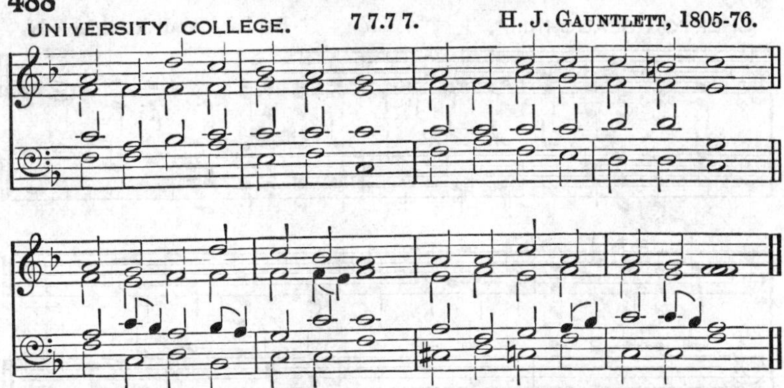

1 OFT in danger, oft in woe,
Onward, Christians, onward go;
Fight the fight, maintain the strife,
Strengthened with the Bread of Life.

2 Shrink not, Christians: will ye yield?
Will ye quit the painful field?
Will ye flee in danger's hour?
Know ye not your Captain's power?

3 Let your drooping hearts be glad;
March in heavenly armour clad:
Fight, nor think the battle long;
Soon shall victory tune your song.

4 Let not sorrow dim your eye,
Soon shall every tear be dry;
Let not fears your course impede,
Great your strength if great your need.

5 Onward then to glory move,
More than conquerors ye shall prove;
Though opposed by many a foe,
Christian soldiers, onward go.

Henry Kirke White, 1785-1806;
Frances Sara Colquhoun, 1809-77.

489

GRAINGER. C.M. G. F. BROCKLESS, 1887-1957.

1 WORKMAN of God! O lose not heart,
But learn what God is like,
And in the darkest battle-field
Thou shalt know where to strike.

2 Thrice blest is he to whom is given
The instinct that can tell
That God is on the field when He
Is most invisible.

3 For God is other than we think;
His ways are far above,
Far beyond reason's height, and reached
Only by childlike love.

4 Then learn to scorn the praise of man,
And learn to lose with God;
For Jesus won the world through shame,
And beckons thee His road.

5 For right is right, since God is God,
And right the day must win;
To doubt would be disloyalty,
To falter would be sin.

Frederick William Faber, 1814-63.

490

SHEPTON-BEAUCHAMP. L.M. English Traditional Melody.

May also be sung to DUKE STREET, No. 784.

1 FIGHT the good fight with all thy might;
Christ is thy strength, and Christ thy right;
Lay hold on life, and it shall be
Thy joy and crown eternally.

2 Run the straight race through God's good grace;
Lift up thine eyes, and seek His face,
Life with its path before thee lies;
Christ is the way, and Christ the prize.

3 Cast care aside, lean on thy Guide,
His boundless mercy will provide;
Lean, and thy trusting soul shall prove,
Christ is thy life, and Christ thy love.

4 Faint not, nor fear, His arm is near;
He changeth not, and thou art dear,
Only believe, and thou shalt see
That Christ is all in all to thee.

John Samuel Bewley Monsell, 1811-75.

491

CAMBERWELL. 7.7.7.3. J. McMURDIE, 1792-1878.

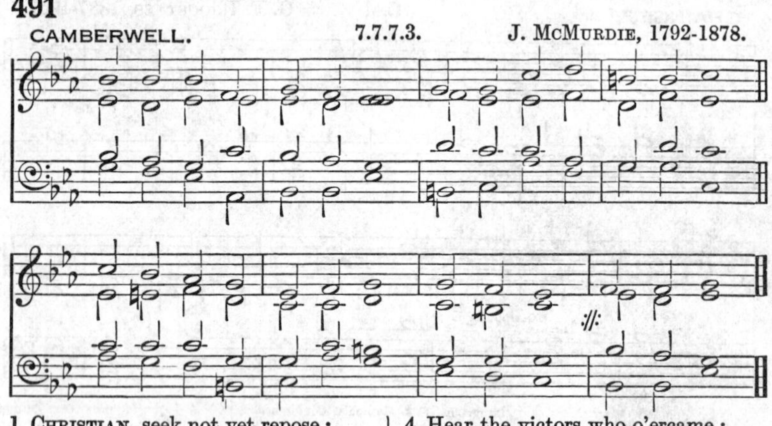

1 CHRISTIAN, seek not yet repose;
Cast thy dreams of ease away;
Thou art in the midst of foes:
Watch and pray.

2 Principalities and powers,
Mustering their unseen array,
Wait for thy unguarded hours:
Watch and pray.

3 Gird thy heavenly armour on;
Wear it ever, night and day;
Ambushed lies the evil one:
Watch and pray.

4 Hear the victors who o'ercame;
Still they mark each warrior's way;
All with one sweet voice exclaim,
Watch and pray.

5 Hear, above all, hear thy Lord,
Him thou lovest to obey;
Hide within thy heart His word:
Watch and pray.

6 Watch, as if on that alone
Hung the issue of the day:
Pray, that help may be sent down:
Watch and pray.

Charlotte Elliott, 1789-1871.

HOLY ROOD. S.M. A. H. BROWN, 1830-1926.

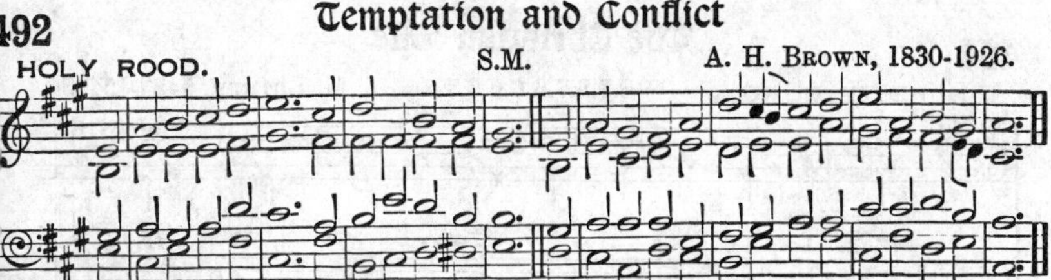

May also be sung to SWABIA, No. 599.

2 *Timothy* iv. 6-8.

1 'I the good fight have fought',
O when shall I declare?
The victory by my Saviour got
I long with Paul to share.

2 O may I triumph so,
When all my warfare 's past,
And, dying, find my latest foe
Under my feet at last.

3 This blessèd word be mine
Just as the port is gained:
Kept by the power of grace divine,
I have the faith maintained.

4 The apostles of my Lord,
To whom it first was given,
They could not speak a greater word,
Nor all the saints in heaven.

Charles Wesley, 1707-88.

Also:

24 O God, my strength
239 Lord Jesus, think on me
352 Oppressed with sin
494 A safe stronghold
499 O safe to the Rock
502 Omnipotent Lord
542 Jesus, my strength

TRUSTFULNESS AND PEACE

493

7.8.7.8.7 7.

RATISBON (JESU, MEINE ZUVERSICHT). J. CRÜGER, 1598-1662.

1 LOVE of love, and Light of light,
Heavenly Father all maintaining;
Wisdom hid in highest height,
To Thy creature fondly deigning;
Maker wonderful and just,
Thou hast call'd my heart to trust.

2 What are life's unnumber'd cares,
Sorrow, torment, passing measure?
O'er my short-lived pains and fears
Surely ruleth Thy good pleasure.
Boundless is Thy love for me,
Boundless then my trust shall be.

3 Every burden weigheth light,
Since in Thee my hope abideth:
Sweetly bright my darkest night,
While on Thee my mind confideth.
Give Thy gift, I Thee implore,
Thee to trust for evermore. Amen.

Robert Seymour Bridges, 1844-1930. *Y.H.*

EIN' FESTE BURG. 8.7.8.7.6 6.6 6.7. M. LUTHER, 1483-1546.

Ein' feste Burg ist unser Gott.

1 A SAFE stronghold our God is still,
A trusty shield and weapon;
He'll help us clear from all the ill
That hath us now o'ertaken.
The ancient prince of hell
Hath risen with purpose fell;
Strong mail of craft and power
He weareth in this hour;
On earth is not his fellow.

2 With force of arms we nothing can,
Full soon were we down-ridden;
But for us fights the proper Man,
Whom God Himself hath bidden.
Ask ye: Who is this same?
Christ Jesus is His name,
The Lord Sabaoth's Son;
He, and no other one,
Shall conquer in the battle.

3 And were this world all devils o'er,
And watching to devour us,
We lay it not to heart so sore;
Not they can overpower us.
And let the prince of ill
Look grim as e'er he will,
He harms us not a whit:
For why? His doom is writ;
A word shall quickly slay him.

4 God's word, for all their craft and force
One moment will not linger,
But, spite of hell, shall have its course;
'Tis written by His finger.
And though they take our life,
Goods, honour, children, wife,
Yet is their profit small:
These things shall vanish all;
The city of God remaineth.

Martin Luther, 1483-1546;
tr. by Thomas Carlyle, 1795-1881.

Trustfulness and Peace

495

WALTON. 4 4.7. (12 lines). W. F. MOULTON, 1866-1929.

Wer Gott vertraut, hat wohl gebaut.

1 WHO puts his trust
In God most just
Hath built his house securely;
He who relies
On Jesus Christ,
Heaven shall be his most surely:
Then fixed on Thee
My trust shall be,
For Thy truth cannot alter;
While mine Thou art,
Not death's worst smart
Shall make my courage falter.

2 Though fiercest foes
My course oppose,
A dauntless front I'll show them;
My champion Thou,
Lord Christ, art now,
Who soon shalt overthrow them!
And if but Thee
I have in me,
With Thy good gifts and Spirit,
Nor death nor hell,
I know full well,
Shall hurt me, through Thy merit.

3 I rest me here
Without a fear—
By Thee shall all be given
That I can need,
O Friend indeed,
For this life or for heaven.
O make me true,
My heart renew,
My soul and flesh deliver!
Lord, hear my prayer,
And in Thy care
Keep me in peace for ever. Amen.

Joachim Magdeburg, 1525-75;
tr. by Catherine Winkworth, 1827-78.

496

INVITATION. L.M. J. F. LAMPE, 1703-51.

1 ETERNAL beam of light divine,
Fountain of unexhausted love,
In whom the Father's glories shine
Through earth beneath and heaven above.

2 Jesu, the weary wanderer's rest,
Give me Thy easy yoke to bear,
With steadfast patience arm my breast,
With spotless love and lowly fear.

3 Thankful I take the cup from Thee,
Prepared and mingled by Thy skill,
Though bitter to the taste it be,
Powerful the wounded soul to heal.

4 Be Thou, O Rock of Ages, nigh!
So shall each murmuring thought be gone,
And grief, and fear, and care shall fly,
As clouds before the midday sun.

5 Speak to my warring passions: Peace!
Say to my trembling heart: Be still!
Thy power my strength and fortress is,
For all things serve Thy sovereign will.

6 O death! Where is thy sting? Where now
Thy boasted victory, O grave?
Who shall contend with God? Or who
Can hurt whom God delights to save?

Charles Wesley, 1707-88.

497

ST. HILARY. 7.6.7.6.7.7.7.6. J. B. DYKES, 1823-76.

1 To the hills I lift mine eyes,
The everlasting hills;
Streaming thence in fresh supplies,
My soul the Spirit feels.
Will He not His help afford?
Help, while yet I ask, is given:
God comes down: the God and Lord
That made both earth and heaven.

2 Faithful soul, pray always; pray,
And still in God confide;
He thy feeble steps shall stay,
Nor suffer thee to slide:
Lean on thy Redeemer's breast;
He thy quiet spirit keeps;
Rest in Him, securely rest;
Thy watchman never sleeps.

3 Neither sin, nor earth, nor hell
Thy keeper can surprise;
Careless slumbers cannot steal
On His all-seeing eyes:
He is Israel's sure defence;
Israel all His care shall prove,
Kept by watchful providence
And ever-waking love.

4 See the Lord, thy keeper, stand
Omnipotently near!
Lo! He holds thee by thy hand,
And banishes thy fear;
Shadows with His wings thy head;
Guards from all impending harms:
Round thee and beneath are spread
The everlasting arms.

5 Christ shall bless thy going out,
Shall bless thy coming in;
Kindly compass thee about,
Till thou art saved from sin;
Like thy spotless Master, thou,
Filled with wisdom, love, and power,
Holy, pure, and perfect, now,
Henceforth, and evermore.

Charles Wesley, 1707-88.

498

REDHEAD No. 76. 7 7.7 7.7 7. R. REDHEAD, 1820-1901.

1 Rock of Ages, cleft for me,
Let me hide myself in Thee;
Let the water and the blood,
From Thy riven side which flowed,
Be of sin the double cure,
Cleanse me from its guilt and power.

2 Not the labours of my hands
Can fulfil Thy law's demands;
Could my zeal no respite know,
Could my tears for ever flow,
All for sin could not atone:
Thou must save, and Thou alone.

3 Nothing in my hand I bring,
Simply to Thy Cross I cling;
Naked, come to Thee for dress;
Helpless, look to Thee for grace;
Foul, I to the fountain fly;
Wash me, Saviour, or I die.

4 While I draw this fleeting breath,
When my eyelids close in death,
When I soar to worlds unknown,
See Thee on Thy judgement-throne:
Rock of Ages, cleft for me,
Let me hide myself in Thee. Amen.

Augustus Montague Toplady, 1740-78.

SHELTER. 11 11.11 11. and refrain. I. D. SANKEY, 1840-1908.

REFRAIN.

1 O SAFE to the Rock that is higher than I,
My soul in its conflicts and sorrows would fly,
So sinful, so weary, Thine, Thine would I be,
Thou blest Rock of Ages, I'm hiding in Thee!
Hiding in Thee! Hiding in Thee!
Thou blest Rock of Ages, I'm hiding in Thee!

2 In the calm of the noontide, in sorrow's lone hour,
In times when temptation casts o'er me its power;
In the tempests of life, on its wide heaving sea,
Thou blest Rock of Ages, I'm hiding in Thee!

3 How oft in the conflict, when pressed by the foe,
I have fled to my refuge, and breathed out my woe:
How often, when trials, like sea-billows roll,
Have I hidden in Thee, O Thou Rock of my soul.

William Orcutt Cushing, 1823-1903.

500

LEICESTER. 8.8.8.8.8.8 8. J. Bishop, 1665-1737.

May also be sung to Euphony, No. 173.

1 Peace, doubting heart! my God's I am:
Who formed me man, forbids my fear;
The Lord hath called me by my name;
The Lord protects, for ever near;
His blood for me did once atone,
And still He loves and guards His own.

2 When, passing through the watery deep,
I ask in faith His promised aid,
The waves an awful distance keep,
And shrink from my devoted head;
Fearless their violence I dare;
They cannot harm, for God is there.

3 To Him mine eye of faith I turn,
And through the fire pursue my way;
The fire forgets its power to burn,
The lambent flames around me play;
I own His power, accept the sign,
And shout to prove the Saviour mine.

4 Still nigh me, O my Saviour, stand!
And guard in fierce temptation's hour;
Hide in the hollow of Thy hand,
Show forth in me Thy saving power,
Still be Thy arms my sure defence,
Nor earth nor hell shall pluck me thence.

5 When darkness intercepts the skies
And sorrow's waves around me roll,
When high the storms of passion rise,
And half o'erwhelm my sinking soul;
My soul a sudden calm shall feel,
And hear a whisper: Peace; be still!

Charles Wesley, 1707-88.

501

SONG 46 (*First Tune*). 10 10. O. GIBBONS, 1583-1625.

PAX TECUM (*Second Tune*). 10 10. G. T. CALDBECK, 1852-1918

1 PEACE, perfect peace, in this dark world of sin?
The blood of Jesus whispers peace within.

2 Peace, perfect peace, by thronging duties pressed?
To do the will of Jesus, this is rest.

3 Peace, perfect peace, with sorrows surging round?
On Jesus' bosom nought but calm is found.

4 Peace, perfect peace, with loved ones far away?
In Jesus' keeping we are safe and they.

5 Peace, perfect peace, our future all unknown?
Jesus we know, and He is on the throne.

6 Peace, perfect peace, death shadowing us and ours?
Jesus has vanquished death and all its powers.

7 It is enough: earth's struggles soon shall cease,
And Jesus call us to heaven's perfect peace.

Edward Henry Bickersteth, 1825-1906.

502

LAUDATE DOMINUM. 10 10.11 11. H. J. GAUNTLETT, 1805-76.

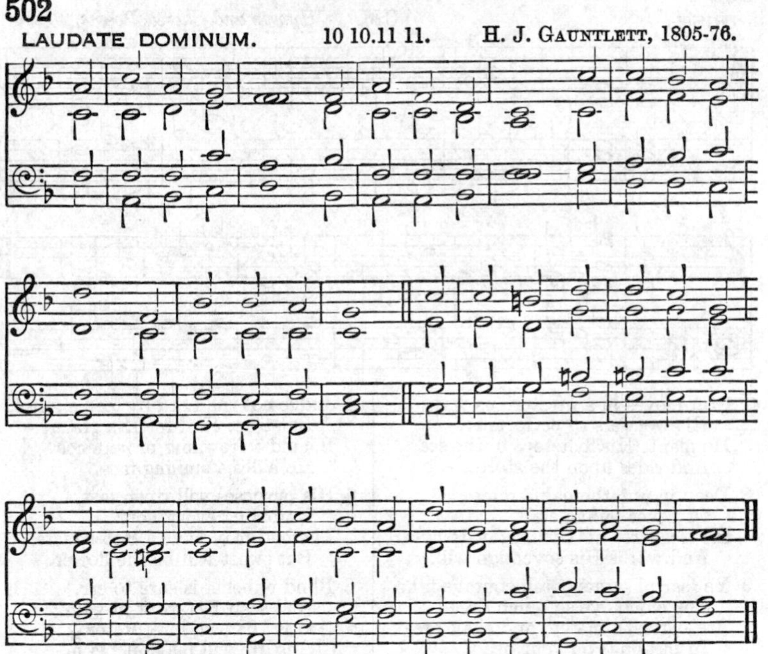

1 OMNIPOTENT Lord, my Saviour and King,
Thy succour afford, Thy righteousness bring:
Thy promises bind Thee compassion to have;
Now, now let me find Thee almighty to save.

2 Rejoicing in hope, and patient in grief,
To Thee I look up for certain relief;
I fear no denial, no danger I fear,
Nor start from the trial, while Jesus is near.

3 I every hour in jeopardy stand;
But Thou art my power, and holdest my hand:
While yet I am calling, Thy succour I feel;
It saves me from falling, or plucks me from hell.

4 O who can explain this struggle for life,
This travail and pain, this trembling and strife:
Plague, earthquake, and famine, and tumult, and war,
The wonderful coming of Jesus declare.

5 Yet God is above men, devils, and sin,
My Jesus's love the battle shall win;
So terribly glorious His coming shall be,
His love all-victorious shall conquer for me.

6 He all shall break through; His truth and His grace
Shall bring me into the plentiful place,
Through much tribulation, through water and fire,
Through floods of temptation and flames of desire.

7 On Jesus, my power, till then I rely,
All evil before His presence shall fly;
When I have my Saviour, my sin shall depart,
And Jesus for ever shall reign in my heart.

Charles Wesley, 1707-88.

503

IRISH. C.M. *Hymns and Sacred Poems*, 1749.

1 God moves in a mysterious way
His wonders to perform;
He plants His footsteps in the sea,
And rides upon the storm.

2 Deep in unfathomable mines
Of never-failing skill
He treasures up His bright designs,
And works His sovereign will.

3 Ye fearful saints, fresh courage take,
The clouds ye so much dread
Are big with mercy, and shall break
In blessings on your head.

4 Judge not the Lord by feeble sense,
But trust Him for His grace;
Behind a frowning providence
He hides a smiling face.

5 His purposes will ripen fast,
Unfolding every hour;
The bud may have a bitter taste,
But sweet will be the flower.

6 Blind unbelief is sure to err,
And scan His work in vain;
God is His own interpreter,
And He will make it plain.

William Cowper, 1731-1800.

504

BREMEN. 8.8.8.8.8.8. G. C. Neumark, 1621-81.

May also be sung to Aldersgate Street, No. 447.

Wer nur den lieben Gott lässt walten.

1 LEAVE God to order all thy ways,
And hope in Him whate'er betide;
Thou'lt find Him in the evil days
Thy all-sufficient strength and guide:
Who trusts in God's unchanging love
Builds on the rock that nought can move.

2 Only thy restless heart keep still,
And wait in cheerful hope, content
To take whate'er His gracious will,
His all-discerning love, hath sent;
Nor doubt our inmost wants are known
To Him who chose us for His own.

3 Sing, pray, and swerve not from His ways,
But do thine own part faithfully;
Trust His rich promises of grace,
So shall they be fulfilled in thee:
God never yet forsook at need
The soul that trusted Him indeed.

Georg Christian Neumark, 1621-81;
tr. by Catherine Winkworth, 1827-78.

505

PSALM 8 (WHITEHALL). L.M. H. LAWES, 1596-1662.

Seelenbräutigam, O du Gotteslamm.

1 O THOU to whose all-searching sight
The darkness shineth as the light,
Search, prove my heart; it pants for Thee;
O burst these bonds, and set it free!

2 Wash out its stains, refine its dross,
Nail my affections to the Cross;
Hallow each thought; let all within
Be clean, as Thou, my Lord, art clean.

3 When rising floods my soul o'erflow,
When sinks my heart in waves of woe,
Jesu, Thy timely aid impart
And raise my head, and cheer my heart.

4 Saviour, where'er Thy steps I see,
Dauntless, untired, I follow Thee;
O let Thy hand support me still,
And lead me to Thy holy hill! Amen.

Nicolaus Ludwig von Zinzendorf, 1700-60;
tr. by John Wesley, 1703-91.

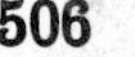

506

IN MEMORIAM. S.M. A. SULLIVAN, 1842-1900.

By permission of Novello and Company, Limited.

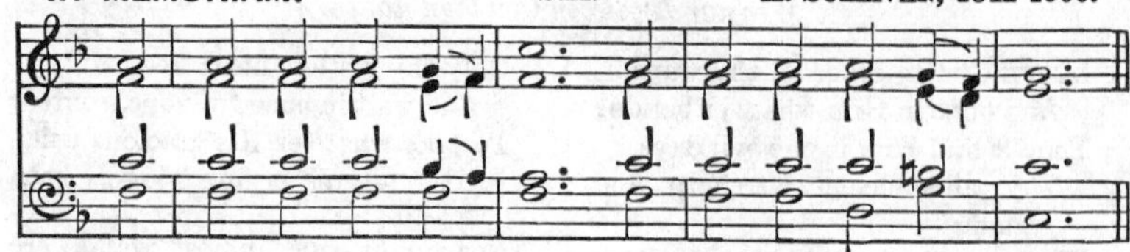

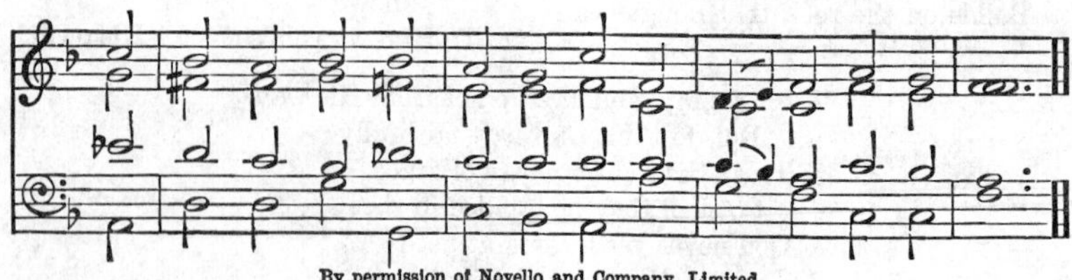

1 My spirit on Thy care
Blest Saviour, I recline;
Thou wilt not leave me in despair,
For Thou art Love divine.

2 In Thee I place my trust,
On Thee I calmly rest;
I know Thee good, I know Thee just,
And count Thy choice the best.

3 Whate'er events betide,
Thy will they all perform;
Safe in Thy breast my head I hide,
Nor fear the coming storm.

4 Let good or ill befall,
It must be good for me;
Secure of having Thee in all,
Of having all in Thee.

Henry Francis Lyte, 1793-1847.

507

FRANCONIA (*First Tune*). S.M. KONIG'S *Choralbuch*, 1738.

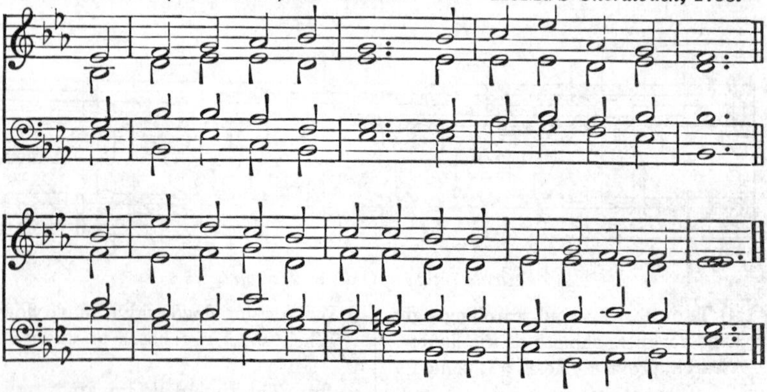

SONG 20 (*Second Tune*). S.M. O. GIBBONS, 1583-1625.

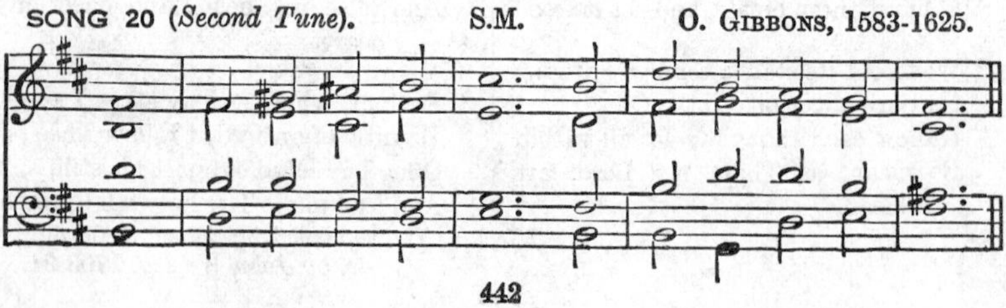

Trustfulness and Peace

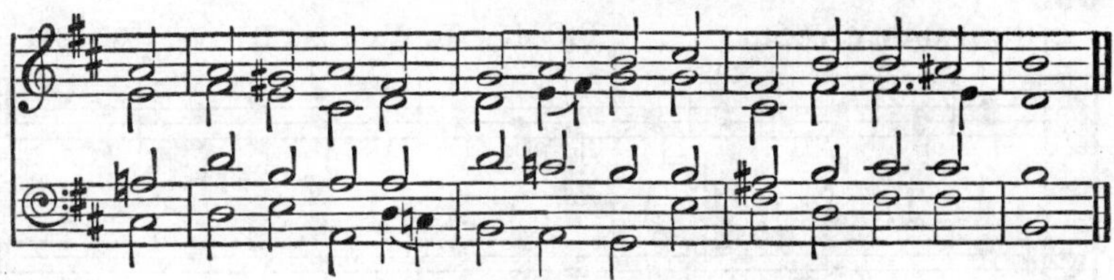

Befiehl du deine Wege.

1 Commit thou all thy griefs
And ways into His hands,
To His sure truth and tender care,
Who heaven and earth commands.

2 Who points the clouds their course,
Whom winds and seas obey,
He shall direct thy wandering feet,
He shall prepare thy way.

3 Thou on the Lord rely,
So safe shalt thou go on;
Fix on His work thy steadfast eye,
So shall thy work be done.

4 No profit canst thou gain
By self-consuming care:
To Him commend thy cause; His ear
Attends the softest prayer.

5 Thy everlasting truth,
Father, Thy ceaseless love,
Sees all Thy children's wants, and knows
What best for each will prove.

6 Thou everywhere hast sway,
And all things serve Thy might;
Thy every act pure blessing is,
Thy path unsullied light.

7 When Thou arisest, Lord,
What shall Thy work withstand?
Whate'er Thy children want, Thou giv'st;
And who shall stay Thy hand?

* * * *

8 Give to the winds thy fears;
Hope, and be undismayed:
God hears thy sighs, and counts thy tears,
God shall lift up thy head.

9 Through waves, and clouds, and storms
He gently clears thy way:
Wait thou His time; so shall this night
Soon end in joyous day.

10 Still heavy is thy heart?
Still sink thy spirits down?
Cast off the weight, let fear depart,
Bid every care be gone.

11 What though thou rulest not?
Yet heaven, and earth, and hell
Proclaim: God sitteth on the throne,
And ruleth all things well!

12 Leave to His sovereign sway
To choose and to command;
So shalt thou wondering own His way
How wise, how strong His hand.

13 Far, far above thy thought
His counsel shall appear,
When fully He the work hath wrought
That caused thy needless fear.

14 Thou seest our weakness, Lord;
Our hearts are known to Thee:
O lift Thou up the sinking hand,
Confirm the feeble knee!

15 Let us in life, in death,
Thy steadfast truth declare,
And publish with our latest breath
Thy love and guardian care.

Paulus Gerhardt, 1607-76;
tr. by John Wesley, 1703-91.

508

CHRISTMAS CAROL. D.C.M. H. WALFORD DAVIES, 1869-1941

May also be sung to LAND OF REST, No. 921.

1 As helpless as a child who clings
Fast to his father's arm,
And casts his weakness on the strength
That keeps him safe from harm:
So I, my Father, cling to Thee,
And thus I every hour
Would link my earthly feebleness
To Thine almighty power.

2 As trustful as a child who looks
Up in his mother's face,
And all his little griefs and fears
Forgets in her embrace:
So I to Thee, my Saviour look,
And in Thy face divine
Can read the love that will sustain
As weak a faith as mine.

3 As loving as a child who sits
Close by his parent's knee,
And knows no want while he can have
That sweet society:
So sitting at Thy feet, my heart
Would all its love outpour,
And pray that Thou wouldst teach me, Lord,
To love Thee more and more.

James Drummond Burns, 1823-64.

509

ST. LEONARD'S. D.C.M. H. Hiles, 1826-1904.

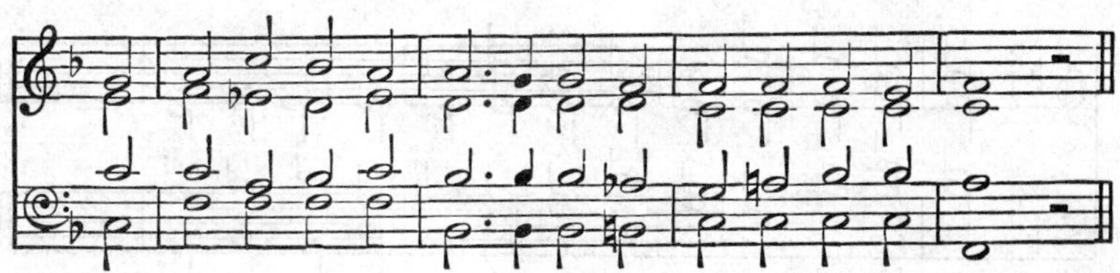

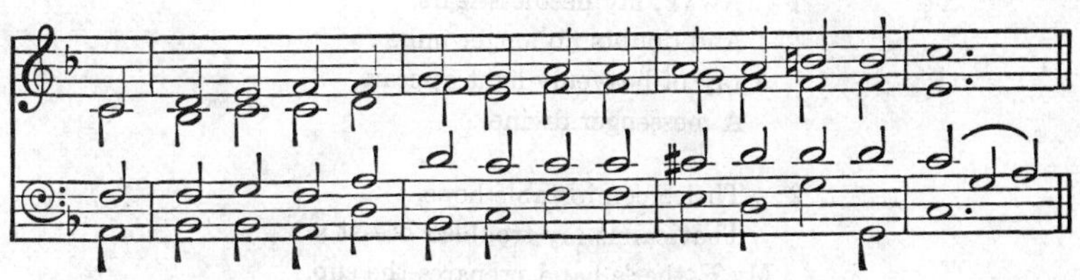

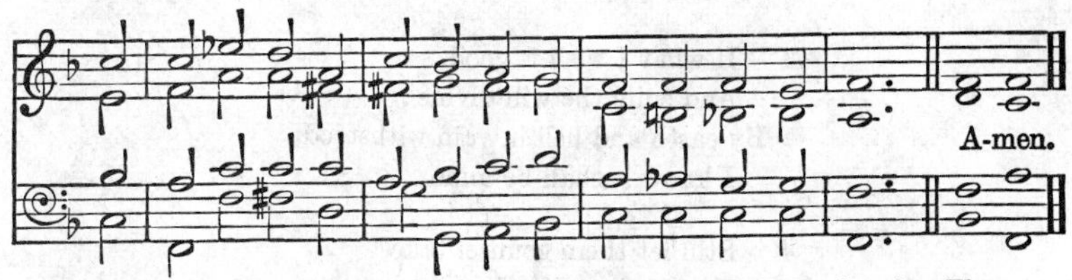

1 The Galilean fishers toil
  All night and nothing take;
But Jesus comes—a wondrous spoil
  Is lifted from the lake.
Lord, when our labours are in vain,
  And vain the help of men,
When fruitless is our care and pain,
  Come, blessèd Jesus, then!

2 The night is dark, the surges fill
  The bark, the wild winds roar;
But Jesus comes; and all is still—
  The ship is at the shore.
O Lord, when storms around us howl,
  And all is dark and drear,
In all the tempests of the soul,
  O blessèd Jesus, hear!

3 A frail one, thrice denying Thee,
  Saw mercy in Thine eyes;
The penitent upon the tree
  Was borne to Paradise.
In hours of sin and deep distress,
  O show us, Lord, Thy face;
In penitential loneliness,
  O give us, Jesus, grace!

4 The faithful few retire in fear,
  To their closed upper room;
But, suddenly, with joyful cheer
  They see their Master come.
Lord, come to us, unloose our bands,
  And bid our terrors cease;
Lift over us Thy blessèd hands,
  Speak, holy Jesus, peace! Amen.

Christopher Wordsworth, 1807-85.

510

CLIFTON. S.M. J. BRABHAM, 1840.

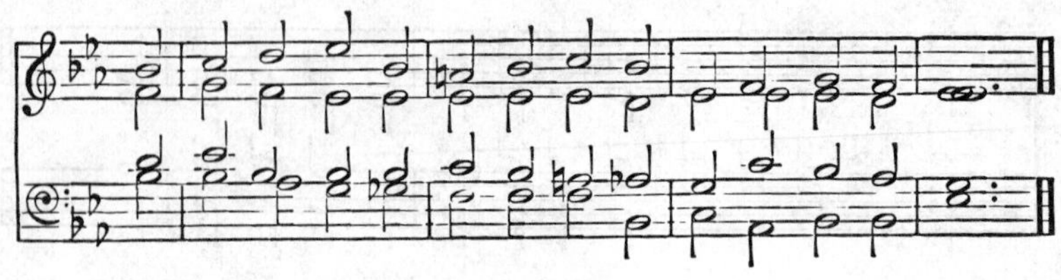

1 AWAY, my needless fears,
And doubts no longer mine;
A ray of heavenly light appears,
A messenger divine.

2 Thrice comfortable hope,
That calms my troubled breast;
My Father's hand prepares the cup,
And what He wills is best.

3 If what I wish is good,
And suits the will divine;
By earth and hell in vain withstood,
I know it shall be mine.

4 Still let them counsel take
To frustrate His decree,
They cannot keep a blessing back
By heaven designed for me.

5 Here then I doubt no more,
But in His pleasure rest,
Whose wisdom, love, and truth, and power
Engage to make me blest.

6 To accomplish His design
The creatures all agree;
And all the attributes divine
Are now at work for me.

Charles Wesley, 1707-88.

511

SPETISBURY. 10 10.11 11. W. Knapp, c. 1688-1768.

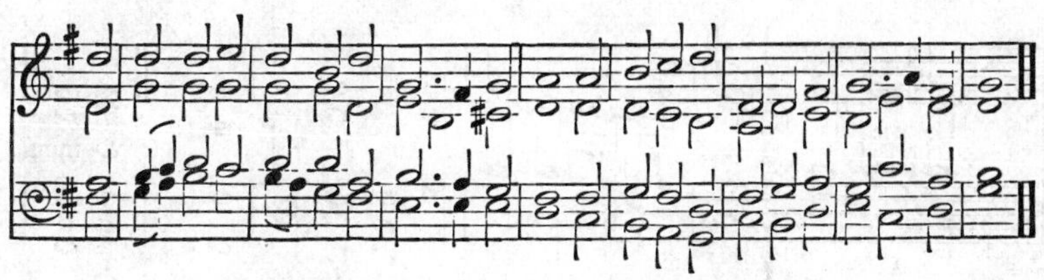

1.

Begone, unbelief; my Saviour is near,
And for my relief will surely appear:
By prayer let me wrestle, and He will perform;
With Christ in the vessel, I smile at the storm.

2.

Though dark be my way, since He is my Guide,
'Tis mine to obey, 'tis His to provide;
Though cisterns be broken and creatures all fail,
The word He hath spoken shall surely prevail.

3.

His love in time past forbids me to think
He'll leave me at last in trouble to sink;
While each Ebenezer I have in review
Confirms His good pleasure to help me quite through.

4.

Why should I complain of want or distress,
Temptation or pain? He told me no less;
The heirs of salvation, I know from His word,
Through much tribulation must follow their Lord.

5.

Since all that I meet shall work for my good,
The bitter is sweet, the medicine food;
Though painful at present, 'twill cease before long;
And then, O how pleasant the conqueror's song!

John Newton, 1725-1807.

512

WIGTOWN. C.M. *Scottish Psalter*, 1635.

1 Lord, as to Thy dear Cross we flee,
And plead to be forgiven,
So let Thy life our pattern be,
And form our souls for heaven.

2 Help us, through good report and ill,
Our daily cross to bear;
Like Thee to do our Father's will,
Our brethren's grief to share.

3 Let grace our selfishness expel,
Our earthliness refine,
And kindness in our bosoms dwell,
As free and true as Thine.

4 If joy shall at Thy bidding fly,
And grief's dark day come on,
We, in our turn, would meekly cry:
Father, Thy will be done!

5 Should friends misjudge, or foes defame,
Or brethren faithless prove,
Then, like Thine own, be all our aim
To conquer them by love.

6 Kept peaceful in the midst of strife,
Forgiving and forgiven,
O may we lead the pilgrims' life,
And follow Thee to heaven. Amen.

John Hampden Gurney, 1802-62.

513

GREEN HILL. C.M. A. L. PEACE, 1844-1912.

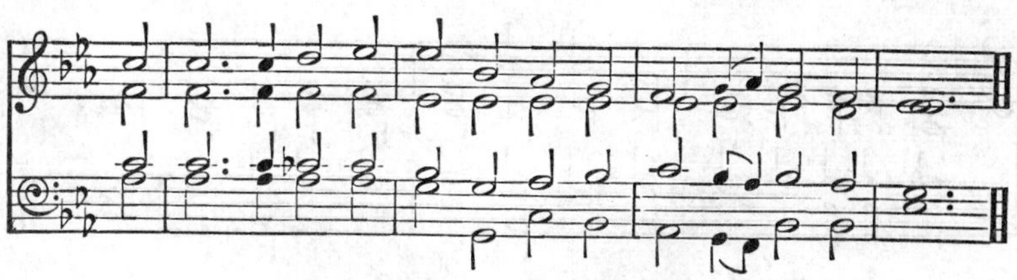

1 Who fathoms the eternal thought?
Who talks of scheme and plan?
The Lord is God! He needeth not
The poor device of man.

2 Here in the maddening maze of things,
When tossed by storm and flood,
To one fixed ground my spirit clings;
I know that God is good!

3 I long for household voices gone,
For vanished smiles I long;
But God hath led my dear ones on,
And He can do no wrong.

4 I know not what the future hath
Of marvel or surprise,
Assured alone that life and death
His mercy underlies.

5 And if my heart and flesh are weak
To bear an untried pain,
The bruisèd reed He will not break,
But strengthen and sustain.

6 No offering of my own I have,
Nor works my faith to prove;
I can but give the gifts He gave,
And plead His love for love.

7 And so beside the silent sea
I wait the muffled oar;
No harm from Him can come to me
On ocean or on shore.

8 I know not where His islands lift
Their fronded palms in air;
I only know I cannot drift
Beyond His love and care.

John Greenleaf Whittier, 1807-92.

514

1 He that is down needs fear no fall,
He that is low, no pride;
He that is humble ever shall
Have God to be his guide.

2 I am content with what I have,
Little be it or much;
And, Lord, contentment still I crave,
Because Thou savest such.

3 Fullness to such a burden is
That go on pilgrimage;
Here little, and hereafter bliss,
Is best from age to age.

John Bunyan, 1628-88.

Trustfulness and Peace

MOAB. 6.6.6.6. D. I. GWYLLT, 1822-77.

A-men.

May also be sung to SUPPLICATION, No. 782.

1 THY way, not mine, O Lord,
However dark it be!
Lead me by Thine own hand;
Choose out the path for me.
Smooth let it be or rough,
It will be still the best;
Winding or straight, it leads
Right onward to Thy rest.

2 I dare not choose my lot;
I would not, if I might:
Choose Thou for me, my God;
So shall I walk aright.
The kingdom that I seek
Is Thine; so let the way
That leads to it be Thine,
Else I must surely stray.

3 Take Thou my cup, and it
With joy or sorrow fill
As best to Thee may seem;
Choose Thou my good and ill.
Not mine, not mine the choice
In things or great or small;
Be Thou my Guide, my Strength,
My Wisdom, and my All. Amen.

Horatius Bonar, 1808-89.

516

TRUST AND OBEY. 6 6.9. D. and refrain. D. B. TOWNER, 1833-96.

REFRAIN.

1 WHEN we walk with the Lord
In the light of His Word
What a glory He sheds on our way!
While we do His good will,
He abides with us still,
And with all who will trust and obey.

Trust and obey, for there's no other way
To be happy in Jesus,
But to trust and obey.

2 Not a shadow can rise,
Not a cloud in the skies,
But His smile quickly drives it away;
Not a doubt nor a fear,
Not a sigh nor a tear,
Can abide while we trust and obey.

3 Not a burden we bear,
Not a sorrow we share,
But our toil He doth richly repay;
Not a grief nor a loss,
Not a frown nor a cross,
But is blest if we trust and obey.

4 But we never can prove
The delights of His love
Until all on the altar we lay;
For the favour He shows,
And the joy He bestows,
Are for them who will trust and obey.

5 Then in fellowship sweet
We will sit at His feet,
Or we'll walk by His side in the way;
What He says we will do,
Where He sends we will go—
Never fear, only trust and obey.

John Henry Sammis, d. 1919.

517

TRUSTING JESUS. 7 7.7 7. and refrain. I. D. SANKEY, 1840-1908.

1 SIMPLY trusting every day,
Trusting through a stormy way;
Even when my faith is small,
Trusting Jesus, that is all.

Trusting as the moments fly,
Trusting as the days go by,
Trusting Him whate'er befall,
Trusting Jesus, that is all.

2 Brightly doth His Spirit shine
Into this poor heart of mine:
While He leads I cannot fall,
Trusting Jesus, that is all.

3 Singing, if my way be clear;
Praying, if the path be drear;
If in danger, for Him call;
Trusting Jesus, that is all.

4 Trusting Him while life shall last,
Trusting Him till earth be past,
Till within the jasper wall;
Trusting Jesus, that is all.

Edgar Page Stites, *b.* 1837.

JESU, MEINE FREUDE. 6 6.5.6 6.5.7.8 6. J. CRÜGER, 1598-1662.

Jesu, meine Freude.

1 JESU, priceless treasure,
Source of purest pleasure,
Truest friend to me;
Ah! how long I've panted,
And my heart hath fainted,
Thirsting, Lord, for Thee!
Thine I am, O spotless Lamb,
I will suffer nought to hide Thee,
Nought I ask beside Thee.

2 In Thine arm I rest me;
Foes who would molest me
Cannot reach me here;
Though the earth be shaking,
Every heart be quaking,
Jesus calms my fear;
Sin and hell in conflict fell
With their bitter storms assail me:
Jesus will not fail me.

3 Hence, all fears and sadness,
For the Lord of gladness,
Jesus, enters in;
Those who love the Father,
Though the storms may gather,
Still have peace within;
Yea, whate'er I here must bear,
Still in Thee lies purest pleasure,
Jesu, priceless treasure!

Johann Franck, 1618-77;
tr. by Catherine Winkworth, 1827-78.

519

ABRIDGE. C.M. I. SMITH, c. 1725-c. 1800.

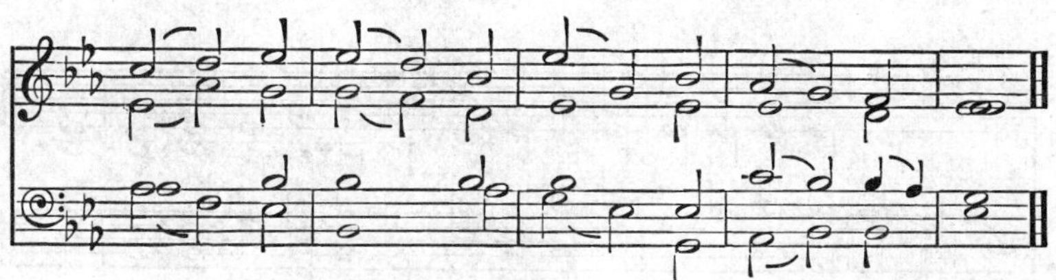

1 THEE, Jesus, full of truth and grace,
  Thee, Saviour, we adore,
Thee in affliction's furnace praise,
  And magnify Thy power.

2 Thy power, in human weakness shown,
  Shall make us all entire;
We now Thy guardian presence own,
  And walk unburned in fire.

3 Thee, Son of Man, by faith we see,
  And glory in our Guide;
Surrounded and upheld by Thee,
  The fiery test abide.

4 The fire our graces shall refine,
  Till, moulded from above,
We bear the character divine,
  The stamp of perfect love.

Charles Wesley, 1707-88.

520

CARINTHIA. 6.6.6.6.8 8. BOOTH'S *Appendix*, 1873.

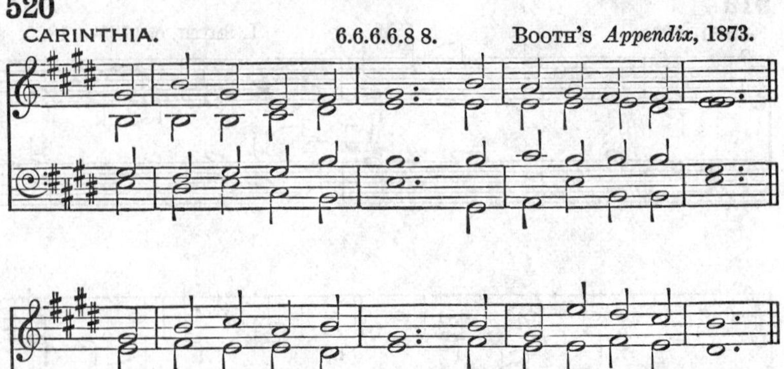

May also be sung to WARRENNE, No. 5 (PEVERIL), A.T. No. 18.

1 I BRING my sins to Thee
The sins I cannot count,
That all may cleansèd be
In Thy once-opened Fount.
I bring them, Saviour, all to Thee;
The burden is too great for me.

2 My heart to Thee I bring,
The heart I cannot read;
A faithless, wandering thing,
An evil heart indeed.
I bring it, Saviour, now to Thee,
That fixed and faithful it may be.

3 To Thee I bring my care,
The care I cannot flee;
Thou wilt not only share,
But bear it all for me.
O loving Saviour, now to Thee
I bring the load that wearies me.

4 I bring my grief to Thee,
The grief I cannot tell;
No words shall needed be,
Thou knowest all so well.
I bring the sorrow laid on me,
O suffering Saviour, now to Thee.

5 My joys to Thee I bring,
The joys Thy love hath given,
That each may be a wing
To lift me nearer heaven.
I bring them, Saviour, all to Thee;
For Thou hast purchased all for me.

6 My life I bring to Thee,
I would not be my own;
O Saviour, let me be
Thine ever, Thine alone.
My heart, my life, my all I bring
To Thee, my Saviour and my King.

Frances Ridley Havergal, 1836-79.

521

EASTERGATE (*First Tune*). 8.5.8.3. J. N. IRELAND, 1879-

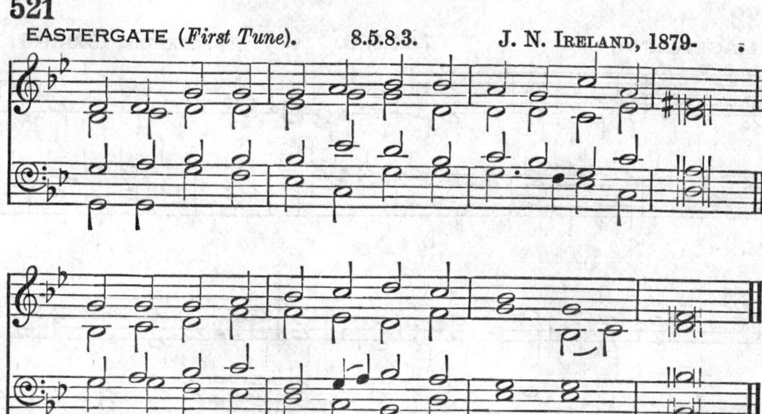

May also be sung to SACRED REST, A.T. No. 22.

TRUST (*Second Tune*). 8.5.8.3. F. R. HAVERGAL, 1836-79.

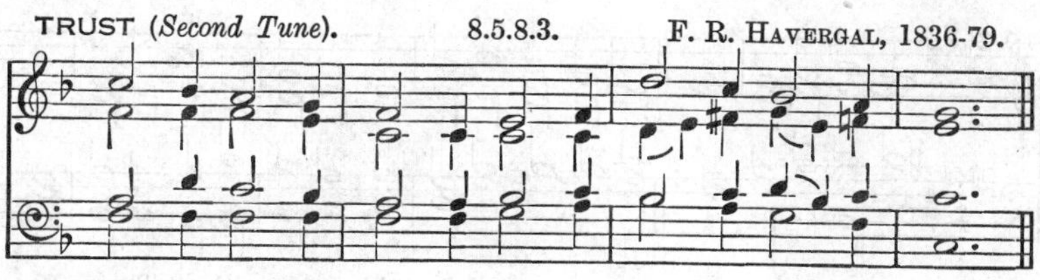

1 I AM trusting Thee, Lord Jesus,
Trusting only Thee;
Trusting Thee for full salvation,
Great and free.

2 I am trusting Thee for pardon,
At Thy feet I bow;
For Thy grace and tender mercy,
Trusting now.

3 I am trusting Thee for cleansing
In the crimson flood;
Trusting Thee to make me holy
By Thy blood.

4 I am trusting Thee to guide me;
Thou alone shalt lead,
Every day and hour supplying
All my need.

5 I am trusting Thee for power,
Thine can never fail;
Words which Thou Thyself shalt give [me
Must prevail.

6 I am trusting Thee, Lord Jesus;
Never let me fall;
I am trusting Thee for ever,
And for all.

Frances Ridley Havergal, 1836-79.

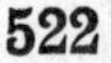

MAGDALENA. 7.6.7.6. D. J. STAINER, 1840-1901.

1 I COULD not do without Thee,
O Saviour of the lost,
Whose precious blood redeemed me
At such tremendous cost;
Thy righteousness, Thy pardon,
Thy precious blood must be
My only hope and comfort,
My glory and my plea.

2 I could not do without Thee,
I cannot stand alone,
I have no strength or goodness,
No wisdom of my own;
But Thou, belovèd Saviour,
Art all in all to me,
And weakness will be power
If leaning hard on Thee.

3 I could not do without Thee;
No other friend can read
The spirit's strange deep longings,
Interpreting its need.
No human heart could enter
Each dim recess of mine,
And soothe, and hush, and calm it,
O blessèd Lord, but Thine.

4 I could not do without Thee;
For years are fleeting fast,
And soon in solemn loneness
The river must be passed:
But Thou wilt never leave me;
And though the waves roll high,
I know Thou wilt be near me
And whisper: It is I.

Frances Ridley Havergal, 1836-79.

523

TENAX. 12.4 4.10.6 6.10.6. A. BEER, 1874-

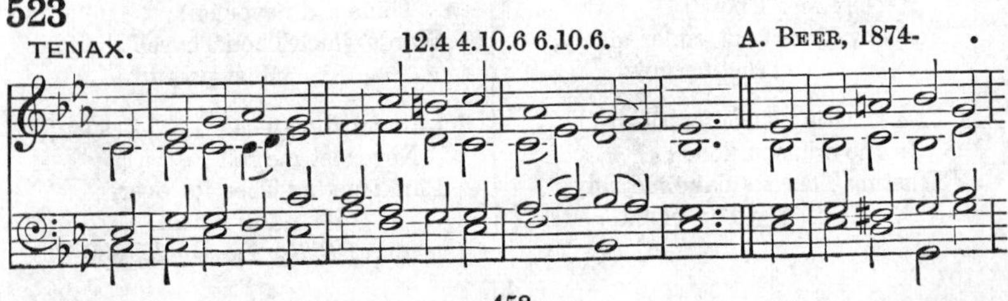

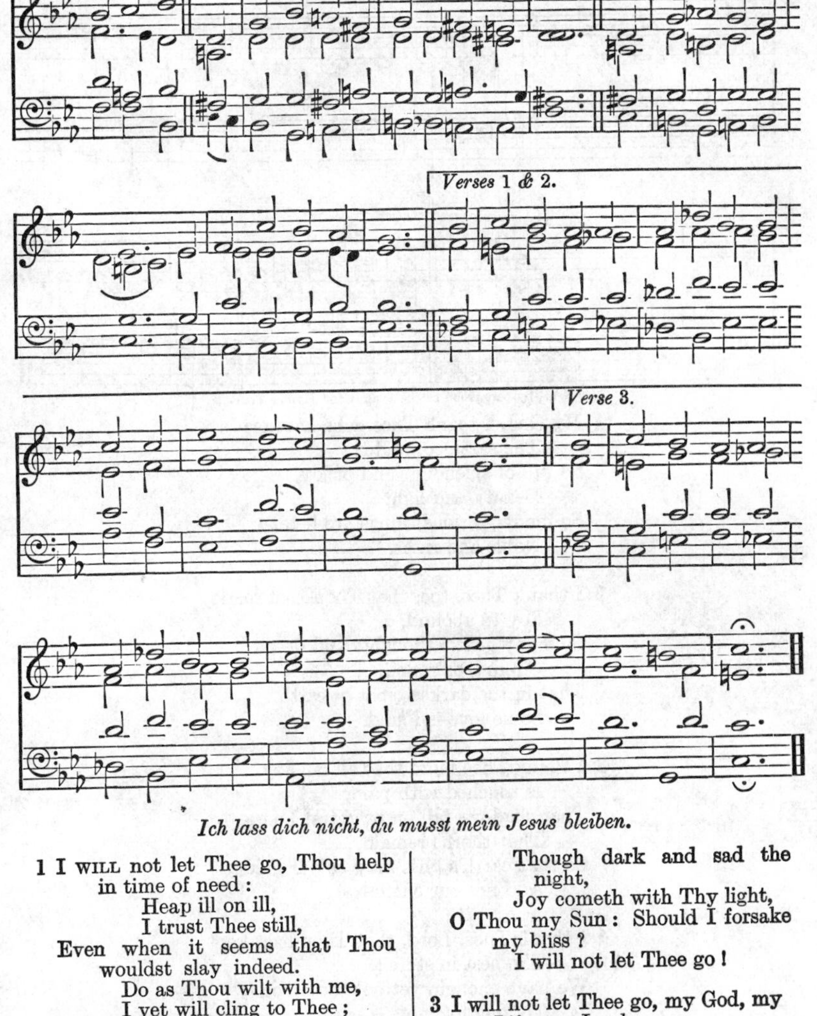

Ich lass dich nicht, du musst mein Jesus bleiben.

1 I WILL not let Thee go, Thou help in time of need:
Heap ill on ill,
I trust Thee still,
Even when it seems that Thou wouldst slay indeed.
Do as Thou wilt with me,
I yet will cling to Thee;
Hide Thou Thy face, yet: Help in time of need,
I will not let Thee go!

2 I will not let Thee go. Should I forsake my bliss?
No, Thou art mine,
And I am Thine;
Thee will I hold when all things else I miss.
Though dark and sad the night,
Joy cometh with Thy light,
O Thou my Sun: Should I forsake my bliss?
I will not let Thee go!

3 I will not let Thee go, my God, my Life, my Lord:
Not death can tear
Me from His care,
Who for my sake His soul in death outpoured.
Thou diedst for love to me;
I say in love to Thee,
Even when my heart shall break, my God, my Life, my Lord,
I will not let Thee go!

Wolfgang Christoph Dessler, 1660-1722;
tr. by Catherine Winkworth, 1827-78.

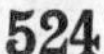

524

WENTWORTH. 8.4.8.4.8.4. F. C. MAKER, 1844-1927.

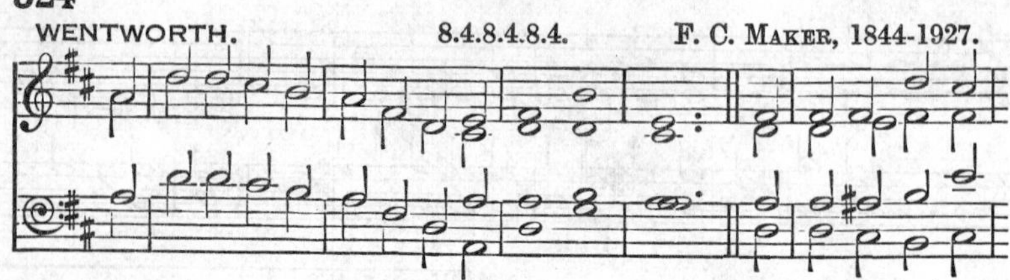

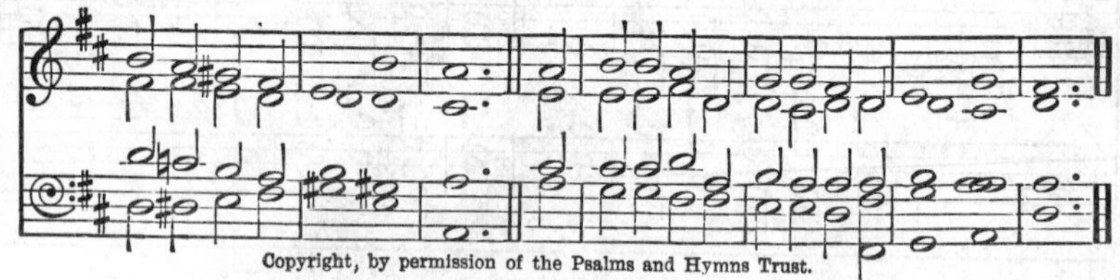

1 My God, I thank Thee, who hast made
The earth so bright,
So full of splendour and of joy,
Beauty and light;
So many glorious things are here,
Noble and right.

2 I thank Thee, too, that Thou hast made
Joy to abound,
So many gentle thoughts and deeds
Circling us round,
That in the darkest spot of earth
Some love is found.

3 I thank Thee more that all our joy
Is touched with pain,
That shadows fall on brightest hours,
That thorns remain,
So that earth's bliss may be our guide,
And not our chain.

4 I thank Thee, Lord, that Thou hast kept
The best in store;
We have enough, yet not too much
To long for more—
A yearning for a deeper peace
Not known before.

5 I thank Thee, Lord, that here our souls,
Though amply blest,
Can never find, although they seek,
A perfect rest,
Nor ever shall, until they lean
On Jesu's breast.

Adelaide Anne Procter, 1825-64.

525

AR HYD Y NOS. 8.4.8.4.8 8 8.4. Welsh Air.

1 THROUGH the love of God our Saviour,
All will be well;
Free and changeless is His favour,
All, all is well:
Precious is the blood that healed us;
Perfect is the grace that sealed us;
Strong the hand stretched forth to shield us,
All must be well.

2 Though we pass through tribulation,
All will be well;
Christ hath purchased full salvation,
All, all is well:
Happy still in God confiding;
Fruitful, if in Christ abiding;
Holy, through the Spirit's guiding;
All must be well

3 We expect a bright to-morrow;
All will be well;
Faith can sing through days of sorrow,
All, all is well:
On our Father's love relying,
Jesus every need supplying,
Then in living or in dying
All must be well.

Mary Peters, 1813-56.

526

NORWICK (*First Tune*). 7.6.7.6. D. B. E. Woods, 1900-

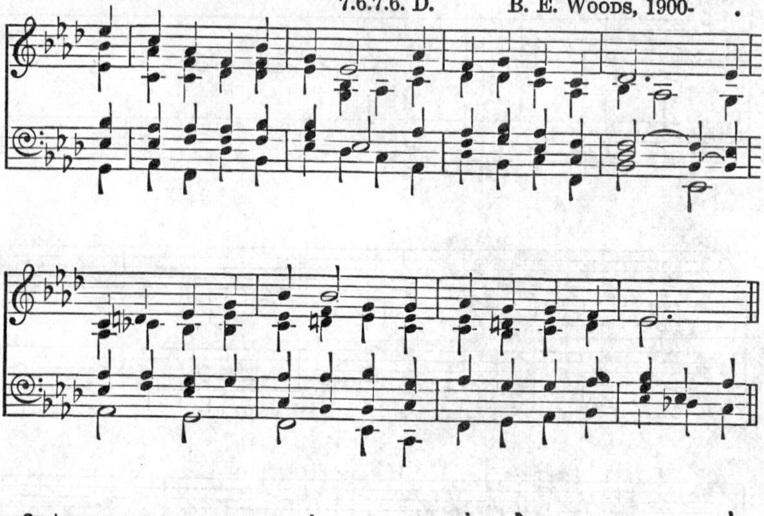

Unison.

Harmony.

A - men.

WOLVERCOTE (*Second Tune*). 7.6.7.6. D. W. H. Ferguson, 1874-1950

Unison.

Trustfulness and Peace

1 O Jesus, I have promised
To serve Thee to the end;
Be Thou for ever near me,
My Master and my Friend:
I shall not fear the battle
If Thou art by my side,
Nor wander from the pathway
If Thou wilt be my Guide.

2 O let me feel Thee near me;
The world is ever near;
I see the sights that dazzle,
The tempting sounds I hear;
My foes are ever near me,
Around me and within;
But Jesus, draw Thou nearer,
And shield my soul from sin.

3 O let me hear Thee speaking
In accents clear and still,
Above the storms of passion,
The murmurs of self-will;
O speak to reassure me,
To hasten or control;
O speak, and make me listen,
Thou Guardian of my soul.

4 O Jesus, Thou hast promised,
To all who follow Thee,
That where Thou art in glory
There shall Thy servant be;
And, Jesus, I have promised
To serve Thee to the end:
O give me grace to follow,
My Master and my Friend. Amen.

John Ernest Bode, 1816-74.

527

PETITION. 7.6.7.6. D. F. J. HAYDN, 1732-1809.

1 SOMETIMES a light surprises
The Christian while he sings;
It is the Lord who rises
With healing in His wings:
When comforts are declining,
He grants the soul again
A season of clear shining,
To cheer it after rain.

2 In holy contemplation,
We sweetly then pursue
The theme of God's salvation,
And find it ever new.
Set free from present sorrow,
We cheerfully can say,
E'en let the unknown to-morrow
Bring with it what it may:

3 It can bring with it nothing
But He will bear us through;
Who gives the lilies clothing
Will clothe His people too:
Beneath the spreading heavens
No creature but is fed;
And He who feeds the ravens
Will give His children bread.

4 Though vine nor fig-tree neither
Their wonted fruit should bear,
Though all the field should wither,
Nor flocks nor herds be there,
Yet, God the same abiding,
His praise shall tune my voice;
For, while in Him confiding,
I cannot but rejoice.

William Cowper, 1731-1800.

528

PENLAN. 7.6.7.6. D. D. Jenkins, 1849-1915.

May also be sung to Nyland, No. 303.

1 In heavenly love abiding,
No change my heart shall fear;
And safe is such confiding,
For nothing changes here:
The storm may roar without me,
My heart may low be laid;
But God is round about me,
And can I be dismayed?

2 Wherever He may guide me,
No want shall turn me back;
My Shepherd is beside me,
And nothing can I lack:
His wisdom ever waketh,
His sight is never dim;
He knows the way He taketh,
And I will walk with Him.

3 Green pastures are before me,
Which yet I have not seen;
Bright skies will soon be o'er me,
Where the dark clouds have been:
My hope I cannot measure,
My path to life is free;
My Saviour has my treasure,
And He will walk with me.

Anna Laetitia Waring, 1820-1910.

529

REDHEAD No. 4. L.M. Adapted by R. REDHEAD, 1820-1901.

1 O BLESSÈD life! the heart at rest
When all without tumultuous seems—
That trusts a higher will, and deems
That higher will, not mine, the best.

2 O blessèd life! the mind that sees,
Whatever change the years may bring,
A mercy still in everything,
And shining through all mysteries.

3 O blessèd life! the soul that soars,
When sense of mortal sight is dim,
Beyond the sense—beyond to Him
Whose love unlocks the heavenly doors.

4 O blessèd life! heart, mind, and soul,
From self-born aims and wishes free,
In all at one with Deity,
And loyal to the Lord's control.

5 O life, how blessèd, how divine!
High life, the earnest of a higher:
Saviour, fulfil my deep desire,
And let this blessèd life be mine.
Amen.

William Tidd Matson, 1833-99.

530

BARNABAS. 7.6.7.6.7.7.7.6. *French Psalter*, 1561.

1 Oft I in my heart have said:
Who shall ascend on high,
Mount to Christ, my glorious Head,
To bring Him from the sky?
Borne on contemplation's wing,
Surely I shall find Him there,
Where the angels praise their King,
And gain the morning star.

2 Oft I in my heart have said:
Who to the deep shall stoop,
Sink with Christ among the dead,
From thence to bring Him up?
Could I but my heart prepare
By unfeigned humility,
Christ would quickly enter there,
And ever dwell with me.

3 But the righteousness of faith
Hath taught me better things:
Inward turn thine eyes, it saith,
While Christ to me it brings;
Christ is ready to impart
Life to all for life who sigh;
In thy mouth and in thy heart
The word is ever nigh.

Charles Wesley, 1707-88.

531

HULL. 8 8.6. D. American, 1798.

1 Light of the world, Thy beams I bless;
On Thee, bright Sun of Righteousness
My faith hath fixed its eye;
Guided by Thee, through all I go,
Nor fear the ruin spread below,
For Thou art always nigh.

2 Not all the powers of hell can fright
A soul that walks with Christ in light;
He walks, and cannot fall:
Clearly he sees, and wins his way,
Shining unto the perfect day,
And more than conquers all.

3 I rest in Thine almighty power;
The name of Jesus is a tower,
That hides my life above:
Thou canst, Thou wilt my Helper be;
My confidence is all in Thee,
The faithful God of love.

4 Wherefore, in never-ceasing prayer,
My soul to Thy continual care
I faithfully commend;
Assured that Thou through life shalt save,
And show Thyself beyond the grave
My everlasting Friend.

Charles Wesley, 1707-88.

532

ST. GREGORY. L.M. *Darmstadt Gesangbuch*, 1698.

1 Let everlasting glories crown
  Thy head, my Saviour and my Lord;
Thy hands have brought salvation down,
  And writ the blessing in Thy word.

2 In vain our trembling conscience seeks
  Some solid ground to rest upon;
With long despair our spirit breaks,
  Till we apply to Thee alone.

3 How well Thy blessèd truths agree;
  How wise and holy Thy commands;
Thy promises, how firm they be;
  How firm our hope and comfort stands!

4 Should all the forms that men devise
  Assault my faith with treacherous art,
I'd call them vanity and lies,
  And bind Thy gospel to my heart.

Isaac Watts, 1674-1748.

Also:

54 My soul, repeat His praise
65 O God of God
68 None is like Jeshurun's God
90 Object of my first desire
98 Thou hidden Source
101 Rest of the weary
147 When the Lord
165 Forty days and forty nights
167 Fierce raged the tempest
357 Jesus, in whom the weary find
375 Now I have found the ground
393 I give my heart to Thee
403 My heart is fixed
458 Long did I toil
459 To the haven of Thy breast
466 My soul, there is a country
551 O Lord, how happy should we be

533

PRAYER

NOX PRÆCESSIT. C.M. J. B. Calkin, 1827-1905.

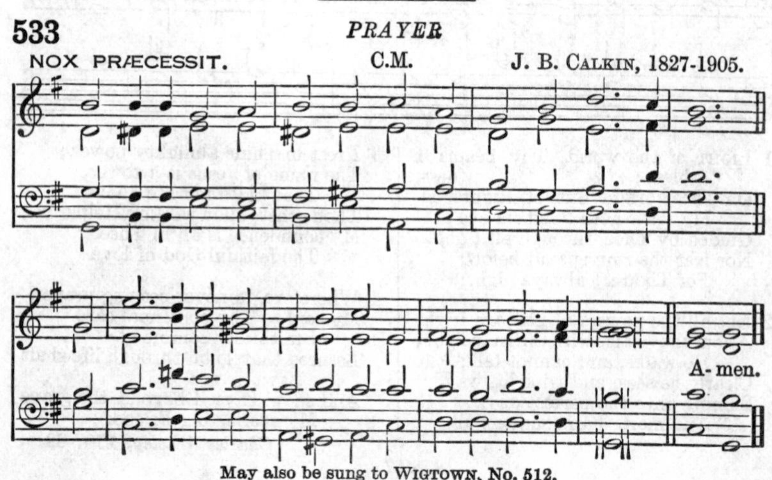

May also be sung to Wigtown, No. 512.

1 Prayer is the soul's sincere desire,
Uttered or unexpressed,
The motion of a hidden fire
That trembles in the breast.

2 Prayer is the burden of a sigh,
The falling of a tear,
The upward glancing of an eye
When none but God is near.

3 Prayer is the simplest form of speech
That infant lips can try;
Prayer the sublimest strains that reach
The majesty on high.

4 Prayer is the contrite sinner's voice
Returning from his ways,
While angels in their songs rejoice,
And cry: Behold he prays!

5 Prayer is the Christian's vital breath,
The Christian's native air,
His watchword at the gates of death;
He enters heaven with prayer.

6 O Thou by whom we come to God,
The Life, the Truth, the Way!
The path of prayer Thyself hast trod:
Lord! teach us how to pray.
Amen.

James Montgomery, 1771-1854.

534

ST. WERBERGH. 8.8.8.8.8 8. J. B. Dykes, 1823-76.

1 Jesus, Thou sovereign Lord of all,
The same through one eternal day,
Attend Thy feeblest followers' call,
And O instruct us how to pray!
Pour out the supplicating grace,
And stir us up to seek Thy face.

2 We cannot think a gracious thought,
We cannot feel a good desire,
Till Thou, who call'dst a world from nought,
The power into our hearts inspire:
The promised Intercessor give,
And let us now Thyself receive.

3 Come in Thy pleading Spirit down
To us who for Thy coming stay;
Of all Thy gifts we ask but one,
We ask the constant power to pray:
Indulge us, Lord, in this request;
Thou canst not then deny the rest.

Charles Wesley, 1707-88.

535

PAVIA. L.M. German, 13th Century

1 From every stormy wind that blows,
From every swelling tide of woes,
There is a calm, a sure retreat;
'Tis found beneath the mercy-seat.

2 There is a place where Jesus sheds
The oil of gladness on our heads—
A place than all beside more sweet;
It is the blood-stained mercy-seat.

3 There is a spot where spirits blend,
And friend holds fellowship with friend;
Though sundered far, by faith they meet
Around one common mercy-seat.

4 There, there on eagle wing we soar,
And time and sense seem all no more;
And heaven comes down our souls to greet,
And glory crowns the mercy-seat.

Hugh Stowell, 1799-1865.

536

MEMORIA (*First Tune*). 8.8.8.4. S. S. Wesley, 1810-76.

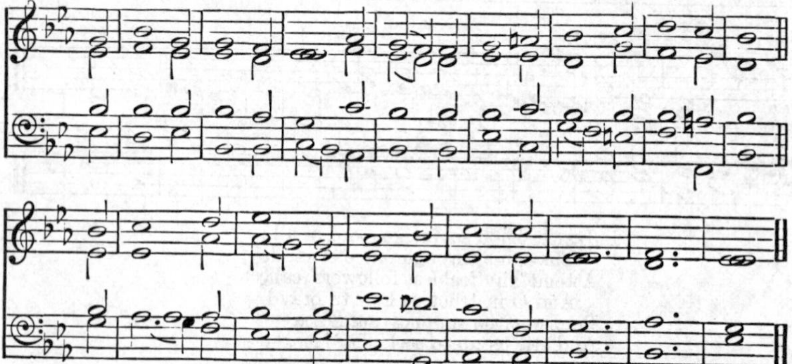

SOUTHPORT (*Second Tune*). 8.8.8.4. G. Lomas, 1834-84.

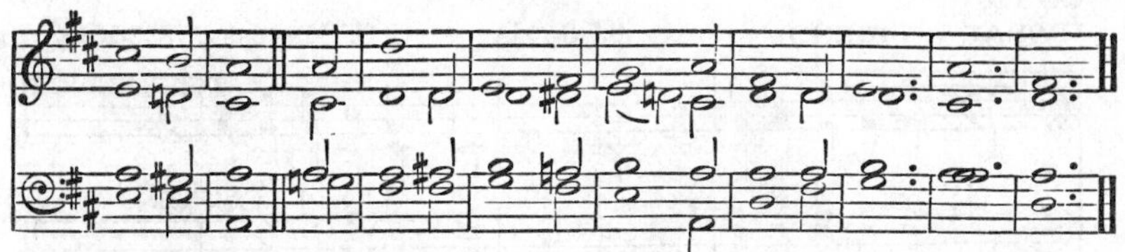

1 My God, is any hour so sweet,
From blush of morn to evening star,
As that which calls me to Thy feet,
The hour of prayer ?

2 Blest be that tranquil hour of morn,
And blest that hour of solemn eve,
When, on the wings of prayer upborne,
The world I leave.

3 For then a day-spring shines on me,
Brighter than morn's ethereal glow;
And richer dews descend from Thee
Than earth can know.

4 Then is my strength by Thee renewed;
Then are my sins by Thee forgiven;
Then dost Thou cheer my solitude
With hope of heaven.

5 No words can tell what blest relief,
There for my every want I find;
What strength for warfare, balm for grief;
What peace of mind.

6 Hushed is each doubt, gone every fear;
My spirit seems in heaven to stay;
And e'en the penitential tear
Is wiped away.

7 Lord, till I reach yon blissful shore,
No privilege so dear shall be,
As thus my inmost soul to pour
In prayer to Thee.

Charlotte Elliott, 1789-1871.

537

REVERENCE. 8 8.8 8.4. M. L. Wostenholm, 1887-

1 'Tis not to ask for gifts alone,
I kneel in prayer before His throne;
But, seeking fellowship divine,
I feel His love, and know it mine,
When I can pray.

2 'Tis prayer that makes my spirit strong
To do the right and fear the wrong,
To know the peace of sins forgiven,
To breathe the atmosphere of heaven;
To live, I pray.

3 I ought to pray, because my voice
Can make the Father's heart rejoice;
He loves His child, and He will meet
And hold communication sweet
With one who prays.

4 Therefore I seek my God, and raise
My grateful thanks, my fervent praise;
While evil passions and deceit
Will vanish when before His feet
I kneel to pray.

5 And if, great Father, when I pray,
Thy answer can be only Nay,
Still Thou wilt comfort me and bless
With visions of Thy righteousness:
Help me to pray.

Mary Russell Olivant, 1852-

WHAT A FRIEND. 8.7.8.7. D. C. C. CONVERSE, 1832-1918.

1 WHAT a Friend we have in Jesus,
All our sins and griefs to bear!
What a privilege to carry
Everything to God in prayer!
O what peace we often forfeit,
O what needless pain we bear,
All because we do not carry
Everything to God in prayer!

2 Have we trials and temptations?
Is there trouble anywhere?
We should never be discouraged:
Take it to the Lord in prayer.
Can we find a friend so faithful,
Who will all our sorrows share?
Jesus knows our every weakness:
Take it to the Lord in prayer.

3 Are we weak and heavy-laden,
Cumbered with a load of care?
Precious Saviour, still our refuge:
Take it to the Lord in prayer.
Do thy friends despise, forsake thee?
Take it to the Lord in prayer;
In His arms He'll take and shield thee,
Thou wilt find a solace there.

Joseph Medlicott Scriven, 1820-86.

539

FARRANT. C.M. (?) J. Hilton, *d.* 1608.

1 Lord, teach us how to pray aright,
With reverence and with fear;
Though dust and ashes in Thy sight,
We may, we must draw near.

2 We perish if we cease from prayer;
O grant us power to pray!
And when to meet Thee we prepare,
Lord, meet us by the way.

3 Give deep humility; the sense
Of godly sorrow give;
A strong desiring confidence
To hear Thy voice and live;

4 Faith in the only Sacrifice
That can for sin atone;
To build our hopes, to fix our eyes,
On Christ, on Christ alone;

5 Patience to watch, and wait, and weep,
Though mercy long delay;
Courage, our fainting souls to keep
And trust Thee, though Thou slay.

6 Give these, and then, Thy will be done:
Thus strengthened with all might,
We through Thy Spirit and Thy Son
Shall pray, and pray aright.

James Montgomery, 1771-1854.

540

CHRIST CHAPEL. 7 7.7 7. C. Steggall, 1826-1905.

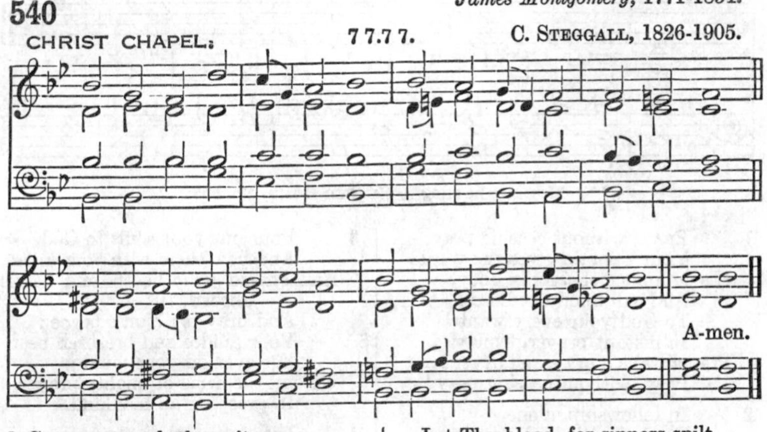

1 Come, my soul, thy suit prepare,
Jesus loves to answer prayer;
He Himself has bid thee pray,
Therefore will not say thee nay.

2 Thou art coming to a King;
Large petitions with thee bring;
For His grace and power are such,
None can ever ask too much.

3 With my burden I begin:
Lord, remove this load of sin;
Let Thy blood, for sinners spilt,
Set my conscience free from guilt.

4 Lord, I come to Thee for rest;
Take possession of my breast;
There Thy blood-bought right maintain,
And without a rival reign.

5 While I am a pilgrim here,
Let Thy love my spirit cheer:
As my Guide, my Guard, my Friend,
Lead me to my journey's end. Amen.

John Newton, 1725-1807.

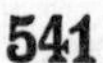

BONAR. D.S.M. C. Steggall, 1826-1905.

May also be sung to Nearer Home, No. 658.

1 Pray, without ceasing pray,
Your Captain gives the word;
His summons cheerfully obey,
And call upon the Lord:
To God your every want
In instant prayer display;
Pray always; pray, and never faint;
Pray, without ceasing pray!

2 In fellowship, alone,
To God with faith draw near,
Approach His courts, besiege His throne
With all the powers of prayer:
Go to His temple, go,
Nor from His altar move;
Let every house His worship know,
And every heart His love.

3 Pour out your souls to God,
And bow them with your knees,
And spread your hearts and hands abroad,
And pray for Zion's peace;
Your guides and brethren bear
For ever on your mind;
Extend the arms of mighty prayer,
In grasping all mankind.

4 From strength to strength go on,
Wrestle, and fight, and pray,
Tread all the powers of darkness down,
And win the well-fought day;
Still let the Spirit cry
In all His soldiers: Come!
Till Christ the Lord descend from high,
And take the conquerors home.

Charles Wesley, 1707-88.

542

LEOMINSTER. D.S.M.

G. W. MARTIN, 1828-81.
Har. by A. SULLIVAN.

1 JESUS, my strength, my hope,
On Thee I cast my care,
With humble confidence look up,
And know Thou hear'st my prayer.
Give me on Thee to wait,
Till I can all things do,
On Thee, almighty to create,
Almighty to renew.

2 I want a godly fear,
A quick-discerning eye
That looks to Thee when sin is near,
And sees the tempter fly:
A spirit still prepared,
And armed with jealous care,
For ever standing on its guard
And watching unto prayer.

3 I want a true regard,
A single, steady aim,
Unmoved by threatening or reward,
To Thee and Thy great name;
A jealous, just concern
For Thine immortal praise;
A pure desire that all may learn
And glorify Thy grace.

4 I rest upon Thy word;
The promise is for me;
My succour and salvation, Lord,
Shall surely come from Thee:
But let me still abide,
Nor from my hope remove,
Till Thou my patient spirit guide
Into Thy perfect love. Amen.

Charles Wesley, 1707-88.

543

EGYPT. S.M. J. Leach, 1762-98.

1 Hear Thou my prayer, O Lord,
And listen to my cry;
Remember now Thy faithful word,
And graciously reply.

2 Do not in judgement rise
Thy servant's life to scan;
For righteous in Thy spotless eyes
Is found no living man.

3 I stretch my longing hands
Toward Thy holy place,
With soul athirst, like weary lands,
For Thy refreshing grace.

4 Haste Thee, O Lord, I pray,
My failing heart to save.
Hide not Thy face: I droop as they
That sink into the grave.

5 Thy mercy's early light
My faith desires to see;
O let me walk before Thy sight!
I lift my soul to Thee.

6 Let Thy good Spirit lead
My feet in righteous ways;
And for Thy name's sake, Lord, my head
Above my troubles raise.
Amen.

Benjamin Hall Kennedy, 1804-89.

Also:

237 There is no sorrow
238 My faith looks up
239 Lord Jesus, think on me
285 O breath of God
335 Pass me not
453 O my Saviour
463 O Jesus Christ
497 To the hills I lift
505 O Thou to whose

544

CHRISTIAN HOLINESS

NEWCASTLE (*First Tune*). 8.6.8 8.6. H. L. Morley, *b.* 1855

ROYAL FORT (*Second Tune*). 8.6.8 8.6. E. J. ORCHARD, 1834-1915.

1 ETERNAL Light! Eternal Light!
How pure the soul must be,
When, placed within Thy searching sight,
It shrinks not, but, with calm delight,
Can live, and look on Thee!

2 The spirits that surround Thy throne
May bear the burning bliss;
But that is surely theirs alone,
Since they have never, never known
A fallen world like this.

3 O how shall I, whose native sphere
Is dark, whose mind is dim,
Before the Ineffable appear,
And on my naked spirit bear
The uncreated beam?

4 There is a way for man to rise
To that sublime abode:
An offering and a sacrifice,
A Holy Spirit's energies,
An Advocate with God—

5 These, these prepare us for the sight
Of holiness above:
The sons of ignorance and night
May dwell in the eternal Light,
Through the eternal Love!

Thomas Binney, 1798-1874.

545

ARFON. 7.7.7.7.7.7. Welsh Hymn Melody.

1 O disclose Thy lovely face !
  Quicken all my drooping powers ;
Gasps my fainting soul for grace,
  As a thirsty land for showers ;
Haste, my Lord, no more delay,
Come, my Saviour, come away !

2 Well Thou know'st I cannot rest
  Till I fully rest in Thee,
Till I am of Thee possessed,
  Till, from every sin set free,
All the life of faith I prove,
All the joy and heaven of love.

3 With me O continue, Lord !
  Keep me, or from Thee I fly ;
Strength and comfort from Thy word
  Imperceptibly supply,
Hold me till I apprehend,
Make me faithful to the end. Amen.

Charles Wesley, 1707-88.

546

WAREHAM. L.M. W. Knapp, *c.* 1688-1768.

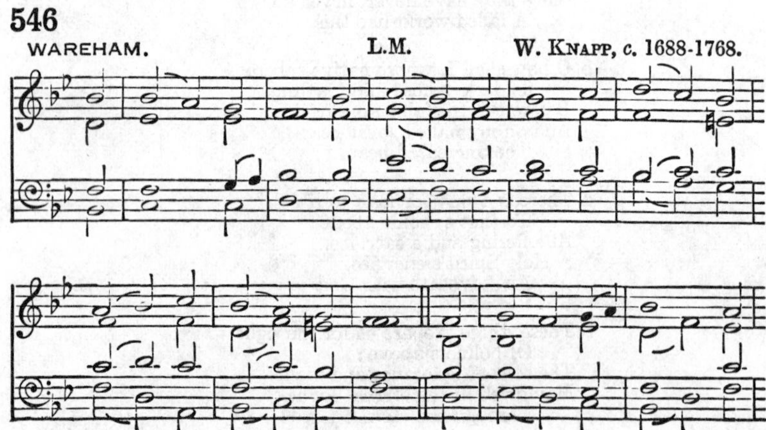

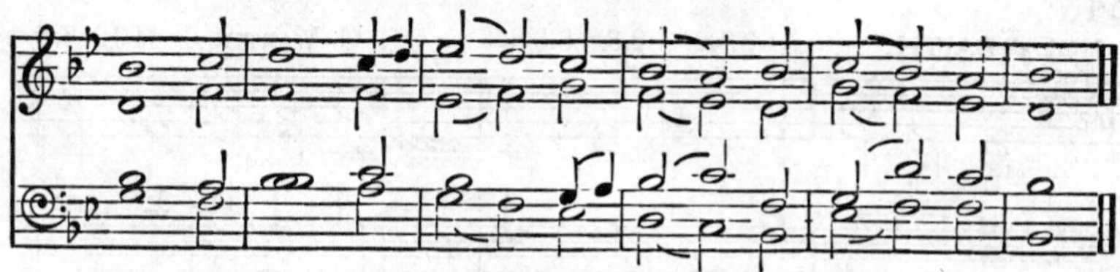

Venez Jésus, mon salutaire.

1 Come, Saviour, Jesus, from above!
Assist me with Thy heavenly grace;
Empty my heart of earthly love,
And for Thyself prepare the place.

2 O let Thy sacred presence fill,
And set my longing spirit free!
Which pants to have no other will,
But day and night to feast on Thee.

3 That path with humble speed I'll seek,
Wherein my Saviour's footsteps shine;
Nor will I hear, nor will I speak,
Of any other love but Thine.

4 Henceforth may no profane delight
Divide this consecrated soul;
Possess it Thou, who hast the right,
As Lord and Master of the whole.

5 Thee I can love, and Thee alone,
With pure delight and inward bliss:
To know Thou tak'st me for Thine own,
O what a happiness is this!

6 Nothing on earth do I desire
But Thy pure love within my breast;
This, only this, will I require,
And freely give up all the rest.

Antoinette Bourignon, 1616-80;
tr. by John Wesley, 1703-91.

547

AYNHOE. S.M. J. Nares, 1715-83.

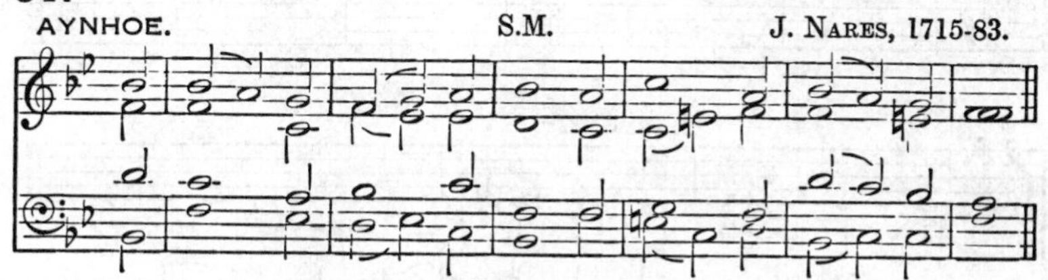

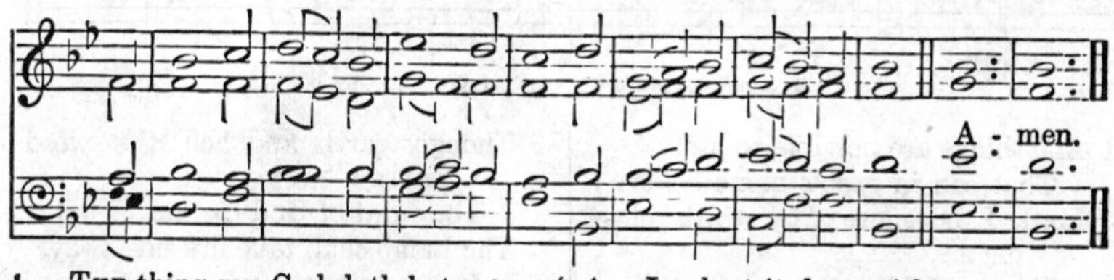

1 The thing my God doth hate
That I no more may do,
Thy creature, Lord, again create,
And all my soul renew.

2 My soul shall then, like Thine,
Abhor the thing unclean,
And, sanctified by love divine,
For ever cease from sin.

3 That blessèd law of Thine,
Jesus, to me impart;
The Spirit's law of life divine,
O write it in my heart!

4 Implant it deep within,
Whence it may ne'er remove,
The law of liberty from sin,
The perfect law of love.

5 Thy nature be my law,
Thy spotless sanctity,
And sweetly every moment draw
My happy soul to Thee.

6 Soul of my soul remain!
Who didst for all fulfil,
In me, O Lord, fulfil again
Thy heavenly Father's will!
Amen.

Charles Wesley, 1707-88.

548

HOLY FAITH. 8.8.8.8.8.8. G. C. Martin, 1844-1916.

1 All things are possible to him
That can in Jesu's name believe:
Lord, I no more Thy truth blaspheme,
Thy truth I lovingly receive;
I can, I do believe in Thee,
All things are possible to me.

2 The most impossible of all
Is, that I e'er from sin should cease;
Yet shall it be, I know it shall:
Jesus, look to Thy faithfulness!
If nothing is too hard for Thee,
All things are possible to me.

3 Though earth and hell the word gainsay,
The word of God can never fail;
The Lamb shall take my sins away,
'Tis certain, though impossible;
The thing impossible shall be,
All things are possible to me.

4 All things are possible to God,
To Christ, the power of God in man,
To me, when I am all renewed,
When I in Christ am formed again,
And witness, from all sin set free,
All things are possible to me.

Charles Wesley, 1707-88.

549

SIMPLICITY. 7 7.7 7. O. GIBBONS, 1583-1625.

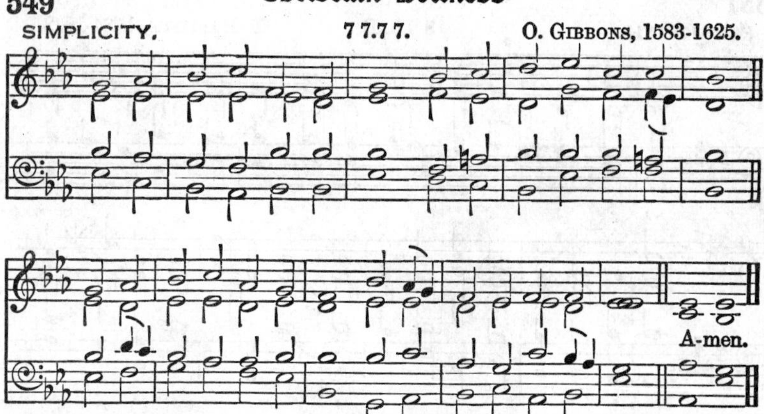

1 LORD, that I may learn of Thee,
Give me true simplicity;
Wean my soul, and keep it low,
Willing Thee alone to know.

2 Let me cast myself aside,
All that feeds my knowing pride,
Not to man, but God submit,
Lay my reasonings at Thy feet;

3 Of my boasted wisdom spoiled,
Docile, helpless, as a child,
Only seeing in Thy light,
Only walking in Thy might.

4 Then infuse the teaching grace,
Spirit of truth and righteousness;
Knowledge, love divine, impart,
Life eternal, to my heart. Amen.

Charles Wesley, 1707-88.

550

ABRIDGE. C.M. I. SMITH, *c.* 1725- *c.* 1800.

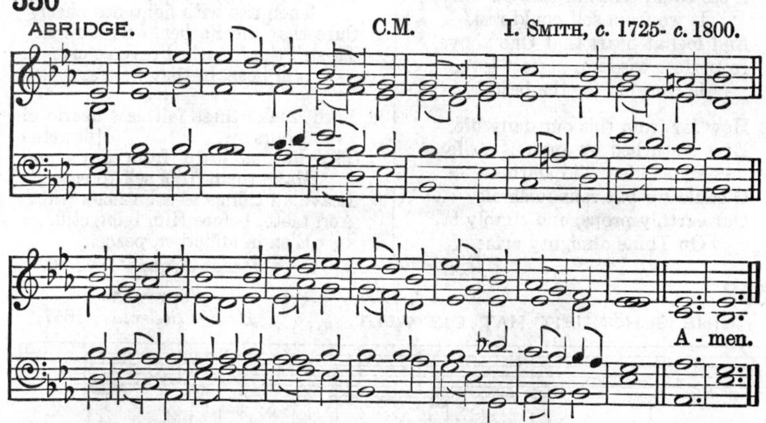

1 O FOR a heart to praise my God,
A heart from sin set free,
A heart that always feels Thy blood
So freely spilt for me.

2 A heart resigned, submissive, meek,
My great Redeemer's throne,
Where only Christ is heard to speak,
Where Jesus reigns alone:

3 A humble, lowly, contrite heart,
Believing, true, and clean;
Which neither life nor death can part
From Him that dwells within:

4 A heart in every thought renewed,
And full of love divine;
Perfect, and right, and pure, and good,
A copy, Lord, of Thine.

5 Thy nature, gracious Lord, impart;
Come quickly from above,
Write Thy new name upon my heart,
Thy new, best name of love. Amen.

Charles Wesley, 1707-88.

551

PLYMOUTH. 8 8.6. D. T. Hastings, 1784-1872.

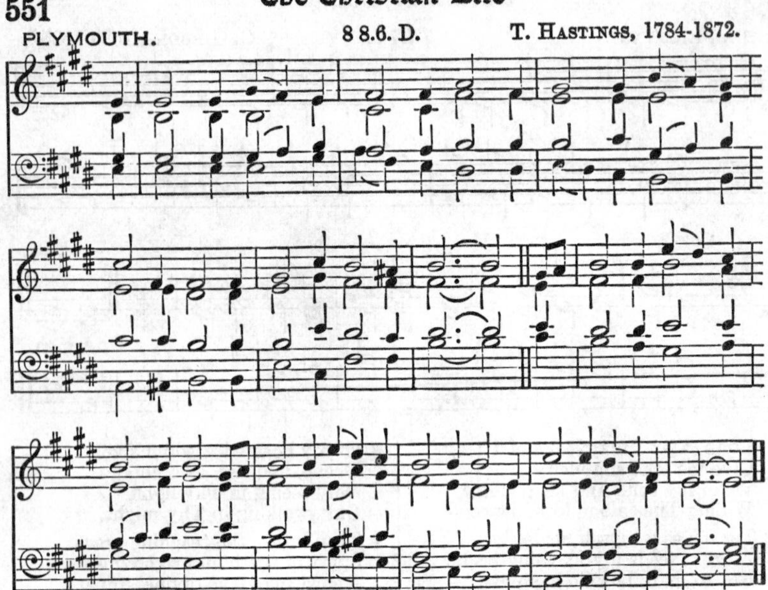

1 O Lord, how happy should we be
If we could cast our care on Thee,
If we from self could rest,
And feel at heart that One above,
In perfect wisdom, perfect love,
Is working for the best.

2 How far from this our daily life,
Ever disturbed by anxious strife,
By sudden wild alarms.
O could we but relinquish all
Our earthly props, and simply fall
On Thine almighty arms.

3 Could we but kneel and cast our load,
E'en while we pray, upon our God,
Then rise with lightened cheer,
Sure that the Father, who is nigh
To still the famished raven's cry,
Will hear, in that we fear.

4 Lord, make these faithless hearts of ours
Thy lessons learn from birds and flowers:
Make them from self to cease,
Leave all things to a Father's will,
And taste, before Him lying still,
E'en in affliction, peace.

Joseph Anstice, 1808-36.

552

KEINE SCHÖNHEIT HAT DIE WELT. 7 7.7 7. Scheffler's *Heilige Seelenlust*, 1657.

1 Jesus, all-atoning Lamb,
Thine, and only Thine, I am:
Take my body, spirit, soul;
Only Thou possess the whole.

2 Thou my one thing needful be;
Let me ever cleave to Thee;
Let me choose the better part;
Let me give Thee all my heart.

3 Fairer than the sons of men,
Do not let me turn again,
Leave the fountain-head of bliss,
Stoop to creature-happiness.

4 Whom have I on earth below?
Thee, and only Thee, I know;
Whom have I in heaven but Thee?
Thou art all in all to me.

5 All my treasure is above,
All my riches is Thy love:
Who the worth of love can tell?
Infinite, unsearchable.

Charles Wesley, 1707-88.

553

TARSUS. 8 8.8. D. J. Goss, 1800-80.

1 Come, Holy Ghost, all-quickening fire!
Come, and my hallowed heart inspire,
Sprinkled with the atoning blood;
Now to my soul Thyself reveal,
Thy mighty working let me feel,
And know that I am born of God.

2 Humble, and teachable, and mild,
O may I, as a little child,
My lowly Master's steps pursue!
Be anger to my soul unknown,
Hate, envy, jealousy, be gone;
In love create Thou all things new.

3 Let earth no more my heart divide,
With Christ may I be crucified,
To Thee with my whole soul aspire;
Dead to the world and all its toys,
Its idle pomp, and fading joys,
Be Thou alone my one desire.

4 My will be swallowed up in Thee;
Light in Thy light still may I see,
Beholding Thee with open face;
Called the full power of faith to prove,
Let all my hallowed heart be love,
And all my spotless life be praise.
Amen.

Charles Wesley, 1707-88.

554

HUDDERSFIELD. S.M. WILLIAMS' *Psalmody*, 1770.

1 O COME and dwell in me,
Spirit of power within !
And bring the glorious liberty
From sorrow, fear, and sin.

2 The seed of sin's disease,
Spirit of health, remove,
Spirit of finished holiness,
Spirit of perfect love.

3 Hasten the joyful day
Which shall my sins consume,
When old things shall be passed away,
And all things new become.

4 I want the witness, Lord,
That all I do is right,
According to Thy will and word,
Well-pleasing in Thy sight.

5 I ask no higher state;
Indulge me but in this,
And soon or later then translate
To my eternal bliss. Amen.

Charles Wesley, 1707-88.

555

PLEYEL. 7 7.7 7. I. J. PLEYEL, 1757-1831.

1 WHEN, my Saviour, shall I be
Perfectly resigned to Thee?
Poor and vile in my own eyes,
Only in Thy wisdom wise:

2 Only Thee content to know,
Ignorant of all below,
Only guided by Thy light,
Only mighty in Thy might!

3 So I may Thy Spirit know,
Let Him as He listeth blow;
Let the manner be unknown,
So I may with Thee be one.

4 Fully in my life express
All the heights of holiness,
Sweetly let my spirit prove
All the depths of humble love.
Amen.

Charles Wesley, 1707-88.

556

BANGOR. C.M. W. Tansur, 1706-83.

1 Deepen the wound Thy hands have made
In this weak, helpless soul;
Till mercy, with its kindly aid,
Descends to make me whole.

2 The sharpness of Thy two-edged sword
Enable me to endure;
Till bold to say: My hallowing Lord
Hath wrought a perfect cure.

3 I see the exceeding broad command,
Which all contains in one:
Enlarge my heart to understand
The mystery unknown.

4 O that with all Thy saints I might
By sweet experience prove
What is the length, and breadth, and height,
And depth of perfect love! Amen.

Charles Wesley, 1707-88.

557

STAFFORD. C.M. S. Howard, 1710-82.

1 What is our calling's glorious hope
But inward holiness?
For this to Jesus I look up,
I calmly wait for this.

2 I wait, till He shall touch me clean,
Shall life and power impart,
Give me the faith that casts out sin
And purifies the heart.

3 This is the dear redeeming grace,
For every sinner free;
Surely it shall on me take place,
The chief of sinners, me.

4 From all iniquity, from all,
He shall my soul redeem;
In Jesus I believe, and shall
Believe myself to Him.

5 When Jesus makes my heart His home,
My sin shall all depart;
And lo, He saith: I quickly come,
To fill and rule thy heart.

6 Be it according to Thy word!
Redeem me from all sin;
Lord, My heart would now receive Thee,
Come in, my Lord, come in! Amen.

Charles Wesley, 1707-88.

ST. CATHERINE. 8.8.8.8.8.8. *Crown of Jesus*, 1864.

1 Saviour from sin, I wait to prove
That Jesus is Thy healing name;
To lose, when perfected in love,
Whate'er I have, or can, or am.
I stay me on Thy faithful word:
The servant shall be as his Lord.

2 Answer that gracious end in me
For which Thy precious life was given;
Redeem from all iniquity;
Restore, and make me meet for heaven:
Unless Thou purge my every stain,
Thy suffering and my faith are vain.

3 Didst Thou not die that I might live
No longer to myself, but Thee,
Might body, soul, and spirit give
To Him who gave Himself for me?
Come then, my Master and my God,
Take the dear purchase of Thy blood.

4 Thy own peculiar servant claim,
For Thy own truth and mercy's sake;
Hallow in me Thy glorious name;
Me for Thine own this moment take,
And change, and throughly purify;
Thine only may I live and die. Amen.

Charles Wesley, 1707-88.

559

BALLERMA. C.M. Adapted by R. Simpson, 1790-1832.

1 Come, O my God, the promise seal,
This mountain, sin, remove;
Now in my fainting soul reveal
The virtue of Thy love.

2 I want Thy life, Thy purity,
Thy righteousness, brought in;
I ask, desire, and trust in Thee,
To be redeemed from sin.

3 Anger and sloth, desire and pride,
This moment be subdued;
Be cast into the crimson tide
Of my Redeemer's blood!

4 Saviour, to Thee my soul looks up,
My present Saviour Thou!
In all the confidence of hope,
I claim the blessing now.

5 'Tis done! Thou dost this moment save,
With full salvation bless;
Redemption through Thy blood I have,
And spotless love and peace.

Charles Wesley, 1707-88.

560

DEVIZES. C.M. I. Tucker, 1761-1825.

May also be sung to St. Flavian, No. 43.

1 Jesus hath died that I might live,
Might live to God alone,
In Him eternal life receive,
And be in spirit one.

2 Saviour, I thank Thee for the grace,
The gift unspeakable!
And wait with arms of faith to embrace,
And all Thy love to feel.

3 My soul breaks out in strong desire
The perfect bliss to prove;
My longing heart is all on fire
To be dissolved in love.

4 Give me Thyself—from every boast,
From every wish set free;
Let all I am in Thee be lost,
But give Thyself to me.

5 Thy gifts, alone, cannot suffice
Unless Thyself be given;
Thy presence makes my paradise,
And where Thou art is heaven.

Charles Wesley, 1707-88.

SOLOMON. C.M. From HANDEL'S *Solomon*, 1748.

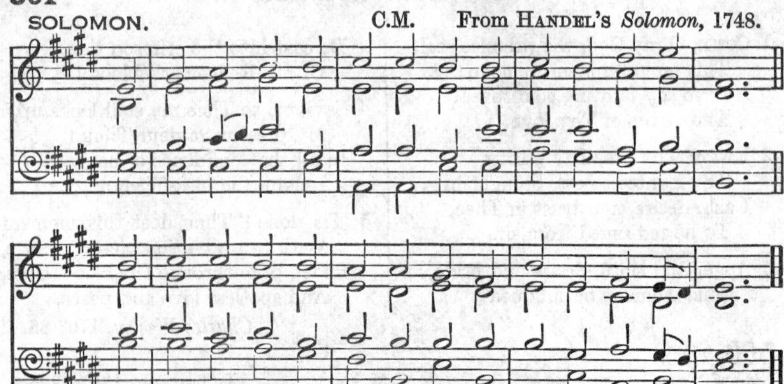

1 FATHER of Jesus Christ, my Lord,
My Saviour, and my Head,
I trust in Thee, whose powerful word
Hath raised Him from the dead.

2 Eternal life to all mankind
Thou hast in Jesus given;
And all who seek, in Him shall find
The happiness of heaven.

3 Faith in Thy power Thou seest I have,
For Thou this faith hast wrought;
Dead souls Thou callest from their grave,
And speakest worlds from nought.

4 In hope, against all human hope,
Self-desperate, I believe;
Thy quickening word shall raise me up,
Thou shalt Thy Spirit give.

5 Faith, mighty faith, the promise sees,
And looks to that alone;
Laughs at impossibilities,
And cries: It shall be done!

Charles Wesley, 1707-88.

562

OMBERSLEY. L.M. W. H. GLADSTONE, 1840-91.

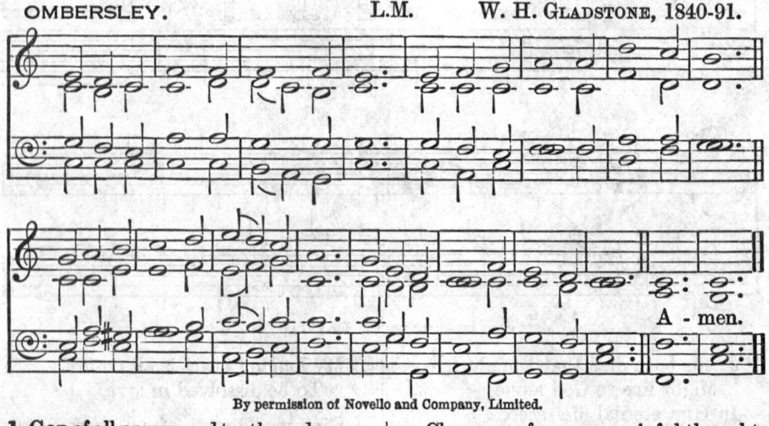

By permission of Novello and Company, Limited.

1 GOD of all power, and truth, and grace,
Which shall from age to age endure,
Whose word, when heaven and earth shall pass,
Remains and stands for ever sure;

2 That I Thy mercy may proclaim,
That all mankind Thy truth may see,
Hallow Thy great and glorious name,
And perfect holiness in me.

3 Purge me from every evil blot;
My idols all be cast aside;
Cleanse me from every sinful thought,
From all the filth of self and pride.

4 Give me a new, a perfect heart,
From doubt, and fear, and sorrow free;
The mind which was in Christ impart,
And let my spirit cleave to Thee.

5 O that I now, from sin released,
Thy word may to the utmost prove,
Enter into the promised rest,
The Canaan of Thy perfect love!
Amen.

Charles Wesley, 1707-88.

563

REDHEAD No. 66. C.M. R. REDHEAD, 1820-1901.

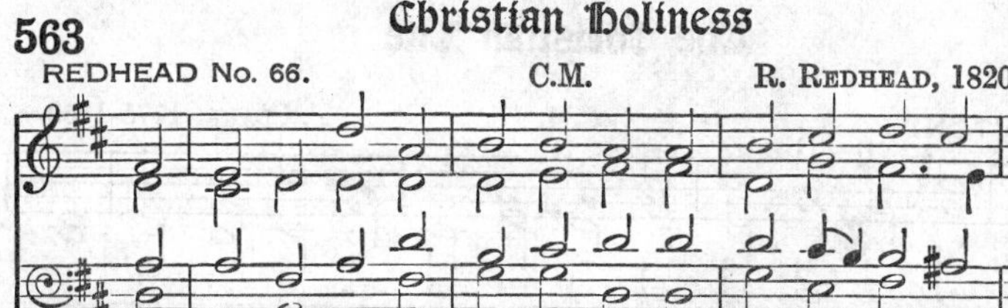

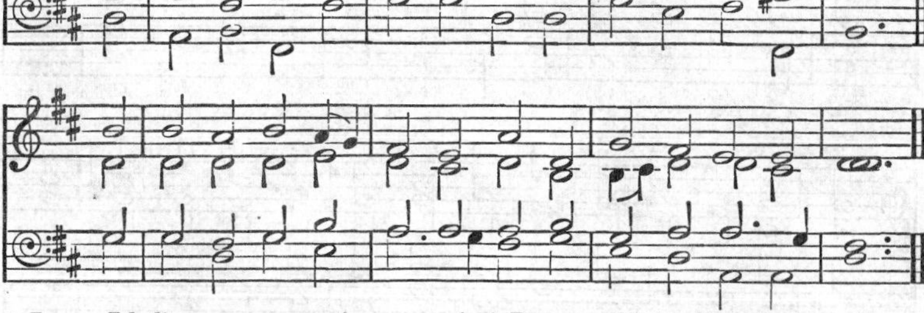

1 LORD, I believe a rest remains
To all Thy people known,
A rest where pure enjoyment reigns,
And Thou art loved alone:

2 A rest, where all our soul's desire
Is fixed on things above;
Where fear, and sin, and grief expire,
Cast out by perfect love.

3 O that I now the rest might know,
Believe, and enter in!
Now, Saviour, now the power bestow,
And let me cease from sin.

4 Remove this hardness from my heart,
This unbelief remove;
To me the rest of faith impart,
The sabbath of Thy love.

5 I would be Thine, Thou know'st I
would,
And have Thee all my own;
Thee, O my all-sufficient Good!
I want, and Thee alone.

6 Thy name to me, Thy nature grant;
This, only this be given:
Nothing beside my God I want,
Nothing in earth or heaven.

Charles Wesley, 1707-88.

564

RIPON. S.M. J. G. NÄGELI, 1768-1836.

1 FATHER, I dare believe
Thee merciful and true:
Thou wilt my guilty soul forgive,
My fallen soul renew.

2 Come then for Jesu's sake,
And bid my heart be clean;
An end of all my troubles make,
An end of all my sin.

3 I will, through grace, I will,
I do, return to Thee;
Take, empty it, O Lord, and fill
My heart with purity.

4 For power I feebly pray:
Thy kingdom now restore,
To-day, while it is called to-day,
And I shall sin no more.

5 I cannot wash my heart,
But by believing Thee,
And waiting for Thy blood to
The spotless purity. [impart

6 While at Thy Cross I lie,
Jesus, the grace bestow,
Now Thy all-cleansing blood apply,
And I am white as snow.

Charles Wesley, 1707-88.

565

CREDITON. C.M. T. CLARK, 1775-1859.

1 I KNOW that my Redeemer lives,
And ever prays for me;
A token of His love He gives,
A pledge of liberty.

2 I find Him lifting up my head,
He brings salvation near,
His presence makes me free indeed,
And He will soon appear.

3 He wills that I should holy be;
What can withstand His will?
The counsel of His grace in me
He surely shall fulfil.

4 Jesus, I hang upon Thy word;
I steadfastly believe
Thou wilt return and claim me, Lord,
And to Thyself receive.

5 When God is mine, and I am His,
Of paradise possessed,
I taste unutterable bliss
And everlasting rest.

Charles Wesley, 1707-88.

566

BENEVENTO. 7.7.7.7. D. S. WEBBE, 1740-1816.

1 God of all redeeming grace,
By Thy pardoning love compelled,
Up to Thee our souls we raise,
Up to Thee our bodies yield:
Thou our sacrifice receive,
Acceptable through Thy Son,
While to Thee alone we live,
While we die to Thee alone.

2 Meet it is, and just, and right,
That we should be wholly Thine,
In Thine only will delight,
In Thy blessèd service join:
O that every work and word
Might proclaim how good Thou [art,
Holiness unto the Lord
Still be written on our heart!
Amen.

Charles Wesley, 1707-88.

567

ST. VICTOR. 7.6.7.6. R. Redhead, 1820-1901.

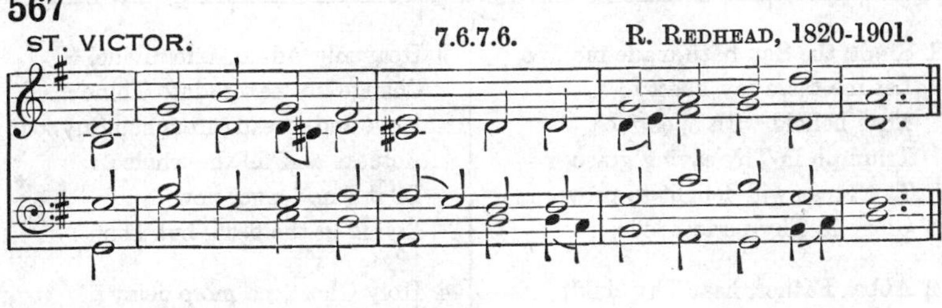

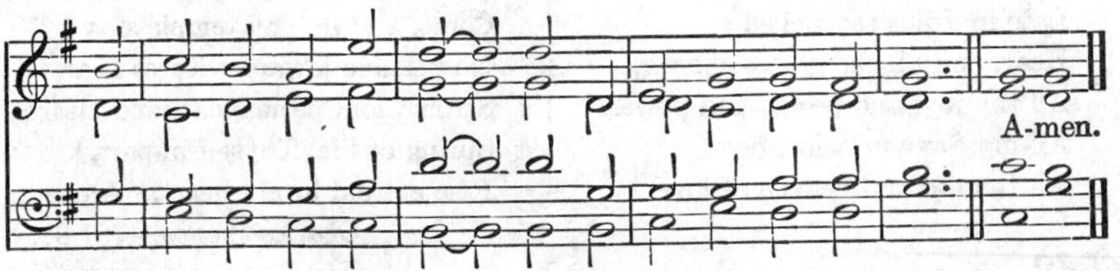

1 In full and glad surrender
I give myself to Thee;
Thine utterly, and only,
And evermore to be.

2 O Son of God, who lov'st me,
I will be Thine alone;
And all I have, and all I am,
Shall henceforth be Thine own.

3 Reign over me, Lord Jesus;
O make my heart Thy throne:
It shall be Thine, my Saviour,
It shall be Thine alone.

4 O come and reign, Lord Jesus,
Rule over everything;
And keep me always loyal
And true to Thee, my King. Amen.

Frances Ridley Havergal, 1836-79.

568

CROWLAND. 7 7.7 7.7 7. J. SCHOP, ?-1664.

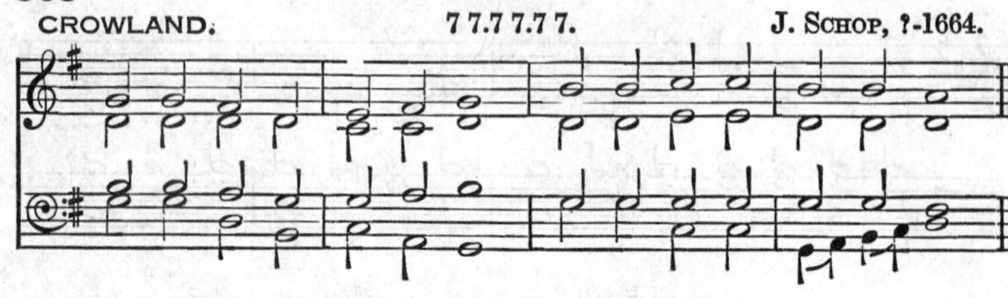

1 SINCE the Son hath made me free,
Let me taste my liberty;
Thee behold with open face,
Triumph in Thy saving grace,
Thy great will delight to prove,
Glory in Thy perfect love.

2 Abba, Father, hear Thy child,
Late in Jesus reconciled;
Hear, and all the graces shower,
All the joy, and peace, and power,
All my Saviour asks above,
All the life and heaven of love.

3 Heavenly Adam, Life divine,
Change my nature into Thine;
Move and spread throughout my soul,
Actuate and fill the whole;
Be it I no longer now
Living in the flesh, but Thou.

4 Holy Ghost, no more delay;
Come, and in Thy temple stay;
Now Thine inward witness bear,
Strong, and permanent, and clear;
Spring of life, Thyself impart,
Rise eternal in my heart. Amen.

Charles Wesley, 1707-88.

569

NEWINGTON. 7 7.7 7. W. D. MACLAGAN, 1826-1910.

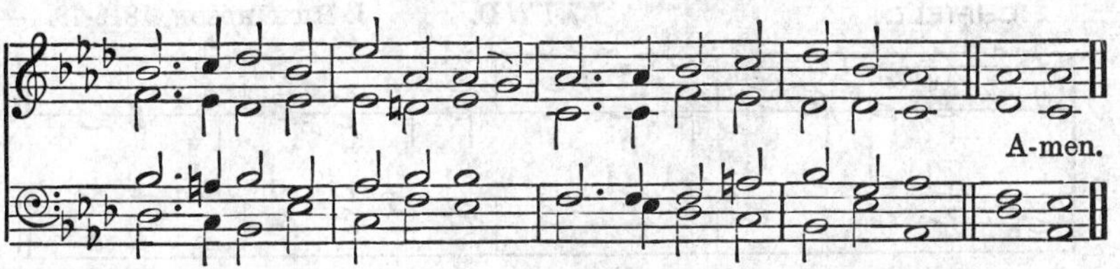

1 THINE for ever! God of love,
Hear us from Thy throne above;
Thine for ever may we be,
Here and in eternity.

2 Thine for ever! Lord of life,
Shield us through our earthly strife:
Thou the Life, the Truth, the Way,
Guide us to the realms of day.

3 Thine for ever! O how blest
They who find in Thee their rest!
Saviour, Guardian, Heavenly Friend,
O defend us to the end!

4 Thine for ever! Shepherd keep
These Thy frail and trembling sheep;
Safe alone beneath Thy care,
Let us all Thy goodness share.

5 Thine for ever! Thou our guide,
All our wants by Thee supplied,
All our sins by Thee forgiven,
Lead us, Lord, from earth to heaven. Amen.

Mary Fawler Maude, 1819-1913.

570

UFFINGHAM. L.M. J. CLARKE, 1659 *or* 1670-1707

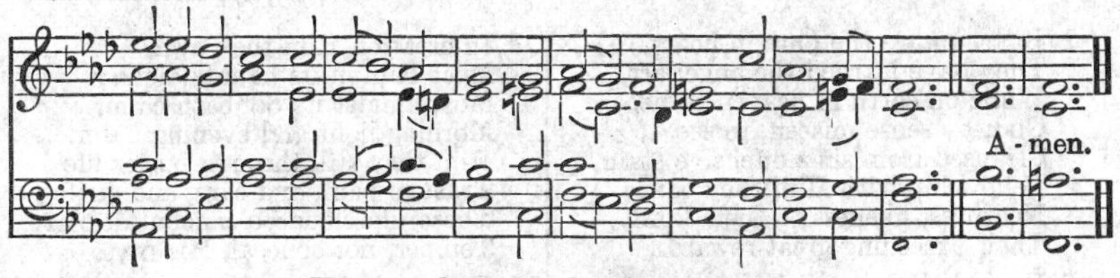

1 HOLY, and true, and righteous Lord,
I wait to prove Thy perfect will;
Be mindful of Thy gracious word,
And stamp me with Thy Spirit's seal.

2 Confound, o'erpower me by Thy grace,
I would be by myself abhorred;
All might, all majesty, all praise,
All glory, be to Christ my Lord.

3 Now let me gain perfection's height,
Now let me into nothing fall,
Be less than nothing in Thy sight,
And feel that Christ is all in all. Amen.

Charles Wesley, 1707-88.

571

TICHFIELD. 7 7.7 7. D. J. RICHARDSON, 1816-79.

1 BLESSÈD are the pure in heart,
They have learned the angel art,
While on earth in heaven to be,
God, by sense unseen, to see.
Cleansed from sin's offensive stain,
Fellowship with Him they gain;
Nearness, likeness to their Lord,
Their exceeding great reward.

2 Worshipping in spirit now,
In His inner court they bow—
Bow before the brightening veil,
God's own radiance through it hail.
Serious, simple of intent,
Teachably intelligent,
Rapt, they search the written Word
Till His very voice is heard.

3 In creation Him they own,
Meet Him in its haunts alone;
Most amidst its Sabbath calm,
Morning light and evening balm.
Him they still through busier life
Trust in pain, and care, and strife;
These, like clouds, o'er noontide blaze,
Temper, not conceal, His rays.

4 Hallowed thus their every breath:
Dying, they shall not see death.
With the Lord in paradise,
Till, like His, their bodies rise.
Nearer than the seraphim
In their flesh shall saints see Him,
With the Father, in the Son,
Through the Spirit, ever one.

William Maclardie Bunting, 1805-66.

Also:

87 Jesus comes with all
105 Jesus, the First
142 Let earth and heaven
229 Ye faithful souls
387 My God! I know
400 Take my life
430 Jesu, Thy boundless love
433 Thou hidden love
464 Jesus, the all-restoring Word
519 Thee, Jesus, full

572

MOZART. 8.8.8.8.8.8 8. From MOZART's *Die Zauberflöte,* 1791.

1 BEHOLD the servant of the Lord!
I wait Thy guiding eye to feel,
To hear and keep Thy every word,
To prove and do Thy perfect will,
Joyful from my own works to cease,
Glad to fulfil all righteousness.

2 Me, if Thy grace vouchsafe to use,
Meanest of all Thy creatures, me:
The deed, the time, the manner choose,
Let all my fruit be found of Thee;
Let all my works in Thee be wrought,
By Thee to full perfection brought.

3 My every weak, though good design,
O'errule, or change, as seems Thee meet;
Jesus, let all my work be Thine!
Thy work, O Lord, is all complete,
And pleasing in Thy Father's sight;
Thou only hast done all things right.

4 Here then to Thee Thy own I leave;
Mould as Thou wilt Thy passive clay;
But let me all Thy stamp receive,
But let me all Thy words obey,
Serve with a single heart and eye,
And to Thy glory live and die.
Amen.

Charles Wesley, 1707-88.

573

PATER OMNIUM. 8.8.8.8.8.8 8. H. J. E. HOLMES, 1852-1938

O Jesu, süsses Licht.

1 O GOD, what offering shall I give
To Thee, the Lord of earth and skies?
My spirit, soul, and flesh receive,
A holy, living sacrifice:
Small as it is, 'tis all my store;
More shouldst Thou have, if I had [more.

2 Now, O my God, Thou hast my soul,
No longer mine, but Thine I am;
Guard Thou Thine own, possess it whole,
Cheer it with hope, with love inflame;
Thou hast my spirit, there display
Thy glory to the perfect day.

3 Thou hast my flesh, Thy hallowed shrine,
Devoted solely to Thy will;
Here let Thy light for ever shine,
This house still let Thy presence fill:
O source of life; live, dwell, and move
In me, till all my life be love!

4 Send down Thy likeness from above,
And let this my adorning be;
Clothe me with wisdom, patience, love,
With lowliness and purity,
Than gold and pearls more precious far,
And brighter than the morning star.

5 Lord, arm me with Thy Spirit's might,
Since I am called by Thy great name;
In Thee let all my thoughts unite,
Of all my works be Thou the aim:
Thy love attend me all my days,
And my sole business be Thy praise.
Amen.

Joachim Lange, 1670-1744;
tr. by John Wesley, 1703-91.

574

WELLSPRING. 7.7.7.7.7.7. D. S. BORTNIANSKI, 1752-1825.
(Adapted.)

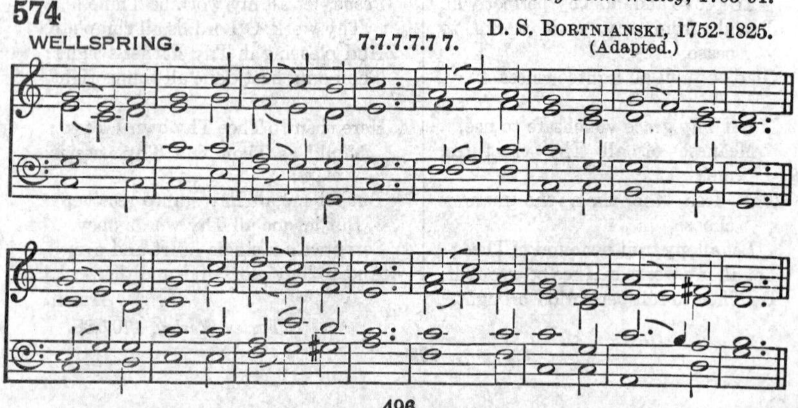

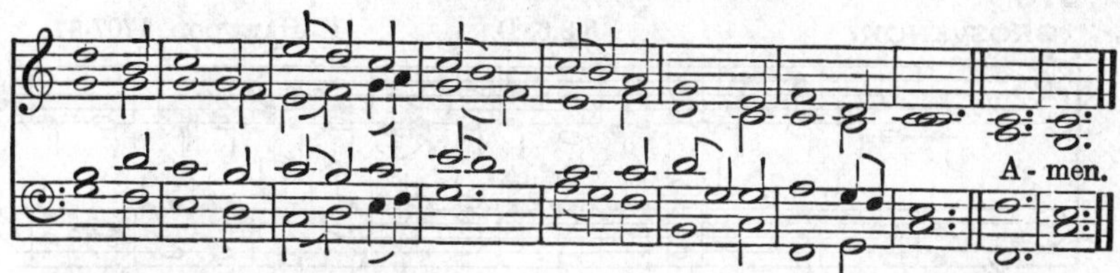

1 FATHER, Son, and Holy Ghost,
One in Three, and Three in One,
As by the celestial host,
Let Thy will on earth be done;
Praise by all to Thee be given,
Glorious Lord of earth and heaven.

2 Vilest of the sinful race,
Lo! I answer to Thy call;
Meanest vessel of Thy grace,
Grace divinely free for all,
Lo! I come to do Thy will,
All Thy counsel to fulfil.

3 If so poor a worm as I
May to Thy great glory live,
All my actions sanctify,
All my words and thoughts receive;
Claim me for Thy service, claim
All I have and all I am.

4 Take my soul and body's powers;
Take my memory, mind, and will,
All my goods, and all my hours,
All I know, and all I feel,
All I think, or speak, or do;
Take my heart, but make it new.

5 Now, O God, Thine own I am,
Now I give Thee back Thine own;
Freedom, friends, and health, and fame
Consecrate to Thee alone:
Thine I live, thrice happy I;
Happier still if Thine I die.

6 Father, Son, and Holy Ghost,
One in Three, and Three in One,
As by the celestial host,
Let Thy will on earth be done;
Praise by all to Thee be given,
Glorious Lord of earth and heaven.
Amen.

Charles Wesley, 1707-88.

575

ST. JAMES. C.M. R. COURTEVILLE, ?-1772.

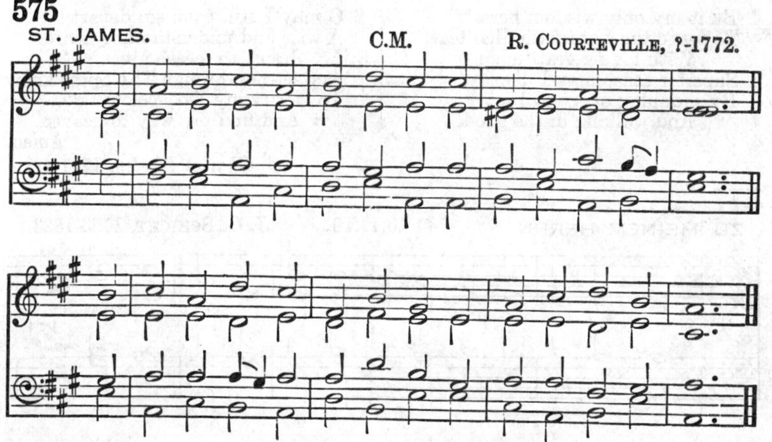

1 SERVANT of all, to toil for man
Thou didst not, Lord, refuse;
Thy majesty did not disdain
To be employed for us.

2 Son of the carpenter, receive
This humble work of mine;
Worth to my meanest labour give,
By joining it to Thine.

3 End of my every action Thou,
In all things Thee I see;
Accept my hallowed labour now,
I do it unto Thee.

4 Thy bright example I pursue,
To Thee in all things rise;
And all I think, or speak, or do
Is one great sacrifice.

5 Careless through outward cares I go,
From all distraction free;
My hands are but engaged below,
My heart is still with Thee.

Charles Wesley, 1707-88.

576

GROSVENOR. 8 8.6. D. E. HARWOOD, 1707-87.

A-men.

1 Be it my only wisdom here
To serve the Lord with filial fear,
With loving gratitude;
Superior sense may I display,
By shunning every evil way,
And walking in the good.

2 O may I still from sin depart!
A wise and understanding heart,
Jesus, to me be given;
And let me through Thy Spirit know
To glorify my God below,
And find my way to heaven.
Amen.

Charles Wesley, 1707-88.

577

ZU MEINEM HERRN. 11.10.11.10. J. G. SCHICHT, 1753-1823.

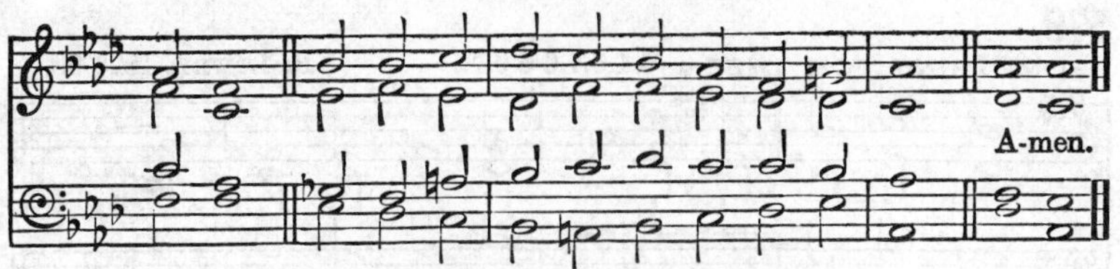

1 O loving Lord, who art for ever seeking
Men of Thy mind, intent to do Thy will,
Strong in Thy strength, Thy power and grace bespeaking;
Faithful to Thee, through good report and ill—

2 To Thee we come, and humbly make confession,
Faithless so oft, in thought and word and deed,
Asking that we may have, in true possession,
Thy free forgiveness in the hour of need.

3 In duties small, be Thou our inspiration,
In large affairs endue us with Thy might;
Through faithful service cometh full salvation,
So may we serve, Thy will our chief delight.

4 Not disobedient to the heavenly vision,
Faithful in all things, seeking not reward,
Then, following Thee, may we fulfil our mission,
True to ourselves, our brethren, and our Lord. Amen.

William Vaughan Jenkins, 1868-1920.

578

CAMBRIDGE. S.M. R. Harrison, 1748-1810.

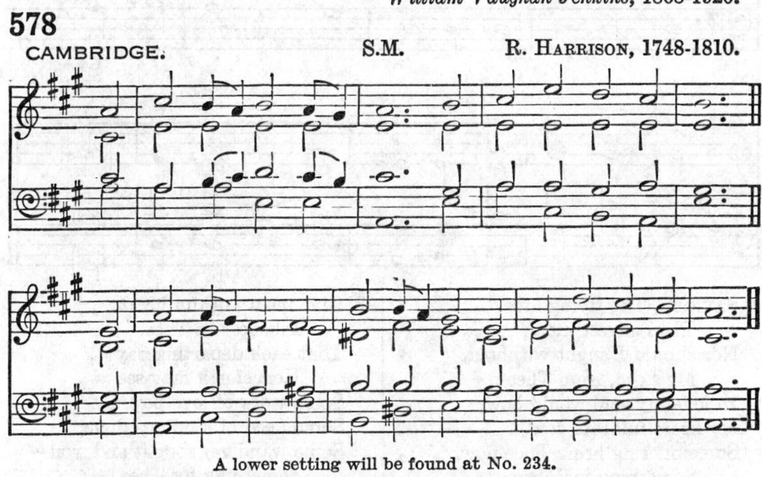

A lower setting will be found at No. 234.
May also be sung to Vigil, A.T. No. 4.

1 A charge to keep I have,
A God to glorify,
A never-dying soul to save,
And fit it for the sky:

2 To serve the present age,
My calling to fulfil:
O may it all my powers engage
To do my Master's will!

3 Arm me with jealous care,
As in Thy sight to live;
And O Thy servant, Lord, prepare
A strict account to give!

4 Help me to watch and pray,
And on Thyself rely,
Assured, if I my trust betray,
I shall for ever die.

Charles Wesley, 1707-88.

579

SOMETHING FOR THEE. 6.4.6.4.6 6 6.4. R. LOWRY, 1826-99.

1 SAVIOUR, Thy dying love
Thou gavest me,
Nor should I aught withhold,
My Lord, from Thee;
In love my soul would bow,
My heart fulfil its vow,
Some offering bring Thee now,
Something for Thee.

2 At the blest mercy-seat
Pleading for me,
My feeble faith looks up,
Jesus, to Thee:
Help me the cross to bear,
Thy wondrous love declare,
Some song to raise, or prayer—
Something for Thee.

3 Give me a faithful heart,
Likeness to Thee,
That each departing day
Henceforth may see
Some work of love begun,
Some deed of kindness done,
Some wanderer sought and won—
Something for Thee.

4 All that I am and have,
Thy gifts so free,
In joy, in grief, through life,
O Lord, for Thee.
And when Thy face I see,
My ransomed soul shall be,
Through all eternity,
Something for Thee.

Sylvanus Dryden Phelps, 1816-95.

580

SPOHR. 8.6.8.6.8.6. From SPOHR'S *Calvary*, 1833.

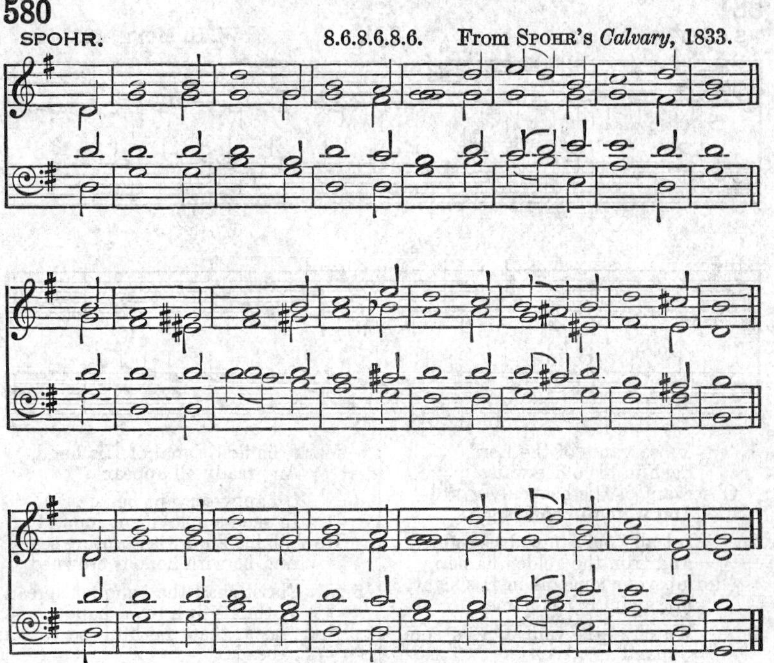

1 DISMISS me not Thy service, Lord,
But train me for Thy will;
For even I, in fields so broad,
Some duties may fulfil;
And I will ask for no reward,
Except to serve Thee still.

2 How many serve, how many more
May to the service come;
To tend the vines, the grapes to store,
Thou dost appoint for some;
Thou hast Thy young men at the war,
Thy little ones at home.

3 All works are good, and each is best
As most it pleases Thee;
Each worker pleases when the rest
He serves in charity;
And neither man nor work unblest
Wilt Thou permit to be.

4 Our Master all the work hath done
He asks of us to-day;
Sharing His service, every one
Share too His sonship may:
Lord, I would serve and be a son;
Dismiss me not, I pray.

Thomas Toke Lynch, 1818-71.

581

ST. ETHELWALD. S.M. W. H. Monk, 1823-89.

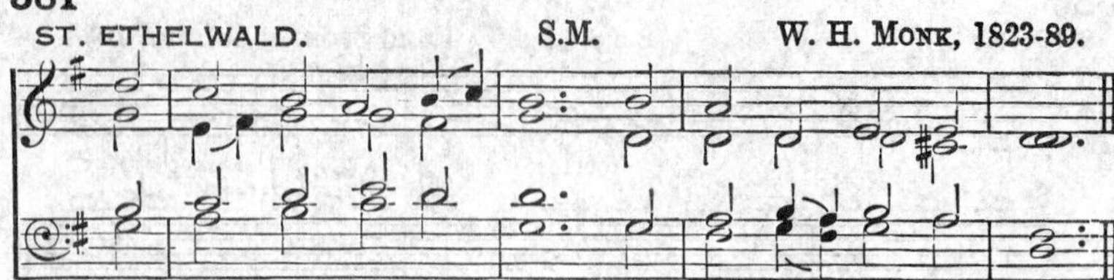

1 Ye servants of the Lord
Each in his office wait,
Observant of His heavenly word,
And watchful at His gate.

2 Let all your lamps be bright,
And trim the golden flame;
Gird up your loins, as in His sight,
For awful is His name.

3 Watch: 'tis your Lord's command;
And, while we speak, He's near;
Mark the first signal of His hand,
And ready all appear.

4 O happy servant he,
In such employment found!
He shall his Lord with rapture see,
And be with honour crowned.

5 Christ shall the banquet spread
With His own royal hand,
And raise that faithful servant's head
Amid the angelic band.

Philip Doddridge, 1702-51.

582

LET THE LOWER LIGHTS. 8.7.8.7. and refrain. P. Bliss, 1838-76.

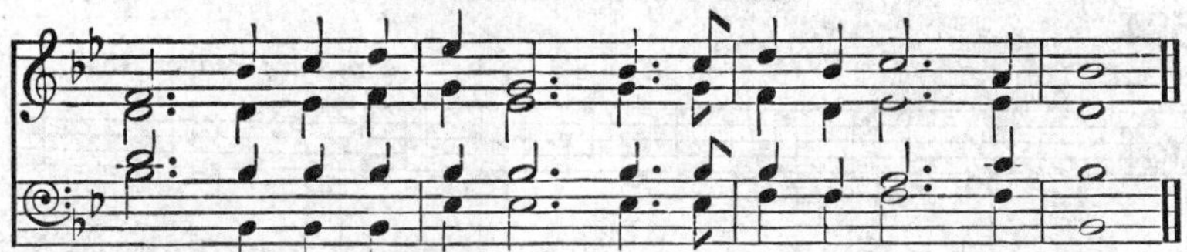

1 Brightly beams our Father's mercy
From His lighthouse evermore;
But to us He gives the keeping
Of the lights along the shore.

Let the lower lights be burning,
Send a gleam across the wave;
Some poor fainting, struggling seaman
You may rescue, you may save.

2 Dark the night of sin has settled,
Loud the angry billows roar;
Eager eyes are watching, longing,
For the lights along the shore.

3 Trim your feeble lamp, my brother,
Some poor sailor tempest-tossed,
Trying now to make the harbour,
In the darkness may be lost.

Philipp Bliss, 1838-76.

583

BEULAH. D.C.M. Gawler's *Hymns and Psalms*, c. 1785.

O hochbeglückte Seele.

1 How blessèd, from the bonds of sin
And earthly fetters free,
In singleness of heart and aim,
Thy servant, Lord, to be;
The hardest toil to undertake
With joy at Thy command,
The meanest office to receive
With meekness at Thy hand;

2 With willing heart and longing eyes
To watch before Thy gate,
Ready to run the weary race,
To bear the heavy weight;
No voice of thunder to expect,
But follow, calm and still:
For love can easily divine
The One Belovèd's will.

3 Thus may I serve Thee, gracious Lord,
Thus ever Thine alone,
My soul and body given to Thee,
The purchase Thou hast won;
Through evil or through good report,
Still keeping by Thy side:
By life or death, in this poor flesh,
Let Christ be magnified.

4 How happily the working days
In this dear service fly!
How rapidly the closing hour,
The time of rest, draws nigh,
When all the faithful gather home,
A joyful company,
And ever where the Master is
Shall His blest servants be.

Carl Johann Philipp Spitta, 1801-59;
tr. by Jane Laurie Borthwick, 1813-97.

584

OLD 113TH. 8 8.8. 8 8.8.D. *Strasburg Psalter*, 1542.

May also be sung to DRESDEN, No. 80.

1 Thou, Jesu, Thou my breast inspire,
And touch my lips with hallowed fire,
And loose a stammering infant's tongue;
Prepare the vessel of Thy grace,
Adorn me with the robes of praise,
And mercy shall be all my song:
Mercy for all who know not God,
Mercy for all in Jesu's blood,
Mercy, that earth and heaven transcends;
Love, that o'erwhelms the saints in light,
The length, and breadth, and depth, [and height
Of love divine which never ends!

2 A faithful witness of Thy grace,
Well may I fill the allotted space,
And answer all Thy great design;
Walk in the works by Thee prepared;
And find annexed the vast reward,
The crown of righteousness divine.
When I have lived to Thee alone,
Pronounce the welcome word: Well done!
And let me take my place above,
Enter into my Master's joy,
And all eternity employ
In praise, and ecstasy, and love.
Amen.

Charles Wesley, 1707-88.

585

WATCHMAN. S.M. J. Leach, 1762-98.

May also be sung to Carlisle, No. 595.

1 Rise up, O men of God!
Have done with lesser things;
Give heart and soul and mind and strength
To serve the King of kings.

2 Rise up, O men of God!
His kingdom tarries long;
Bring in the day of brotherhood,
And end the night of wrong.

3 Rise up, O men of God!
The Church for you doth wait,
Her strength unequal to her task;
Rise up and make her great.

4 Lift high the Cross of Christ!
Tread where His feet have trod;
As brothers of the Son of Man
Rise up, O men of God!

William Pierson Merrill, 1867-

UNDE ET MEMORES. 10 10.10 10.10 10. W. H. Monk, 1823-89.

1 Stay, Master, stay upon this heavenly hill:
A little longer let us linger still;
With all the mighty ones of old beside,
Near to the awful Presence still abide;
Before the throne of light we trembling stand,
And catch a glimpse into the spirit-land.

2 Stay, Master, stay! We breathe a purer air;
This life is not the life that waits us there:
Thoughts, feelings, flashes, glimpses come and go;
We cannot speak them—nay, we do not know;
Wrapt in this cloud of light we seem to be
The thing we fain would grow—eternally.

3 No, saith the Lord, the hour is past, we go;
Our home, our life, our duties lie below.
While here we kneel upon the mount of prayer,
The plough lies waiting in the furrow there.
Here we sought God that we might know His will;
There we must do it, serve Him, seek Him still.

4 If man aspires to reach the throne of God,
O'er the dull plains of earth must lie the road:
He who best does his lowly duty here,
Shall mount the highest in a nobler sphere:
At God's own feet our spirits seek their rest,
And he is nearest Him who serves Him best.

Samuel Greg, 1804-76.

587

NICOLAUS (LOB'T GOTT). 8.6.8 8.6. N. HERMANN, 1485-1561.

1 O LORD of every lovely thing,
  The Maker of them all,
Who from the winter's gloomy wing
Dost shed the splendours of the spring,
  On Thy great name we call.

2 With flowers that through the valleys teach
  Thy love and truth divine,
With streams that sing, and hills that preach,
With waves that laugh on every beach,
  We praise Thee we are Thine!

3 Not Thine alone because from Thee
  Our life and breath we hold;
But Thine because in Christ we see
The grace that sets our spirits free,
  And for the truth makes bold.

4 Count us amongst the radiant choir
  That sounds Thy name abroad,
Set in our hands the heavenly lyre,
With songs of love our hearts inspire,
  The mighty love of God.

5 Until with those who toiled and dreamed
  To build Thy kingdom here,
With those the world hath ne'er esteemed,
With all the hosts of Thy redeemed,
  We in Thy home appear.

Robert Wilfrid Callin, 1886-1951

588

SHELTERED DALE. 8.6.8.6.8.6. German Traditional Melody.

1 AWAKE, awake to love and work,
The lark is in the sky,
The fields are wet with diamond dew,
The worlds awake to cry
Their blessings on the Lord of Life,
As He goes meekly by.

2 Come, let thy voice be one with theirs,
Shout with their shout of praise;
See how the giant sun soars up,
Great lord of years and days!
So let the love of Jesus come,
And set thy soul ablaze.

3 To give and give, and give again,
What God hath given thee;
To spend thy self nor count the cost,
To serve right gloriously
The God who gave all worlds that are,
And all that are to be.

Geoffrey Anketell Studdert-Kennedy, 1883-1929.

589

GRENOBLE. L.M. Grenoble Church Melody.
UNISON.

May also be sung to PENTECOST, No. 817.

1 Go, labour on; spend, and be spent,
Thy joy to do the Father's will:
It is the way the Master went;
Should not the servant tread it still?

2 Go, labour on; 'tis not for nought,
Thy earthly loss is heavenly gain:
Men heed thee, love thee, praise thee not;
The Master praises; what are men?

3 Go, labour on, while it is day;
The world's dark night is hastening on:
Speed, speed thy work, cast sloth away;
It is not thus that souls are won.

4 Men die in darkness at your side,
Without a hope to cheer the tomb:
Take up the torch, and wave it wide,
The torch that lights time's thickest gloom.

5 Toil on, faint not, keep watch, and pray;
Be wise, the erring soul to win;
Go forth into the world's highway,
Compel the wanderer to come in.

6 Toil on, and in thy toil rejoice;
For toil comes rest, for exile home:
Soon shalt thou hear the Bridegroom's voice,
The midnight peal: Behold, I come!

Horatius Bonar, 1808-89.

590

ANTWERP. L.M. W. SMALLWOOD, 1831-97.

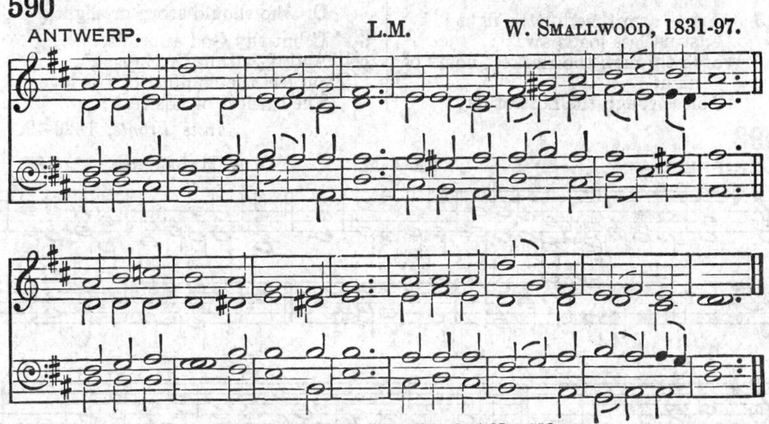

A higher setting will be found at No. 153.

1 FORTH in Thy name, O Lord, I go,
My daily labour to pursue,
Thee, only Thee, resolved to know
In all I think, or speak, or do.

2 The task Thy wisdom hath assigned
O let me cheerfully fulfil,
In all my works Thy presence find,
And prove Thy acceptable will.

3 Thee may I set at my right hand,
Whose eyes my inmost substance see,
And labour on at Thy command,
And offer all my works to Thee.

4 Give me to bear Thy easy yoke,
And every moment watch and pray,
And still to things eternal look,
And hasten to Thy glorious day:

5 For Thee delightfully employ
Whate'er Thy bounteous grace hath given,
And run my course with even joy,
And closely walk with Thee to heaven.

Charles Wesley, 1707-88.

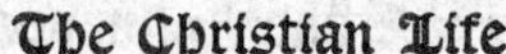

591

ST. THOMAS. S.M. A. WILLIAMS, 1731-76.

1 BELIEVE not those who say
The upward path is smooth,
Lest thou shouldst stumble in the way
And faint before the truth.

2 It is the only road
Unto the realms of joy;
But he who seeks that blest abode
Must all his powers employ.

3 Arm—arm thee for the fight!
Cast useless loads away;
Watch through the darkest hours of night;
Toil through the hottest day.

4 To labour and to love,
To pardon and endure,
To lift thy heart to God above,
And keep thy conscience pure—

5 Be this thy constant aim,
Thy hope, thy chief delight;
What matter who should whisper blame
Or who should scorn or slight:

6 If but thy God approve,
And if, within thy breast,
Thou feel the comfort of His love,
The earnest of His rest?

Anne Brontë, 1820-49.

592

CRIPPLEGATE. D.C.M. G. A. MACFARREN, 1813-87.

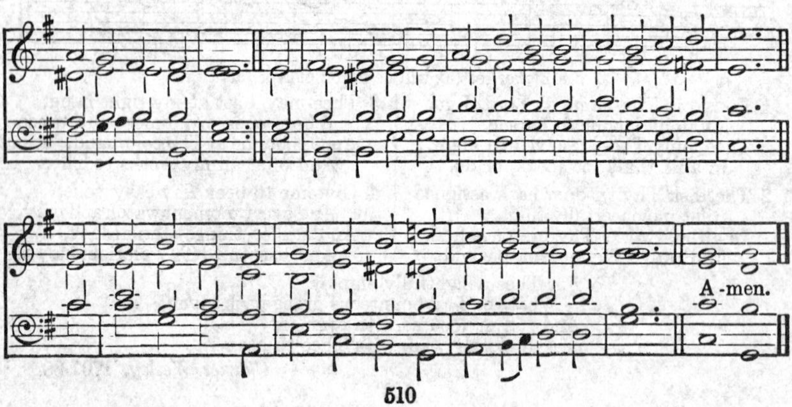

A-men.

1 I HOPED that with the brave and strong
My portioned task might lie;
To toil amid the busy throng,
With purpose pure and high:
But God has fixed another part,
And He has fixed it well;
I said so with my breaking heart,
When first this trouble fell.

2 These weary hours will not be lost,
These days of misery,
These nights of darkness, tempest-
Can I but turn to Thee, [tossed,
With secret labour to sustain
In patience every blow,
To gather fortitude from pain,
And holiness from woe.

3 If Thou shouldst bring me back to life,
More humble I should be,
More wise, more strengthened for the
More apt to lean on Thee; [strife,
Should death be standing at the gate,
Thus should I keep my vow:
But, Lord, whatever be my fate,
O let me serve Thee now! Amen.

Anne Brontë, 1820-49.

593

RETIREMENT. 7.8.7.8.7 7.7 7. G. F. BROCKLESS, 1887-1957.

1 O'ER the harvest reaped or lost
Falls the eve; our tasks are over:
Purpose crowned or purpose crossed,
None may mar and none recover.
Now, O merciful and just,
Trembling lay we down the trust;
Slender fruit of thriftless day,
Father, at Thy feet we lay.

2 Yea, but Thou, O Judge and Lord,
Yea, but Thou, O strong and holy,
Take, and in Thy bosom stored,
By Thy pure hands changing wholly,
Turn to gold the things of naught,
Failing deed and failing thought:
Love, how faint, yet love, we give;
Thou within Thee make it live.

3 Gracious task our heart shall bear
Now, for sweeter call has found us:
Airs of home and days that were
Wind re-woven chains around us;
By the hearthstone, whence we came,
Love shall trim her gentle flame,
Kindling new from undefiled
Ancient altars of the child.

4 Brothers, whom the wider life
Summons to a man's endeavour,
Bear our blessing to the strife,
Comrades once and comrades ever:
Yours and ours, one saving star,
Here and on your fields afar,
Lightens from beside the throne,
Where the one Lord makes us one.

John Huntley Skrine, 1848-1923.

594

ST. MICHAEL. S.M. DAY'S *Psalter*, 1562.

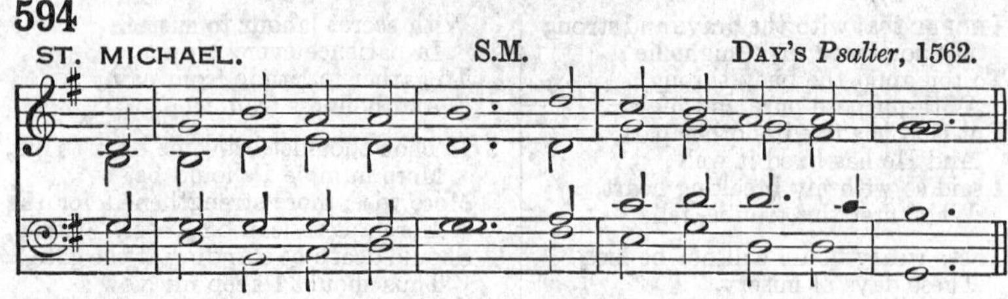

1 LORD, in the strength of grace,
With a glad heart and free,
Myself, my residue of days,
I consecrate to Thee.

2 Thy ransomed servant, I
Restore to Thee Thy own;
And, from this moment, live or die
To serve my God alone.

Charles Wesley, 1707-88.

595

CARLISLE. S.M. C. LOCKHART, 1745-1815.

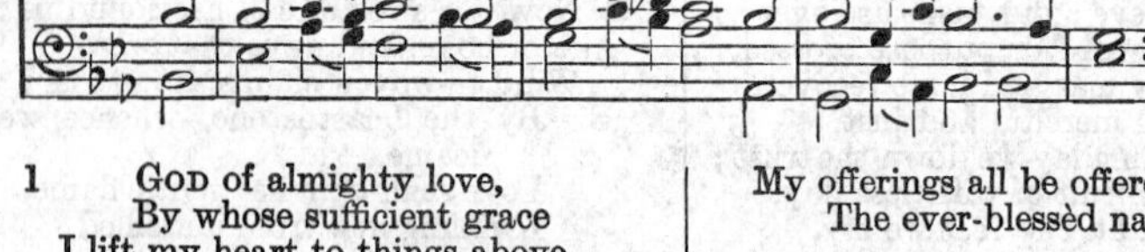

1 GOD of almighty love,
By whose sufficient grace
I lift my heart to things above,
And humbly seek Thy face:

2 Through Jesus Christ the Just
My faint desires receive,
And let me in Thy goodness trust
And to Thy glory live.

3 Whate'er I say or do,
Thy glory be my aim;
My offerings all be offered through
The ever-blessèd name.

4 Jesu, my single eye
Be fixed on Thee alone:
Thy name be praised on earth, on high;
Thy will by all be done.

5 Spirit of faith, inspire
My consecrated heart;
Fill me with pure, celestial fire,
With all Thou hast and art.
Amen.

Charles Wesley, 1707-88.

596

LLANLLYFNI. D.S.M. J. JONES, 1797-1857. Arranged by D. JENKINS.

May also be sung to LEOMINSTER, No. 542.

1 MAKE me a captive, Lord,
And then I shall be free;
Force me to render up my sword,
And I shall conqueror be.
I sink in life's alarms
When by myself I stand;
Imprison me within Thine arms,
And strong shall be my hand.

2 My heart is weak and poor
Until it master find;
It has no spring of action sure—
It varies with the wind.
It cannot freely move,
Till Thou hast wrought its chain;
Enslave it with Thy matchless love,
And deathless it shall reign.

3 My power is faint and low
Till I have learned to serve;
It wants the needed fire to glow,
It wants the breeze to nerve;
It cannot drive the world,
Until itself be driven;
Its flag can only be unfurled
When Thou shalt breathe from heaven.

4 My will is not my own
Till Thou hast made it Thine;
If it would reach a monarch's throne
It must its crown resign;
It only stands unbent,
Amid the clashing strife,
When on Thy bosom it has leant
And found in Thee its life.

George Matheson, 1842-1906.

597

SANDYS. S.M. SANDYS' *Collection*, 1833.

1 TEACH me, my God and King,
In all things Thee to see;
And what I do in anything,
To do it as for Thee.

2 A man that looks on glass,
On it may stay his eye;
Or if he pleaseth, through it pass,
And then the heaven espy.

3 All may of Thee partake:
Nothing can be so mean,
Which with this tincture: For Thy sake,
Will not grow bright and clean.

4 A servant with this clause
Makes drudgery divine;
Who sweeps a room, as for Thy laws,
Makes that and the action fine.

5 This is the famous stone
That turneth all to gold:
For that which God doth touch and own,
Cannot for less be told.

George Herbert, 1593-1632.

598

SYRIA. 7 7.7 7. D. *Union Tune Book*, 1842.

1 Holy Lamb, who Thee confess,
Followers of Thy holiness,
Thee they ever keep in view,
Ever ask: What shall we do?
Governed by Thy only will,
All Thy words we would fulfil,
Would in all Thy footsteps go,
Walk as Jesus walked below.

2 While Thou didst on earth appear,
Servant to Thy servants here,
Mindful of Thy place above,
All Thy life was prayer and love.
Such our whole employment be,
Works of faith and charity;
Works of love on man bestowed,
Secret intercourse with God.

3 Early in the temple met,
Let us still our Saviour greet;
Nightly to the mount repair,
Join our praying Pattern there.
There by wrestling faith obtain
Power to work for God again,
Power His image to retrieve,
Power, like Thee, our Lord, to live.

4 Vessels, instruments of grace,
Pass we thus our happy days
'Twixt the mount and multitude,
Doing or receiving good;
Glad to pray and labour on,
Till our earthly course is run,
Till we, on the sacred tree,
Bow the head and die like Thee.

Charles Wesley, 1707-88.

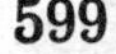

599

SWABIA. S.M. Spiess's *Gesangbuch*, 1745.

1 Sow in the morn thy seed,
At eve hold not thine hand;
To doubt and fear give thou no heed,
Broadcast it o'er the land.

2 Beside all waters sow,
The highway furrows stock,
Drop it where thorns and thistles grow,
Scatter it on the rock.

3 The good, the fruitful ground,
Expect not here nor there;
O'er hill and dale, by plots 'tis found:
Go forth, then, everywhere.

4 And duly shall appear,
In verdure, beauty, strength,
The tender blade, the stalk, the ear,
And the full corn at length.

5 Thou canst not toil in vain;
Cold, heat, and moist, and dry,
Shall foster and mature the grain
For garners in the sky.

6 Thence, when the glorious end,
The day of God is come,
The angel reapers shall descend,
And heaven cry: Harvest home!

James Montgomery, 1771-1854.

600

KETTERING. D.L.M. J. Sheeles, c. 1720.

May also be sung to Stanley, No. 168.

1 O Master, let me walk with Thee
In lowly paths of service free;
Thy secret tell; help me to bear
The strain of toil, the fret of care;
Help me the slow of heart to move
By some clear winning word of love;
Teach me the wayward feet to stay,
And guide them in the homeward way.

2 Teach me Thy patience; still with Thee
In closer, dearer company,
In work that keeps faith sweet and strong,
In trust that triumphs over wrong,
In hope that sends a shining ray
Far down the future's broadening way,
In peace that only Thou canst give,
With Thee, O Master, let me live! Amen.

Washington Gladden, 1836-1918.

601

EVERTON. 8 7.8 7. D. H. Smart, 1813-79.

1 They who tread the path of labour follow where My feet have trod;
They who work without complaining do the holy will of God;
Nevermore thou needest seek Me; I am with thee everywhere;
Raise the stone, and thou shalt find Me; cleave the wood and I am there.

2 Where the many toil together, there am I among My own;
Where the tired workman sleepeth, there am I with him alone.
I, the Peace that passeth knowledge, dwell amid the daily strife;
I, the Bread of heaven, am broken in the sacrament of life.

3 Every task, however simple, sets the soul that does it free;
Every deed of love and mercy done to man, is done to Me.
Nevermore thou needest seek Me; I am with thee everywhere;
Raise the stone, and thou shalt find Me; cleave the wood and I am there.

Henry Van Dyke, 1852-1933.

602

ARABIA (*First Tune*). 8.6.8.6.8.6. W. WILSON, c. 1830.

LEBANON (*Second Tune*). 8.6.8.6.8.6. From SPOHR'S *Quartet in A minor*.

1 FATHER, I know that all my life
Is portioned out for me,
And the changes that are sure to come
I do not fear to see;
But I ask Thee for a present mind,
Intent on pleasing Thee.

2 I ask Thee for a thoughtful love,
Through constant watching wise,
To meet the glad with joyful smiles,
And wipe the weeping eyes,
And a heart at leisure from itself
To soothe and sympathize.

3 I would not have the restless will
That hurries to and fro,
Seeking for some great thing to do
Or secret thing to know;
I would be treated as a child,
And guided where I go.

4 Wherever in the world I am,
In whatsoe'er estate,
I have a fellowship with hearts
To keep and cultivate,
And a work of lowly love to do
For the Lord on whom I wait.

5 I ask Thee for the daily strength
To none that ask denied,
And a mind to blend with outward life,
Still keeping at Thy side,
Content to fill a little space
If Thou be glorified.

6 In a service which Thy will appoints
There are no bonds for me;
For my inmost soul is taught the truth
That makes Thy children free;
And a life of self-renouncing love
Is a life of liberty.

Anna Laetitia Waring, 1820-1910.

603

ATTERCLIFFE. C.M. W. MATHER, 1756-1808.

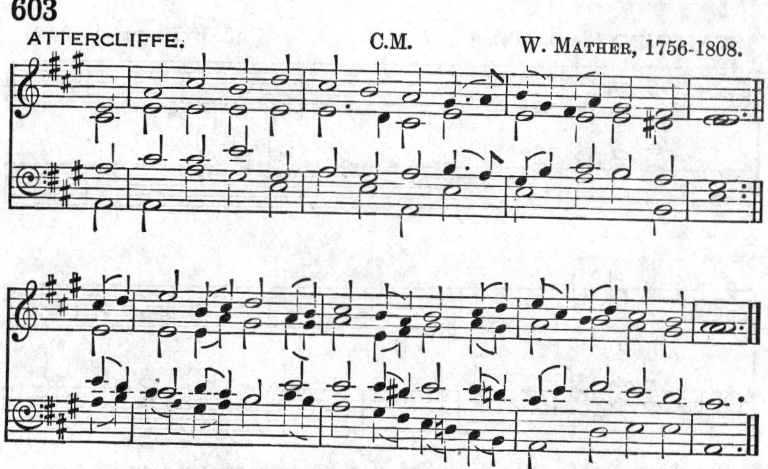

1 JESUS, let all Thy lovers shine
Illustrious as the sun:
And, bright with borrowed rays divine,
Their glorious circuit run.

2 Beyond the reach of mortals, spread
Their light where'er they go;
And heavenly influences shed
On all the world below.

3 As the bright Sun of Righteousness,
Their healing wings display;
And let their lustre still increase
Unto the perfect day.

Charles Wesley, 1707-88.

604

ST. FULBERT (*First Tune*). C.M. H. J. GAUNTLETT, 1805-76.

BEATITUDO (*Second Tune*). C.M. J. B. DYKES, 1823-76.

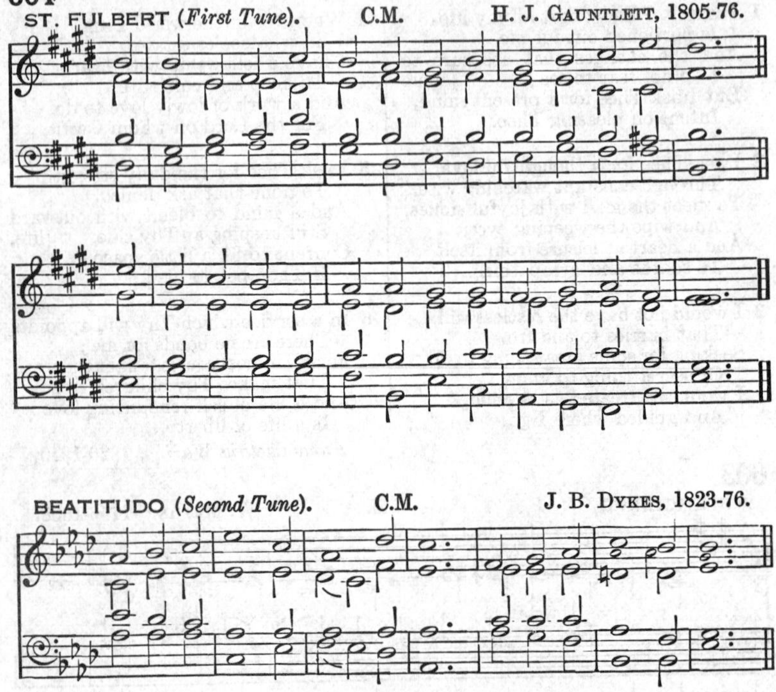

1 FILL Thou my life, O Lord my God,
In every part with praise,
That my whole being may proclaim
Thy being and Thy ways.

2 Not for the lip of praise alone,
Nor e'en the praising heart,
I ask, but for a life made up
Of praise in every part:

3 Praise in the common things of life,
Its goings out and in;
Praise in each duty and each deed,
However small and mean.

4 Fill every part of me with praise;
Let all my being speak
Of Thee and of Thy love, O Lord,
Poor though I be and weak.

5 So shalt Thou, Lord, from me, e'en me,
Receive the glory due;
And so shall I begin on earth
The song for ever new.

6 So shall no part of day or night
From sacredness be free;
But all my life, in every step,
Be fellowship with Thee.

Horatius Bonar, 1808-89.

Service and Influence

605

COLCHESTER. 8.8.8.8.8 8. S. S. Wesley, 1810-76.

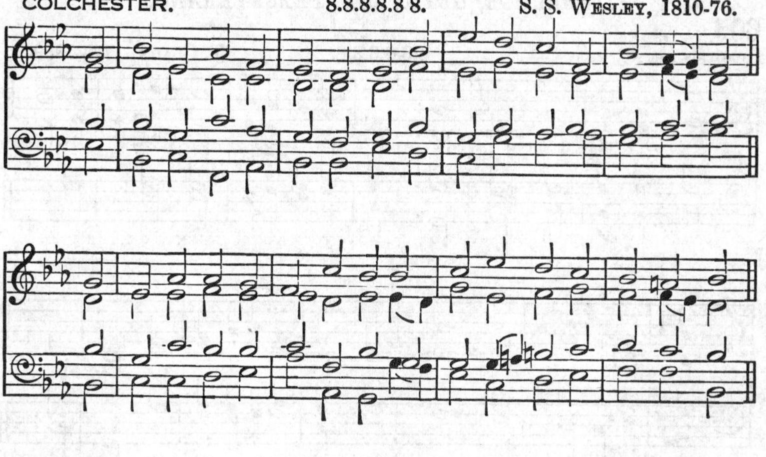

1 Jesus, the gift divine I know,
The gift divine I ask of Thee;
That living water now bestow,
Thy Spirit and Thyself, on me;
Thou, Lord, of life the Fountain art,
Now let me find Thee in my heart.

2 Thee let me drink, and thirst no more
For drops of finite happiness;
Spring up, O well, in heavenly power,
In streams of pure perennial peace,
In joy that none can take away,
In life which shall for ever stay.

3 Father, on me the grace bestow,
Unblamable before Thy sight,
Whence all the streams of mercy flow;
Mercy, Thy own supreme delight,
To me, for Jesu's sake, impart,
And plant Thy nature in my heart.

4 Thy mind throughout my life be shown,
While, listening to the sufferer's cry,
The widow's and the orphan's groan,
On mercy's wings I swiftly fly,
The poor and helpless to relieve,
My life, my all, for them to give.

5 Thus may I show the Spirit within,
Which purges me from every stain;
Unspotted from the world and sin,
My faith's integrity maintain;
The truth of my religion prove
By perfect purity and love.

Charles Wesley, 1707-88.

Also:

103 O Lord and Master
158 Thou say'st: Take up
198 Never further than Thy Cross
320 Art thou weary
390 Give me the faith
418 Awake, our souls!
452 What shall I do
546 Come, Saviour, Jesus
731 O Christ, our God
780 Master, speak!
781 Lord, speak to me
895 Where cross the crowded ways
923 We give Thee but Thine own

PILGRIMAGE, GUIDANCE, PERSEVERANCE

606

WARSAW. 6.6.6.6.8 8. T. Clark, 1775-1859.

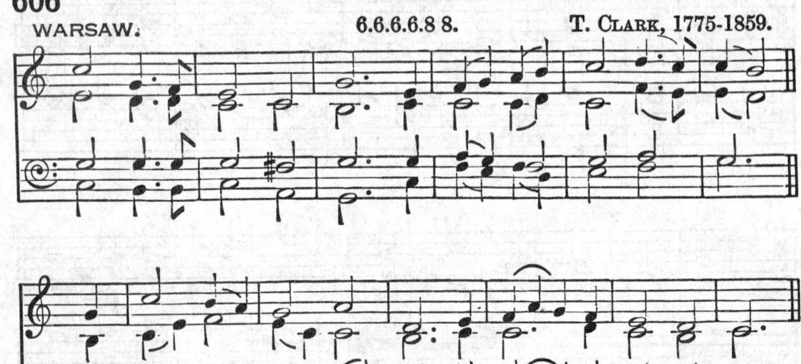

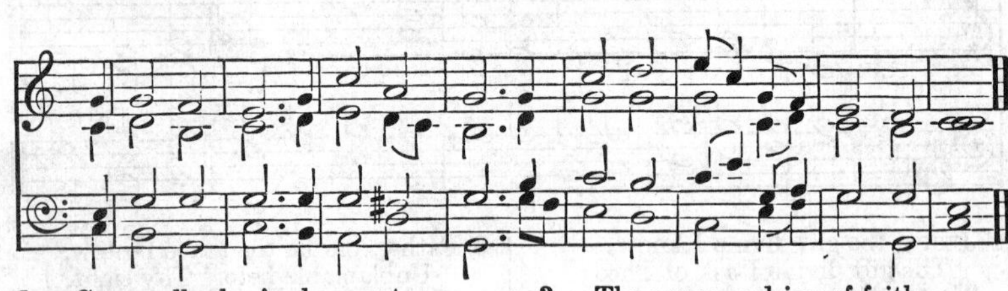

1 Come, all whoe'er have set
Your faces Zion-ward,
In Jesus let us meet,
And praise our common Lord;
In Jesus let us still go on,
Till all appear before His throne.

2 Nearer, and nearer still,
We to our country come,
To that celestial hill,
The weary pilgrim's home:
The new Jerusalem above,
The seat of everlasting love.

3 The peace and joy of faith
Each moment may we feel;
Redeemed from sin and wrath,
From earth, and death, and hell,
We to our Father's house repair,
To meet our elder Brother there.

4 Our Brother, Saviour, Head,
Our all in all, is He;
And in His steps who tread
We soon His face shall see;
Shall see Him with our glorious friends,
And then in heaven our journey ends.

Charles Wesley, 1707-88.

607

TALLIS' ORDINAL. C.M. T. Tallis, *c.* 1510-85.

May also be sung to STRACATHRO, No. 102.

1 O God of Bethel, by whose hand
Thy people still are fed;
Who through this weary pilgrimage
Hast all our fathers led:

2 Our vows, our prayers, we now present
Before Thy throne of grace;
God of our fathers, be the God
Of their succeeding race.

3 Through each perplexing path of life
Our wandering footsteps guide;
Give us each day our daily bread,
And raiment fit provide.

4 O spread Thy covering wings around,
Till all our wanderings cease,
And at our Father's loved abode
Our souls arrive in peace.

5 Such blessings from Thy gracious hand
Our humble prayers implore;
And Thou shalt be our chosen God,
And portion evermore. Amen.

Philip Doddridge, 1702-51.

608

MARIENLYST. 8.8.8.8.8.8. J. W. David, 1837-1902.

1 Captain of Israel's host, and Guide
Of all who seek the land above,
Beneath Thy shadow we abide,
The cloud of Thy protecting love;
Our strength, Thy grace; our rule, Thy word;
Our end, the glory of the Lord.

2 By Thine unerring Spirit led,
We shall not in the desert stray;
We shall not full direction need,
Nor miss our providential way;
As far from danger as from fear,
While love, almighty love, is near.

Charles Wesley, 1707-88.

609

LEWES. 8.7.8.7.4.7. J. RANDALL, 1715-99.

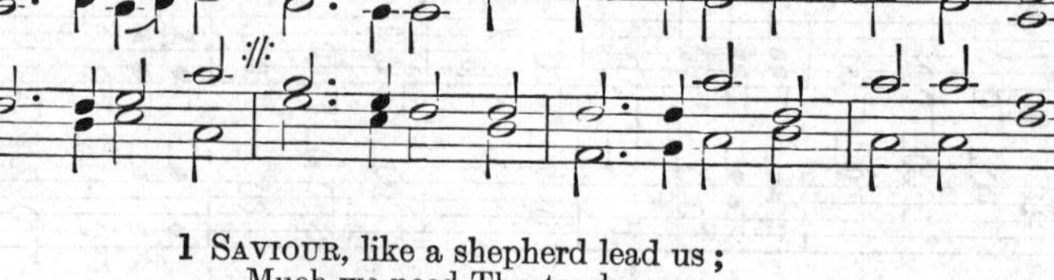

1 SAVIOUR, like a shepherd lead us;
Much we need Thy tender care;
In Thy pleasant pastures feed us,
For our use Thy folds prepare:
Blessèd Jesus,
Thou hast bought us, Thine we are.

2 We are Thine, do Thou befriend us;
Be the Guardian of our way;
Keep Thy flock, from sin defend us,
Seek us when we go astray:
Blessèd Jesus,
Hear us when we praise and pray.

3 Thou hast promised to receive us,
Poor and sinful though we be;
Thou hast mercy to relieve us,
Grace to cleanse, and make us free:
Blessèd Jesus,
Early let us turn to Thee.

4 Early let us seek Thy favour;
Early let us do Thy will;
Gracious Lord, our only Saviour,
With Thyself our bosoms fill:
Blessèd Jesus,
Thou hast loved us—love us still.

Dorothy Ann Thrupp: Hymns for the Young, 1836.

MOUNT BEACON. 8.8.8.8.8.8. A. BEER, 1874-

May also be sung to ST. WERBERGH, No. 534.

1 LEADER of faithful souls, and Guide
Of all that travel to the sky,
Come and with us, even us, abide,
Who would on Thee alone rely,
On Thee alone our spirits stay,
While held in life's uneven way.

2 Strangers and pilgrims here below,
This earth, we know, is not our place;
But hasten through the vale of woe,
And, restless to behold Thy face,
Swift to our heavenly country move,
Our everlasting home above.

3 We have no abiding city here,
But seek a city out of sight;
Thither our steady course we steer,
Aspiring to the plains of light,
Jerusalem, the saints' abode,
Whose founder is the living God.

4 Patient the appointed race to run,
This weary world we cast behind;
From strength to strength we travel on
The new Jerusalem to find;
Our labour this, our only aim,
To find the new Jerusalem.

5 Through Thee, who all our sins hast borne,
Freely and graciously forgiven,
With songs to Zion we return,
Contending for our native heaven;
That palace of our glorious King,
We find it nearer while we sing.

6 Raised by the breath of love divine,
We urge our way with strength renewed;
The Church of the first-born to join,
We travel to the mount of God,
With joy upon our heads arise,
And meet our Captain in the skies.

Charles Wesley, 1707-88.

611

MANNHEIM. 8.7.8.7.8.7. F. FILITZ, 1804-76.

1 LEAD us, heavenly Father, lead us
O'er the world's tempestuous sea;
Guard us, guide us, keep us, feed us,
For we have no help but Thee,
Yet possessing every blessing
If our God our Father be.

2 Saviour, breathe forgiveness o'er us;
All our weakness Thou dost know;
Thou didst tread this earth before us,
Thou didst feel its keenest woe;
Lone and dreary, faint and weary,
Through the desert Thou didst go.

3 Spirit of our God, descending,
Fill our hearts with heavenly joy,
Love with every passion blending,
Pleasure that can never cloy;
Thus provided, pardoned, guided,
Nothing can our peace destroy.

James Edmeston, 1791-1867.

612

SANDON. 10.4.10.4.10 10. C. H. Purday, 1799-1885.

1 Lead, kindly Light, amid the encircling gloom
Lead Thou me on!
The night is dark, and I am far from home;
Lead Thou me on!
Keep Thou my feet; I do not ask to see
The distant scene: one step enough for me.

2 I was not ever thus, nor prayed that Thou
Shouldst lead me on.
I loved to choose and see my path, but now
Lead Thou me on!
I loved the garish day, and, spite of fears,
Pride ruled my will: remember not past years.

3 So long Thy power hath blest me, sure it still
Will lead me on
O'er moor and fen, o'er crag and torrent, till
The night is gone;
And with the morn those angel faces smile
Which I have loved long since, and lost awhile.

John Henry Newman, 1801-90.

613

ALL SOULS. 10.10.10.10. J. YOAKLEY, 1860-1932.

1 LEAD us, O Father, in the paths of peace;
Without Thy guiding hand we go astray,
And doubts appal, and sorrows still increase;
Lead us through Christ, the true and living way.

2 Lead us, O Father, in the paths of truth;
Unhelped by Thee, in error's maze we grope,
While passion stains and folly dims our youth,
And age comes on uncheered by faith and hope.

3 Lead us, O Father, in the paths of right;
Blindly we stumble when we walk alone,
Involved in shadows of a darksome night,
Only with Thee we journey safely on.

4 Lead us, O Father, to Thy heavenly rest,
However rough and steep the path may be,
Through joy or sorrow, as Thou deemest best,
Until our lives are perfected in Thee. Amen.

William Henry Burleigh, 1812-71.

614

SALVATOR. 8.7.8.7. D. J. P. JEWSON, 1825-89.

1 HEAVENLY Father, Thou hast brought us
Safely to the present day,
Gently leading on our footsteps,
Watching o'er us all the way.
Friend and Guide through life's long journey,
Grateful hearts to Thee we bring;
But for love so true and changeless
How shall we fit praises sing?

2 Mercies new and never-failing
Brightly shine through all the past,
Watchful care and loving-kindness
Always near from first to last,
Tender love, divine protection
Ever with us day and night;
Blessings more than we can number
Strow the path with golden light.

3 Shadows deep have crossed our pathway;
We have trembled in the storm;
Clouds have gathered round so darkly
That we could not see Thy form:
Yet Thy love hath never left us
In our griefs alone to be,
And the help each gave the other
Was the strength that came from Thee.

4 Many that we loved have left us,
Reaching first their journey's end;
Now they wait to give us welcome,
Brother, sister, child, and friend.
When at last our journey's over,
And we pass away from sight,
Father, take us through the darkness
Into everlasting light. Amen.

Hester Periam Hawkins: Home Hymn Book, 1885.

615

CWM RHONDDA (*First Tune*). 8.7.8.7.4.7. J. HUGHES, 1873-1932.

By permission of the widow of the late John Hughes.

ORIEL (*Second Tune*). 8.7.8.7.4.7. ETT'S *Cantica Sacra*, 1840.

Arglwydd, arwain trwy'r anialwch.

1.

GUIDE me, O Thou great Jehovah,
  Pilgrim through this barren land;
I am weak, but Thou art mighty;
  Hold me with Thy powerful hand:
    Bread of heaven!
  Feed me now and evermore.

2.

Open Thou the crystal fountain,
  Whence the healing stream shall flow;
Let the fiery, cloudy pillar
  Lead me all my journey through:
    Strong Deliverer!
  Be Thou still my help and shield.

3.

When I tread the verge of Jordan,
  Bid my anxious fears subside;
Death of death, and hell's Destruction,
  Land me safe on Canaan's side:
    Songs of praises
  I will ever give to Thee.

William Williams, 1717-91;
tr. by Peter Williams, 1722-96.

616

EBENEZER (*First Tune*). 8.7.8.7. D. T. J. WILLIAMS, 1869-1944

MARCHING (*Second Tune*). 8.7.8.7. M. SHAW, 1876-

Igjennem Nat og Traengsel.

1 THROUGH the night of doubt and sorrow,
Onward goes the pilgrim band,
Singing songs of expectation,
Marching to the promised land.

2 Clear before us through the darkness
Gleams and burns the guiding light;
Brother clasps the hand of brother,
Stepping fearless through the night.

3 One the light of God's own presence,
O'er His ransomed people shed,
Chasing far the gloom and terror,
Brightening all the path we tread:

4 One the object of our journey,
One the faith which never tires,
One the earnest looking forward,
One the hope our God inspires:

5 One the strain that lips of thousands
Lift as from the heart of one;
One the conflict, one the peril,
One the march in God begun:

6 One the gladness of rejoicing
On the far eternal shore,
Where the one almighty Father
Reigns in love for evermore.

7 Onward therefore, pilgrim brothers,
Onward with the Cross our aid!
Bear its shame, and fight its battle,
Till we rest beneath its shade.

8 Soon shall come the great awaking,
Soon the rending of the tomb;
Then the scattering of all shadows,
And the end of toil and gloom.

Bernhardt Severin Ingemann, 1789-1862;
tr. by Sabine Baring-Gould, 1834-1924.

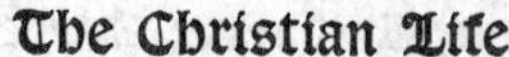

617

ARMAGEDDON. 6.5.6.5. D. and refrain. Adapted by J. Goss, 1800-80.

REFRAIN.

1 Brightly gleams our banner,
 Pointing to the sky,
Waving on Christ's soldiers
 To their home on high.
Marching through the desert,
 Gladly thus we pray,
Still with hearts united
 Singing on our way.

Brightly gleams our banner,
 Pointing to the sky,
Waving on Christ's soldiers
 To their home on high.

2 Jesus, Lord and Master,
 At Thy sacred feet,
Here, with hearts rejoicing,
 See Thy children meet.
Often have we left Thee,
 Often gone astray;
Keep us, mighty Saviour,
 In the narrow way.

3 All our days direct us
 In the way we go;
Lead us on victorious
 Over every foe;
Bid Thine angels shield us
 When the storm-clouds lower;
Pardon Thou and save us
 In the last dread hour.

4 Then with saints and angels
 May we join above,
Offering prayers and praises
 At Thy throne of love.
When the march is over,
 Then come rest and peace,
Jesus in His beauty,
 Songs that never cease.

Thomas Joseph Potter, 1827-73;
William Walsham How, 1823-97, *and others.*

618

KNECHT. 7.6.7.6. J. H. KNECHT, 1752-1817.

May also be sung to CHERRY TREE CAROL, No. 954.

1 O HAPPY band of pilgrims,
If onward ye will tread,
With Jesus as your Fellow,
To Jesus as your Head!

2 O happy if ye labour
As Jesus did for men:
O happy if ye hunger
As Jesus hungered then!

3 The Cross that Jesus carried,
He carried as your due:
The crown that Jesus weareth,
He weareth it for you.

4 The faith by which ye see Him,
The hope in which ye yearn,
The love that through all troubles
To Him alone will turn,

5 The trials that beset you,
The sorrows ye endure,
The manifold temptations
That death alone can cure:

6 What are they but His jewels
Of right celestial worth?
What are they but the ladder
Set up to heaven on earth?

7 O happy band of pilgrims,
Look upward to the skies,
Where such a light affliction
Shall win you such a prize.

John Mason Neale, 1818-66; *based on Joseph the Hymnographer*, 9*th cent.*

619

6.5. (twelve lines).

FORWARD! BE OUR WATCHWORD. H. ALFORD, 1810-71.

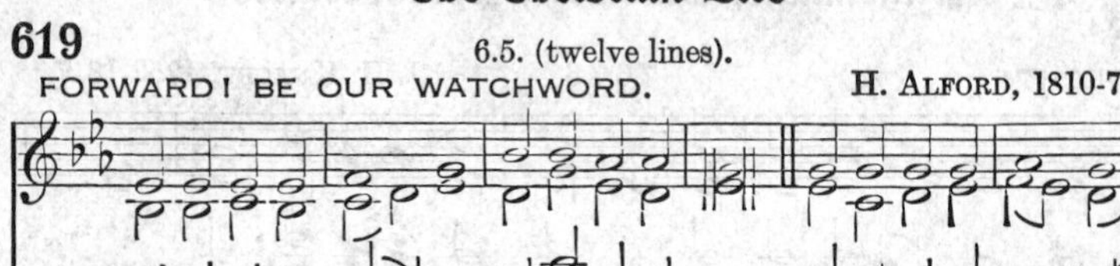

1 FORWARD! be our watchword,
  Steps and voices joined;
Seek the things before us,
  Not a look behind;
Burns the fiery pillar
  At our army's head;
Who shall dream of shrinking,
  By our Captain led?
    Forward through the desert,
      Through the toil and fight;
    Jordan flows before us,
      Zion beams with light.

2 Glories upon glories
  Hath our God prepared,
By the souls that love Him
  One day to be shared;
Eye hath not beheld them
  Ear hath never heard,
Nor of these hath uttered
  Thought or speech a word.
    Forward, ever forward,
      Clad in armour bright,
    Till the veil be lifted,
      Till our faith be sight.

3 Far o'er yon horizon
  Rise the City towers,
Where our God abideth;
  That fair home is ours:
Flash the gates with jasper,
  Shine the streets with gold,
Flows the gladdening river,
  Shedding joys untold.
    Thither, onward thither,
      In the Spirit's might;
    Pilgrims to your country,
      Forward into light.

Henry Alford, 1810-71.

620

MONKS GATE. 6.5.6.5.6 6 6.5. English Traditional Melody.

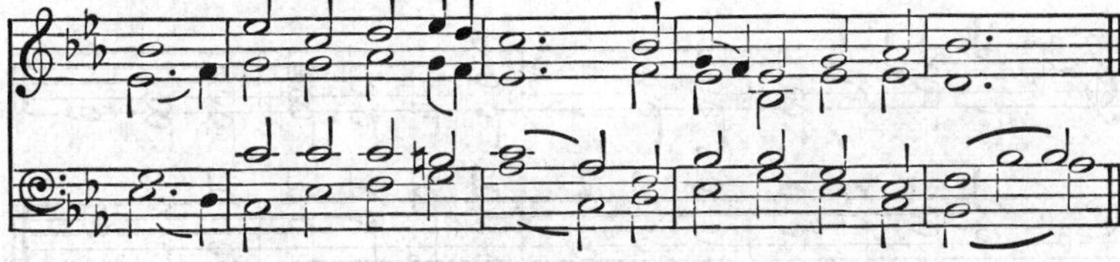

1 Who would true valour see,
Let him come hither;
One here will constant be,
Come wind, come weather;
There's no discouragement
Shall make him once relent
His first avowed intent
To be a pilgrim.

2 Whoso beset him round
With dismal stories,
Do but themselves confound;
His strength the more is.
No lion can him fright,
He'll with a giant fight,
But he will have a right
To be a pilgrim.

3 Hobgoblin nor foul fiend
Can daunt his spirit;
He knows he at the end
Shall life inherit.
Then fancies fly away;
He'll fear not what men say;
He'll labour night and day
To be a pilgrim.

John Bunyan, 1628-88.

621

BREAD OF HEAVEN. 7.7.7.7.7 7. W. D. MACLAGAN, 1826-1910.

1 JESUS the good Shepherd is;
   Jesus died the sheep to save;
He is mine, and I am His;
   All I want in Him I have,
Life, and health, and rest, and food,
All the plenitude of God.

2 Jesus loves and guards His own;
   Me in verdant pastures feeds;
Makes me quietly lie down,
   By the streams of comfort leads:
Following Him where'er He goes,
Silent joy my heart o'erflows.

3 He in sickness makes me whole,
   Guides into the paths of peace;
He revives my fainting soul,
   Stablishes in righteousness;
Who for me vouchsafed to die,
Loves me still—I know not why!

4 Love divine shall still embrace,
   Love shall keep me to the end;
Surely all my happy days
   I shall in Thy temple spend,
Till I to Thy house remove,
Thy eternal house above!

Charles Wesley, 1707-88.

CORDS OF LOVE. 6.4.6.4.10 10. J. BARNBY, 1838-96.

May also be sung to SURSUM CORDA, No. 451.

1 SHOW me the way, O Lord,
And make it plain;
I would obey Thy Word,
Speak yet again;
I will not take one step until I know
Which way it is that Thou wouldst have me go.

2 O Lord, I cannot see!
Vouchsafe me light:
The mist bewilders me,
Impedes my sight:
Hold Thou my hand, and lead me by Thy side;
I dare not go alone: be Thou my Guide.

3 I will be patient, Lord,
Trustful and still;
I will not doubt Thy Word;
My hopes fulfil:
How can I perish, clinging to Thy side,
My Comforter, my Saviour, and my Guide?

Jane Euphemia Saxby, 1811-98.

623

NACHTLIED. 10 10.10 10.10 10. H. SMART, 1813-79.

May also be sung to SONG 1., No. 458.

1 I DARED not hope that Thou wouldst deign to come
And make this lowly heart of mine Thy home,
That Thou wouldst deign, O King of kings, to be
E'en for one hour a sojourner in me:
Yet art Thou always here to help, and bless,
And lift the load of my great sinfulness.

2 I dared not ever hope for such a Guide
To walk with me my faltering steps beside,
To help me when I fall, and, when I stray,
Constrain me gently to the better way:
Yet art Thou always at my side to be
A Counsellor and Comforter to me.

3 I do not always go where Thou dost lead,
I do not always Thy soft whispers heed;
I follow other lights, and, in my sin,
I vex with many a slight my Friend within:
Yet dost Thou not, though grieved, from me depart,
But guardest still Thy place within my heart.

Edwin Hatch, 1835-89.

SPIRE. 5 5.8 8.5 5. A. Drese, 1620-1701.

Jesu geh' voran.

1 Jesus, still lead on,
Till our rest be won,
And, although the way be cheerless,
We will follow, calm and fearless:
Guide us by Thy hand
To our Fatherland.

2 If the way be drear,
If the foe be near,
Let not faithless fears o'ertake us,
Let not love and hope forsake us,
For, through many a foe,
To our home we go.

3 When we seek relief
From a long-felt grief,
When oppressed by new temptations,
Lord increase and perfect patience:
Show us that bright shore
Where we weep no more.

4 When sweet earth and skies
Fade before our eyes; [heaven,
When through death we look to
And our sins are all forgiven,
From Thy bright abode,
Call us home to God.

5 Jesus, still lead on,
Till our rest be won;
Heavenly Leader, still direct us,
Still support, console, protect us,
Till we safely stand
In our Fatherland. Amen.

Nicolaus Ludwig von Zinzendorf, 1700-60;
tr. by Jane Laurie Borthwick [*H.L.L.*], 1813-97.

625

DUNDEE (FRENCH) C.M. *Scottish Psalter*, 1615.

1 I to the hills will lift mine eyes,
From whence doth come mine aid;
My safety cometh from the Lord,
Who heaven and earth hath made.

2 Thy foot He'll not let slide, nor will
He slumber that thee keeps:
Behold, He that keeps Israel,
He slumbers not, nor sleeps.

3 The Lord thee keeps, the Lord thy shade
On thy right hand doth stay:
The moon by night thee shall not [smite,
Nor yet the sun by day.

4 The Lord shall keep thy soul; He [shall
Preserve thee from all ill:
Henceforth thy going out and in
God keep for ever will. Amen.

Scottish Psalter, 1750.

626

ALBANO. C.M. V. Novello, 1781-1861.

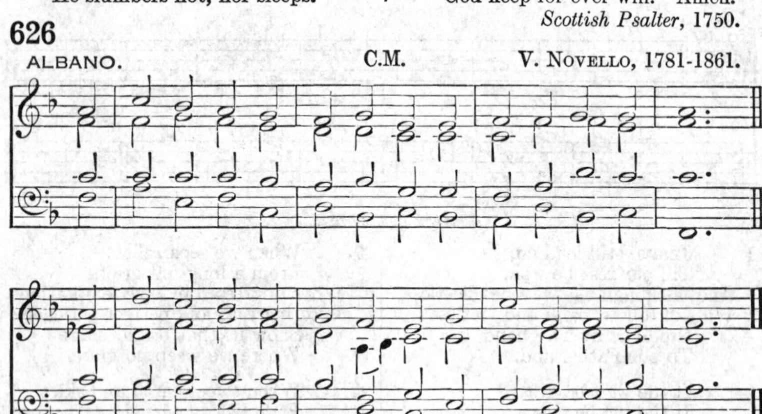

1 I want a principle within
Of jealous, godly fear,
A sensibility of sin,
A pain to feel it near.

2 I want the first approach to feel
Of pride or fond desire,
To catch the wandering of my will,
And quench the kindling fire.

3 That I from Thee no more may part,
No more Thy goodness grieve,
The filial awe, the fleshly heart,
The tender conscience, give.

4 Quick as the apple of an eye,
O God, my conscience make;
Awake my soul when sin is nigh,
And keep it still awake.

5 O may the least omission pain
My well instructed soul,
And drive me to the blood again
Which makes the wounded whole.

Charles Wesley, 1707-88.

627

SPES CELESTIS. D.C.M. W. A. SMITH, 1877.

1 How happy every child of grace,
Who knows his sins forgiven!
This earth, he cries, is not my place,
I seek my place in heaven!
A country far from mortal sight;
Yet O by faith I see
The land of rest, the saints' delight,
The heaven prepared for me.

2 A stranger in the world below,
I calmly sojourn here;
Nor can its happiness or woe
Provoke my hope or fear:
Its evils in a moment end,
Its joys as soon are past;
But O the bliss to which I tend
Eternally shall last.

3 To that Jerusalem above
With singing I repair;
While in the flesh, my hope and love,
My heart and soul, are there:
There my exalted Saviour stands,
My merciful High-priest,
And still extends His wounded hands
To take me to His breast.

4 O what a blessèd hope is ours,
While here on earth we stay,
We more than taste the heavenly [powers,
And antedate that day:
We feel the resurrection near,
Our life in Christ concealed,
And with His glorious presence here
Our earthen vessels filled.

Charles Wesley, 1707-88.

628

TRURO. 7 7.7 7.7 7. W. E. Miller, 1766-1839.

1 Ye that do your Master's will,
Meek in heart, be meeker still:
Day by day your sins confess,
Ye that walk in righteousness:
Gracious souls in grace abound,
Seek the Lord, whom ye have found.

2 Sing ye happy souls, that press
Toward the height of holiness;
All His promises receive,
All the grace He hath to give;
Follow on, nor slack your pace
Till ye see His glorious face.

Charles Wesley, 1707-88.

629

ST. AUSTIN. C.M. English Traditional Melody.

1 All as God wills, who wisely heeds
To give or to withhold,
And knoweth more of all my needs
Than all my prayers have told.

2 Enough that blessings undeserved
Have marked my erring track;
That whereso'er my feet have swerved,
His chastening turned me back;

3 That more and more a providence
Of love is understood,
Making the springs of time and sense
Sweet with eternal good;

4 That death seems but a covered way
Which opens into light
Wherein no blinded child can stray
Beyond the Father's sight;

5 That care and trial seem at last,
Through memory's sunset air,
Like mountain ranges overpast,
In purple distance fair;

6 That all the jarring notes of life
Seem blending in a psalm,
And all the angles of its strife
Slow rounding into calm.

7 And so the shadows fall apart,
And so the west winds play;
And all the windows of my heart
I open to the day.

John Greenleaf Whittier, 1807-92.

630

ALSTONE. L.M. C. E. Willing, 1830-1904.

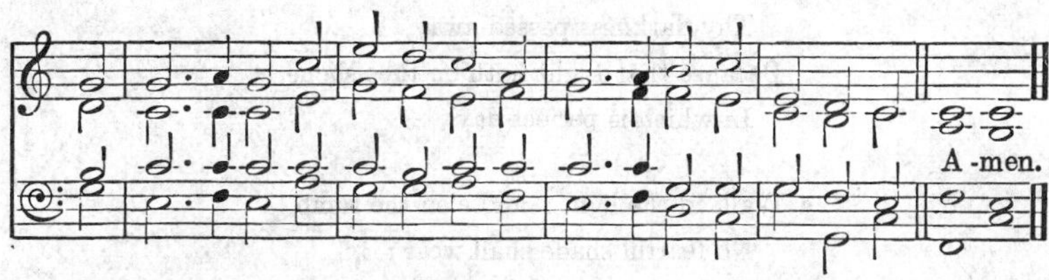

1 O grant us light, that we may know
The wisdom Thou alone canst give;
That truth may guide where'er we go
And virtue bless where'er we live.

2 O grant us light, that we may see,
Where error lurks in human lore,
And turn our doubting minds to Thee,
And love Thy simple Word the more.

3 O grant us light, that we may learn
How dead is life from Thee apart;
How sure is joy for all who turn
To Thee an undivided heart.

4 O grant us light, in grief and pain,
To lift our burdened hearts above,
And count the very cross a gain,
And bless our Father's hidden love.

5 O grant us light, when soon or late
All earthly scenes shall pass away,
In Thee to find the open gate
To deathless home and endless day. Amen.

Lawrence Tuttiett, 1825-97.

631

TILTEY ABBEY. C.M. A. H. BROWN, 1830-1926.

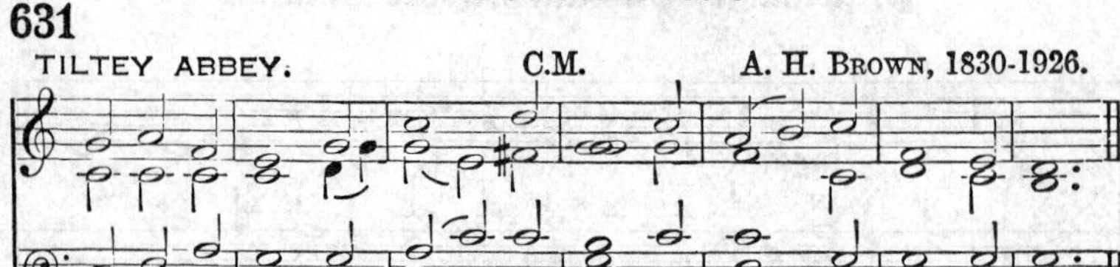

1 WALK in the light: so shalt thou know
 That fellowship of love
His Spirit only can bestow,
 Who reigns in light above.

2 Walk in the light: and thou shalt find
 Thy heart made truly His,
Who dwells in cloudless light enshrined,
 In whom no darkness is.

3 Walk in the light: and thou shalt own
 Thy darkness passed away,
Because that Light hath on thee shone,
 In which is perfect day.

4 Walk in the light: and e'en the tomb
 No fearful shade shall wear;
Glory shall chase away its gloom,
 For Christ hath conquered there.

5 Walk in the light: and thine shall be
 A path, though thorny, bright;
For God, by grace, shall dwell in thee,
 And God Himself is Light.

Bernard Barton, 1784-1849.

SLANE.

UNISON. Irregular. Irish Traditional Melody.

HARMONY.

A- men.

* The note-values of this bar apply to verses 1 and 4. The remaining verses should be sung as under:—

Verse 2. Wis - - dom,
Verse 3. bat - tle - shield,
Verse 5. heaven, . . . af - ter

Rob tu mo bhoile, a Comdi cride.

1 Be Thou my Vision, O Lord of my heart;
Naught be all else to me, save that Thou art—
Thou my best thought, by day or by night,
Waking or sleeping, Thy presence my light.

2 Be Thou my Wisdom, Thou my true Word;
I ever with Thee, Thou with me, Lord;
Thou my great Father, I Thy true son;
Thou in me dwelling, and I with Thee one.

3 Be Thou my battle-shield, sword for the fight,
Be Thou my dignity, Thou my delight.
Thou my soul's shelter, Thou my high tower:
Raise Thou me heavenward, O Power of my power.

4 Riches I heed not, nor man's empty praise,
Thou mine inheritance, now and always:
Thou and Thou only, first in my heart,
High King of heaven, my treasure Thou art.

5 High King of heaven, after victory won,
May I reach heaven's joys, O bright heaven's Sun!
Heart of my own heart, whatever befall,
Still be my Vision, O Ruler of all. Amen.

Ancient Irish, tr. by Mary Elizabeth Byrne, 1880-1931;
versified by Eleanor Henrietta Hull, 1860-1935

633

ST. CYRIL. 10 10. C. VINCENT, 1852-1934

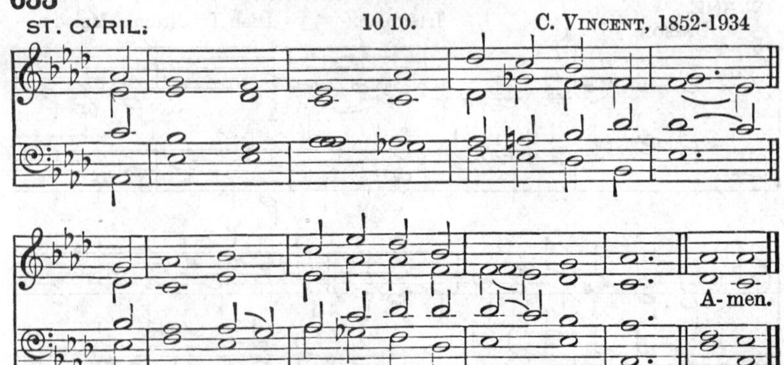

1 O KING of mercy, from Thy throne on high
Look down in love, and hear our humble cry.

2 Thou tender Shepherd of the blood-bought sheep,
Thy feeble wandering flock in safety keep.

3 O gentle Saviour, by Thy death we live;
To contrite sinners life eternal give.

4 Thou art the Bread of heaven, on Thee we feed;
Be near to help our souls in time of need.

5 Thou art the mourner's Stay, the sinner's Friend,
Sweet Fount of joy and blessings without end.

6 O come and cheer us with Thy heavenly grace;
Reveal the brightness of Thy glorious face.

7 In cooling cloud by day, in fire by night,
Be near our steps, and make our darkness light.

8 Go where we go, abide where we abide,
In life, in death, our Comfort, Strength and Guide.

9 O lead us daily with Thine eye of love,
And bring us safely to our home above. Amen.

Thomas Rawson Birks, 1810-83.

634

Irregular and refrain.

WILL YOUR ANCHOR HOLD? W. J. KIRKPATRICK, 1838-1921.

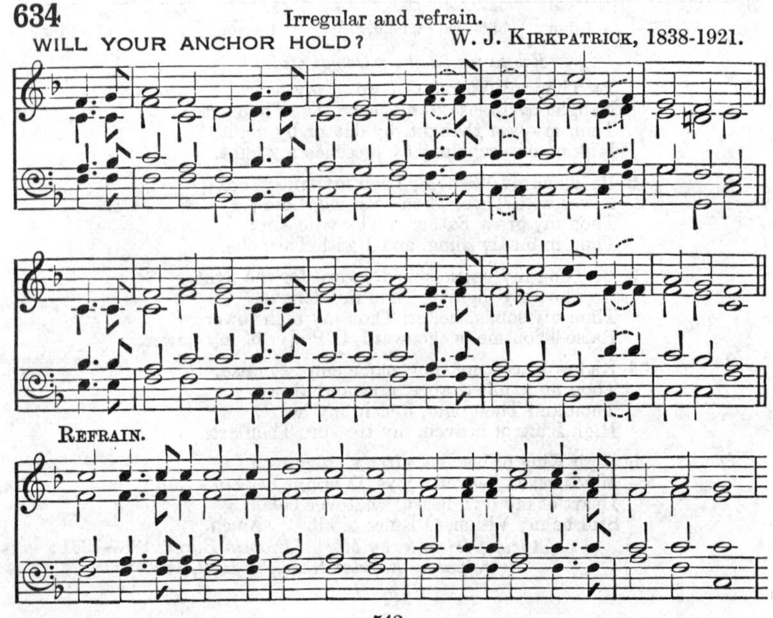

1 WILL your anchor hold in the storms of life,
When the clouds unfold their wings of strife ?
When the strong tides lift, and the cables strain,
Will your anchor drift, or firm remain ?

We have an anchor that keeps the soul
Steadfast and sure while the billows roll ;
Fastened to the Rock which cannot move,
Grounded firm and deep in the Saviour's love !

2 Will your anchor hold in the straits of fear ?
When the breakers roar and the reef is near ;
While the surges rave, and the wild winds blow,
Shall the angry waves then your bark o'erflow ?

3 Will your anchor hold in the floods of death,
When the waters cold chill your latest breath ?
On the rising tide you can never fail,
While your anchor holds within the veil.

4 Will your eyes behold through the morning light
The city of gold and the harbour bright ?
Will you anchor safe by the heavenly shore,
When life's storms are past for evermore ?

Priscilla Jane Owens, 1829-99.

635

POTSDAM. S.M. From J. S. BACH, 1685-1750.

1 JESU, my Truth, my Way,
My sure, unerring Light,
On Thee my feeble steps I stay,
Which Thou wilt guide aright.

2 My Wisdom and my Guide,
My Counsellor Thou art ;
O never let me leave Thy side,
Or from Thy paths depart !

3 Teach me the happy art
In all things to depend
On Thee ; O never, Lord, depart,
But love me to the end !

4 Through fire and water bring
Into the wealthy place ;
And teach me the new song to sing,
When perfected in grace.

5 O make me all like Thee,
Before I hence remove !
Settle, confirm, and stablish me,
And build me up in love.

6 Let me Thy witness live,
When sin is all destroyed ;
And then my spotless soul receive,
And take me home to God.
Amen.

Charles Wesley, 1707-88.

BARTON. 10.4.10.4.10 10. J. T. LIGHTWOOD, 1856-1944

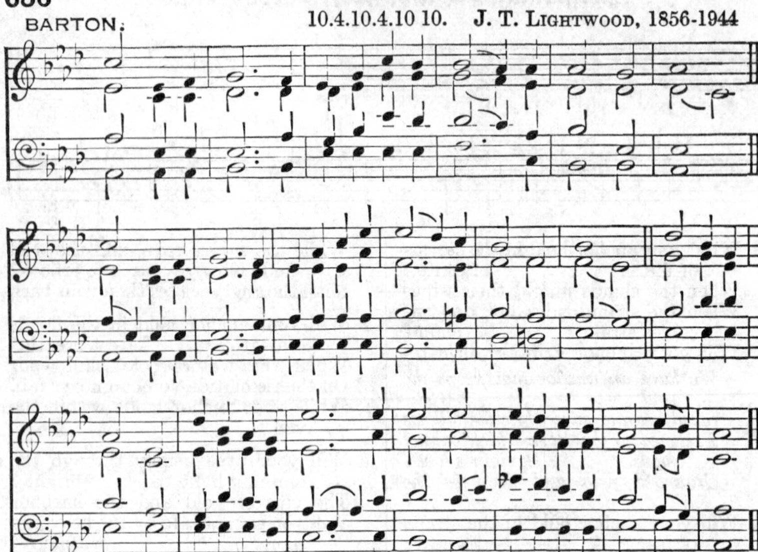

May also be sung to SANDON, No. 612.

1 LIGHT of the world, faint were our weary feet
With wandering far;
But Thou didst come our lonely hearts to greet,
O Morning Star; [on high,
And Thou didst bid us lift our gaze
To see the glory of the glowing sky.

2 In days long past we missed our homeward way;
We could not see;
Blind were our eyes, our feet were bound to stray:
How blind to Thee!
But Thou didst pity, Lord, our gloomy plight;
And Thou didst touch our eyes, and give them sight.

3 Now hallelujahs rise along the road
Our glad feet tread;
Thy love hath shared our sorrow's heavy load;
There's light o'erhead:
Glory to Thee whose love hath led us on,
Glory for all the great things Thou hast done.

4 Where is death's sting, where, grave, thy victory,
Where all the pain,
Now that thy King the veil that hung o'er thee
Hath rent in twain?
Light of the world, we hear Thee bid us come [home.
To light and love in Thine eternal

Laura Ormiston Chant, 1848-1923.

637

RUTHERFORD. 7.6.7.6.7.6.7.5. C. D'URHAN, 1790-1845.

1 The sands of time are sinking;
The dawn of heaven breaks;
The summer morn I've sighed for,
The fair, sweet morn, awakes.
Dark, dark hath been the midnight;
But day-spring is at hand,
And glory, glory dwelleth
In Immanuel's land.

2 The King there, in His beauty,
Without a veil is seen;
It were a well-spent journey,
Though seven deaths lay between:
The Lamb, with His fair army,
Doth on Mount Zion stand,
And glory, glory dwelleth
In Immanuel's land.

3 O Christ! He is the fountain,
The deep, sweet well of love;
The streams on earth I've tasted
More deep I'll drink above;
There to an ocean fullness
His mercy doth expand,
And glory, glory dwelleth
In Immanuel's land.

4 With mercy and with judgement
My web of time He wove,
And aye the dews of sorrow
Were lustred by His love;
I'll bless the hand that guided,
I'll bless the heart that planned,
When throned where glory dwelleth
In Immanuel's land.

Anne Ross Cousin, 1824-1906.

638

ST. AUGUSTINE. S.M. J. S. Bach's *Choralgesänge*, 1784-7

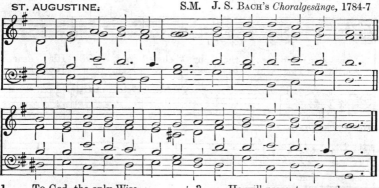

1 To God, the only Wise,
Our Saviour and our King,
Let all the saints below the skies
Their humble praises bring.

2 'Tis His almighty love,
His counsels, and His care,
Preserve us safe from sin and death,
And every hurtful snare.

3 He will present our souls,
Unblemished and complete,
Before the glory of His face,
With joys divinely great.

4 Then all the chosen seed
Shall meet around the throne,
Shall bless the conduct of His grace,
And make His wonders known.

Isaac Watts, 1674-1748.

Also:

30 From glory to glory
52 O Love of God
69 This, this is the God
76 The King of love [ground
89 Christ, of all my hopes the
132 As with gladness
135 Stupendous height
169 My Saviour, Thou
238 My faith looks up
282 Spirit of wisdom
404 How blest is life
515 Thy way, not mine
569 Thine for ever!
696 Children of the heavenly King

639 *DEATH, JUDGEMENT, THE FUTURE LIFE*

CAMBRIDGE. 6 6.6.5.6.5. C. WOOD, 1866-1926.

ORGAN.
Ped.
VOICES. HARMONY.
1. CHRIST, who knows all . . His sheep, Will all . . in safe - ty
take my spi - rit, I trust Thy life and
keep; He will not lose His blood, Nor in - ter -
mer - it; Take home this wand - 'ring sheep, For Thou hast
- ces - sion: Nor we . . the pur - chased good, Of His dear
sought it: This soul in safe - ty keep, For Thou hast
Small notes Organ.
pas - sion.
bought it.
ORGAN.

Unison.
2. I know my God is just, To Him I whol - ly
Fine (small notes).
trust All that I have, and am, All that I hope for:
All's sure and seen to Him, Which I . . here grope for.
Harmony.
3. Lord Je - sus,

Richard Baxter, 1615-91.

N.B.—If desired, the music of this hymn can follow verse 1 throughout.

640

CROSSING THE BAR. Irregular. J. F. BRIDGE, 1844-1924.

1. SUN-SET and eve-ning star, And one clear call for
moan-ing of the bar, *cresc.*
me! And may there be no moan - - ing When
moan-ing of the bar, *cresc.*
moan - - ing
I put out to sea, But such a tide as mov - ing
rall.
seems a - sleep, Too full for sound and foam, When
seems a - sleep, Too full for sound and foam,
Adagio.
that which drew from out the bound-less deep Turns a-gain home.

2. Twi-light and eve-ning bell, And af-ter that the dark! And
sad-ness of fare-well When I em-
may there be no sad - - ness When I em
sad-ness of fare-well . .
sad - - ness When I em - -
- bark; For though from out our bourne . . . of time . . and
place The flood may bear me far, I hope to see my
place The flood may bear me far,
Adagio.
Pi-lot face to face When I have crost the bar.
Alfred Tennyson, 1809-92.
p
cresc.
f
rall
pp

T

641

ANNUE CHRISTE. LA FEILLÉE,
UNISON. *In free rhythm.* 6.6.6.6. D. *Méthode du Plain-Chant*, 1808.

May also be sung to MOAB, No. 515.

1 WHILE ebbing nature grieves,
My God, my portion be,
Until the hour which gives
My spirit unto Thee.
When flesh and life decline,
Stretch out Thy hand and take
My nature into Thine,
Till I in Thee awake.

2 The morning sun will glow,
The evening light will die;
So change the lights below,
They never change on high.
Friend turns from friend his face,
One mourns upon the shore;
But from Thy holy place
Thy sons go out no more.

3 The cloud broods o'er us still;
We hope, yet fear to fall;
We long toward yonder hill
Whence comes the help of all:
It glimmers through the night
The dead have overpast
To Thee the dawning Light;
O fail us not at last! Amen.

James Smetham, 1821-89.

GIFFORD. 11.10.11.6. T. C. L. PRITCHARD, 1885-

Verses 1-4.
D.S.
Organ.
Verse 5.
The life for which I long, The life for which I long. A - men.

1 WHEN on my day of life the night is falling,
And in the winds, from unsunned spaces blown,
I hear far voices out of darkness calling
My feet to paths unknown,

2 Be near me when all else is from me drifting—
Earth, sky, home's pictures, days of shade and shine,
And kindly faces, to my own uplifting
The love which answers mine.

3 I have but Thee, my Father; let Thy Spirit
Be with me then to comfort and uphold;
No gate of pearl, no branch of palm I merit,
Nor street of shining gold.

4 Suffice it if—my good and ill unreckoned,
And both forgiven through Thy abounding grace—
I find myself by hands familiar beckoned
Unto my fitting place,

5 There, from the music round about me stealing,
I fain would learn the new and holy song,
And find at last, beneath Thy trees of healing,
The life for which I long. Amen.

John Greenleaf Whittier, 1807-92.

643

PRESSBURG. 7 7.7 7.7 7.

FREYLINGHAUSEN'S *Gesangbuch*, 1714.

A-men.

1 WHEN this passing world is done,
When has sunk yon glaring sun,
When we stand with Christ in glory,
Looking o'er life's finished story,
Then, Lord, shall I fully know,
Not till then, how much I owe.

2 When I stand before the throne,
Dressed in beauty not my own,
When I see Thee as Thou art,
Love Thee with unsinning heart,
Then, Lord, shall I fully know,
Not till then, how much I owe.

3 When the praise of heaven I hear,
Loud as thunders to the ear,
Loud as many waters' noise,
Sweet as harp's melodious voice,
Then, Lord, shall I fully know,
Not till then, how much I owe.

4 Chosen not for good in me,
Wakened up from wrath to flee,
Hidden in the Saviour's side,
By the Spirit sanctified,
Teach me, Lord, on earth to show,
By my love, how much I owe. Amen.

Robert Murray McCheyne, 1813-43.

644

DINBYCH. D.S.M. J. PARRY, 1841-1903.

1 THOU Judge of quick and dead,
Before whose bar severe,
With holy joy, or guilty dread,
We all shall soon appear:
Our cautioned souls prepare
For that tremendous day,
And fill us now with watchful care,
And stir us up to pray.

2 To pray, and wait the hour,
That awful hour unknown,
When robed in majesty and power,
Thou shalt from heaven come down,
The immortal Son of Man,
To judge the human race,
With all Thy Father's dazzling train,
With all Thy glorious grace.

3 O may we thus be found
Obedient to His word,
Attentive to the trumpet's sound,
And looking for our Lord.
O may we thus ensure
A lot among the blest;
And watch a moment to secure
An everlasting rest. Amen.

Charles Wesley, 1707-88.

645

LLEF. L.M. G. H. JONES, 1849-1919.

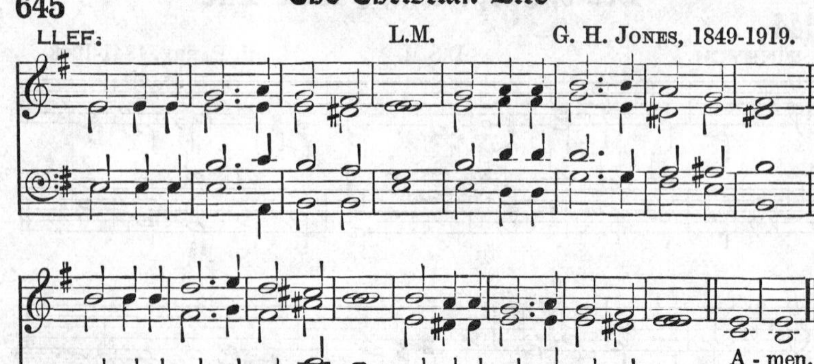

1 THAT day of wrath, that dreadful day
When heaven and earth shall pass away:
What power shall be the sinner's stay?
How shall we meet that dreadful day?

2 When, shrivelling like a parchèd scroll,
The flaming heavens together roll,
When louder yet, and yet more dread,
Swells the high trump that wakes the dead.

3 O! On that day, that wrathful day,
When man to judgement wakes from clay,
Be Thou, O Christ, the sinner's stay,
Though heaven and earth shall pass away. Amen.

Walter Scott, 1771-1832.

646

DIES IRÆ. 888. A. H. BROWN, 1830-1926.

Dies iræ, dies illa.

1 DAY of wrath! O day of mourning!
See fulfilled the prophet's warning,
Heaven and earth to ashes burning.

2 O what fear man's bosom rendeth,
When from heaven the Judge descendeth,
On whose sentence all dependeth.

3 Wondrous sound the trumpet flingeth,
Through earth's sepulchres it ringeth,
All before the throne it bringeth.

4 Death is struck, and nature quaking,
All creation is awaking,
To its Judge an answer making.

5 Lo! The Book, exactly worded,
Wherein all hath been recorded;
Thence shall judgement be awarded.

6 When the Judge His seat attaineth
And each hidden deed arraigneth,
Nothing unavenged remaineth.

7 What shall I, frail man, be pleading,
Who for me be interceding,
When the just are mercy needing?

8 King of majesty tremendous,
Who dost free salvation send us,
Fount of pity, then befriend us.

9 Think, good Jesu, my salvation
Caused Thy wondrous incarnation;
Leave me not to reprobation.

10 Faint and weary Thou hast sought me,
On the Cross of suffering bought me;
Shall such grace be vainly brought me?

11 Righteous Judge; for sin's pollution
Grant Thy gift of absolution,
Ere that day of retribution.

12 Guilty, now I pour my moaning,
All my shame with anguish owning;
Spare, O God, Thy suppliant groaning.

13 Thou the sinful woman savèdst,
Thou the dying thief forgavest,
And to me a hope vouchsafest.

14 Worthless are my prayers and sighing;
Yet, good Lord, in grace complying,
Rescue me from fires undying.

15 With Thy favoured sheep O place me,
Nor among the goats abase me,
But to Thy right hand upraise me.

16 Low I kneel, with heart-submission;
See, like ashes, my contrition;
Help me in my last condition.

17 Ah, that day of tears and mourning!
From the dust of earth returning,
Man for judgement must prepare him.

18 Spare, O God, in mercy spare him.
Lord all pitying, Jesu blest
Grant us Thine eternal rest!
Amen.

Thomas of Celano, 13*th cent.*;
tr. by William Josiah Irons, 1812-83.

647

CHESHIRE. C.M. ESTE'S *Psalter*, 1592.

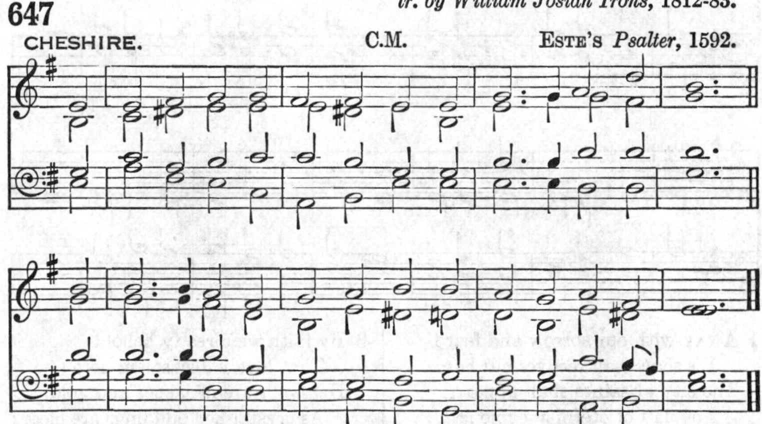

1 LORD, it belongs not to my care
Whether I die or live;
To love and serve Thee is my share,
And this Thy grace must give.

2 If life be long, I will be glad
That I may long obey;
If short, yet why should I be sad
To soar to endless day?

3 Christ leads me through no darker rooms
Than He went through before;
He that into God's kingdom comes
Must enter by this door.

4 Come, Lord, when grace has made me meet
Thy blessèd face to see;
For if Thy work on earth be sweet,
What will Thy glory be?

5 Then shall I end my sad complaints,
And weary, sinful days,
And join with the triumphant saints
That sing Jehovah's praise.

6 My knowledge of that life is small,
The eye of faith is dim;
But 'tis enough that Christ knows all,
And I shall be with Him.

Richard Baxter, 1615-91.

648

8.8.8.8. D.

HYMN OF EVE (UXBRIDGE). ARNE'S *Death of Abel*, 1755.

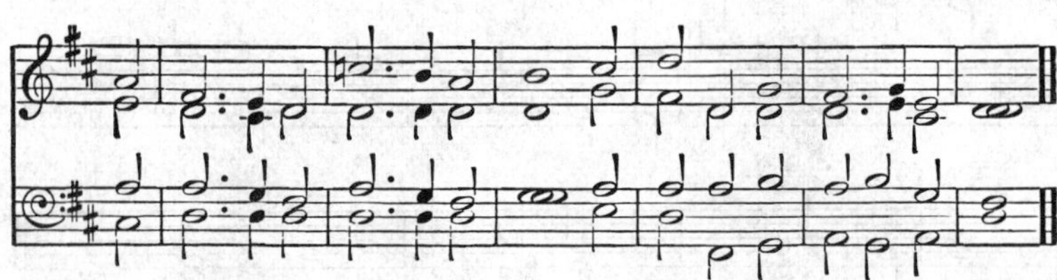

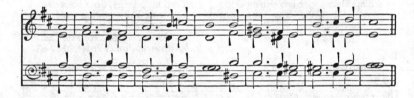

1 AWAY with our sorrow and fear!
 We soon shall recover our home,
The city of saints shall appear,
 The day of eternity come:
From earth we shall quickly remove,
 And mount to our native abode,
The house of our Father above,
 The palace of angels and God.

2 Our mourning is all at an end,
 When, raised by the life-giving word,
We see the new city descend,
 Adorned as a bride for her Lord;
The city so holy and clean,
 No sorrow can breathe in the air;
No gloom of affliction or sin,
 No shadow of evil is there.

3 By faith we already behold
 That lovely Jerusalem here;
Her walls are of jasper and gold,
 As crystal her buildings are clear:
Immovably founded in grace,
 She stands as she ever hath stood,
And brightly her Builder displays,
 And flames with the glory of God.

4 No need of the sun in that day,
 Which never is followed by night,
Where Jesus's beauties display
 A pure and a permanent light:
The Lamb is their light and their sun,
 And lo, by reflection they shine,
With Jesus ineffably one,
 And bright in effulgence divine.

Charles Wesley, 1707-88.

BEULAH. C.M. G. M. GARRETT, 1834-97.

1 THERE is a land of pure delight,
Where saints immortal reign;
Infinite day excludes the night,
And pleasures banish pain.

2 There everlasting spring abides,
And never-withering flowers;
Death, like a narrow sea, divides
This heavenly land from ours.

3 Sweet fields beyond the swelling flood
Stand dressed in living green;
So to the Jews old Canaan stood,
While Jordan rolled between.

4 But timorous mortals start and [shrink
To cross this narrow sea,
And linger, shivering on the brink,
And fear to launch away.

5 O could we make our doubts remove,
Those gloomy thoughts that rise,
And see the Canaan that we love
With unbeclouded eyes:

6 Could we but climb where Moses stood,
And view the landscape o'er, [flood,
Not Jordan's stream, nor death's cold
Should fright us from the shore!

Isaac Watts, 1674-1748.

650

JERUSALEM. C.M. S. GROSVENOR, *c.* 1840.

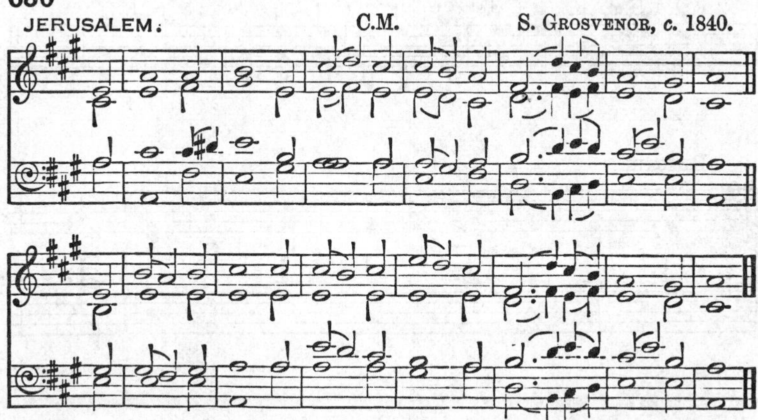

1 JERUSALEM, my happy home,
Name ever dear to me!
When shall my labours have an end,
In joy, and peace, and thee?

2 When shall these eyes thy heaven-built [walls
And pearly gates behold,
Thy bulwarks with salvation strong,
And streets of shining gold?

3 There happier bowers than Eden's [bloom,
Nor sin nor sorrow know:
Blest seats, through rude and stormy [scenes
I onward press to you.

4 Why should I shrink at pain and woe,
Or feel, at death, dismay?
I've Canaan's goodly land in view,
And realms of endless day.

5 Apostles, martyrs, prophets there
Around my Saviour stand;
And soon my friends in Christ below
Will join the glorious band.

6 Jerusalem, my happy home,
My soul still pants for thee!
Then shall my labours have an end,
When I thy joys shall see.

Joseph Bromehead, 1748-1826.

651

11.10.11.10. and refrain.

LA SUISSESSE (*First Tune*). J. N. GOULÉ, 1774-1818.

1.

Hark! hark, my soul! Angelic songs are swelling
O'er earth's green fields and ocean's wave-beat shore:
How sweet the truth those blessèd strains are telling
Of that new life when sin shall be no more!

Angels of Jesus, angels of light,
Singing to welcome the pilgrims of the night!

2.

Onward we go; for still we hear them singing:
Come, weary souls, for Jesus bids you come;
And through the dark, its echoes sweetly ringing,
The music of the gospel leads us home.

3.

Far, far away, like bells at evening pealing,
The voice of Jesus sounds o'er land and sea,
And laden souls, by thousands meekly stealing,
Kind Shepherd, turn their weary steps to Thee.

4.

Rest comes at length; though life be long and dreary,
The day must dawn and darksome night be past;
Faith's journey ends in welcomes to the weary,
And heaven, the heart's true home, will come at last.

5.

Angels, sing on, your faithful watches keeping;
Sing us sweet fragments of the songs above,
Till morning's joy shall end the night of weeping,
And life's long shadows break in cloudless love.

Frederick William Faber, 1814-63.

651 11.10.11.10. and refrain.

PILGRIMS (*Second Tune*). H. SMART, 1813-79.

1.

HARK! hark, my soul! Angelic songs are swelling
O'er earth's green fields and ocean's wave-beat shore:
How sweet the truth those blessèd strains are telling
Of that new life when sin shall be no more!

Angels of Jesus, angels of light,
Singing to welcome the pilgrims of the night!

2.

Onward we go; for still we hear them singing:
Come, weary souls, for Jesus bids you come;
And through the dark, its echoes sweetly ringing,
The music of the gospel leads us home.

3.

Far, far away, like bells at evening pealing,
The voice of Jesus sounds o'er land and sea,
And laden souls, by thousands meekly stealing,
Kind Shepherd, turn their weary steps to Thee.

4.

Rest comes at length; though life be long and dreary,
The day must dawn and darksome night be past;
Faith's journey ends in welcomes to the weary,
And heaven, the heart's true home, will come at last.

5.

Angels, sing on, your faithful watches keeping;
Sing us sweet fragments of the songs above,
Till morning's joy shall end the night of weeping,
And life's long shadows break in cloudless love.

Frederick William Faber, 1814-63.

652

EWING (*First Tune*). 7.6.7.6. D. A. Ewing, 1830-95.

ST. ALPHEGE (*Second Tune*). 7.6.7.6. H. J. Gauntlett, 1805-76.

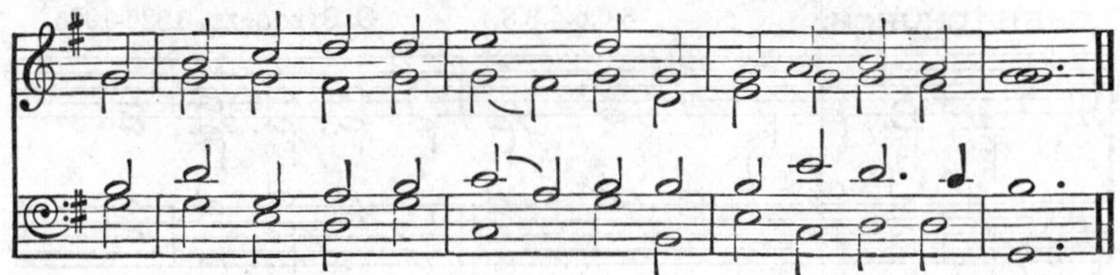

Hora novissima.

1 Brief life is here our portion,
Brief sorrow, short-lived care;
The life that knows no ending,
The tearless life, is there.
O happy retribution!
Short toil, eternal rest;
For mortals and for sinners,
A mansion with the blest!

2 That we should look, poor wanderers
To have our home on high!
That worms should seek for dwellings
Beyond the starry sky!
And now we fight the battle,
But then shall wear the crown
Of full and everlasting
And passionless renown.

3 And now we watch and struggle,
And now we live in hope,
And Zion in her anguish
With Babylon must cope;
But He whom now we trust in
Shall then be seen and known,
And they that know and see Him
Shall have Him for their own.

4 O sweet and blessèd country,
The home of God's elect!
O sweet and blessèd country,
That eager hearts expect!
Jesu, in mercy bring us
To that dear land of rest,
Who art, with God the Father
And Spirit, ever blest.

* * * *

5 Jerusalem the golden,
With milk and honey blessed,
Beneath thy contemplation
Sink heart and voice oppressed.
I know not, O I know not,
What joys await us there,
What radiancy of glory,
What bliss beyond compare!

6 They stand, those halls of Zion,
All jubilant with song,
And bright with many an angel
And all the martyr throng;
The Prince is ever in them;
The daylight is serene;
The pastures of the blessèd
Are decked in glorious sheen.

7 There is the throne of David,
And there, from care released,
The shout of them that triumph,
The song of them that feast;
And they who, with their Leader,
Have conquered in the fight,
For ever and for ever
Are clad in robes of white.

8 Strive, man, to win that glory;
Toil, man, to gain that light;
Send hope before to grasp it,
Till hope be lost in sight.
Exult, O dust and ashes;
The Lord shall be thy part:
His only, His for ever
Thou shalt be, and thou art.

Bernard of Cluny, *12th cent.*;
tr. by John Mason Neale, 1818-66.

653

CHRISTCHURCH. 6.6.6.6.8.8. C. STEGGALL, 1826-1905.

1 SWEET place: sweet place alone!
The court of God most high,
The heaven of heavens, the throne
Of spotless majesty!
O happy place! When shall I be
My God, with Thee, to see Thy face?

2 There dwells my Lord, my King,
Judged here unfit to live;
There angels to Him sing,
And lowly homage give.

3 The patriarchs of old
There from their travels cease;
The prophets there behold
Their longed-for Prince of Peace.

4 The Lamb's apostles there
I might with joy behold;
The harpers I might hear
Harping on harps of gold.

5 The faithful martyrs, they
Within those courts are found;
All clothed in pure array,
Their scars with glory crowned.

6 Jerusalem on high
My song and city is,
My home whene'er I die,
The centre of my bliss.

Samuel Crossman, c. 1624-83.

654

HOMELAND.
Irregular.
A. SULLIVAN, 1842-1900.
1. THE home - land! The home - land! The land of the free - born;
2. My Lord is in the home - land, With an - gels bright and fair;
3. For those I love in the home - land Are call - ing me a - way
There's no . . . night in the home - land, But aye the fade - less morn;
There's no . . . sin in the home - land, And no temp - ta - tion there;
To the rest and peace of the home - land, And the life be - yond de - cay:
I'm sigh - ing for the home - land, My heart is ach - ing here;
The voi - ces of the home - land Are ring - ing in my ears,
For there's no . . . death in the home - land, There is no grief a - bove:
There's no . . pain in the home - land, To which I'm draw - ing near.
And when I think of the home - land, My eyes are filled with tears.
Christ bring us all to the home - land Of His e - ter - nal love. A - men.
Hugh Reginald Haweis, 1839-1901.

655

BOCKING (*First Tune*). C.M. F. L. Wiseman, 1858-1944

A - men.

DIANA (*Second Tune*). C.M. 16th Century Air.

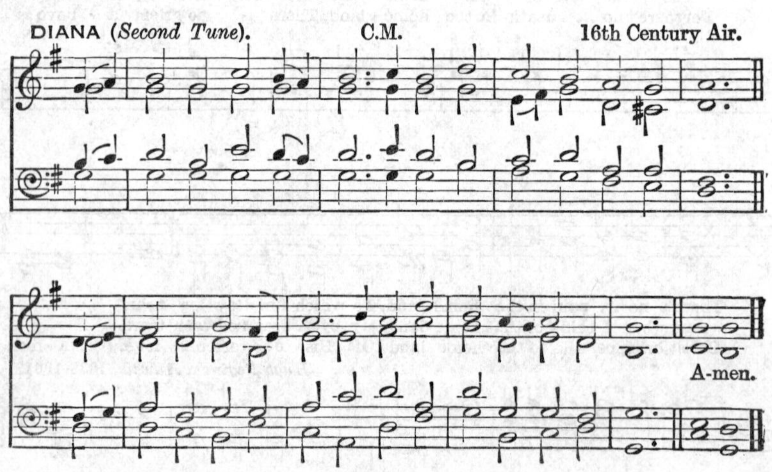

1 JERUSALEM, my happy home,
When shall I come to thee ?
When shall my sorrows have an end ?
Thy joys when shall I see ?

2 O happy harbour of the saints !
O sweet and pleasant soil !
In thee no sorrow may be found,
No grief, no care, no toil.

3 Thy walls are made of precious stones,
Thy bulwarks diamonds square ;
Thy gates are of right orient pearl,
Exceeding rich and rare ;

4 Thy turrets and thy pinnacles
With carbuncles do shine ;
Thy very streets are paved with gold
Surpassing clear and fine.

5 Thy vineyards and thy orchards are
Most beautiful and fair,
Full furnishèd with trees and fruits
Most wonderful and rare.

6 Thy gardens and thy gallant walks
Continually are green,
There grow such sweet and pleasant flowers
As nowhere else are seen.

7 Quite through the streets with silver sound,
The flood of life doth flow ;
Upon whose banks on every side
The wood of life doth grow.

8 Thy saints are crowned with glory great,
They see God face to face ;
They triumph still, they still rejoice,
Most happy is their case.

9 There David stands with harp in hand
As master of the quire,
Ten thousand times that man were blest
That might this music hear.

10 There Magdalene hath left her moan,
And cheerfully doth sing
With blessèd Saints, whose harmony
In every street doth ring.

11 Jerusalem, Jerusalem,
God grant me once to see
Thy endless joys, and of the same
Partaker aye to be. Amen.

F.B.P., 16*th or* 17*th cent.*

656

GLORY. 8.6.8.6. and refrain. *The Tune Book*, 1842.

REFRAIN.

1 AROUND the throne of God in heaven
  Thousands of children stand,
Children, whose sins are all forgiven,
  A holy, happy band,
    Singing: Glory, glory, glory!

2 In flowing robes of spotless white
  See every one arrayed,
Dwelling in everlasting light
  And joys that never fade.

3 What brought them to that world above,
  That heaven so bright and fair,
Where all is peace, and joy, and love?
  How came those children there?

4 Because the Saviour shed His blood
  To wash away their sin;
Bathed in that pure and precious flood,
  Behold them white and clean.

5 On earth they sought the Saviour's grace,
  On earth they loved His name;
So now they see His blessèd face,
  And stand before the Lamb.

Anne Shepherd, 1809-57.

657

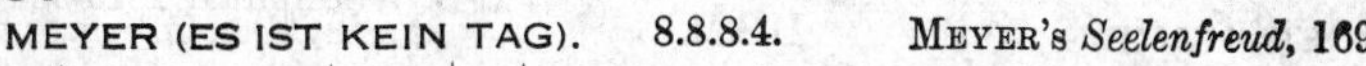

MEYER (ES IST KEIN TAG). 8.8.8.4. MEYER's *Seelenfreud*, 1692

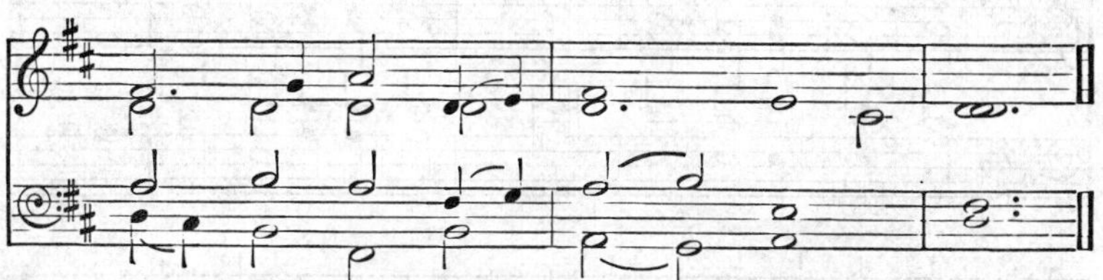

1 For those we love within the veil,
Who once were comrades of our way,
We thank Thee, Lord; for they have won
To cloudless day;

2 And life for them is life indeed,
The splendid goal of earth's strait race;
And where no shadows intervene
They see Thy face.

3 Not as we knew them any more,
Toilworn, and sad with burdened care—
Erect, clear-eyed, upon their brows
Thy name they bear.

4 Free from the fret of mortal years,
And knowing now Thy perfect will,
With quickened sense and heightened joy
They serve Thee still.

5 O fuller, sweeter is that life,
And larger, ampler is the air:
Eye cannot see nor heart conceive
The glory there;

6 Nor know to what high purpose Thou
Dost yet employ their ripened powers,
Nor how at Thy behest they touch
This life of ours.

7 There are no tears within their eyes;
With love they keep perpetual tryst;
And praise and work and rest are one,
With Thee, O Christ.

William Charter Piggott, 1872-1943

658

NEARER HOME. D.S.M. I. B. WOODBURY, 1819-58. Arr. by A. SULLIVAN.

By permission of Novello and Company, Limited.

1 For ever with the Lord!
Amen; so let it be:
Life from the dead is in that word,
'Tis immortality.
Here in the body pent,
Absent from Him I roam,
Yet nightly pitch my moving tent
A day's march nearer home.

2 My father's house on high,
Home of my soul, how near
At times, to faith's foreseeing eye,
Thy golden gates appear!
Ah! then my spirit faints
To reach the land I love,
The bright inheritance of saints,
Jerusalem above.

3 For ever with the Lord!
Father, if 'tis Thy will,
The promise of that faithful word
Even here to me fulfil.
Be Thou at my right hand,
Then can I never fail;
Uphold Thou me, and I shall stand;
Fight, and I must prevail.

4 So when my latest breath
Shall rend the veil in twain,
By death I shall escape from death
And life eternal gain.
Knowing as I am known,
How shall I love that word,
And oft repeat before the throne:
For ever with the Lord!

James Montgomery, 1771-1854.

Also:

104 Thou great Redeemer
202 O sacred Head
213 Thine be the glory
215 The strife is o'er
216 Jesus lives! thy terrors now
247 Rejoice, the Lord is King!
264 Lo! He comes
370 Jesu, Thy blood
408 My God, the spring
429 God of my life
492 I the good fight
498 Rock of Ages
501 Peace, perfect peace
637 The sands of time
725 Lord, in this
824 Come, let us join
825 The saints of God
948 Abide with me
974 God of the living

659

THE LORD'S DAY

MUNICH. 7.6.7.6. D. STORL'S *Gesangbuch*, 1710.

May also be sung to AURELIA, No. 701.

1 O DAY of rest and gladness,
O day of joy and light,
O balm of care and sadness,
Most beautiful, most bright!
On thee the high and lowly,
Through ages joined in tune,
Sing: Holy, holy, holy,
To the great God Triune.

2 On thee, at the creation,
The light first had its birth;
On thee, for our salvation,
Christ rose from depths of earth;
On thee, our Lord victorious
The Spirit sent from heaven:
And thus on thee most glorious
A triple light was given.

3 To-day on weary nations
The heavenly manna falls;
To holy convocations
The silver trumpet calls,
Where gospel light is glowing
With pure and radiant beams,
And living water flowing
With soul-refreshing streams.

4 New graces ever gaining
From this our day of rest,
We reach the rest remaining
To spirits of the blest.
To Holy Ghost be praises,
To Father, and to Son;
The Church her voice upraises
To Thee, blest Three in One. Amen.

Christopher Wordsworth, 1807-85.

660

DULWICH COLLEGE. S.M. E. D. RENDALL, 1858-1920.

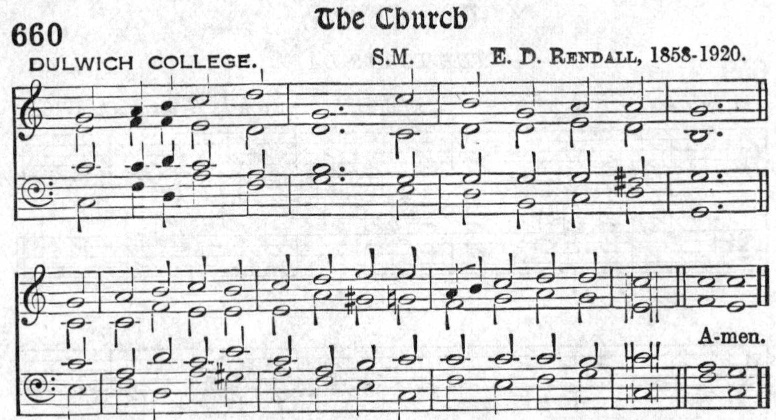

1 This is the day of light:
Let there be light to-day;
O Day-spring, rise upon our night,
And chase its gloom away.

2 This is the day of rest:
Our failing strength renew;
On weary brain and troubled breast
Shed Thou Thy freshening dew.

3 This is the day of peace:
Thy peace our spirits fill;
Bid Thou the blasts of discord cease,
The waves of strife be still.

4 This is the day of prayer:
Let earth to heaven draw near;
Lift up our hearts to seek Thee there,
Come down to meet us here.

5 This is the first of days:
Send forth Thy quickening breath,
And wake dead souls to love and praise,
O Vanquisher of death! Amen.

John Ellerton, 1826-93.

661

PLYMOUTH DOCK. 8 8.8 8.8 8 8. Unknown.

A-men.

1 COME, let us with our Lord arise,
Our Lord, who made both earth and skies;
Who died to save the world He made,
And rose triumphant from the dead;
He rose, the Prince of life and peace,
And stamped the day for ever His.

2 This is the day the Lord hath made,
That all may see His love displayed,
May feel His resurrection's power,
And rise again to fall no more,
In perfect righteousness renewed,
And filled with all the life of God.

3 Then let us render Him His own,
With solemn prayer approach the throne,
With meekness hear the gospel word,
With thanks His dying love record;
Our joyful hearts and voices raise,
And fill His courts with songs of praise.

4 Honour and praise to Jesus pay
Throughout His consecrated day;
Be all in Jesu's praise employed,
Nor leave a single moment void;
With utmost care the time improve,
And only breathe His praise and love. Amen.

Charles Wesley, 1707-88.

662

WOOLMER'S. L.M. F. A. G. OUSELEY, 1825-89.

1 SWEET is the sunlight after rain,
And sweet the sleep which follows pain,
And sweetly steals the Sabbath rest
Upon the world's work-wearied breast.

2 Of heaven the sign, of earth the calm;
The poor man's birthright, and his balm;
God's witness of celestial things;
A sun with healing in its wings.

3 New rising in this gospel time,
And in its sevenfold light sublime,
Blest day of God! we hail its dawn,
To gratitude and worship drawn.

4 O nought of gloom and nought of pride
Should with the sacred hours abide;
At work for God, in loved employ,
We lose the duty in the joy.

5 Breathe on us, Lord, our sins forgive,
And make us strong in faith to live:
Our utmost, sorest need supply,
And make us strong in faith to die. Amen.

William Morley Punshon, 1824-81.

663

LÜNEBURG. 7.8.7.8.7 7. J. S. BACH'S *Choralgesänge*, 1784-7

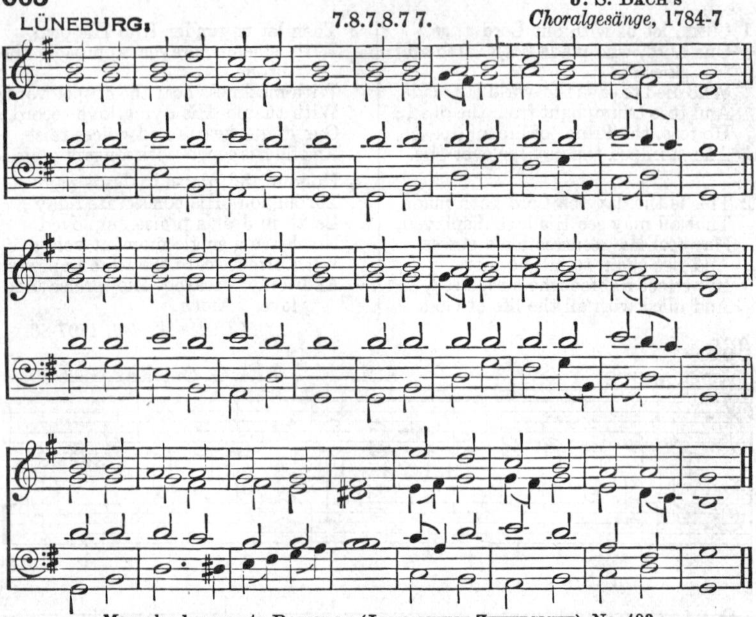

May also be sung to RATISBON (JESU, MEINE ZUVERSICHT), No. 493.

Licht vom Licht, erleuchte mich.

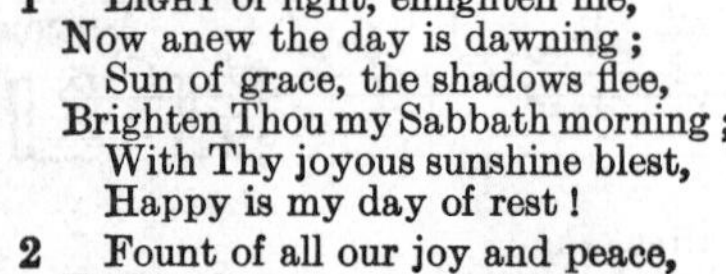

1 LIGHT of light, enlighten me,
Now anew the day is dawning;
Sun of grace, the shadows flee,
Brighten Thou my Sabbath morning;
With Thy joyous sunshine blest,
Happy is my day of rest!

2 Fount of all our joy and peace,
To Thy living waters lead me;
Thou from earth my soul release,
And with grace and mercy feed me;
Bless Thy word that it may prove
Rich in fruits that Thou dost love.

3 Kindle Thou the sacrifice
That upon my lips is lying;
Clear the shadows from mine eyes,
That, from every error flying,
No strange fire may in me glow
Which Thine altar doth not know.

4 Let me with my heart to-day,
Holy, holy, holy, singing,
Rapt awhile from earth away,
All my soul to Thee upspringing,
Have a foretaste inly given
How they worship Thee in heaven.

5 Rest in me and I in Thee,
Build a paradise within me;
O reveal Thyself to me,
Blessèd Love, who diedst to win me;
Fed from Thine exhaustless urn,
Pure and bright my lamp shall burn.

6 Hence all care and vanity,
For the day to God is holy;
Come, Thou glorious Majesty,
Deign to fill this temple lowly;
Nought to-day my soul shall move
Simply resting in Thy love.

Benjamin Schmolck, 1672-1737;
tr. by Catherine Winkworth, 1827-78.

664

ST. OSWALD. 8.7.8.7. J. B. DYKES, 1823-76.

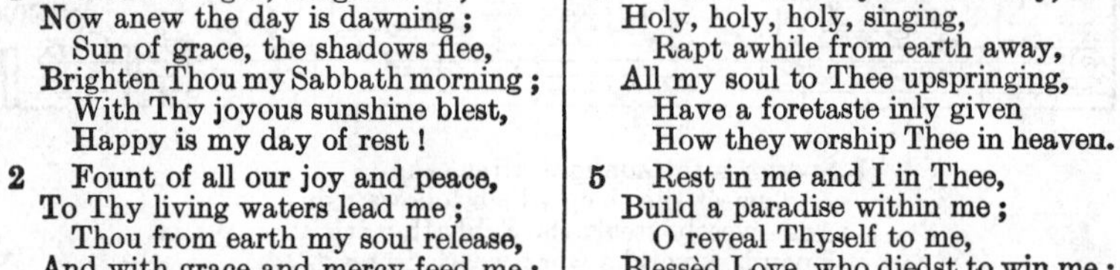

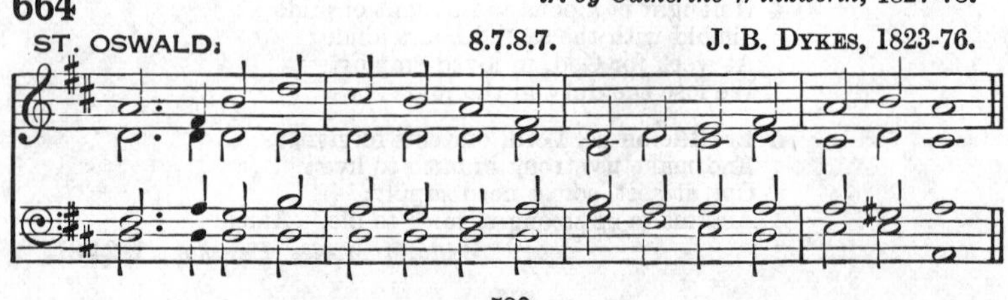

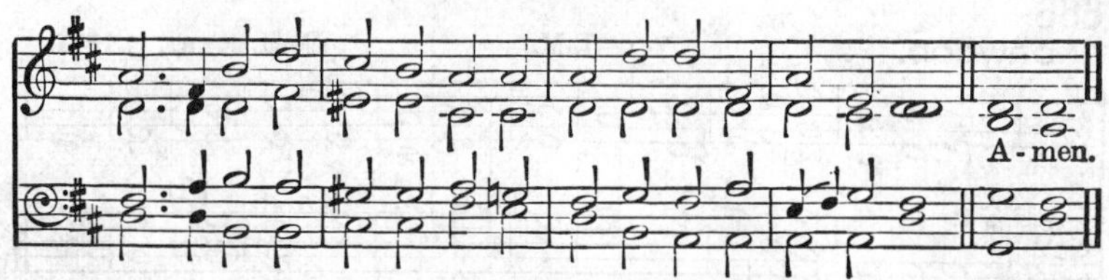

O wie freun wir uns der Stunde.

1 O HOW blest the hour, Lord Jesus,
When we can to Thee draw near,
Promises so sweet and precious
From Thy gracious lips to hear.

2 Be with us this day to bless us,
That we may not hear in vain;
With the saving truths impress us
Which the words of life contain.

3 Open Thou our minds, and lead us
Safely on our heavenward way;
With the lamp of truth precede us,
That we may not go astray.

4 Make us gentle, meek, and humble,
And yet bold in doing right:
Scatter darkness, lest we stumble;
Men walk safely in the light.

5 Lord, endue Thy word from heaven
With such light, and love, and [power,
That in us its silent leaven
May work on from hour to hour.

6 Give us grace to bear our witness
To the truths we have embraced;
And let others both their sweetness
And their quickening virtue taste.
Amen.

Carl Johann Philipp Spitta, 1801-59;
tr. by Richard Massie, 1800-87.

665

EIGNBROOK. L.M. *The Hallelujah*, 1849.

1 SWEET is the work, my God, my King,
To praise Thy name, give thanks, [and sing;
To show Thy love by morning light,
And talk of all Thy truth at night.

2 Sweet is the day of sacred rest,
No mortal cares disturb my breast:
O may my heart in tune be found
Like David's harp of solemn sound!

3 My heart shall triumph in the Lord,
And bless His works, and bless His word:
Thy works of grace, how bright they shine!
How deep Thy counsels, how divine!

4 And I shall share a glorious part,
When grace has well refined my heart,
And fresh supplies of joy are shed,
Like holy oil to cheer my head.

5 Then shall I see, and hear, and know
All I desired and wished below;
And every power find sweet employ
In that eternal world of joy.

Isaac Watts, 1674-1748.

666

NORWOOD. L.M. W. H. Hart, c. 1877.

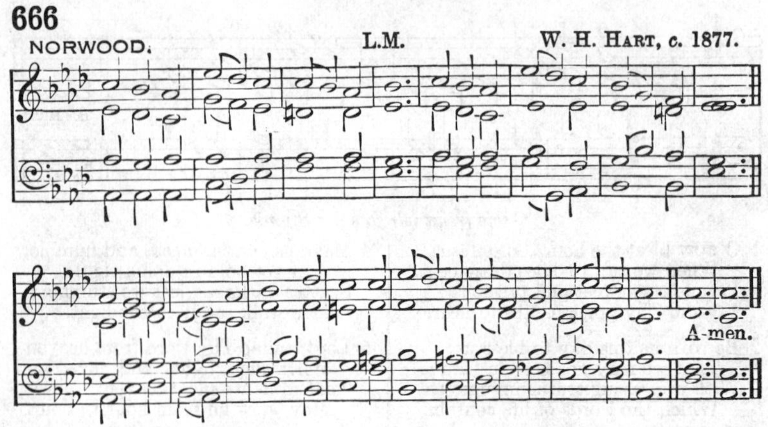

1 We rose to-day with anthems sweet
To sing before the mercy-seat,
And ere the darkness round us fell
We bade the grateful vespers swell.

2 Whate'er has risen from heart sincere,
Each upward glance of filial fear,
Each true resolve, each solemn vow,
Jesus our Lord, accept it now.

3 Whate'er beneath Thy searching eyes
Has wrought to spoil our sacrifice,
Mid this sweet stillness while we bow,
Jesus our Lord, forgive us now.

4 O teach us erring souls to win,
And hide a multitude of sin,
To tread in Christ's long-suffering way,
And grow more like Him day by day.
Amen.

William Morley Punshon, 1824-81.

667

RADFORD (*First Tune*). 9.8.9.8. S. S. Wesley, 1810-76.

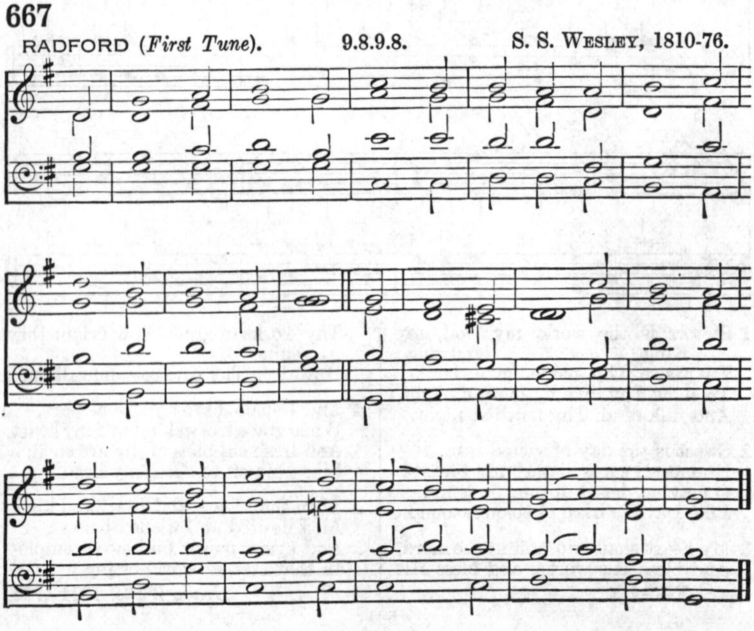

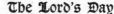

ST. CLEMENT (*Second Tune*). 9.8.9.8. C. C. SCHOLEFIELD, 1839-1904.

9.8.9.8.
LES COMMANDEMENS DE DIEU (*Third Tune*). L. BOURGEOIS, *c.* 1510-*c.* 1561

1 THE day Thou gavest, Lord, is ended,
The darkness falls at Thy behest;
To Thee our morning hymns ascended,
Thy praise shall sanctify our rest.

2 We thank Thee that Thy Church unsleeping,
While earth rolls onward into light,
Through all the world her watch is keeping,
And rests not now by day or night.

3 As o'er each continent and island
The dawn leads on another day,
The voice of prayer is never silent,
Nor dies the strain of praise away.

4 The sun that bids us rest is waking
Our brethren 'neath the western sky,
And hour by hour fresh lips are making
Thy wondrous doings heard on high.

5 So be it, Lord; Thy throne shall never,
Like earth's proud empires, pass away;
Thy kingdom stands, and grows for ever,
Till all Thy creatures own Thy sway.

John Ellerton, 1826-93.

668 WORSHIP IN THE SANCTUARY

EIDE (*First Tune*). 8.5.8.5.8 4.3. A. BEER, 1874-

ANGEL VOICES (*Second Tune*). 8.5.8.5.8 4.3. E. G. MONK, 1819-1900.

Worship in the Sanctuary

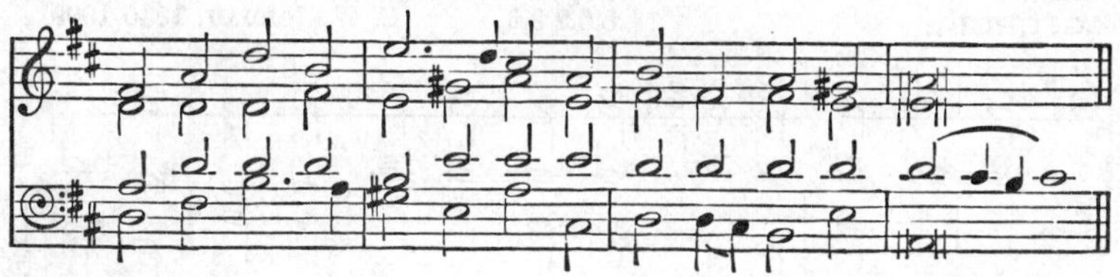

1 ANGEL voices, ever singing
Round Thy throne of light,
Angel harps, for ever ringing,
Rest not day nor night;
Thousands only live to bless Thee,
And confess Thee
Lord of might.

2 Thou who art beyond the farthest
Mortal eye can scan,
Can it be that Thou regardest
Songs of sinful man?
Can we know that Thou art near us
And wilt hear us?
Yea, we can.

3 Yea, we know that Thou rejoicest
O'er each work of Thine;
Thou didst ears, and hands, and voices
For Thy praise design;
Craftsman's art and music's measure
For Thy pleasure
All combine.

4 In Thy house, great God, we offer
Of Thine own to Thee,
And for Thine acceptance proffer,
All unworthily,
Hearts, and minds, and hands, and voices
In our choicest
Psalmody.

5 Honour, glory, might, and merit
Thine shall ever be,
Father, Son, and Holy Spirit,
Blessèd Trinity.
Of the best that Thou hast given
Earth and heaven
Render Thee. Amen.

Francis Pott, 1832-1909.

669

GEORGIA. 8.6.8 8.6. C. W. JORDAN, 1840-1909.

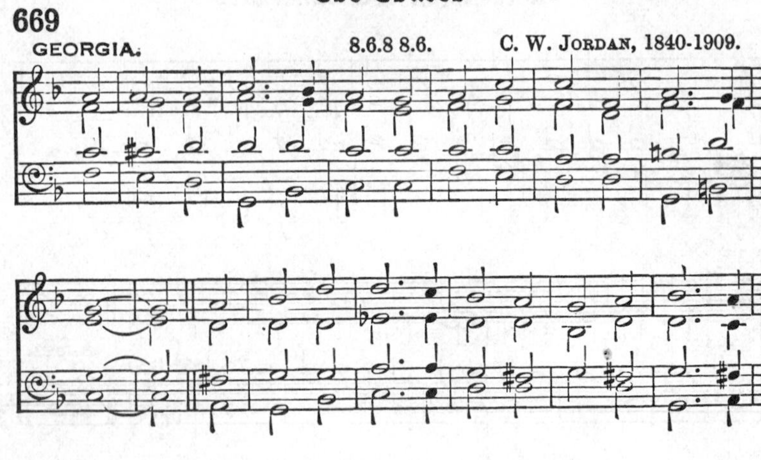

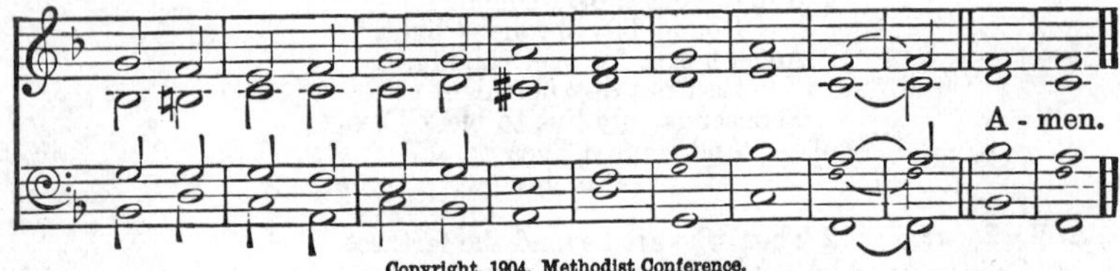

May also be sung to REST, A.T. No. 23.

1 DEAR Lord and Father of mankind,
Forgive our foolish ways;
Re-clothe us in our rightful mind;
In purer lives Thy service find,
In deeper reverence, praise.

2 In simple trust like theirs who heard,
Beside the Syrian sea,
The gracious calling of the Lord,
Let us, like them, without a word
Rise up and follow Thee.

3 O Sabbath rest by Galilee!
O calm of hills above,
Where Jesus knelt to share with Thee
The silence of eternity,
Interpreted by love!

4 With that deep hush subduing all
Our words and works that drown
The tender whisper of Thy call,
As noiseless let Thy blessing fall
As fell Thy manna down.

5 Drop Thy still dews of quietness,
Till all our strivings cease;
Take from our souls the strain and stress,
And let our ordered lives confess
The beauty of Thy peace.

6 Breathe through the heats of our desire
Thy coolness and Thy balm;
Let sense be dumb, let flesh retire;
Speak through the earthquake, wind, and fire,
O still small voice of calm!
Amen.

John Greenleaf Whittier, 1807-92.

670

GROSVENOR. 8 8.6. D. E. HARWOOD, 1707-87.

1 Jesus, Thou soul of all our joys,
For whom we now lift up our voice
And all our strength exert,
Vouchsafe the grace we humbly claim,
Compose into a thankful frame,
And tune Thy people's heart.

2 While in the heavenly work we join,
Thy glory be our whole design,
Thy glory, not our own:
Still let us keep our end in view,
And still the pleasing task pursue,
To please our God alone.

3 The secret pride, the subtle sin,
O let it never more steal in,
To offend Thy glorious eyes,
To desecrate our hallowed strain,
And make our solemn service vain,
And mar our sacrifice.

4 With calmly reverential joy,
O let us all our lives employ
In setting forth Thy love;
And raise in death our triumph higher,
And sing with all the heavenly choir
That endless song above! Amen.

Charles Wesley, 1707-88.

671

ALLELUIA PERENNE. 10 10.7. W. H. Monk, 1823-89.

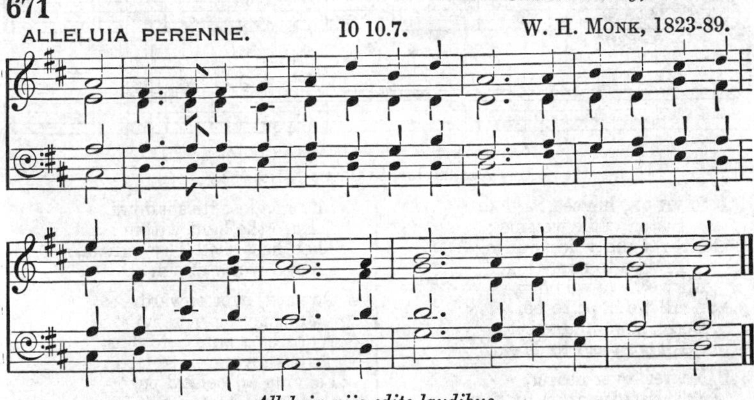

Alleluia piis edite laudibus.

1 Sing Alleluia forth in duteous praise, [raise
O citizens of heaven, and sweetly
An endless Alleluia!

2 The Holy City shall take up your strain, [again
And with glad songs resounding wake
An endless Alleluia!

3 There, in one grand acclaim, for ever ring [your King,
The strains which tell the honour of
An endless Alleluia!

4 This is the rest for weary ones brought back, [shall lack,
This is the food and drink which none
An endless Alleluia!

5 While Thee, by whom were all things made, we praise [lays
For ever, and tell out in sweetest
An endless Alleluia!

6 To Thee, Eternal Son, our voices sing; [we bring
With them, O Holy Ghost, to Thee
An endless Alleluia!

Mozarabic Breviary, 5th cent.;
tr. by John Ellerton, 1826-93.

672

NORFOLK PARK. 6.5.6.5. D. H. Coward, 1849-1944

May also be sung to Goshen, No. 981.

1 Saviour, blessèd Saviour,
Listen while we sing;
Hearts and voices raising
Praises to our King:
All we have we offer,
All we hope to be,
Body, soul, and spirit,
All we yield to Thee.

2 Nearer, ever nearer,
Christ, we draw to Thee,
Deep in adoration
Bending low the knee.
Thou, for our redemption,
Cam'st on earth to die;
Thou, that we might follow,
Hast gone up on high.

3 Clearer still, and clearer,
Dawns the light from heaven,
In our sadness bringing
News of sin forgiven;
Life has lost its shadows,
Pure the light within;
Thou hast shed Thy radiance
On a world of sin.

4 Onward, ever onward,
Journeying o'er the road
Worn by saints before us,
Journeying on to God;
Leaving all behind us,
May we hasten on,
Backward never looking
Till the prize is won.

5 Higher then, and higher,
Bear the ransomed soul,
Earthly toils forgotten,
Saviour, to its goal;
Where, in joys unthought of,
Saints with angels sing,
Never weary, raising
Praises to their King. Amen.

Godfrey Thring, 1823-1903.

673

RUTH. 6.5.6.5. D. S. Smith, 1821-1917.

By permission of Novello and Company, Limited.

May also be sung to PRINCETHORPE, No. 966.

1 Summer suns are glowing
Over land and sea;
Happy light is flowing,
Bountiful and free.
Everything rejoices
In the mellow rays;
All earth's thousand voices
Swell the psalm of praise.

2 God's free mercy streameth
Over all the world,
And His banner gleameth,
Everywhere unfurled.
Broad, and deep, and glorious,
As the heaven above,
Shines in might victorious
His eternal love.

3 Lord, upon our blindness
Thy pure radiance pour;
For Thy loving-kindness
Make us love Thee more.
And when clouds are drifting
Dark across our sky,
Then, the veil uplifting,
Father, be Thou nigh.

4 We will never doubt Thee,
Though Thou veil Thy light;
Life is dark without Thee,
Death with Thee is bright.
Light of Light, shine o'er us
On our pilgrim way;
Go Thou still before us
To the endless day. Amen.

William Walsham How, 1823-97.

BOSTON. L.M. L. Mason, 1792-1872.

1 O Love Divine! whose constant beam
Shines on the eyes that will not see,
And waits to bless us, while we dream
Thou leav'st us when we turn from [Thee.

2 All souls that struggle and aspire,
All hearts of prayer, by Thee are lit;
And, dim or clear, Thy tongues of fire
On dusky tribes and centuries sit.

3 Nor bounds nor clime nor creed Thou know'st,
Wide as our need Thy favours fall;
The white wings of the Holy Ghost
Stoop unseen o'er the heads of all.

4 Truth, which the sage and prophet saw,
Long sought without, but found [within,
The law of love beyond all law,
The life o'erflooding death and sin.

5 Shine, Light of God! Make broad Thy scope
To all who sin and suffer; more
And better than we dare to hope
Make with Thy love our longings poor. Amen.

John Greenleaf Whittier, 1807-92.

675

REDHEAD No. 4. L.M. Adapted by R. Redhead, 1820-1901.

1 Jesus, where'er Thy people meet,
There they behold Thy mercy-seat;
Where'er they seek Thee Thou art found,
And every place is hallowed ground.

2 For Thou, within no walls confined,
Inhabitest the humble mind;
Such ever bring Thee where they come,
And going take Thee to their home.

3 Dear Shepherd of Thy chosen few,
Thy former mercies here renew;
Here to our waiting hearts proclaim
The sweetness of Thy saving name.

4 Here may we prove the power of prayer,
To strengthen faith and sweeten care,
To teach our faint desires to rise,
And bring all heaven before our eyes.

5 Lord, we are few, but Thou art near,
Nor short Thine arm, nor deaf Thine ear;
O rend the heavens, come quickly [down,
And make a thousand hearts Thine own! Amen.

William Cowper, 1731-1800.

676

ST. GEORGE. S.M. H. J. Gauntlett, 1805-76.

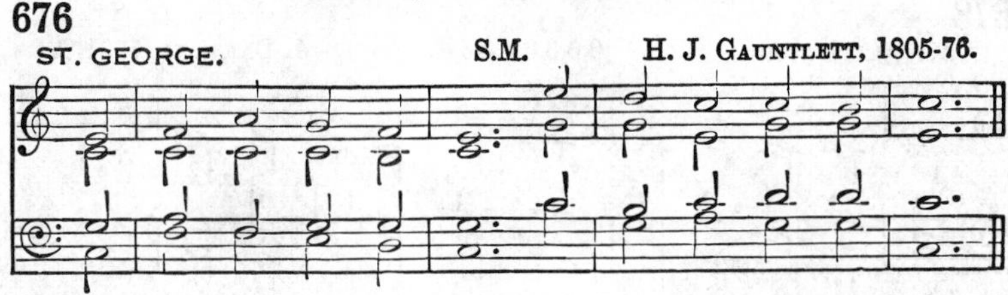

1 Great is the Lord our God,
And let His praise be great;
He makes His churches His abode,
His most delightful seat.

2 These temples of His grace,
How beautiful they stand!
The honours of our native place,
And bulwarks of our land.

3 In Zion God is known
A refuge in distress;
How bright has His salvation shone
Through all her palaces!

4 In every new distress
We'll to His house repair;
We'll think upon His wondrous grace,
And seek deliverance there.

Isaac Watts, 1674-1748.

677

QUAM DILECTA. 6.6.6.6. H. L. Jenner, 1820-98.

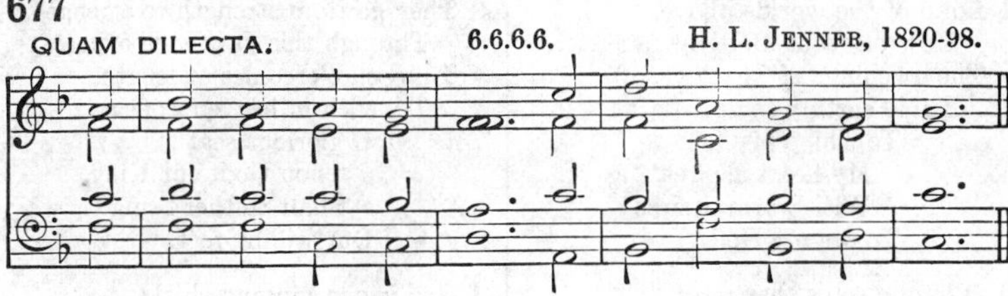

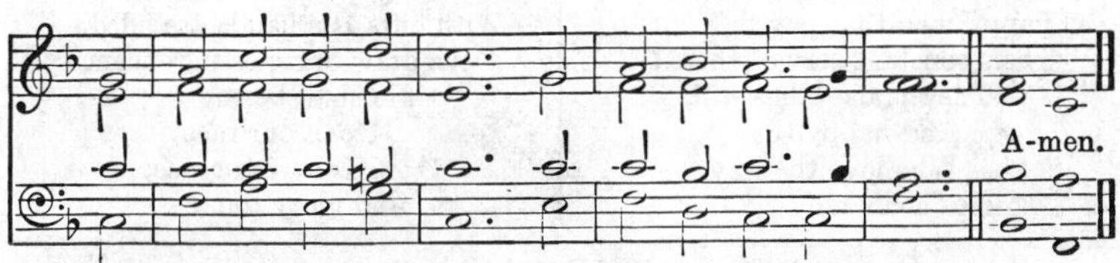

1 We love the place, O God,
Wherein Thine honour dwells;
The joy of Thine abode
All earthly joy excels.

2 It is the house of prayer,
Wherein Thy servants meet;
And Thou, O Lord, art there,
Thy chosen flock to greet.

3 We love the word of life,
The word that tells of peace,
Of comfort in the strife
And joys that never cease.

4 We love to sing below
Of mercies freely given;
But O we long to know
The triumph song of heaven!

5 Lord Jesus, give us grace,
On earth to love Thee more,
In heaven to see Thy face,
And with Thy saints adore. Amen.

William Bullock, 1798-1874, *and*
Henry Williams Baker 1821-77.

678

DARWALL'S 148TH: 6.6.6.6.4.4 4.4. J. DARWALL, 1731-89.

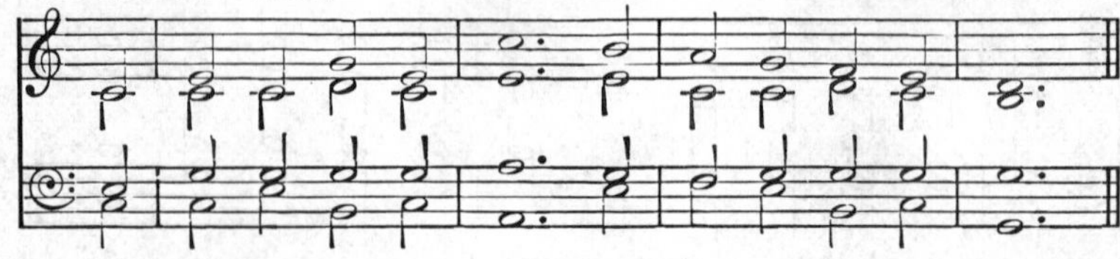

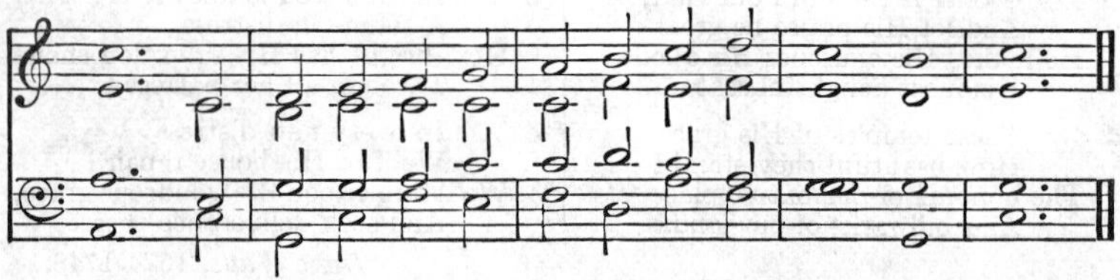

1 LORD of the worlds above,
How pleasant and how fair
The dwellings of Thy love,
Thine earthly temples, are!
To Thine abode
My heart aspires,
With warm desires
To see my God.

2 O happy souls that pray
Where God delights to hear!
O happy men that pay
Their constant service there!
They praise Thee still,
And happy they
Who love the way
To Zion's hill!

3 They go from strength to strength,
Through this dark vale of tears,
Till each o'ercomes at length,
Till each in heaven appears:
O glorious seat!
Thou God, our King,
Shalt thither bring
Our willing feet.

4 God is our sun and shield,
Our light and our defence;
With gifts His hands are filled,
We draw our blessings thence:
He shall bestow
Upon our race
His saving grace,
And glory too.

5 The Lord His people loves;
His hand no good withholds
From those His heart approves,
From holy, humble souls:
Thrice happy he,
O Lord of Hosts,
Whose spirit trusts
Alone in Thee!

Isaac Watts, 1674-1748.

679

MAIDSTONE. 7 7.7 7. D. W. B. GILBERT, 1829-1910.

By permission of Novello and Company, Limited.

1 PLEASANT are Thy courts above,
In the land of light and love;
Pleasant are Thy courts below,
In this land of sin and woe.
O my spirit longs and faints
For the converse of Thy saints,
For the brightness of Thy face,
For Thy fullness, God of grace!

2 Happy birds that sing and fly
Round Thy altars, O Most High!
Happier souls that find a rest
In a heavenly Father's breast!
Like the wandering dove that found
No repose on earth around,
They can to their ark repair,
And enjoy it ever there.

3 Happy souls! Their praises flow
In this vale of sin and woe;
Waters in the desert rise,
Manna feeds them from the skies.
On they go from strength to strength,
Till they reach Thy throne at length;
At Thy feet adoring fall,
Who hast led them safe through all.

4 Lord, be mine this prize to win:
Guide me through a world of sin;
Keep me by Thy saving grace;
Give me at Thy side a place.
Sun and shield alike Thou art;
Guide and guard my erring heart:
Grace and glory flow from Thee;
Shower, O shower them, Lord, on me! Amen.

Henry Francis Lyte, 1793-1847.

FALCON STREET. S.M. I. SMITH, *c.* 1725-*c.* 1800.

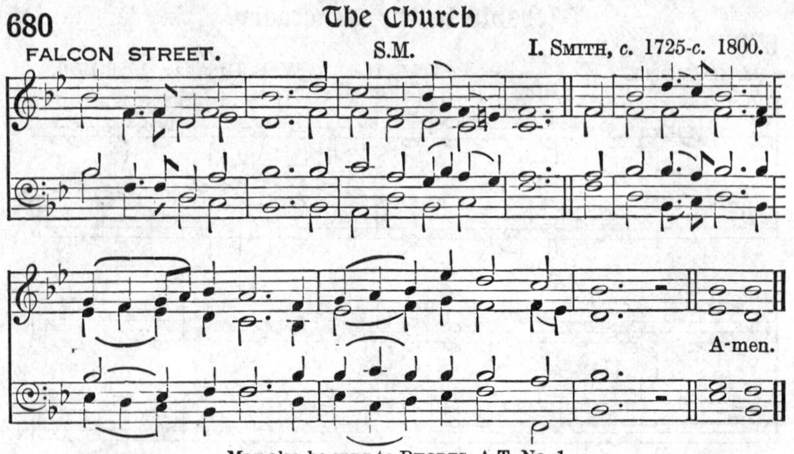

May also be sung to RHODES, A.T. No. 1.

1 GLAD was my heart to hear
My old companions say:
Come, in the house of God appear,
For 'tis a holy day.

2 Our willing feet shall stand
Within the temple door,
While young and old, in many a band,
Shall throng the sacred floor.

3 Thither the tribes repair,
Where all are wont to meet,
And joyful in the house of prayer
Bend at the mercy-seat.

4 Pray for Jerusalem,
The city of our God;
The Lord from heaven be kind to them
That love the dear abode!

5 Within these walls may peace
And harmony be found;
Zion, in all thy palaces
Prosperity abound!

6 For friends and brethren dear
Our prayer shall never cease;
Oft as they meet for worship here,
God send His people peace!
Amen.

James Montgomery, 1771-1854.

681

DIX. 7 7.7 7.7 7. C. KOCHER, 1786-1872.

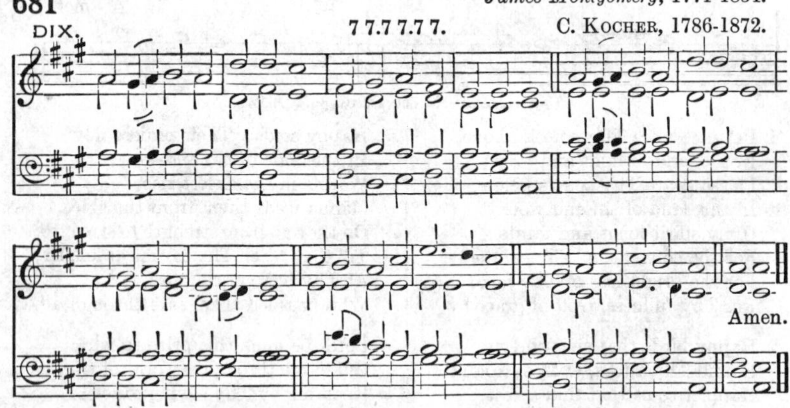

May also be sung to TE LAUDANT OMNIA, No. 29.

1 GOD of mercy, God of grace,
Show the brightness of Thy face;
Shine upon us, Saviour, shine,
Fill Thy Church with light divine;
And Thy saving health extend
Unto earth's remotest end.

2 Let the peoples praise Thee, Lord;
Be by all that live adored;
Let the nations shout and sing
Glory to their Saviour King;
At Thy feet their tribute pay,
And Thy holy will obey.

3 Let the peoples praise Thee, Lord;
Earth shall then her fruits afford;
God to man His blessing give,
Man to God devoted live;
All below, and all above,
One in joy, and light, and love. Amen.

Henry Francis Lyte, 1793-1847.

682

HUDDERSFIELD (*First Tune*). 7 7 7.5. W. PARRATT, 1841-1924.

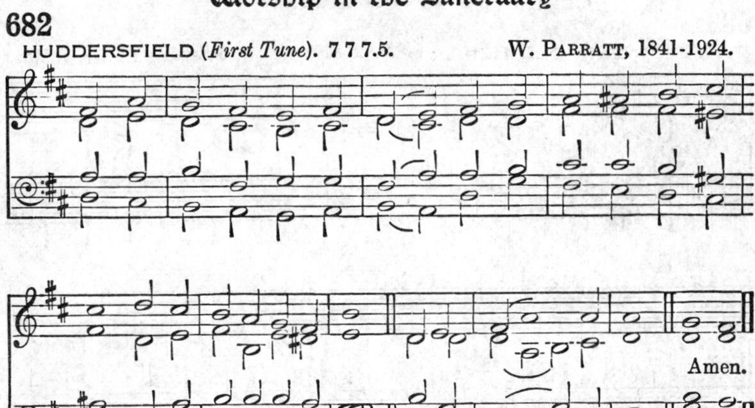

CAPETOWN (*Second Tune*). 7 7 7.5. F. FILITZ, 1804-76.

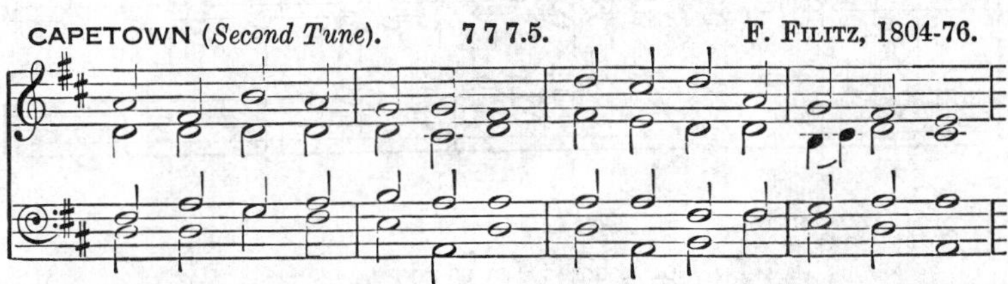

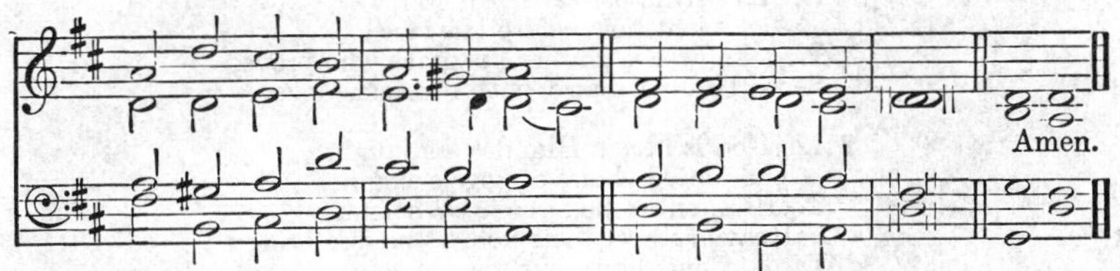

1 GOD of pity, God of grace,
When we humbly seek Thy face,
Bend from heaven, Thy dwelling-place;
Hear, forgive and save.

2 When we in Thy temple meet,
Spread our wants before Thy feet,
Pleading at Thy mercy-seat,
Look from heaven and save.

3 When Thy love our hearts shall fill,
And we long to do Thy will,
Turning to Thy holy hill,
Lord, accept and save.

4 Should we wander from Thy fold,
And our love to Thee grow cold,
With a pitying eye behold;
Lord, forgive and save.

5 Should the hand of sorrow press,
Earthly care and want distress,
May our souls Thy peace possess;
Jesus, hear and save.

6 And whate'er our cry may be,
When we lift our hearts to Thee,
From our burden set us free;
Hear, forgive and save. Amen.

Eliza Fanny Morris, 1821-74.

683

VATER UNSER (OLD 112TH). 8.8.8.8.8.8. *Geistliche Lieder*, 1539

Gott ist gegenwärtig.

1 Lo, God is here! Let us adore,
And own how dreadful is this place!
Let all within us feel His power,
And silent bow before His face;
Who know His power, His grace who prove,
Serve Him with awe, with reverence love.

2 Lo, God is here! Him day and night
The united choirs of angels sing;
To Him, enthroned above all height,
Heaven's host their noblest praises bring:
Disdain not, Lord, our meaner song,
Who praise Thee with a stammering tongue.

3 Being of beings! May our praise
Thy courts with grateful fragrance fill;
Still may we stand before Thy face,
Still hear and do Thy sovereign will;
To Thee may all our thoughts arise,
Ceaseless, accepted sacrifice.

4 As flowers their opening leaves display,
And glad drink in the solar fire,
So may we catch Thy every ray,
So may Thy influence us inspire;
Thou Beam of the eternal Beam,
Thou purging Fire, Thou quickening Flame. Amen.

Gerhard Tersteegen, 1697-1769;
tr. by John Wesley, 1703-91.

684

CASWALL. 6.5.6.5. F. FILITZ, 1804-76.

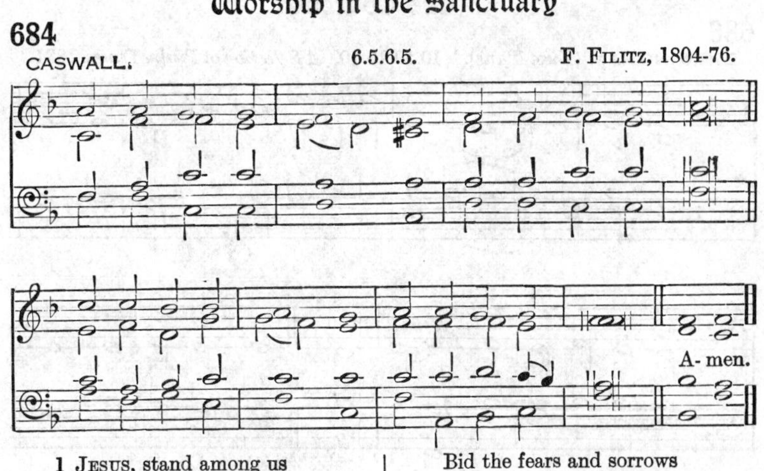

1 JESUS, stand among us
In Thy risen power;
Let this time of worship
Be a hallowed hour.

2 Breathe the Holy Spirit
Into every heart;
Bid the fears and sorrows
From each soul depart.

3 Thus with quickened footsteps
We'll pursue our way,
Watching for the dawning
Of eternal day. Amen.

William Pennefather, 1816-73.

685

DONCASTER (BETHLEHEM). S.M. S. WESLEY, 1766-1837.

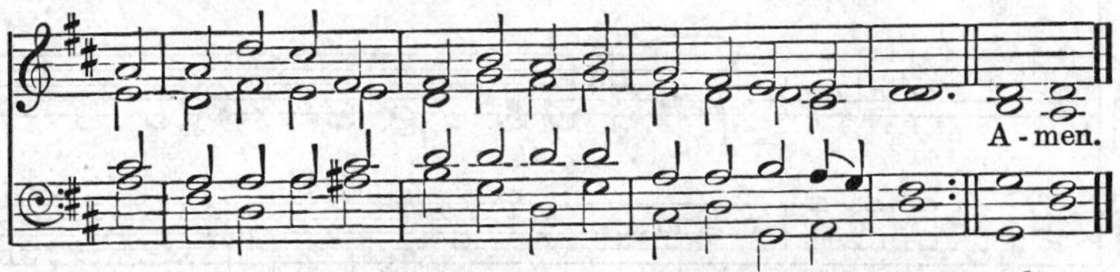

1 STAND up and bless the Lord,
Ye people of His choice;
Stand up and bless the Lord your God,
With heart and soul and voice.

2 Though high above all praise,
Above all blessing high,
Who would not fear His holy name,
And laud and magnify?

3 O for the living flame
From His own altar brought,
To touch our lips, our minds inspire,
And wing to heaven our thought!

4 There, with benign regard,
Our hymns He deigns to hear;
Though unrevealed to mortal sense,
Our spirits feel Him near.

5 God is our strength and song,
And His salvation ours;
Then be His love in Christ proclaimed
With all our ransomed powers.

6 Stand up and bless the Lord,
The Lord your God adore;
Stand up and bless His glorious name
Henceforth for evermore. Amen.

James Montgomery, 1771-1854.

686

BIRMINGHAM (*First Tune*). 10 10.10 10. *A Selection of Psalm Tunes*, 1834.

WOODLANDS (*Second Tune*). 10 10.10 10. W. Greatorex, 1877-1949

Unison.

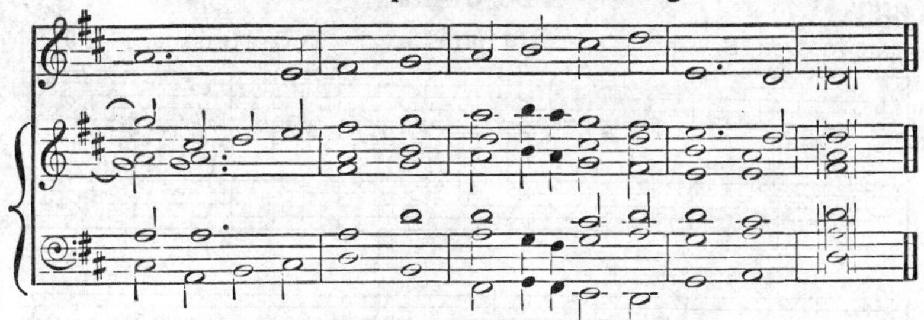

1 Lift up your hearts! We lift them, Lord, to Thee;
Here at Thy feet none other may we see;
Lift up your hearts! E'en so, with one accord,
We lift them up, we lift them to the Lord.

2 Above the level of the former years,
The mire of sin, the slough of guilty fears,
The mist of doubt, the blight of love's decay,
O Lord of Light, lift all our hearts to-day!

3 Above the swamps of subterfuge and shame,
The deeds, the thoughts that honour may not name,
The halting tongue that dares not tell the whole,
O Lord of Truth, lift every Christian soul!

4 Lift every gift that Thou Thyself hast given;
Low lies the best till lifted up to heaven:
Low lie the bounding heart, the teeming brain,
Till, sent from God, they mount to God again.

5 Then, as the trumpet-call, in after years:
Lift up your hearts, rings pealing in our ears,
Still shall those hearts respond, with full accord:
We lift them up, we lift them to the Lord!

Henry Montagu Butler, 1833-1918.

687

ERSKINE. 8 8 8.6. W. H. Gladstone, 1840-91.

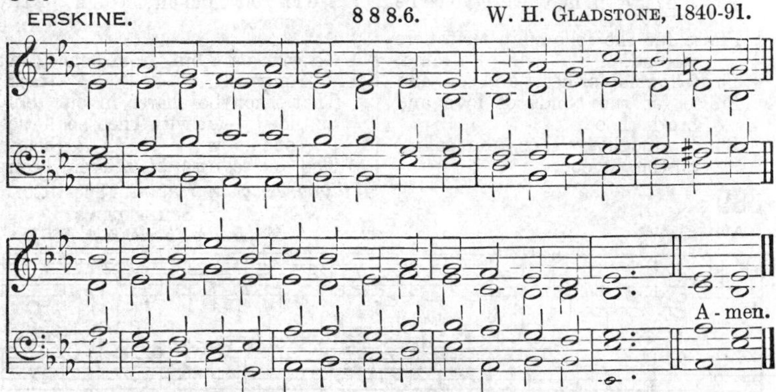

1 I bow in silence at Thy feet;
Come to my soul and make it meet
To hold divine communion sweet,
My Lord, my life, my all.

2 Thou know'st the evil thoughts within,
That make it hard for me to win
The victory over self and sin,
My Lord, my life, my all.

3 Thou too art man and knowest all
That would my love from Thee recall;
Wilt Thou be near me, lest I fall,
My Lord, my life, my all?

4 I have no power save Thine alone,
Help me to make this heart Thine own,
Rule Thou my life, there find Thy throne,
My Lord, my life, my all.

5 I bow in silence at Thy feet,
Hear Thou the prayer which I repeat,
O make my sacrifice complete,
My Lord, my life, my all.
Amen.

James Robert Batey, 1878-

688

MORECAMBE.

10 10.10 10.

F. C. Atkinson, 1841-97.

May also be sung to Birmingham, No. 686.

1 O God our Father, who dost make us one,
Heart bound to heart, in love of Thy dear Son,
Now as we part and go our several ways,
Touch every lip, may every voice be praise—

2 Praise for the fellowship that here we find,
The fellowship of heart and soul and mind,
Praise for the bonds of love and brotherhood,
Bonds wrought by Thee, who makest all things good.

3 Lord, make us strong, for Thou alone dost know
How oft we turn our faces from the foe;
How oft, when claimed by dark temptation's hour,
We lose our hold on Thee, and of Thy power.

4 Go with us, Lord, from hence; we only ask
That Thou be sharer in our daily task;
So, side by side with Thee, shall each one know
The blessedness of heaven begun below.

William Vaughan Jenkins, 1868-1920.

689

ANGELUS. L.M.

Scheffler's *Heilige Seelenlust*, 1657.

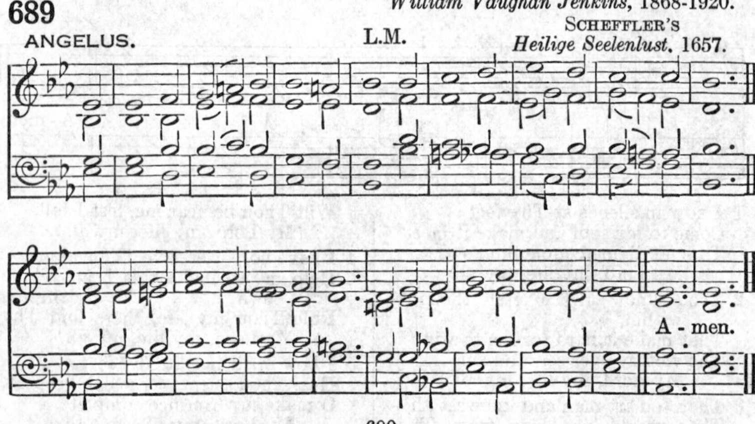

1 At even, ere the sun was set,
The sick, O Lord, around Thee lay;
O in what divers pains they met!
O with what joy they went away!

2 Once more 'tis eventide, and we,
Oppressed with various ills, draw near;
What if Thy form we cannot see?
We know and feel that Thou art here.

3 O Saviour Christ, our woes dispel:
For some are sick, and some are sad,
And some have never loved Thee well
And some have lost the love they had.

4 And some have found the world is vain,
Yet from the world they break not free;
And some have friends who give them pain,
Yet have not sought a friend in Thee.

5 And all, O Lord, crave perfect rest,
And to be wholly free from sin;
And they who fain would serve Thee best
Are conscious most of wrong within.

6 O Saviour Christ, Thou too art Man;
Thou hast been troubled, tempted, tried;
Thy kind but searching glance can scan
The very wounds that shame would hide.

7 Thy touch has still its ancient power;
No word from Thee can fruitless fall:
Hear in this solemn evening hour,
And in Thy mercy heal us all. Amen.

Henry Twells, 1823-1900.

690

FRANCONIA. S.M. König's *Choralbuch*, 1738.

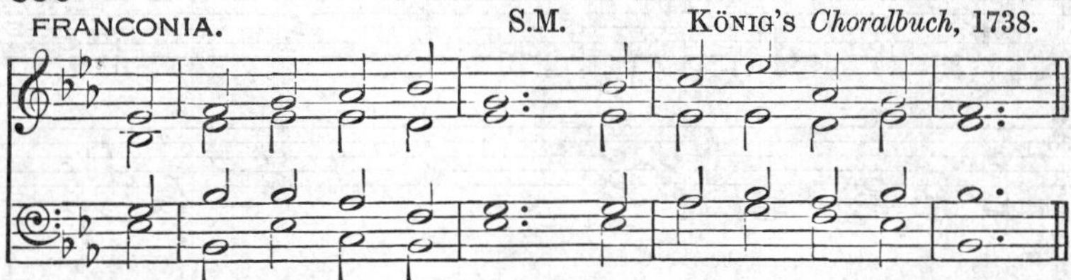

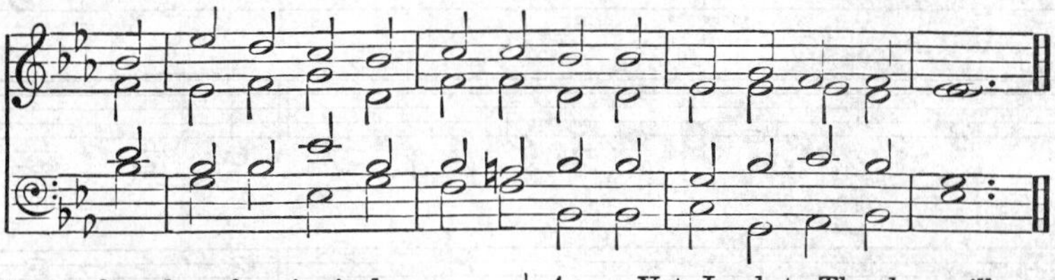

1 Our day of praise is done,
The evening shadows fall;
But pass not from us with the sun,
True Light, that lightenest all!

2 Around the throne on high,
Where night can never be,
The white-robed harpers of the sky
Bring ceaseless hymns to Thee.

3 Too faint our anthems here,
Too soon of praise we tire;
But O the strains, how full and clear,
Of that eternal choir!

4 Yet, Lord, to Thy dear will,
If Thou attune the heart,
We in Thine angels' music still
May bear our lower part.

5 'Tis Thine each soul to calm,
Each wayward thought reclaim,
And make our life a daily psalm
Of glory to Thy name.

6 A little while, and then
Shall come the glorious end,
And songs of angels and of men
In perfect praise shall blend.

John Ellerton, 1826-93.

ELLERS (*First Tune*). 10 10.10 10. E. J. Hopkins, 1818-1901.

ADORO TE (*Second Tune*). 10 10.10 10. Solesmes Version.

1 Saviour, again to Thy dear name we raise
With one accord our parting hymn of praise;
We stand to bless Thee ere our worship cease,
Then, lowly kneeling, wait Thy word of peace.

2 Grant us Thy peace upon our homeward way;
With Thee began, with Thee shall end the day;
Guard Thou the lips from sin, the hearts from shame,
That in this house have called upon Thy name.

3 Grant us Thy peace, Lord, through the coming night,
Turn Thou for us its darkness into light;
From harm and danger keep Thy children free,
For dark and light are both alike to Thee.

4 Grant us Thy peace throughout our earthly life,
Our balm in sorrow, and our stay in strife;
Then, when Thy voice shall bid our conflict cease,
Call us, O Lord, to Thine eternal peace.
Amen.

John Ellerton, 1826-93.

692

ST. MATTHIAS. 8.8.8.8.8.8 8. W. H. Monk, 1823-89.

1 O Saviour, bless us ere we go ;
Thy word into our minds instil ;
And make our lukewarm hearts to glow
With lowly love and fervent will.
Through life's long day and death's dark night,
O gentle Jesus, be our light.

2 The day is done, its hours have run,
And Thou hast taken count of all—
The scanty triumphs grace hath won,
The broken vow, the frequent fall.

3 Grant us, dear Lord, from evil ways
True absolution and release ;
And bless us, more than in past days,
With purity and inward peace.

4 Do more than pardon : give us joy,
Sweet fear and sober liberty,
And loving hearts without alloy
That only long to be like Thee.

5 For all we love, the poor, the sad,
The sinful, unto Thee we call ;
O let Thy mercy make us glad ;
Thou art our Jesus and our all. Amen.

Frederick William Faber, 1814-63.

693

DISMISSAL. 8.7.8.7.4.7. W. L. VINER, 1790-1867.

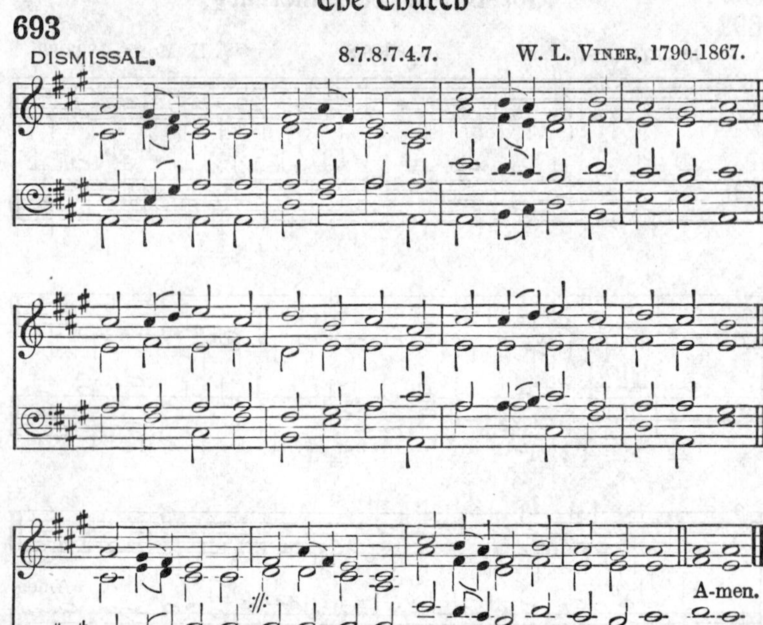

May also be sung to ST. THOMAS, No. 808.

1 LORD, dismiss us with Thy blessing,
Fill our hearts with joy and peace;
Let us each, Thy love possessing,
Triumph in redeeming grace;
O refresh us,
Travelling through this wilderness.

2 Thanks we give, and adoration,
For Thy gospel's joyful sound;
May the fruits of Thy salvation
In our hearts and lives abound;
May Thy presence
With us evermore be found. Amen.

John Fawcett, 1740-1817.

Also:

2 All people that
3 Before Jehovah's
9 O worship the Lord
11 With gladness we worship
17 Meet and right
25 Round the Lord
31 God reveals His presence
205 Jesus Christ is risen
240 O word of pity
289 Spirit divine
469 That mystic Word
535 From every stormy wind
587 O Lord of every lovely thing
633 O King of mercy
932 O splendour of God's glory bright
983 Be with us, gracious Lord

694

DETTINGEN. 8.7.8.7.8 8.7.

Christliche Lieder, Wittenberg, 1524.

1 LORD, Thou hast been our dwelling-
In every generation ; [place
Thy people still have known Thy grace,
And blessed Thy consolation ;
Through every age Thou heardst our cry ;
Through every age we found Thee nigh,
Our strength and our salvation.

2 Our cleaving sins we oft have wept,
And oft Thy patience provèd ;
But still Thy faith we fast have kept ;
Thy name we still have lovèd ;
And Thou hast kept and loved us well,
Hast granted us in Thee to dwell,
Unshaken, unremovèd.

3 Lord, nothing from Thine arms of love
Shall Thine own people sever :
Our helper never will remove,
Our God will fail us never.
Thy people, Lord, have dwelt in Thee :
Our dwelling-place Thou still wilt be
For ever and for ever.

Thomas Hornblower Gill, 1819-1906.

695

MAINZER. L.M. J. MAINZER, 1801-51.

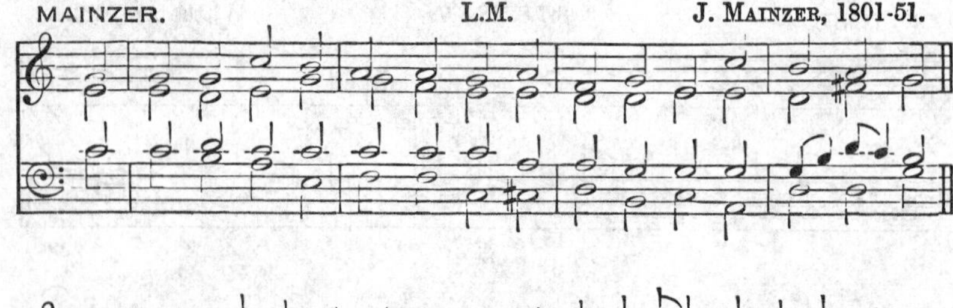

1 PRAISE, Lord, for Thee in Zion waits;
Prayer shall besiege Thy temple gates;
All flesh shall to Thy throne repair,
And find, through Christ, salvation there.

2 Our spirits faint, our sins prevail;
Leave not our trembling hearts to fail:
O Thou that hearest prayer, descend,
And still be found the sinner's friend.

3 How blest Thy saints; how safely led;
How surely kept; how richly fed!
Saviour of all in earth and sea,
How happy they who rest in Thee!

4 Thy hand sets fast the mighty hills,
Thy voice the troubled ocean stills;
Evening and morning hymn Thy praise,
And earth Thy bounty wide displays.

5 The year is with Thy goodness crowned,
Thy clouds drop wealth the world around;
Through Thee the deserts laugh and sing,
And nature smiles, and owns her King.

6 Lord, on our souls Thy Spirit pour;
The moral waste within restore;
O let Thy love our spring-tide be,
And make us all bear fruit to Thee.
Amen.

Henry Francis Lyte, 1793-1847.

696

TRULL (*First Tune*). 7 7.7 7. C. L. WISEMAN, 1893- .

MELLING (*Second Tune*). 77.77. J. FAWCETT, 1789-1867.

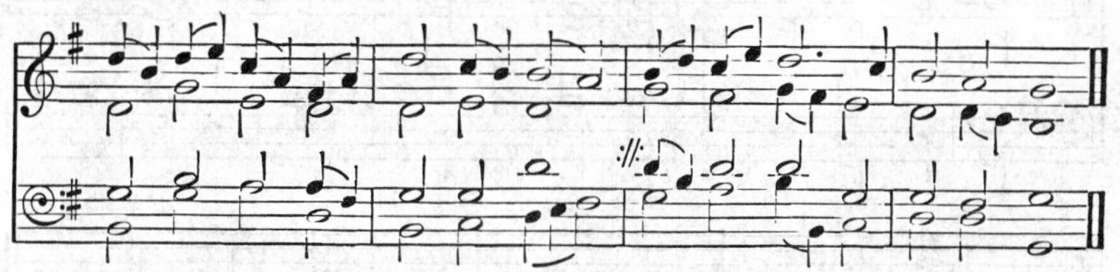

1 CHILDREN of the heavenly King,
As ye journey, sweetly sing;
Sing your Saviour's worthy praise,
Glorious in His works and ways.

2 We are travelling home to God
In the way the fathers trod;
They are happy now, and we
Soon their happiness shall see.

3 Shout, ye little flock and blest;
You on Jesu's throne shall rest;
There your seat is now prepared,
There your kingdom and reward.

4 Lift your eyes, ye sons of light;
Zion's city is in sight;
There our endless home shall be,
There our Lord we soon shall see.

5 Fear not, brethren; joyful stand
On the borders of your land;
Jesus Christ, your Father's Son,
Bids you undismayed go on.

6 Lord, obediently we go,
Gladly leaving all below;
Only Thou our leader be,
And we still will follow Thee.

John Cennick, 1718-55.

697

ABNEY. L.M. F. L. WISEMAN, 1858-1944

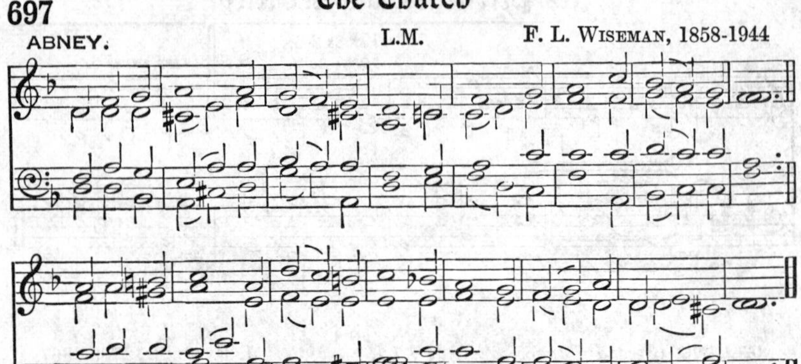

1 BLEST are the humble souls that see
Their emptiness and poverty;
Treasures of grace to them are given,
And crowns of joy laid up in heaven.

2 Blest are the men of broken heart,
Who mourn for sin with inward smart;
The blood of Christ divinely flows,
A healing balm for all their woes.

3 Blest are the souls that long for grace,
Hunger and thirst for righteousness;
They shall be well supplied and fed
With living streams and living bread.

4 Blest are the pure, whose hearts are clean
From the defiling power of sin;
With endless pleasure they shall see
The God of spotless purity.

5 Blest are the sufferers, who partake
Of pain and shame for Jesu's sake;
Their souls shall triumph in the Lord;
Glory and joy are their reward.

Isaac Watts, 1674-1748.

698

ABBEY. C.M. *Scottish Psalter*, 1615.

May also be sung to JAZER, A.T. No. 7.

Ach bleib mit deiner Gnade.

1 ABIDE among us with Thy grace,
Lord Jesus, evermore;
Nor let us e'er to sin give place,
Nor grieve Him we adore.

2 Abide among us with Thy word,
Redeemer whom we love;
Thy help and mercy here afford,
And life with Thee above.

3 Abide among us with Thy ray,
O Light that lighten'st all,
And let Thy truth preserve our way,
Nor suffer us to fall.

4 Abide with us to bless us still,
O bounteous Lord of peace;
With grace and power our spirits fill,
Our faith and love increase.

5 Abide among us as our shield,
O Captain of Thy host,
That to the world we may not yield,
Nor e'er forsake our post.

6 Abide with us in faithful love,
Our God and Saviour be;
Thy help in need, O let us prove,
And keep us true to Thee. Amen.

Josua Stegmann, 1588-1632;
tr. by Catherine Winkworth, 1827-78.

699

JOSIAH. 7.6.7.6.7.7.7.6. W. ARNOLD, 1768-1832.

1 GREAT is our redeeming Lord
In power, and truth, and grace;
Him, by highest heaven adored,
His Church on earth doth praise:
In the city of our God,
In His holy mount below,
Publish, spread His name abroad,
And all His greatness show.

2 For Thy loving-kindness, Lord,
We in Thy temple stay;
Here Thy faithful love record,
Thy saving power display:
With Thy name Thy praise is known,
Glorious Thy perfections shine;
Earth's remotest bounds shall own
Thy works are all divine.

3 See the Gospel Church secure,
And founded on a rock;
All her promises are sure;
Her bulwarks who can shock?
Count her every precious shrine;
Tell, to after-ages tell,
Fortified by power divine,
The Church can never fail.

4 Zion's God is all our own,
Who on His love rely;
We His pardoning love have known,
And live to Christ, and die:
To the new Jerusalem
He our faithful Guide shall be:
Him we claim, and rest in Him,
Through all eternity.

Charles Wesley, 1707-88.

ISHMAEL.

UNISON. D.S.M. C. VINCENT, 1852-1934

HARMONY.

1 Who in the Lord confide,
And feel His sprinkled blood,
In storms and hurricanes abide,
Firm as the mount of God:
Steadfast and fixed and sure,
His Zion cannot move;
His faithful people stand secure
In Jesu's guardian love.

2 As round Jerusalem
The hilly bulwarks rise,
So God protects and covers them
From all their enemies.
On every side He stands,
And for His Israel cares;
And safe in His almighty hands
Their souls for ever bears.

3 But let them still abide
In Thee, all-gracious Lord,
Till every soul is sanctified
And perfectly restored:
The men of heart sincere
Continue to defend;
And do them good, and save them here,
And love them to the end.

Charles Wesley, 1707-88.

701

AURELIA. 7.6.7.6. D. S. S. WESLEY, 1810-76.

1 THE Church's one foundation
Is Jesus Christ her Lord;
She is His new creation
By water and the word;
From heaven He came and sought her
To be His holy bride;
With His own blood He bought her,
And for her life He died.

2 Elect from every nation,
Yet one o'er all the earth,
Her charter of salvation
One Lord, one faith, one birth,
One holy name she blesses,
Partakes one holy food,
And to one hope she presses,
With every grace endued.

3 Though with a scornful wonder
Men see her sore oppressed,
By schisms rent asunder,
By heresies distressed;
Yet saints their watch are keeping,
Their cry goes up: How long?
And soon the night of weeping
Shall be the morn of song.

4 Mid toil and tribulation,
And tumult of her war,
She waits the consummation
Of peace for evermore,
Till with the vision glorious
Her longing eyes are blest,
And the great Church victorious
Shall be the Church at rest.

5 Yet she on earth hath union
With God the Three in One,
And mystic sweet communion
With those whose rest is won.
O happy ones and holy!
Lord, give us grace that we,
Like them, the meek and lowly,
On high may dwell with Thee.
Amen.

Samuel John Stone, 1839-1900.

702

HARWOOD. 6.6.6.6.8.8. S. S. WESLEY, 1810-76.

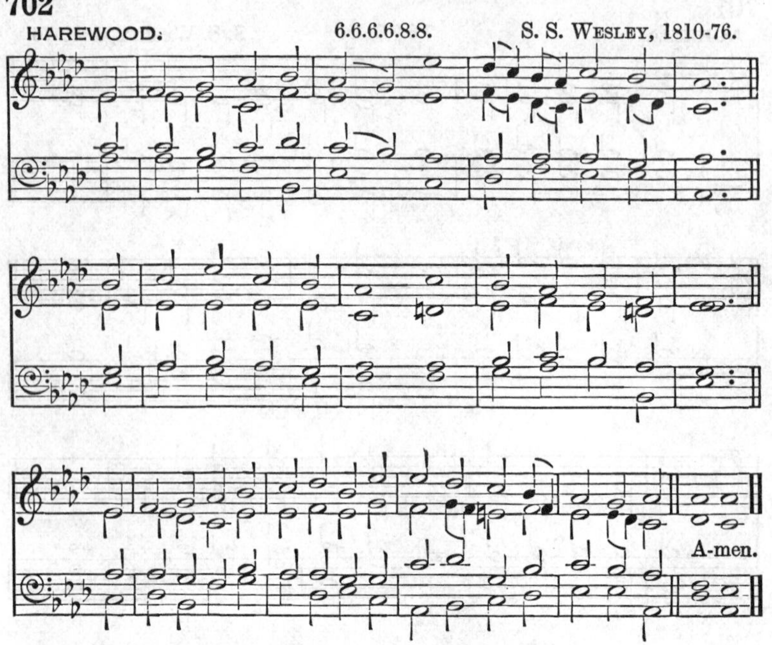

Angularis fundamentum.

1 CHRIST is our corner-stone,
On Him alone we build;
With His true saints alone
The courts of heaven are filled:
On His great love our hopes we place
Of present grace and joys above.

2 O then with hymns of praise
These hallowed courts shall ring;
Our voices we will raise
The Three in One to sing,
And thus proclaim in joyful song,
Both loud and long, that glorious name.

3 Here, gracious God, do Thou
For evermore draw nigh;
Accept each faithful vow,
And mark each suppliant sigh;
In copious shower on all who pray
Each holy day Thy blessings pour.

4 Here may we gain from heaven
The grace which we implore;
And may that grace, once given,
Be with us evermore,
Until that day when all the blest
To endless rest are called away. Amen.

Anonymous, 6th or 7th cent.;
tr. by John Chandler, 1806-76.

RICHMOND (*First Tune*). C.M. T. Haweis, 1734-1820.

BRISTOL (*Second Tune*). C.M. Ravenscroft's *Psalter*, 1621.

1 City of God, how broad and far
Outspread thy walls sublime!
The true thy chartered freemen are,
Of every age and clime.

2 One holy Church, one army strong,
One steadfast high intent,
One working band, one harvest song,
One King Omnipotent.

3 How purely hath thy speech come down
From man's primeval youth!
How grandly hath thine empire grown
Of freedom, love, and truth!

4 How gleam thy watch-fires through the night
With never-fainting ray!
How rise thy towers, serene and bright
To meet the dawning day!

5 In vain the surge's angry shock,
In vain the drifting sands;
Unharmed upon the eternal Rock
The eternal City stands.

Samuel Johnson, 1822-82.

704

SLEEPERS, WAKE. 8 9.8.D.6 6.4.4 4 8. P. NICOLAI, 1556-1608.

Gottes Stadt steht festgegründet.

1 By the holy hills surrounded,
On her firm base securely founded,
Stands fast the city of the Lord:
None shall rend her walls asunder;
On her men look with fear and wonder, [and ward.
And mark who here keeps watch
He slumbers not, nor sleeps,
Who His loved Israel keeps.
Hallelujah!
Happy the race
Who through God's grace
Shall have in her their dwelling-place!

2 Zion's gates Jehovah loveth,
And with especial grace approveth;
He maketh fast her bolts and bars;
Those who dwell in her He blesses,
And comforts them in their distresses
Who cast on Him their griefs and cares.
How wonderful the grace
With which He doth embrace
All His people!
City of God,
How sweet the abode
On which such blessings are bestowed!

3 Taught in thee is a salvation
Unknown to every other nation;
There great and holy things are heard;
In the midst of thee abiding, [ing,
Enlightening, comforting, and guid-
Thou hast the Spirit and the Word;
There breathing peace around
Is heard the joyful sound,
Grace and mercy!
How sweet that is,
Which here speaks peace,
There crowns with everlasting bliss.

Carl Johann Philipp Spitta, 1801-59;
tr. by Richard Massie, 1800-87.

705

LASUS. L.M. A. H. Mann, 1850-1930.

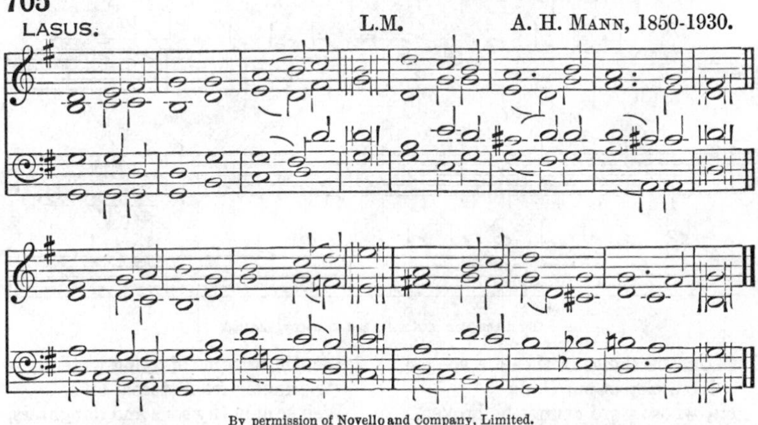

By permission of Novello and Company, Limited.

1 God is the refuge of His saints,
When storms of sharp distress invade;
Ere we can offer our complaints,
Behold Him present with His aid!

2 Let mountains from their seats be hurled
Down to the deep, and buried there,
Convulsions shake the solid world,
Our faith shall never yield to fear.

3 Loud may the troubled ocean roar;
In sacred peace our souls abide;
While every nation, every shore,
Trembles, and dreads the swelling tide.

4 There is a stream whose gentle flow
Makes glad the city of our God,
Life, love, and joy still gliding through,
And watering our divine abode.

5 This sacred stream, Thy vital word,
Thus all our raging fear controls;
Sweet peace Thy promises afford,
And give new strength to fainting souls.

6 Zion enjoys her Monarch's love,
Secure against the threatening hour;
Nor can her firm foundation move,
Built on His faithfulness and power.

Isaac Watts, 1674-1748.

706

LUX EOI. 8.7.8.7. D. A. SULLIVAN, 1842-1900.

1 GLORIOUS things of thee are spoken,
Zion, city of our God;
He, whose word cannot be broken,
Formed thee for His own abode.
On the Rock of Ages founded,
What can shake thy sure repose?
With salvation's walls surrounded,
Thou may'st smile at all thy foes.

2 See, the streams of living waters,
Springing from eternal love,
Well supply thy sons and daughters,
And all fear of want remove:
Who can faint, while such a river
Ever flows their thirst to assuage?
Grace which, like the Lord, the Giver,
Never fails from age to age.

3 Saviour, if of Zion's city
I, through grace, a member am,
Let the world deride or pity,
I will glory in Thy name:
Fading is the worldling's pleasure,
All his boasted pomp and show;
Solid joys and lasting treasure
None but Zion's children know.

John Newton, 1725-1807.

707

OLD 120TH. 6.6.6.6.6 6. ESTE'S *Psalter*, 1592.

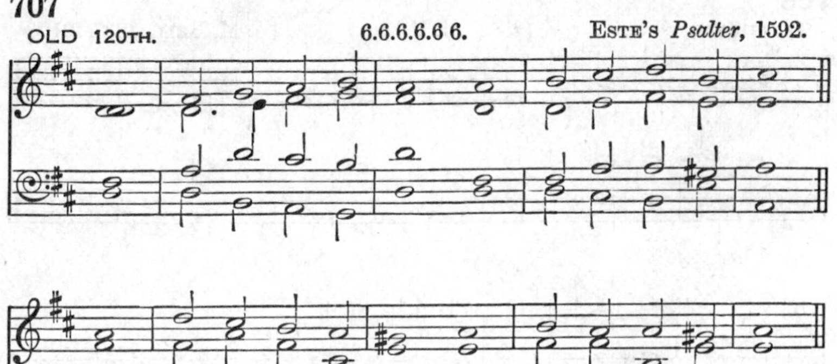

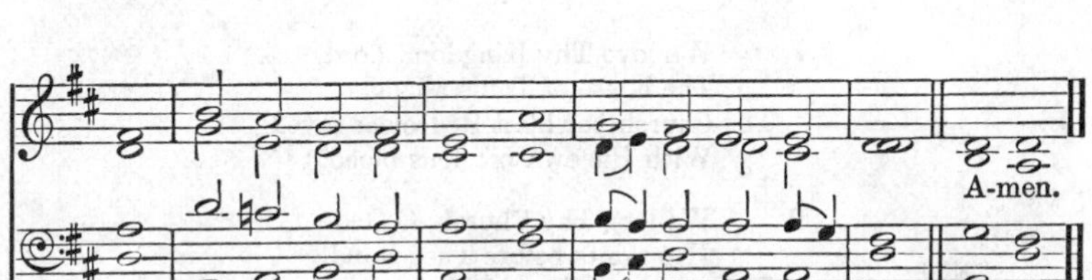

1 O THOU not made with hands,
Not throned above the skies,
Nor walled with shining walls,
Nor framed with stones of price,
More bright than gold or gem,
God's own Jerusalem.

2 Where'er the gentle heart
Finds courage from above;
Where'er the heart forsook
Warms with the breath of love;
Where faith bids fear depart,
City of God, thou art.

3 Thou art where'er the proud
In humbleness melts down;
Where self itself yields up;
Where martyrs win their crown;
Where faithful souls possess
Themselves in perfect peace.

4 Where in life's common ways
With cheerful feet we go;
Where in His steps we tread
Who trod the way of woe;
Where He is in the heart,
City of God, thou art.

5 Not throned above the skies,
Nor golden-walled afar,
But where Christ's two or three
In His name gathered are,
Be in the midst of them,
God's own Jerusalem. Amen.

Francis Turner Palgrave, 1824-97.

ST. GILES. S.M. J. M. BELL, 1837-1910.

1 We love Thy Kingdom, Lord,
The house of Thine abode,
The Church our blest Redeemer saved
With His own precious blood.

2 We love Thy Church, O God:
Her saints before Thee stand,
Dear as the apple of Thine eye,
And graven on Thy hand.

3 For her our tears shall fall,
For her our prayers ascend,
To her our cares and toils be given,
Till toils and cares shall end.

4 Beyond our highest joy
We prize her heavenly ways,
Her sweet communion, solemn vows,
Her hymns of love and praise.

5 Jesus, Thou Friend divine,
Our Saviour, and our King,
Thy hand from every snare and foe
Shall great deliverance bring.

6 Sure as Thy truth shall last,
To Zion shall be given
The brightest glories earth can yield,
And brighter bliss of heaven.

Timothy Dwight, 1752-1817.

Also:

363 Spirit of faith
441 Riches unsearchable
571 Blessèd are the pure
678 Lord of the worlds

709

FALCON STREET. S.M. I. SMITH, *c.* 1725-*c.* 1800.

DOXOLOGY.
Praise ye the Lord, Hal-le-lu-jah, Praise ye the Lord, Hal-le-lu-jah,
Hal-le-lu-jah, Hal-le-lu-jah, Hal-le-lu-jah, Praise ye the Lord.

1 AND are we yet alive,
And see each other's face?
Glory and praise to Jesus give
For His redeeming grace!

2 Preserved by power divine
To full salvation here,
Again in Jesu's praise we join,
And in His sight appear.

3 What troubles have we seen,
What conflicts have we passed,
Fightings without, and fears within,
Since we assembled last!

4 But out of all the Lord
Hath brought us by His love;
And still He doth His help afford,
And hides our life above.

5 Then let us make our boast
Of His redeeming power,
Which saves us to the uttermost,
Till we can sin no more:

6 Let us take up the cross,
Till we the crown obtain;
And gladly reckon all things loss,
So we may Jesus gain.

Charles Wesley, 1707-88.

OTTERBOURNE. L.M. F. J. HAYDN, 1732-1809.

1 BRETHREN in Christ, and well beloved,
To Jesus and His servants dear,
Enter, and show yourselves approved;
Enter, and find that God is here.

2 Welcome from earth: lo, the right hand
Of fellowship to you we give;
With open hearts and hands we stand,
And you in Jesu's name receive.

3 Jesu, Thyself in love reveal:
Are we not met in Thy great name?
Thee in the midst we wait to feel,
We wait to catch the spreading flame.

4 Thou God that answerest by fire,
The Spirit of burning now impart;
And let the flames of pure desire
Rise from the altar of our heart.

5 Truly our fellowship below
With Thee and with the Father is:
In Thee eternal life we know,
And heaven's unutterable bliss.

Charles Wesley, 1707-88.

711

NICOMACHUS. L.M. A. H. MANN, 1850-1930.

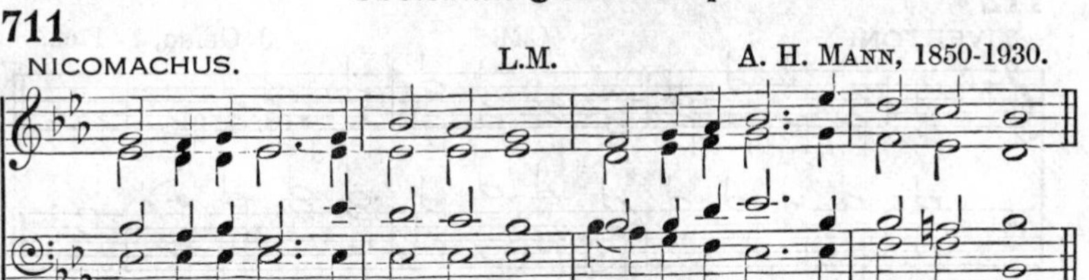

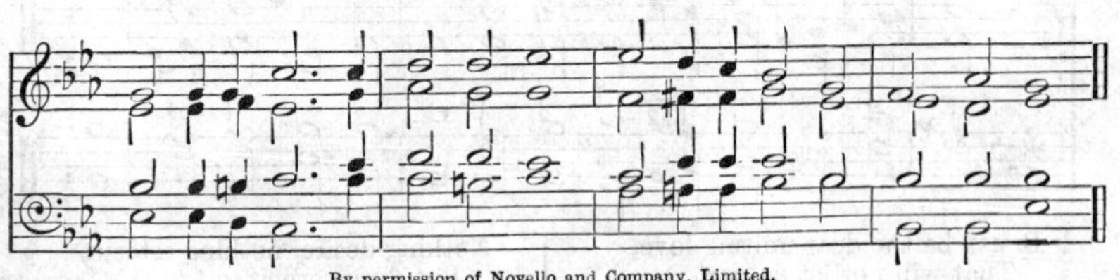

By permission of Novello and Company, Limited.

1.

How pleasant, how divinely fair,
O Lord of Hosts, Thy dwellings are!
With strong desire my spirit faints
To meet the assemblies of Thy saints.

2.

Blest are the saints that sit on high,
Around Thy throne of majesty;
Thy brightest glories shine above,
And all their work is praise and love.

3.

Blest are the souls that find a place
Within the temple of Thy grace;
Here they behold Thy gentler rays,
And seek Thy face, and learn Thy praise.

4.

Blest are the men whose hearts are set
To find the way to Zion's gate;
God is their strength, and through the road
They lean upon their helper God.

5.

Cheerful they walk with growing strength,
Till all shall meet in heaven at length;
Till all before Thy face appear,
And join in nobler worship there.

Isaac Watts, 1674-1748.

712

TIVERTON. C.M. J. Grigg, ?- 1768.

1 Blest be the dear uniting love,
That will not let us part;
Our bodies may far off remove,
We still are one in heart.

2 Joined in one spirit to our Head,
Where He appoints we go;
And still in Jesu's footsteps tread,
And show His praise below.

3 O may we ever walk in Him,
And nothing know beside,
Nothing desire, nothing esteem,
But Jesus crucified!

4 Closer and closer let us cleave
To His beloved embrace;
Expect His fullness to receive,
And grace to answer grace.

5 Partakers of the Saviour's grace,
The same in mind and heart,
Nor joy, nor grief, nor time, nor place,
Nor life, nor death can part.

Charles Wesley, 1707-88.

713

LOVE-FEAST. 7 7.7 7. D. *Foundery Collection*, 1742.

May also be sung to HART'S, No. 748.

1 LET us join—'tis God commands—
Let us join our hearts and hands;
Help to gain our calling's hope,
Build we each the other up:
Still forget the things behind,
Follow Christ in heart and mind,
Toward the mark unwearied press,
Seize the crown of righteousness.

2 While we walk with God in light,
God our hearts doth still unite;
Dearest fellowship we prove,
Fellowship in Jesu's love:
Sweetly each, with each combined,
In the bonds of duty joined,
Feels the cleansing blood applied,
Daily feels that Christ hath died.

3 Still, O Lord, our faith increase,
Cleanse from all unrighteousness:
Thee the unholy cannot see;
Make, O make us meet for Thee!
Every vile affection kill,
Root out every seed of ill,
Utterly abolish sin,
Write Thy law of love within.

4 Hence may all our actions flow,
Love the proof that Christ we know;
Mutual love the token be,
Lord, that we belong to Thee:
Love, Thine image, love impart!
Stamp it on our face and heart!
Only love to us be given!
Lord, we ask no other heaven.

Charles Wesley, 1707-88.

714

O JESU MI DULCISSIME. L.M. *Clausener Gesangbuch*, 1653.

1 HE wants not friends that hath Thy love,
And may converse and walk with Thee,
And with Thy saints here and above,
With whom for ever I must be.

2 In the communion of the saints
Is wisdom, safety and delight;
And, when my heart declines and faints,
It's raisèd by their heat and light!

3 As for my friends, they are not lost;
The several vessels of Thy fleet,
Though parted now, by tempests tost,
Shall safely in the haven meet.

4 Still we are centred all in Thee,
Members, though distant, of one Head;
In the same family we be,
By the same faith and spirit led.

5 Before Thy throne we daily meet,
As joint petitioners to Thee;
In spirit we each other greet,
And shall again each other see.

6 The heavenly hosts, world without end,
Shall be my company above;
And Thou, my best and surest Friend,
Who shall divide me from Thy love?

Richard Baxter, 1615-91.

715

MOUNTAIN CHRISTIANS. Irregular. J. MANNIN (Adapted).

1 FOR the might of Thine arm we bless Thee, our God, our fathers' God;
Thou hast kept Thy pilgrim people by the strength of Thy staff and rod;
Thou hast called us to the journey which faithless feet ne'er trod;
For the might of Thine arm we bless Thee, our God, our fathers' God.

2 For the love of Christ constraining, that bound their hearts as one;
For the faith in truth and freedom in which their work was done;
For the peace of God's evangel wherewith their feet were shod;
For the might of Thine arm we bless Thee, our God, our fathers' God.

3 We are watchers of a beacon whose light must never die;
We are guardians of an altar that shows Thee ever nigh;
We are children of Thy freemen who sleep beneath the sod;
For the might of Thine arm we bless Thee, our God, our fathers' God.

4 May the shadow of Thy presence around our camp be spread;
Baptize us with the courage Thou gavest to our dead;
O keep us in the pathway their saintly feet have trod;
For the might of Thine arm we bless Thee, our God, our fathers' God.

Charles Silvester Horne, 1865-1914.

716

ST. GODRIC. 6.6.6.6.8 8. J. B. DYKES, 1823-76.

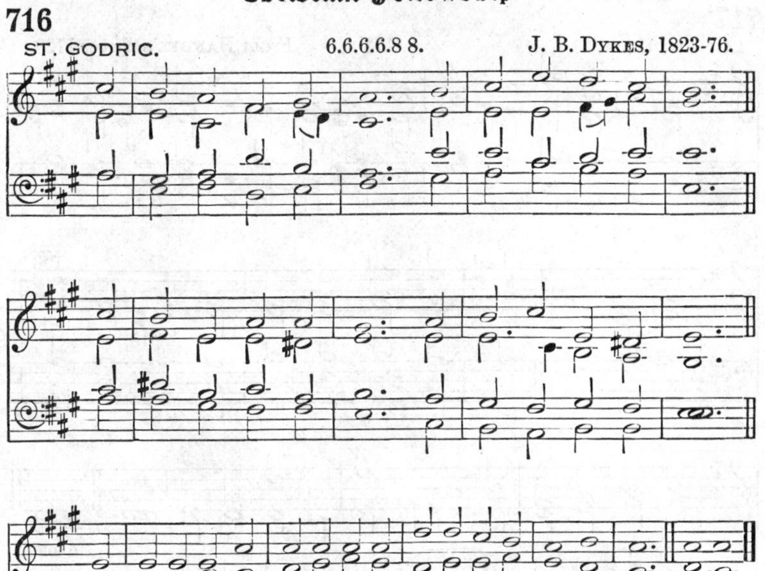

1 THOU God of truth and love,
We seek Thy perfect way,
Ready Thy choice to approve,
Thy providence to obey:
Enter into Thy wise design,
And sweetly lose our will in Thine.

2 Why hast Thou cast our lot
In the same age and place,
And why together brought
To see each other's face;
To join with loving sympathy,
And mix our friendly souls in Thee?

3 Didst Thou not make us one,
That we might one remain,
Together travel on,
And bear each other's pain;
Till all Thy utmost goodness prove,
And rise renewed in perfect love?

4 Then let us ever bear
The blessèd end in view,
And join, with mutual care,
To fight our passage through;
And kindly help each other on,
Till all receive the starry crown.

5 O may Thy Spirit seal
Our souls unto that day,
With all Thy fullness fill,
And then transport away:
Away to our eternal rest,
Away to our Redeemer's breast. Amen.

Charles Wesley, 1707-88.

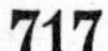

717

LUNENBURG. C.M. From HANDEL's *Siroe*, 1728.

1 HELP us to help each other, Lord,
  Each other's cross to bear,
Let each his friendly aid afford,
  And feel his brother's care.

2 Help us to build each other up,
  Our little stock inprove ;
Increase our faith, confirm our hope,
  And perfect us in love.

3 Up into Thee, our living Head,
  Let us in all things grow,
Till Thou hast made us free indeed,
  And spotless here below.

4 Then, when the mighty work is wrought,
  Receive Thy ready bride ;
Give us in heaven a happy lot
  With all the sanctified. Amen.

Charles Wesley, 1707-88.

718

REUBEN. S.M. S. WAKELEY, 1820- *c*. 82.

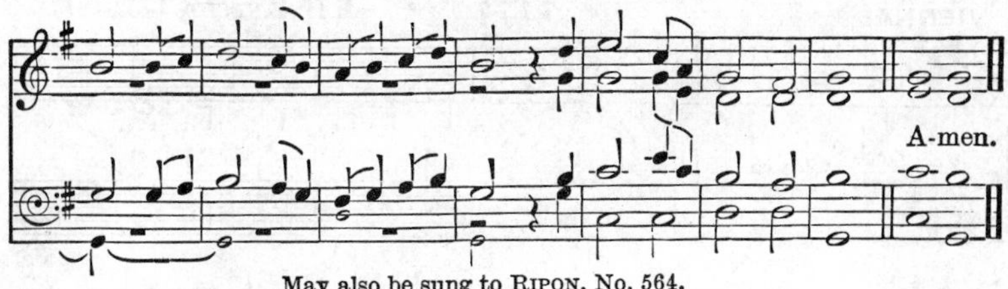

May also be sung to RIPON, No. 564.

1 JESUS, we look to Thee,
Thy promised presence claim;
Thou in the midst of us shalt be,
Assembled in Thy name.

2 Thy name salvation is,
Which here we come to prove;
Thy name is life and health and [peace
And everlasting love.

3 We meet, the grace to take
Which Thou hast freely given;
We meet on earth for Thy dear sake,
That we may meet in heaven.

4 Present we know Thou art,
But O Thyself reveal!
Now, Lord, let every bounding heart
The mighty comfort feel.

5 O may Thy quickening voice
The death of sin remove;
And bid our inmost souls rejoice
In hope of perfect love! Amen.

Charles Wesley, 1707-88.

719

BISHOPTHORPE. C.M. J. CLARKE, 1659 *or* 1670-1707

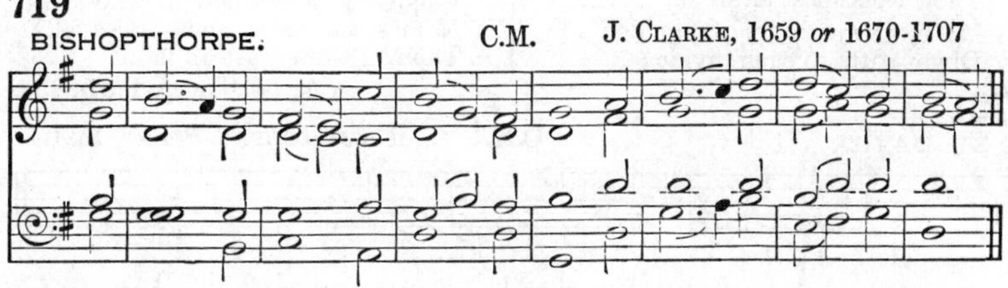

1 SEE, Jesu, Thy disciples see,
The promised blessing give;
Met in Thy name, we look to Thee,
Expecting to receive.

2 Thee we expect, our faithful Lord,
Who in Thy name are joined;
We wait, according to Thy word,
Thee in the midst to find.

3 With us Thou art assembled here;
But O Thyself reveal!
Son of the living God, appear!
Let us Thy presence feel.

4 Whom now we seek, O may we meet!
Jesus the crucified,
Show us Thy bleeding hands and feet,
Thou who for us hast died.

5 Cause us the record to receive,
Speak, and the tokens show—
O be not faithless, but believe
In Me, who died for you!

Charles Wesley, 1707-88.

720

VIENNA. 7 7.7 7. J. H. KNECHT, 1752-1817.

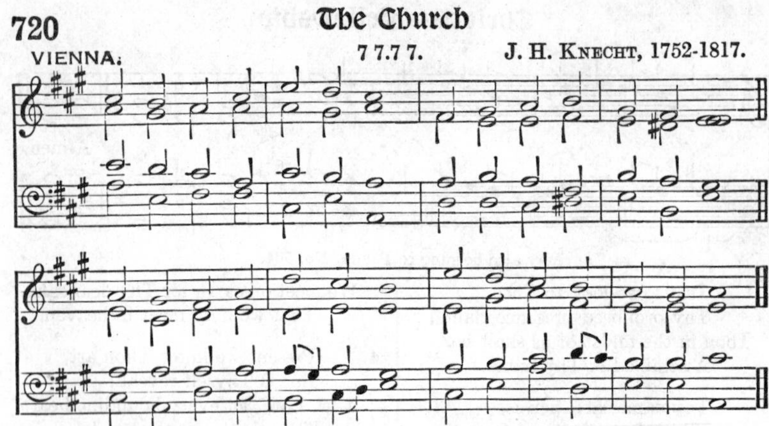

1 CHRIST, from whom all blessings flow,
Perfecting the saints below,
Hear us, who Thy nature share,
Who Thy mystic body are.

2 Join us, in one spirit join,
Let us still receive of Thine;
Still for more on Thee we call,
Thou who fillest all in all.

3 Move, and actuate, and guide:
Divers gifts to each divide;
Placed according to Thy will,
Let us all our work fulfil;

4 Sweetly may we all agree,
Touched with loving sympathy:
Kindly for each other care;
Every member feel its share.

5 Love, like death, hath all destroyed,
Rendered all distinctions void;
Names, and sects, and parties fall:
Thou, O Christ, art all in all.

Charles Wesley, 1707-88.

721

ST. DAVID. C.M. RAVENSCROFT'S *Psalter*, 1621.

1 JESUS, united by Thy grace
And each to each endeared,
With confidence we seek Thy face,
And know our prayer is heard.

2 Still let us own our common Lord,
And bear Thine easy yoke,
A band of love, a threefold cord,
Which never can be broke.

3 Make us into one spirit drink;
Baptize into Thy name;
And let us always kindly think
And sweetly speak the same.

4 Touched by the loadstone of Thy love,
Let all our hearts agree,
And ever toward each other move,
And ever move toward Thee.

5 To Thee, inseparably joined,
Let all our spirits cleave;
O may we all the loving mind
That was in Thee receive.

6 This is the bond of perfectness,
Thy spotless charity;
O let us, still we pray, possess
The mind that was in Thee. Amen.

Charles Wesley, 1707-88.

722

CHIMES. C.M. *Sacred Melody*, 1765.

1 Lift up your hearts to things above,
Ye followers of the Lamb,
And join with us to praise His love
And glorify His name.

2 To Jesu's name give thanks and sing,
Whose mercies never end :
Rejoice ! rejoice ! The Lord is King ;
The King is now our Friend !

3 We, for His sake, count all things loss ;
On earthly good look down ;
And joyfully sustain the cross,
Till we receive the crown.

4 O let us stir each other up,
Our faith by works to approve,
By holy, purifying hope,
And the sweet task of love.

5 You on our minds we ever bear,
Whoe'er to Jesus bow ;
Stretch out the arms of faith and prayer,
And lo, we reach you now.

6 Mercy and peace your portion be,
To carnal minds unknown,
The hidden manna, and the tree
Of life, and the white stone.

7 The blessings all on you be shed,
Which God in Christ imparts ;
We pray the Spirit of our Head
Into your faithful hearts.

8 Live till the Lord in glory come,
And wait His heaven to share :
Our Saviour now prepares our home :
Go on ; we'll meet you there.

Charles Wesley, 1707-88.

Also :

535 From every stormy wind
745 All praise to our
818 Happy the souls

723 THE COMMUNION OF SAINTS: THE CHURCH IN PRAYER

VATER UNSER (OLD 112TH). 8.8.8.8.8.8. *Geistliche Lieder*, 1539.

A-men.

May also be sung to EATON, No. 750.

1 O God of our forefathers, hear,
And make Thy faithful mercies known;
To Thee through Jesus we draw near,
Thy suffering, well belovèd Son,
In whom Thy smiling face we see,
In whom Thou art well pleased with me.

2 With solemn faith we offer up,
And spread before Thy glorious eyes,
That only ground of all our hope,
That precious, bleeding sacrifice,
Which brings Thy grace on sinners down,
And perfects all our souls in one.

3 Acceptance through His only name,
Forgiveness in His blood, we have;
But more abundant life we claim
Through Him who died our souls to save,
To sanctify us by His blood,
And fill with all the life of God.

4 Father, behold Thy dying Son,
And hear the blood that speaks above;
On us let all Thy grace be shown,
Peace, righteousness, and joy, and love,
Thy kingdom come to every heart,
And all Thou hast, and all Thou art.
Amen.

Charles Wesley, 1707-88.

724

JORDAN. 8.7.8.7.4.7. Welsh Melody.

1 Jesus, Lord of life and glory,
Bend from heaven Thy gracious ear;
While our waiting souls adore Thee,
Friend of helpless sinners, hear:
By Thy mercy,
O deliver us, good Lord!

2 From the depths of nature's blindness,
From the hardening power of sin,
From all malice and unkindness,
From the pride that lurks within:

3 When temptation sorely presses,
In the day of Satan's power,
In our times of deep distresses,
In each dark and trying hour:

4 When the world around is smiling,
In the time of wealth and ease,
Earthly joys our hearts beguiling,
In the day of health and peace:

5 In the weary hours of sickness,
In the time of grief and pain,
When we feel our mortal weakness,
When the creature's help is vain:

6 In the solemn hour of dying,
In the awful judgement day,
May our souls, on Thee relying,
Find Thee still our hope and stay:

John James Cummins, 1795-1867.

725

ST. PHILIP. 7 7 7. W. H. Monk, 1823-89.

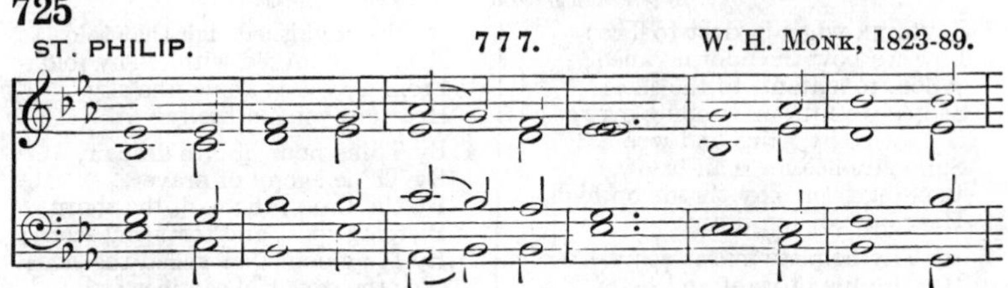

1 Lord, in this Thy mercy's day,
Ere it pass for aye away,
Humbly at Thy feet we pray.

2 Holy Jesus, grant us tears,
Fill us with heart-searching fears,
Ere that awful doom appears.

3 Lord, on us Thy Spirit pour,
Kneeling lowly at Thy door,
Ere it close for evermore.

4 By Thy night of agony,
By Thy supplicating cry,
By Thy willingness to die,

5 By Thy tears of bitter woe,
For Jerusalem below,
Let us not Thy love forego.

6 Judge and Saviour of our race,
When we see Thee face to face,
Grant us 'neath Thy wings a place.
Amen.

Isaac Williams, 1802-65.

726

ABERYSTWYTH. 7 7.7 7. D. J. Parry, 1841-1903.

A-men.

By permission of Messrs. Hughes & Son, Wrexham.

1 Saviour, when in dust to Thee
Low we bow the adoring knee;
When, repentant, to the skies
Scarce we lift our weeping eyes:
O by all Thy pains and woe
Suffered once for man below,
Bending from Thy throne on high,
Hear our solemn litany.

2 By Thy helpless infant years,
By Thy life of want and tears,
By Thy days of sore distress
In the savage wilderness,
By the dread, mysterious hour
Of the insulting tempter's power:
Turn, O turn a favouring eye,
Hear our solemn litany.

3 By the sacred grief that wept
O'er the grave where Lazarus slept,
By the boding tears that flowed
Over Salem's loved abode,
By the anguished sigh that told
Treachery lurked within Thy fold:
From Thy seat above the sky,
Hear our solemn litany.

4 By Thine hour of dire despair,
By Thine agony of prayer,
By the Cross, the nail, the thorn,
Piercing spear and torturing scorn;
By the gloom that veiled the skies
O'er the dreadful sacrifice:
Listen to our humble cry,
Hear our solemn litany.

5 By Thy deep expiring groan,
By the sad sepulchral stone,
By the vault whose dark abode
Held in vain the rising God:
O from earth to heaven restored,
Mighty re-ascended Lord,
Listen, listen to the cry
Of our solemn litany. Amen.

Robert Grant, 1785-1838

727

AGAPÉ. 7 7 7.6. G. Herbert, 1862.

1 Jesus, with Thy Church abide;
Be her Saviour, Lord, and Guide,
While on earth her faith is tried:
We beseech Thee, hear us.

2 Keep her life and doctrine pure;
Grant her patience to endure,
Trusting in Thy promise sure:
We beseech Thee, hear us.

3 May her voice be ever clear,
Warning of a judgement near,
Telling of a Saviour dear:
We beseech Thee, hear us.

4 All her fettered powers release;
Bid all strife and envy cease;
Grant the heavenly gift of peace:
We beseech Thee, hear us.

5 May she guide the poor and blind,
Seek the lost until she find,
And the broken-hearted bind:
We beseech Thee, hear us.

6 May her lamp of truth be bright;
Bid her bear aloft its light
Through the realms of heathen night:
We beseech Thee, hear us.

7 May she holy triumphs win,
Overthrow the hosts of sin,
Gather all the nations in:
We beseech Thee, hear us. Amen.

Thomas Benson Pollock, 1836-96.

728

AMOR DEI. 8 8 8.6. *Kirchen Gesänge*, 1707.

1 O God of mercy, God of might,
In love and pity infinite,
Teach us, as ever in Thy sight,
To live our life to Thee.

2 And Thou, who cam'st on earth to die,
That fallen man might live thereby,
O hear us, for to Thee we cry,
In hope, O Lord, to Thee.

3 Teach us the lesson Thou hast taught,
To feel for those Thy blood hath bought,
That every word and deed and thought
May work a work for Thee.

4 For all are brethren, far and wide,
Since Thou, O Lord, for all hast died:
Then teach us, whatsoe'er betide,
To love them all in Thee.

5 In sickness, sorrow, want, or care,
Whate'er it be, 'tis ours to share;
May we, where help is needed, there
Give help as unto Thee.

6 And may Thy Holy Spirit move
All those who live, to live in love,
Till Thou shalt greet in heaven above
All those who live to Thee.
Amen.

Godfrey Thring, 1823-1903.

729

CLOISTERS. 11 11 11.5. J. BARNBY, 1838-96.

A - men.

Christe, du Beistand deiner Kreuzgemeine.

1 LORD of our life, and God of our salvation,
Star of our night, and hope of every nation,
Hear and receive Thy Church's supplication,
Lord God Almighty.

2 See round Thine ark the hungry billows curling;
See how Thy foes their banners are unfurling;
Lord, while their darts envenomed they are hurling,
Thou canst preserve us.

3 Lord, Thou canst help when earthly armour faileth;
Lord, Thou canst save when deadly sin assaileth;
Lord, o'er Thy rock nor death nor hell prevaileth:
Grant us Thy peace, Lord.

4 Grant us Thy help till foes are backward driven;
Grant them Thy truth that they may be forgiven;
Grant peace on earth, and, after we have striven,
Peace in Thy heaven. Amen.

Matthäus Apelles von Löwenstern, 1594-1648;
free tr. by Philip Pusey, 1799-1855.

The Church in Prayer

730

STAMFORD. 8 8.8. D. S. REAY, 1822-1905.

1 FATHER of everlasting grace,
Thy goodness and Thy truth we praise, [prove;
Thy goodness and Thy truth we
Thou hast, in honour of Thy Son,
The gift unspeakable sent down,
The Spirit of life, and power, and love.

2 Send us the Spirit of Thy Son,
To make the depths of Godhead known,
To make us share the life divine;
Send Him the sprinkled blood to apply,
Send Him our souls to sanctify,
And show and seal us ever Thine.

3 So shall we pray, and never cease,
So shall we thankfully confess
Thy wisdom, truth, and power, and love;
With joy unspeakable adore,
And bless and praise Thee evermore,
And serve Thee as Thy hosts above:

4 Till, added to that heavenly choir,
We raise our songs of triumph higher,
And praise Thee in a bolder strain,
Out-soar the first-born seraph's flight,
And sing, with all our friends in light,
Thy everlasting love to man.
Amen.

Charles Wesley, 1707-88.

731

CŒNA DOMINI. 10 10. A. SULLIVAN, 1842-1900.

By permission of Novello and Company, Limited.

1 O CHRIST, our God, who with Thine own hast been,
Our spirits cleave to Thee, the Friend unseen.

2 Vouchsafe that all, who on Thy bounty feed
May heed Thy love and prize Thy gifts indeed.

3 Make every heart that is Thy dwelling-place
A watered garden, filled with fruits of grace.

4 Each holy purpose help us to fulfil;
Increase our faith to feed upon Thee still.

5 Illuminate our minds that we may see
In all around us holy signs of Thee.

6 And may such witness in our lives appear,
That all may know Thou hast been with us here.

7 So shalt Thou be for ever, loving Lord,
Our shield and our exceeding great reward.

George Hugh Bourne, 1840-1928.

732

SOUTHPORT. S.M. J. DAVIES, 1889.

1 Sweetly the holy hymn
Breaks on the morning air :
Before the world with smoke is dim
We meet to offer prayer.

2 While flowers are wet with dews,
Dew of our souls, descend ;
Ere yet the sun the day renews,
O Lord, Thy Spirit send !

3 Upon the battle-field,
Before the fight begins, [shield
We seek, O Lord, Thy sheltering
To guard us from our sins.

4 Ere yet our vessel sails
Upon the stream of day,
We plead, O Lord, for heavenly gales
To speed us on our way.

5 On the lone mountain side,
Before the morning's light,
The Man of Sorrows wept and cried,
And rose refreshed with might.

6 O hear us, then, for we
Are very weak and frail ;
We make the Saviour's name our
And surely must prevail. [plea,

Charles Haddon Spurgeon, 1834-92.

733

LUX PRIMA. 7.7.7.7.7 3. G. A. Macfarren, 1813-87.

Morgenglanz der Ewigkeit.

1 Jesus, Sun of Righteousness,
Brightest beam of love divine,
With the early morning rays,
Do Thou on our darkness shine,
And dispel with purest light
All our night.

2 As on drooping herb and flower
Falls the soft refreshing dew,
Let Thy Spirit's grace and power
All our weary souls renew ;
Showers of blessing over all
Softly fall.

3 Like the sun's reviving ray,
May Thy love with tender glow
All our coldness melt away,
Warm and cheer us forth to go,
Gladly serve Thee and obey
All the day.

4 O our only Hope and Guide,
Never leave us nor forsake ;
Keep us ever at Thy side
Till the eternal morning break,
Moving on to Zion's hill,
Homeward still. Amen.

Christian Knorr von Rosenroth, 1636-89 ;
tr. by Jane Laurie Borthwick [*H.L.L.*], 1813-97.

734

ST. CONSTANTINE. 6.5.6.5. W. H. Monk, 1823-89.

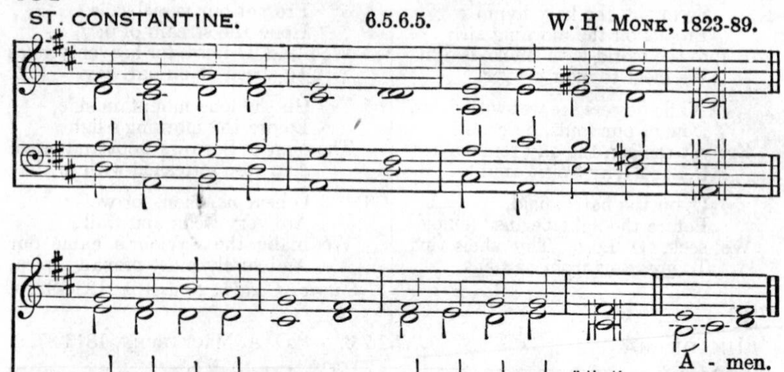

1.

Jesus, meek and gentle,
  Son of God most high,
Pitying, loving Saviour,
  Hear Thy children's cry.

2.

Pardon our offences,
  Loose our captive chains,
Break down every idol
  Which our soul detains.

3.

Give us holy freedom,
  Fill our hearts with love,
Draw us, holy Jesus,
  To the realms above.

4.

Lead us on our journey,
  Be Thyself the way
Through earth's passing darkness
  To heaven's endless day.

5.

Jesus, meek and gentle,
  Son of God most high,
Pitying, loving Saviour,
  Hear Thy children's cry. Amen.

George Rundle Prynne, 1818-1903.

735

INTERCESSION. 7.5.7.5.7.5.7.5.8 8. W. H. CALLCOTT. 1807-82.
Last two lines from MENDELSSOHN'S 'Elijah.'

1 WHEN the weary, seeking rest,
To Thy goodness flee;
When the heavy-laden cast
All their load on Thee;
When the troubled, seeking peace,
On Thy name shall call;
When the sinner, seeking life,
At Thy feet shall fall:

Hear then in love, O Lord, the cry,
In heaven, Thy dwelling-place on high.

2 When the child, with grave fresh lip,
Youth, or maiden fair;
When the agèd, weak and grey,
Seek Thy face in prayer;
When the widow weeps to Thee
Sad, and lone, and low;
When the orphan brings to Thee
All his orphan woe:

3 When the worldling, sick at heart,
Lifts his soul above;
When the prodigal looks back
To his Father's love;
When the proud man from his pride
Stoops to seek Thy face;
When the burdened brings his guilt
To Thy throne of grace: Amen.

Horatius Bonar, 1808-89.

ARNOLD'S. C.M. S. ARNOLD, 1740-1802.

1 SHEPHERD divine, our wants relieve
In this our evil day,
To all Thy tempted followers give
The power to watch and pray.

2 Long as our fiery trials last,
Long as the cross we bear,
O let our souls on Thee be cast
In never-ceasing prayer!

3 The Spirit of interceding grace
Give us in faith to claim;
To wrestle till we see Thy face,
And know Thy hidden name.

4 Till Thou Thy perfect love impart,
Till Thou Thyself bestow,
Be this the cry of every heart:
I will not let Thee go—

5 I will not let Thee go, unless
Thou tell Thy name to me,
With all Thy great salvation bless,
And make me all like Thee.

6 Then let me on the mountain-top
Behold Thy open face,
Where faith in sight is swallowed up,
And prayer in endless praise. Amen.

Charles Wesley, 1707-88.

737

CHESHUNT COLLEGE. 8.8.8.8.8.8 8. J. BARNBY, 1838-96.

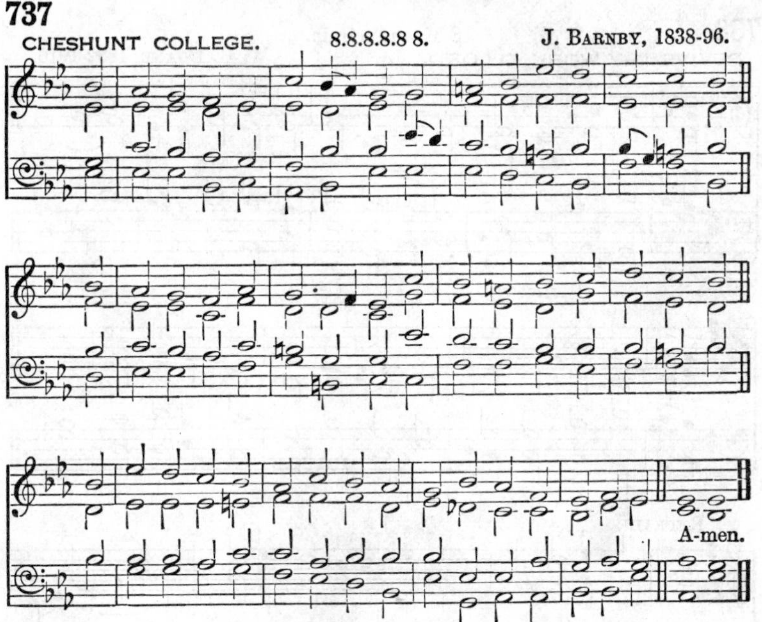

1 JESU, to Thee our hearts we lift—
  May all our hearts with love o'erflow—
With thanks for Thy continued gift,
  That still Thy precious name we know,
Retain our sense of sin forgiven,
And wait for all our inward heaven.

2 What mighty troubles hast Thou shown
  Thy feeble, tempted followers here!
We have through fire and water gone,
  But saw Thee on the floods appear,
But felt Thee present in the flame,
And shouted our Deliverer's name.

3 All are not lost or wandered back;
  All have not left Thy Church and Thee;
There are who suffer for Thy sake,
  Enjoy Thy glorious infamy,
Esteem the scandal of the cross,
And only seek divine applause.

4 Thou who hast kept us to this hour,
  O keep us faithful to the end:
When, robed with majesty and power,
  Our Jesus shall from heaven descend.
His friends and witnesses to own,
And seat us on His glorious throne. Amen.

Charles Wesley, 1707-88.

738

S.M. and refrain.

REVIVE THY WORK, O LORD.

W. H. DOANE, 1832-1916.

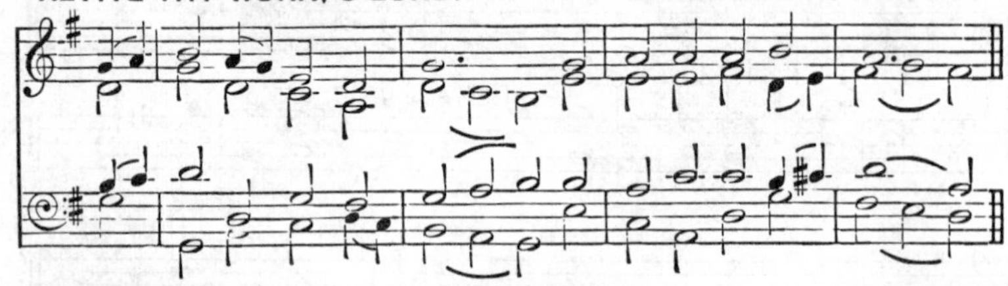

REFRAIN.

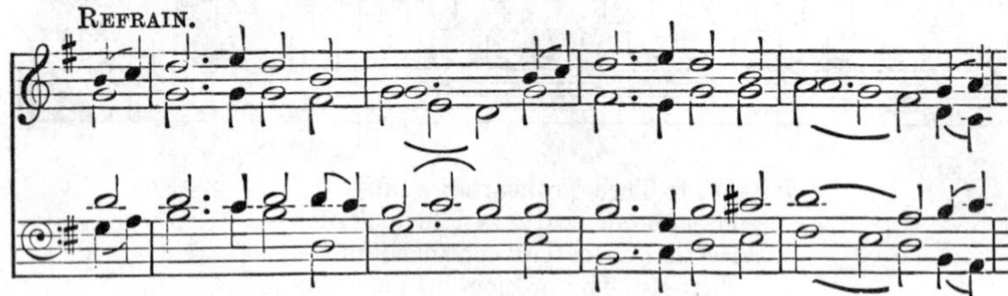

1 REVIVE Thy work, O Lord,
Thy mighty arm make bare;
Speak with the voice that wakes the dead,
And make Thy people hear.

Revive Thy work, O Lord,
While here to Thee we bow;
Descend, O gracious Lord, descend!
O come and bless us now.

2 Revive Thy work, O Lord,
Create soul-thirst for Thee;
And hungering for the Bread of Life,
O may our spirits be.

3 Revive Thy work, O Lord,
Exalt Thy precious name;
And, by the Holy Ghost, our love
For Thee and Thine inflame.

4 Revive Thy work, O Lord:
Give power unto Thy word;
Grant that Thy blessèd Gospel may
In living faith be heard.

5 Revive Thy work, O Lord,
And give refreshing showers;
The glory shall be all Thine own,
The blessing, Lord, be ours.

Albert Midlane, 1825-1909.

739

ABERDEEN. C.M. Bremner's *Collection*, 1763.

1 Our Father, hear our longing prayer,
And help this prayer to flow,
That humble thoughts, which are Thy care,
May live in us and grow.

2 For lowly hearts shall understand
The peace, the calm delight
Of dwelling in Thy heavenly land,
A pleasure in Thy sight.

3 Give us humility, that so
Thy reign may come within,
And when Thy children homeward go,
We too may enter in.

4 Hear us, our Saviour ! Ours Thou art,
Though we are not like Thee ;
Give us Thy spirit in a heart
Large, lowly, trusting, free. Amen.

George MacDonald, 1824-1905.

740

BEVAN. 6.6.6.6.8 8. J. Goss, 1800-80.

1 Father of all, to Thee
With loving hearts we pray,
Through Him, in mercy given,
The life, the truth, the way;
From Heaven, Thy Throne, in mercy shed
Thy blessings on each bended head.

2 Father of all, to Thee
Our contrite hearts we raise,
Unstrung by sin and pain,
Long voiceless in Thy praise;
Breathe Thou the silent chords along,
Until they tremble into song.

3 Father of all, to Thee
We breathe unuttered fears,
Deep-hidden in our souls,
That have no voice but tears;
Take Thou our hand, and through the wild
Lead gently on each trustful child.

4 Father of all, may we
In praise our tongues employ,
When gladness fills the soul
With deep and hallowed joy;
In storm and calm give us to see
The path of peace which leads to Thee. Amen.

John Julian, 1839-1913.

741

CREDO. 8.8.8.8.8 8. J. Stainer, 1840-1901.

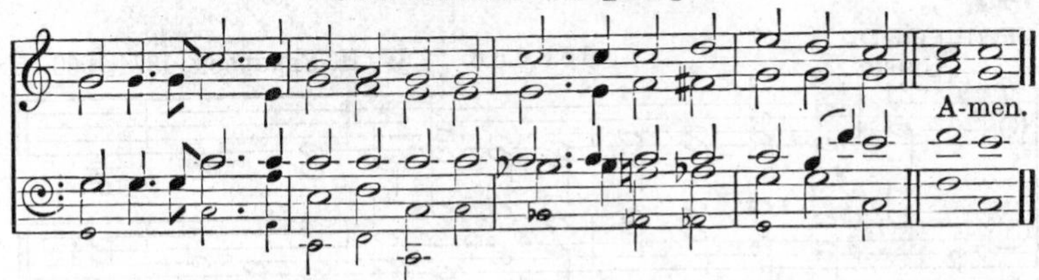

1 We have not known Thee as we ought,
Nor learned Thy wisdom, grace, and power;
The things of earth have filled our thought,
And trifles of the passing hour:
Lord, give us light Thy truth to see,
And make us wise in knowing Thee.

2 We have not feared Thee as we ought,
Nor bowed beneath Thine awful eye,
Nor guarded deed, and word, and thought,
Remembering that God was nigh:
Lord, give us faith to know Thee near,
And grant the grace of holy fear.

3 We have not loved Thee as we ought,
Nor cared that we are loved by Thee;
Thy presence we have coldly sought,
And feebly longed Thy face to see:
Lord, give a pure and loving heart
To feel and know the Love Thou art.

4 We have not served Thee as we ought;
Alas the duties left undone,
The work with little fervour wrought,
The battles lost or scarcely won!
Lord, give the zeal, and give the might,
For Thee to toil, for Thee to fight.

5 When shall we know Thee as we ought,
And fear, and love, and serve aright?
When shall we, out of trial brought,
Be perfect in the land of light?
Lord, may we day by day prepare
To see Thy face and serve Thee there. Amen.

Thomas Benson Pollock, 1836-96.

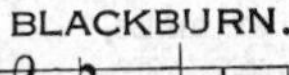

742

BLACKBURN. C.M. HARRISON'S *Sacred Harmony*, 1784.

1 Thy kingdom come—on bended knee
The passing ages pray;
And faithful souls have yearned to see
On earth that kingdom's day.

2 But the slow watches of the night
Not less to God belong,
And for the everlasting right
The silent stars are strong.

3 And lo, already on the hills
The flags of dawn appear;
Gird up your loins, ye prophet souls,
Proclaim the day is near:

4 The day in whose clear-shining light
All wrong shall stand revealed,
When justice shall be clothed with might,
And every hurt be healed:

5 When knowledge, hand in hand with peace
Shall walk the earth abroad—
The day of perfect righteousness,
The promised day of God.

Frederick Lucian Hosmer, 1840-1929.

FRILFORD. UNISON. 6.6.6.6.6.6. W. H. FERGUSON, 1874-1950

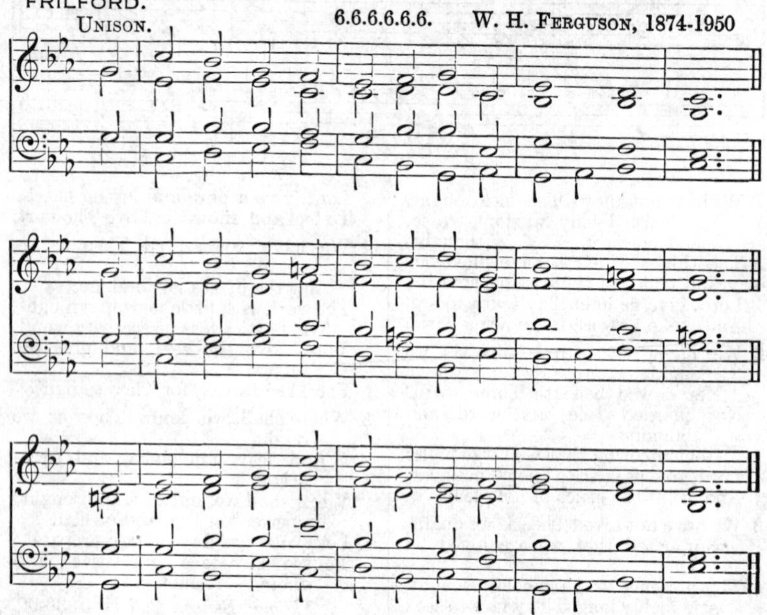

1 NOT for our sins alone
Thy mercy, Lord, we sue;
Let fall Thy pitying glance
On our devotions too—
What we have done for Thee,
And what we think to do.

2 The holiest hours we spend
In prayer upon our knees,
The times when most we deem
Our songs of praise will please,
Thou searcher of all hearts,
Forgiveness pour on these.

3 And all the gifts we bring,
And all the vows we make,
And all the acts of love
We plan for Thy dear sake,
Into Thy pardoning thought,
O God of mercy, take.

4 And most when we, Thy flock,
Before Thine altar bend,
And strange bewildering thoughts
With those sweet moments blend,
By Him whose death we plead,
Good Lord, Thy help extend.

5 Bow down Thine ear and hear:
Open Thine eyes and see:
Our very love is shame;
And we must come to Thee
To make it, of Thy grace,
What Thou wouldst have it be.

Henry Twells, 1823-1900.

Also:

363 Spirit of faith, come down
534 Jesus, Thou sovereign Lord
541 Pray, without ceasing
675 Jesus, where'er
682 God of pity

The Communion of Saints: Lovefeast and Covenant Services

744

HAPPY DAY. L.M. and refrain. *Wesleyan Sacred Harp*, 1855.

May also be sung to **Samson**, No. 418.

1 O happy day that fixed my choice
On Thee, my Saviour and my God!
Well may this glowing heart rejoice,
And tell its raptures all abroad.

Happy day! Happy day!
When Jesus washed my sins away;
He taught me how to watch and pray,
And live rejoicing every day;
Happy day! Happy day!
When Jesus washed my sins away.

2 O happy bond that seals my vows
To Him who merits all my love!
Let cheerful anthems fill His house,
While to that sacred shrine I move.

3 'Tis done, the great transaction's done!
I am my Lord's, and He is mine;
He drew me, and I followed on,
Charmed to confess the voice divine.

4 Now rest, my long-divided heart;
Fixed on this blissful centre, rest:
Nor ever from thy Lord depart,
With Him of every good possessed.

5 High heaven, that heard the solemn vow,
That vow renewed shall daily hear,
Till in life's latest hour I bow,
And bless in death a bond so dear.

Philip Doddridge, 1702-51.

745

LUCIUS. C.M. *Templi Carmina*, 1829.

1 All praise to our redeeming Lord,
Who joins us by His grace,
And bids us, each to each restored,
Together seek His face.

2 He bids us build each other up;
And, gathered into one,
To our high calling's glorious hope
We hand in hand go on.

3 The gift which He on one bestows,
We all delight to prove;
The grace through every vessel flows,
In purest streams of love.

4 Even now we think and speak the same,
And cordially agree;
Concentred all, through Jesu's name,
In perfect harmony.

5 We all partake the joy of one,
The common peace we feel,
A peace to sensual minds unknown,
A joy unspeakable.

6 And if our fellowship below
In Jesus be so sweet,
What heights of rapture shall we know
When round His throne we meet.

Charles Wesley, 1707-88.

746 

DRAW ME NEARER. 10.7.10.7. and refrain. W. H. Doane, 1832-1916.

Refrain.

nearer, nearer,

1 I am Thine, O Lord; I have heard Thy voice,
And it told Thy love to me;
But I long to rise in the arms of faith,
And be closer drawn to Thee.

Draw me nearer, nearer, blessèd Lord,
To the Cross where Thou hast died:
Draw me nearer, nearer, nearer, blessèd Lord,
To Thy precious, bleeding side.

2 Consecrate me now to Thy service, Lord,
By the power of grace divine;
Let my soul look up with a steadfast hope,
And my will be lost in Thine.

3 O the pure delight of a single hour
That before Thy throne I spend,
When I kneel in prayer, and with Thee, my God,
I commune as friend with friend.

4 There are depths of love that I cannot know
Till I cross the narrow sea;
There are heights of joy that I may not reach
Till I rest in peace with Thee.

Frances Jane van Alstyne, 1820-1915.

747

ST. IGNATIUS. 5.5.5.5.6.5.6.5. J. BEAUMONT, 1762-1822.

1 All thanks to the Lamb,
  Who gives us to meet:
His love we proclaim,
  His praises repeat;
We own Him our Jesus,
  Continually near
To pardon and bless us,
  And perfect us here.

2 In Him we have peace,
  In Him we have power,
Preserved by His grace
  Throughout the dark hour,
In all our temptation
  He keeps us, to prove
His utmost salvation,
  His fullness of love.

3 Through pride and desire
  Unhurt we have gone,
Through water and fire
  In Him we went on;
The world and the devil
  Through Him we o'ercame,
Our Saviour from evil,
  For ever the same.

4 O what shall we do
  Our Saviour to love?
To make us anew,
  Come, Lord, from above:
The fruit of Thy passion,
  Thy holiness, give,
Give us the salvation
  Of all that believe.

5 Pronounce the glad word,
  And bid us be free;
Ah! hast Thou not, Lord,
  A blessing for me?
The peace Thou hast given
  This moment impart,
And open Thy heaven
  Of love in my heart.

6 Come, Jesus, and loose
  The stammerer's tongue,
And teach even us
  The spiritual song;
Let us without ceasing
  Give thanks for Thy grace,
And glory, and blessing,
  And honour, and praise. Amen.

Charles Wesley, 1707-88.

748

HART'S. 7 7.7 7. B. MILGROVE, *c.* 1731-1810.

May also be sung to LOVE-FEAST, No. 713.

1 COME, and let us sweetly join
Christ to praise in hymns divine;
Give we all, with one accord,
Glory to our common Lord.

2 Hands and hearts and voices raise
Sing as in the ancient days;
Antedate the joys above,
Celebrate the feast of love.

3 Strive we, in affection strive;
Let the purer flame revive,
Such as in the martyrs glowed,
Dying champions for their God.

4 We, like them, may live and love;
Called we are their joys to prove,
Saved with them from future wrath,
Partners of like precious faith.

5 Sing we then in Jesu's name,
Now as yesterday the same;
One in every time and place,
Full for all of truth and grace.

6 We for Christ, our Master, stand,
Lights in a benighted land:
We our dying Lord confess;
We are Jesu's witnesses.

7 Witnesses that Christ hath died,
We with Him are crucified;
Christ hath burst the bands of death,
We His quickening Spirit breathe.

8 Christ is now gone up on high,
Thither all our wishes fly;
Sits at God's right hand above,
There with Him we reign in love.

Charles Wesley, 1707-88.

749

DUNDEE (FRENCH). C.M. *Scottish Psalter*, 1615.

1 COME, let us use the grace divine,
  And all, with one accord,
In a perpetual covenant join
  Ourselves to Christ the Lord:

2 Give up ourselves, through Jesu's [power,
  His name to glorify;
And promise, in this sacred hour,
  For God to live and die.

3 The covenant we this moment make
  Be ever kept in mind:
We will no more our God forsake,
  Or cast His words behind.

4 We never will throw off His fear
  Who hears our solemn vow;
And if Thou art well pleased to hear,
  Come down, and meet us now.

5 To each the covenant blood apply,
  Which takes our sins away;
And register our names on high,
  And keep us to that day. Amen.

Charles Wesley, 1707-88.

750

EATON. 8.8.8.8.8.8. Z. WYVILL, 1763-1837.

A-men.

1 O God, how often hath Thine ear
To me in willing mercy bowed!
While worshipping Thine altar near,
Lowly I wept, and strongly vowed;
But ah! the feebleness of man!
Have I not vowed and wept in vain?

2 Return, O Lord of hosts, return!
Behold Thy servant in distress;
My faithlessness again I mourn;
Again forgive my faithlessness;
And to Thine arms my spirit take,
And bless me for the Saviour's sake.

3 In pity of the soul Thou lov'st,
Now bid the sin Thou hat'st expire;
Let me desire what Thou approv'st,
Thou dost approve what I desire;
And Thou wilt deign to call me Thine,
And I will dare to call Thee mine.

4 This day the covenant I sign,
The bond of sure and promised peace;
Nor can I doubt its power divine,
Since sealed with Jesu's blood it is:
That blood I trust, that blood alone,
And make the covenant peace mine own.

5 But, that my faith no more may know
Or change, or interval, or end,
Help me in all Thy paths to go,
And now, as e'er, my voice attend,
And gladden me with answers mild,
And commune, Father, with Thy child. Amen.

William Maclardie Bunting, 1805-66.

Also:

406 My God, I am Thine
407 How happy are they
475 I need Thee every hour
560 Jesus hath died
717 Help us to help each other
956 Come, let us anew

THE SACRAMENTS: BAPTISM

751

DUBLIN. C.M. J. A. Stevenson, 1762-1833.

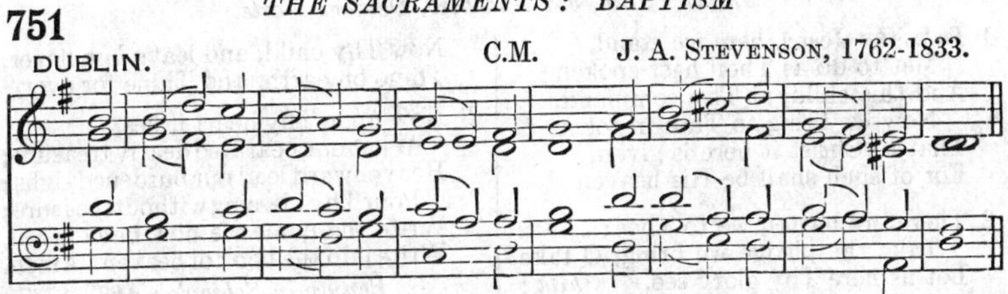

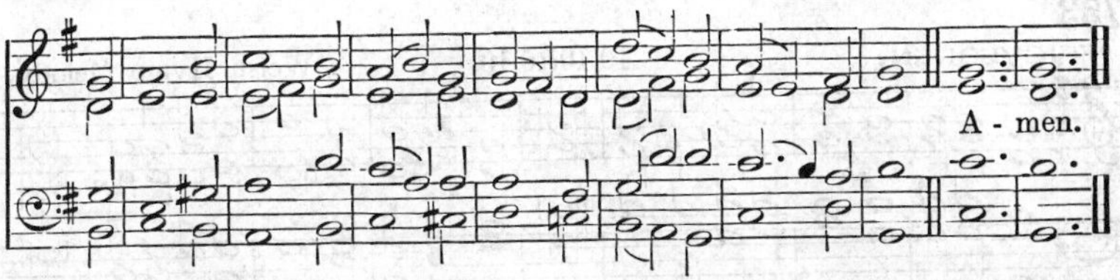

1 See Israel's gentle Shepherd stand
With all-engaging charms;
Hark how He calls the tender lambs,
And folds them in His arms!

2 Permit them to approach, He cries,
Nor scorn their humble name;
For 'twas to bless such souls as these
The Lord of Angels came.

3 We bring them, Lord, in thankful hands,
And yield them up to Thee;
Joyful that we ourselves are Thine,
Thine let our children be. Amen.

Philip Doddridge, 1702-51.

752

ST. MARK. 7.8.7.8 8 8. J. R. AHLE, 1625-73.

A -men.

Liebster Jesu, wir sind hier, Deinem Worte.

1 BLESSÈD Jesus, here we stand,
Met to do as Thou hast spoken;
And this child, at Thy command,
Now we bring to Thee in token
That to Christ it here is given,
For of such shall be His heaven.

2 Therefore hasten we to Thee;
Take the pledge we bring, O take *him*;
Let us here Thy glory see,
And in tender pity make *him*
Now Thy child, and leave *him* never,
Thine on earth, and Thine for ever.

3 Now upon Thy heart it lies,
What our hearts so dearly treasure;
Heavenward lead our burdened sighs;
Pour Thy blessing without measure;
Write the name we now have given,
Write it in the book of heaven. Amen.

Benjamin Schmolck, 1672-1737;
tr. by Catherine Winkworth, 1827-78.

753

FFIGYSBREN. 10 10.10 10. Welsh Hymn Melody.

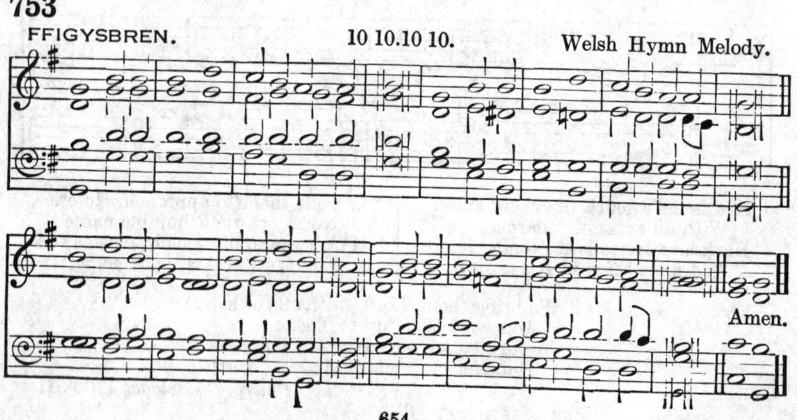

1 Friend of the home, as when in Galilee
The mothers brought their little ones to Thee,
So we, dear Lord, would now the children bring,
And seek for them the shelter of Thy wing.

2 Thine are they, by Thy love's eternal claim,
Thine we baptize them in the threefold Name:
Yet not the sign we trust, Lord, but the grace
That in Thy fold prepared the lambs a place.

3 Lord, may Thy Church, as with a mother's care,
For Thee the lambs within her bosom bear;
And grant, as morning fades to noon, that they
Still in her love and holy service stay.

4 Draw through the child the parents nearer Thee,
Endue their home with growing sanctity:
And gather all, by earthly homes made one,
In heaven, O Christ, when earthly days are done. Amen.

Howell Elvet Lewis, 1860-1953.

754

Baptism of Adults.

KERRY. S.M. J. Jowett, 1784-1856.

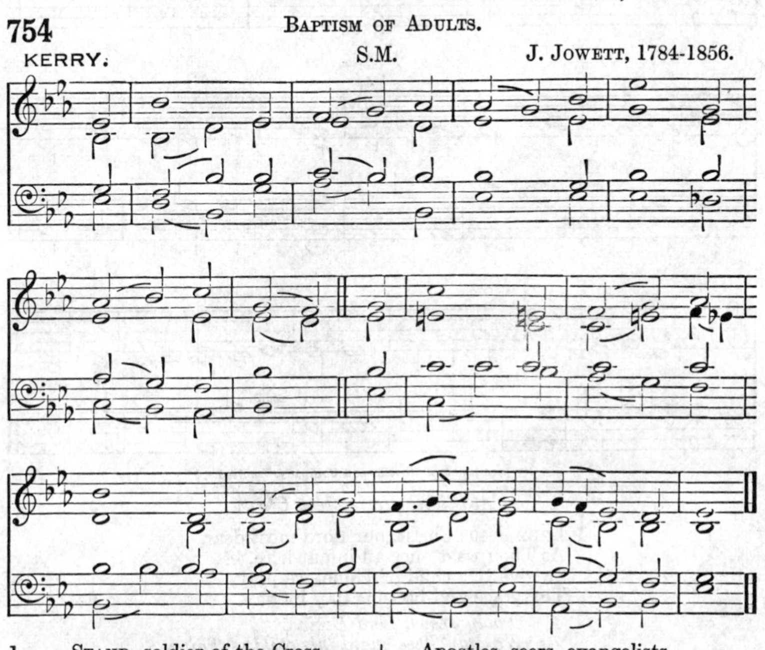

1 Stand, soldier of the Cross,
Thy high allegiance claim,
And vow to hold the world but loss
For thy Redeemer's name.

2 Arise, and be baptized,
And wash thy sins away;
Thy league with God be solemnized,
Thy faith avouched to-day.

3 No more thine own, but Christ's
With all the saints of old,
Apostles, seers, evangelists,
And martyr throngs enrolled—

4 In God's whole armour strong,
Front hell's embattled powers:
The warfare may be sharp and long,
The victory must be ours.

5 O bright the conqueror's crown,
The song of triumph sweet,
When faith casts every trophy down
At our great Captain's feet!

Edward Henry Bickersteth, 1825-1906.

755

8 8.8 8.8 8 8.

ST. CHRYSOSTOM (BARNBY). J. Barnby, 1838-96.

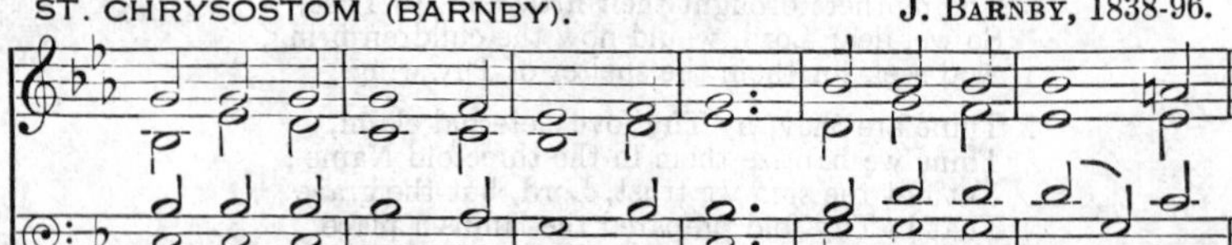

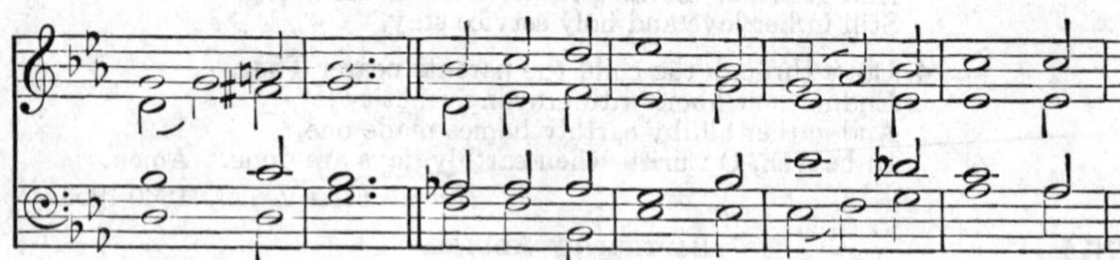

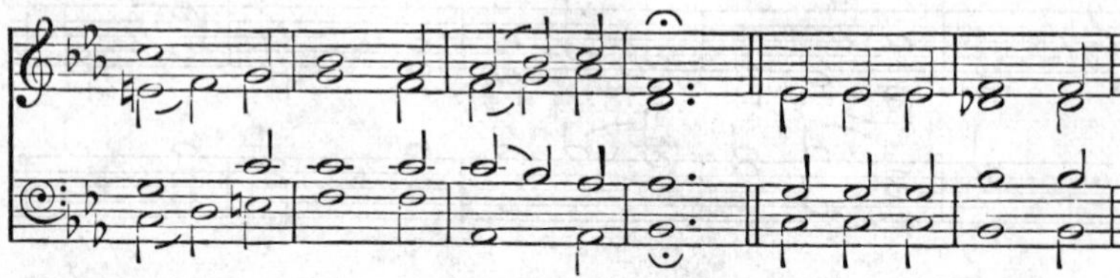

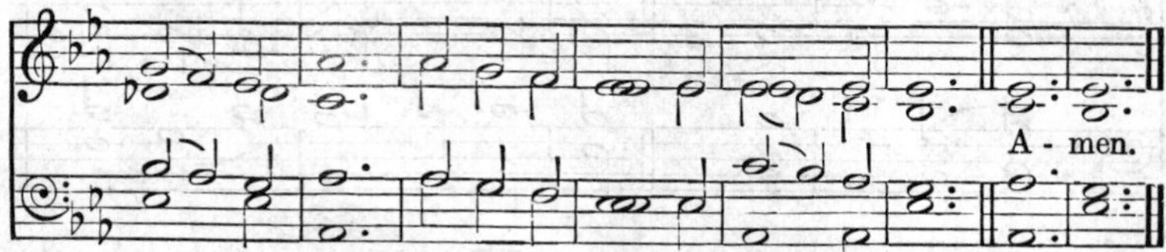

By permission of Novello and Company, Limited.

Ach lieber Herre, Jesu Christ.

1 Lord Jesus Christ, our Lord most dear,
As Thou wast once an infant here,
So give this child of Thine, we pray,
Thy grace and blessing day by day.
O holy Jesus, Lord Divine,
We pray Thee guard this child of Thine.

2 As in Thy heavenly Kingdom, Lord,
All things obey Thy sacred word,
Do Thou Thy mighty succour give,
And shield this child by morn and eve.

3 Their watch let angels round *him* keep
Where'er *he* be, awake, asleep;
Thy holy cross now let *him* bear,
That *he* Thy crown with saints may wear. Amen.

Heinrich von Laufenberg, 15*th cent.*;
tr. by Catherine Winkworth, 1827-78

756

RENDEZ À DIEU. 9.8.9.8. D. *Genevan Psalter*, 1543.

Bread of the world, in mercy broken;
  Wine of the soul, in mercy shed;
By whom the words of life were spoken,
  And in whose death our sins are dead:
Look on the heart by sorrow broken,
  Look on the tears by sinners shed,
And be Thy feast to us the token
  That by Thy grace our souls are fed.

Reginald Heber, 1783-1826.

757

CULBACH. 7.7.7.7. Scheffler's *Heilige Seelenlust*, 1657.

1 Spread the table of the Lord,
  Break the bread and pour the wine;
Gathered at the sacred board,
  We would taste the feast divine.

2 Saints and martyrs of the faith
  To the Cross have turned their eyes,
Sharing, in their life and death,
  That eternal sacrifice.

3 Humbly now our place we claim
  In that glorious company,
Proud confessors of the name,
  Breaking bread, O Christ, with Thee.

4 By the memory of Thy love,
  To the glory of the Lord,
Here we raise Thy Cross above,
  Gird us with Thy Spirit's sword.

5 Guided by Thy mighty hand,
  All Thy mind we would fulfil,
Loyal to Thy least command,
  Serving Thee with steadfast will.

George Osborn Gregory, 1881- .

758

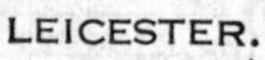
LEICESTER. C.M. W. Hurst, 1849-1934

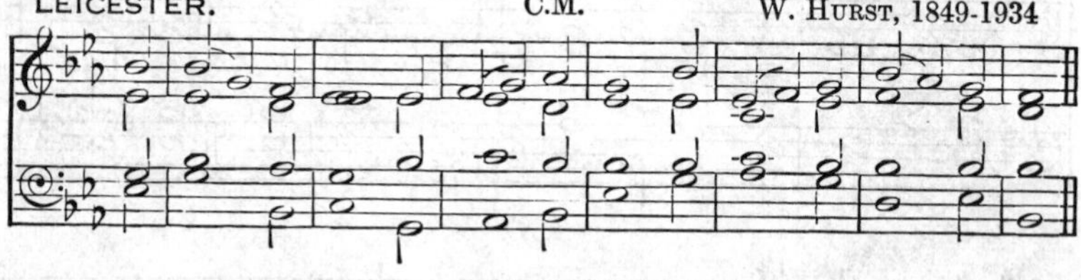

1 I am not worthy, holy Lord,
  That Thou shouldst come to me;
Speak but the word: one gracious word
  Can set the sinner free.

2 I am not worthy; cold and bare
  The lodging of my soul;
How canst Thou deign to enter there?
  Lord, speak, and make me whole.

3 I am not worthy; yet, my God,
  How can I say Thee nay,
Thee, who didst give Thy flesh and blood
  My ransom-price to pay?

4 O come, in this sweet morning hour,
  Feed me with food divine;
And fill with all Thy love and power
  This worthless heart of mine.
    Amen.

Henry Williams Baker, 1821-77.

759

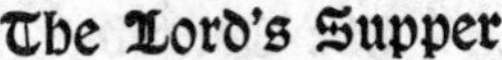

UNDE ET MEMORES. 10.10.10.10.10 10. W. H. MONK, 1823-89.

A-men.

May also be sung to SONG I., No. 458.

1 AND now, O Father, mindful of the love
   That bought us, once for all, on Calvary's tree,
And having with us Him that pleads above,
   We here present, we here spread forth to Thee
That only offering perfect in Thine eyes,
The one true, pure, immortal sacrifice.

2 Look, Father, look on His anointed face,
   And only look on us as found in Him;
Look not on our misusings of Thy grace,
   Our prayer so languid, and our faith so dim:
For lo! between our sins and their reward
We set the passion of Thy Son our Lord.

3 And then for those, our dearest and our best,
   By this prevailing presence we appeal;
O fold them closer to Thy mercy's breast,
   O do Thine utmost for their souls' true weal;
From tainting mischief keep them white and clear,
And crown Thy gifts with strength to persevere.

4 And so we come: O draw us to Thy feet,
   Most patient Saviour, who canst love us still;
And by this food, so awful and so sweet,
   Deliver us from ev'ry touch of ill:
In Thine own service make us glad and free,
And grant us never more to part with Thee. Amen.

William Bright, 1824-1901.

760

DEVOTION. 6 6.7.7.7.7. C. GARBUTT, 1904.

A-men.

1 SAVIOUR, and can it be
That Thou shouldst dwell with me?
From Thy high and lofty throne,
Throne of everlasting bliss,
Will Thy Majesty stoop down
To so mean a house as this?

2 I am not worthy, Lord,
So foul, so self-abhorred,
Thee, my God, to entertain
In this poor polluted heart:
I a frail and sinful man;
All my nature cries: Depart!

3 Yet come, Thou heavenly Guest,
And purify my breast;
Come, Thou great and glorious King,
While before Thy Cross I bow;
With Thyself salvation bring,
Cleanse the house by entering now. Amen.

Charles Wesley, 1707-88.

761

ST. AUGUSTINE. S.M. J. S. BACH's *Choralgesänge*, 1784-7

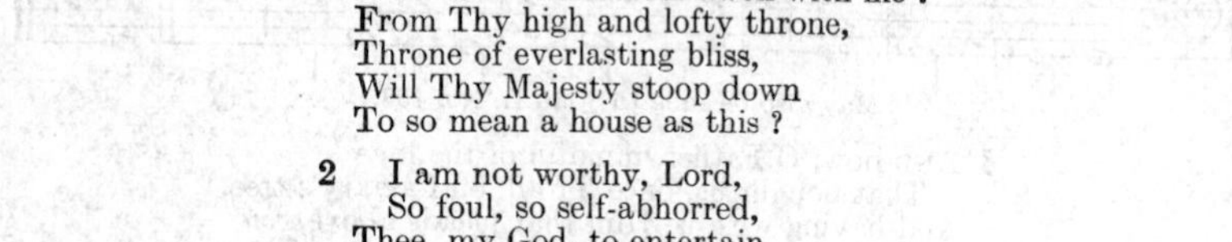

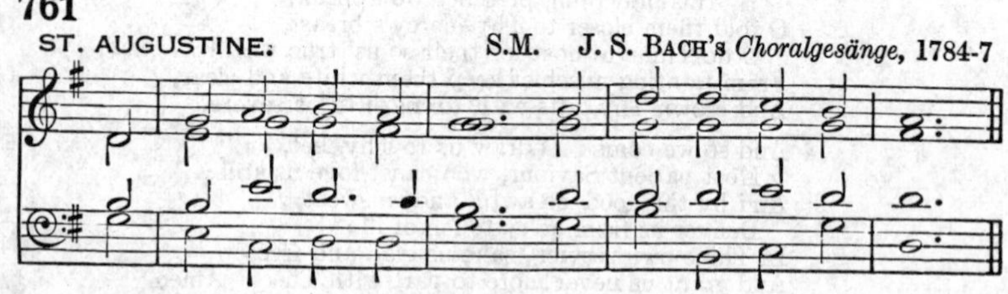

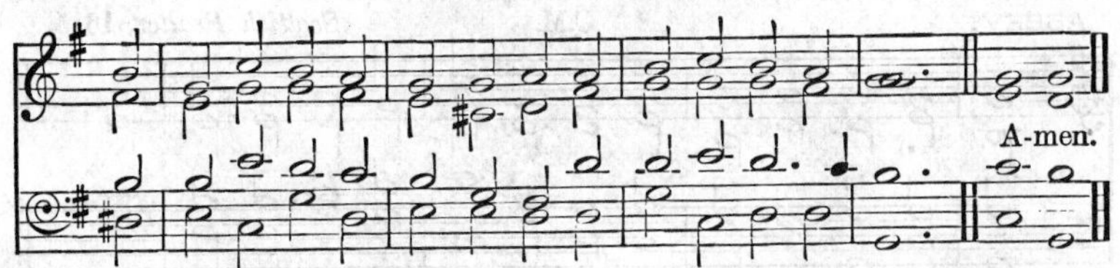

1 Jesus, we thus obey
Thy last and kindest word;
Here, in Thine own appointed way,
We come to meet Thee, Lord.

2 Our hearts we open wide,
To make the Saviour room;
And lo! the Lamb, the Crucified,
The sinner's Friend, is come.

3 Thy presence makes the feast;
Now let our spirits feel
The glory not to be expressed,
The joy unspeakable.

4 With high and heavenly bliss
Thou dost our spirits cheer;
Thy house of banqueting is this,
And Thou hast brought us here.

5 Now let our souls be fed
With manna from above,
And over us Thy banner spread
Of everlasting love. Amen.

Charles Wesley, 1707-88.

762

ARNOLD'S. C.M. S. Arnold, 1740-1802.

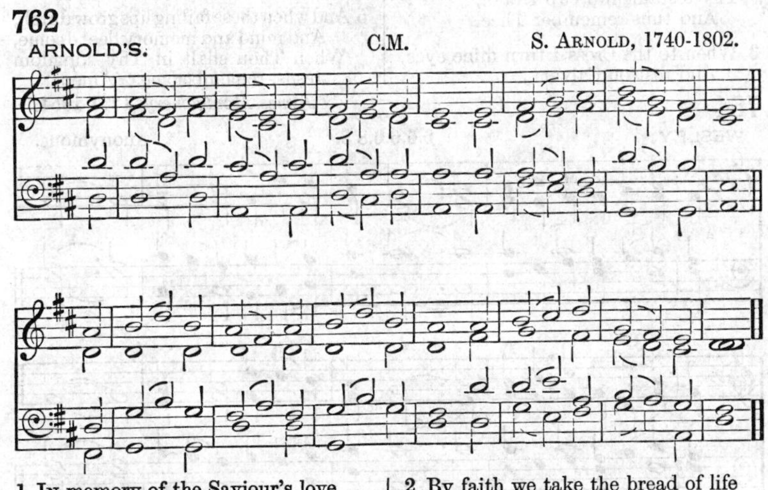

1 In memory of the Saviour's love
We keep the sacred feast,
Where every humble, contrite heart
Is made a welcome guest.

2 By faith we take the bread of life
With which our souls are fed,
The cup in token of His blood
That was for sinners shed.

3 Under His banner thus we sing
The wonders of His love,
And thus anticipate by faith
The heavenly feast above.

Thomas Cotterill, 1779-1823.

763

ABBEY. C.M. *Scottish Psalter*, 1615.

A-men.

1 According to Thy gracious word,
In meek humility,
This will I do, my dying Lord,
I will remember Thee.

2 Thy body, broken for my sake,
My bread from heaven shall be;
Thy testamental cup I take,
And thus remember Thee.

3 When to the Cross I turn mine eyes,
And rest on Calvary,
O Lamb of God, my sacrifice,
I must remember Thee—

4 Remember Thee, and all Thy pains,
And all Thy love to me;
Yea, while a breath, a pulse remains,
Will I remember Thee.

5 And when these failing lips grow dumb,
And mind and memory flee,
When Thou shalt in Thy kingdom come,
Jesus, remember me. Amen.

James Montgomery, 1771-1854.

764

WESLEY. 6.6.6.6.8 8. Anonymous.

A-men.

1 Author of life divine,
Who hast a table spread,
Furnished with mystic wine
And everlasting bread,
Preserve the life Thyself hast given,
And feed and train us up for heaven.

2 Our needy souls sustain
With fresh supplies of love,
Till all Thy life we gain,
And all Thy fullness prove,
And, strengthened by Thy perfect grace
Behold without a veil Thy face.
Amen.

Charles Wesley, 1707-88.

765

SICILIAN MARINERS. 8.7.8.7. Tattersall's *Psalmody*, 1794

A-men.

1 Come, Thou everlasting Spirit,
Bring to every thankful mind
All the Saviour's dying merit,
All His sufferings for mankind:

2 True Recorder of His passion,
Now the living faith impart,
Now reveal His great salvation,
Preach His gospel to our heart.

3 Come, Thou Witness of His dying;
Come, Remembrancer divine,
Let us feel Thy power, applying
Christ to every soul, and mine. Amen.

Charles Wesley, 1707-88.

766

BELMONT. C.M. *Islington Psalmody*, 1854.

1 Be known to us in breaking bread,
But do not then depart;
Saviour, abide with us, and spread
Thy table in our heart.

2 There sup with us in love divine;
Thy body and Thy blood, [wine,
That living bread, that heavenly
Be our immortal food. Amen.

James Montgomery, 1771-1854.

767

HAMPSTEAD. C.M. E. F. HORNER, 1864-1928.

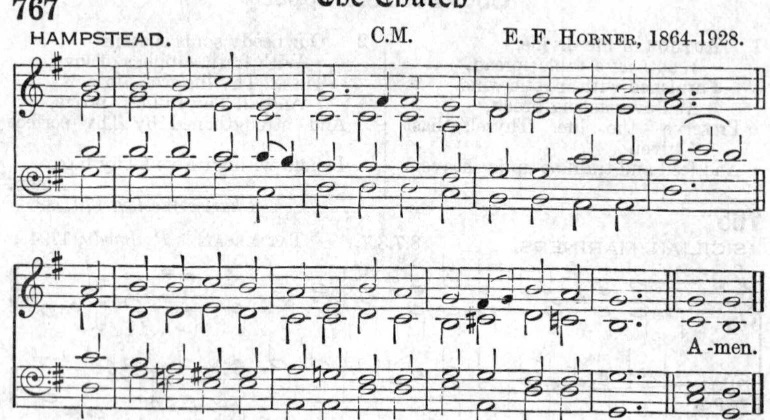

1 COME, Holy Ghost, Thine influence shed,
And realize the sign;
Thy life infuse into the bread,
Thy power into the wine.

2 Effectual let the tokens prove,
And made, by heavenly art,
Fit channels to convey Thy love
To every faithful heart. Amen.

Charles Wesley, 1707-88.

768

PASSION CHORALE. 7.6.7.6. D. H. L. HASSLER, 1564-1612.

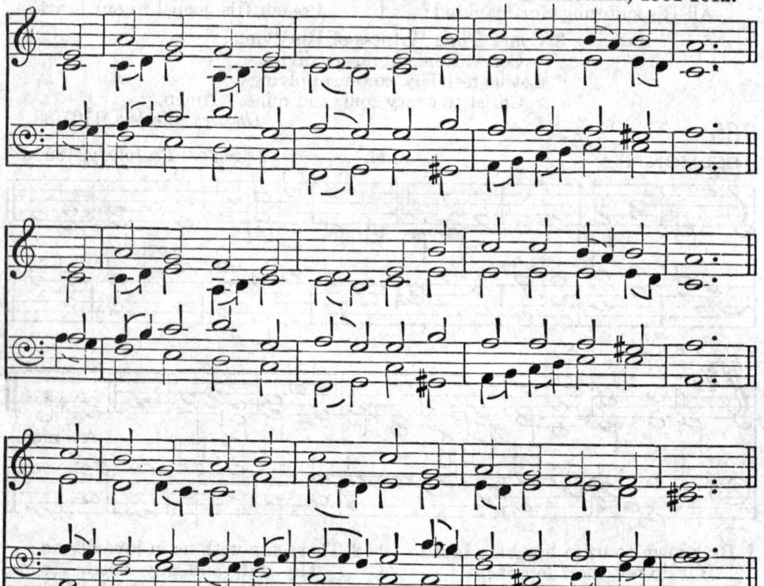

O esca viatorum.

1 O Bread to pilgrims given,
O Food that angels eat,
O Manna sent from heaven,
For heaven-born natures meet,
Give us, for Thee long pining,
To eat till richly filled ;
Till, earth's delights resigning,
Our every wish is stilled.

2 O Water, life bestowing,
Forth from the Saviour's heart,
A fountain purely flowing,
A fount of love Thou art :
O let us, freely tasting,
Our burning thirst assuage ;
Thy sweetness, never wasting,
Avails from age to age.

3 Jesus, this feast receiving,
We Thee unseen adore ;
Thy faithful word believing,
We take, and doubt no more :
Give us, Thou true and loving,
On earth to live in Thee ;
Then, death the veil removing,
Thy glorious face to see. Amen.

Thomas Aquinas, c. 1227-74 ;
tr. by Ray Palmer 1808-87.

769

SPANISH CHANT. 7 7.7 7.7 7. Burgoyne's *Collection*, 1827.

1 Bread of heaven, on Thee I feed,
For Thy flesh is meat indeed :
Ever may my soul be fed
With this true and living bread ;
Day by day with strength supplied
Through the life of Him who died.

2 Vine of heaven, Thy blood supplies
This blest cup of sacrifice :
'Tis Thy wounds my healing give ;
To Thy Cross I look and live :
Thou my life, O let me be
Rooted, grafted, built on Thee !
Amen.

Josiah Conder, 1789-1855.

770

TYHOLLAND. 777. German Carol Melody, adapted by D. F. R. WILSON, 1871-1957.

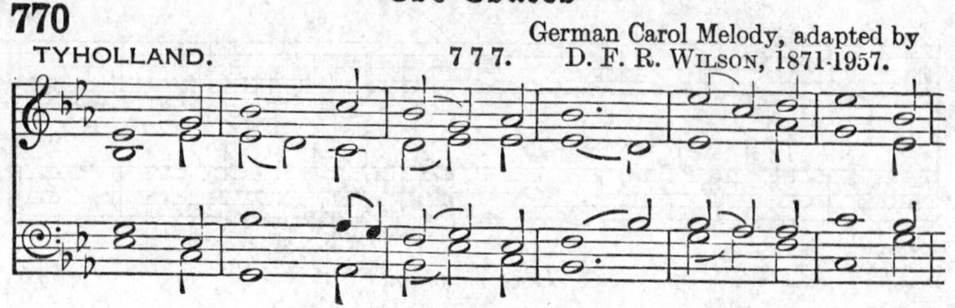

1 JESUS, to Thy table led,
Now let every heart be fed
With the true and living Bread.

2 While in penitence we kneel,
Thy sweet presence let us feel,
All Thy wondrous love reveal.

3 While on Thy dear Cross we gaze,
Mourning o'er our sinful ways,
Turn our sadness into praise.

4 When we taste the mystic wine,
Of Thine outpoured blood the sign,
Fill our hearts with love divine.

5 Draw us to Thy wounded side,
Whence there flowed the healing tide;
There our sins and sorrows hide.

6 From the bonds of sin release,
Cold and wavering faith increase,
Lamb of God, grant us Thy peace.

7 Lead us by Thy piercèd hand
Till around Thy throne we stand
In the bright and better land. Amen.

Robert Hall Baynes, 1831-95.

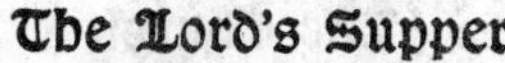

771

EUPHONY. 8.8.8.8.8 8. H. DENNIS, 1818-87.

A-men.

1 VICTIM divine, Thy grace we claim,
  While thus Thy precious death we show:
Once offered up, a spotless Lamb,
  In Thy great temple here below,
Thou didst for all mankind atone,
And standest now before the throne.

2 Thou standest in the holy place,
  As now for guilty sinners slain:
The blood of sprinkling speaks, and prays,
  All prevalent for helpless man;
Thy blood is still our ransom found,
And speaks salvation all around.

3 We need not now go up to heaven,
  To bring the long-sought Saviour down;
Thou art to all already given,
  Thou dost ev'n now Thy banquet crown:
To every faithful soul appear,
And show Thy real presence here. Amen.

Charles Wesley, 1707-88.

772

ST. AGNES. 10.10.10.10. J. LANGRAN, 1835-1909.

By permission of Novello and Company, Limited.

1 HERE, O my Lord, I see Thee face to face;
Here would I touch and handle things unseen,
Here grasp with firmer hand the eternal grace,
And all my weariness upon Thee lean.

2 Here would I feed upon the bread of God,
Here drink with Thee the royal wine of heaven;
Here would I lay aside each earthly load,
Here taste afresh the calm of sin forgiven.

3 This is the hour of banquet and of song;
This is the heavenly table spread for me;
Here let me feast, and, feasting, still prolong
The brief, bright hour of fellowship with Thee.

* * * * *

4 I have no help but Thine; nor do I need
Another arm save Thine to lean upon;
It is enough, my Lord, enough indeed;
My strength is in Thy might, Thy might alone.

5 Mine is the sin, but Thine the righteousness;
Mine is the guilt, but Thine the cleansing blood;
Here is my robe, my refuge, and my peace—
Thy blood, Thy righteousness, O Lord, my God.

6 Feast after feast thus comes and passes by,
Yet, passing, points to the glad feast above,
Giving sweet foretaste of the festal joy,
The Lamb's great bridal feast of bliss and love.

Horatius Bonar, 1808-89.

773

MEMORIA (*First Tune*). 8 8 8.4. S. S. Wesley, 1810-76.

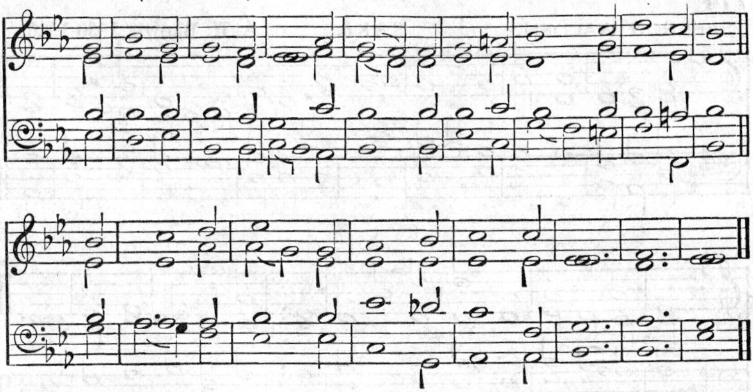

WILLENHALL (*Second Tune*). 8 8 8.4. J. Cluley, 1856-1940

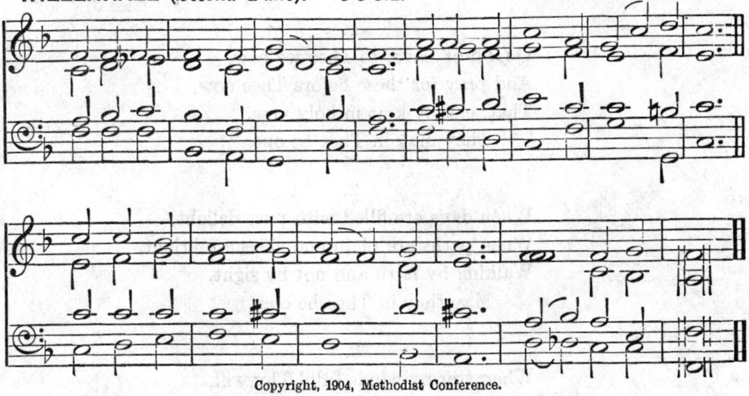

1 By Christ redeemed, in Christ restored,
We keep the memory adored,
And show the death of our dear Lord
Until He come.

2 His body, broken in our stead,
Is here in this memorial bread,
And so our feeble love is fed
Until He come.

3 The drops of His dread agony,
His life-blood shed for us, we see;
The wine shall tell the mystery
Until He come.

4 And thus that dark betrayal night
With the last advent we unite,
By one blest chain of loving rite,
Until He come.

5 O blessèd hope! With this elate,
Let not our hearts be desolate,
But, strong in faith, in patience wait
Until He come.

George Rawson, 1807-89.

Also:

95 Jesus, Sun and Shield art Thou
109 Jesu, Thou joy
181 Lamb of God, whose dying love
182 When I survey
382 Let Him to whom
462 I hunger and I thirst
723 O God of our forefathers

774

MARRIAGE

SAFFRON WALDEN. 8 8 8.6. A. H. Brown, 1830-1926.

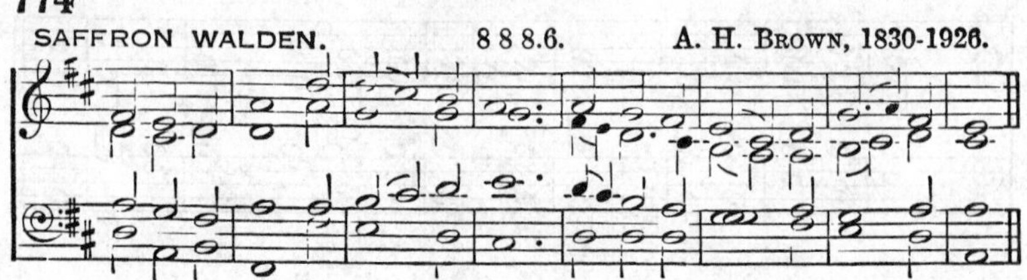

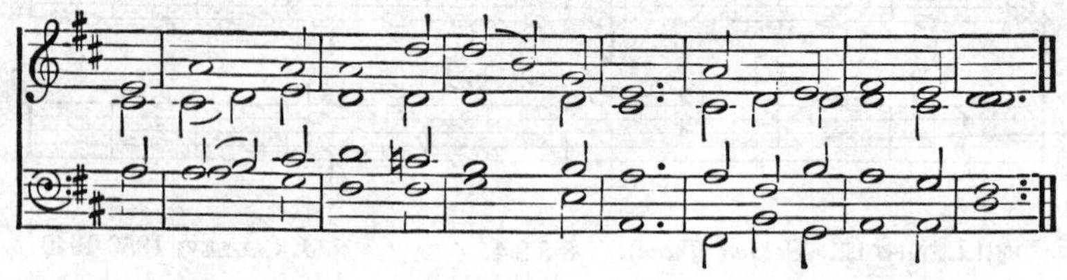

1.

O God of Love, to Thee we bow,
And pray for these before Thee now,
That, closely knit in holy vow,
They may in Thee be one.

2.

When days are filled with pure delight,
When paths are plain and skies are bright,
Walking by faith and not by sight,
May they in Thee be one.

3.

When stormy winds fulfil Thy will,
And all their good seems turned to ill,
Then, trusting Thee completely, still
May they in Thee be one.

4.

Whate'er in life shall be their share
Of quickening joy or burdening care,
In power to do and grace to bear,
May they in Thee be one.

5.

Eternal Love, with them abide;
In Thee for ever may they hide,
For even death cannot divide
Those whom Thou makest one.

William Vaughan Jenkins, 1868-1920.

775

ST. ALPHEGE. 7.6.7.6. H. J. GAUNTLETT, 1805-76.

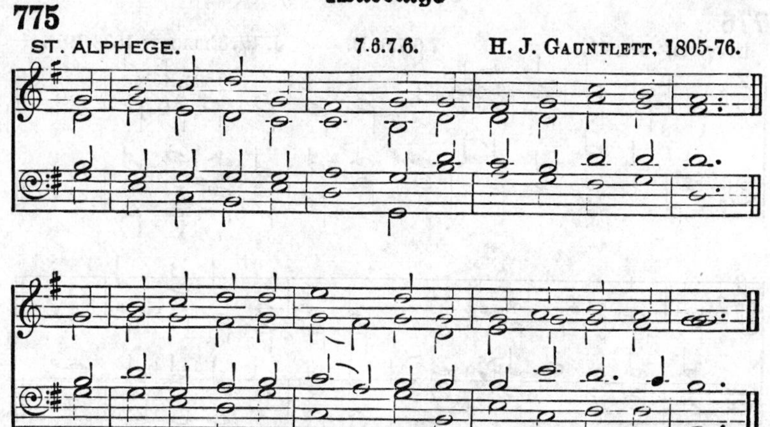

1 THE voice that breathed o'er Eden,
  That earliest wedding-day,
The primal marriage blessing,
  It hath not passed away.

2 Still in the pure espousal
  Of Christian man and maid
The Holy Three are with us,
  The threefold grace is said,

3 For dower of blessèd children,
  For love and faith's sweet sake,
For high mysterious union
  Which nought on earth may break.

4 Be present, heavenly Father,
  To give away this bride,
As Eve Thou gav'st to Adam
  Out of his own pierced side.

5 Be present, gracious Saviour,
  To join their loving hands,
As Thou didst bind two natures
  In Thine eternal bands.

6 Be present, Holy Spirit,
  To bless them as they kneel,
As Thou for Christ the Bridegroom
  The heavenly spouse dost seal.

7 O spread Thy pure wings o'er them!
  Let no ill power find place,
When onward through life's journey
  The hallowed path they trace,

8 To cast their crowns before Thee,
  In perfect sacrifice,
Till to the home of gladness
  With Christ's own bride they rise.

John Keble, 1792-1866.

776

DAY OF REST. 7.6.7.6. D. J. W. ELLIOTT, 1833-1915.

By permission of Novello and Company, Limited.

1 O FATHER, all creating,
Whose wisdom, love, and power
First bound two lives together
In Eden's primal hour.
To-day to these Thy children
Thine earliest gifts renew:
A home by Thee made happy,
A love by Thee kept true.

2 O Saviour, Guest most bounteous
Of old in Galilee,
Vouchsafe to-day Thy presence
With those who call on Thee;
Their store of earthly gladness
Transform to heavenly wine,
And teach them in the tasting
To know the gift is Thine.

3 O Spirit of the Father,
Breathe on them from above,
So mighty in Thy pureness,
So tender in Thy love,
That, guarded by Thy presence,
From sin and strife kept free,
Their lives may own Thy guidance,
Their hearts be ruled by Thee.

4 Except Thou build it, Father,
The house is built in vain;
Except Thou, Saviour, bless it,
The joy will turn to pain:
But nought can break the union
Of hearts in Thee made one;
And love Thy Spirit hallows
Is endless love begun.

John Ellerton, 1826-93.

777

O PERFECT LOVE. 11.10.11.10. J. BARNBY, 1838-96.

A- men.

By permission of Novello and Company, Limited.

1 O PERFECT Love, all human thought transcending,
Lowly we kneel in prayer before Thy throne,
That theirs may be the love which knows no ending
Whom Thou for evermore dost join in one.

2 O perfect Life, be Thou their full assurance
Of tender charity and steadfast faith,
Of patient hope, and quiet brave endurance,
With childlike trust that fears nor pain nor death.

3 Grant them the joy which brightens earthly sorrow,
Grant them the peace which calms all earthly strife;
And to life's day the glorious unknown morrow
That dawns upon eternal love and life. Amen.

Dorothy Frances Gurney, 1858-1932.

Also:
716 Thou God of truth

MINISTERS AND TEACHERS

778

DAY OF PRAISE. S.M. C. STEGGALL, 1826-1905.

1 How beauteous are their feet
Who stand on Zion's hill,
Who bring salvation in their tongues,
And words of peace reveal!

2 How cheering is their voice,
How sweet the tidings are!
Zion, behold thy Saviour King;
He reigns and triumphs here.

3 How blessèd are our ears
That hear this joyful sound,
Which kings and prophets waited for,
And sought, but never found.

4 How blessèd are our eyes
That see this heavenly light,
Prophets and kings desirèd long,
But died without the sight.

5 The watchmen join their voice,
And tuneful notes employ;
Jerusalem breaks forth in songs,
And deserts learn the joy.

6 The Lord makes bare His arm
Through all the earth abroad:
Let all the nations now behold
Their Saviour and their God.

Isaac Watts, 1674-1748.

779

VENI CREATOR. L.M. Ancient Plain-song.
UNISON.

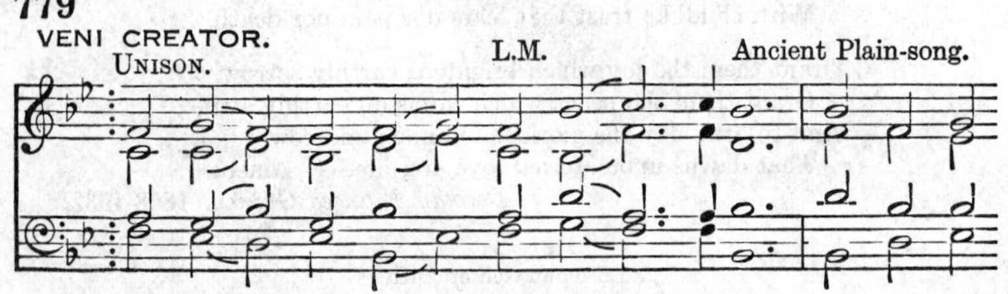

All praise to Thy .. e - ter - nal me - rit,
O Fa - ther, Son, .. and Ho - ly Spi - rit! A - men. . .

Veni, Creator Spiritus.

1 Come, Holy Ghost, our souls inspire,
And lighten with celestial fire;
Thou the anointing Spirit art,
Who dost Thy sevenfold gifts impart:

2 Thy blessèd unction from above
Is comfort, life, and fire of love;
Enable with perpetual light
The dullness of our blinded sight:

3 Anoint and cheer our soilèd face
With the abundance of Thy grace:
Keep far our foes, give peace at home;
Where Thou art Guide no ill can come.

4 Teach us to know the Father, Son,
And Thee, of both, to be but One;
That through the ages all along
This, this may be our endless song:

All praise to Thy eternal merit,
O Father, Son, and Holy Spirit! Amen.

Anonymous, 9th or 10th cent.;
tr. by John Cosin, 1594-1672.

780
ST. LEONARD (First Tune). 8.7.8.7.7 7. J. C. BACH, 1643-1703.
A-men.
OTTAWA (Second Tune). 8.7.8.7.7 7. L. MASON, 1792-1872.
A - men.

1 Master, speak! Thy servant heareth,
Waiting for Thy gracious word,
Longing for Thy voice that cheereth;
Master, let it now be heard.
I am listening, Lord, for Thee;
What hast Thou to say to me?

2 Speak to me by name, O Master,
Let me know it is to me;
Speak, that I may follow faster,
With a step more firm and free,
Where the Shepherd leads the flock
In the shadow of the Rock.

3 Master, speak! Though least and lowest,
Let me not unheard depart;
Master, speak! For O Thou knowest
All the yearning of my heart,
Knowest all its truest need;
Speak, and make me blest indeed.

4 Master, speak: and make me ready,
When Thy voice is truly heard,
With obedience glad and steady
Still to follow every word.
I am listening, Lord, for Thee;
Master, speak! O speak to me! Amen.

Frances Ridley Havergal, 1836-79.

781

GALILEE. L.M. P. Armes, 1836-1908.

1 Lord, speak to me, that I may speak
In living echoes of Thy tone;
As Thou hast sought, so let me seek
Thy erring children lost and lone.

2 O lead me, Lord, that I may lead
The wandering and the wavering feet;
O feed me, Lord, that I may feed
Thy hungering ones with manna sweet.

3 O strengthen me, that, while I stand
Firm on the rock, and strong in Thee,
I may stretch out a loving hand
To wrestlers with the troubled sea.

4 O teach me, Lord, that I may teach
The precious things Thou dost impart;
And wing my words, that they may reach
The hidden depths of many a heart.

5 O give Thine own sweet rest to me,
That I may speak with soothing power
A word in season, as from Thee,
To weary ones in needful hour.

6 O fill me with Thy fullness, Lord,
Until my very heart o'erflow
In kindling thought and glowing word,
Thy love to tell, Thy praise to show.

7 O use me, Lord, use even me,
Just as Thou wilt, and when, and where,
Until Thy blessèd face I see,
Thy rest, Thy joy, Thy glory share.
Amen.

Frances Ridley Havergal, 1836-79.

SUPPLICATION.

UNISON. 6.6.6.6. D. G. F. VINCENT, 1855-1928.

A - men.

1 SHINE Thou upon us, Lord,
True Light of men, to-day;
And through the written word
Thy very self display;
That so, from hearts which burn
With gazing on Thy face,
The little ones may learn
The wonders of Thy grace.

2 Breathe Thou upon us, Lord,
Thy Spirit's living flame,
That so with one accord
Our lips may tell Thy name;
Give Thou the hearing ear,
Fix Thou the wandering thought,
That those we teach may hear
The great things Thou hast wrought.

3 Speak Thou for us, O Lord,
In all we say of Thee;
According to Thy word
Let all our teaching be;
That so Thy lambs may know
Their own true Shepherd's voice,
Where'er He leads them go,
And in His love rejoice.

4 Live Thou within us, Lord;
Thy mind and will be ours;
Be Thou beloved, adored,
And served, with all our powers;
That so our lives may teach
Thy children what Thou art,
And plead, by more than speech,
For Thee with every heart.
Amen.

John Ellerton, 1826-93.

783

BIRSTAL. L.M. A. WIDDOP, *c.* 1750-1801.

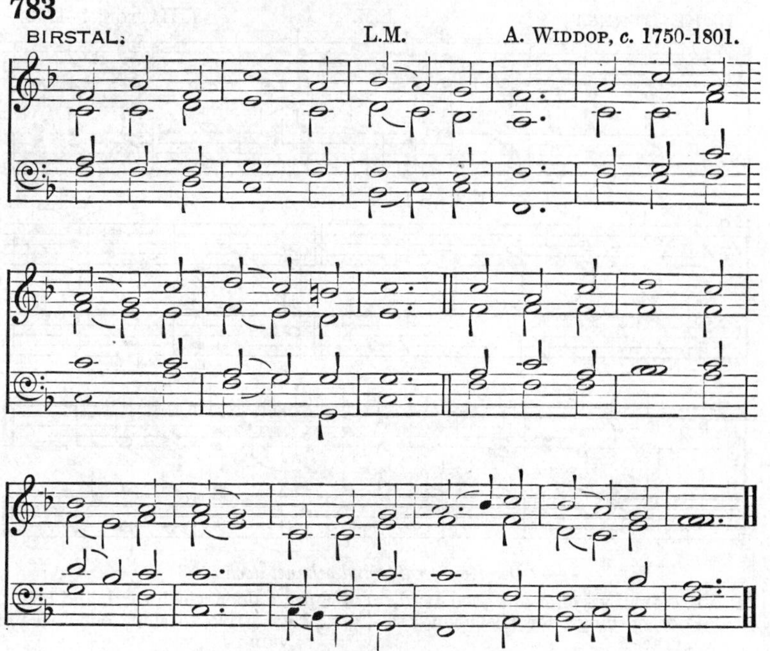

Sollt ich aus Furcht vor Menschenkindern.

1 SHALL I, for fear of feeble man,
The Spirit's course in me restrain?
Or, undismayed, in deed and word
Be a true witness for my Lord?

2 Saviour of men, Thy searching eye
Doth all my inmost thoughts descry;
Doth aught on earth my wishes raise,
Or the world's pleasures or its praise?

3 The love of Christ doth me constrain
To seek the wandering souls of men;
With cries, entreaties, tears, to save,
To snatch them from the gaping grave.

4 My life, my blood, I here present,
If for Thy truth they may be spent:
Fulfil Thy sovereign counsel, Lord;
Thy will be done, Thy name adored.

5 Give me Thy strength, O God of power;
Then, let winds blow or thunders roar,
Thy faithful witness will I be:
'Tis fixed; I can do all through Thee!

Johann Joseph Winckler, 1670-1722;
tr. by John Wesley, 1703-91.

784

DUKE STREET. L.M. J. HATTON, ? -1793.

Der König ruht, und schauet doch.

1 WHAT shall we offer our good Lord,
Poor nothings, for His boundless grace ?
Fain would we His great name record
And worthily set forth His praise.

2 Great object of our growing love,
To whom our more than all we owe,
Open the fountain from above,
And let it our full souls o'erflow.

3 So shall our lives Thy power proclaim,
Thy grace for every sinner free ;
Till all mankind shall learn Thy name,
Shall all stretch out their hands to Thee.

4 Open a door which earth and hell
May strive to shut, but strive in vain ;
Let Thy word richly in us dwell,
And let our gracious fruit remain.

5 O multiply the sower's seed !
And fruit we every hour shall bear,
Throughout the world Thy gospel spread,
Thy everlasting truth declare.

6 We all, in perfect love renewed,
Shall know the greatness of Thy power,
Stand in the temple of our God
As pillars, and go out no more.

August Gottlieb Spangenberg, 1704-92 ;
tr. by John Wesley, 1703-91.

785

OLD 44TH. D.C.M. *Anglo-Genevan Psalter*, 1556.

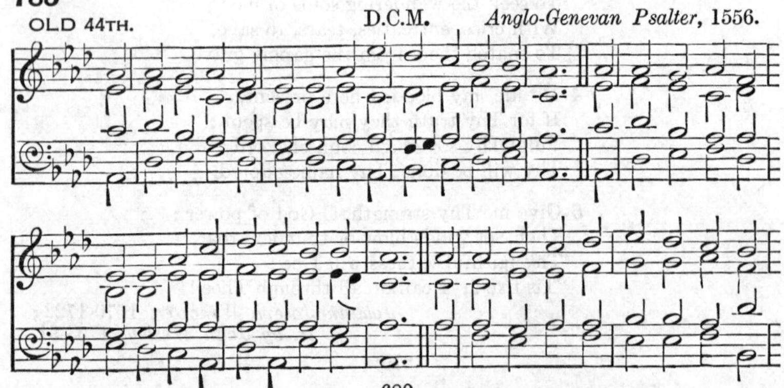

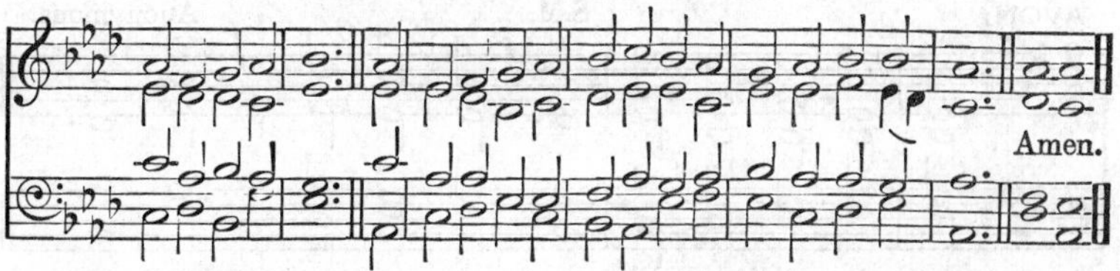

1 Jesus, if we aright confess
Our heartfelt poverty,
We own the conscious want of grace
Itself a gift from Thee;
And who our poverty retain,
More gifts we shall receive,
Multiplied grace and blessings gain,
And all a God can give.

2 Our scanty stock as soon as known,
Our insufficiency
For feeding famished souls we own,
And bring it, Lord, to Thee;
Our want received into Thy hand
Shall rich abundance prove,
Answer the multitude's demand,
And fill them with Thy love. Amen.

Charles Wesley, 1707-88.

786

LOTHIAN. 8 8.6. D. J. F. Bridge, 1844-1924.

1 Lord, grant us, like the watching five,
To wait Thy coming, and to strive
Each one her lamp to trim;
And, since the oil Thou dost impart,
Pour daily grace into each heart,
Lest any lamp grow dim.

2 May we not wait in selfish sloth,
But mingle prayer and work, that both
May trim the shining light;
So from the midnight of their sin
May many, with us, enter in,
To banquet in Thy sight.

3 We would not come alone, dear Lord,
To Thy great feast, and at Thy board
In rapture sit and gaze;
But bring the lost, the sick, the lone,
The little ones to be Thine own,
And look into Thy face.

Thomas Bowman Stephenson, 1839-1912.

787

AVON. S.M. Anonymous.

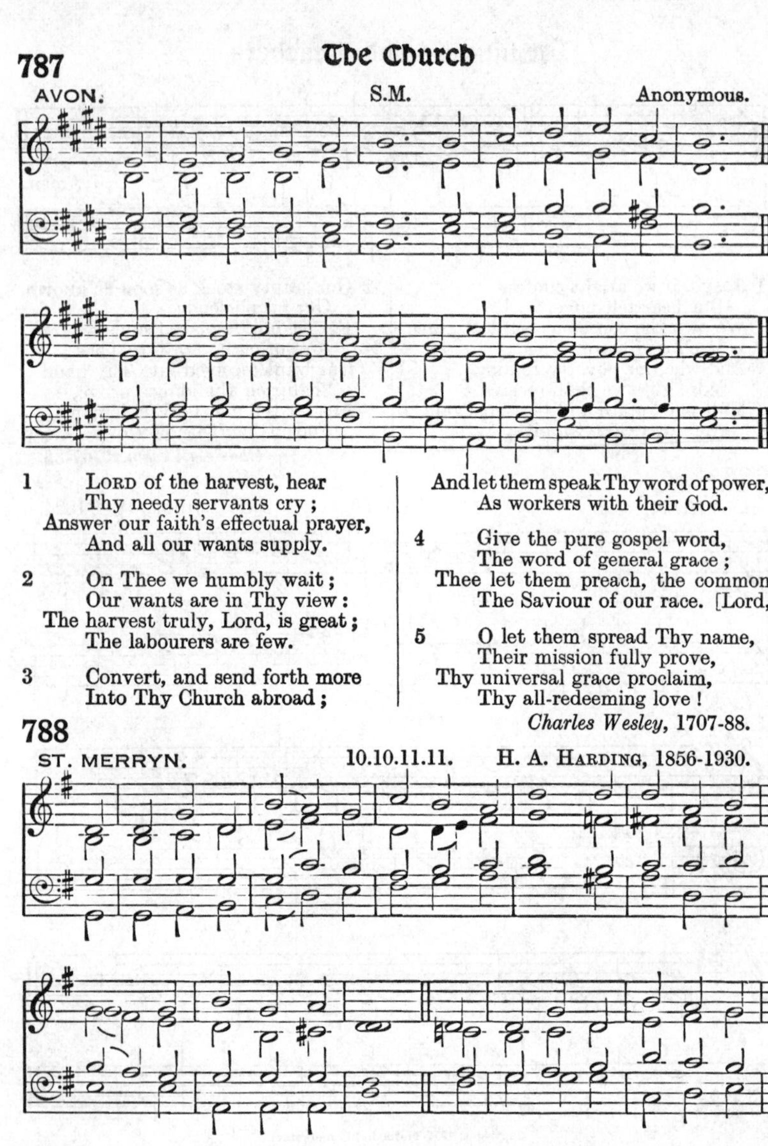

1 Lord of the harvest, hear
Thy needy servants cry;
Answer our faith's effectual prayer,
And all our wants supply.

2 On Thee we humbly wait;
Our wants are in Thy view:
The harvest truly, Lord, is great;
The labourers are few.

3 Convert, and send forth more
Into Thy Church abroad;
And let them speak Thy word of power,
As workers with their God.

4 Give the pure gospel word,
The word of general grace;
Thee let them preach, the common Lord,
The Saviour of our race.

5 O let them spread Thy name,
Their mission fully prove,
Thy universal grace proclaim,
Thy all-redeeming love!

Charles Wesley, 1707-88.

788

ST. MERRYN. 10.10.11.11. H. A. Harding, 1856-1930.

May also be sung to Laudate Dominum, No. 426.

Supreme quales, Arbiter.

1 Disposer Supreme, and Judge of the earth,
Who choosest for Thine the weak and the poor;
To frail earthen vessels and things of no worth
Entrusting Thy riches, which aye shall endure:

2 Those vessels soon fail, though full of Thy light,
And at Thy decree are broken and gone;
Then brightly appeareth Thy truth in its might,
As through the clouds riven the lightnings have shone.

3 Like clouds are they borne to do Thy great will,
And swift as the winds about the world go;
The word with His wisdom their spirits doth fill,
They thunder, they lighten, the waters o'erflow.

4 Their sound goeth forth: Christ Jesus is Lord!
Then Satan doth fear, his citadels fall:
As when the dread trumpets went forth at Thy word,
And one long blast shattered the Canaanite's wall.

5 Then loud be their trump, and stirring their sound,
To rouse us, O Lord, from slumber of sin;
The lights Thou hast kindled in darkness around,
O may they illumine our spirits within!

6 All honour and praise, dominion and might,
To God Three in One eternally be;
Who round us hath shed His marvellous light,
And called us from darkuess His glory to see!

Jean-Baptiste de Santeüil, 1630-97;
tr. by Isaac Williams, 1802-65.

789

FRITWELL. 8 8. G. F. Brockless, 1887-1957.

1 Forget them not, O Christ, who stand
Thy vanguard in the distant land.

2 In flood, in flame, in dark, in dread,
Sustain, we pray, each lifted head.

3 Exalt them over every fear,
In peril come Thyself more near.

4 Thine is the work they strive to do,
Their foes so many, they so few.

5 Be with Thine own, Thy loved, who stand,
Christ's vanguard, in the storm-swept land.

Margaret Elizabeth Sangster, 1838-1912.

790

FULDA. L.M. Gardiner's *Sacred Melodies*, 1812.

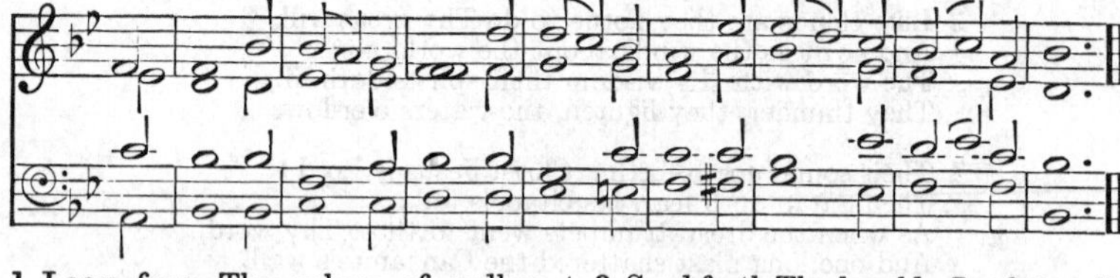

1 Look from Thy sphere of endless day,
O God of mercy and of might;
In pity look on those who stray
Benighted in this land of light.

2 In peopled vale, in lonely glen,
In crowded mart, by stream or sea,
How many of the sons of men
Hear not the message sent from Thee.

3 Send forth Thy heralds, Lord, to call
The thoughtless young, the hardened old,
A scattered homeless flock, till all
Be gathered to Thy peaceful fold.

4 Send them Thy mighty word to speak,
Till faith shall dawn and doubt depart,
To awe the bold, to stay the weak,
And bind and heal the broken heart.

5 Then all these wastes, a dreary scene,
That make us sadden as we gaze,
Shall grow, with living waters, green,
And lift to heaven the voice of praise.

William Cullen Bryant, 1794-1878.

791

ELIM (HESPERUS). L.M. H. Baker, 1835-1910.

1 Jesus, Thy wandering sheep behold!
See, Lord, with tenderest pity see
The sheep that cannot find the fold,
Till sought and gathered in by Thee.

2 Lost are they now, and scattered wide,
In pain, and weariness, and want;
With no kind shepherd near to guide
The sick, and spiritless, and faint.

3 Thou, only Thou, the kind and good
And sheep-redeeming Shepherd art:
Collect Thy flock, and give them food,
And pastors after Thine own heart.

4 Give the pure word of general grace,
And great shall be the preachers' crowd;
Preachers, who all the sinful race
Point to the all-atoning blood.

5 Open their mouth, and utterance give;
Give them a trumpet-voice, to call
On all mankind to turn and live,
Through faith in Him who died for all.

6 Thy only glory let them seek;
O let their hearts with love o'erflow!
Let them believe, and therefore speak,
And spread Thy mercy's praise below.

Charles Wesley, 1707-88.

792

MOUNT EPHRAIM. S.M. B. Milgrove, *c.* 1731-1810.

1 Lord, if at Thy command
The word of life we sow,
Watered by Thy almighty hand,
The seed shall surely grow:

2 The virtue of Thy grace
A large increase shall give,
And multiply the faithful race
Who to Thy glory live.

3 Now then the ceaseless shower
Of gospel blessings send,
And let the soul-converting power
Thy ministers attend.

4 On multitudes confer
The heart-renewing love,
And by the joy of grace prepare
For fuller joys above.

Charles Wesley, 1707-88.

HERRNHUT. 7.6.7.6. D. J. CRÜGER, 1598-1662.

1 LORD of the living harvest
That whitens o'er the plain,
Where angels soon shall gather
Their sheaves of golden grain,
Accept these hands to labour,
These hearts to trust and love,
And deign with them to hasten
Thy kingdom from above.

2 As labourers in Thy vineyard,
Lord, send them out to be,
Content to bear the burden
Of weary days for Thee,
Content to ask no wages
When Thou shalt call them home,
But to have shared the travail
That makes Thy kingdom come.

3 Be with them, God the Father,
Be with them, God the Son,
Be with them, God the Spirit,
Eternal Three in One!
Make them a royal priesthood,
Thee rightly to adore,
And fill them with Thy fullness
Now and for evermore. Amen.

John Samuel Bewley Monsell, 1811-75.

Also:

251 Omnipotent Redeemer
262 All thanks be to God
481 Hark, how the watchmen
489 Workman of God!
709 And are we yet alive
807 And let our bodies
808 Speed Thy servants
913 With the sweet word

794

ST. PANCRAS. L.M. J. BATTISHILL, 1738-1801.

1 ETERNAL Son, eternal Love,
Take to Thyself Thy mighty power;
Let all earth's sons Thy mercy prove,
Let all Thy saving grace adore.

2 The triumphs of Thy love display,
In every heart reign Thou alone,
Till all Thy foes confess Thy sway,
And glory ends what grace begun.

3 Spirit of grace, and health, and power,
Fountain of light and love below,
Abroad Thy healing influence shower,
O'er all the nations let it flow.

4 Inflame our hearts with perfect love,
In us the work of faith fulfil;
So not heaven's host shall swifter move
Than we on earth, to do Thy will.

5 Blessing and honour, praise and love,
Co-equal, co-eternal Three,
In earth below, and heaven above,
By all Thy works be paid to Thee.

6 Thrice Holy! Thine the kingdom is,
The power omnipotent is Thine;
And when created nature dies,
Thy never-ceasing glories shine.

John Wesley, 1703-91.

KINGSLAND. 6.6.6.6. W. BOYCE, 1710-79.

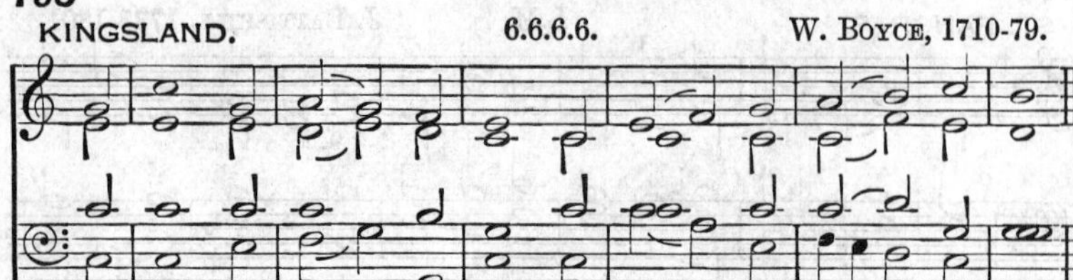

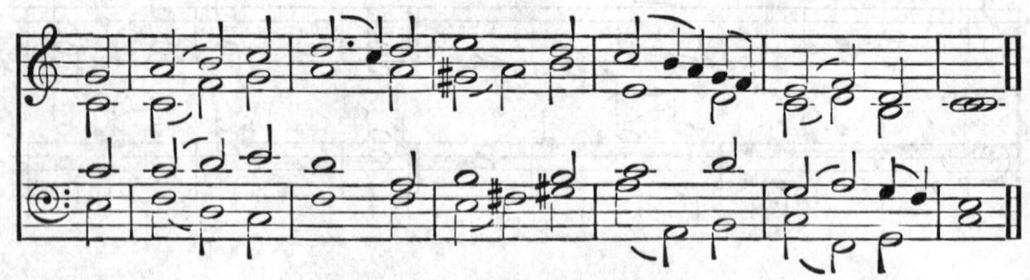

1 O CHURCH of God, arise,
And take thy lamp of love,
The light that never dies
On earth, in heaven above!

2 With wisdom and with truth
Keep quick and straight the flame,
The light of love and youth,
To save a world of shame.

3 Rebuke the devil's mart,
The souls in prison release,
Bind up the broken heart,
Give joy and mirth and peace!

4 Whatever things are fair,
Whatever things are just,
Go, make them free as air
And plenteous as the dust!

5 In every darkest place
Let radiant warmth be shed,
Till in each dreary face
The joy of God is read.

6 Tell every man on earth,
The greatest and the least,
Love called him from his birth
To be a king and priest.

Annie Matheson, 1853-1924.

796

CONTEMPLATION. 8.7.8.7. D. MENDELSSOHN, 1809-47.

1 LORD, Thy ransomed Church is waking
 Out of slumber far and near,
Knowing that the morn is breaking
 When the Bridegroom shall appear;
Waking up to claim the treasure
 With Thy precious life-blood bought,
And to trust in fuller measure
 All Thy wondrous death hath wrought.

2 Praise to Thee for this glad shower,
 Precious drops of latter rain;
Praise, that by Thy Spirit's power
 Thou hast quickened us again;
That Thy gospel's priceless treasure
 Now is borne from land to land,
And that all the Father's pleasure
 Prospers in Thy piercèd hand.

3 Praise to Thee for saved ones yearning
 O'er the lost and wandering throng;
Praise for voices daily learning
 To upraise the glad new song;
Praise to Thee for sick ones hasting
 Now to touch Thy garment's hem;
Praise for souls believing, tasting
 All Thy love has won for them.

4 Set on fire our heart's devotion
 With the love of Thy dear name;
Till o'er every land and ocean
 Lips and lives Thy Cross proclaim:
Fix our eyes on Thy returning,
 Keeping watch till Thou shalt come,
Loins well girt, lamps brightly burning;
 Then, Lord, take Thy servants home. Amen.

Sarah Geraldina Stock, 1838-98.

797

STAPLES. 7 7.7 7. English, 16th century

1 ONCE again, dear Lord, we pray
For the children far away,
Who have never even heard
Name of Jesus, sweetest word.

2 Little lips that Thou hast made,
'Neath the far-off temples' shade
Give to gods of wood and stone
Praise that should be all Thine own.

3 Little hands, whose wondrous skill
Thou hast given to do Thy will,
Offerings bring, and serve with fear
Gods that cannot see or hear.

4 Teach them, O Thou heavenly King,
All their gifts and praise to bring
To Thy Son, who died to prove
Thy forgiving, saving love.

Mary Jane Willcox, 1835-1919.

798

PARTING. 10.10.10.10. JANE RHODES, 1910.

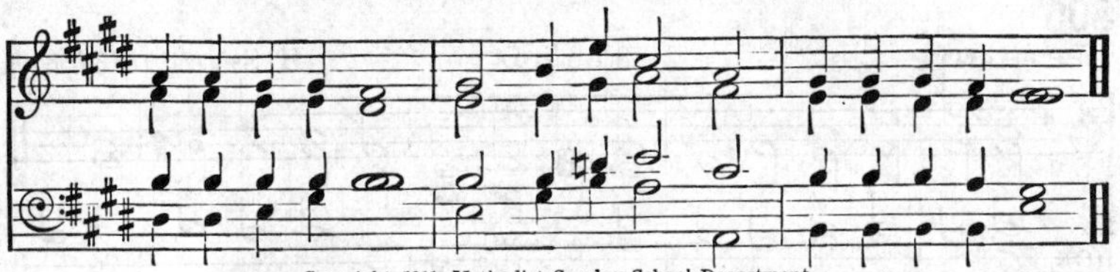

May also be sung to WOODLANDS, No. 686.

1 FAR round the world Thy children sing their song:
From East and West their voices sweetly blend,
Praising the Lord in whom young lives are strong,
Jesus our Guide, our Hero, and our Friend.

2 Where Thy wide ocean, wave on rolling wave,
Beats through the ages, on each island shore,
They praise their Lord, whose hand alone can save,
Whose sea of love surrounds them evermore.

3 Thy sun-kissed children on earth's spreading plain,
Where Asia's rivers water all the land,
Sing, as they watch Thy fields of glowing grain,
Praise to the Lord who feeds them with His hand.

4 Still there are lands where none have seen Thy face,
Children whose hearts have never shared Thy joy;
Yet Thou wouldst pour on these Thy radiant grace,
Give Thy glad strength to every girl and boy.

5 All round the world let children sing Thy song:
From East and West their voices sweetly blend,
Praising the Lord in whom young lives are strong,
Jesus our Guide, our Hero, and our Friend.

Basil Joseph Mathews, 1879-

799

COLVEND. 5.6.6.5.9. F. L. WISEMAN, 1858-1944

1 THE fields are all white,
And the reapers are few;
We children are willing,
But what can we do
To work for our Lord in His harvest?

2 Our hands are so small,
And our words are so weak:
We cannot teach others;
How then shall we seek
To work for our Lord in His harvest.

3 We'll work by our prayers,
By the offerings we bring,
By small self-denials;
The least little thing
May work for our Lord in His harvest:

4 Until by and by,
As the years pass, at length
We too may be reapers,
And go forth in strength,
To work for our Lord in His harvest.

The Book of Praise for Children, 1881.

800

BETHANY. 8.7.8.7. D. H. SMART, 1813-79.

A-men.

1 SAVIOUR, quicken many nations,
Fruitful let Thy sorrows be;
By Thy pains and consolations
Draw the Gentiles unto Thee:
Of Thy Cross the wondrous story
Be to all the nations told;
Let them see Thee in Thy glory
And Thy mercy manifold.

2 Far and wide, though all unknowing,
Pants for Thee each mortal breast;
Human tears for Thee are flowing,
Human hearts in Thee would rest:
Thirsting, as for dews of even,
As the new-mown grass for rain,
Thee they seek as God of heaven,
Thee as Man for sinners slain.

3 Saviour, lo! the isles are waiting,
Stretched the hand and strained the sight,
For Thy Spirit, new creating,
Love's pure flame, and wisdom's light;
Give the word, and of the preacher
Speed the foot, and touch the tongue,
Till on earth by every creature
Glory to the Lamb be sung. Amen.

Arthur Cleveland Coxe, 1818-96.

801

MISSIONARY. 7.6.7.6. D. L. MASON, 1792-1872.

1 FROM Greenland's icy mountains,
From India's coral strand,
Where Afric's sunny fountains
Roll down their golden sand,
From many an ancient river,
From many a palmy plain,
They call us to deliver
Their land from error's chain.

2 Can we, whose souls are lighted
With wisdom from on high,
Can we to men benighted
The lamp of life deny ?
Salvation ! O salvation !
The joyful sound proclaim,
Till each remotest nation
Has learned Messiah's name.

3 Waft, waft, ye winds, His story,
And you, ye waters, roll,
Till, like a sea of glory,
It spreads from pole to pole ;
Till o'er our ransomed nature,
The Lamb for sinners slain,
Redeemer, King, Creator,
In bliss returns to reign. Amen.

Reginald Heber, 1783-1826.

802

NEW SABBATH. L.M. T. PHILLIPS, 1735-1807.

1 THE heavens declare Thy glory, Lord,
In every star Thy wisdom shines;
But when our eyes behold Thy word,
We read Thy name in fairer lines.

2 The rolling sun, the changing light,
And night and day, Thy power confess;
But the blest volume Thou hast writ
Reveals Thy justice and Thy grace.

3 Sun, moon, and stars convey Thy praise
Round the whole earth, and never stand;
So when Thy truth began its race,
It touched and glanced on every land.

4 Nor shall Thy spreading gospel rest
Till through the world Thy truth has run;
Till Christ has all the nations blest,
That see the light or feel the sun.

5 Great Sun of Righteousness, arise,
Bless the dark world with heavenly light:
Thy gospel makes the simple wise;
Thy laws are pure, Thy judgements right.

6 Thy noblest wonders here we view,
In souls renewed, and sins forgiven;
Lord, cleanse my sins, my soul renew,
And make Thy word my guide to heaven. Amen.

Isaac Watts, 1674-1748.

803

MALVERN. 6 6.4.6 6 6.4. *The Hallelujah*, 1849.

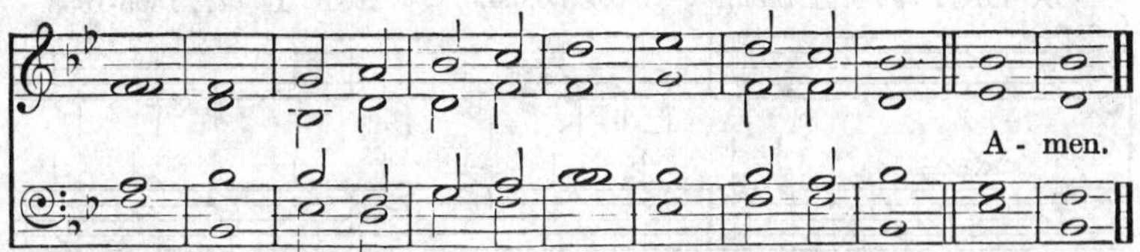

May also be sung to Moscow, No. 880.

1 Thou whose almighty word
Chaos and darkness heard,
And took their flight,
Hear us, we humbly pray,
And where the gospel day
Sheds not its glorious ray
Let there be light!

2 Thou who didst come to bring
On Thy redeeming wing
Healing and sight,
Health to the sick in mind,
Sight to the inly blind,
O now to all mankind
Let there be light!

3 Spirit of truth and love,
Life-giving, holy Dove,
Speed forth Thy flight:
Move on the water's face,
Spreading the beams of grace,
And in earth's darkest place
Let there be light!

4 Blessèd and holy Three,
Glorious Trinity,
Grace, love, and might,
Boundless as ocean's tide
Rolling in fullest pride,
Through the world far and wide
Let there be light! Amen.

John Marriott, 1780-1825.

804

DENT DALE. 77.77. English Traditional Melody.

Walte, fürder, nah und fern.

1 Spread, O spread, thou mighty word,
Spread the kingdom of the Lord,
Wheresoe'er His breath has given
Life to beings meant for heaven.

2 Word of life, most pure and strong,
Lo! for thee the nations long;
Spread, till from its dreary night
All the world awakes to light.

3 Up! the ripening fields ye see,
Mighty shall the harvest be;
But the reapers still are few,
Great the work they have to do.

4 Lord of harvest, let there be
Joy and strength to work for Thee,
Till the nations far and near
See Thy light and learn Thy fear.
Amen.

Jonathan Friedrich Bahnmaier, 1774-1841;
tr. by Catherine Winkworth, 1827-78.

DOXFORD (*First Tune*). 6 6.4.6 6 6.4. R. R. TERRY, 1865-1938

EDINBURGH (*Second Tune*). 6 6.4.6 6 6.4. E. S. LAMPLOUGH, 1860-1940

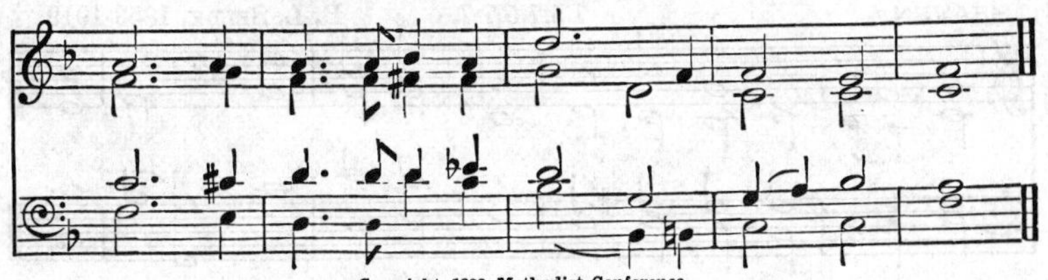

1.

Christ for the world, we sing:
The world to Christ we bring
With loving zeal;
The poor, and them that mourn,
The faint and overborne,
Sin-sick and sorrow-worn,
Whom Christ doth heal.

2.

Christ for the world, we sing:
The world to Christ we bring
With fervent prayer;
The wayward and the lost,
By restless passions tossed,
Redeemed at countless cost
From dark despair.

3.

Christ for the world, we sing:
The world to Christ we bring
With one accord;
With us the work to share,
With us reproach to dare,
With us the cross to bear
For Christ our Lord.

4.

Christ for the world, we sing:
The world to Christ we bring
With joyful song;
The new-born souls, whose days,
Reclaimed from error's ways,
Inspired with hope and praise,
To Christ belong.

Samuel Wolcott, 1813-86.

806

HEAVEN. 7.5.7.5.7 7. B. L. SELBY, 1853-1919.

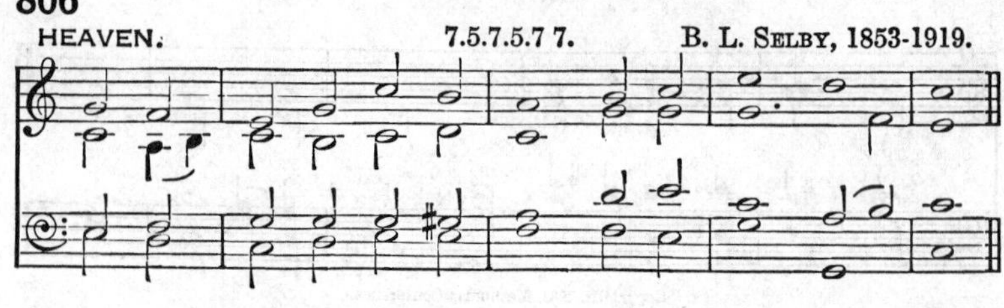

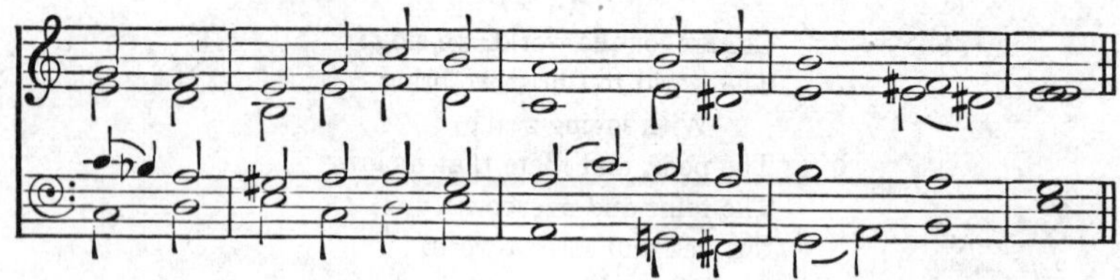

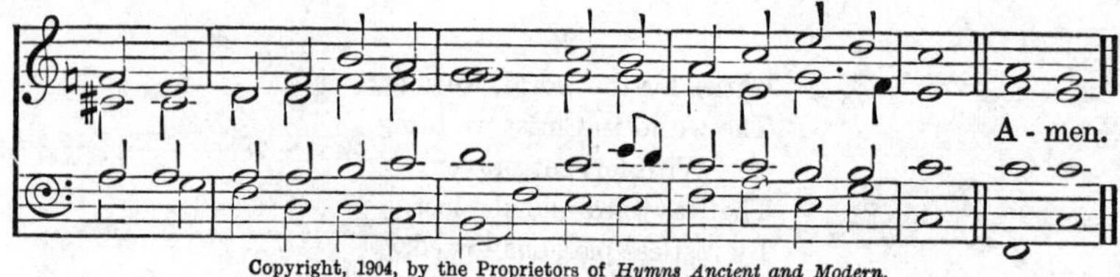

1 LET the song go round the earth:
Jesus Christ is Lord,
Sound His praises, tell His worth,
Be His name adored;
Every clime and every tongue
Join the grand, the glorious song.

2 Let the song go round the earth,
From the eastern sea,
Where the daylight has its birth,
Glad, and bright, and free;
China's millions join the strains,
Waft them on to India's plains.

3 Let the song go round the earth,
Lands where Islam's sway
Darkly broods o'er home and hearth,
Cast their bonds away;
Let His praise from Afric's shore
Rise and swell her wide lands o'er.

4 Let the song go round the earth,
Where the summer smiles,
Let the notes of holy mirth
Break from distant isles;
Inland forests, dark and dim,
Snow-bound coasts give back the hymn.

5 Let the song go round the earth:
Jesus Christ is King,
With the story of His worth,
Let the whole world ring,
Him creation all adore
Evermore and evermore. Amen.

Sarah Geraldina Stock, 1838-98.

807

S.M.

BETHLEHEM (DONCASTER) (*First Tune*). S. WESLEY, 1766-1837.

CANADA (*Second Tune*). S.M. W. MATHER, 1756-1808.

1 AND let our bodies part,
To different climes repair;
Inseparably joined in heart
The friends of Jesus are.

2 Jesus, the corner-stone,
Did first our hearts unite,
And still He keeps our spirits one,
Who walk with Him in white.

3 O let us still proceed
In Jesu's work below;
And, following our triumphant Head,
To further conquests go.

4 The vineyard of their Lord
Before His labourers lies;
And, lo! We see the vast reward
Which waits us in the skies.

5 O let our heart and mind
Continually ascend,
That haven of repose to find
Where all our labours end:

6 Where all our toils are o'er,
Our suffering and our pain;
Who meet on that eternal shore,
Shall never part again.

7 O happy, happy place,
Where saints and angels meet,
There we shall see each other's face,
And all our brethren greet.

8 The Church of the first-born;
We shall with them be blest
And, crowned with endless joy, return
To our eternal rest.

Charles Wesley, 1707-88.

808

ST. THOMAS. 8.7.8.7.4.7. J. F. WADE'S *MS. Book*, 1751 (Stonyhurst).

Missions at Home and Abroad

1 Speed Thy servants, Saviour, speed them;
Thou art Lord of winds and waves:
They were bound, but Thou hast freed them;
Now they go to free the slaves.
Be Thou with them:
'Tis Thine arm alone that saves.

2 Friends, and home, and all forsaking,
Lord, they go at Thy command;
As their stay Thy promise taking,
While they traverse sea and land:
O be with them!
Lead them safely by the hand.

3 When they reach the land of strangers,
And the prospect dark appears,
Nothing seen but toils and dangers,
Nothing felt but doubts and fears,
Be Thou with them,
Hear their sighs, and count their tears.

4 Where no fruit appears to cheer them,
And they seem to toil in vain,
Then in mercy, Lord, draw near them,
Then their sinking hopes sustain;
Thus supported,
Let their zeal revive again.

5 In the midst of opposition,
Let them trust, O Lord, in Thee;
When success attends their mission,
Let Thy servants humbler be;
Never leave them,
Till Thy face in heaven they see:

6 There to reap in joy for ever
Fruit that grows from seed here sown,
There to be with Him who never
Ceases to preserve His own,
And with gladness
Give the praise to Him alone. Amen.

Thomas Kelly, 1769-1854.

809

LONDONDERRY AIR. Irregular.

PETRIE'S *Ancient Music of Ireland*, 1855.

Arr. by G. F. BROCKLESS.

UNISON.

1 I CANNOT tell why He, whom angels worship,
Should set His love upon the sons of men,
Or why, as Shepherd, He should seek the wanderers,
To bring them back, they know not how or when.
But this I know, that He was born of Mary,
When Bethlehem's manger was His only home,
And that He lived at Nazareth and laboured,
And so the Saviour, Saviour of the world, is come.

2 I cannot tell how silently He suffered,
As with His peace He graced this place of tears,
Or how His heart upon the Cross was broken,
The crown of pain to three and thirty years.
But this I know, He heals the broken-hearted,
And stays our sin, and calms our lurking fear,
And lifts the burden from the heavy laden,
For yet the Saviour, Saviour of the world, is here.

3 I cannot tell how He will win the nations,
How He will claim His earthly heritage,
How satisfy the needs and aspirations
Of East and West, of sinner and of sage.
But this I know, all flesh shall see His glory,
And He shall reap the harvest He has sown,
And some glad day His sun shall shine in splendour
When He the Saviour, Saviour of the world, is known.

4 I cannot tell how all the lands shall worship,
When, at His bidding, every storm is stilled,
Or who can say how great the jubilation
When all the hearts of men with love are filled.
But this I know, the skies will thrill with rapture,
And myriad, myriad human voices sing,
And earth to heaven, and heaven to earth, will answer:
At last the Saviour, Saviour of the world, is King!

William Young Fullerton, 1857-1932.

810

7.7.7.7.

DA CHRISTUS GEBOREN WAR. *Vierstimmiges Choralbuch,* 1785.

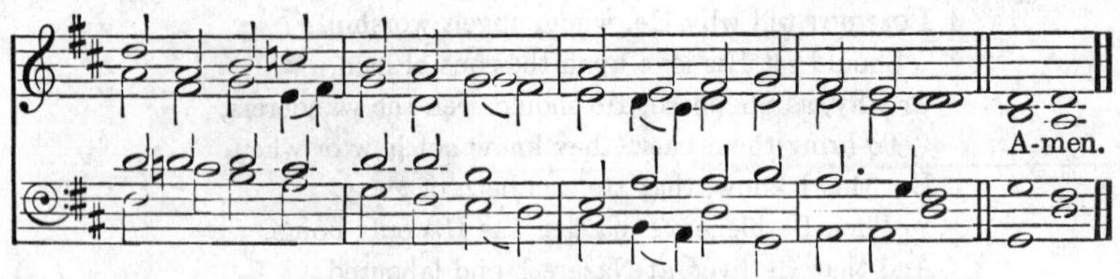

May also be sung to BUCKLAND, No. 277.

1 FATHER, let Thy kingdom come,
Let it come with living power;
Speak at length the final word,
Usher in the triumph hour.

2 As it came in days of old,
In the deepest hearts of men,
When Thy martyrs died for Thee,
Let it come, O God, again!

3 Tyrant thrones and idol shrines,
Let them from their place be hurled:
Enter on Thy better reign,
Wear the crown of Thine own world.

4 O what long, sad years have gone,
Since Thy Church was taught this prayer;
O what eyes have watched and wept
For the dawning everywhere!

5 Break, triumphant day of God!
Break at last, our hearts to cheer;
Throbbing souls and holy songs
Wait to hail Thy dawning here.

6 Empires, temples, sceptres, thrones—
May they all for God be won;
And, in every human heart,
Father, let Thy kingdom come! Amen.

John Page Hopps, 1834-1912.

811

ST. CECILIA. 6.6.6.6. L. G. Hayne, 1836-83.

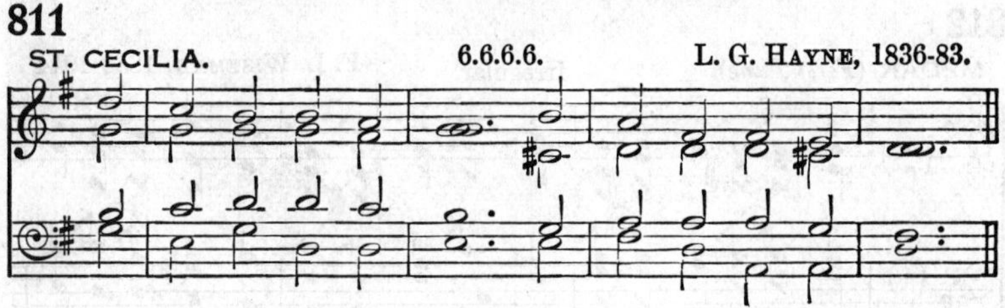

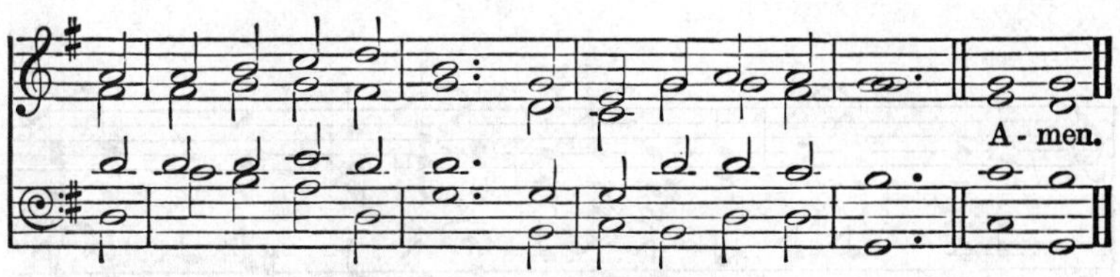

1 Thy kingdom come, O God,
  Thy rule, O Christ, begin;
Break with Thine iron rod
  The tyrannies of sin.

2 Where is Thy reign of peace,
  And purity, and love?
When shall all hatred cease,
  As in the realms above?

3 When comes the promised time
  That war shall be no more—
Oppression, lust, and crime
  Shall flee Thy face before?

4 We pray Thee, Lord, arise,
  And come in Thy great might;
Revive our longing eyes,
  Which languish for Thy sight.

5 Men scorn Thy sacred name,
  And wolves devour Thy fold;
By many deeds of shame
  We learn that love grows cold.

6 O'er heathen lands afar
  Thick darkness broodeth yet:
Arise, O morning Star,
  Arise, and never set! Amen.

Lewis Hensley, 1824-1905.

812

MEDAK (*First Tune*). Irregular. F. L. WISEMAN, 1858-1944

Missions at Home and Abroad

1.

God is working His purpose out, as year succeeds to year;
God is working His purpose out, and the time is drawing near—
Nearer and nearer draws the time—the time that shall surely be,
When the earth shall be filled with the glory of God, as the waters cover the sea.

2.

From utmost east to utmost west, where'er man's foot hath trod,
By the mouth of many messengers goes forth the voice of God:
Give ear to Me, ye continents—ye isles, give ear to Me,
That the earth may be filled with the glory of God, as the waters cover the sea.

3.

What can we do to work God's work, to prosper and increase
The brotherhood of all mankind—the reign of the Prince of Peace?
What can we do to hasten the time—the time that shall surely be,
When the earth shall be filled with the glory of God, as the waters cover the sea?

4.

March we forth in the strength of God, with the banner of Christ unfurled,
That the light of the glorious gospel of truth may shine throughout the world:
Fight we the fight with sorrow and sin, to set their captives free,
That the earth may be filled with the glory of God, as the waters cover the sea.

5.

All we can do is nothing worth, unless God blesses the deed;
Vainly we hope for the harvest-tide, till God gives life to the seed;
Yet nearer and nearer draws the time—the time that shall surely be,
When the earth shall be filled with the glory of God, as the waters cover the sea.

Arthur Campbell Ainger, 1841-1919.

812

PURPOSE (*Second Tune*). Irregular. M. SHAW, 1876-

1.

God is working His purpose out, as year succeeds to year;
God is working His purpose out, and the time is drawing near—
Nearer and nearer draws the time—the time that shall surely be,
When the earth shall be filled with the glory of God, as the waters cover the sea.

2.

From utmost east to utmost west, where'er man's foot hath trod,
By the mouth of many messengers goes forth the voice of God:
Give ear to Me, ye continents—ye isles, give ear to Me,
That the earth may be filled with the glory of God, as the waters cover the sea.

3.

What can we do to work God's work, to prosper and increase
The brotherhood of all mankind—the reign of the Prince of Peace?
What can we do to hasten the time—the time that shall surely be,
When the earth shall be filled with the glory of God, as the waters cover the sea?

4.

March we forth in the strength of God, with the banner of Christ unfurled,
That the light of the glorious gospel of truth may shine throughout the world:
Fight we the fight with sorrow and sin, to set their captives free,
That the earth may be filled with the glory of God, as the waters cover the sea.

5.

All we can do is nothing worth, unless God blesses the deed;
Vainly we hope for the harvest-tide, till God gives life to the seed;
Yet nearer and nearer draws the time—the time that shall surely be,
When the earth shall be filled with the glory of God, as the waters cover the sea.

Arthur Campbell Ainger, 1841-1919.

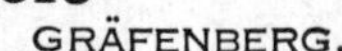

C.M. *Praxis Pietatis Melica*, 1653.

1.

The Lord will come, and not be slow;
His footsteps cannot err;
Before Him righteousness shall go,
His royal harbinger.

2.

Truth from the earth, like to a flower,
Shall bud and blossom then;
And justice, from her heavenly bower,
Look down on mortal men.

3.

Rise, Lord, judge Thou the earth in might,
This longing earth redress;
For Thou art He who shall by right
The nations all possess.

4.

The nations all whom Thou hast made
Shall come, and all shall frame
To bow them low before Thee, Lord,
And glorify Thy name.

5.

For great Thou art, and wonders great
By Thy strong hand are done:
Thou in Thine everlasting seat
Remainest God alone. Amen.

John Milton, 1608-74.

814

DOVERSDALE. L.M. S. Stanley, 1767-1822.

1 Head of Thy Church, whose Spirit fills
And flows through every faithful soul,
Unites in mystic love, and seals
Them one, and sanctifies the whole:

2 Come, Lord! Thy glorious Spirit cries;
And souls beneath the altar groan:
Come, Lord! The bride on earth replies;
And perfect all our souls in one.

3 Pour out the promised gift on all,
Answer the universal: Come!
The fullness of the Gentiles call,
And take Thine ancient people home.

4 To Thee let all the nations flow,
Let all obey the gospel word;
Let all their suffering Saviour know,
Filled with the glory of the Lord.

5 O for Thy truth and mercy's sake
The purchase of Thy passion claim!
Thine heritage, the nations, take,
And cause the world to know Thy name. Amen.

Charles Wesley, 1707-88.

815

LITTLE CORNARD.
6.6.6.6.8 8.
M. SHAW, 1876-
UNISON. vv. 1, 3, 5.
HARMONY. vv. 2 & 4.
Lulled be your
Lulled be
Lulled be your
Lulled be

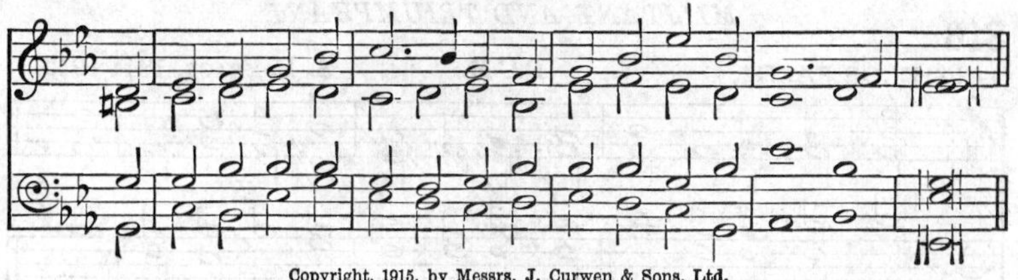

1 Hills of the North, rejoice,
River and mountain-spring,
Hark to the advent voice,
Valley and lowland, sing:
Though absent long, your Lord is nigh;
He judgement brings and victory.

2 Isles of the Southern seas,
Deep in your coral caves
Pent be each warring breeze,
Lulled be your restless waves:
He comes to reign with boundless sway,
And makes your wastes His great highway.

3 Lands of the East, awake,
Soon shall your sons be free;
The sleep of ages break,
And rise to liberty:
On your far hills, long cold and grey,
Has dawned the everlasting day.

4 Shores of the utmost West,
Ye that have waited long,
Unvisited, unblest,
Break forth to swelling song:
High raise the note, that Jesus died,
Yet lives and reigns—the Crucified!

5 Shout while ye journey home,
Songs be in every mouth;
Lo! from the North we come,
From East, and West, and South.
City of God, the bond are free;
We come to live and reign in thee.

Charles Edward Oakley, 1832-65.

Also:

The Church

MILITANT AND TRIUMPHANT

816

FIGHT OF FAITH. D.C.M. A. L. PEACE, 1844-1912.

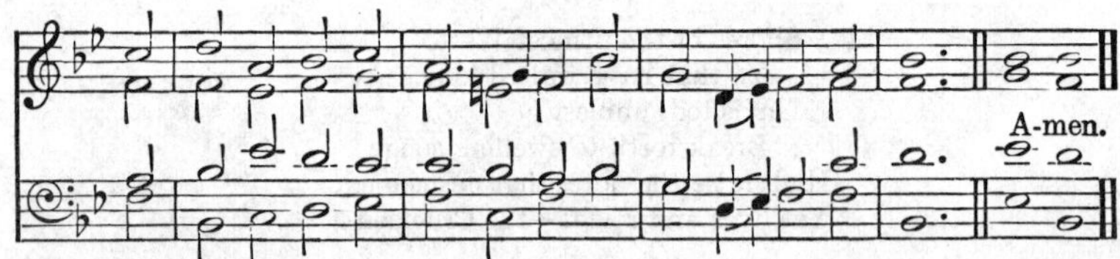

1 THE Son of God goes forth to war,
  A kingly crown to gain;
His blood-red banner streams afar:
  Who follows in His train?
Who best can drink his cup of woe,
  Triumphant over pain,
Who patient bears his cross below,
  He follows in His train.

2 The martyr first, whose eagle eye
  Could pierce beyond the grave,
Who saw his Master in the sky,
  And called on Him to save;
Like Him, with pardon on his tongue
  In midst of mortal pain,
He prayed for them that did the
  wrong:
  Who follows in his train?

3 A glorious band, the chosen few
  On whom the Spirit came, [knew,
Twelve valiant saints, their hope they
  And mocked the cross and flame;
They met the tyrant's brandished
  The lion's gory mane, [steel,
They bowed their necks the death to
  Who follows in their train? [feel:

4 A noble army, men and boys,
  The matron and the maid,
Around the Saviour's throne rejoice,
  In robes of light arrayed;
They climbed the steep ascent of
  heaven,
  Through peril, toil, and pain:
O God, to us may grace be given
  To follow in their train. Amen.

Reginald Heber, 1783-1826.

817

PENTECOST. L.M. W. BOYD, 1847-1928.

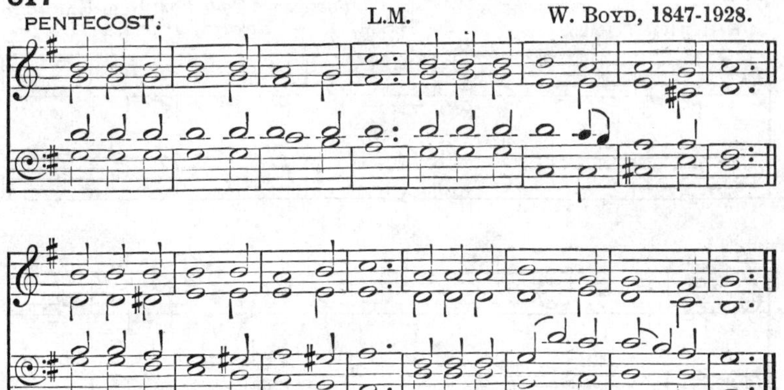

By permission of Novello and Company, Limited.

1 FLING out the banner! Let it float
Skyward and seaward, high and wide;
The sun shall light its shining folds,
The Cross on which the Saviour died.

2 Fling out the banner! Angels bend
In anxious silence o'er the sign;
And vainly seek to comprehend
The wonder of the Love Divine.

3 Fling out the banner! Heathen lands
Shall see from far the glorious sight,
And nations, crowding to be born,
Baptize their spirits in its light.

4 Fling out the banner! Let it float
Skyward and seaward, high and wide,
Our glory, only in the Cross;
Our only hope, the Crucified!

5 Fling out the banner! Wide and high,
Seaward and skyward, let it shine;
Nor skill, nor might, nor merit ours:
We conquer only in that sign.

George Washington Doane, 1799-1859.

818

ST. LEONARD. C.M. H. SMART, 1813-79.

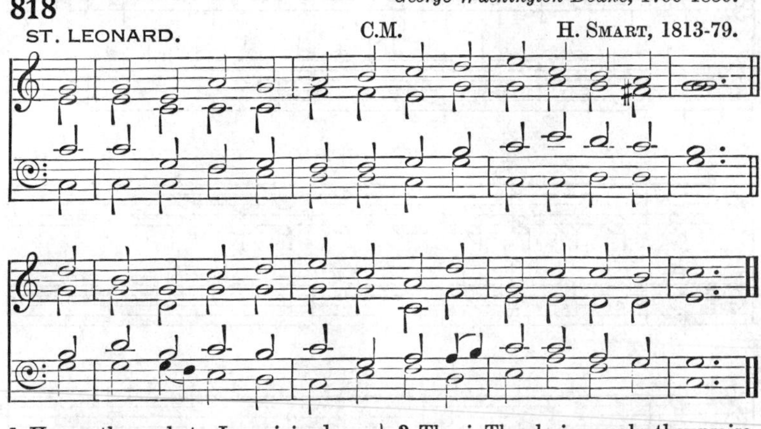

1 HAPPY the souls to Jesus joined,
And saved by grace alone,
Walking in all His ways, they find
Their heaven on earth begun.

2 The Church triumphant in Thy love,
Their mighty joys we know;
They sing the Lamb in hymns above,
And we in hymns below.

3 Thee in Thy glorious realm they praise,
And bow before Thy throne,
We in the kingdom of Thy grace:
The kingdoms are but one.

4 The holy to the holiest leads,
From thence our spirits rise,
And he that in Thy statutes treads
Shall meet Thee in the skies.

Charles Wesley, 1707-88.

819

JERICHO TUNE. D.S.M. *'Foundery' Collection*, from HANDEL'S *Riccardo Primo*, 1727.

1 Forth rode the knights of old
With armour gleaming bright,
By noble deeds and actions bold
To fight for God and right.
To lay the tyrant low,
To set the captive free,
The hosts of evil to o'erthrow
By might of purity.

2 A vision flamed above,
A voice within spoke clear,
The symbol of Christ's mighty love
Shone radiant and near.
Then, burning with desire,
By zeal and love possessed,
The knights of old with heart afire
Rode out upon the quest.

3 In every age the same,
From hut and princely hall,
The pilgrim knights who bear His name
Have followed at His call.
Now each with glory crowned,
And waiting on His will,
They stand His splendid throne around
And serve more nobly still.

4 Still, still the vision glows,
Still calls the voice divine;
Still sink the weak, oppressed by foes,
And still the captives pine;
Still loyal to their Lord,
With zeal and patience shod,
With shield of faith and mystic sword,
Go forth the knights of God.

Vera Evaline Walker, 1887-

820

The Church

HERMAS. 6.5. (twelve lines). F. R. HAVERGAL, 1836-79.

May also be sung to ARMAGEDDON, No. 617.

Militant and Triumphant

1 Who is on the Lord's side ?
Who will serve the King ?
Who will be His helpers
Other lives to bring ?
Who will leave the world's side ?
Who will face the foe ?
Who is on the Lord's side ?
Who for Him will go ?
By Thy call of mercy,
By Thy grace divine,
We are on the Lord's side ;
Saviour, we are Thine.

2 Jesus, Thou hast bought us,
Not with gold or gem,
But with Thine own life-blood,
For Thy diadem.
With Thy blessing filling
Each who comes to Thee,
Thou hast made us willing,
Thou hast made us free.
By Thy great redemption,
By Thy grace divine,
We are on the Lord's side ;
Saviour, we are Thine.

3 Fierce may be the conflict,
Strong may be the foe ;
But the King's own army
None can overthrow.
Round His standard ranging,
Victory is secure ;
For His truth unchanging
Makes the triumph sure.
Joyfully enlisting,
By Thy grace divine,
We are on the Lord's side ;
Saviour, we are Thine.

4 Chosen to be soldiers
In an alien land,
Chosen, called, and faithful,
For our Captain's band,
In the service royal
Let us not grow cold ;
Let us be right loyal,
Noble, true, and bold.
Master, Thou wilt keep us,
By Thy grace divine,
Always on the Lord's side,
Saviour, always Thine. Amen.

Frances Ridley Havergal, 1836-79.

821

MORNING LIGHT. 7.6.7.6. D. G. J. WEBB, 1803-87.

May also be sung to ST. THEODULPH, No. 84.

1 STAND up, stand up for Jesus !
Ye soldiers of the Cross ;
Lift high His royal banner ;
It must not suffer loss.
From victory unto victory
His army shall He lead,
Till every foe is vanquished
And Christ is Lord indeed.

2 Stand up, stand up for Jesus !
The trumpet-call obey ;
Forth to the mighty conflict
In this His glorious day !
Ye that are men, now serve Him
Against unnumbered foes ;
Let courage rise with danger,
And strength to strength oppose.

3 Stand up, stand up for Jesus !
Stand in His strength alone :
The arm of flesh will fail you ;
Ye dare not trust your own.
Put on the Christian's armour,
And watching unto prayer,
Where duty calls, or danger,
Be never wanting there.

4 Stand up, stand up for Jesus !
The strife will not be long ;
This day the noise of battle,
The next the victor's song.
To him that overcometh
A crown of life shall be ;
He with the King of Glory
Shall reign eternally.

George Duffield, 1818-88.

822

ST. GERTRUDE. 6.5.6.5. D. and refrain. A. SULLIVAN, 1842-1900.

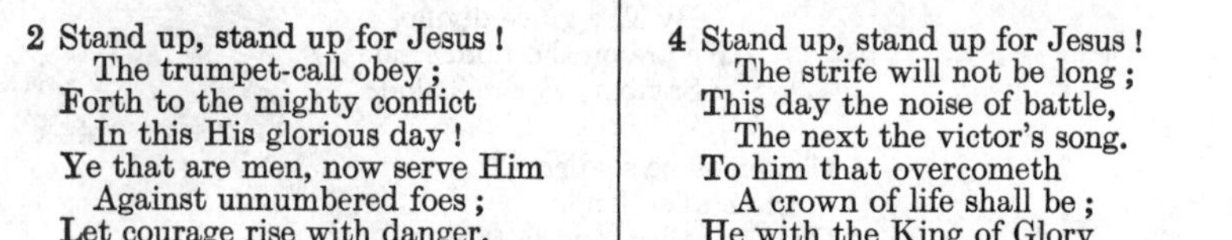

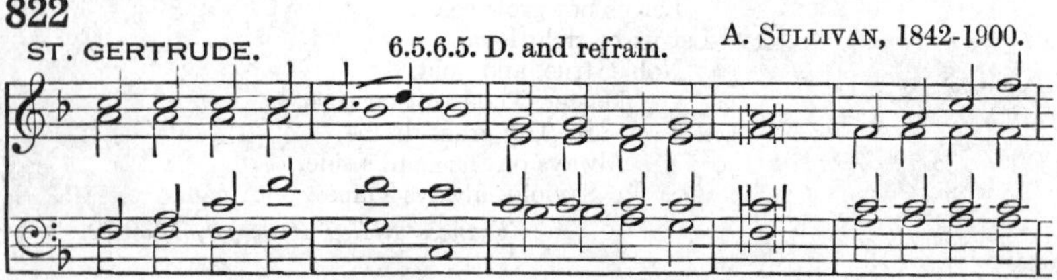

Militant and Triumphant

By permission of Novello and Company, Limited.

1 Onward! Christian soldiers,
Marching as to war,
With the Cross of Jesus
Going on before.
Christ, the royal Master,
Leads against the foe;
Forward into battle,
See! His banners go.
Onward! Christian soldiers,
Marching as to war,
With the Cross of Jesus
Going on before.

2 At the sign of triumph
Satan's host doth flee;
On then, Christian soldiers,
On to victory!
Hell's foundations quiver
At the shout of praise;
Brothers, lift your voices,
Loud your anthems raise.

3 Like a mighty army
Moves the Church of God;
Brothers, we are treading
Where the saints have trod.
We are not divided,
All one body we,
One in hope, in doctrine,
One in charity.

4 Crowns and thrones may perish.
Kingdoms rise and wane,
But the Church of Jesus
Constant will remain.
Gates of hell can never
'Gainst that Church prevail;
We have Christ's own promise,
And that cannot fail.

5 Onward then, ye people!
Join our happy throng;
Blend with ours your voices
In the triumph song:
Glory, laud, and honour
Unto Christ the King!
This through countless ages
Men and angels sing.

Sabine Baring-Gould, 1834-1924.

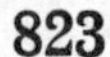

823

ST. LAWRENCE. C.M. R. A. SMITH, 1780-1829.

May also be sung to WARWICK, No. 387.

1 OUR life is hid with Christ in God;
Our Life shall soon appear,
And shed His glory all abroad
In all His members here.

2 Our souls are in His mighty hand,
And He shall keep them still;
And you and I shall surely stand
With Him on Zion's hill.

3 O what a joyful meeting there!
In robes of white arrayed,
Palms in our hands we all shall bear,
And crowns upon our head.

4 Then let us lawfully contend,
And fight our passage through:
Bear in our faithful minds the end,
And keep the prize in view.

Charles Wesley, 1707-88.

824

ST. MATTHEW. D.C.M. W. CROFT, 1678-1727.

A higher setting will be found at No. 919

1 COME, let us join our friends above
  That have obtained the prize,
And on the eagle wings of love
  To joys celestial rise :
Let all the saints terrestrial sing,
  With those to glory gone ;
For all the servants of our King,
  In earth and heaven, are one.

2 One family we dwell in Him,
  One Church, above, beneath,
Though now divided by the stream,
  The narrow stream of death :
One army of the living God,
  To His command we bow ;
Part of His host have crossed the flood,
  And part are crossing now.

3 Ten thousand to their endless home
  This solemn moment fly ;
And we are to the margin come,
  And we expect to die ;
Ev'n now by faith we join our hands
  With those that went before,
And greet the blood-besprinkled bands
  On the eternal shore.

4 Our spirits too shall quickly join,
  Like theirs with glory crowned,
And shout to see our Captain's sign,
  To hear His trumpet sound.
O that we now might grasp our Guide !
  O that the word were given !
Come, Lord of hosts, the waves divide,
  And land us all in heaven. Amen.

Charles Wesley, 1707-88.

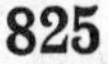

825

REST. 8 8.8 8.8 8. J. STAINER, 1840-1901.

UNISON. HARMONY.

A-men.

By permission of Novello and Company, Limited.

1 THE saints of God, their conflict past,
And life's long battle won at last,
No more they need the shield or sword;
They cast them down before their Lord:
O happy saints! For ever blest,
At Jesu's feet how safe their rest.

2 The saints of God, their wanderings done,
No more their weary course they run,
No more they faint, no more they fall,
No foes oppress, no fears appal:
O happy saints! For ever blest,
In that dear home, how sweet their rest.

3 The saints of God, life's voyage o'er,
Safe landed on that blissful shore,
No stormy tempests now they dread,
No roaring billows lift their head:
O happy saints! For ever blest,
In that calm haven of their rest.

4 O God of saints, to Thee we cry;
O Saviour, plead for us on high;
O Holy Ghost, our Guide and Friend,
Grant us Thy grace till life shall end:
That with all saints our rest may be
In that bright paradise with Thee. Amen.

William Dalrymple Maclagan, 1826-1910.

826

ST. JUSTIN. 8 8.6. D. *St. Alban's Tune Book*, 1865.

1 O God, to whom the faithful dead
Still live, united to their Head,
Their Lord and ours the same;
For all Thy saints, to memory dear,
Departed in Thy faith and fear,
We bless Thy holy name.

2 By the same grace upheld, may we
So follow those who followed Thee,
As with them to partake
The full reward of heavenly bliss:
Merciful Father, grant us this
For our Redeemer's sake. Amen.

Josiah Conder, 1789-1855.

827

FROGMORE. 6.4.6.4. W. PARRATT, 1841-1924.

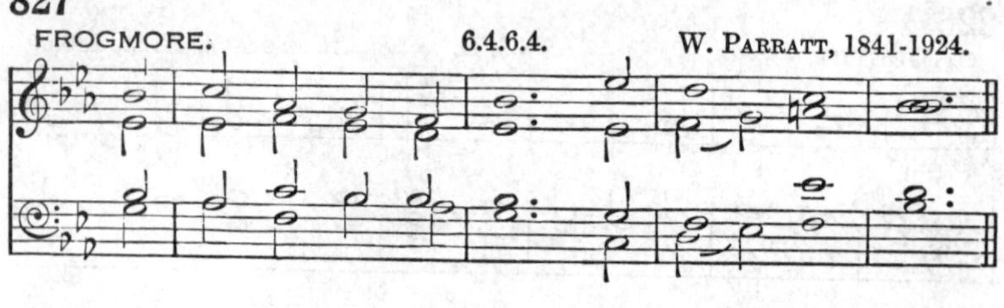

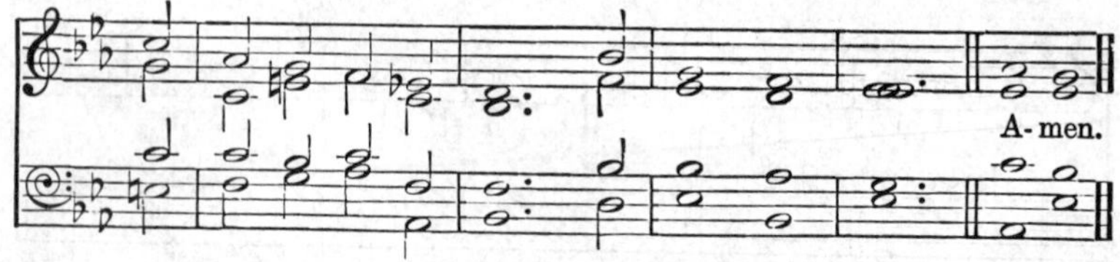

1 THEIR names are names of kings
  Of heavenly line;
The bliss of earthly things
  They did resign.

2 Chieftains they were, who warred
  With sword and shield;
Victors for God the Lord
  On foughten field.

3 Sad were their days on earth,
  Mid hate and scorn,
A life of pleasure's dearth,
  A death forlorn;

4 Yet blest that end in woe,
  And those sad days;
Only man's blame below;
  Above—God's praise.

5 A city of great name
  Is built for them,
Of glorious golden fame—
  Jerusalem!

6 Redeemed with precious blood
  From death and sin,
Sons of the Triune God,
  They enter in.

7 So doth the life of pain
  In glory close;
Lord God, may we attain
  Their grand repose. Amen.

Samuel John Stone, 1839-1900.

828

ALFORD. 7.6.8.6. D. J. B. Dykes, 1823-76.

1 Ten thousand times ten thousand,
In sparkling raiment bright,
The armies of the ransomed saints
Throng up the steeps of light;
'Tis finished, all is finished,
Their fight with death and sin;
Fling open wide the golden gates,
And let the victors in.

2 What rush of hallelujahs
Fills all the earth and sky!
What ringing of a thousand harps
Bespeaks the triumph nigh!
O day for which creation
And all its tribes were made!
O joy, for all its former woes
A thousand-fold repaid!

3 O then what raptured greetings
On Canaan's happy shore,
What knitting severed friendships up
Where partings are no more!
Then eyes with joy shall sparkle
That brimmed with tears of [late;
Orphans no longer fatherless,
Nor widows desolate.

4 Bring near Thy great salvation,
Thou Lamb for sinners slain;
Fill up the roll of Thine elect,
Then take Thy power and reign;
Appear, Desire of nations—
Thine exiles long for home;
Show in the heaven Thy promised sign;
Thou Prince and Saviour, come.
Amen.

Henry Alford, 1810-71.

829

THANKSGIVING. 7 7.7 7. D. W. B. GILBERT, 1829-1910.

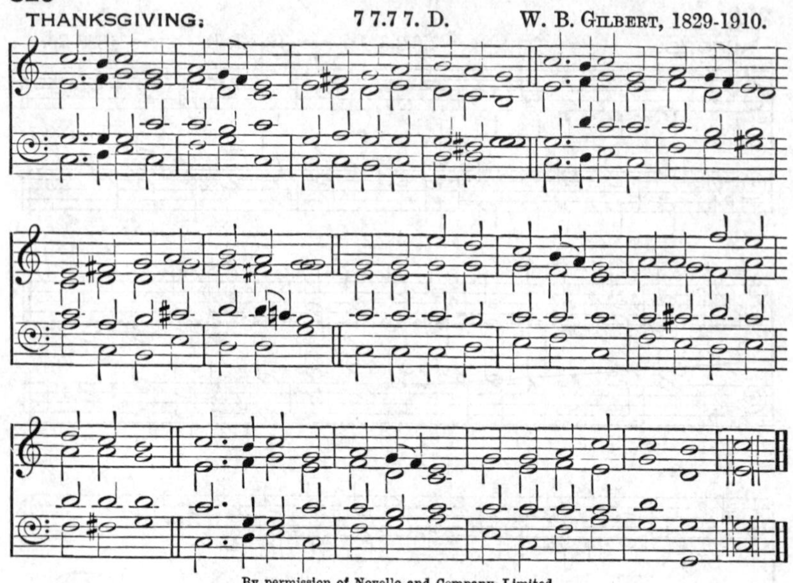

By permission of Novello and Company, Limited.

1 HARK! The song of jubilee,
Loud as mighty thunders' roar:
Or the fullness of the sea,
When it breaks upon the shore.
Hallelujah! For the Lord
God Omnipotent shall reign:
Hallelujah! Let the word
Echo round the earth and main.

2 Hallelujah! Hark! The sound,
From the depths unto the skies,
Wakes above, beneath, around,
All creation's harmonies:
See Jehovah's banner furled:
Sheathed His sword; He speaks—
'tis done:
And the kingdoms of this world
Are the kingdoms of His Son.

3 He shall reign from pole to pole
With illimitable sway:
He shall reign, when, like a scroll,
Yonder heavens have passed away;
Then the end—beneath His rod
Man's last enemy shall fall;
Hallelujah! Christ in God,
God in Christ, is All in all.

James Montgomery, 1771-1854.

830

DEERHURST. 8.7.8.7. D. J. LANGRAN, 1835-1909.

By permission of Novello and Company, Limited.

1 HARK! The sound of holy voices,
Chanting at the crystal sea:
Hallelujah! Hallelujah!
Hallelujah! Lord, to Thee:
Multitude, which none can number,
Like the stars in glory stand,
Clothed in white apparel, holding
Palms of victory in their hand.

2 They have come from tribulation,
And have washed their robes in blood,
Washed them in the blood of Jesus;
Tried they were, and firm they stood;
Mocked, imprisoned, stoned, tormented,
Sawn asunder, slain with sword,
They have conquered death and Satan
By the might of Christ the Lord.

3 Marching with Thy Cross their banner,
They have triumphed, following
Thee, the Captain of salvation,
Thee, their Saviour and their King.
Gladly, Lord, with Thee they suffered;
Gladly, Lord, with Thee they died;
And, by death, to life immortal
They were born and glorified.

4 God of God, the One-begotten,
Light of Light, Immanuel,
In whose body joined together
All the saints for ever dwell,
Pour upon us of Thy fullness,
That we may for evermore
God the Father, God the Son, and
God the Holy Ghost adore. Amen.

Christopher Wordsworth, 1807-85.

831

MYLON. C.M. J. A. NAUMANN, 1741-1801.

1 GIVE me the wings of faith to rise
Within the veil, and see
The saints above, how great their joys,
How bright their glories be.

2 Once they were mourners here below,
And poured out cries and tears;
They wrestled hard, as we do now,
With sins, and doubts, and fears.

3 I ask them whence their victory came;
They, with united breath,
Ascribe their conquest to the Lamb,
Their triumph to His death.

4 They marked the footsteps that He trod,
His zeal inspired their breast;
And, following their incarnate God,
Possess the promised rest.

5 Our glorious Leader claims our praise
For His own pattern given;
While the long cloud of witnesses
Show the same path to heaven.

Isaac Watts, 1674-1748.

832 The Church
SINE NOMINE (First Tune). 10 10 10.4.
Verses 1, 2, and 3. Unison.
R. Vaughan Williams, 1872-
1. For all the saints who from their la - bours rest,
2. Thou wast their Rock, their For - tress, and their Might;
3. O may Thy sol - - diers, faith - ful, true and bold,
Who Thee . . by faith be - fore the world con - fessed,
Thou, Lord, their Cap - tain in the well-fought fight;
Fight as the saints who no - bly fought of old,
(crotchets v. 2.)
Thy Name, O Je - - su, be for ev - er blest.
Thou in the dark - - ness drear their one true Light.
And win, with them, the vic - tor's crown of gold!
Al - - le - lu - - ia! Al - le - lu - ia!
Verses 4, 5, and 6. Harmony.
4. O blest com - mu - nion, fel - low - ship di - vine!
5. And when the strife is fierce, the war - fare long,
6. The gold - en eve - ning bright - ens in the west;
We fee - bly strug - gle; They in glo - ry shine,
Steals on the ear the dis - tant tri - umph song,
Soon, soon to faith - ful war - riors com - eth rest;

Militant and Triumphant
(small notes v. 6.)
Yet all are... one in Thee, for all are Thine.
And hearts are... brave a - gain, and arms are strong.
Sweet is the calm of Pa - ra - dise the blest.
Al - le - lu - ia! Al - le - lu - ia!
Verses 7 and 8. UNISON.
7. But lo! there breaks a yet more glo-rious day:
8. From earth's wide bounds, from o-cean's farthest coast,
The saints tri - um - phant rise in bright ar - ray; . . . .
Through gates of pearl streams in the count-less host, ...
(crotchets v. 8.)
The King of Glo - - ry pass-es on His way.
Sing - ing to Fa - - ther, Son, and Ho - ly Ghost.
Al - le - lu - ia! Al - le - lu - ia!
William Walsham How, 1823-97.

832

10 10 10.4.

FOR ALL THE SAINTS (*Second Tune*). J. BARNBY, 1838-96.

1 FOR all the saints who from their labours rest,
Who Thee by faith before the world confessed,
Thy name, O Jesu, be for ever blest.
Alleluia!

2 Thou wast their Rock, their Fortress, and their Might;
Thou, Lord, their Captain in the well fought fight;
Thou in the darkness drear their one true Light.
Alleluia!

3 O may Thy soldiers, faithful, true, and bold,
Fight as the saints who nobly fought of old,
And win, with them, the victor's crown of gold!
Alleluia!

4 O blest communion, fellowship divine!
We feebly struggle; they in glory shine,
Yet all are one in Thee, for all are Thine.
Alleluia!

5 And when the strife is fierce, the warfare long,
Steals on the ear the distant triumph song,
And hearts are brave again, and arms are strong.
Alleluia!

6 The golden evening brightens in the west;
Soon, soon to faithful warriors cometh rest;
Sweet is the calm of paradise the blest.
Alleluia!

7 But lo! there breaks a yet more glorious day:
The saints triumphant rise in bright array;
The King of Glory passes on His way.
Alleluia!

8 From earth's wide bounds, from ocean's farthest coast,
Through gates of pearl streams in the countless host,
Singing to Father, Son, and Holy Ghost:
Alleluia!

William Walsham How, 1823-97.

833

BENEVENTO. 7.7.7.7.D. S. WEBBE, 1740-1816.

1 WHAT are these arrayed in white,
Brighter than the noonday sun?
Foremost of the sons of light,
Nearest the eternal throne?
These are they that bore the cross,
Nobly for their Master stood;
Sufferers in His righteous cause,
Followers of the dying God.

2 Out of great distress they came,
Washed their robes by faith below
In the blood of yonder Lamb,
Blood that washes white as snow:
Therefore are they next the throne,
Serve their Maker day and night;
God resides among His own,
God doth in His saints delight.

3 More than conquerors at last,
Here they find their trials o'er;
They have all their sufferings past,
Hunger now and thirst no more;
No excessive heat they feel
From the sun's directer ray,
In a milder clime they dwell,
Region of eternal day.

4 He that on the throne doth reign,
Them the Lamb shall always feed,
With the tree of life sustain,
To the living fountains lead;
He shall all their sorrows chase,
All their wants at once remove,
Wipe the tears from every face,
Fill up every soul with love.

Charles Wesley, 1707-88.

Also:

219 God is gone up
243 Jesus, the Conqueror
252 God is with us
494 A safe stronghold
585 Rise up, O men of God
616 Through the night
619 Forward! be our watchword

For Children

834

CHILDREN'S VOICES. 6.6.6.6.4.4 4.4. E. J. HOPKINS, 1818-1901.

By permission of A. Weekes & Co., Ltd.

1 ABOVE the clear blue sky,
In heaven's bright abode,
The angel-host on high
Sing praises to their God:
Hallelujah!
They love to sing
To God their King:
Hallelujah!

2 But God from infant tongues
On earth receiveth praise;
We then our cheerful songs
In sweet accord will raise:
Hallelujah!
We too will sing
To God our King:
Hallelujah!

3 O blessèd Lord, Thy truth
In love to us impart,
And teach us in our youth
To know Thee as Thou art.
Hallelujah!
Then shall we sing
To God our King:
Hallelujah!

4 O may Thy holy word
Spread all the world around;
And all with one accord
Uplift the joyful sound:
Hallelujah!
All then shall sing
To God their King:
Hallelujah!

John Chandler, 1806-76.

For Children

835

TOURS. 7.6.7.6. D. B. TOURS, 1838-97.

By permission of Novello and Company, Limited.

1 WHEN, His salvation bringing,
  To Zion Jesus came,
The children all stood singing
  Hosanna to His name;
Nor did their zeal offend Him,
  But, as He rode along,
He let them still attend Him,
  And smiled to hear their song.

2 And, since the Lord retaineth
  His love for children still,
Though now as King He reigneth
  On Zion's heavenly hill,
We'll flock around His banner
  Who sits upon the throne,
And cry aloud: Hosanna
  To David's royal Son!

3 For, should we fail proclaiming
  Our great Redeemer's praise,
The stones, our silence shaming,
  Would their hosannas raise.
But shall we only render
  The tribute of our words?
No! while our hearts are tender,
  They too shall be the Lord's.

John King, 1789-1858.

For Children

ELLACOMBE. 7.6.7.6. D. *Mainz Gesangbuch*, 1833.

A-men.

1 Hosanna, loud hosanna,
The little children sang;
Through pillared court and temple,
The lovely anthem rang;
To Jesus, who had blessed them,
Close folded to His breast,
The children sang their praises,
The simplest and the best.

2 From Olivet they followed,
Midst an exultant crowd,
Waving the victor palm branch,
And shouting clear and loud.
Bright angels joined the chorus,
Beyond the cloudless sky:
Hosanna in the highest,
Glory to God on high!

3 Fair leaves of silvery olive
They strewed upon the ground,
Whilst Salem's circling mountains
Echoed the joyful sound.
The Lord of men and angels
Rode on in lowly state,
Nor scorned that little children
Should on His bidding wait.

4 Hosanna in the highest!
That ancient song we sing;
For Christ is our Redeemer,
The Lord of heaven our King:
O may we ever praise Him,
With heart and life and voice,
And in His blissful presence
Eternally rejoice. Amen.

Jeannette Threlfall, 1821-80.

For Children

837

INFANT PRAISE. 7 7.7 7. and refrain. *The Tune Book*, 1842.

Refrain.
Hark, hark, hark! while in-fant voi-ces sing, Hark, hark,
hark! while in- fant voi -ces sing Loud . . ho - san-nas,
loud . . ho-sannas, loud . . ho - san - nas to our King.

1 Children of Jerusalem
Sang the praise of Jesu's name:
Children, too, of modern days,
Join to sing the Saviour's praise.
Hark! While infant voices sing
Loud hosannas to our King.

2 We are taught to love the Lord,
We are taught to read His Word,
We are taught the way to heaven:
Praise for all to God be given.

3 Parents, teachers, old and young,
All unite to swell the song;
Higher and yet higher rise,
Till hosannas reach the skies.

John Henley, 1800-1842.

838

GLENFINLAS. 6.5.6.5. K. G. FINLAY, 1882-

May also be sung to NORTH COATES, No. 286.

1 JESUS, high in glory,
Lend a listening ear;
When we bow before Thee,
Children's praises hear.

2 Though Thou art so holy,
Heaven's almighty King,
Thou wilt stoop to listen
When Thy praise we sing.

3 We are little children,
Weak and apt to stray;
Saviour, guide and keep us
In the heavenly way.

4 Save us, Lord, from sinning;
Watch us day by day;
Help us now to love Thee;
Take our sins away.

5 Then, when Thou shalt call us
To our heavenly home,
We will gladly answer:
Saviour, Lord, we come!

Harriet Burn McKeever, 1807-86.

839

IN MEMORIAM. 8.6.7.6.7.6.7.6. J. STAINER, 1840-1901.

1 THERE'S a Friend for little children
Above the bright blue sky,
A Friend who never changeth,
Whose love can never die.
Unlike our friends by nature,
Who change with changing years,
This Friend is always worthy
The precious name He bears.

2 There's a home for little children
Above the bright blue sky,
Where Jesus reigns in glory,
A home of peace and joy.
No home on earth is like it,
Or can with it compare;
For every one is happy,
Nor could be happier, there.

3 There's a song for little children
Above the bright blue sky,
A song that will not weary
Though sung continually,
A song which even angels
Can never, never sing;
They know not Christ as Saviour,
But worship Him as King.

4 There's a robe for little children
Above the bright blue sky,
And a harp of sweetest music,
And a palm of victory.
All, all above is treasured,
And found in Christ alone;
O come, dear little children,
That all may be your own.

Albert Midlane, 1825-1909.

840

PEACEFIELD. 7 7.7 7. Old Irish Melody.

1 GOD, my Father, loving me,
Gave His Son, my friend to be:
Gave His Son, my form to take,
Bearing all things for my sake.

2 Jesus still remains the same
As in days of old He came;
As my brother by my side,
Still He seeks my steps to guide.

3 How can I repay Thy love,
Lord of all the hosts above?
What have I, a child, to bring
Unto Thee, Thou heavenly King?

4 I have but myself to give:
Let me to Thy glory live;
Let me follow, day by day,
Where Thou showest me the way.

George Wallace Briggs, 1875-

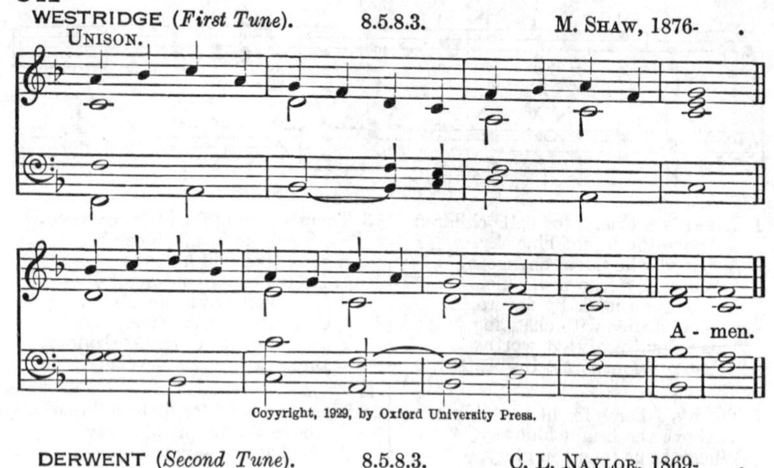

1 Jesus, Friend of little children,
Be a Friend to me;
Take my hand and ever keep me
Close to Thee.

2 Teach me how to grow in goodness
Daily as I grow;
Thou hast been a child and surely
Thou dost know.

3 Step by step, O lead me onward,
Upward into youth;
Wiser, stronger, still becoming
In Thy truth.

4 Never leave me nor forsake me,
Ever be my Friend,
For I need Thee from life's dawning
To its end. Amen.

Walter John Mathams, 1853-1931.

For Children

842

INNOCENTS (*First Tune*). 7 7.7 7. *Parish Choir*, 1851.

GENTLE JESUS (*Second Tune*). 7 7.7 7. M. SHAW, 1876- .

1 GENTLE Jesus, meek and mild,
Look upon a little child,
Pity my simplicity,
Suffer me to come to Thee.

2 Fain I would to Thee be brought;
Gracious Lord, forbid it not;
In the kingdom of Thy grace
Give a little child a place.

3 Fain I would be as Thou art;
Give me Thy obedient heart:
Thou art pitiful and kind;
Let me have Thy loving mind.

4 Let me above all fulfil
God my heavenly Father's will;
Never His good Spirit grieve,
Only to His glory live.

5 Lamb of God, I look to Thee;
Thou shalt my example be:
Thou art gentle, meek, and mild;
Thou wast once a little child.

6 Thou didst live to God alone;
Thou didst never seek Thine own;
Thou Thyself didst never please:
God was all Thy happiness.

7 Loving Jesus, gentle Lamb,
In Thy gracious hands I am:
Make me, Saviour, what Thou art;
Live Thyself within my heart.

8 I shall then show forth Thy praise,
Serve Thee all my happy days;
Then the world shall always see
Christ, the holy Child, in me.

Charles Wesley, 1707-88.

* * * *

843

CASTLE EDEN. 6.5.6.5. R. W. DIXON, 1875.

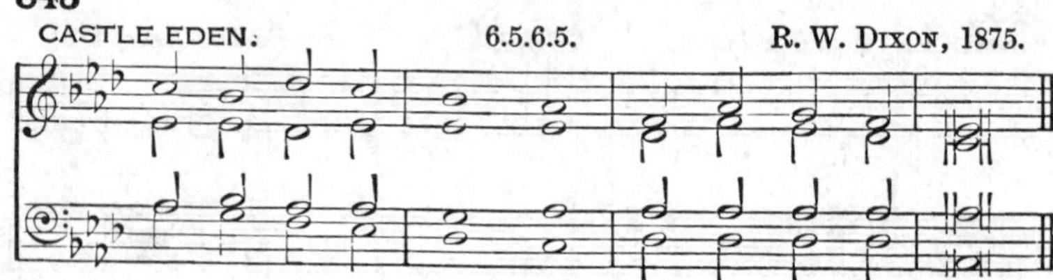

1 IN our dear Lord's garden,
Planted here below,
Many tiny flowerets
In sweet beauty grow.

2 Christ, the loving Gardener,
Tends these blossoms small;
Loves the little lilies
As the cedars tall.

3 Nothing is too little
For His gentle care;
Nothing is too lowly
In His love to share.

4 Jesus loves the children,
Children such as we;
Blest them when their mothers
Brought them to His knee.

5 Jesus calls the children,
Bids them come and stand
In His pleasant garden,
Watered by His hand.

6 Lord, Thy call we answer
Take us in Thy care;
Train us in Thy garden,
In Thy work to share.

Ella Sophia Armitage, 1841-1931.

844

EVENING PRAYER.
UNISON. 8.7.8.7. J. STAINER, 1840-1901.

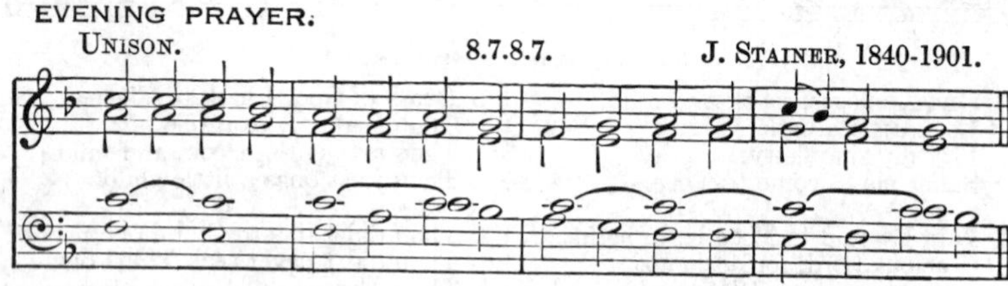

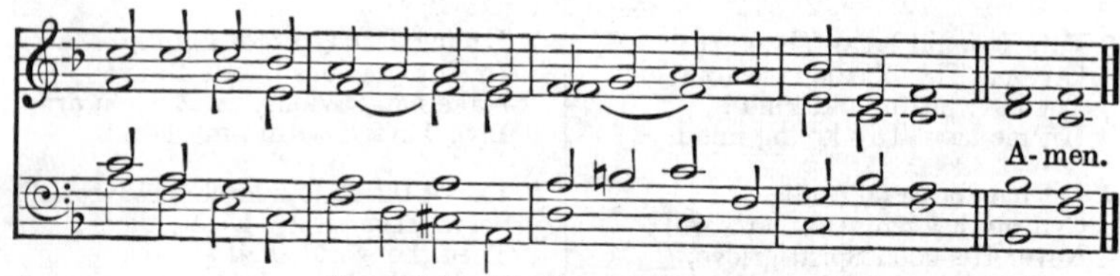

By permission of Novello and Company, Limited.

May also be sung to SICILIAN MARINERS, No. 765.

1 Jesus, tender Shepherd, hear me;
Bless Thy little lamb to-night;
Through the darkness be Thou near me;
Keep me safe till morning light.

2 All this day Thy hand has led me,
And I thank Thee for Thy care;
Thou hast clothed me, warmed and fed me;
Listen to my evening prayer.

3 Let my sins be all forgiven;
Bless the friends I love so well;
Take me, when I die, to heaven,
Happy there with Thee to dwell. Amen.

Mary Duncan, 1814-40.

845

CAPEL. C.M. English Traditional Melody.

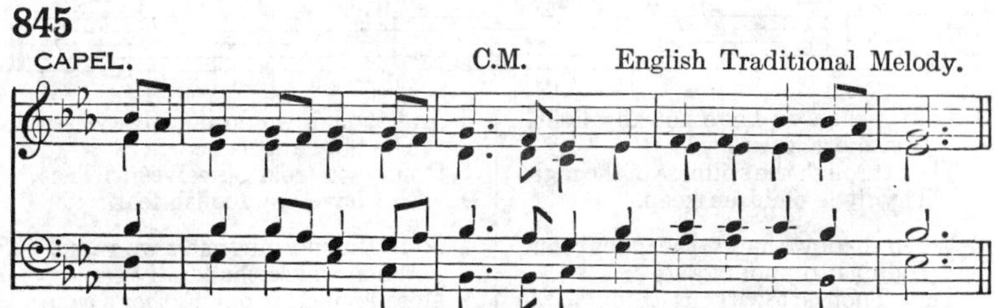

1 God make my life a little light
Within the world to glow;
A little flame that burneth bright,
Wherever I may go.

2 God make my life a little flower
That giveth joy to all,
Content to bloom in native bower,
Although the place be small.

3 God make my life a little song
That comforteth the sad,
That helpeth others to be strong,
And makes the singer glad.

4 God make my life a little staff
Whereon the weak may rest,
That so what health and strength I have
May serve my neighbours best.

5 God make my life a little hymn
Of tenderness and praise,
Of faith, that never waxeth dim,
In all His wondrous ways.

Matilda Barbara Betham-Edwards, 1836-1919.

846

THIS ENDRIS NYGHT. C.M. English Carol, 15th Century.

1 LORD, when we have not any light,
And mothers are asleep,
Then through the stillness of the night
Thy little children keep.

2 When shadows haunt the quiet room,
Help us to understand
That Thou art with us through the [gloom,
To hold us by the hand.

3 And though we do not always see
The holy angels near,
O may we trust ourselves to Thee,
Nor have one foolish fear.

4 So in the morning may we wake,
When wakes the kindly sun,
More loving for our Father's sake
To each unloving one.

Annie Matheson, 1853-1924.

847

SOLOTHURN. L.M. Swiss Traditional Melody.
UNISON.

1 O JESUS, we are well and strong,
And we can run about and play;
But there are children who are sick,
And have to lie in bed all day.

2 We thank Thee for our health and strength; [bless
And, loving Lord, we pray Thee
The children who are weak and ill
And suffer pain and weariness.

3 Lord, give us thoughtful, loving hearts, [done
Show us kind deeds which may be
By us, for Jesu's sake, to help
Some sad or suffering little one.
Amen.

Edith Florence Boyle Macalister, 1873-

848

SAMUEL. 6.6.6.6.8 8. A. SULLIVAN, 1842-1900.

By permission of Novello and Company, Limited.

1 HUSHED was the evening hymn,
The temple courts were dark,
The lamp was burning dim
Before the sacred ark,
When suddenly a voice divine
Rang through the silence of the shrine.

2 The old man, meek and mild,
The priest of Israel, slept;
His watch the temple child,
The little Levite, kept:
And what from Eli's sense was sealed
The Lord to Hannah's son revealed.

3 O give me Samuel's ear,
The open ear, O Lord,
Alive and quick to hear
Each whisper of Thy word;
Like him to answer at Thy call,
And to obey Thee first of all.

4 O give me Samuel's heart,
A lowly heart, that waits
Where in Thy house Thou art
Or watches at Thy gates
By day and night—a heart that still
Moves at the breathing of Thy will.

5 O give me Samuel's mind,
A sweet unmurmuring faith,
Obedient and resigned
To Thee in life and death,
That I may read with childlike eyes
Truths that are hidden from the wise.

James Drummond Burns, 1823-64.

849

SUPPLICATION. 7 7.7 7. J. B. Calkin, 1827-1905.

1 Father, lead me day by day
Ever in Thine own sweet way;
Teach me to be pure and true,
Show me what I ought to do.

2 When in danger, make me brave;
Make me know that Thou canst save;
Keep me safe by Thy dear side;
Let me in Thy love abide.

3 When I'm tempted to do wrong,
Make me steadfast, wise and strong;
And when all alone I stand,
Shield me with Thy mighty hand.

4 When my heart is full of glee,
Help me to remember Thee,
Happy most of all to know
That my Father loves me so.

5 When my work seems hard and dry,
May I press on cheerily;
Help me patiently to bear
Pain and hardship, toil and care.

6 May I see the good and bright
When they pass before my sight;
May I hear the heavenly voice
When the pure and wise rejoice.
Amen.

John Page Hopps, 1834-1912.

850

EXCELSIOR. 7.6.7.6., Trochaic. J. Booth, 1852-1930.

1 Looking upward every day,
Sunshine on our faces;
Pressing onward every day
Toward the heavenly places.

2 Growing every day in awe,
For Thy name is holy;
Learning every day to love
With a love more lowly.

3 Walking every day more close
To our elder Brother;
Growing every day more true
Unto one another.

4 Every day more gratefully
Kindnesses receiving,
Every day more readily
Injuries forgiving.

5 Lord, so pray we every day,
Hear us in Thy pity,
That we enter in at last
To the holy City. Amen.

Mary Butler, 1841-1916.

851

ALL THINGS BRIGHT AND BEAUTIFUL (KEATS) (*First Tune*).
Verse 1 *and* REFRAIN. 7.6.7.6. and refrain. W. H. MONK, 1823-89.

1 *All things bright and beautiful,*
All creatures great and small,
All things wise and wonderful,
The Lord God made them all.

2 Each little flower that opens,
Each little bird that sings,
He made their glowing colours,
He made their tiny wings.
All things—

3 The purple-headed mountain,
The river running by,
The sunset, and the morning
That brightens up the sky.
All things—

4 The cold wind in the winter,
The pleasant summer sun,
The ripe fruits in the garden,
He made them every one.
All things—

5 He gave us eyes to see them,
And lips that we might tell
How great is God Almighty,
Who has made all things well.
All things—

Cecil Frances Alexander, 1823-95.

851

ROYAL OAK (*Second Tune*).
UNISON.

7.6.7.6. and refrain.

Adapted from an English Traditional Melody by M. SHAW.

NOTE.—The pause (𝄐) is for the last time only.

1 *All things bright and beautiful,*
All creatures great and small,
All things wise and wonderful,
The Lord God made them all.

2 Each little flower that opens,
Each little bird that sings,
He made their glowing colours,
He made their tiny wings.
All things—

3 The purple-headed mountain,
The river running by,
The sunset, and the morning
That brightens up the sky.
All things—

4 The cold wind in the winter,
The pleasant summer sun,
The ripe fruits in the garden,
He made them every one.
All things—

5 He gave us eyes to see them,
And lips that we might tell
How great is God Almighty,
Who has made all things well.
All things—

Cecil Frances Alexander, 1823-95.

852

RODMELL. C.M. English Traditional Melody.

1 All things which live below the sky,
Or move within the sea,
Are creatures of the Lord most high,
And brothers unto me.

2 I love to hear the robin sing,
Perched on the highest bough;
To see the rook with purple wing
Follow the shining plough.

3 I love to watch the swallow skim
The river in his flight;
To mark, when day is growing dim,
The glow-worm's silvery light;

4 The sea-gull whiter than the foam,
The fish that dart beneath;
The lowing cattle coming home;
The goats upon the heath.

5 Beneath His heaven there's room for all;
He gives to all their meat;
He sees the meanest sparrow fall
Unnoticed in the street.

6 Almighty Father, King of kings,
The Lover of the meek,
Make me a friend of helpless things,
Defender of the weak. Amen.

Edward John Brailsford, 1841-1921.

853

NEWLAND. S.M. H. J. Gauntlett, 1805-76.

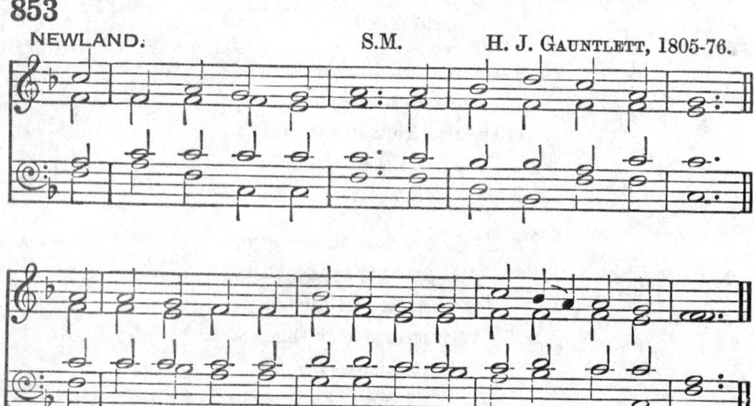

1 A LITTLE child may know
Our Father's name of Love;
'Tis written on the earth below,
And on the sky above.

2 Around me when I look,
His handiwork I see;
This world is like a picture book
To teach His name to me.

3 The thousand little flowers
Within our garden found,
The rainbow and the soft spring showers,
And every pleasant sound.

4 The birds that sweetly sing,
The moon that shines by night;
With every tiny living thing
Rejoicing in the light.

5 And every star above,
Set in the deep blue sky,
All tell me that our God is love,
All tell me He is nigh.

Jane Eliza Leeson, 1807-82.

854

HERONGATE. L.M. English Traditional Melody.

1 IT is a thing most wonderful,
Almost too wonderful to be,
That God's own Son should come from heaven,
And die to save a child like me.

2 And yet I know that it is true;
He chose a poor and humble lot,
And wept and toiled and mourned and died,
For love of those who loved Him [not.

3 I sometimes think about the Cross,
And shut my eyes and try to see
The cruel nails and crown of thorns,
And Jesus crucified for me.

4 But even could I see Him die,
I could but see a little part
Of that great love which like a fire
Is always burning in His heart.

5 I cannot tell how He could love
A child so weak and full of sin;
His love must be most wonderful,
If He could die my love to win.

6 It is most wonderful to know
His love for me so free and sure;
But 'tis more wonderful to see
My love for Him so faint and poor.

7 And yet I want to love Thee, Lord;
O light the flame within my heart,
And I will love Thee more and more,
Until I see Thee as Thou art.

William Walsham How, 1823-97.

NEWBURY. C.M. English Traditional Melody.

1 I LOVE to think, though I am young,
My Saviour was a child;
That Jesus walked this earth along,
With feet all undefiled.

2 He kept His Father's word of truth,
As I am taught to do; [youth,
And while He walked the paths of
He walked in wisdom too.

3 I love to think that He who spake
And made the blind to see,
And called the sleeping dead to
Was once a child like me. [wake,

4 That He who wore the thorny crown,
And tasted death's despair,
Had a kind mother like my own,
And knew her love and care.

5 I know 'twas all for love of me
That He became a child,
And left the heavens, so fair to see,
And trod earth's pathway wild.

6 Then, Saviour, who wast once a child,
A child may come to Thee;
And O in all Thy mercy mild,
Dear Saviour, come to me! Amen.

Edwin Paxton Hood, 1820-85.

856

ANGELS' STORY. 7.6.7.6. D. A. H. MANN, 1850-1930.

1 I LOVE to hear the story
Which angel voices tell,
How once the King of Glory
Came down on earth to dwell.
I am both weak and sinful,
But this I surely know:
The Lord came down to save me,
Because He loved me so.

2 I'm glad my blessèd Saviour
Was once a child like me,
To show how pure and holy
His little ones might be;
And if I try to follow
His footsteps here below,
He never will forsake me,
Because He loves me so.

3 To sing His love and mercy
My sweetest songs I'll raise;
And though I cannot see Him,
I know He hears my praise:
For He has kindly promised
That even I may go
To sing among His angels,
Because He loves me so.

Emily Huntington Miller, 1833-1913.

857

THE STORY OF JESUS. Irregular. C. B. JUTSON, 1870-1930.

UNISON.

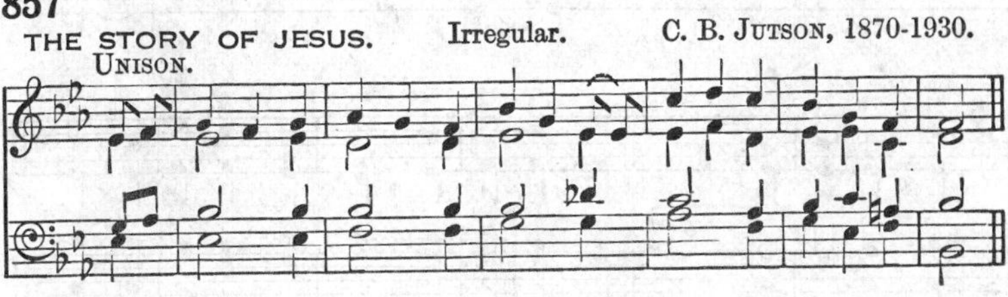

1 GOD has given us a Book full of stories,
Which was made for His people of old,
It begins with the tale of a garden,
And ends with the city of gold.

2 But the best is the story of Jesus,
Of the Babe with the ox in the stall,
Of the song that was sung by the angels,
The most beautiful story of all.

3 There are stories for parents and children,
For the old who are ready to rest,
But for all who can read them or listen,
The story of Jesus is best.

4 For it tells how He came from the Father,
His far-away children to call,
To bring the lost sheep to their Shepherd,
The most beautiful story of all.

Maria Matilda Penstone, 1859-1910.

STORIES OF JESUS.
UNISON OR DUET. 8.4.8.4.5.4.5.4. F. A. CHALLINOR, 1866-1952

1 TELL me the stories of Jesus
I love to hear;
Things I would ask Him to tell me
If He were here:
Scenes by the wayside,
Tales of the sea,
Stories of Jesus,
Tell them to me.

2 First let me hear how the children
Stood round His knee;
And I shall fancy His blessing
Resting on me:
Words full of kindness,
Deeds full of grace,
All in the love-light
Of Jesu's face.

3 Tell how the sparrow that twitters
On yonder tree
And the sweet meadow-side lily
May speak to me;
Give me their message,
For I would hear
How Jesus taught us
Our Father's care.

4 Tell me, in accents of wonder,
How rolled the sea,
Tossing the boat in a tempest
On Galilee;
And how the Master,
Ready and kind,
Chided the billows
And hushed the wind.

5 Into the city I'd follow
The children's band,
Waving a branch of the palm-tree
High in my hand;
One of His heralds,
Yes, I would sing
Loudest hosannas!
Jesus is King!

6 Show me that scene, in the Garden,
Of bitter pain;
And of the Cross where my Saviour
For me was slain:
Sad ones or bright ones,
So that they be
Stories of Jesus,
Tell them to me.

William Henry Parker, 1845-1929.

859

IRBY. 8.7.8.7.7 7. H. J. GAUNTLETT, 1805-76.

1 ONCE in royal David's city
Stood a lowly cattle-shed,
Where a mother laid her baby
In a manger for His bed.
Mary was that mother mild,
Jesus Christ her little child.

2 He came down to earth from heaven
Who is God and Lord of all,
And His shelter was a stable,
And His cradle was a stall.
With the poor, and mean, and lowly
Lived on earth our Saviour holy.

3 And through all His wondrous childhood
He would honour and obey,
Love, and watch the lowly maiden
In whose gentle arms He lay.
Christian children all must be
Mild, obedient, good as He.

4 For He is our childhood's pattern:
Day by day like us He grew;
He was little, weak, and helpless;
Tears and smiles like us He knew;
And He feeleth for our sadness,
And He shareth in our gladness.

5 And our eyes at last shall see Him,
Through His own redeeming love;
For that child so dear and gentle
Is our Lord in heaven above;
And He leads His children on
To the place where He is gone.

Cecil Frances Alexander, 1823-95.

AWAY IN A MANGER. 11 11.11 11. W. J. KIRKPATRICK, 1838-1921.

UNISON.

1 AWAY in a manger, no crib for a bed,
The little Lord Jesus laid down His sweet head,
The stars in the bright sky looked down where He lay,
The little Lord Jesus asleep on the hay.

2 The cattle are lowing, the Baby awakes,
But little Lord Jesus no crying He makes,
I love Thee, Lord Jesus! Look down from the sky,
And stay by my side until morning is nigh.

3 Be near me, Lord Jesus; I ask Thee to stay
Close by me for ever, and love me, I pray.
Bless all the dear children in Thy tender care,
And fit us for heaven, to live with Thee there.

Anonymous.

861

TEMPLE FORTUNE. 11 11.11 11. G. F. BROCKLESS, 1887-1957.

Ihr Kinderlein kommet

1 O COME little children, I pray ye come all,
And join with the shepherds at Bethlehem's stall;
There see what the Father, to do us delight,
Hath sent to the earth on this glorious night.

2 O bow, little children, O bend low and pray,
With little hands folded thank God, as did they;
Sing lustily, children, with glad tuneful voice,
O sing with the angels, and like them rejoice!

C. von Schmidt, 17*th. cent.*

862

WORSHIP. 6.5.6.5. A. H. MANN, 1850-1930.

1 WISE men, seeking Jesus,
Travelled from afar,
Guided on their journey
By a beauteous star.

2 But if we desire Him,
He is close at hand;
For our native country
Is our Holy Land.

3 Prayerful souls may find Him
By our quiet lakes,
Meet Him on our hillsides
When the morning breaks.

4 In our fertile cornfields
While the sheaves are bound,
In our busy markets,
Jesus may be found.

5 Fishermen talk with Him
By the great North Sea,
As the first disciples
Did in Galilee.

6 Every peaceful village
In our land might be
Made by Jesu's presence
Like sweet Bethany.

7 He is more than near us,
If we love Him well;
For He seeketh ever
In our hearts to dwell.

James Thomas East, 1860-1937

863

CHRISTINA. Irregular. F. L. WISEMAN, 1858-1944

1 THE shepherds had an angel,
The wise men had a star;
But what have I, a little child,
To guide me home from far,
Where glad stars sing together,
And singing angels are?

2 Lord Jesus is my guardian,
So I can nothing lack:
The lambs lie in His bosom,
Along life's dangerous track;
The wilful lambs that go astray
He, bleeding, fetches back.

3 Those shepherds through the lonely night
Sat watching by their sheep,
Until they saw the heavenly host
Who neither tire nor sleep,
All singing Glory, glory
In festival they keep.

4 Christ watches me, His little lamb,
Cares for me day and night,
That I may be His own in heaven:
So angels clad in white
Shall sing their Glory, glory
For my sake in the height.

5 Lord, bring me nearer day by day,
Till I my voice unite,
And sing my Glory, glory
With angels clad in white,
All Glory, glory given to Thee
Through all the heavenly height.

Christina Georgina Rossetti, 1830-94.

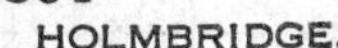

864

HOLMBRIDGE. 7.6.7.6. D. J. T. LIGHTWOOD, 1856-1944

1 REMEMBER all the people
Who live in far-off lands
In strange and lovely cities,
Or roam the desert sands,
Or farm the mountain pastures,
Or till the endless plains [fields
Where children wade through rice-
And watch the camel-trains :

2 Some work in sultry forests
Where apes swing to and fro,
Some fish in mighty rivers,
Some hunt across the snow.
Remember all God's children,
Who yet have never heard
The truth that comes from Jesus,
The glory of His word.

3 God bless the men and women
Who serve Him oversea ;
God raise up more to help them
To set the nations free,
Till all the distant people
In every foreign place
Shall understand His Kingdom
And come into His grace.

Percy Dearmer, 1867-1938

ATHENS. Irregular. Greek Melody.

1 I THINK, when I read that sweet story of old,
When Jesus was here among men,
How He called little children as lambs to His fold,
I should like to have been with them then;
I wish that His hands had been placed on my head,
That His arms had been thrown around me,
And that I might have seen His kind look when He said:
Let the little ones come unto Me!

2 Yet still to His footstool in prayer I may go,
And ask for a share in His love;
And if I now earnestly seek Him below,
I shall see Him and hear Him above,
In that beautiful place He is gone to prepare
For all who are washed and forgiven;
And many dear children are gathering there,
For of such is the kingdom of heaven.

3 But thousands and thousands who wander and fall
Never heard of that heavenly home;
I should like them to know there is room for them all,
And that Jesus has bid them to come.
I long for the joy of that glorious time,
The sweetest and brightest and best,
When the dear little children of every clime
Shall crowd to His arms and be blessed.

Jemima Luke, 1813-1906.

866

SALEM. Irregular. German Students' Song.

1 When mothers of Salem,
Their children brought to Jesus,
The stern disciples drove them back
And bade them depart;
But Jesus saw them ere they fled,
And sweetly smiled, and kindly said:
Suffer the children to come unto Me.

2 How kind was our Saviour
To bid those children welcome;
But there are many thousands
Who have never heard His name;
Dear Saviour, hear us when we pray,
That they may hear Thee to them say:
Suffer the children to come unto Me.

3 And soon may the heathen
Of every tribe and nation
Fulfil Thy blessèd word, and cast
Their idols all away;
O shine upon them from above,
And show Thyself a God of love;
Teach them, dear Saviour, to come unto Thee.

William Medlen Hutchings, 1827-76.

Also:

84 All glory, laud, and honour
124 See, amid the winter's snow
125 O little town of Bethlehem
137 In the bleak mid-winter
146 Jesus, who lived above the sky
180 There is a green hill
286 Holy Spirit, hear us
609 Saviour, like a Shepherd lead us
656 Around the throne of God in heaven
797 Once again, dear Lord
798 Far round the world
799 The fields are all white
871 In our work and in our play

867

SLINGSBY. 8.7.8.7. E. S. CARTER, 1845-1923.

May also be sung to LAUS DEO, No. 13.

1 DAY by day we magnify Thee,
When, as each new day is born,
On our knees at home, we bless Thee
For the mercies of the morn.

2 Day by day we magnify Thee,
When our hymns in school we [raise,
Daily work begun and ended
With the daily voice of praise.

3 Day by day we magnify Thee
In our hymns before we sleep;
Angels hear them, watching by us,
Christ's dear lambs all night to keep.

4 Day by day we magnify Thee,
Not in words of praise alone;
Truthful lips and meek obedience
Show Thy glory in Thine own.

5 Day by day we magnify Thee,
When for Jesu's sake we try
Every wrong to bear with patience,
Every sin to mortify.

6 Day by day we magnify Thee,
Till our days on earth shall cease,
Till we rest from these our labours,
Waiting for Thy day in peace.

John Ellerton, 1826-93.

868

BOYCE (SHARON). 7 7.7 7. W. BOYCE, 1710-79.

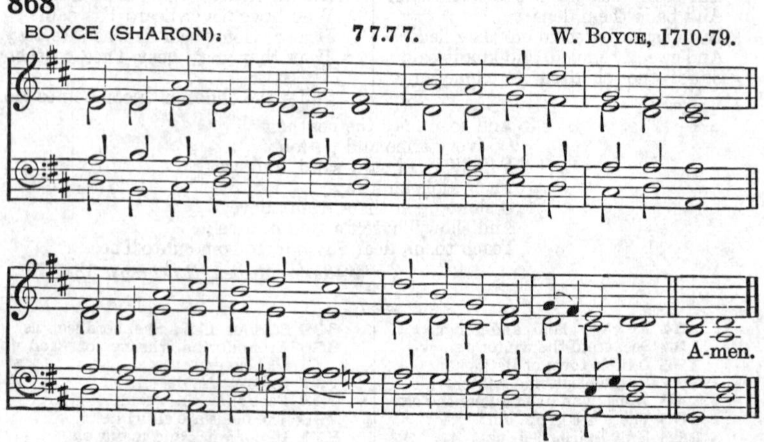

1 LORD and Saviour, true and kind,
Be the master of my mind;
Bless and guide and strengthen still
All my powers of thought and will.

2 While I ply the scholar's task,
Jesus Christ, be near, I ask;
Help the memory, clear the brain,
Knowledge still to seek and gain.

3 Here I train for life's swift race;
Let me do it in Thy grace:
Here I arm me for life's fight;
Let me do it in Thy might.

4 Thou hast made me mind and soul;
I for Thee would use the whole:
Thou hast died that I might live;
All my powers to Thee I give.

5 Striving, thinking, learning still,
Let me follow thus Thy will,
Till my whole glad nature be
Trained for duty and for Thee. Amen.

Handley Carr Glyn Moule, 1841-1920.

869

BEDE. 11.10.11.10. Dactylic.

Adapted by JOHN GOSS, 1800-80.

1 PRAISE to our God, who with love never swerving
Guides our endeavours, enfolds us from harm,
Peace and prosperity, past our deserving,
Showering upon us with bountiful arm.

2 Gone are the labours, the joy, and the sorrow;
Lo, at the end we draw near to adore,
Ere our full life is begun on the morrow,
Childhood behind us and manhood before.

3 Shepherd of souls, O door of salvation,
Keep Thou Thy flock in Thine infinite care,
Fold them as one in their last adoration,
Ere in the distance divided they fare.

4 Though nevermore in one place all may gather,
Though in life's battle we struggle apart,
One be our Saviour, and One be our Father,
Bind us together in faith and in heart. Amen.

Herbert Branston Gray, 1851-1929.

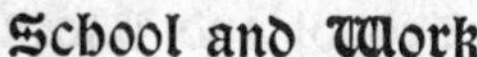

870

PILGRIMAGE (*First Tune*). 8.7.8.7.4.7. G. J. ELVEY, 1816-93.

A-men.

8.7.8.7.4.7.

TONBRIDGE SCHOOL (*Second Tune*). Anonymous.

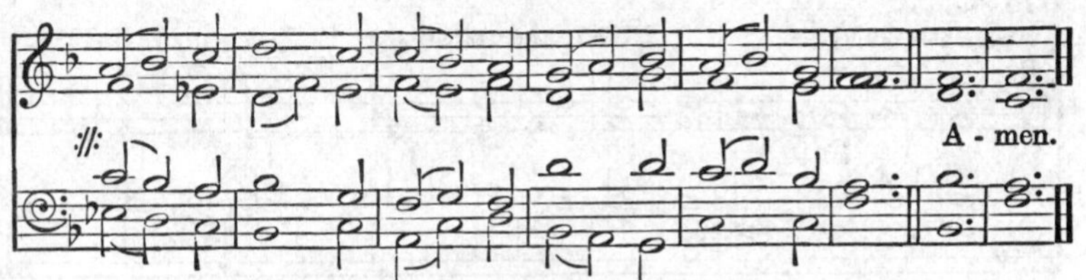

May also be sung to DISMISSAL, No. 693.

Assembly.

1 LORD, behold us with Thy blessing,
Once again assembled here;
Onward be our footsteps pressing,
In Thy love, and faith, and fear;
Still protect us
By Thy presence ever near.

2 For Thy mercy we adore Thee,
For this rest upon our way;
Lord, again we bow before Thee,
Speed our labours day by day;
Mind and spirit
With Thy choicest gifts array.

3 Keep the spell of home affection
Still alive in every heart;
May its power, with mild direction,
Draw our love from self apart,
Till Thy children
Feel that Thou their Father art. Amen.

* * * * *

Dismissal.

4 Lord, dismiss us with Thy blessing
Thanks for mercies past receive;
Pardon all, their faults confessing;
Time that's lost may all retrieve;
May Thy children
Ne'er again Thy Spirit grieve.

5 By Thy kindly influence cherish
All the good we here have gained;
May all taint of evil perish,
By Thy mightier power restrained;
Seek we ever
Knowledge pure and love unfeigned.

6 Let Thy Father-hand be shielding
All who here shall meet no more;
May their seed-time past be yielding
Year by year a richer store;
Those returning
Make more faithful than before. Amen.

Henry James Buckoll, 1803-71.

871

ASHBURTON. 7 7.7 7. and refrain. R. JACKSON, 1842-1914.

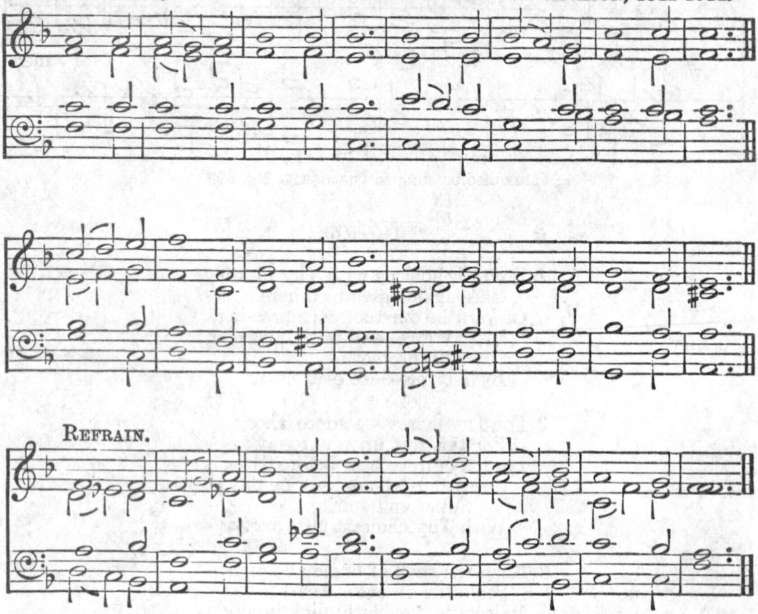

REFRAIN.

1 IN our work and in our play,
Jesus, ever with us stay;
May we always strive to be
True and faithful unto Thee.

Then we truthfully can sing:
We are children of the King.

2 May we in Thy strength subdue
Evil tempers, words untrue,
Thoughts impure and deeds unkind,
All things hateful to Thy mind.

3 Jesus, from Thy throne above
Deign to fill us with Thy love,
So that all around may see
We belong, dear Lord, to Thee.

4 Children of the King are we,
May we loyal to Him be;
Try to please Him every day,
In our work and in our play.

Whitfield Glanville Wills, 1841-91.

872

CHILTON FOLIAT. 10 10.10 10. G. C. MARTIN, 1844-1916.

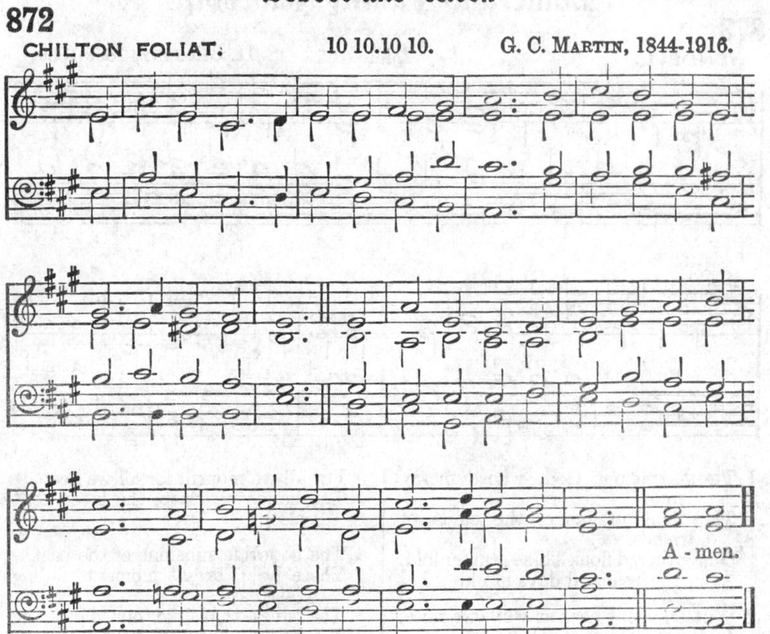

1 WE bless Thee, Lord, for all this common life
Can give of rest and joy amidst its strife;
For earth and trees and sea and clouds and springs;
For work, and all the lessons that it brings;

2 For Pisgah gleams of newer, fairer truth,
Which ever ripening still renews our youth;
For fellowship with noble souls and wise,
Whose hearts beat time to music of the skies;

3 For each achievement human toil can reach;
For all that patriots win, and poets teach;
For the old light that gleams on history's page
For the new hope that shines on each new age.

4 May we to these our lights be ever true,
Find hope and strength and joy for ever new,
To heavenly visions still obedient prove,
The Eternal Law, writ by the Almighty Love! Amen.

Frederick M. White: South Place Hymn Book, 1873.

Also:

549 Lord, that I may learn of Thee
849 Father, lead me **850** Looking upward

873

WENDELL. L.M. S. H. GREGORY, 1869-1950

A-men.

1 THOU gracious God, whose mercy lends
The light of home, the smile of friends,
Our gathered flock Thine arms enfold,
As in the peaceful days of old.

2 Wilt Thou not hear us while we raise,
In sweet accord of solemn praise,
The voices that have mingled long
In joyous flow of mirth and song?

3 For all the blessings life has brought,
For all its sorrowing hours have taught,
For all we mourn, for all we keep,
The hands we clasp, the loved that sleep:

4 The noontide sunshine of the past,
These brief, bright moments fading fast,
The stars that gild our darkening years,
The twilight ray from holier spheres:

5 We thank Thee, Father; let Thy grace
Our loving circle still embrace,
Thy mercy shed its heavenly store,
Thy peace be with us evermore.
Amen.

Oliver Wendell Holmes, 1809-94.

874

BUILTH. 5 6.9.6 6.9. *Sacred Melody*, 1761.

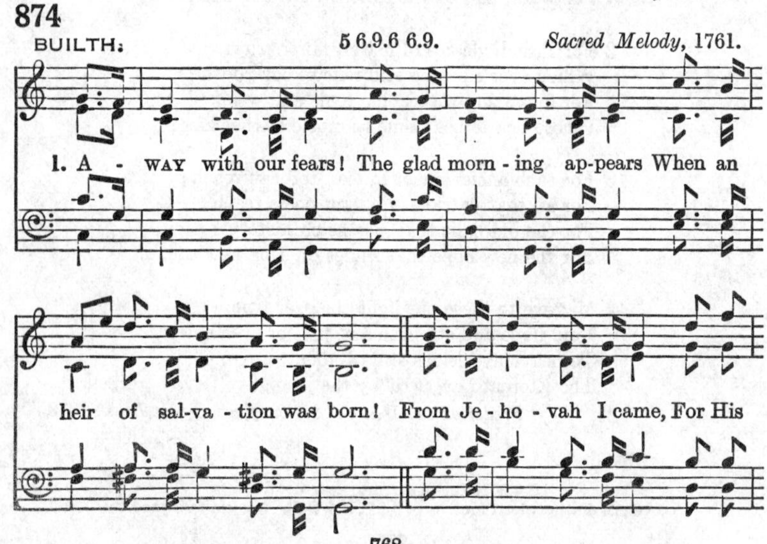
1. A - WAY with our fears! The glad morn - ing ap-pears When an
heir of sal-va - tion was born! From Je - ho - vah I came, For His

glo - ry I am, And to Him I with sing - ing re - turn.
From Je - ho - vah I came, For His glo - ry I am, And to
Him I with sing - ing re - turn, And to Him I with sing - ing re - turn.

May also be sung to HUNGERFORD, No. 407.

Wesleys' Birthday Hymn.

1 Away with our fears!
The glad morning appears
When an heir of salvation was born!
From Jehovah I came,
For His glory I am,
And to Him I with singing return.

2 I sing of Thy grace,
From my earliest days
Ever near to allure and defend;
Hitherto Thou hast been
My Preserver from sin,
And I trust Thou wilt save to the end.

3 O the infinite cares,
And temptations, and snares
Thy hand hath conducted me through!
O the blessings bestowed
By a bountiful God,
And the mercies eternally new!

4 What a mercy is this,
What a heaven of bliss,
How unspeakably happy am I;
Gathered into the fold,
With Thy people enrolled,
With Thy people to live and to die.

5 All honour and praise
To the Father of grace,
To the Spirit, and Son, I return;
The business pursue
He hath made me to do,
And rejoice that I ever was born.

6 In a rapture of joy
My life I employ
The God of my life to proclaim;
'Tis worth living for, this,
To administer bliss
And salvation in Jesus's name.

7 My remnant of days
I spend in His praise,
Who died the whole world to redeem:
Be they many or few,
My days are His due,
And they all are devoted to Him.

Charles Wesley, 1707-88.

875

STRENGTH AND STAY. 11.10.11.10. J. B. DYKES, 1823-76.

O selig Haus, wo man dich aufgenommen.

1 O HAPPY home where Thou art loved the dearest,
Thou loving Friend, and Saviour of our race,
And where among the guests there never cometh
One who can hold such high and honoured place!

2 O happy home where two in heart united
In holy faith and blessèd hope are one,
Whom death a little while alone divideth,
And cannot end the union here begun!

3 O happy home whose little ones are given
Early to Thee, in humble faith and prayer,
To Thee, their Friend, who from the heights of heaven
Guides them, and guards with more than mother's care!

4 O happy home where each one serves Thee, lowly,
Whatever his appointed work may be,
Till every common task seems great and holy,
When it is done, O Lord, as unto Thee!

5 O happy home where Thou art not forgotten
When joy is overflowing, full and free;
O happy home where every wounded spirit
Is brought, Physician, Comforter, to Thee.

6 Until at last, when earth's day's work is ended,
All meet Thee in the blessèd home above,
From whence Thou camest, where Thou hast ascended,
Thy everlasting home of peace and love!

Carl Johann Philipp Spitta, 1801-59;
tr. by Sarah Laurie Findlater [*Borthwick*], 1823-1907.

876

BENEVENTO. 7.7.7.7. D. S. WEBBE, 1740-1816.

1 OMNIPRESENT God, whose aid
No one ever asked in vain,
Be this night about my bed,
Every evil thought restrain;
Lay Thy hand upon my soul,
God of my unguarded hours;
All my enemies control,
Hell, and earth, and nature's powers.

2 Loose me from the chains of sense,
Set me from the body free,
Draw with stronger influence
My unfettered soul to Thee;
In me, Lord, Thyself reveal,
Fill me with a sweet surprise;
Let me Thee when waking feel,
Let me in Thy image rise.

3 Let me of Thy life partake,
Thy own holiness impart,
O that I might sweetly wake
With my Saviour in my heart!
O that I might know Thee mine!
O that I might Thee receive!
Only live the life divine,
Only to Thy glory live.

4 Or if Thou my soul require
Ere I see the morning light,
Grant me, Lord, my heart's desire,
Perfect me in love to-night:
Finish Thy great work of love,
Cut it short in righteousness,
Fit me for the realms above,
Change, and bid me die in peace.
Amen.

Charles Wesley, 1707-88.

877

SAXBY. L.M. T. R. MATTHEWS, 1826-1910.

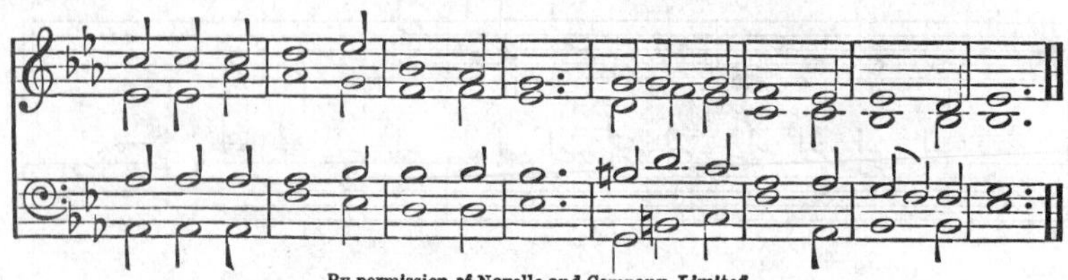

By permission of Novello and Company, Limited.

1 How do Thy mercies close me round!
  For ever be Thy name adored!
I blush in all things to abound;
  The servant is above his Lord!

2 Inured to poverty and pain,
  A suffering life my Master led;
The Son of God, the Son of Man,
  He had not where to lay His head.

3 But, lo, a place He hath prepared
  For me, whom watchful angels keep;
Yea, He Himself becomes my guard,
  He smooths my bed, and gives me sleep.

4 Jesus protects; my fears, begone!
  What can the Rock of Ages move?
Safe in Thy arms I lay me down,
  Thy everlasting arms of love.

5 While Thou art intimately nigh,
  Who, who shall violate my rest?
Sin, earth, and hell I now defy;
  I lean upon my Saviour's breast.

6 I rest beneath the Almighty's shade,
  My griefs expire, my troubles cease:
Thou, Lord, on whom my soul is stayed,
  Wilt keep me still in perfect peace.

7 Me for Thine own Thou lov'st to take,
  In time and in eternity;
Thou never, never wilt forsake
  A helpless soul that trusts in Thee.

Charles Wesley, 1707-88.

Also:

310 When quiet in my house I sit
339 Come, O Thou Traveller unknown
465 Open, Lord, my inward ear
592 I hoped that with the brave
593 O'er the harvest reaped or lost
953 O Lord, who by Thy presence

878 QUEEN AND NATION

ST. ANNE. C.M. W. CROFT, 1678-1727.

From Psalm xc.

1 O GOD, our help in ages past,
  Our hope for years to come,
Our shelter from the stormy blast,
  And our eternal home:

2 Under the shadow of Thy throne,
  Thy saints have dwelt secure;
Sufficient is Thine arm alone,
  And our defence is sure.

3 Before the hills in order stood,
  Or earth received her frame,
From everlasting Thou art God,
  To endless years the same.

4 A thousand ages in Thy sight
  Are like an evening gone;
Short as the watch that ends the night
  Before the rising sun.

5 The busy tribes of flesh and blood,
  With all their cares and fears,
Are carried downward by the flood,
  And lost in following years.

6 Time, like an ever-rolling stream,
  Bears all its sons away;
They fly forgotten, as a dream
  Dies at the opening day.

7 O God, our help in ages past,
  Our hope for years to come,
Be Thou our guard while troubles last,
  And our eternal home. Amen.

Isaac Watts, 1674-1748.

879

NATIONAL ANTHEM. 6 6.4.6 6 6.4. *Gentleman's Magazine*, 1745.

1.

GOD save our gracious Queen;
Long live our noble Queen;
God save the Queen!
Send her victorious,
Happy and glorious,
Long to reign over us:
God save the Queen!

2.

Thy choicest gifts in store
On her be pleased to pour;
Long may she reign;
May she defend our laws,
And ever give us cause
To sing with heart and voice,
God save the Queen!

Attrib. to Henry Carey, d. 1743.

Queen and Nation

880

MOSCOW. 6 6.4.6 6 6.4. F. GIARDINI, 1716-96.

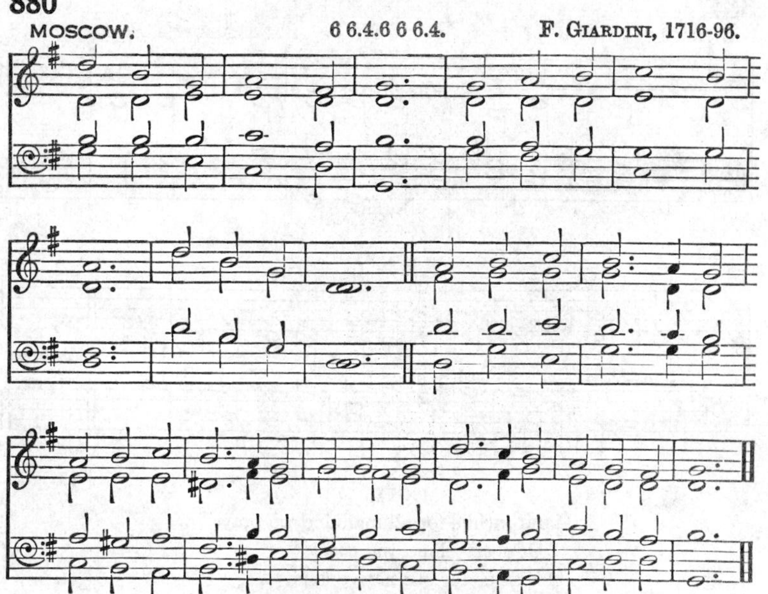

1 GOD bless our native land!
May heaven's protecting hand
Still guard our shore:
May peace her power extend,
Foe be transformed to friend,
And Britain's rights depend
On war no more.

2 O Lord, our monarch bless
With strength and righteousness:
Long may she reign:
Her heart inspire and move
With wisdom from above;
And in a nation's love
Her throne maintain.

3 May just and righteous laws
Uphold the public cause,
And bless our isle:
Home of the brave and free,
Thou land of liberty,
We pray that still on thee
Kind heaven may smile.

4 Nor on this land alone,
But be God's mercies known
From shore to shore:
Lord make the nations see
That men should brothers be,
And form one family
The wide world o'er.

William Edward Hickson, 1803-70.

881

LINCOLN. C.M. Ravenscroft's *Psalter*, 1621.

1.

Lord, while for all mankind we pray,
Of every clime and coast,
O hear us for our native land,
The land we love the most.

2.

Our father's sepulchres are here,
And here our kindred dwell,
Our children too: how should we love
Another land so well?

3.

O guard our shores from every foe;
With peace our borders bless:
With prosperous times our cities crown,
Our fields with plenteousness.

4.

Unite us in the sacred love
Of knowledge, truth, and Thee;
And let our hills and valleys shout
The songs of liberty.

5.

Lord of the nations, thus to Thee
Our country we commend;
Be Thou her refuge and her trust,
Her everlasting Friend. Amen.

John Reynell Wreford, 1800-81.

882

GONFALON ROYAL. L.M. P. C. BUCK, 1871-1947.

UNISON.

HARMONY.

A - - - men.

1.

REJOICE, O land, in God thy might.
His will obey, Him serve aright.
For thee the saints uplift their voice:
Fear not, O land, in God rejoice.

2.

Glad shalt thou be, with blessing crowned,
With joy and peace thou shalt abound.
Yea, love with thee shall make his home,
Until thou see God's kingdom come.

3.

He shall forgive thy sins untold.
Remember thou His love of old.
Walk in His way, His word adore,
And keep His truth for evermore. Amen.

Robert Seymour Bridges, 1844-1930, *Y.H.*

883

RHUDDLAN. 8.7.8.7.8.7. Welsh Traditional Melody.

1 Judge eternal, throned in splendour,
Lord of lords, and King of kings,
With Thy living fire of judgement
Purge this realm of bitter things;
Solace all its wide dominion
With the healing of Thy wings.

2 Still the weary folk are pining
For the hour that brings release;
And the city's crowded clangour
Cries aloud for sin to cease;
And the homesteads and the woodlands
Plead in silence for their peace.

3 Crown, O God, Thine own endeavour:
Cleave our darkness with Thy sword:
Feed the faint and hungry heathen
With the richness of Thy Word:
Cleanse the body of this empire
Through the glory of the Lord. Amen.

Henry Scott Holland, 1847-1918.

884

STRASBURG. 8 8.8 8.8 8. *Strasburg Psalter*, 1525.

1 BEFORE Thy throne, O God, we kneel;
Give us a conscience quick to feel,
A ready mind to understand
The meaning of Thy chastening hand;
Whate'er the pain and shame may be,
Bring us, O Father, nearer Thee.

2 Search out our hearts and make us true,
Wishful to give to all their due;
From love of pleasure, lust of gold,
From sins which make the heart grow cold,
Wean us and train us with Thy rod;
Teach us to know our faults, O God.

3 For sins of heedless word and deed,
For pride ambitious to succeed;
For crafty trade and subtle snare
To catch the simple unaware;
For lives bereft of purpose high,
Forgive, forgive, O Lord, we cry.

4 Let the fierce fires, which burn and try,
Our inmost spirits purify:
Consume the ill; purge out the shame;
O God! be with us in the flame;
A new-born people may we rise,
More pure, more true, more nobly wise. Amen.

William Boyd Carpenter, 1841-1918.

885

GLORIA IN EXCELSIS. 8.7.8.7.6 6.6 6.7. J. W. ELLIOTT, 1833-1915.

UNISON.

Queen and Nation

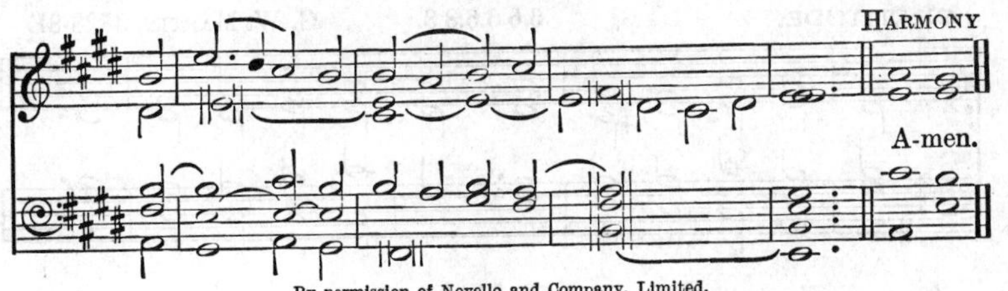

By permission of Novello and Company, Limited.

May also be sung to EIN' FESTE BURG, No. 494.

1.

REJOICE to-day with one accord,
Sing out with exultation;
Rejoice and praise our mighty Lord,
Whose arm hath brought salvation;
His works of love proclaim
The greatness of His name;
For He is God alone,
Who hath His mercy shown;
Let all His saints adore Him.

2.

When in distress to Him we cried,
He heard our sad complaining;
O trust in Him, whate'er betide,
His love is all-sustaining;
Triumphant songs of praise
To Him our hearts shall raise;
Now every voice shall say
O praise our God alway;
Let all His saints adore Him.

3.

Rejoice to-day with one accord,
Sing out with exultation;
Rejoice and praise our mighty Lord,
Whose arm hath brought salvation;
His works of love proclaim
The greatness of His name;
For He is God alone,
Who hath His mercy shown;
Let all His saints adore Him. Amen.

Henry Williams Baker, 1821-77.

886

GRATITUDE. 6.6.6.6.8 8. G. W. MARTIN, 1828-81.

May also be sung to CROFT'S 136, No. 26.

1 To Thee our God we fly,
For mercy and for grace;
O hear our lowly cry,
And hide not Thou Thy face!

O Lord, stretch forth Thy mighty hand,
And guard and bless our fatherland.

2 Arise, O Lord of Hosts;
Be jealous for Thy name,
And drive from out our coasts
The sins that put to shame.

3 Thy best gifts from on high
In rich abundance pour,
That we may magnify
And praise Thee more and more.

4 The powers ordained by Thee
With heavenly wisdom bless;
May they Thy servants be,
And rule in righteousness.

5 The Church of Thy dear Son
Inflame with love's pure fire;
Bind her once more in one,
And life and truth inspire.

6 The pastors of Thy fold
With grace and power endue,
That faithful, pure, and bold,
They may be pastors true.

7 O let us love Thy house
And sanctify Thy day,
Bring unto Thee our vows
And loyal homage pay.

8 Give peace, Lord, in our time;
O let no foe draw nigh,
Nor lawless deed of crime
Insult Thy majesty.

9 Though weak and wayward, still
Thy people, Lord, are we;
And for our God we will
None other have but Thee. Amen.

William Walsham How, 1823-97.

1 God of our fathers, unto Thee
Our fathers cried in danger's hour,
And then Thou gavest them to see
The acts of Thine almighty power.
They cried to Thee, and Thou didst hear;
They called on Thee, and Thou didst save;
And we their sons to-day draw near
Thy name to praise, Thy help to crave.

Lord God of Hosts, uplift Thine hand,
Protect and bless our fatherland.

2 Thine is the majesty, O Lord,
And Thine dominion over all;
When Thou commandest, at Thy word
Great kings and nations rise or fall.
For eastern realms, for western coasts,
For islands washed by every sea,
The praise be given, O God of Hosts,
Not unto us but unto Thee.

3 If in Thy grace Thou shouldst allow
Our fame to wax through coming days,
Still grant us humbly, then as now,
Thy help to crave, Thy name to praise.
Not all alike in speech or birth,
Alike we bow before Thy throne:
One fatherland throughout the earth
Our Father's noble acts we own.
Amen.

Arthur Campbell Ainger, 1841-1919.

888

REX REGUM. D.C.M. J. STAINER, 1840-1901.

1 O KING of kings, O Lord of hosts, whose throne is lifted high
Above the nations of the earth, the armies of the sky,
The spirits of the perfected may give their nobler songs,
And we, Thy children, worship Thee, to whom all praise belongs.

2 Thou who didst lead Thy people forth, and make the captive free,
Hast drawn around our native land the curtain of the sea,
To make another holy place, where golden lamps should shine,
And human hearts keep loving watch around the ark divine.

3 Thou who hast sown the sky with stars, setting Thy thoughts in gold,
Hast crowned our nation's life, and ours, with blessings manifold;
Thy mercies have been numberless; Thy love, Thy grace, Thy care,
Were wider than our utmost need, and higher than our prayer.

4 O King of kings, O Lord of hosts, our fathers' God and ours!
Be with us in the future years; and if the tempest lowers,
Look through the cloud with light of love, and smile our tears away,
And lead us through the brightening years to heaven's eternal day. Amen.

Henry Burton, 1840-1930.

LEST WE FORGET. 8.8.8.8.8.8 8. G. F. Blanchard, 1868-1926.

Verses 1-4.

Last verse.

A - men.

1 God of our fathers, known of old,
Lord of our far-flung battle line,
Beneath whose awful hand we hold
Dominion over palm and pine—
Lord God of Hosts, be with us yet,
Lest we forget—lest we forget!

2 The tumult and the shouting dies,
The captains and the kings depart;
Still stands Thine ancient sacrifice,
A humble and a contrite heart.
Lord God of Hosts, be with us yet,
Lest we forget—lest we forget!

3 Far-called, our navies melt away,
On dune and headland sinks the [fire;
Lo, all our pomp of yesterday
Is one with Nineveh and Tyre!
Judge of the nations, spare us yet,
Lest we forget—lest we forget!

4 If, drunk with sight of power, we loose [in awe,
Wild tongues that have not Thee
Such boasting as the Gentiles use,
Or lesser breeds without the law—
Lord God of Hosts, be with us yet,
Lest we forget—lest we forget!

5 For heathen heart that puts her trust
In reeking tube and iron shard,
All valiant dust that builds on dust,
And guarding, calls not Thee to guard:
For frantic boast and foolish word—
Thy mercy on Thy people, Lord! Amen.

Rudyard Kipling, 1865-1936

Also:

2 All people that on earth do dwell
3 Before Jehovah's awful throne
10 Now thank we all our God
61 Earth, with all thy thousand voices
64 Praise to the Lord, the Almighty
694 Lord, Thou hast been

890

CITIZENSHIP AND SERVICE

MARAZION. 8 8.8 8.8 8.6 6. M. L. WOSTENHOLM, 1887-
UNISON.

1. LIFT up your heads, ye migh - ty gates, Be -
- hold the King of glo - ry.. waits! . . . The King of
kings is draw - ing near, The Sav - iour of the world is
here;
(vv. 2, 3, & 5) Life and sal - va - tion

(vv. 3, 4, & 5)
doth He.. bring, Where-fore re- joice and glad - ly .. sing.
We praise Thee, Fa-ther, now, Cre - a - tor, wise art Thou!
rall.
HARMONY.
rall.
A-men.

* Omit in Verse 2.

Macht hoch die Thür, das Thor macht weit.

1 LIFT up your heads, ye mighty gates,
Behold the King of glory waits!
The King of kings is drawing near,
The Saviour of the world is here;
Life and salvation doth He bring,
Wherefore rejoice and gladly sing.
We praise Thee, Father, now,
Creator, wise art Thou!

2 The Lord is just, a helper tried,
Mercy is ever at His side;
His kingly crown is holiness;
His sceptre, pity in distress;
The end of all our woe He brings,
Wherefore the earth is glad and sings.
We praise Thee, Saviour, now,
Mighty in deed art Thou!

3 O blest the land, the city blest,
Where Christ the ruler is confest!
O happy hearts and happy homes,
To whom this King in triumph comes!
The cloudless Sun of joy He is,
Who bringeth pure delight and bliss.
O Comforter Divine,
What boundless grace is Thine!

4 Fling wide the portals of your heart,
Make it a temple set apart
From earthly use, for heaven's employ,
Adorned with prayer, and love, and joy;
So shall your Sovereign enter in,
And new and nobler life begin.
To Thee, O God, be praise,
For word and deed and grace.

5 Redeemer, come, we open wide
Our heart to Thee; here, Lord abide!
Thine inner presence let us feel,
Thy grace and love in us reveal,
Thy Holy Spirit guide us on,
Until the glorious goal is won.
Eternal praise and fame
We offer to Thy name. Amen

Georg Weissel, 1590-1635;
tr. by Catherine Winkworth, 1827-78.

URBIS REX. 7.6.7.6.7.4. J. A. BENSON, 1848-1931.

1 KING of the City Splendid,
Eternal in the height,
May all our country's cities
Be holy in Thy sight:
Cleansed from the deeds of darkness—
Cities of light.

2 Teach love to gladden children
That know not childhood's mirth,
Wronged of their rights—no beauty
In their scant reach of earth;
To hope's large sunshine give them
A second birth.

3 Lord, end the spell of passion,
Break Thou the drunkard's lure:
Thou art the one Physician
The human heart to cure;
The wavering will to strengthen,
Foul life make pure.

4 Give joy to all the joyless,
Song's voice to sorrows dumb,
May light invade with blessing
Each dark and deathly slum;
Into earth's realms of horror
Thy kingdom come!

5 Soon may our country's cities,
Thy robe of glory wear;
Each place of toil a Temple,
Each house a home of prayer;
Each city's name of beauty—
The Lord is there!

George Thomas Coster, 1835-1912.

892

SONG 1. 10.10.10.10.10 10. O. GIBBONS, 1583-1625.

1 ETERNAL Ruler of the ceaseless round
Of circling planets singing on their way,
Guide of the nations from the night profound
Into the glory of the perfect day:
Rule in our hearts, that we may ever be
Guided and strengthened and upheld by Thee.

2 We are of Thee, the children of Thy love,
The brothers of Thy well-belovèd Son;
Descend, O Holy Spirit, like a dove,
Into our hearts, that we may be as one;
As one with Thee, to whom we ever tend;
As one with Him, our Brother and our Friend.

3 We would be one in hatred of all wrong,
One in our love of all things sweet and fair,
One with the joy that breaketh into song,
One with the grief that trembleth into prayer,
One in the power that makes the children free
To follow truth, and thus to follow Thee.

4 O clothe us with Thy heavenly armour, Lord,
Thy trusty shield, Thy sword of love divine;
Our inspiration be Thy constant word;
We ask no victories that are not Thine:
Give or withhold, let pain or pleasure be;
Enough to know that we are serving Thee.

John White Chadwick, 1840-1904.

893

DELHI. 8 8 8. E. F. Rimbault, 1816-76.

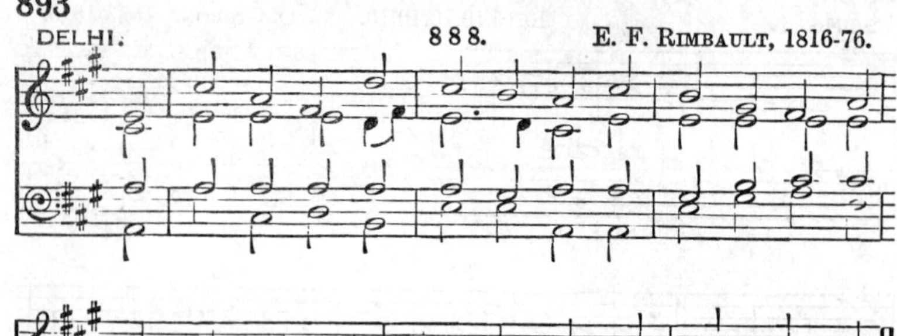

1 O ye who taste that love is sweet,
Set waymarks for all doubtful feet
That stumble on in search of it.

2 Sing notes of love: that some who hear
Far off, inert, may lend an ear,
Rise up and wonder and draw near.

3 Lead lives of love; that others who
Behold your life may kindle too
With love, and cast their lot with you.

Christina Georgina Rossetti, 1830-94.

894

8 8 8.7.

QUEM PASTORES LAUDAVERE. German Traditional Melody.

1 Father, who on man dost shower
Gifts of plenty from Thy dower,
To Thy people give the power
All Thy gifts to use aright.

2 Give pure happiness in leisure,
Temperance in every pleasure,
Holy use of earthly treasure,
Bodies clear and spirits bright.

3 Lift from this and every nation
All that brings us degradation;
Quell the forces of temptation;
Put Thine enemies to flight.

4 Be with us, Thy strength supplying,
That with energy undying,
Every foe of man defying,
We may rally to the fight.

5 Thou who art our Captain ever,
Lead us on to great endeavour;
May Thy Church the world deliver:
Give us wisdom, courage, might.

6 Father, who hast sought and found us,
Son of God, whose love has bound us,
Holy Ghost, within us, round us—
Hear us, Godhead infinite.
Amen.

Percy Dearmer, 1867-1938

895

ST. BARTHOLOMEW. L.M. H. DUNCALF, 1762.

May also be sung to FULDA, No. 790.

1 WHERE cross the crowded ways of life,
Where sound the cries of race and clan,
Above the noise of selfish strife,
We hear Thy voice, O Son of Man.

2 In haunts of wretchedness and need,
On shadowed thresholds dark with fears,
From paths where hide the lures of greed,
We catch the vision of Thy tears.

3 From tender childhood's helplessness,
From woman's grief, man's burdened toil,
From famished souls, from sorrow's stress,
Thy heart has never known recoil.

4 The cup of water given for Thee
Still holds the freshness of Thy grace;
Yet long these multitudes to see
The sweet compassion of Thy face.

5 O Master, from the mountain side,
Make haste to heal these hearts of pain;
Among these restless throngs abide,
O tread the city's streets again:

6 Till sons of men shall learn Thy love,
And follow where Thy feet have trod;
Till glorious from Thy heaven above,
Shall come the City of our God.

Frank Mason North, 1850-1936

896

BRYNHYFRYD. 8.7.8.7., Iambic. Welsh Hymn Melody.

May also be sung to **DOMINUS REGIT ME**, No. 76.

1 Now praise we great and famous men,
The fathers, named in story;
And praise the Lord who now as then
Reveals in man His glory.

2 Praise we the wise and brave and strong,
Who graced their generation;
Who helped the right, and fought the wrong,
And made our folk a nation.

3 Praise we the great of heart and mind,
The singers sweetly gifted,
Whose music like a mighty wind
The souls of men uplifted.

4 Praise we the peaceful men of skill
Who builded homes of beauty,
And, rich in art, made richer still
The brotherhood of duty.

5 Praise we the glorious names we know;
And they—whose names have perished,
Lost in the haze of long ago—
In silent love be cherished.

6 In peace their sacred ashes rest,
Fulfilled their day's endeavour;
They blest the earth, and they are blest
Of God and man, for ever.

7 So praise we great and famous men,
The fathers, named in story;
And praise the Lord who now as then
Reveals in man His glory.

William George Tarrant, 1853-1928.

897

FOREST GREEN. D.C.M. English Traditional Melody.

1 What service shall we render thee
O Fatherland we love ?
What gift of hand, or heart, or brain
May our devotion prove ?
The coming age invokes our aid,
Thy voice of old inspires ;
Shall we, thy sons and daughters, be
Less worthy than our sires ?

2 The service of the commonwealth
Is not in arms alone ;
A nobler chivalry shall rise
Than war has ever known ;
Glad rivalries in arts of peace,
True ministries of life,
Shall supersede the arts of war
And calm our feverish strife.

3 Too long the pagan rule of force
Has held the world in thrall,
Too long the clash of arms has drowned
The higher human call.
O comrades, seek a nobler quest !
O keep a worthier tryst !
The laws of hate have had their day ;
Proclaim the laws of Christ !

4 Lord of the nations, far and near,
Send forth Thy quickening breath,
Equip us for the tasks of life,
Save us from deeds of death :
Enlist us in Thy ranks to fight
Fair freedom's holy war,
Whose battle-cry is Brotherhood,
Far-flung from shore to shore.

Ernest Dodgshun, 1876-1944

898

ADRIAN. 8.7.8.7. D. R. P. STEWART, 1825-94.

May also be sung to EBENEZER, No. 616.

1 Once to every man and nation
Comes the moment to decide,
In the strife of truth with falsehood,
For the good or evil side;
Some great cause, God's new Messiah,
Offering each the bloom or blight—
And the choice goes by for ever
'Twixt that darkness and that light.

2 Then to side with truth is noble,
When we share her wretched crust,
Ere her cause bring fame and profit,
And 'tis prosperous to be just;
Then it is the brave man chooses,
While the coward stands aside,
Till the multitude make virtue
Of the faith they had denied.

3 By the light of burning martyrs,
Christ, Thy bleeding feet we track
Toiling up new Calvaries ever
With the Cross that turns not back.
New occasions teach new duties;
Time makes ancient good uncouth;
They must upward still and onward
Who would keep abreast of truth.

4 Though the cause of evil prosper,
Yet 'tis truth alone is strong;
Though her portion be the scaffold,
And upon the throne be wrong—
Yet that scaffold sways the future,
And, behind the dim unknown,
Standeth God within the shadow,
Keeping watch above His own.

James Russell Lowell, 1819-91.

LAND OF OUR BIRTH.

Unison.
Verses 1 and 8. L.M. A. E. Floyd, 1877-

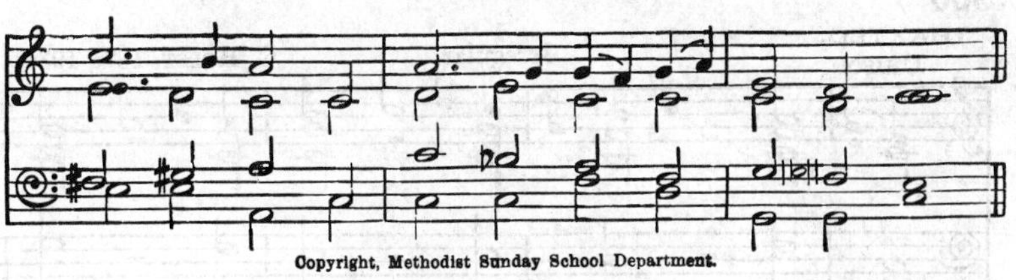

1 *Land of our Birth, we pledge to thee*
Our love and toil in the years to be;
When we are grown, and take our place
As men and women with our race.

2 Father in heaven, who lovest all,
O help Thy children when they call;
That they may build from age to age,
An undefilèd heritage.

3 Teach us to bear the yoke in youth,
With steadfastness and careful truth;
That, in our time, Thy grace may give
The truth whereby the nations live.

4 Teach us to rule ourselves alway,
Controlled and cleanly night and day;
That we may bring, if need arise,
No maimed or worthless sacrifice.

5 Teach us to look, in all our ends,
On Thee for Judge, and not our friends;
That we, with Thee, may walk uncowed
By fear or favour of the crowd.

6 Teach us the strength that cannot seek,
By deed or thought, to hurt the weak;
That, under Thee, we may possess
Man's strength to succour man's distress.

7 Teach us delight in simple things,
And mirth that has no bitter springs;
Forgiveness free of evil done,
And love to all men 'neath the sun!

8 *Land of our Birth, our faith, our pride,*
For whose dear sake our fathers died;
O Motherland, we pledge to thee,
Head, heart, and hand through the years to be.

Rudyard Kipling, 1865-1936

900

THAXTED.

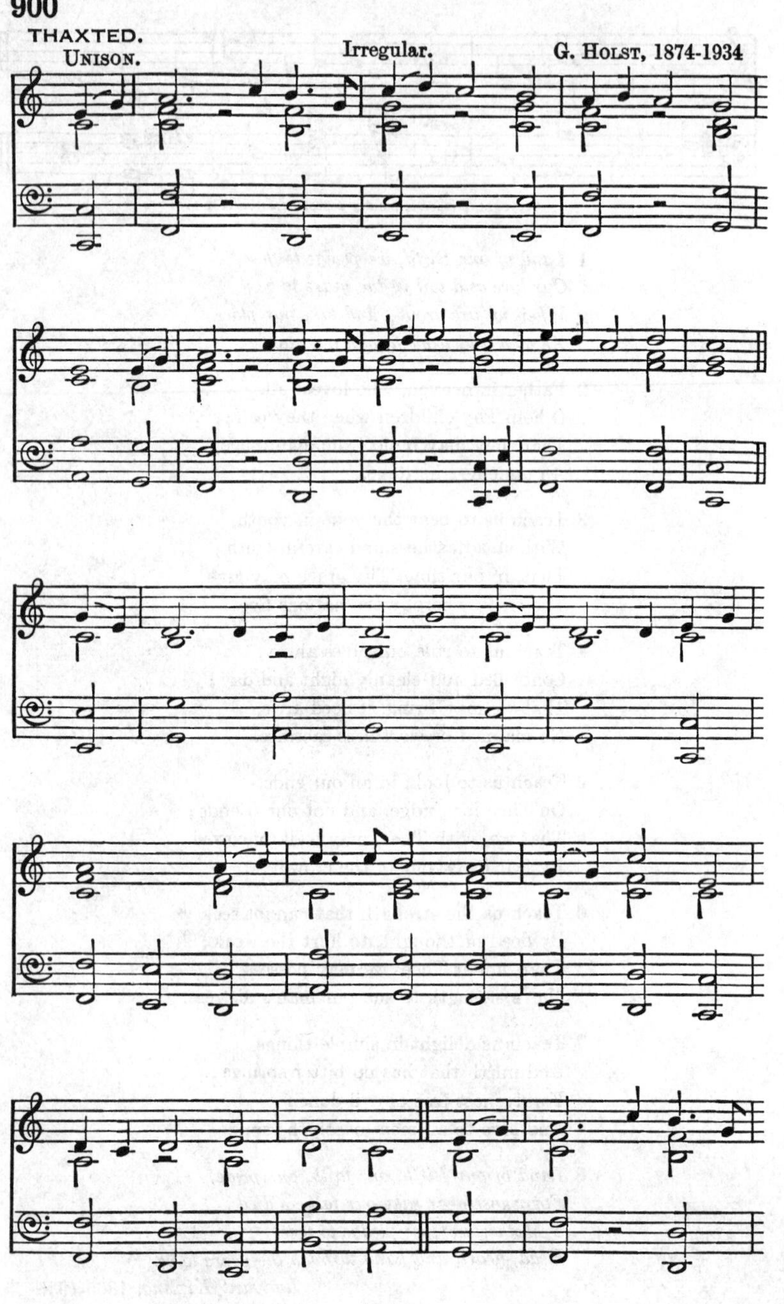
UNISON.
Irregular.
G. HOLST, 1874-1934

1.

I vow to thee, my country, all earthly things above,
Entire and whole and perfect, the service of my love;
The love that asks no question, the love that stands the test,
That lays upon the altar the dearest and the best;
The love that never falters, the love that pays the price,
The love that makes undaunted the final sacrifice.

2.

And there's another country, I've heard of long ago,
Most dear to them that love her, most great to them that know;
We may not count her armies, we may not see her King;
Her fortress is a faithful heart, her pride is suffering;
And soul by soul and silently her shining bounds increase,
And her ways are ways of gentleness and all her paths are peace.

Cecil Spring-Rice, 1859-1918.

Also:

57 In all my vast concerns with Thee
241 O Son of Man, our hero
256 There's a light
260 Mine eyes have seen
401 God's trumpet wakes
484 Soldiers of Christ
489 Workman of God
578 A charge to keep
588 Awake, awake to love and work
707 O thou not made with hands
872 We bless Thee, Lord
922 O Thou before whose presence

901

WORLD PEACE AND BROTHERHOOD

RUSSIA. 11.10.11.9. A. Lvov, 1799-1871.

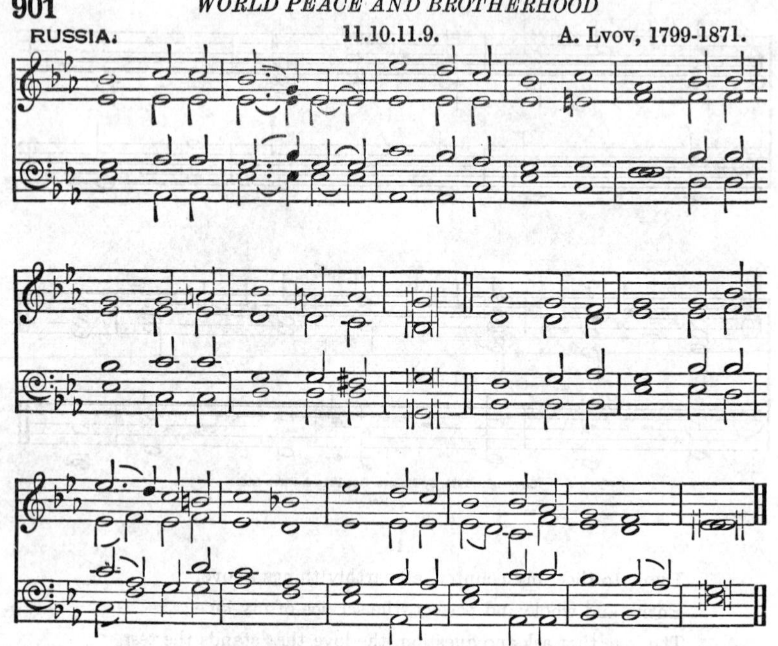

1 God the All-terrible! King, who ordainest
Great winds Thy clarions, the lightnings Thy sword;
Show forth Thy pity on high where Thou reignest;
Give to us peace in our time, O Lord.

2 God the All-merciful! Earth hath forsaken
Thy way of blessedness, slighted Thy word;
Bid not Thy wrath in its terrors awaken;
Give to us peace in our time, O Lord.

3 God the All-righteous One! Man hath defied Thee;
Yet to eternity standeth Thy word;
Falsehood and wrong shall not tarry beside Thee;
Give to us peace in our time, O Lord.

4 God the All-wise! By the fire of Thy chastening,
Earth shall to freedom and truth be restored;
Through the thick darkness Thy kingdom is hastening;
Thou wilt give peace in Thy time, O Lord.

5 So shall Thy children in thankful devotion
Laud Him who saved them from peril abhorred,
Singing in chorus from ocean to ocean:
Peace to the nations and praise to the Lord.

Henry Fothergill Chorley, 1808-72;
John Ellerton, 1826-93.

World Peace and Brotherhood

902

ST. CYPRIAN. 8.8.8.8. D. J. Goss, 1800-80.

1 All glory to God in the sky,
And peace upon earth be restored!
O Jesus, exalted on high,
Appear our omnipotent Lord!
Who, meanly in Bethlehem born,
Didst stoop to redeem a lost race,
Once more to Thy creatures return,
And reign in Thy kingdom of grace.

2 When Thou in our flesh didst appear,
All nature acknowledged Thy birth;
Arose the acceptable year,
And heaven was opened on earth:
Receiving its Lord from above,
The world was united to bless
The Giver of concord and love,
The Prince and the Author of peace.

3 O wouldst Thou again be made known!
Again in Thy Spirit descend,
And set up in each of Thine own
A kingdom that never shall end.
Thou only art able to bless,
And make the glad nations obey,
And bid the dire enmity cease,
And bow the whole world to Thy sway.

4 Come then to Thy servants again,
Who long Thy appearing to know,
Thy quiet and peaceable reign
In mercy establish below;
All sorrow before Thee shall fly,
And anger and hatred be o'er,
And envy and malice shall die,
And discord afflict us no more.

Charles Wesley, 1707-88.

903

ERHALT' UNS, HERR. L.M. *Geistliche Lieder*, 1547.

1 O God of love, O King of peace,
Make wars throughout the world to cease;
The wrath of sinful man restrain:
Give peace, O God, give peace again.

2 Remember, Lord, Thy works of old,
The wonders that our fathers told;
Remember not our sin's dark stain:
Give peace, O God, give peace again.

3 Whom shall we trust but Thee, O Lord?
Where rest but on Thy faithful word?
None ever called on Thee in vain:
Give peace, O God, give peace again.

4 Where saints and angels dwell above,
All hearts are knit in holy love;
O bind us in that heavenly chain:
Give peace, O God, give peace again.
Amen.

Henry Williams Baker, 1821-77.

904

GLASGOW. C.M. MOORE'S *Psalm-Singer's Pocket Companion*, 1756.

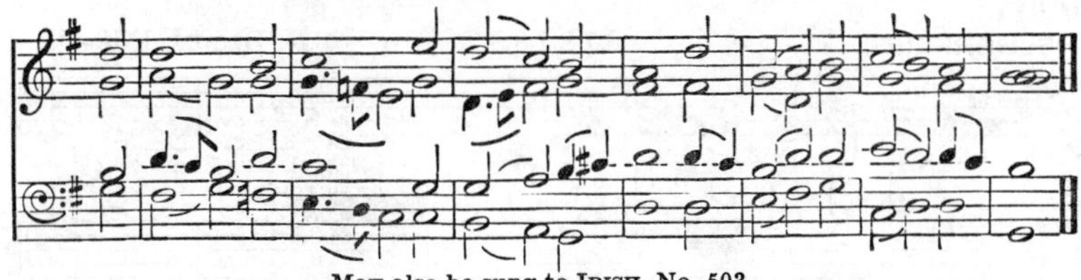

May also be sung to IRISH, No. 503.

1 BEHOLD, the mountain of the Lord
In latter days shall rise
On mountain-tops above the hills,
And draw the wondering eyes.

2 To this the joyful nations round,
All tribes and tongues, shall flow;
Up to the hill of God, they'll say,
And to His house, we'll go.

3 The beam that shines from Zion's hill
Shall lighten every land;
The King who reigns in Salem's towers
Shall all the world command.

4 Among the nations He shall judge;
His judgements truth shall guide;
His sceptre shall protect the just,
And quell the sinner's pride.

5 No strife shall rage, nor hostile feuds
Disturb those peaceful years;
To ploughshares men shall beat their swords,
To pruning-hooks their spears.

6 No longer hosts, encountering hosts,
Shall crowds of slain deplore;
They hang the trumpet in the hall,
And study war no more.

7 Come then, O house of Jacob, come
To worship at His shrine;
And, walking in the light of God,
With holy beauties shine.

Michael Bruce, 1746-67.

905

GRENOBLE. L.M. Grenoble Church Melody.

UNISON.

Ring out, wild bells, to the wild sky,
The flying cloud, the frosty light:
The year is dying in the night;
Ring out, wild bells, and let him die.

1 RING out the grief that saps the mind,
For those that here we see no more;
Ring out the feud of rich and poor,
Ring in redress to all mankind.

2 Ring out a slowly dying cause,
And ancient forms of party strife;
Ring in the nobler modes of life,
With sweeter manners, purer laws.

3 Ring out false pride in place and blood,
The civic slander and the spite;
Ring in the love of truth and right,
Ring in the common love of good.

4 Ring out old shapes of foul disease;
Ring out the narrowing lust of gold!
Ring out the thousand wars of old,
Ring in the thousand years of peace.

5 Ring in the valiant man and free,
The larger heart, the kindlier hand;
Ring out the darkness of the land,
Ring in the Christ that is to be.

Alfred Tennyson, 1809-92.

906

ELBERFELD. 8.7.8.7.8 8.7. N. Decius, 1519-41.

1 Lord Christ, when first Thou cam'st to men,
Upon a Cross they bound Thee;
And mocked Thy saving Kingship then
By thorns with which they crowned Thee:
And still our wrongs may weave Thee now
New thorns to pierce that steady brow,
And robe of sorrow round Thee.

2 O awful love which found no room
In life where sin denied Thee,
And, doomed to death, must bring to doom
The power which crucified Thee,
Till not a stone was left on stone,
And all a nation's pride o'erthrown
Went down to dust beside Thee.

3 New advent of the love of Christ,
Shall we again refuse Thee,
Till in the night of hate and war
We perish as we lose Thee?
From old unfaith our souls release
To seek the Kingdom of Thy peace,
By which alone we choose Thee.

4 O wounded hands of Jesus, build
In us Thy new creation;
Our pride is dust, our vaunt is stilled,
We wait Thy revelation:
O love that triumphs over loss,
We bring our hearts before Thy Cross,
To finish Thy salvation.

Walter Russell Bowie, 1882-

907

VERMONT. L.M. A. E. Floyd, 1877-

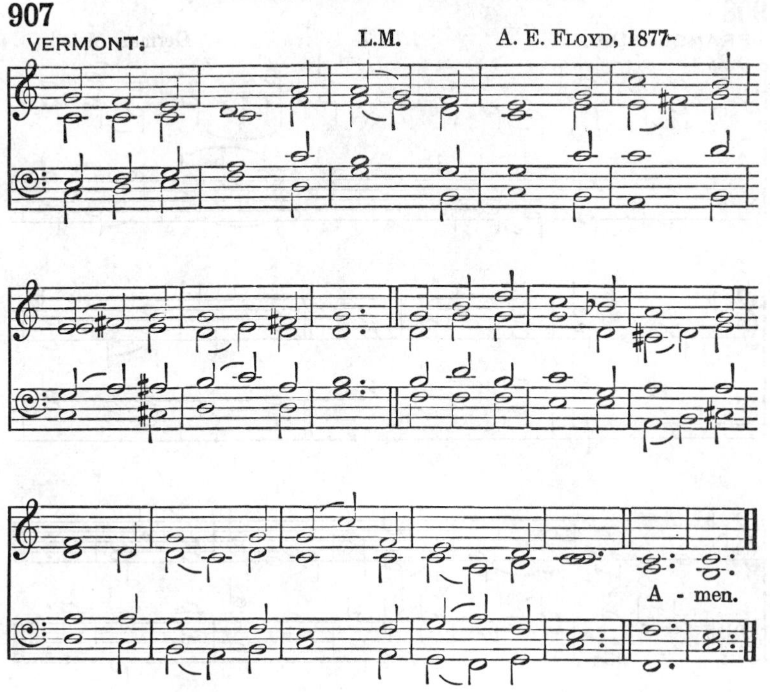

1 Almighty Father, who dost give
The gift of life to all who live,
Look down on all earth's sin and strife,
And lift us to a nobler life.

2 Lift up our hearts, O King of kings,
To brighter hopes and kindlier things,
To visions of a larger good,
And holier dreams of brotherhood.

3 Thy world is weary of its pain,
Of selfish greed and fruitless gain,
Of tarnished honour, falsely strong,
And all its ancient deeds of wrong.

4 Hear Thou the prayer Thy servants pray,
Uprising from all lands to-day,
And o'er the vanquished powers of sin
O bring Thy great salvation in. Amen.

John Howard Bertram Masterman, 1867-1933.

908

BRANDENBURG. 7.7.7.7. German Melody.

1 Life of ages, richly poured,
Love of God, unspent and free,
Flowing in the prophet's word,
And the people's liberty.

2 Never was to chosen race
That unstinted tide confined:
Thine are every time and place,
Fountain sweet of heart and mind:

3 Breathing in the thinker's creed,
Pulsing in the hero's blood,
Nerving noblest thought and deed,
Freshening time with truth and good:

4 Consecrating art and song,
Holy book and pilgrim way,
Quelling strife and tyrant wrong,
Widening freedom's sacred sway.

5 Life of ages, richly poured,
Love of God, unspent and free,
Flowing in the prophet's word,
And the people's liberty.

Samuel Johnson, 1822-82.

World Peace and Brotherhood

909

COMMONWEALTH. 7.6.7.6.8 8 8.5. J. BOOTH, 1852-1930.

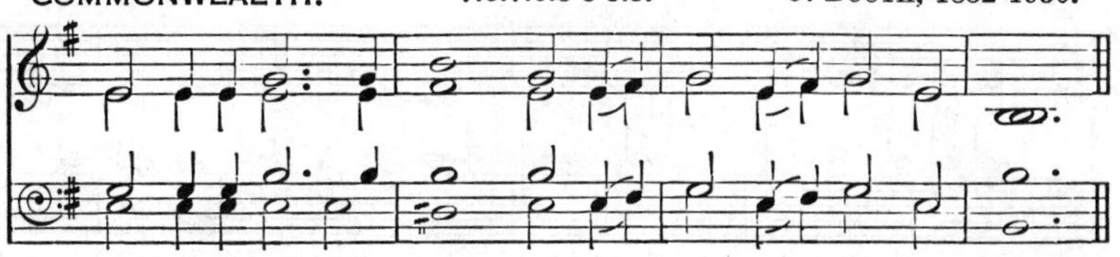

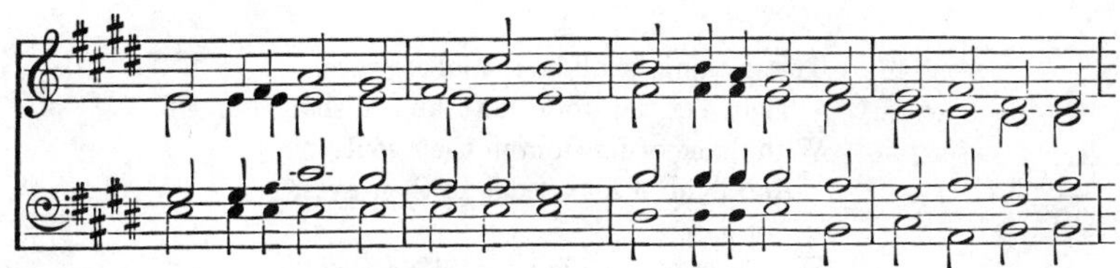

1 WHEN wilt Thou save the people ?
O God of mercy, when ?
The people, Lord, the people,
Not thrones and crowns, but men !
Flowers of Thy heart, O God, are they ;
Let them not pass like weeds away,
Their heritage a sunless day.
God save the people !

2 Shall crime bring crime for ever,
Strength aiding still the strong ?
Is it Thy will, O Father,
That man shall toil for wrong ?
No ! say Thy mountains : No ! Thy skies ;
Man's clouded sun shall brightly rise,
And songs be heard instead of sighs:
God save the people !

3 When wilt Thou save the people ?
O God of mercy, when ?
The people, Lord, the people,
Not thrones and crowns, but men !
God save the people ; Thine they are,
Thy children, as Thine angels fair ;
From vice, oppression, and despair,
God save the people !

Ebenezer Elliott, 1781-1849.

910

ARIZONA. L.M. R. H. Earnshaw, 1856-1929.

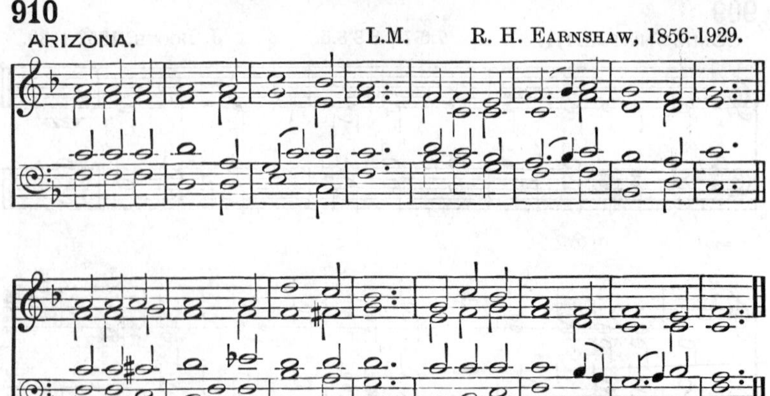

May also be sung to Simeon, No. 301.

1.

These things shall be: a loftier race
Than e'er the world hath known shall rise,
With flame of freedom in their souls
And light of knowledge in their eyes.

2.

They shall be gentle, brave, and strong
To spill no drop of blood, but dare
All that may plant man's lordship firm
On earth, and fire, and sea, and air.

3.

Nation with nation, land with land,
Inarmed shall live as comrades free;
In every heart and brain shall throb
The pulse of one fraternity.

4.

Man shall love man, with heart as pure
And fervent as the young-eyed throng
Who chant their heavenly psalms before
God's face with undiscordant song.

5.

New arts shall bloom of loftier mould,
And mightier music thrill the skies,
And every life shall be a song,
When all the earth is paradise.

John Addington Symonds, 1840-93.

911

INTERCESSOR. 11.10.11.10. C. H. H. PARRY, 1848-1918.

1 O BROTHER man, fold to thy heart thy brother!
Where pity dwells, the peace of God is there;
To worship rightly is to love each other,
Each smile a hymn, each kindly deed a prayer.

2 For he whom Jesus loved hath truly spoken:
The holier worship which He deigns to bless
Restores the lost, and binds the spirit broken,
And feeds the widow and the fatherless.

3 Follow with reverent steps the great example
Of Him whose holy work was doing good;
So shall the wide earth seem our Father's temple,
Each loving life a psalm of gratitude.

4 Then shall all shackles fall; the stormy clangour
Of wild war-music o'er the earth shall cease;
Love shall tread out the baleful fire of anger,
And in its ashes plant the tree of peace.

John Greenleaf Whittier, 1807-92.

912

OLD 124TH. 10.10.10 10.10. *Genevan Psalter*, 1551.

1 TURN back, O man, forswear thy foolish ways;
Old now is earth, and none may count her days,
Yet thou, her child, whose head is crowned with flame,
Still wilt not hear thine inner God proclaim:
Turn back, O man, forswear thy foolish ways.

2 Earth might be fair and all men glad and wise,
Age after age their tragic empires rise,
Built while they dream, and in that dreaming weep:
Would man but wake from out his haunted sleep,
Earth might be fair and all men glad and wise.

3 Earth shall be fair, and all her people one:
Nor till that hour shall God's whole will be done;
Now, even now, once more from earth to sky,
Peals forth in joy man's old undaunted cry:
Earth shall be fair, and all her folk be one.

Clifford Bax, 1886-

Also:

16 Raise the psalm
129 While shepherds watched
130 It came upon the midnight
134 Glory be to God
219 God is gone up
253 Break, day of God
271 Crown Him with many crowns
810 Father, let Thy kingdom
811 Thy kingdom come
829 Hark! The song

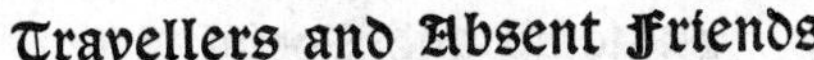

913

VERBUM PACIS. 6.6.8.4. G. Lomas, 1834-84.

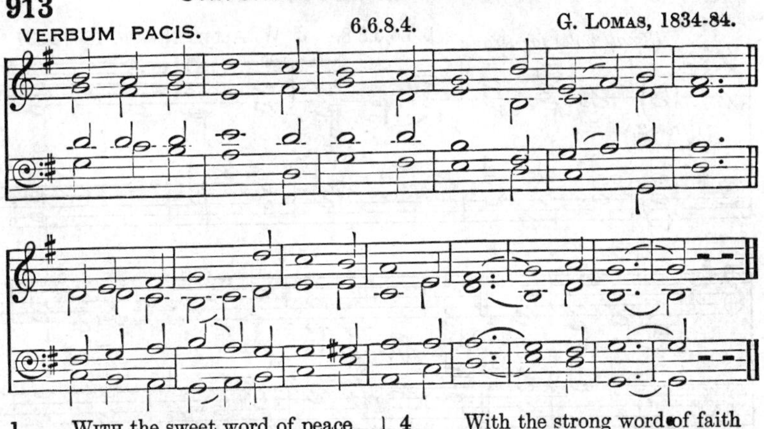

1 With the sweet word of peace
We bid our brethren go ;
Peace, as a river, to increase
And ceaseless flow.

2 With the calm word of prayer
We earnestly commend
Our brethren to Thy watchful care,
Eternal Friend !

3 With the dear word of love
We give our brief farewell ;
Our love below, and Thine above,
With them shall dwell.

4 With the strong word of faith
We stay ourselves on Thee ;
That Thou, O Lord, in life and death
Their help shall be.

5 Then the bright word of hope
Shall on our parting gleam,
And tell of joys beyond the scope
Of earth-born dream.

6 Farewell ; in hope, and love,
In faith, and peace, and prayer ;
Till He whose home is ours above
Unite us there.

George Watson, 1816-98.

914

RANDOLPH. 9.8 8.9. R. Vaughan Williams, 1872-1958.

1 God be with you till we meet again,
By His counsels guide, uphold you,
With His sheep securely fold you :
God be with you till we meet again.

2 God be with you till we meet again,
'Neath His wings protecting hide you,
Daily manna still provide you :
God be with you till we meet again.

3 God be with you till we meet again,
When life's perils thick confound you,
Put His arms unfailing round you :
God be with you till we meet again.

4 God be with you till we meet again,
Keep love's banner floating o'er you,
[before you :
Smite death's threatening wave
God be with you till we meet again !

Jeremiah Eames Rankin, 1828-1904.

INGS. (*Small notes for Organ.*) 6.6.6.6.8 8. J. W. ALLEN NORTH, 1869-1937

May also be sung to SAMUEL, No. 848.

1 FATHER, who art alone
Our helper and our stay,
O hear us, as we plead
For loved ones far away,
And shield with Thine almighty hand
Our wanderers by sea and land.

2 For Thou, our Father God,
Art present everywhere,
And bendest low Thine ear
To catch the faintest prayer,
Waiting rich blessings to bestow
On all Thy children here below.

3 O compass with Thy love
The daily path they tread;
And may Thy light and truth
Upon their hearts be shed,
That, one in all things with Thy will,
Heaven's peace and joy their souls may fill.

4 Guard them from every harm
When dangers shall assail,
And teach them that Thy power
Can never, never fail;
We cannot with our loved ones be,
But trust them, Father, unto Thee.

5 We all are travellers here
Along life's various road,
Meeting and parting oft
Till we shall mount to God;
At home at last, with those we love,
Within the fatherland above.

Edith Jones: Home Hymn Book, 1885.

916

ST. HELEN'S. 8.5.8.3. R. P. STEWART, 1825-94.

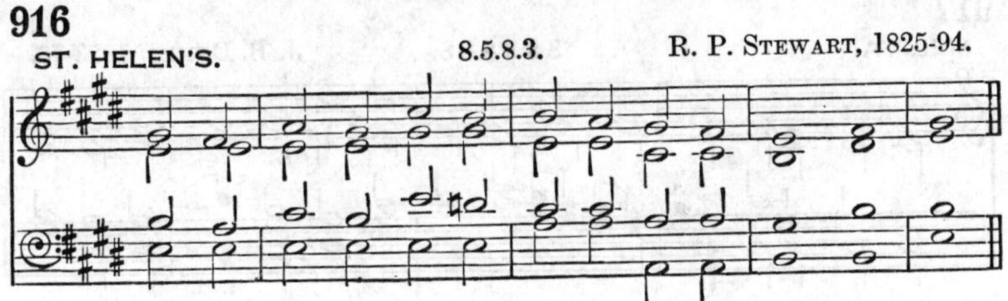

May also be sung to BULLINGER, A.T. No. 21.

1 HOLY Father, in Thy mercy,
Hear our anxious prayer;
Keep our loved ones, now far distant,
'Neath Thy care.

2 Jesus, Saviour, let Thy presence
Be their light and guide;
Keep, O keep them, in their weakness,
At Thy side.

3 When in sorrow, when in danger,
When in loneliness,
In Thy love look down and comfort
Their distress.

4 May the joy of Thy salvation
Be their strength and stay;
May they love and may they praise Thee
Day by day.

5 Holy Spirit, let Thy teaching
Sanctify their life;
Send Thy grace that they may conquer
In the strife.

6 Father, Son, and Holy Spirit,
God, the One in Three,
Bless them, guide them, save them, keep them
Near to Thee. Amen.

Isabel Stephana Stevenson, 1843-90.

917

MELITA. 8 8.8 8.8 8 8. J. B. DYKES, 1823-76.

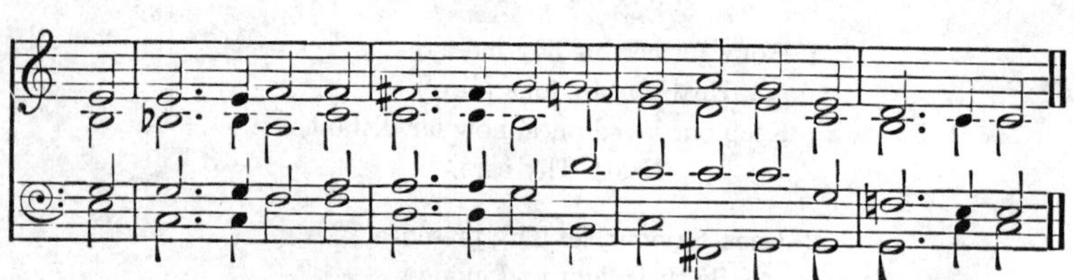

1 ETERNAL Father, strong to save,
Whose arm doth bind the restless wave,
Who bidd'st the mighty ocean deep
Its own appointed limits keep:
O hear us when we cry to Thee
For those in peril on the sea!

2 O Saviour, whose almighty word
The winds and waves submissive heard,
Who walkèdst on the foaming deep,
And calm amid its rage didst sleep:
O hear us when we cry to Thee
For those in peril on the sea!

3 O Sacred Spirit, who didst brood
Upon the chaos dark and rude,
Who bad'st its angry tumult cease,
And gavest light, and life, and peace:
O hear us when we cry to Thee
For those in peril on the sea!

4 O Trinity of love and power,
Our brethren shield in danger's hour;
From rock and tempest, fire and foe,
Protect them wheresoe'er they go;
And ever let there rise to Thee
Glad hymns of praise from land and sea.

William Whiting, 1825-78.

918

ST. PETROX. L.M. R. F. Dale, 1845-1919.

1 O Love divine, that stooped to share
Our sharpest pang, our bitterest tear,
On Thee we cast each earth-born care;
We smile at pain while Thou art near.

2 Though long the weary way we tread,
And sorrow crown each lingering year,
No path we shun, no darkness dread,
Our hearts still whispering: Thou art near.

3 When drooping pleasure turns to grief,
And trembling faith is changed to fear,
The murmuring wind, the quivering leaf,
Shall softly tell us: Thou art near.

4 On Thee we fling our burdening woe,
O Love divine, for ever dear;
Content to suffer, while we know,
Living and dying, Thou art near.

Oliver Wendell Holmes, 1808-94.

919

ST. MATTHEW. D.C.M. W. CROFT, 1678-1727.

A lower setting will be found at No. 824.

1 THINE arm, O Lord, in days of old,
Was strong to heal and save;
It triumphed o'er disease and death,
O'er darkness and the grave.
To Thee they went—the blind, the dumb,
The palsied, and the lame,
The leper with his tainted life,
The sick with fevered frame.

2 And, lo, Thy touch brought life and health,
Gave speech, and strength, and sight;
And youth renewed and frenzy calmed
Owned Thee, the Lord of light:
And now, O Lord, be near to bless,
Almighty as of yore,
In crowded street, by restless couch,
As by Gennesaret's shore.

3 Be Thou our great Deliverer still,
Thou Lord of life and death;
Restore and quicken, soothe and bless,
With Thine almighty breath;
To hands that work and eyes that see
Give wisdom's heavenly lore,
That whole and sick, and weak and strong,
May praise Thee evermore. Amen.

Edward Hayes Plumptre, 1821-91.

920

EVENSONG. 8.7.8.7.7 7. J. Summers, 1843-1916.

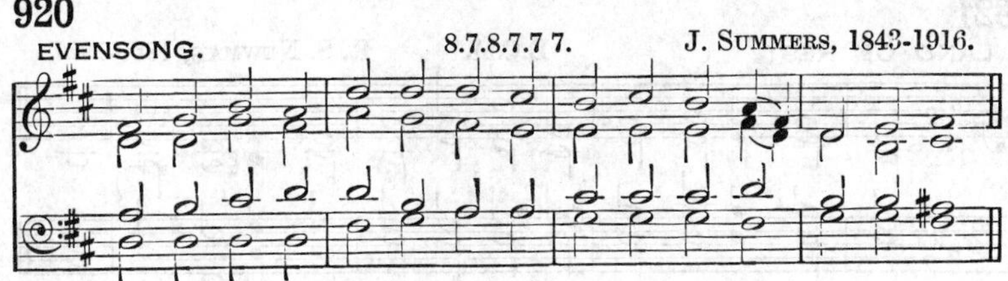

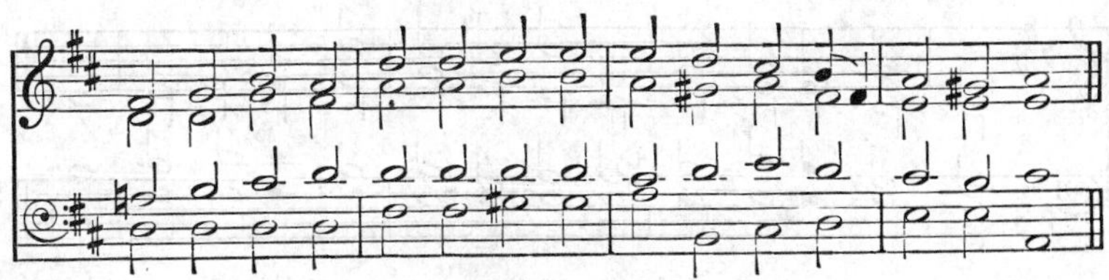

1 Thou to whom the sick and dying
  Ever came, nor came in vain,
Still with healing words replying
  To the wearied cry of pain,
Hear us, Jesu, as we meet,
Suppliants at Thy mercy-seat.

2 Every care, and every sorrow,
  Be it great, or be it small,
Yesterday, to-day, to-morrow,
  When, where'er it may befall,
Lay we humbly at Thy feet,
Suppliants at Thy mercy-seat.

3 Still the weary, sick, and dying
  Need a brother's, sister's care;
On Thy higher help relying,
  May we now their burden share,
Bringing all our offerings meet,
Suppliants at Thy mercy-seat.

4 May each child of Thine be willing,
  Willing both in hand and heart,
All the law of love fulfilling,
  Ever comfort to impart,
Ever bringing offerings meet,
Suppliant to Thy mercy-seat.

5 So may sickness, sin, and sadness
  To Thy healing power yield,
Till the sick and sad, in gladness,
  Rescued, ransomed, cleansèd, healed,
One in Thee together meet,
Pardoned at Thy judgement-seat. Amen.

Godfrey Thring, 1823-1903.

921

LAND OF REST. D.C.M. R. S. Newman, 1850-1927.

1 From Thee all skill and science flow,
All pity, care, and love,
All calm and courage, faith and hope:
O pour them from above;
And part them, Lord, to each and all,
As each and all shall need,
To rise like incense, each to Thee,
In noble thought and deed.

2 And hasten, Lord, that perfect day
When pain and death shall cease,
And Thy just rule shall fill the earth
With health, and light, and peace;
When ever blue the sky shall gleam,
And ever green the sod,
And man's rude work deface no more
The paradise of God.

Charles Kingsley, 1819-75.

922

KOMM, SEELE. 7.6.7.6. D. J. W. FRANCK, 1641-88.

1 O THOU before whose presence
Nought evil may come in,
Yet who dost look in mercy
Down on this world of sin;
O give us noble purpose
To set the sin-bound free,
And Christ-like tender pity
To seek the lost for Thee.

2 Our foe is fierce and subtle;
The forces at his hand,
With woes that none can number,
Despoil the pleasant land:
All they who war against them,
In strife so keen and long,
Must in their Saviour's armour
Be stronger than the strong.

3 'Tis Thou hast wrought among us
The great things that we see:
For things that are we thank Thee,
And for the things to be;
For bright hope that confirmeth
Faint hands and feeble knees
To strive beneath Thy blessing
For greater things than these.

4 Lead on, O Love and Mercy,
O Purity and Power!
Lead on till peace eternal
Shall close this battle-hour;
Till all who prayed and struggled
To set their brethren free,
In triumph meet to praise Thee,
Most Holy Trinity. Amen.

Samuel John Stone, 1839-1900.

923

WINDERMERE. S.M. A. SOMERVELL, 1863-1937

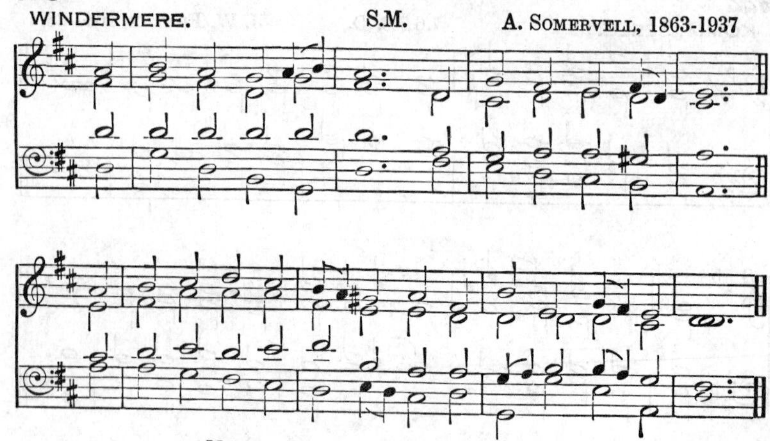

May also be sung to IN MEMORIAM, No. 506.

1 WE give Thee but Thine own,
Whate'er the gift may be;
All that we have is Thine alone,
A trust, O Lord, from Thee.

2 May we Thy bounties thus
As stewards true receive,
And gladly, as Thou blessest us,
To Thee our first-fruits give.

3 O hearts are bruised and dead,
And homes are bare and cold,
And lambs, for whom the Shepherd bled,
Are straying from the fold.

4 To comfort and to bless,
To find a balm for woe,
To tend the lone and fatherless
Is angels' work below.

5 The captive to release,
To God the lost to bring,
To teach the way of life and peace,
It is a Christ-like thing.

6 And we believe Thy word,
Though dim our faith may be;
Whate'er for Thine we do, O Lord,
We do it unto Thee.

William Walsham How, 1823-97.

Also:

153 Jesus, Thy far-extended fame
944 Now the day is over
945 The night is come

MORNING AND EVENING

924

HEATHLANDS. 7.7.7.7.7.7. H. SMART, 1813-79.

May also be sung to SPANISH CHANT, No. 769.

1 CHRIST, whose glory fills the skies,
Christ, the true, the only Light,
Sun of Righteousness, arise,
Triumph o'er the shades of night;
Day-spring from on high, be near;
Day-star, in my heart appear.

2 Dark and cheerless is the morn
Unaccompanied by Thee:
Joyless is the day's return,
Till Thy mercy's beams I see,
Till Thou inward light impart,
Glad my eyes, and warm my heart.

3 Visit then this soul of mine;
Pierce the gloom of sin and grief;
Fill me, Radiancy divine;
Scatter all my unbelief;
More and more Thyself display,
Shining to the perfect day.

Charles Wesley, 1707-88.

925

MOSELEY. 6.6.8.4. H. Smart, 1813-79.

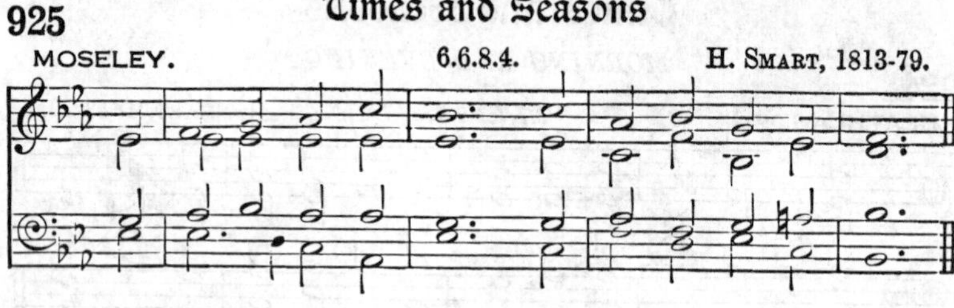

Jam lucis orto sidere.

1 The star of morn has risen:
O Lord, to Thee we pray
O uncreated Light of Light,
Guide Thou our way.

2 Sinless be tongue and hand,
And innocent the mind;
Let simple truth be on our lips,
Our hearts be kind.

3 As the swift day rolls on,
Still, Lord, our guardian be;
And keep the portals of our hearts
From evil free.

4 Grant that our daily toil
May to Thy glory tend;
And as our hours begin with Thee,
So may they end.

Anonymous, c. 8th cent.;
tr. by Greville Phillimore, 1821-84.

926

ST. TIMOTHY. C.M. H. W. Baker, 1821-77.

1 My Father, for another night
Of quiet sleep and rest,
For all the joy of morning light
Thy holy name be blest.

2 Now with the new-born day I give
Myself anew to Thee,
That as Thou willest I may live,
And what Thou willest be.

3 Whate'er I do, things great or small,
Whate'er I speak or frame,
Thy glory may I seek in all,
Do all in Jesu's name.

4 My Father, for His sake, I pray,
Thy child accept and bless;
And lead me by Thy grace to-day
In paths of righteousness.

Henry Williams Baker, 1821-77.

927

MELCOMBE. L.M. S. WEBBE, 1740-1816.

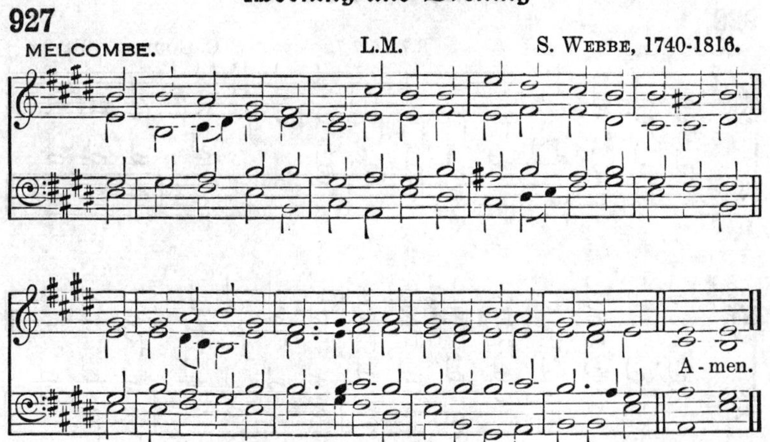

1 O TIMELY happy, timely wise,
Hearts that with rising morn arise,
Eyes that the beam celestial view
Which evermore makes all things new.

2 New every morning is the love
Our wakening and uprising prove,
Through sleep and darkness safely brought,
Restored to life, and power, and thought.

3 New mercies each returning day
Hover around us while we pray;
New perils past, new sins forgiven,
New thoughts of God, new hopes of heaven.

4 If on our daily course our mind
Be set to hallow all we find,
New treasures still of countless price
God will provide for sacrifice.

5 Old friends, old scenes, will lovelier be,
As more of heaven in each we see;
Some softening gleam of love and prayer
Shall dawn on every cross and care.

6 The trivial round, the common task,
Will furnish all we ought to ask;
Room to deny ourselves, a road
To bring us daily nearer God.

7 Only, O Lord, in Thy great love,
Fit us for perfect rest above;
And help us, this and every day,
To live more nearly as we pray. Amen.

John Keble, 1792-1866.

928

GOUNOD. 8.7.8.7.7 7. C. GOUNOD, 1818-93.

By permission of Novello and Company, Limited.

1 MORNING comes with light all-cheering,
  Shades of night have fled apace;
Source of light, by Thine appearing,
  From our minds all darkness chase:
Thou hast blest us in our sleep;
Through the day direct and keep.

2 Earth refreshed Thy praise is sounding,
  All Thy works Thy glory sing;
May our hearts, with love abounding,
  Gratefully their tribute bring:
Thou hast taught the birds their lays;
Teach our hearts to sing Thy praise.

3 All day long to praise Thee help us,
  And to strive against all sin;
Finding all our help in Jesus,
  Who for us the fight did win:
He was tempted here below,
And doth all our weakness know.

4 Man goes to his work till evening
  Brings again the needed rest;
Grant that we, Thy grace receiving,
  May in all we do be blest:
And wherever we may be
Find our joy in pleasing Thee. Amen.

James Englebert Vanner, 1831-1906.

929

MEINE ARMUTH. 8 4.7. D. FREYLINGHAUSEN'S *Gesangbuch*, 1704.

Seele du musst munter werden.

1 Come, my soul, thou must be waking,
Now is breaking
O'er the earth another day;
Come to Him who made this splendour,
See thou render
All thy feeble strength can pay.

2 Gladly hail the sun returning;
Ready burning
Be the incense of thy powers;
For the night is safely ended,
God hath tended
With His care thy helpless hours.

3 Pray that He may prosper ever
Each endeavour,
When thine aim is good and true;
But that He may ever thwart thee,
And convert thee,
When thou evil wouldst pursue.

4 Think that He thy ways beholdeth,
He unfoldeth
Every fault that lurks within;
He the hidden shame glossed over
Can discover,
And discern each deed of sin.

5 Mayest thou on life's last morrow,
Free from sorrow,
Pass away in slumber sweet;
And, released from death's dark sadness,
Rise in gladness
That far brighter Sun to greet.

6 Our God's bounteous gifts abuse not,
Light refuse not,
But His Spirit's voice obey:
Thou with Him shalt dwell, beholding
Light unfolding
All things in unclouded day.

Friedrich Rudolph Ludwig von Canitz, 1654-99;
tr. by Henry James Buckoll, 1803-71.

930

DORKING. C.M. English Traditional Melody.

May also be sung to ST. STEPHEN, No. 56.

1.

O LORD of life, Thy quickening voice
Awakes my morning song ;
In gladsome words I would rejoice
That I to Thee belong.

2.

I see Thy light, I feel Thy wind,
The world, it is Thy word ;
Whatever wakes my heart and mind,
Thy presence is, my Lord.

3.

Therefore I choose my highest part,
And turn my face to Thee ;
Therefore I stir my inmost heart
To worship fervently.

4.

Lord, let me live and will this day.
Keep rising from the dead ;
Lord, make my spirit good and gay,
Give me my daily bread.

5.

Within my heart, speak, Lord, speak on,
My heart alive to keep,
Till comes the night, and, labour done,
In Thee I fall asleep.

George MacDonald, 1824-1905.

931

MORNING HYMN. L.M. F. H. BARTHÉLÉMON, 1741-1808.

1 AWAKE, my soul, and with the sun
Thy daily stage of duty run ;
Shake off dull sloth, and joyful rise,
To pay thy morning sacrifice.

2 Redeem thy misspent moments past,
And live this day as if thy last ;
Thy talents to improve take care ;
For the great day thyself prepare.

3 Let all thy converse be sincere,
Thy conscience as the noonday clear ;
For God's all-seeing eye surveys
Thy secret thoughts, thy words and ways.

4 Wake, and lift up thyself, my heart,
And with the angels bear thy part,
Who all night long unwearied sing
High praise to the eternal King.

5 All praise to Thee, who safe hast kept,
And hast refreshed me whilst I slept.
Grant, Lord, when I from death shall wake,
I may of endless life partake.

6 Lord, I my vows to Thee renew ;
Disperse my sins as morning dew ;
Guard my first springs of thought and will,
And with Thyself my spirit fill.

7 Direct, control, suggest, this day,
All I design, or do, or say,
That all my powers, with all their might,
In Thy sole glory may unite.

8 Praise God, from whom all blessings flow ;
Praise Him, all creatures here below ;
Praise Him above, ye heavenly host ;
Praise Father, Son, and Holy Ghost. Amen.

Thomas Ken, 1637-1711.

932

By permission of Novello and Company, Limited.

Splendor Paternae gloriae.

1 O SPLENDOUR of God's glory bright,
O Thou that bringest light from light,
O Light of light, light's living spring,
O Day, all days illumining.

2 O Thou true Sun, on us Thy glance
Let fall in royal radiance,
The Spirit's sanctifying beam
Upon our earthly senses stream.

3 The Father, too, our prayers implore,
Father of glory evermore;
The Father of all grace and might,
To banish sin from our delight:

4 To guide whate'er we nobly do,
With love all envy to subdue,
To make ill-fortune turn to fair,
And give us grace our wrongs to bear.

* * * *

5 Our mind be in His keeping placed,
Our body true to Him and chaste,
Where only faith her fire shall feed,
To burn the tares of Satan's seed.

6 And Christ to us for food shall be,
From Him our drink that welleth free,
The Spirit's wine, that maketh whole,
And, mocking not, exalts the soul.

7 Rejoicing may this day go hence,
Like virgin dawn our innocence,
Like fiery noon our faith appear,
Nor know the gloom of twilight drear.

8 Morn in her rosy car is borne;
Let Him come forth, our perfect Morn,
The Word in God the Father one,
The Father perfect in the Son. Amen.

Ambrosius, 340-97;
tr. by Robert Seymour Bridges, 1844-1930. ***Y. H.***

933

ST. JOHN. 7 7.7 7.7 7. R. CECIL, 1748-1810.

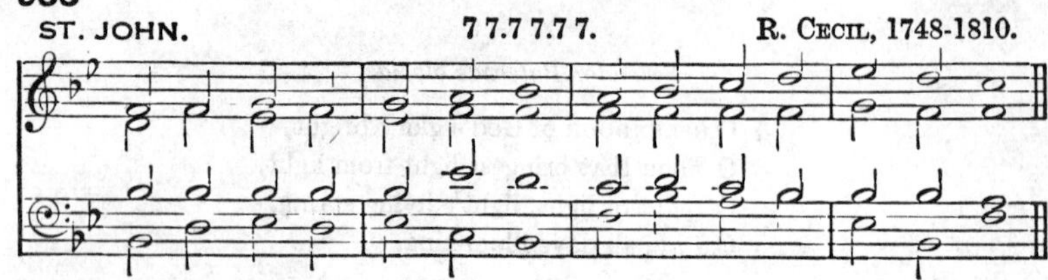

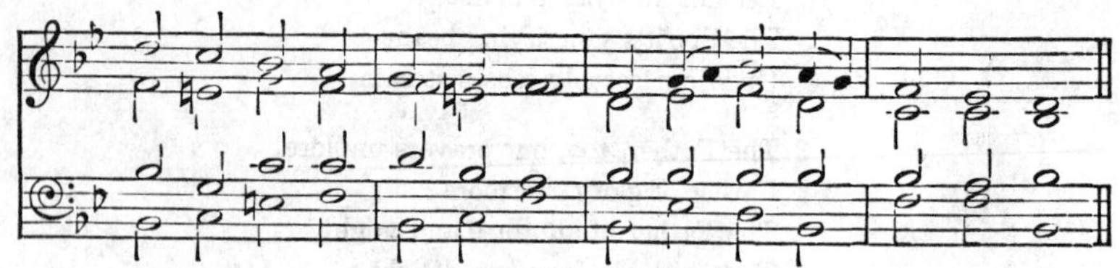

1 AT Thy feet, O Christ, we lay
Thine own gift of this new day;
Doubt of what it holds in store
Makes us crave Thine aid the more;
Lest it prove a time of loss,
Mark it, Saviour, with Thy Cross.

2 If it flow on calm and bright,
Be Thyself our chief delight;
If it bring unknown distress,
Good is all that Thou canst bless;
Only, while its hours begin,
Pray we, keep them clear of sin.

3 We in part our weakness know,
And in part discern our foe;
Well for us, before Thine eyes
All our danger open lies;
Turn not from us while we plead
Thy compassions and our need.

4 Fain would we Thy word embrace,
Live each moment in Thy grace,
All ourselves to Thee consign,
Fold up all our wills in Thine.
Think, and speak, and do, and be
Simply that which pleases Thee.

5 Hear us, Lord, and that right soon;
Hear, and grant the choicest boon
That Thy love can e'er impart,
Loyal singleness of heart;
So shall this and all our days,
Christ our God, show forth Thy praise.

William Bright, 1824-1901.

934

EPWORTH. C.M. C. Wesley, 1757-1834.

1.

All praise to Him who dwells in bliss,
Who made both day and night,
Whose throne is darkness in the abyss
Of uncreated light.

2.

Each thought and deed His piercing eyes
With strictest search survey;
The deepest shades no more disguise
Than the full blaze of day.

3.

Whom Thou dost guard, O King of kings,
No evil shall molest;
Under the shadow of Thy wings
Shall they securely rest.

4.

Thy angels shall around their beds
Their constant stations keep;
Thy faith and truth shall shield their heads
For Thou dost never sleep.

5.

May we, with calm and sweet repose
And heavenly thoughts refreshed,
Our eyelids with the morn's unclose,
And bless the Ever-blessed. Amen.

Charles Wesley, 1707-88.

935

MOTHERLAND. L.M. T. HUTCHINSON, 1854-1917.

1 FATHER Divine, I come to Thee,
I yield, a captive, to Thy sway,
That love's gold chain may set me free
For all the burden of the day.

2 I come not to avoid my care,
I come not to desert the strife;
I come to seek new strength to bear,
I fly to find new power for life.

3 Many there be that seek Thy face
To meet the hour of parting breath,
But 'tis for earth I need Thy grace—
Life is more solemn still than death.

4 When morning gilds the porch of day,
I feel so vile amid the glow
That I should faint, didst Thou not say:
I make thee whiter than the snow.

5 When noontide brings its work to all,
I find my task so hard to be,
That I should sink, didst Thou not call:
My strength is perfected in thee.

6 When darkness leads the world to rest,
The silent burden of the night
Would crush, but for Thy message blest:
At evening time there shall be light.

7 O may these streams of golden light
To all my desert way be given,
Till faith itself is lost in sight,
And days on earth be days of heaven.

George Matheson, 1842-1906.

936

BRINDLEY. 6 6.7. D. C. T. GROVES, 1888-1955.

* Slurs for Verse 1.

Φῶς ἱλαρὸν ἁγίας δόξης.

1 O GLADSOME light, O grace
Of God the Father's face,
The eternal splendour wearing;
Celestial, holy, blest,
Our Saviour Jesus Christ,
Joyful in Thine appearing.

2 Now, ere day fadeth quite,
We see the evening light,
Our wonted hymn outpouring;
Father of might unknown,
Thee, His incarnate Son,
And Holy Spirit adoring.

3 To Thee of right belongs
All praise of holy songs,
O Son of God, lifegiver;
Thee, therefore, O Most High,
The world doth glorify,
And shall exalt for ever.

Anonymous, c. 3rd cent.;
tr. by Robert Seymour Bridges, 1844-1930, *Y.H.*

937 φῶς ἱλαρὸν ἁγίας δόξης.

SEBASTE. Irregular. J. Stainer, 1840-1901.

Hail, gladdening Light, of His pure glo - ry poured,
Who is the immortal Fa - ther, heaven - ly, blest,
Ho - li - est of Ho - lies, Je - sus Christ, our Lord!
Now we come to the sun's hour of rest. The lights of evening round us shine,

Morning and Evening

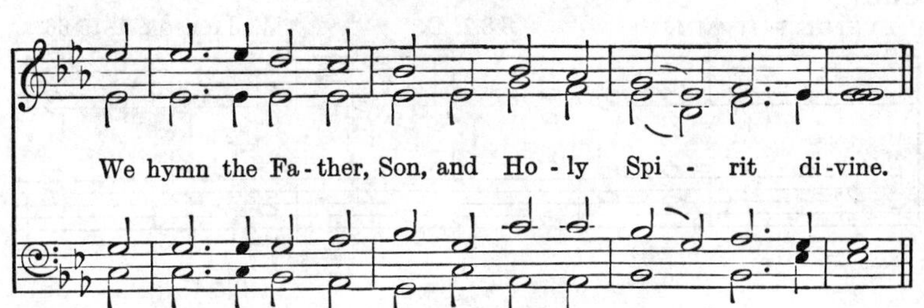

We hymn the Fa-ther, Son, and Ho-ly Spi - rit di-vine.

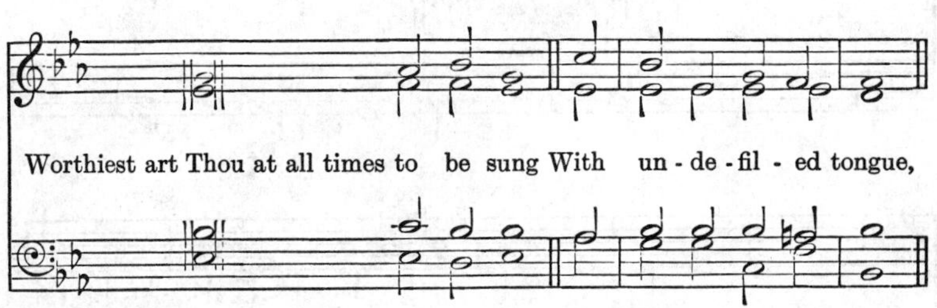

Worthiest art Thou at all times to be sung With un-de-fil-ed tongue,

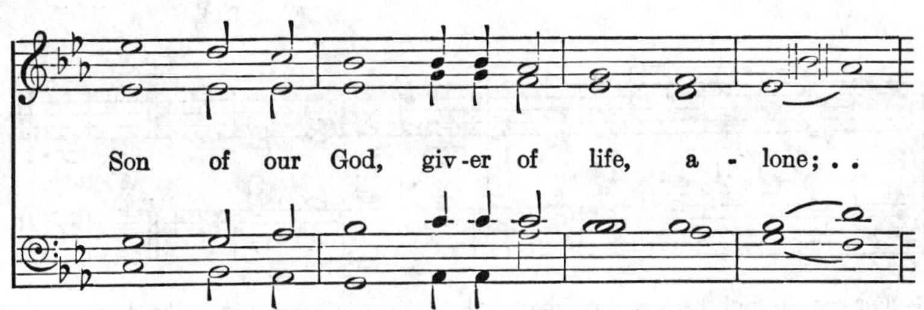

Son of our God, giv-er of life, a - lone; . .

rall.
There-fore in all the world Thy glo-ries, Lord, they own.

Anonymous, c. 3rd cent.; tr. by John Keble, 1792-1866.

938

EVENING HYMN. 8 8.7. D. W. JACKSON, 1815-66.

1 FATHER, in high heaven dwelling,
May our evening song be telling
Of Thy mercy large and free:
Through the day Thy love hath fed us,
Through the day Thy care hath led us,
With divinest charity.

2 This day's sins, O pardon, Saviour!
Evil thoughts, perverse behaviour,
Envy, pride, and vanity;
From the world, the flesh, deliver,
Save us now, and save us ever,
O Thou Lamb of Calvary!

3 From enticements of the devil,
From the might of spirits evil,
Be our shield and panoply;
Let Thy power this night defend us,
And a heavenly peace attend us,
And angelic company.

4 Whilst the night-dews are distilling,
Holy Ghost, each heart be filling,
With Thine own serenity;
Softly let our eyes be closing,
While on Thee the soul reposing,
Ever-blessèd Trinity. Amen.

George Rawson, 1807-89.

ST. COLUMBA. 6.4.6.6. H. S. IRONS, 1834-1905.

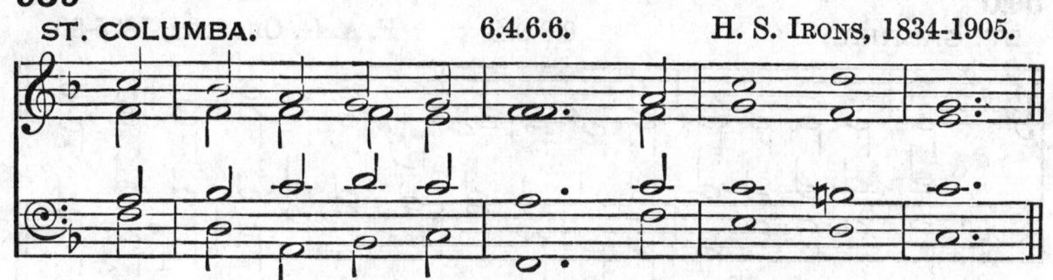

Sol praeceps rapitur.

1 THE sun is sinking fast,
The daylight dies;
Let love awake, and pay
Her evening sacrifice.

2 As Christ upon the Cross
His head inclined
And to His Father's hands
His parting soul resigned:

3 So now herself my soul
Would wholly give
Into His sacred charge,
In whom all spirits live:

4 So now beneath His eye
Would calmly rest,
Without a wish or thought
Abiding in the breast—

5 Save that His will be done,
Whate'er betide;
Dead to herself, and dead
In Him to all beside.

6 Thus would I live; yet now
Not I, but He,
In all His power and love,
Henceforth alive in me.

7 One sacred Trinity,
One Lord Divine,
Thine may I ever be,
And Thou for ever mine. Amen.

Anonymous, c. 18th cent.;
tr. by Edward Caswall, 1814-78.

940

ST. GABRIEL. 8.8.8.4. F. A. G. Ouseley, 1825-89.

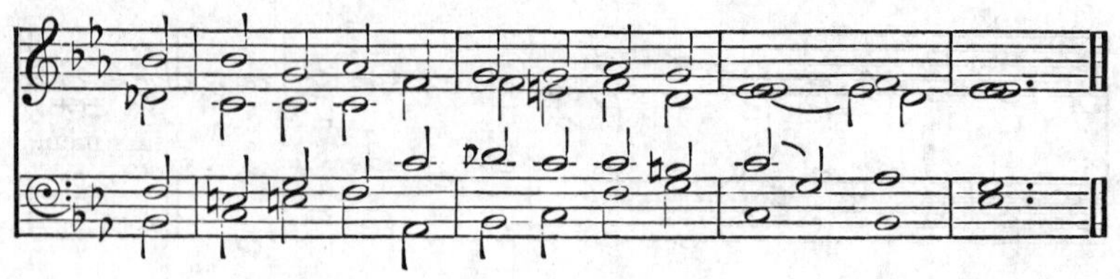

1.

The radiant morn hath passed away,
  And spent too soon her golden store;
The shadows of departing day
    Creep on once more.

2.

Our life is but an autumn day,
  Its glorious noon how quickly past:
Lead us, O Christ, Thou living Way,
    Safe home at last.

3.

O by Thy soul-inspiring grace
  Uplift our hearts to realms on high;
Help us to look to that bright place
    Beyond the sky:

4.

Where light and life and joy and peace
  In undivided empire reign,
And thronging angels never cease
    Their deathless strain:

5.

Where saints are clothed in spotless white,
  And evening shadows never fall;
Where Thou, eternal Light of light,
    Art Lord of all.

Godfrey Thring, 1823-1903.

941

COMPANION. 8.8.8.8.8.8 8. R. S. NEWMAN, 1850-1927.

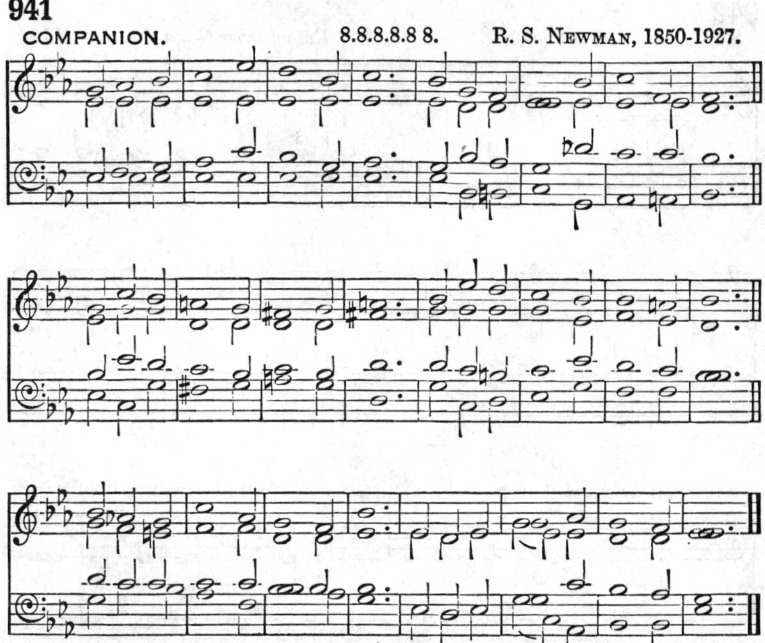

1 LORD JESUS, in the days of old
Two walked with Thee in waning light; [bold
And love's blind instinct made them
To crave Thy presence through the night. [pray:
As night descends, we too would
O leave us not at close of day!

2 Did not their hearts within them burn? [to know,
And though their Lord they failed
Did not their spirits inly yearn?
They could not let the Stranger go.
Much more must we who know Thee pray:
O leave us not at close of day!

3 Perchance we have not always wist
Who has been with us by the way;
Amid day's uproar we have missed
Some word that Thou hast had to say.
In silent night, O Saviour dear,
We would not fail Thy voice to hear.

4 Day is far spent, and night is nigh;
Stay with us, Saviour, through the night;
Talk with us, touch us tenderly,
Lead us to peace, to rest, to light;
Dispel our darkness with Thy face,
Radiant with resurrection grace.

5 Nor this night only, blessèd Lord,
We, every day and every hour,
Would walk with Thee Emmaus-ward
To hear Thy voice of love and power;
And every night would by Thy side
Look, listen, and be satisfied.

James Ashcroft Noble, 1844-96.

942

HURSLEY (*First Tune*). L.M. *Katholisches Gesangbuch*, c. 1774.

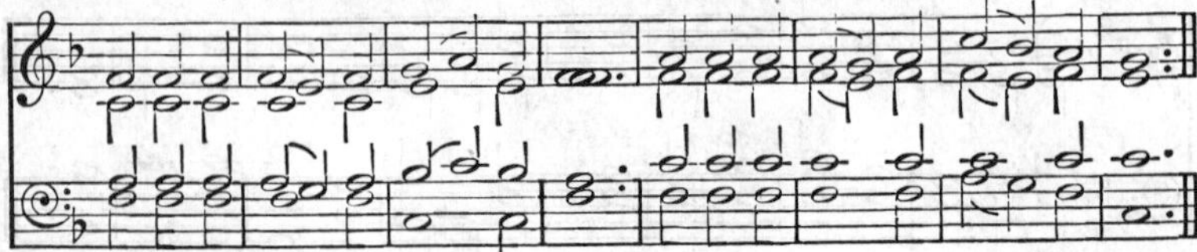

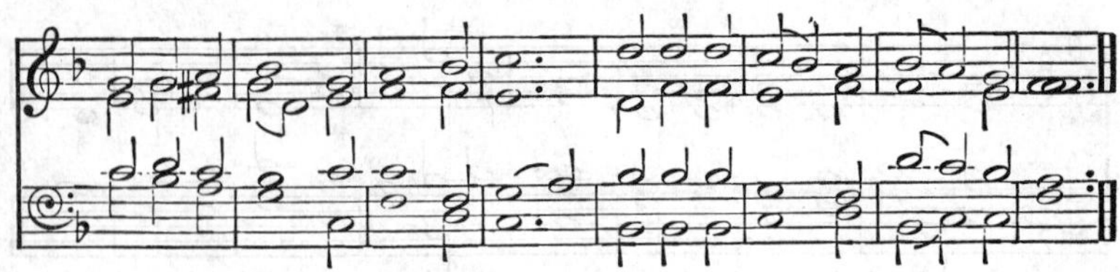

ABENDS (*Second Tune*). L.M. H. S. Oakeley, 1830-1903.

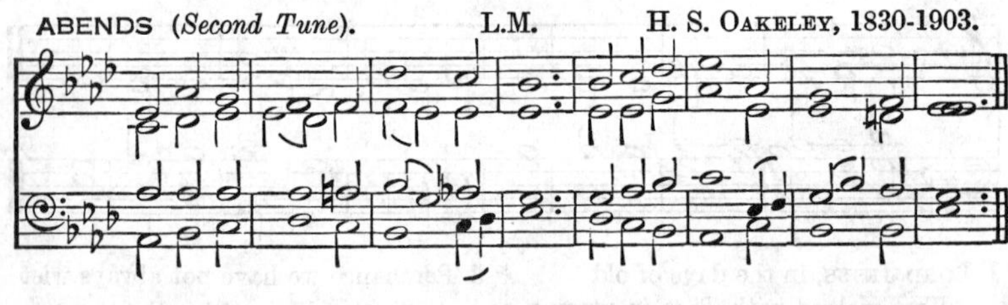

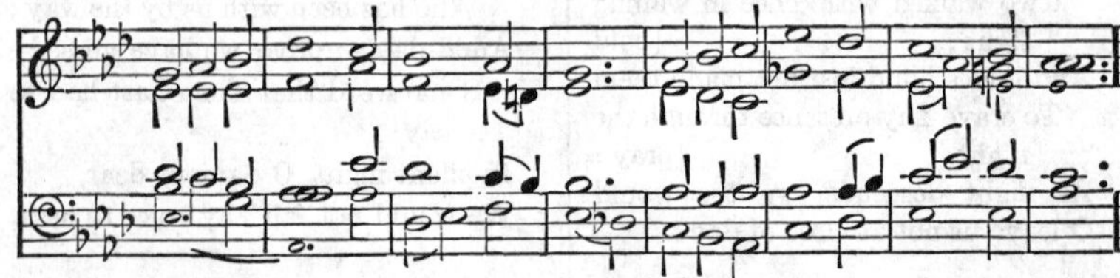

1 Sun of my soul, Thou Saviour dear,
It is not night if Thou be near;
O may no earth-born cloud arise
To hide Thee from Thy servant's eyes!

2 When the soft dews of kindly sleep
My wearied eyelids gently steep,
Be my last thought: How sweet to rest
For ever on my Saviour's breast!

3 Abide with me from morn till eve,
For without Thee I cannot live;
Abide with me when night is nigh,
For without Thee I dare not die.

4 If some poor wandering child of Thine
Have spurned to-day the voice divine,
Now, Lord, the gracious work begin;
Let him no more lie down in sin.

5 Watch by the sick; enrich the poor
With blessings from Thy boundless store;
Be every mourner's sleep to-night,
Like infant's slumbers, pure and light.

6 Come near and bless us when we wake,
Ere through the world our way we take,
Till in the ocean of Thy love
We lose ourselves in heaven above.

John Keble, 1792-1866.

TALLIS' CANON. L.M. T. Tallis, c. 1510-85.

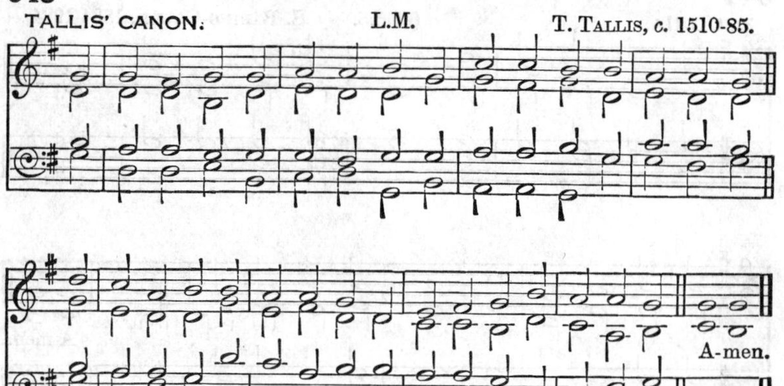

1 Glory to Thee, my God, this night,
For all the blessings of the light:
Keep me, O keep me, King of kings,
Beneath Thine own almighty wings.

2 Forgive me, Lord, for Thy dear Son,
The ill that I this day have done;
That with the world, myself, and Thee,
I, ere I sleep, at peace may be.

3 Teach me to live, that I may dread
The grave as little as my bed;
Teach me to die, that so I may
Rise glorious at the awful day.

4 O may my soul on Thee repose,
And may sweet sleep mine eyelids close;
Sleep that may me more vigorous make
To serve my God when I awake.

5 If in the night I sleepless lie,
My soul with heavenly thoughts supply;
Let no ill dreams disturb my rest,
No powers of darkness me molest.

6 O may I always ready stand
With my lamp burning in my hand;
May I in sight of heaven rejoice,
Whene'er I hear the Bridegroom's voice.

7 All praise to Thee in light arrayed,
Who light Thy dwelling-place hast made;
A boundless ocean of bright beams
From Thy all-glorious Godhead streams.

8 Praise God, from whom all blessings flow,
Praise Him, all creatures here below;
Praise Him above, ye heavenly host:
Praise Father, Son and Holy Ghost. Amen.

Thomas Ken, 1637-1711.

944

EUDOXIA. 6.5.6.5. S. Baring-Gould, 1834-1924.

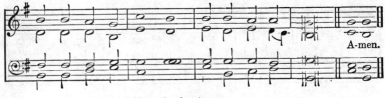

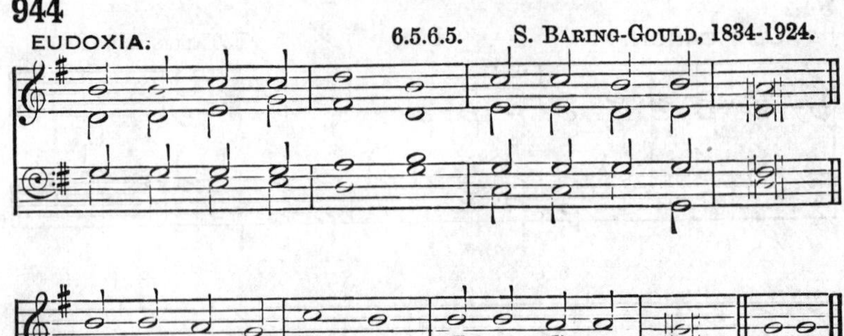

1 Now the day is over,
  Night is drawing nigh,
Shadows of the evening
  Steal across the sky.

2 Now the darkness gathers,
  Stars their watches keep,
Birds and beasts and flowers
  Soon will be asleep.

3 Jesus, give the weary
  Calm and sweet repose;
With Thy tenderest blessing
  May their eyelids close.

4 Grant to little children
  Visions bright of Thee;
Guard the sailors tossing
  On the angry sea.

5 Comfort every sufferer
  Watching late in pain;
Those who plan some evil
  From their sin restrain.

6 Through the long night-watches
  May Thine angels spread
Their white wings above me,
  Watching round my bed.

7 When the morning wakens,
  Then may I arise
Pure and fresh and sinless,
  In Thy holy eyes.

8 Glory to the Father,
  Glory to the Son,
And to Thee, blest Spirit,
  Whilst all ages run. Amen.

Sabine Baring-Gould, 1834-1924.

THE BLESSED REST. 10 10.10 4. J. BARNBY, 1838-96.

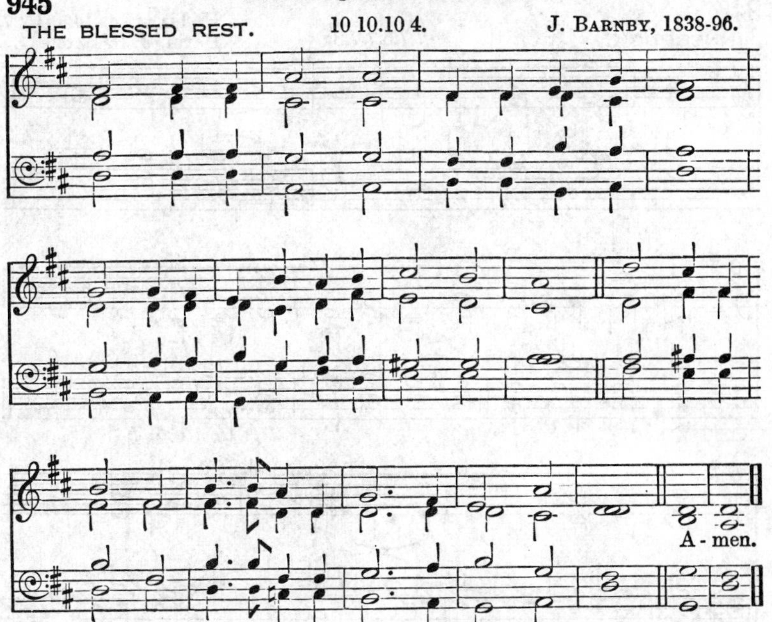

By permission of Novello and Company, Limited.

Die Nacht ist kommen drin wir ruhen sollen.

1 THE night is come, wherein at last we rest;
God order this and all things for the best:
Beneath His blessing fearless we may lie,
Since He is nigh.

2 Drive evil thoughts and spirits far away;
Master, watch o'er us till the dawning day,
Body and soul alike from harm defend,
Thine angel send.

3 Let holy prayers and thoughts our latest be;
Let us awake with joy still close to Thee,
In all things serve Thee, in each deed and thought
Thy praise be sought.

4 Give to the sick as Thy belovèd sleep,
And help the captive, comfort those who weep,
Care for the widows' and the orphans' woe,
Keep far our foe.

5 For we have none on whom for help to call
Save Thee, O God in heaven, who car'st for all,
And wilt forsake them never, day or night,
Who love Thee right.

6 Father, Thy name be praised, Thy kingdom come,
Thy will be wrought as in our heavenly home;
Keep us in life, forgive our sins, deliver
Us now and ever. Amen.

Petrus Herbert, d. 1571;
tr. by Catherine Winkworth, 1827-78.

946

INNSBRUCK. 776.778. H. ISAAK, c. 1450-1527. Harm. J. S. BACH

Nun ruhen alle Wälder.

1 Now all the woods are sleeping,
And night and stillness creeping
O'er city, man and beast;
But thou, my heart, awake thee,
To prayer awhile betake thee,
And praise thy Maker ere thou rest.

2 The last faint beam is going,
The golden stars are glowing
In yonder dark-blue deep;
And such the glory given
When called of God to heaven,
On earth no more we pine and weep.

3 Now thought and labour ceases,
For night the tired releases
And bids sweet rest begin:
My heart, there comes a morrow
Shall set thee free from sorrow
And all the dreary toil of sin.

4 My Jesus, stay Thou by me,
And let no foe come nigh me,
Safe sheltered by Thy wing;
But would the foe alarm me,
O let him never harm me,
But still Thine angels round me sing.

5 My loved ones, rest securely,
From every peril surely
Our God will guard your heads;
And happy slumbers send you,
And bid His hosts attend you,
And golden-armed watch o'er your beds.

Paulus Gerhardt, 1607-76;
tr. by Catherine Winkworth, 1827-78.

947

EVENSONG. 8.3 3.6. O. J. Stimpson, b. 1835

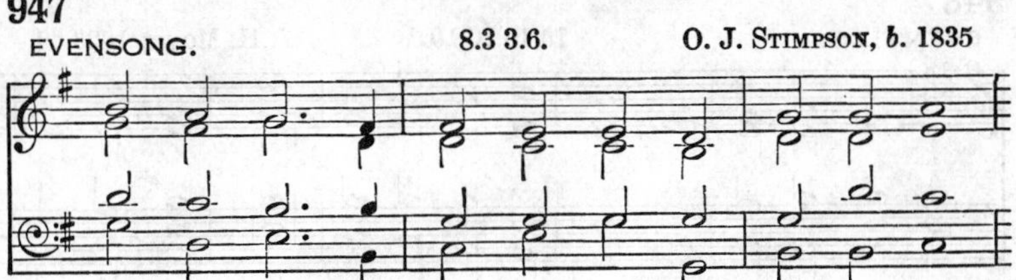

1 Ere I sleep, for every favour
This day showed
By my God,
I will bless my Saviour.

2 O my Lord, what shall I render
To Thy name,
Still the same,
Merciful and tender?

3 Thou hast ordered all my goings
In Thy way,
Heard me pray,
Sanctified my doings.

4 Leave me not, but ever love me;
Let Thy peace
Be my bliss,
Till Thou hence remove me.

5 Thou my rock, my guard, my tower,
Safely keep,
While I sleep,
Me, with all Thy power.

6 So, whene'er in death I slumber,
Let me rise
With the wise,
Counted in their number.

John Cennick, 1718-55.

948

EVENTIDE. 10 10.10 10. W. H. MONK, 1823-89.

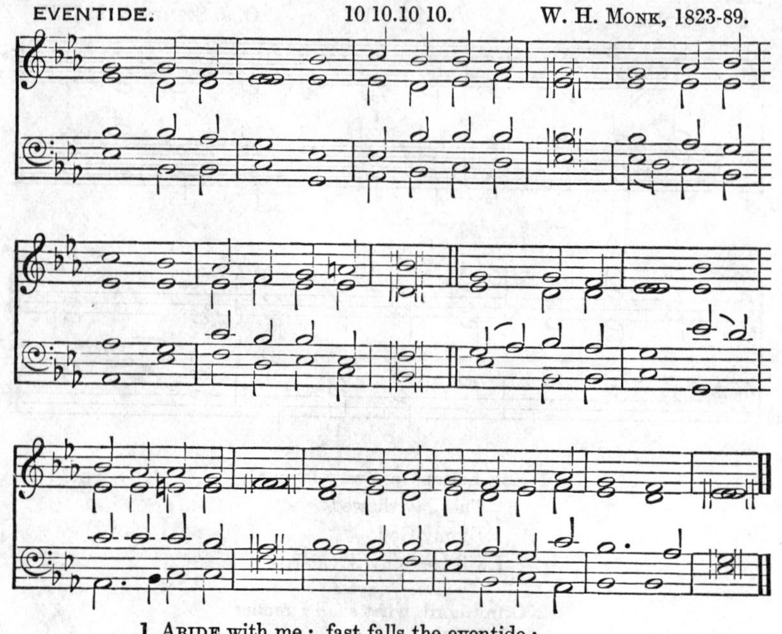

1 ABIDE with me; fast falls the eventide;
The darkness deepens; Lord, with me abide;
When other helpers fail, and comforts flee,
Help of the helpless, O abide with me.

2 Swift to its close ebbs out life's little day;
Earth's joys grow dim, its glories pass away;
Change and decay in all around I see:
O Thou who changest not, abide with me!

3 I need Thy presence every passing hour;
What but Thy grace can foil the tempter's power?
Who like Thyself my guide and stay can be?
Through cloud and sunshine, O abide with me.

4 I fear no foe, with Thee at hand to bless;
Ills have no weight, and tears no bitterness;
Where is death's sting? where, grave, thy victory?
I triumph still, if Thou abide with me.

5 Hold Thou Thy Cross before my closing eyes,
Shine through the gloom, and point me to the skies;
Heaven's morning breaks, and earth's vain shadows flee:
In life, in death, O Lord, abide with me!

Henry Francis Lyte, 1793-1847.

Also:

113 When morning gilds the skies
474 Still, still with Thee
667 The day Thou gavest
689 At even, ere the sun was set
691 Saviour, again to Thy dear name
692 O Saviour, bless us ere we go
732 Sweetly the holy hymn
876 Omnipresent God, whose aid
952 God the Father, be Thou near

949

ST. BERNARD. C.M. J. Richardson, 1816-79.

1 Behold us, Lord, a little space
From daily tasks set free,
And met within Thy holy place
To rest awhile with Thee.

2 Around us rolls the ceaseless tide
Of business, toil, and care,
And scarcely can we turn aside
For one brief hour of prayer.

3 Yet these are not the only walls
Wherein Thou may'st be sought;
On homeliest work Thy blessing falls
In truth and patience wrought.

4 Thine is the loom, the forge, the mart,
The wealth of land and sea,
The worlds of science and of art,
Revealed and ruled by Thee.

5 Then let us prove our heavenly birth
In all we do and know,
And claim the kingdom of the earth
For Thee, and not Thy foe.

6 Work shall be prayer, if all be wrought
As Thou wouldst have it done;
And prayer, by Thee inspired and taught,
Itself with work be one.

John Ellerton, 1826-93.

950

EGHAM. S.M. W. Turner, 1651-1740.

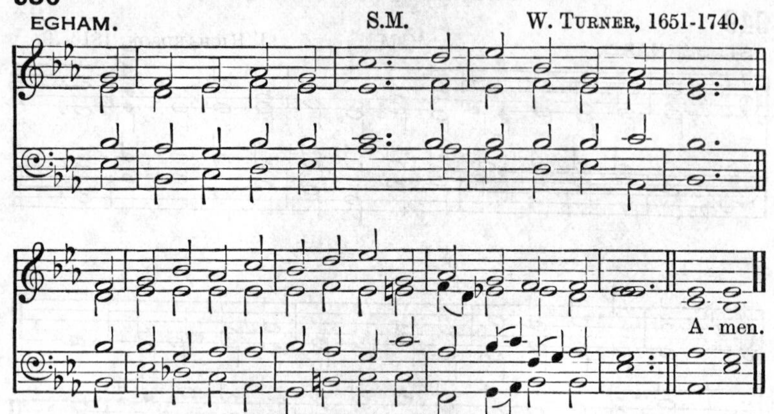

1 Blest are the pure in heart,
For they shall see our God;
The secret of the Lord is theirs,
Their soul is Christ's abode.

2 The Lord, who left the sky
Our life and peace to bring,
And dwelt in lowliness with men,
Their Pattern and their King—

3 Still to the lowly soul
He doth Himself impart;
And for His cradle and His throne
Chooseth the pure in heart.

4 Lord, we Thy presence seek;
May ours this blessing be;
Give us a pure and lowly heart,
A temple meet for Thee. Amen.

John Keble, vv. 1, 3, 1792-1866;
William John Hall, vv. 2, 4, 1793-1861.

951

7.6.7.6.8 8.

ST. ANATOLIUS (1) (*First Tune*). A. H. Brown, 1830-1926.

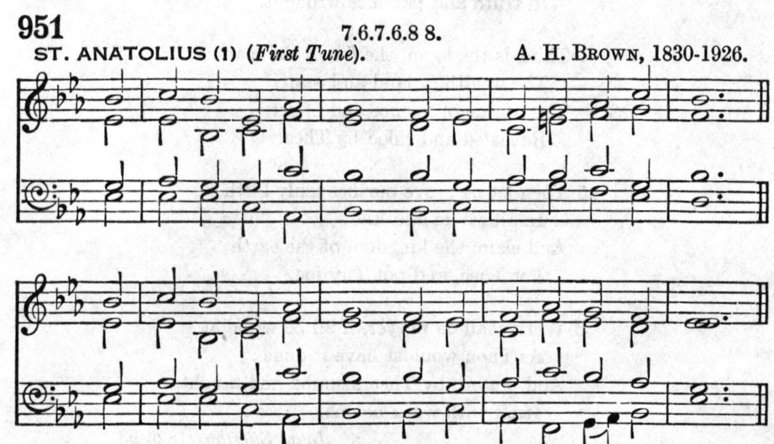

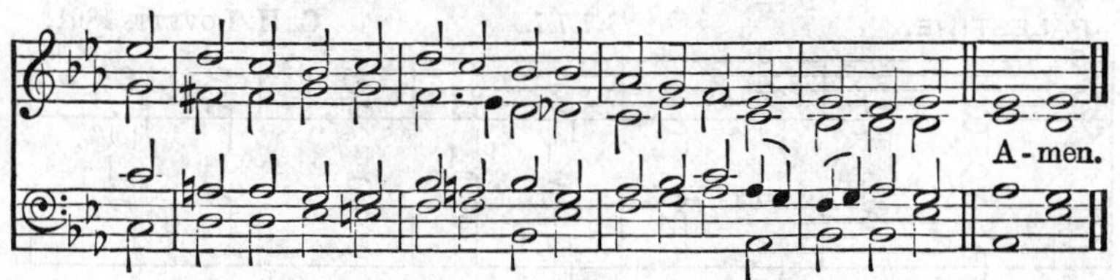

7.6.7.6.8 8.

ST. ANATOLIUS (2) (*Second Tune*). J. B. DYKES, 1823-76.

A-men.

Τὴν ἡμέραν διελθών.

1 THE day is past and over;
All thanks, O Lord, to Thee;
We pray Thee now that sinless
The hours of dark may be:
O Jesu, keep us in Thy sight,
And guard us through the coming night.

2 The joys of day are over;
We lift our hearts to Thee,
And ask Thee that offenceless
The hours of dark may be:
O Jesu, make their darkness light,
And guard us through the coming night.

3 The toils of day are over;
We raise our hymn to Thee,
And ask that free from peril
The hours of dark may be:
O Jesu, keep us in Thy sight,
And guard us through the coming night.

4 Be Thou our soul's Preserver,
For Thou, O God, dost know
How many are the perils
Awaiting us below:
O loving Jesu, hear our call,
And guard and save us from them all. Amen.

Anatolius, 8th or 9th cent.;
tr. by John Mason Neale, 1818-66.

952

PALESTINE. 7.7.7.7. C. H. LOVETT, 1861.

May also be sung to CHRISTUS, No. 288.

1 GOD the Father, be Thou near,
Save from every harm to-night;
Make us all Thy children dear,
In the darkness be our light.

2 God the Saviour, be our peace,
Put away our sins to-night;
Speak the word of full release,
Turn our darkness into light.

3 Holy Spirit, deign to come,
Sanctify us all to-night;
In our hearts prepare Thy home,
Turn our darkness into light.

4 Holy Trinity, be nigh;
Mystery of love adored,
Help to live, and help to die;
Lighten all our darkness, Lord! Amen.

George Rawson, 1807-89.

953

TOULON. 10.10.10.10. *Genevan Psalter*, 1551.

Herr, des Tages Mühen und Beschwerden.

1 O Lord, who by Thy presence hast made light
The heat and burden of the toilsome day,
Be with me also in the silent night,
Be with me when the daylight fades away.

2 Fraught with rich blessing, breathing sweet repose,
The calm of evening settles on my breast;
If Thou be with me when my labours close,
No more is needed to complete my rest.

3 Come then, O Lord, and deign to be my Guest,
After the day's confusion, toil, and din;
O come to bring me peace and joy and rest,
To give salvation, and to pardon sin.

4 Bind up the wounds, assuage the aching smart
Left in my bosom from the day just past,
And let me on a Father's loving heart
Forget my griefs, and find sweet rest at last. Amen.

Carl Johann Philipp Spitta, 1801-59;
tr. by Richard Massie, 1800-87.

Also:

23 King of glory
410 Come, ye that love
470 Still with Thee
664 O how blest the hour
697 Blest are the humble souls that see
718 Jesus, we look to Thee
719 See, Jesu, Thy disciples see
872 We bless Thee, Lord
941 Lord Jesus, in the days of old

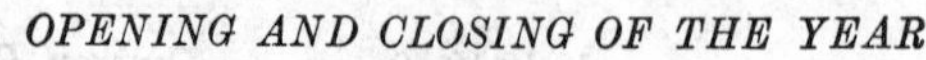

OPENING AND CLOSING OF THE YEAR

954

ANOTHER YEAR (*First Tune*). 7.6.7.6. G. F. BROCKLESS, 1887-1957.

CHERRY TREE CAROL (*Second Tune*). 7.6.7.6. Traditional English Carol Melody.

1 ANOTHER year is dawning:
Dear Master, let it be,
In working or in waiting,
Another year for Thee:

2 Another year of mercies,
Of faithfulness and grace;
Another year of gladness
In the shining of Thy face:

3 Another year of progress,
Another year of praise,
Another year of proving
Thy presence all the days:

4 Another year of service,
Of witness for Thy love;
Another year of training
For holier work above.

5 Another year is dawning:
Dear Master, let it be,
On earth, or else in heaven,
Another year for Thee. Amen.

Frances Ridley Havergal, 1836-79.

Opening and Closing of the Year

955

FYLDE. 6.5.6.5. D. and refrain. J. T. Lightwood, 1856-1944

1 Standing at the portal
Of the opening year,
Words of comfort meet us,
Hushing every fear,
Spoken through the silence
By our Father's voice,
Tender, strong, and faithful,
Making us rejoice.

Onward, then, and fear not,
Children of the day!
For His word shall never,
Never pass away!

2 I, the Lord, am with thee,
Be thou not afraid!
I will help and strengthen,
Be thou not dismayed!
Yea, I will uphold thee
With My own right hand;
Thou art called and chosen
In My sight to stand.

3 For the year before us,
O what rich supplies!
For the poor and needy
Living streams shall rise;
For the sad and sinful
Shall His grace abound,
For the faint and feeble
Perfect strength be found.

4 He will never fail us,
He will not forsake;
His eternal covenant
He will never break!
Resting on His promise,
What have we to fear?
God is all-sufficient
For the coming year.

Frances Ridley Havergal, 1836-79.

956

DERBE. 5 5.5 11. *Sacred Harmony*, 1780.

1 Come, let us anew
Our journey pursue,
Roll round with the year,
And never stand still till the Master appear.

2 His adorable will
Let us gladly fulfil,
And our talents improve,
By the patience of hope and the labour of love.

3 Our life is a dream
Our time as a stream
Glides swiftly away,
And the fugitive moment refuses to stay.

4 The arrow is flown,
The moment is gone;
The millennial year
Rushes on to our view, and eternity 's here.

5 O that each in the day
Of His coming may say:
I have fought my way through,
I have finished the work Thou didst give me to do!

6 O that each from his Lord
May receive the glad word:
Well and faithfully done;
Enter into My joy, and sit down on My throne!

Charles Wesley, 1707-88.

957

DEDICATION. 7.5.7.5. D. G. A. MACFARREN, 1813-87.

1 FATHER, let me dedicate
All this year to Thee,
In whatever worldly state
Thou wilt have me be:
Not from sorrow, pain, or care,
Freedom dare I claim;
This alone shall be my prayer:
Glorify Thy name.

2 Can a child presume to choose
Where or how to live?
Can a Father's love refuse
All the best to give?
More Thou givest every day
Than the best can claim,
Nor withholdest aught that may
Glorify Thy name.

3 If in mercy Thou wilt spare
Joys that yet are mine;
If on life, serene and fair,
Brighter rays may shine;
Let my glad heart, while it sings,
Thee in all proclaim,
And, whate'er the future brings,
Glorify Thy name.

4 If Thou callest to the cross,
And its shadow come,
Turning all my gain to loss,
Shrouding heart and home;
Let me think how Thy dear Son
To His glory came,
And in deepest woe pray on:
Glorify Thy name. Amen.

Lawrence Tuttiett, 1825-97.

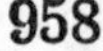

958

HEBER. 7.6.7.6. D. Greek Air

May also be sung to AURELIA, No. 701.

1 O GOD, the Rock of Ages,
Who evermore hast been,
What time the tempest rages,
Our dwelling-place serene:
Before Thy first creations,
O Lord, the same as now,
To endless generations
The everlasting Thou!

2 Our years are like the shadows
On sunny hills that lie,
Or grasses in the meadows
That blossom but to die:
A sleep, a dream, a story
By strangers quickly told,
An unremaining glory
Of things that soon are old.

3 O Thou, who canst not slumber,
Whose light grows never pale,
Teach us aright to number
Our years before they fail.
On us Thy mercy lighten,
On us Thy goodness rest,
And let Thy Spirit brighten
The hearts Thyself hast blessed.

4 Lord, crown our faith's endeavour
With beauty and with grace,
Till, clothed in light for ever,
We see Thee face to face:
A joy no language measures,
A fountain brimming o'er,
An endless flow of pleasures,
An ocean without shore.

Edward Henry Bickersteth, 1825-1906.

959

NORTHROP. C.M. A. NORTHROP, 1863-1938

May also be sung to RICHMOND, No. 703.

1 SING to the great Jehovah's praise;
All praise to Him belongs;
Who kindly lengthens out our days
Demands our choicest songs.

2 His providence hath brought us through
Another various year;
We all with vows and anthems new
Before our God appear.

3 Father, Thy mercies past we own;
Thy still continued care;
To Thee presenting, through Thy Son,
Whate'er we have or are.

4 Our lips and lives shall gladly show
The wonders of Thy love,
While on in Jesu's steps we go
To see Thy face above.

5 Our residue of days or hours
Thine, wholly Thine, shall be;
And all our consecrated powers
A sacrifice to Thee.

Charles Wesley, 1707-88.

960

WINCHESTER OLD. C.M. G. KIRBYE, ? -1634.

1.

JOIN, all ye ransomed sons of grace,
The holy joy prolong,
And shout to the Redeemer's praise
A solemn midnight song.

2.

Blessing and thanks and love and might
Be to our Jesus given,
Who turns our darkness into light,
Who turns our hell to heaven.

3.

Thither our faithful souls He leads,
Thither He bids us rise,
With crowns of joy upon our heads,
To meet Him in the skies.

Charles Wesley, 1707-88.

961

THE GOLDEN CHAIN. 8.7.8.7.8 8.7. J. BARNBY, 1838-96.

By permission of Novello and Company, Limited.

May also be sung to ELBERFELD, No. 906.

1 ACROSS the sky the shades of night
This winter's eve are fleeting ;
We come to Thee, the Life and Light,
In solemn worship meeting ;
And as the year's last hours go by
We lift to Thee our earnest cry,
Once more Thy love entreating.

2 Before the Cross subdued we bow,
To Thee our prayers addressing ;
Recounting all Thy mercies now,
And all our sins confessing ;
Beseeching Thee, this coming year,
To hold us in Thy faith and fear,
And crown us with Thy blessing.

3 We gather up in this brief hour
The memory of Thy mercies ;
Thy wondrous goodness, love, and power
Our grateful song rehearses :
For Thou hast been our strength and stay
In many a dark and dreary day
Of sorrow and reverses.

4 Then, O great God, in years to come,
Whatever fate betide us,
Right onward through our journey home
Be Thou at hand to guide us ;
Nor leave us till, at close of life,
Safe from all peril, toil, and strife,
Heaven shall receive and hide us.

James Hamilton, 1819-96.

Also:

607 O God of Bethel

878 O God, our help
905 Ring out, wild bells

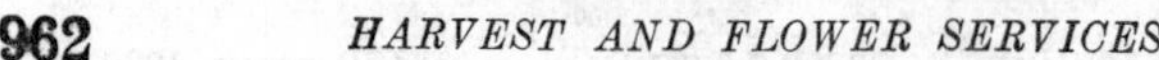

962

HARVEST AND FLOWER SERVICES

ST. GEORGE'S, WINDSOR. 7 7.7 7. D. G. J. ELVEY, 1816-93.

1 COME, ye thankful people, come,
Raise the song of harvest home:
All is safely gathered in,
Ere the winter storms begin;
God our Maker doth provide
For our wants to be supplied:
Come to God's own temple, come,
Raise the song of harvest home!

2 All the world is God's own field,
Fruit unto His praise to yield;
Wheat and tares together sown,
Unto joy or sorrow grown;
First the blade, and then the ear,
Then the full corn shall appear:
Grant, O harvest Lord, that we
Wholesome grain and pure may be.

3 For the Lord our God shall come,
And shall take His harvest home;
From His field shall in that day
All offences purge away;
Give His angels charge at last
In the fire the tares to cast;
But the fruitful ears to store
In His garner evermore.

4 Even so, Lord, quickly come;
Bring Thy final harvest home:
Gather Thou Thy people in,
Free from sorrow, free from sin;
There, for ever purified,
In Thy garner to abide:
Come, with all Thine angels, come,
Raise the glorious harvest-home!
Amen.

Henry Alford, 1810-71.

963

WIR PFLÜGEN. 7.6.7.6. D. and refrain. J. A. P. SCHULZ, 1747-1800.

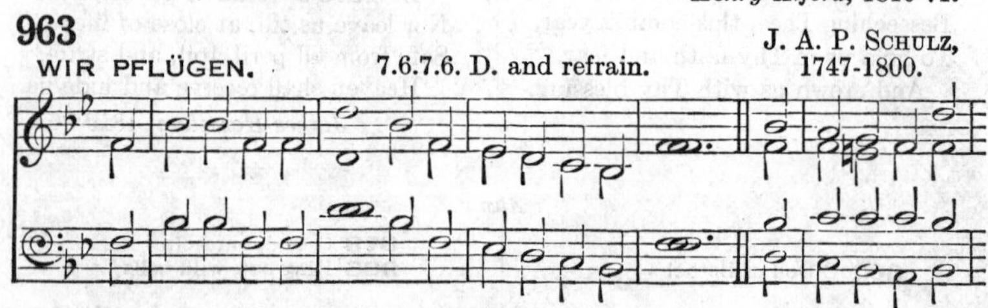

Harvest and Flower Services

Wir pflügen und wir streuen.

1 We plough the fields, and scatter
The good seed on the land,
But it is fed and watered
By God's almighty hand;
He sends the snow in winter,
The warmth to swell the grain,
The breezes, and the sunshine,
And soft refreshing rain.

All good gifts around us
Are sent from heaven above;
Then thank the Lord, O thank the [Lord,
For all His love.

2 He only is the Maker
Of all things near and far;
He paints the wayside flower,
He lights the evening star;
The winds and waves obey Him,
By Him the birds are fed;
Much more to us, His children,
He gives our daily bread.

3 We thank Thee then, O Father,
For all things bright and good,
The seed-time and the harvest,
Our life, our health, our food;
Accept the gifts we offer
For all Thy love imparts,
And, what Thou most desirest,
Our humble, thankful hearts.
Amen.

Matthias Claudius, 1740-1815;
tr. by Jane Montgomery Campbell, 1817-78.

964

8.7.8.7. D. Iambic.

GOLDEN SHEAVES (*First Tune*). A. SULLIVAN, 1842-1900.

By permission of Novello and Company, Limited.

8.7.8.7. D. Iambic.

BISHOPGARTH (*Second Tune*). A. SULLIVAN, 1842-1900.

By permission of Novello and Company, Limited.

1 To Thee, O Lord, our hearts we raise
In hymns of adoration,
To Thee bring sacrifice of praise
With shouts of exultation;
Bright robes of gold the fields adorn,
The hills with joy are ringing,
The valleys stand so thick with corn
That even they are singing.

2 And now, on this our festal day,
Thy bounteous hand confessing,
Before Thee thankfully we lay
The first-fruits of Thy blessing.
By Thee the souls of men are fed
With gifts of grace supernal;
Thou who dost give us earthly bread,
Give us the bread eternal.

3 We bear the burden of the day,
And often toil seems dreary;
But labour ends with sunset ray,
And rest comes for the weary:
May we, the angel-reaping o'er,
Stand at the last accepted,
Christ's golden sheaves for evermore
To garners bright elected.

4 O blessèd is that land of God
Where saints abide for ever,
Where golden fields spread far and broad,
Where flows the crystal river.
The strains of all its holy throng
With ours to-day are blending;
Thrice blessèd is that harvest song
Which never hath an ending.

William Chatterton Dix, 1837-98.

965

SANDYS. S.M. English Traditional Carol.

1 The spring again is here,
Life wakes from winter's gloom;
In field and forest far and near
Sweet opening flowerets bloom.

2 O mystery strange and sweet,
That life so dumbly bound
Should rise, our thankful gaze to greet,
And break from underground.

3 The morn is fresh and bright,
The slow dark hours depart:
Let days unstained and pure delight
Bring sunshine to the heart.

4 Lord, touch our careless eyes;
New life, new ardour bring,
That we may read Thy mysteries,
The wonder of Thy spring.

Arthur Christopher Benson, 1862-1925.

966

PRINCETHORPE. 6.5.6.5. D. W. Pitts, 1829-1903.

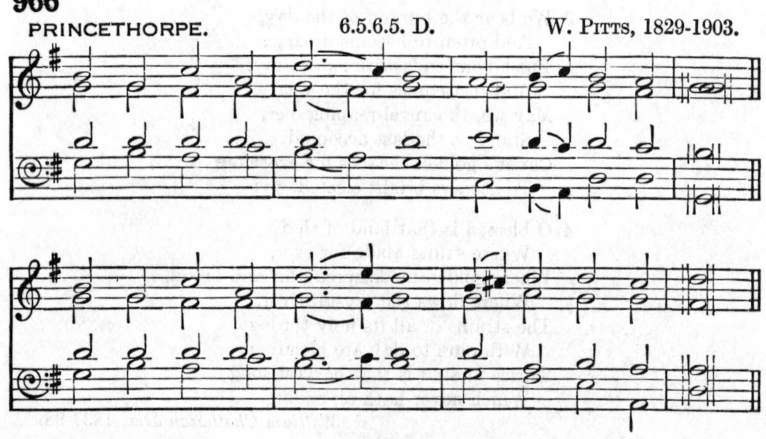

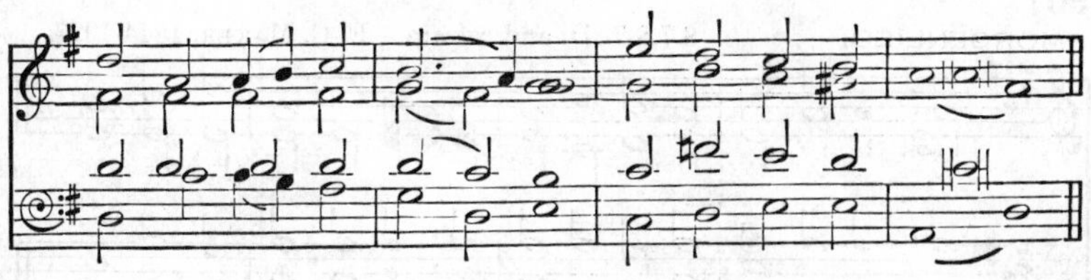

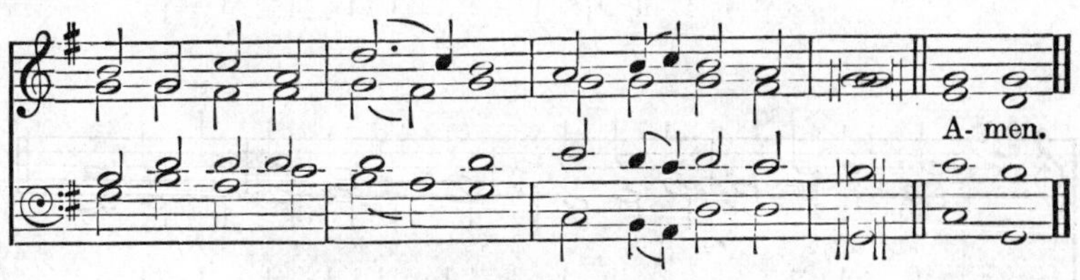

1 Earth below is teeming,
Heaven is bright above;
Every brow is beaming
In the light of love;
Every eye rejoices,
Every thought is praise;
Happy hearts and voices
Gladden nights and days.

2 Every youth and maiden,
On the harvest plain,
Round the waggons laden
With their golden grain,
Swell the happy chorus
On the evening air,
Unto Him who o'er us
Bends with constant care.

3 For the sun and showers,
For the rain and dew,
For the happy hours
Spring and summer knew;
For the golden autumn
And its precious stores,
For the love that brought them
Teeming to our doors.

4 Earth's broad harvest whitens
In a brighter sun
Than the orb that lightens
All we tread upon.
Send our labourers, Father,
Where fields ripening wave;
And the nations gather,
Gather in and save. Amen.

John Samuel Bewley Monsell, 1811-75.

967

MORGENLIED. 8.7.8.7. D. and refrain. F. C. MAKER, 1844-1927.

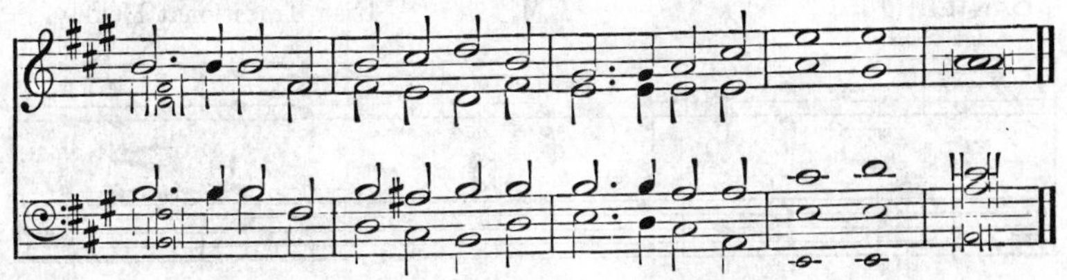

A lower setting will be found at No. 206.

1.

Now the year is crowned with blessing
As we gather in the grain ;
And, our grateful thanks expressing,
Loud we raise a joyous strain.
Bygone days of toil and sadness
Cannot now our peace destroy ;
For the hills are clothed with gladness,
And the valleys shout for joy.

To the Lord their first-fruits bringing
All His thankful people come,
To the Father praises singing
For the joy of harvest home.

2.

In the spring the smiling meadows
Donned their robes of living green,
As the sunshine chased the shadows
Swiftly o'er the changing scene ;
In the summer-time the story
Of a riper hope was told ;
Then the rich autumnal glory
Decked the fields in cloth of gold.

3.

Shall not we, whose hearts are swelling
With the thought of former days,
Sing a joyous song foretelling
Future gladness, fuller praise ?
For the cloud the bow retaineth
With its covenant of peace,
That, as long as earth remaineth,
Harvest-time shall never cease.

Ellen Thorneycroft Fowler [*Mrs. Felkin*], 1860-1929.

968

DANIEL (*First Tune*). L.M. Irish Traditional Melody.

Unison.

WILLIAMS (*Second Tune*). L.M. From *Templi Carmina*, 1829.

1 Yes, God is good—in earth and sky,
From ocean depths and spreading wood,
Ten thousand voices seem to cry:
God made us all, and God is good.

2 The sun that keeps his trackless way,
And downward pours his golden flood,
Night's sparkling hosts, all seem to say
In accents clear, that God is good.

3 The merry birds prolong the strain,
Their song with every spring renewed;
And balmy air, and falling rain,
Each softly whispers: God is good.

4 I hear it in the rushing breeze;
The hills that have for ages stood,
The echoing sky and roaring seas,
All swell the chorus: God is good.

5 Yes, God is good, all nature says,
By God's own hand with speech endued;
And man, in louder notes of praise,
Should sing for joy that God is good.

6 For all Thy gifts we bless Thee, Lord,
But chiefly for our heavenly food;
Thy pardoning grace, Thy quickening word,
These prompt our song, that God is good.

John Hampden Gurney, 1802-62.

969

ALMSGIVING. 8 8 8 4. J. B. DYKES, 1823-76.

1 O LORD of heaven and earth and sea,
To Thee all praise and glory be;
How shall we show our love to Thee,
Who givest all?

2 The golden sunshine, vernal air,
Sweet flowers and fruits Thy love declare;
Where harvests ripen, Thou art there,
Who givest all.

3 For peaceful homes and healthful days,
For all the blessings earth displays,
We owe Thee thankfulness and praise,
Who givest all.

4 Thou didst not spare Thine only Son,
But gav'st Him for a world undone,
And freely with that blessèd One
Thou givest all.

5 Thou giv'st the Spirit's blessèd dower,
Spirit of life, and love, and power,
And dost His sevenfold graces shower
Upon us all.

6 For souls redeemed, for sins forgiven,
For means of grace and hopes of heaven,
Father, all praise to Thee be given,
Who givest all.

Christopher Wordsworth, 1807-85.

970

Manx Fishermen's *Evening Hymn.*

PEEL CASTLE. 10.10 10.10. Adapted by W. H. GILL, 1839-1923.

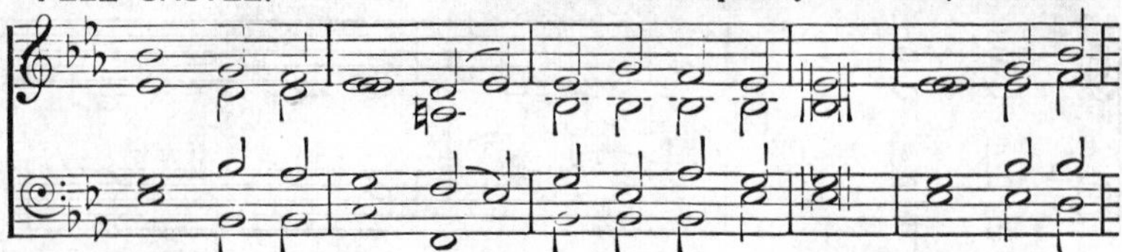

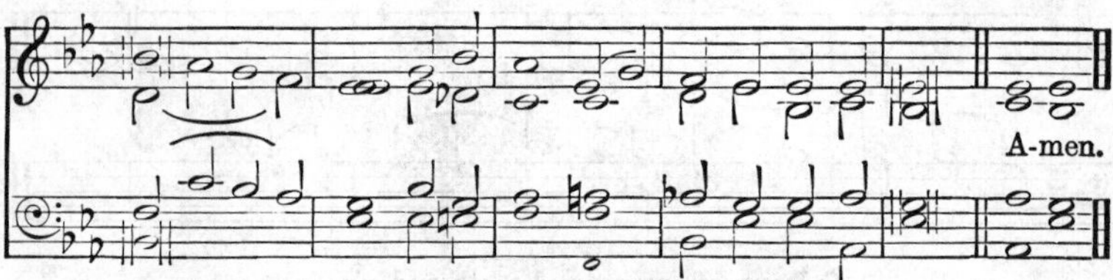

1 HEAR us, O Lord, from heaven, Thy dwelling-place:
Like them of old, in vain we toil all night,
Unless with us Thou go, who art the Light;
Come then, O Lord, that we may see Thy face.

2 Thou, Lord, dost rule the raging of the sea,
When loud the storm and furious is the gale:
Strong is Thine arm; our little barques are frail:
Send us Thy help; remember Galilee.

3 Our wives and children we commend to Thee:
For them we plough the land and plough the deep
For them by day the golden corn we reap,
By night the silver harvest of the sea.

4 We thank Thee, Lord, for sunshine, dew, and rain,
Broadcast from heaven by Thine almighty hand—
Source of all life, unnumbered as the sand—
Bird, beast, and fish, herb, fruit, and golden grain.

5 O Bread of Life, Thou in Thy word hast said:
Who feeds in faith on Me shall never die!
In mercy hear Thy hungry children's cry:
Father, give us this day our daily bread!

6 Sow in our hearts the seeds of Thy dear love,
That we may reap contentment, joy, and peace;
And when at last our earthly labours cease,
Grant us to join Thy harvest home above. Amen.

William Henry Gill, 1839-1923.

971

THE BLESSED NAME. 8.7.8.7. Iambic, and refrain. J. BARNBY, 1838-96.

REFRAIN.

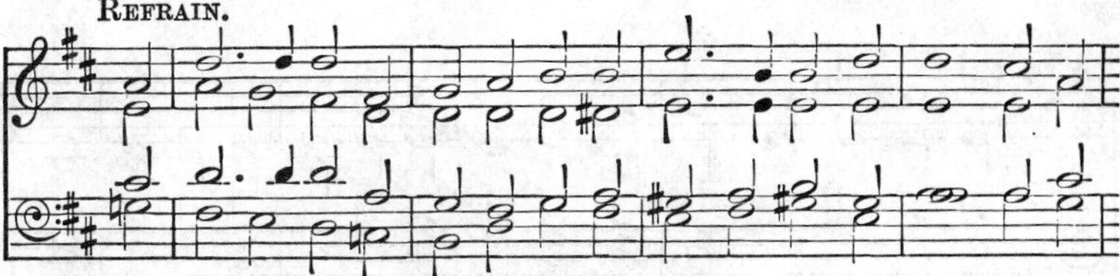

By permission of Novello and Company, Limited.

1 A GLADSOME hymn of praise we sing,
And thankfully we gather,
To bless the love of God above,
Our everlasting Father.

In Him rejoice with heart and voice,
Whose glory fadeth never,
Whose providence is our defence,
Who lives and loves for ever.

2 From shades of night He calls the light,
And from the sod the flower;
From every cloud His blessings break,
In sunshine or in shower.

3 Full in His sight His children stand,
By His strong arm defended;
And He whose wisdom guides the world,
Our footsteps hath attended.

4 For nothing falls unknown to Him
Or care or joy or sorrow;
And He whose mercy ruled the past,
Will be our stay to-morrow.

5 Then praise the Lord with one accord,
To His great name give glory,
And of His never-changing love
Repeat the wondrous story.

Ambrose Nichols Blatchford, 1842-1924.

972

SPRINGFIELD. 11.10.11.10. Dactylic. H. J. GAUNTLETT, 1805-76.

1 HERE, Lord, we offer Thee all that is fairest,
Bloom from the garden, and flowers from the field,
Gifts for the stricken ones, knowing Thou carest
More for the love than the wealth that we yield.

2 Send, Lord, by these to the sick and the dying;
Speak to their hearts with a message of peace;
Comfort the sad, who in weakness are lying;
Grant the departing a gentle release.

3 Raise, Lord, to health again those who have sickened,
Fair be their lives as the roses in bloom;
Give of Thy grace to the souls Thou hast quickened,
Gladness for sorrow, and brightness for gloom.

Abel Gerald Wilson Blunt, 1827-1902.

Also

19 Praise, O praise
35 For the beauty of the earth
45 My soul, praise the Lord!
49 Thy ceaseless, unexhausted love
79 Praise ye the Lord!
409 The glory of the spring
414 We thank Thee, Lord
524 My God, I thank Thee
593 O'er the harvest
599 Sow in the morn
851 All things bright and beautiful

973

DAVID. 8.8.8.8. D. From HANDEL'S *Sosarme*, 1732.

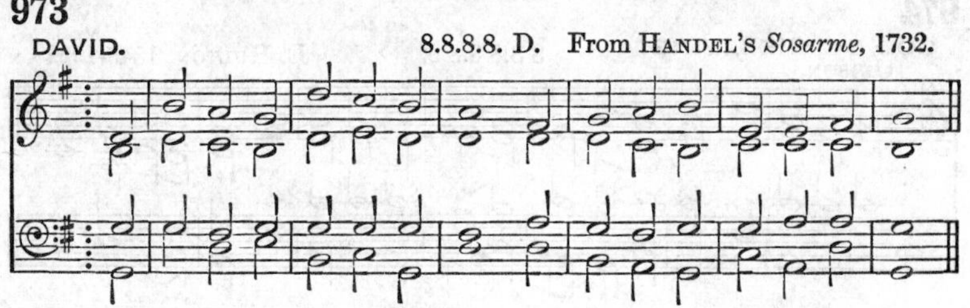

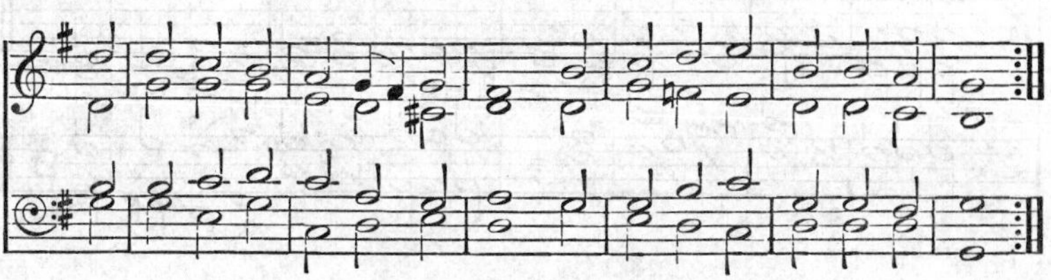

1 REJOICE for a brother deceased,
Our loss is his infinite gain;
A soul out of prison released,
And freed from its bodily chain;
With songs let us follow his flight,
And mount with his spirit above,
Escaped to the mansions of light,
And lodged in the Eden of love.

2 Our brother the haven hath gained,
Out-flying the tempest and wind,
His rest he hath sooner obtained,
And left his companions behind,
Still tossed on a sea of distress,
Hard toiling to make the blest shore,
Where all is assurance and peace,
And sorrow and sin are no more.

3 There all the ship's company meet
Who sailed with the Saviour beneath,
With shouting each other they greet,
And triumph o'er trouble and death:
The voyage of life's at an end,
The mortal affliction is past;
The age that in heaven they spend
For ever and ever shall last.

Charles Wesley, 1707-88.

974

GOD OF THE LIVING. 8 8.8 8.8 8. E. HULTON, 1845-1922

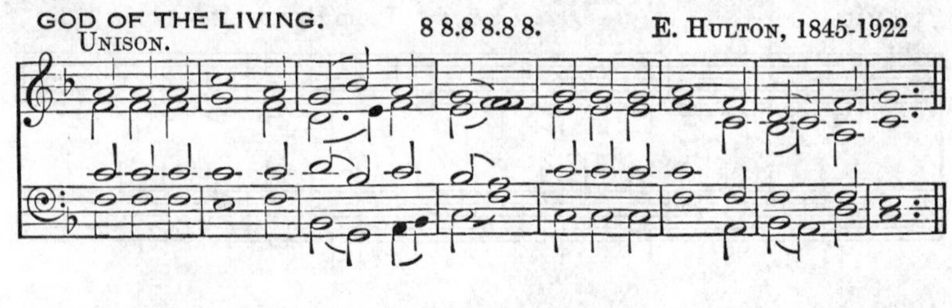

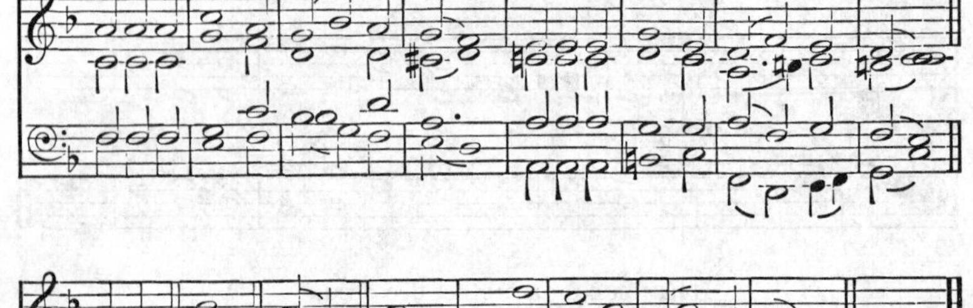

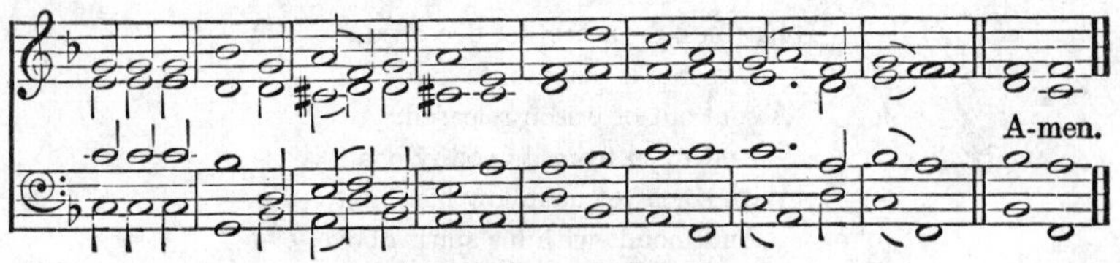

1 God of the living, in whose eyes
Unveiled Thy whole creation lies,
All souls are Thine ; we must not say
That those are dead who pass away ;
From this our world of flesh set free,
We know them living unto Thee.

2 Released from earthly toil and strife,
With Thee is hidden still their life ;
Thine are their thoughts, their works, their powers,
All Thine, and yet most truly ours ;
For well we know, where'er they be,
Our dead are living unto Thee.

3 Thy word is true, Thy will is just :
To Thee we leave them, Lord, in trust ;
And bless Thee for the love which gave
Thy Son to fill a human grave,
That none might fear that world to see
Where all are living unto Thee.

4 O Giver unto man of breath,
O Holder of the keys of death,
O Quickener of the life within,
Save us from death, the death of sin ;
That body, soul, and spirit be
For ever living unto Thee ! Amen.

John Ellerton, 1826-93.

975

IRENE. 7 7 7.5. C. C. Scholefield, 1839-1904.

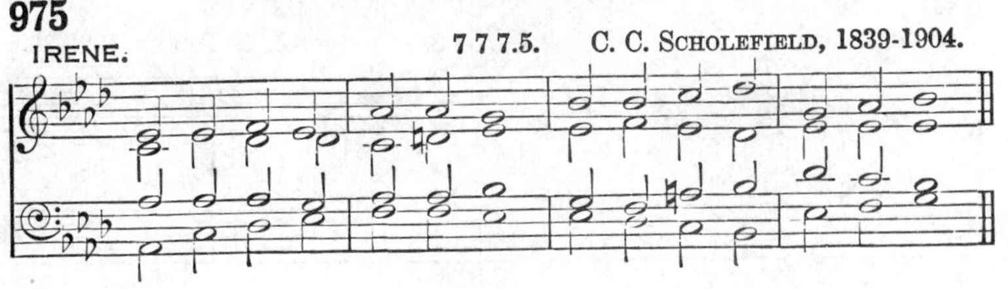

1 When the day of toil is done,
When the race of life is run,
Father, grant Thy wearied one
Rest for evermore.

2 When the strife of sin is stilled,
When the foe within is killed,
Be Thy gracious word fulfilled—
Peace for evermore.

3 When the darkness melts away
At the breaking of the day,
Bid us hail the cheering ray—
Light for evermore.

4 When the heart by sorrow tried
Feels at length its throbs subside,
Bring us, where all tears are dried,
Joy for evermore.

5 When for vanished days we yearn,
Days that never can return,
Teach us in Thy love to learn
Love for evermore.

6 When the breath of life is flown,
When the grave must claim its own,
Lord of Life, be ours Thy crown—
Life for evermore. Amen.

John Ellerton, 1826-93.

REQUIESCAT. 7.7.7.7.8 8. J. B. DYKES, 1823-76.

1 Now the labourer's task is o'er,
Now the battle-day is past;
Now upon the farther shore
Lands the voyager at last.

Father, in Thy gracious keeping
Leave we now Thy servant sleeping.

2 There the tears of earth are dried;
There its hidden things are clear;
There the work of life is tried
By a juster Judge than here.

3 There the Shepherd, bringing home
Many a lamb forlorn and strayed,
Shelters each, no more to roam,
Where the wolf can ne'er invade.

4 There the penitents who turn
To the Cross their dying eyes,
All the love of Jesus learn
At His feet in paradise.

5 There no more the powers of hell
Can prevail to mar their peace;
Christ the Lord shall guard them well,
He who died for their release.

6 Earth to earth, and dust to dust,
Calmly now the words we say;
Left behind, we wait in trust
For the resurrection day.

John Ellerton, 1826-93.

977

SAFE HOME. 6.6.6.6.8 8. A. SULLIVAN, 1842-1900.

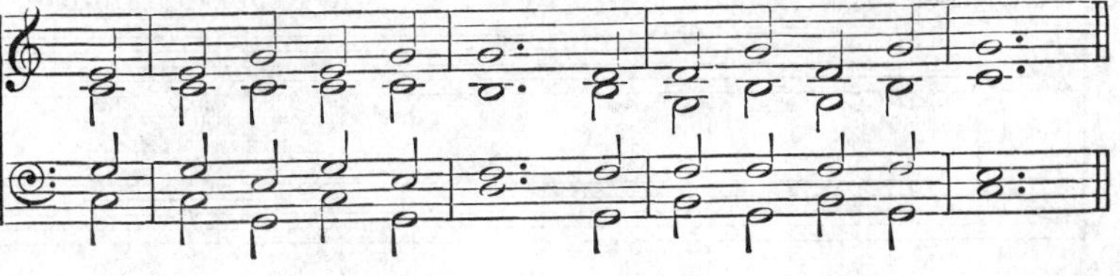

Κόπον τε καὶ κάματον.

1 SAFE home, safe home in port!
Rent cordage, shattered deck,
Torn sails, provision short,
And only not a wreck;
But O the joy upon the shore
To tell the voyage-perils o'er!

2 The prize, the prize secure!
The athlete nearly fell;
Bare all he could endure,
And bare not always well:
But he may smile at troubles gone
Who sets the victor-garland on.

3 No more the foe can harm:
No more of leaguered camp,
And cry of night alarm,
And need of ready lamp:
And yet how nearly had he failed,
How nearly had that foe prevailed!

4 The exile is at home:
O nights and days of tears!
O longings not to roam!
O sins, and doubts, and fears!
What matters now grief's darkest day?
The King has wiped those tears away.

Joseph The Hymnographer, 9th cent.;
free tr. by John Mason Neale, 1818-66.

978

REDHEAD No. 47.

7 7.7 7.

R. REDHEAD, 1820-1901.

1.

WHEN our heads are bowed with woe,
When our bitter tears o'erflow,
When we mourn the lost, the dear,
Jesu, Son of Mary, hear.

2.

When the heart is sad within
With the thought of all its sin,
When the spirit shrinks with fear,
Jesu, Son of Mary, hear.

3.

Thou our throbbing flesh hast worn,
Thou our mortal griefs hast borne,
Thou hast shed the human tear;
Jesu, Son of Mary, hear.

4.

Thou hast bowed the dying head,
Thou the blood of life hast shed,
Thou hast filled a mortal bier;
Jesu, Son of Mary, hear.

Henry Hart Milman, 1791-1868.

Also:

216 Jesus lives! thy terrors now
498 Rock of Ages, cleft for me
513 Who fathoms the eternal thought
649 There is a land of pure delight
658 For ever with the Lord
825 The saints of God
826 O God, to whom the faithful dead
832 For all the saints
833 What are these arrayed in white?
873 Thou gracious God, whose mercy lends
878 O God, our help in ages past

979

MEIRIONYDD. 7.6.7.6. D. WILLIAM LLOYD, 1786-1852

1 OUR Father, by whose servants
  Our house was built of old,
Whose hand hath crowned her children
  With blessings manifold,
For thine unfailing mercies
  Far-strewn along our way,
With all who passed before us,
  We praise Thy name to-day.

2 The changeful years unresting
  Their silent course have sped,
New comrades ever bringing
  In comrades' steps to tread:
And some are long forgotten,
  Long spent their hopes and fears;
Safe rest they in Thy keeping,
  Who changest not with years.

3 They reap not where they laboured,
  We reap what we have sown;
Our harvest may be garnered
  By ages yet unknown.
The days of old have dowered us
  With gifts beyond all praise:
Our Father, make us faithful
  To serve the coming days.

4 Before us and beside us,
  Still holden in Thine hand,
A cloud unseen of witness,
  Our elder comrades stand:
One family unbroken,
  We join, with one acclaim,
One heart, one voice uplifting,
  To glorify Thy name.

George Wallace Briggs, 1875-

980

ST. FRANCIS XAVIER. C.M. J. STAINER, 1840-1901.

By permission of Novello and Company, Limited.

May also be sung to BISHOPTHORPE, No. 719.

1 O LIGHT, from age to age the same,
O ever-living Word,
Here have we felt Thy kindling flame,
Thy voice within have heard.

2 Here holy thought and hymn and prayer
Have winged the spirit's powers,
And made these walls divinely fair,
Thy temple, Lord, and ours.

3 What visions rise above the years;
What tender memories throng,
Till the eye fills with happy tears,
The heart with happy song.

4 Vanish the mists of time and sense;
They come, the loved of yore,
And one encircling providence
Holds all for evermore.

5 O not in vain their toil, who wrought
To build faith's freer shrine;
Nor theirs, whose steadfast love and thought
Have watched the fire divine.

6 Burn, holy Fire, and shine more wide!
While systems rise and fall,
Faith, hope, and charity abide,
The heart and soul of all.

Frederick Lucian Hosmer, 1840-1929.

981

GOSHEN. 6.5.6.5. D. *Bible Class Magazine*, 1860

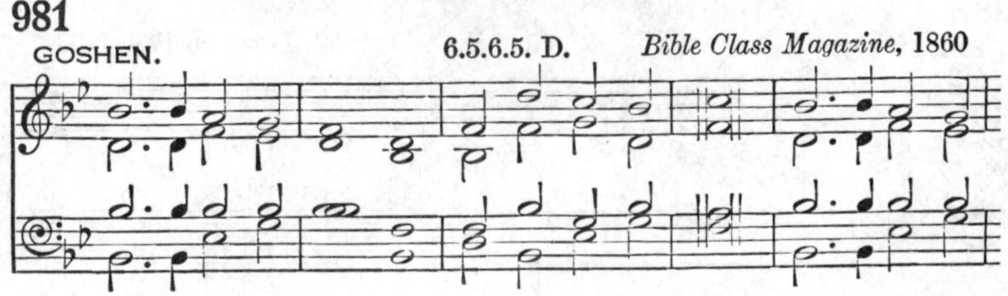

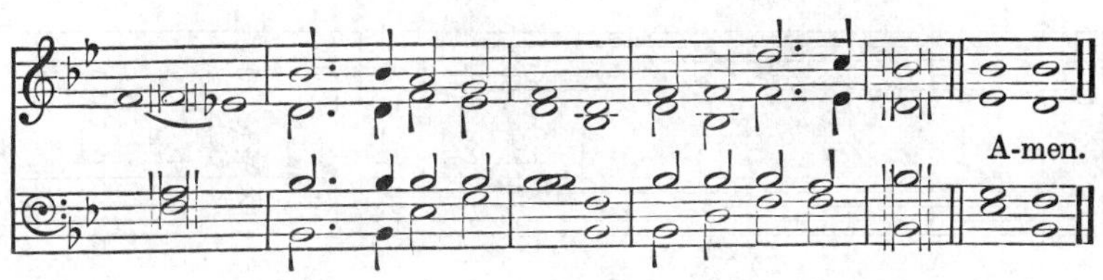

1.

CHRIST is the foundation
  Of the house we raise;
Be its walls salvation,
  And its gateways praise:
May its threshold lowly
  To the Lord be dear;
May the hearts be holy
  That shall worship here.

2.

Here the vow be sealèd
  By Thy Spirit, Lord;
Here the sick be healèd,
  And the lost restored;
Here the broken-hearted
  Thy forgiveness prove;
Here the friends long parted
  Be restored to love.

3.

Here may every token
  Of Thy presence be;
Here may chains be broken,
  Prisoners here set free;
Here may light illumine
  Every soul of Thine,
Lifting up the human
  Into the divine.

4.

Here may God the Father,
  Christ the Saviour—Son,
With the Holy Spirit,
  Be adored as One;
Till the whole creation
  At Thy footstool fall,
And in adoration
  Own Thee Lord of all. Amen.

John Samuel Bewley Monsell, 1811-75.

982

EXETER. 8 8 8. D. W. Jackson, 1730-1803.

1 Father of men, in whom are one
All humankind beneath Thy sun,
Stablish our work in Thee begun.
Except the house be built of Thee,
In vain the builders' toil must be:
O strengthen our infirmity!

2 Man lives not for himself alone,
In others' good he finds his own.
Life's worth in fellowship is known.
We, friends and comrades on life's way,
Gather within these walls to pray:
Bless Thou our fellowship to-day.

3 O Christ, our elder Brother, who
By serving man God's will didst do,
Help us to serve our brethren too.
Guide us to seek the things above,
The base to shun, the pure approve,
To live by Thy free law of love.

4 In all our work, in all our play,
Be with us, Lord, our friend, our stay;
Lead onward to the perfect day:
Then may we know, earth's lesson o'er,
With comrades missed or gone before,
Heaven's fellowship for evermore.
Amen.

Henry Cary Shuttleworth, 1850-1900.

983

WINCHESTER NEW. L.M. FREYLINGHAUSEN'S *Gesangbuch*, 1704.

1 Be with us, gracious Lord, to-day;
This house we dedicate to Thee:
O hear Thy servants as they pray,
And let Thine ear attentive be!

2 Within these walls let holy peace,
Let love and truth be always found;
May burdened hearts find sweet release,
And souls with richest grace be crowned.

3 May here be heard the suppliant's sigh,
The weary enter into rest;
Here may the contrite to Thee cry,
And waiting souls be richly blessed.

4 Here, when the gospel sound is heard,
And here proclaimed the saving name,
May hearts be quickened, moved, and stirred,
And souls be kindled into flame.

5 Here may the dead be made to live,
The dumb to sing, the deaf to hear;
And do Thou to the humble give
Pardon and peace instead of fear.

6 Make this, O Lord, Thine own abode;
Thy presence in these courts be given;
Be this, indeed, the house of God,
And this in truth the gate of heaven. Amen.

Charles Dent Bell, 1818-98.

984

JUBILATE. 7.6.7.6. D. C. H. H. PARRY, 1848-1918.

A-men.

1 O THOU whose hand hath brought us
  Unto this joyful day,
Accept our glad thanksgiving,
  And listen as we pray;
And may our preparation
  For this day's service be
With one accord to offer
  Ourselves, O Lord, to Thee.

2 For this new house we praise Thee,
Reared at Thine own command,
For every generous bosom,
And every willing hand;
And now within Thy temple
Thy glory let us see,
For all its strength and beauty
Are nothing without Thee.

3 And oft as here we gather,
And hearts in worship blend,
May truth reveal its power,
And fervent prayer ascend;
Here may the busy toiler
Rise to the things above,
The young, the old, be strengthened,
And all men learn Thy love.

4 And as the years roll onward,
And strong affections twine,
And tender memories gather
About this sacred shrine,
May this its chiefest honour,
Its glory, ever be,
That multitudes within it
Have found their way to Thee.

5 Lord God, our fathers' helper,
Our joy, and hope, and stay,
Grant now a gracious earnest
Of many a coming day.
Our yearning hearts Thou knowest;
We wait before Thy throne:
O come, and by Thy presence
Make this new house Thine own. Amen.

Frederick William Goadby, 1845-80.

Also:

676 Great is the Lord
678 Lord of the worlds
679 Pleasant are Thy courts
701 The Church's one foundation
702 Christ is our corner-stone
708 We love Thy Kingdom
709 And are we yet alive
874 Away with our fears!

Amens

I.
W. Byrd, 1538-1623.
A - - - - - - - men.
II.
O. Gibbons, 1583-1625.
A - - - men. . . . .
A - - - - - - men.
III. DRESDEN AMEN.
Arranged by J. Stainer, 1840-1901.
p
A - - - - - - men.
p
By permission of Novello and Company, Limited.
IV.
From T. Tallis, c. 1510-1585.
A - - men, A - - - men.
A - - - men,

Amens

V. SEVENFOLD AMEN. J. STAINER, 1840-1901.

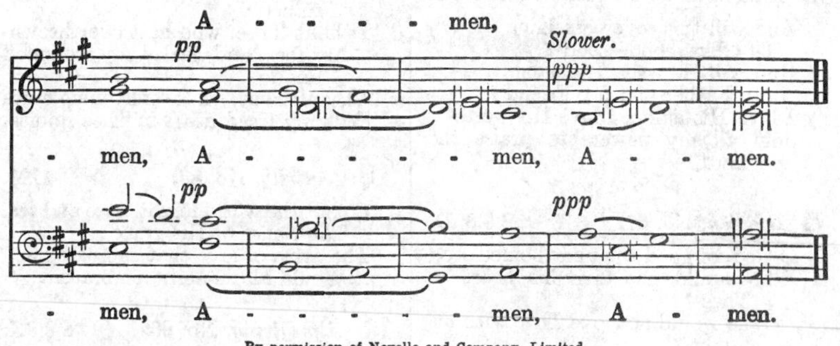

By permission of Novello and Company, Limited.

Verses

A suitable Tune is indicated at the head of each verse; others may be found in the Metrical Index.

1 *Sannox*, No. 887. D.L.M.

And did those feet in ancient time
Walk upon England's mountains green?
And was the Holy Lamb of God
On England's pleasant pastures seen?
And did the countenance divine
Shine forth upon our clouded hills?
And was Jerusalem builded here
Among these dark satanic mills?

Bring me my bow of burning gold!
Bring me my arrows of desire!
Bring me my spear! O clouds, unfold!
Bring me my chariot of fire!
I will not cease from mental fight,
Nor shall my sword sleep in my hand,
Till we have built Jerusalem
In England's green and pleasant land.

William Blake, 1757-1827.

2 *Stamford*, No. 730. 8 8.8. D.

Thou art my God, and Thee I praise;
Thou art my God, I sing Thy grace,
And call mankind to extol Thy name:
All glory to our gracious Lord!
His name be praised, His love adored,
Through all eternity the same.

3 *Millennium*, No. 114. 6.6.6.6.8 8.

And will this sovereign King
Of Glory condescend?
And will He write His name,
My Father and my Friend?
I love His name, I love His word,
Join all my powers to praise the Lord!

4 *Dresden*, No. 67. 8 8.8. D.

O God, of good the unfathomed sea!
Who would not give his heart to Thee?
Who would not love Thee with his might?
O Jesu, Lover of mankind,
Who would not his whole soul and mind,
With all his strength, to Thee unite?

5 *Confidence*, No. 370. L.M.

The Lord my Righteousness I praise;
I triumph in the love divine,
The wisdom, wealth, and strength of grace,
In Christ to endless ages mine.

6 *Laudes Domini*, No. 113. 6 6.6. D.

Let earth's wide circle round
In joyful notes resound:
May Jesus Christ be praised!
Let air, and sea, and sky,
From depth to height, reply:
May Jesus Christ be praised!

7 *Adeste Fideles*, No. 118.

O come, let us adore Him,
Christ the Lord.

8 *St. Bernard*, No. 949. C.M.

O for this love let rocks and hills
Their lasting silence break,
And all harmonious human tongues
The Saviour's praises speak!

Angels, assist our mighty joys,
Strike all your harps of gold;
But when you raise your highest notes,
His love can ne'er be told.

9 *St. Chrysostom* (*Barnby*), No. 755. 8.8.8.8.8 8.

I thank Thee, uncreated Sun,
That Thy bright beams on me have shined;
I thank Thee, who hast overthrown
My foes, and healed my wounded mind;
I thank Thee, whose enlivening voice
Bids my freed heart in Thee rejoice.

10 *Nativity*, No. 85. C.M.

O that the world might taste and see,
The riches of His grace;
The arms of love that compass me
Would all mankind embrace.

11 *Almsgiving*, No. 969. 8 8 8.4.

For souls redeemed, for sins forgiven,
For means of grace and hopes of heaven,
Father, all praise to Thee be given,
Who givest all.

12 *Old 104th*, No. 329. 10 10.11 11.

Ye mountains and vales, in praises abound,
Ye hills and ye dales, continue the sound,
Break forth into singing, ye trees of the wood,
For Jesus is bringing lost sinners to God.

13 *At the Cross.* Irregular.

At the Cross! At the Cross! where I first saw the light,
And the burden of my heart rolled away,
It was there by faith I received my sight,
And now I am happy all the day!

14 *Grosvenor*, No. 670. 8 8.6. D.

Plenteous He is in truth and grace;
He wills that all the fallen race
Should turn, repent, and live;
His pardoning grace for all is free;
Transgression, sin, iniquity,
He freely doth forgive.

Mercy He doth for thousands keep;
He goes and seeks the one lost sheep,
And brings His wanderer home;
And every soul that sheep might be:
Come then, my Lord, and gather me,
My Jesus, quickly come!

15 *Pembroke*, No. 282. 8 8.6. D.

Tired with the greatness of my way,
From Him I would no longer stray,
But rest in Jesus have;
Weary of sin, from sin would cease,
Weary of mine own righteousness,
And stoop, myself to save.

Weary of passions unsubdued,
Weary of vows in vain renewed,
Of forms without the power,
Of prayers, and hopes, complaints, and groans,
My fainting soul in silence owns
I can hold out no more.

16 *Harwich*, No. 66. 5 5 11. D.

For you and for me
He prayed on the tree:
The prayer is accepted, the sinner is free.
That sinner am I,
Who on Jesus rely,
And come for the pardon God cannot deny.

My pardon I claim:
For a sinner I am,
A sinner believing in Jesus's name.
He purchased the grace
Which now I embrace:
O Father, Thou know'st He hath died in my place.

17 *Christus*, No. 288. 7 7.7 7.

There for me the Saviour stands;
Shows His wounds and spreads His hands;
God is love! I know, I feel;
Jesus lives, and loves me still.

18 *Sawley*, A.T. No. 9. C.M.

Thou canst o'ercome this heart of mine,
Thou wilt victorious prove,
For everlasting strength is Thine,
And everlasting love.

19 *Cambridge*, No. 578. S.M.

Grant me my sins to feel,
And then the load remove;
Wound, and pour in my wounds to heal,
The balm of pardoning love.

20 *Benevento*, No. 876. 7 7.7 7. D.

Jesus, mighty to renew,
Work in me to will and do;
Turn my nature's rapid tide,
Stem the torrent of my pride,
Stop the whirlwind of my will,
Speak, and bid the sun stand still;
Now Thy love almighty show,
Make ev'n me a creature new.

21 *Harwich*, No. 406. 5 5 11. D.

My soul, don't delay,
Christ calls thee away.
Rise! Follow thy Saviour, and bless the glad day!
No mortal can know
What He can bestow;
What peace, love and comfort: Go after Him, go!

22 *Shirland*, No. 341. S.M.

And can I yet delay
My little all to give?
To tear my soul from earth away,
For Jesus to receive?

Nay, but I yield, I yield!
I can hold out no more,
I sink, by dying love compelled,
And own Thee conqueror.

23 *Melcombe*, No. 927. L.M.

Stay, Thou insulted Spirit, stay,
Though I have done Thee such despite,
Nor cast the sinner quite away,
Nor take Thine everlasting flight.

24 *Tottenham*, No. 383. C.M.

Faith, mighty faith, the promise sees,
And looks to that alone;
Laughs at impossibilities,
And cries: It shall be done!

25 *Irish*, No. 503. C.M.

That mighty faith on me bestow
Which cannot ask in vain,
Which holds, and will not let Thee go,
Till I my suit obtain.

26 *Farrant*, No. 539. C.M.

I will accept His offer now,
From every sin depart,
Perform my oft repeated vow,
And render Him my heart.

27 *Job*, A.T. No. 14. L.M.

Take my poor heart, and let it be
For ever closed to all but Thee;
Seal Thou my breast, and let me wear
That pledge of love for ever there.

28 *Vigil*, A.T. No. 4. S.M.

What shall I do to keep
The blessèd hope I feel?
Still let me pray, and watch, and weep,
And serve Thy pleasure still.

29 *St. Cross*, No. 187. L.M.

Remember, Lord, my sins no more,
That them I may no more forget;
But, sunk in guiltless shame, adore
With speechless wonder at Thy feet.

O'erwhelmed with Thy stupendous grace,
I shall not in Thy presence move,
But breathe unutterable praise,
And rapturous awe, and silent love.

30 *Leamington*, No. 465. 7.6.7.6.7.7.7.6.

Lord, my time is in Thy hand,
My soul to Thee convert;
Thou canst make me understand,
Though I am slow of heart;
Thine in whom I live and move,
Thine the work, the praise is Thine;
Thou art wisdom, power, and love,
And all Thou art is mine.

31 *Jeshurun*, No. 68. 7.6.7.6.7.7.7.6.

Give me the enlarged desire,
And open, Lord, my soul,
Thy own fullness to require,
And comprehend the whole:
Stretch my faith's capacity
Wider, and yet wider still;
Then with all that is in Thee
My soul for ever fill!

32 *Belmont*, No. 766. C.M.

When Jesus makes my heart His home,
My sin shall all depart;
And lo, He saith: I quickly come,
To fill and rule thy heart.

Be it according to Thy word!
Redeem me from all sin;
My heart would now receive Thee, Lord,
Come in, my Lord, come in!

33 *Arnold's*, No. 762. C.M.

O that the perfect grace were given,
The love diffused abroad!
O that our hearts were all a heaven,
For ever filled with God!

34 *Dundee* (*French*), No. 749. C.M.

Deepen the wound Thy hands have made
In this weak, helpless soul;
Till mercy, with its kindly aid,
Descends to make me whole.

The sharpness of Thy two-edged sword
Enable me to endure;
Till bold to say: My hallowing Lord
Hath wrought a perfect cure!

35 *Sawley*, A.T. No. 9. C.M.

Scatter the last remains of sin,
And seal me Thine abode;
O make me glorious all within,
A temple built by God!

36 *Eden*, No. 449. L.M.

Now let me gain perfection's height,
Now let me into nothing fall,
Be less than nothing in Thy sight,
And feel that Christ is all in all.

37 *Farrant*, No. 539. C.M.

When God is mine, and I am His,
Of paradise possest,
I taste unutterable bliss,
And everlasting rest.

38 *Monmouth*, No. 428. 8 8.6. D.

How shall I thank Thee for the grace,
The trust I have to see Thy face,
When sin shall all be purged away!
The night of doubts and fears is past;
The morning star appears at last,
And I shall see the perfect day.

39 *Bedford*, No. 155. C.M.

Be it according to Thy word;
This moment let it be!
The life I lose for Thee, my Lord,
I find again in Thee.

40 *Attercliffe*, No. 603. C.M.

'Tis done! Thou dost this moment save,
With full salvation bless;
Redemption through Thy blood I have,
And spotless love and peace.

41 *Hanover*, No. 8. 10 10.11 11.

I wrestle not now, but trample on sin,
For with me art Thou, and shalt be within;
While stronger and stronger in Jesus's power,
I go on to conquer, till sin is no more.

42 *Amsterdam*, No. 17. 7.6.7.6.7.8.7.6.

Make our earthly souls a field
Which God delights to bless;
Let us in due season yield
The fruits of righteousness;
Make us trees of paradise,
Which more and more Thy praise may show,
Deeper sink, and higher rise,
And to perfection grow.

43 *Tichfield*, No. 571. 7 7.7 7. D.

Build us in one body up,
Called in one high calling's hope:
One the Spirit whom we claim,
One the pure baptismal flame,
One the faith, and common Lord,
One the Father lives adored,
Over, through, and in us all,
God incomprehensible.

44 *Abridge*, No. 550. C.M.

Touched by the loadstone of Thy love,
Let all our hearts agree,
And ever toward each other move,
And ever move toward Thee.

45 *Worsley*, No. 270. 8 8.8 8.8 8.

A spark of that ethereal fire,
Still let it to its source aspire,
To Thee in every wish return,
Intensely for Thy glory burn;
While all our souls fly up to Thee,
And blaze through all eternity.

46 *Derbe*, No. 262. 5 5.5 11. D.

Then let us attend
Our heavenly Friend,
In His members distressed,
By want, or affliction, or sickness oppressed:
The prisoner relieve,
The stranger receive,
Supply all their wants,
And spend and be spent in assisting His saints.

47 *Marylebone*, A.T. No. 32. 8 8.8 8.8 8.

In age and feebleness extreme,
Who shall a helpless worm redeem?
Jesus! my only hope Thou art,
Strength of my failing flesh and heart;
O could I catch one smile from Thee,
And drop into eternity!

48 *Derbe*, No. 956. 5 5.5 11.

O that each in the day
Of His coming may say:
I have fought my way through,
I have finished the work Thou didst give me to do!

O that each from his Lord
May receive the glad word:
Well and faithfully done;
Enter into My joy, and sit down on My throne!

49 *Franconia*, No. 507. S.M.

This blessèd word be mine,
Just as the port is gained:
Kept by the power of grace divine,
I have the faith maintained.

50 *Hungerford*, No. 407. 5 6.9.6 6.9.

Who on earth can conceive
How happy we live,
In the palace of God, the great King?
What a concert of praise,
When our Jesus's grace
The whole heavenly company sing!

Additional Tunes

Additional Tunes

4

VIGIL. S.M. T. BAIRSTOW, 1840.

5

COVENANTERS. C.M. American Melody.

LLOYD. C.M. *See* No. 29.

6

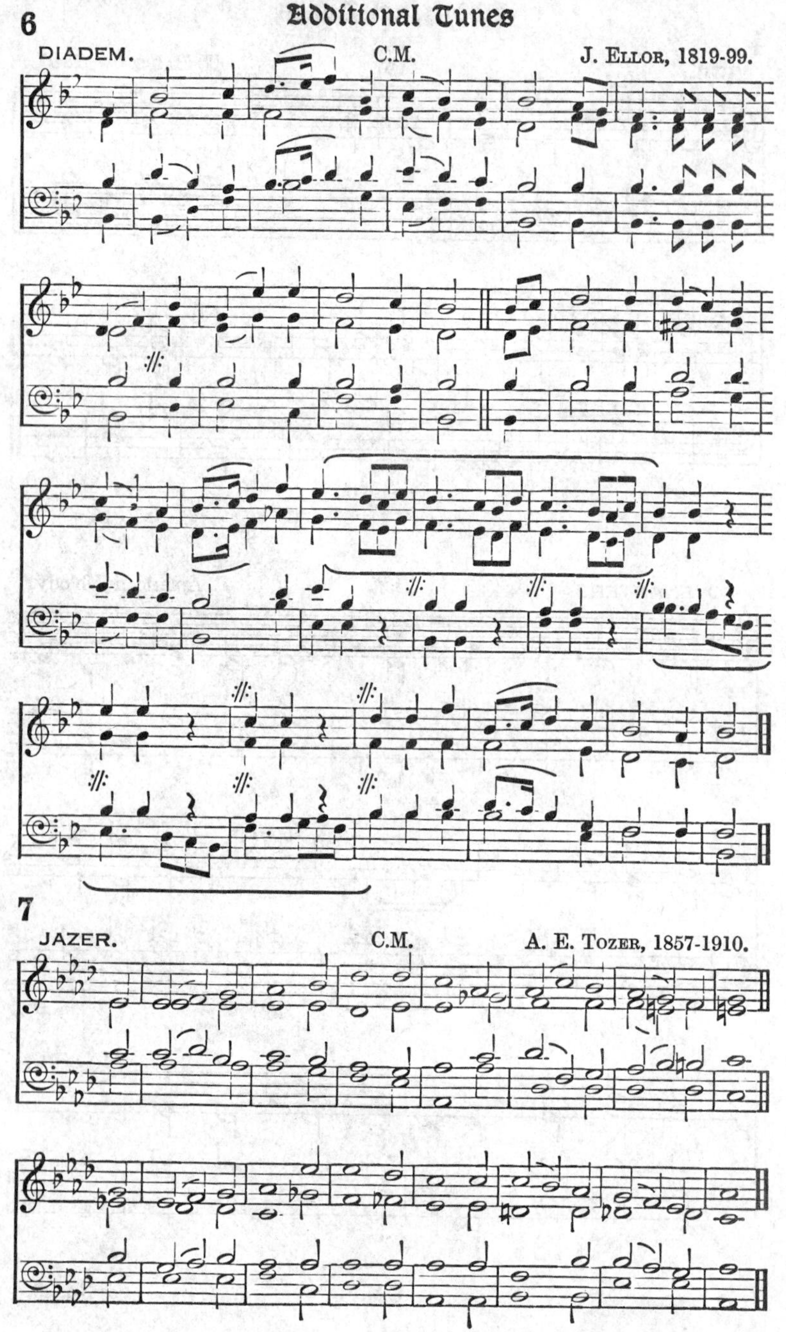
DIADEM.
C.M.
J. ELLOR, 1819-99.
7
JAZER.
C.M.
A. E. TOZER, 1857-1910.

8
LYNGHAM. C.M. T. JARMAN, 1776-1861.
9
SAWLEY. C.M. J. WALCH, 1837-1901.

10

CASTLE RISING.
D.C.M.
F. A. J. Hervey, 1846-1910.
By permission of Novello and Company, Limited.
11
NORSEMAN.
D.C.M.
Norse Air.

12
ATHLONE.
L.M.
T. O'CAROLAN, 1670-1738.
13
L.M.
CASTLE STREET (LUTHER'S CHANT).
H. C. ZEUNER, 1795-1857.

14

JOB.
L.M.
W. Arnold, 1768-1832.
15
RIMINGTON.
L.M.
F. Duckworth, 1862-1941

Additional Tunes

Additional Tunes

21

BULLINGER. 8.5.8.3. E. W. BULLINGER, 1837-1913.

22

SACRED REST. 8.5.8.3. J. B. BIRKBECK, 1831-1917.

Additional Tunes

23

REST. 8.6.8.8.6. F. C. MAKER, 1844-1927.

24

GRACE (*Hymn* 315). 8.7.8.7.4.7. Traditional.

Additional Tunes

25

LEIPSIC. 8.7.8.7.4.7. French *Psalter*, 1565.

26

ROUSSEAU. 8.7.8.7.4.7. J. J. Rousseau, 1712-78.

Additional Tunes

Note.—There is strong reason to believe that this is the tune sung by John Wesley on the night of his conversion, May 24, 1738. He subsequently inserted it in his 'Foundery' Collection of Tunes.

Additional Tunes

29

LLOYD. C.M. C. HOWARD, 1856-1927.

Copyright, John T. Park, Stainland.

30

WONDERFUL LOVE (2). 10.4.10.7.4.10. A. WATSON, 1845-1912.

By permission of J. Curwen & Sons, Ltd.

31
EPIPHANY (HOPKINS).
11.10.11.10.
E. J. Hopkins, 1818-1901.
32
MARYLEBONE.
8 8.8 8.8 8.
C. H. H. Parry, 1848-1918.
p
In age and fee - bleness ex - treme,
fee-ble-ness ex - treme,
Who shall a
help - less worm re - deem?
cresc.
Je - sus, my on - ly
hope Thou art, Strength of my fail - ing flesh and heart;
dim.

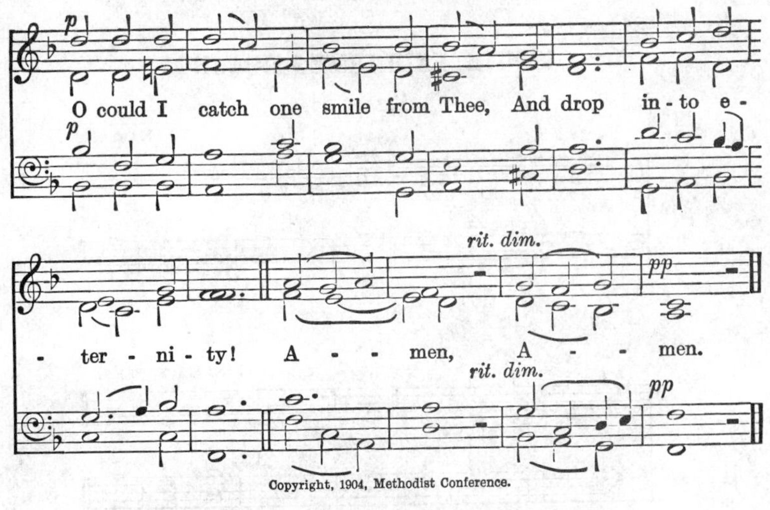
O could I catch one smile from Thee, And drop in - to e - ter - ni - ty! A - - - men, A - - - men.
rit. dim.
pp
Copyright, 1904, Methodist Conference.

ANCIENT HYMNS, CANTICLES AND PSALMS

EXPLANATORY NOTE

The Ancient Hymns, Canticles and Psalms have been pointed on the principles of speech rhythm, in so far as the limitations of the Anglican Chant will permit. Where this system has not been in use, the following particulars will be of service.

The music chosen comprises the ordinary single and double section Chants found in any modern Psalter.

Each verse, except where bracketed, is divided into halves, separated by a double stop (:), represented in the Chant by a double bar. The bar lines in the words and music correspond. No punctuation mark is to be observed except in those verses with a long reciting note where the proper pause is indicated by a breath mark (v).

A bracket ([) indicates lines or verses intended to be sung to a single section.

Where more than two words or syllables occur in any one bar, the correct method of sub-division will be found by reciting the verse aloud.

The Chants set have been selected mainly for their adaptability, but any others may be substituted, although it will be recognized that those which contain crotchets will be difficult to fit into a free rhythm.

It cannot be sufficiently stressed that in order to obtain good psalm-singing, regular practice is essential both for choir and congregation.

Ancient Hymns and Canticles

1

VENITE, EXULTEMUS DOMINO

PSALM 95.

A

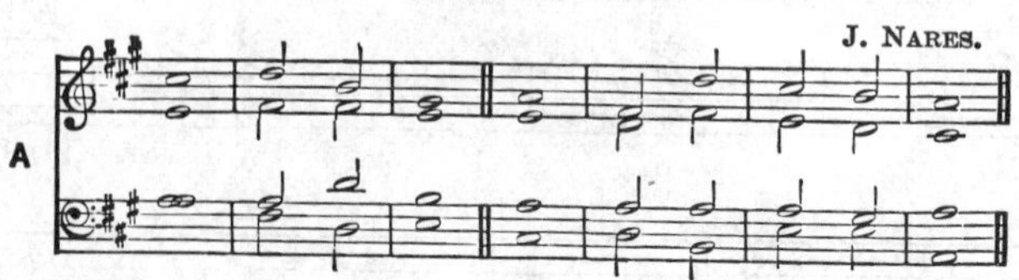

B

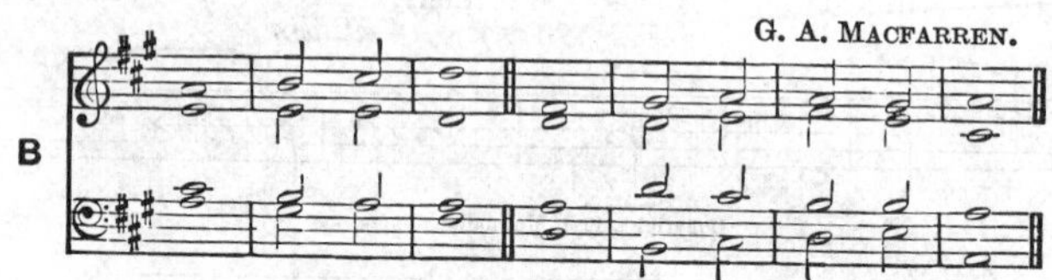

C

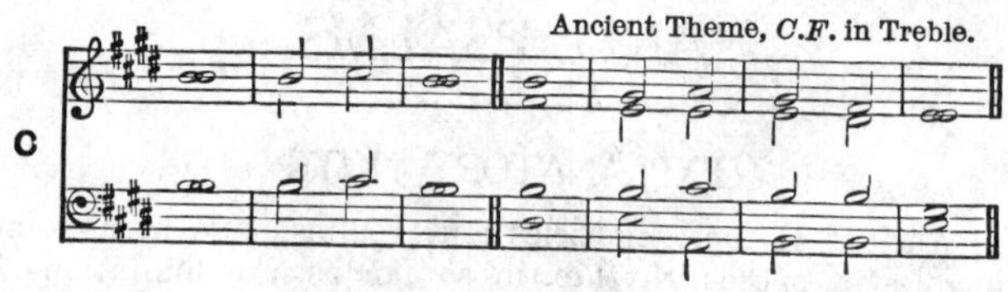

D

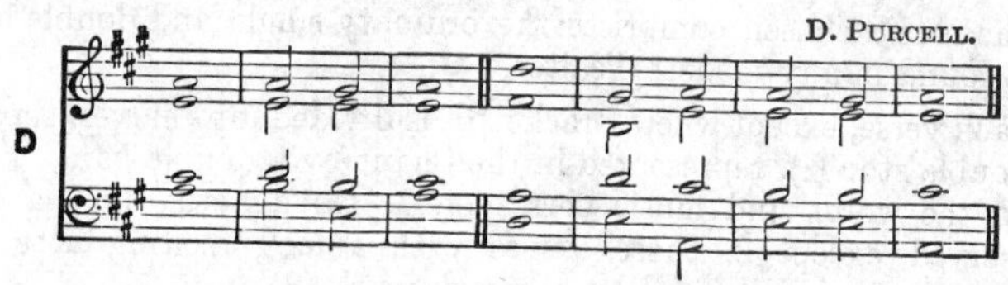

E

1 O COME, let us | sing unto the | Lord : let us heartily rejoice in the | strength of | our sal- | vation.

2 Let us come before His | presence with | thanksgiving : and show ourselves | glad in | Him with | psalms.

3 For the | Lord is a | great God : and a great | King a- | bove all | gods.

4 In His hand are all the corners | of the | earth : and the | strength of the | hills is His | also.

5 The sea is | His, and He | made it : and His | hands pre- | pared the dry | land.

6 O come, let us | worship, and fall | down : and kneel be- | fore the | Lord our | Maker.

7 For He is the | Lord our | God : and we are the people of His | pasture, and the | sheep of His | hand.

8 To-day if ye will hear His voice,ᵛ harden | not your | hearts : as in the provocation,ᵛ and as in the day of temp- | tation | in the | wilderness ;

9 When your fathers | tempted | Me : proved | Me, and | saw My | works.

10 Forty years long was I grieved with this gener- | ation, and | said : It is a people that do err in their hearts,ᵛ for they | have not | known My | ways.

11 Unto whom I | sware in My | wrath : that they should not | enter | into My | rest.

Glory be to the Father, | and to the | Son : and | to the | Holy | Ghost ;
As it was in the beginning,ᵛ is now, and | ever | shall be : world | without | end. A- | men.

2

TE DEUM LAUDAMUS

FIRST SETTING.

1 WE praise | Thee, O | God : we acknowledge | Thee to | be the | Lord.

2 All the | earth doth | worship Thee : the | Father | ever- | lasting.

3 To Thee all angels | cry a- | loud : the heavens, and | all the | powers there- | in.

4 To Thee | cherubin, and | seraphin : con- | tinual- | ly do | cry,

5 Holy, | holy, | holy : Lord | God of | Saba- | oth ;

6 Heaven and | earth are | full : of the | majesty | of Thy | glory.

[7 The glorious company of the a- | postles | praise Thee :
8 The goodly fellowship | of the | prophets | praise Thee.

[9 The noble army of | martyrs | praise Thee :
10 The holy Church throughout | all the | world doth ac- | knowledge Thee ;

11 The | Fa- | ther : of an | infinite | majes- | ty ;

[12 Thine honourable, true and | only | Son :
13 Also the | Holy | Ghost the | Comforter.

Change

[14 Thou art the King of | Glory O | Christ :
15 Thou art the ever- | lasting | Son of the | Father.

16 When Thou tookest upon Thee to de- | liver | man : Thou didst not ab- | hor the | Virgin's | womb.

17 When Thou hadst overcome the | sharpness of | death : Thou didst open the Kingdom of | Heaven to | all be- | lievers.

18 Thou sittest at the right | hand of | God : in the | glory | of the | Father.

[19 We believe that Thou shalt come to | be our | Judge :
20 We therefore pray Thee, help Thy servants,ᵛ whom Thou hast re- | deemed with Thy | precious | blood.

21 Make them to be numbered | with Thy | saints : in | glory | ever- | lasting.

Change

[22 O Lord, save Thy people and | bless Thine | heritage :
23 Govern them and | lift them | up for | ever.

[24 Day by day we | magnify | Thee :
25 And we worship Thy | name ever | world without | end.

[26 Vouchsafe, O Lord to keep us this | day without | sin :
27 O Lord, have mercy up- | on us have | mercy up- | on us.

[28 O Lord, let Thy mercy lighten upon us as our | trust is in | Thee :
29 O Lord, in Thee have I trusted,ᵛ let me | never | be con- | founded.

2 TE DEUM LAUDAMUS

THIRD SETTING.
S. WESLEY.
J. GOSS.
J. TURLE.
FOURTH SETTING.
J. STAINER.
Copyright, 1899, by Novello and Company, Limited.
S. MATTHEWS.
G. C. MARTIN.
Copyright, 1909, by Novello and Company, Limited.

1 WE praise | Thee, O | God : we acknowledge | Thee to | be the | Lord.

2 All the | earth doth | worship Thee : the | Father | ever- | lasting.

3 To Thee all angels | cry a- | loud : the heavens, and | all the | powers there- | in.

4 To Thee | cherubin, and | seraphin : con- | tinual- | ly do | cry,

5 Holy, | holy, | holy : Lord | God of | Saba- | oth ;

6 Heaven and | earth are | full : of the | majesty | of Thy | glory.

[7 The glorious company of the a- | postles | praise Thee :
8 The goodly fellowship | of the | prophets | praise Thee.

[9 The noble army of | martyrs | praise Thee :
10 The holy Church throughout | all the | world doth ac- | knowledge Thee ;

11 The | Fa- | ther : of an | infinite | majes- | ty ;

[12 Thine honourable, true and | only | Son :
13 Also the | Holy | Ghost the | Comforter.

Change

[14 Thou art the King of | Glory O | Christ :
15 Thou art the ever- | lasting | Son of the | Father.

16 When Thou tookest upon Thee to de- | liver | man : Thou didst not ab- | hor the | Virgin's | womb.

17 When Thou hadst overcome the | sharpness of | death : Thou didst open the Kingdom of | Heaven to | all be- | lievers.

18 Thou sittest at the right | hand of | God : in the | glory | of the | Father.

[19 We believe that Thou shalt come to | be our | Judge :
20 We therefore pray Thee, help Thy servants,ᵛ whom Thou hast re- | deemed with Thy | precious | blood.

21 Make them to be numbered | with Thy | saints : in | glory | ever- | lasting.

Change

[22 O Lord, save Thy people and | bless Thine | heritage :
23 Govern them and | lift them | up for | ever.

[24 Day by day we | magnify | Thee :
25 And we worship Thy | name ever | world without | end.

[26 Vouchsafe, O Lord to keep us this | day without | sin :
27 O Lord, have mercy up- | on us have | mercy up- | on us.

[28 O Lord, let Thy mercy lighten upon us as our | trust is in | Thee :
29 O Lord, in Thee have I trusted,ᵛ let me | never | be con- | founded.

3 BENEDICITE, OMNIA OPERA

G. F. BROCKLESS.

Verse 7.
Yea, let it
GLORIA.
Glory be to the Father, and to the Son: and to the Ho - ly Ghost;
As it was in the beginning, is now and ev - er shall be: World with-out end. A - men.

1 O ALL ye works of the Lord, | bless ye the | Lord : | Praise Him, and | magnify | Him for | ever.

2 O ye angels of the Lord, | bless ye the | Lord : | Praise Him, and | magnify | Him for | ever.

3 O ye heavens, | bless ye the | Lord : | Praise Him, and | magnify | Him for | ever.

4 O ye sun, moon and stars | bless ye the | Lord : | Praise Him, and | magnify | Him for | ever.

5 O ye winter and summer, | bless ye the | Lord : | Praise Him, and | magnify | Him for | ever.

6 O ye nights and days, | bless ye the | Lord : | Praise Him, and | magnify | Him for | ever.

7 O let the earth | bless the | Lord : Yea, let it | praise Him, and | magnify | Him for | ever.

8 O ye seas and floods, | bless ye the | Lord : | Praise Him, and | magnify | Him for | ever.

9 O all ye that move in the waters, | bless ye the | Lord : | Praise Him, and | magnify | Him for | ever.

10 O ye fowls of the air, | bless ye the | Lord : | Praise Him, and | magnify | Him for | ever.

11 O ye beasts and cattle, | bless ye the | Lord : | Praise Him, and | magnify | Him for | ever.

12 O ye children of men, | bless ye the | Lord : | Praise Him, and | magnify | Him for | ever.

13 O ye servants of the Lord, | bless ye the | Lord : | Praise Him, and | magnify | Him for | ever.

14 O ye souls of the righteous, | bless ye the | Lord : | Praise Him, and | magnify | Him for | ever.

15 O ye holy and humble men of heart, | bless ye the | Lord : | Praise Him, and | magnify | Him for | ever.

GLORIA.

4 CANTEMUS CUNCTI

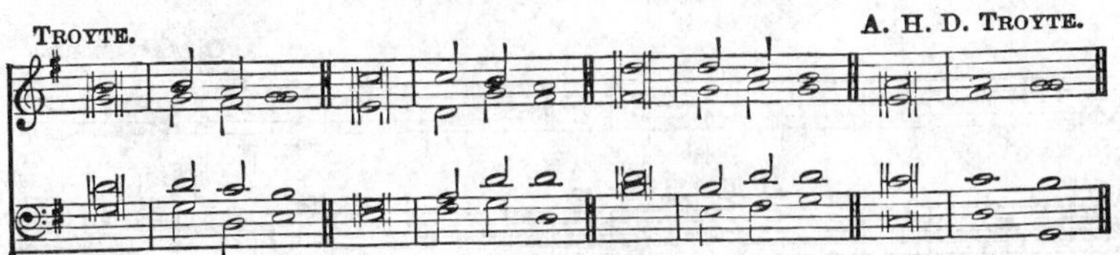

1 THE strain upraise of joy and praise, Halle- | lujah. | To the glory of their King, shall the ransomed | people sing | Halle- | lujah, | Halle- | lujah.

2 And the choirs that | dwell on high | shall re-echo | through the sky | Halle- | lujah, | Halle- | lujah.

3 They in the rest of para- | dise who dwell, | the blessèd ones, with joy the | chorus swell, | Halle- | lujah, | Halle- | lujah.

4 The planets beaming on their | heavenly way, | the shining constellations | join, and say | Halle- | lujah, | Halle- | lujah.

5 Ye clouds that onward sweep, ye winds on | pinions light, | ye thunders, echoing loud and deep, ye lightnings | wildly bright, | in sweet con- | sent unite | your Halle- | lujah.

6 Ye floods and ocean billows, ye storms and | winter snow, | ye days of cloudless beauty, hoar-frost and | summer glow, | ye groves that wave in spring, and glorious | forests, sing | Halle- | lujah.

7 First let the birds, with painted | plumage gay, | exalt their great Creator's | praise, and say | Halle- | lujah, | Halle- | lujah.

8 Then let the beasts of earth, with | varying strain, | join in creation's hymn, and | cry again | Halle- | lujah, | Halle- | lujah.

9 Here let the mountains thunder forth son- | orous | Halle- | lujah. | There let the valleys sing in gentler | chorus | Halle- | lujah.

10 Thou jubilant abyss of | ocean, cry | Halle- | lujah. | Ye tracts of earth and conti- | nents, reply | Halle- | lujah.

11 To God, who all cre- | ation made, | the frequent hymn be | duly paid : | Halle- | lujah, | Halle- | lujah.

12 This is the strain, the eternal strain, the Lord Al- | mighty loves : | Halle- | lujah. | This is the song, the heavenly song, that Christ the | King approves : | Halle- | lujah.

13 Wherefore we sing, both heart and voice a- | waking, | Halle- | lujah. | And children's voices echo, answer | making, | Halle- | lujah.

14 Now from all men | be outpoured | Hallelujah | to the Lord ; | with Hallelujah | evermore | the Son and Spirit | we adore.

15 Praise be done to the | Three in One, | Halle- | lujah ! | Halle- | lujah ! | Halle- | lujah !

5

BENEDICTUS

LUKE 1. 68—79.

A

A. C. MACKENZIE.

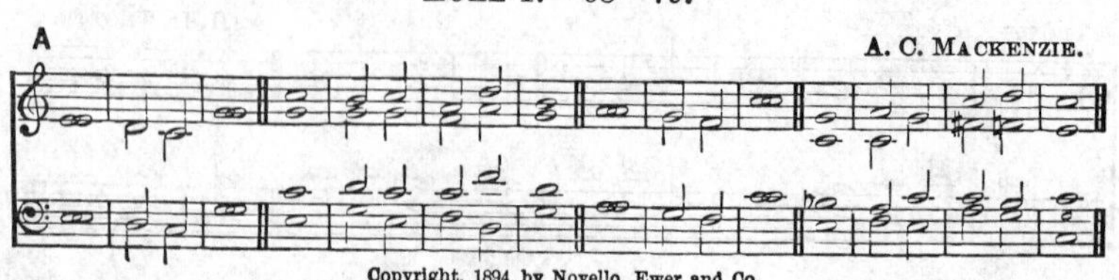

B

G. M. GARRETT.

C

W. GLOVER.

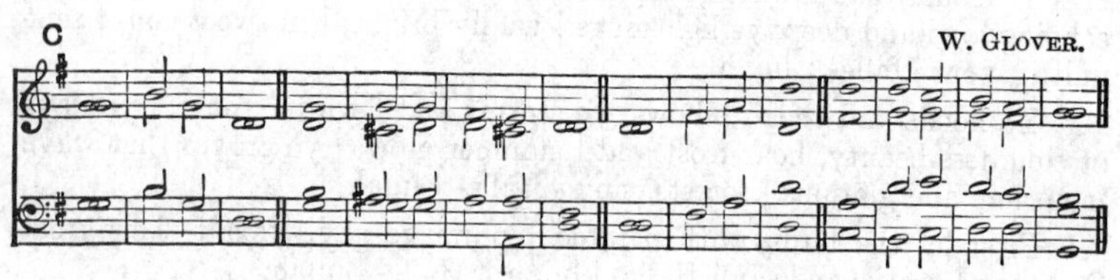

D

E. ELGAR.

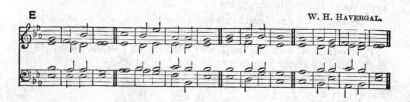

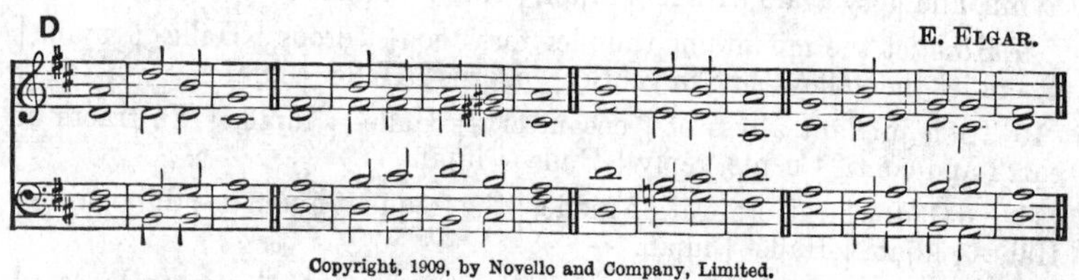

E

W. H. HAVERGAL.

1 BLESSÈD be the Lord | God of | Israel : for He hath visited, | and re- | deemed His | people ;

2 And hath raised up a mighty sal- | vation | for us : in the | house of His | servant | David ;

3 As He spake by the mouth of His | holy | prophets : which have been | since the | world be- | gan ;

4 That we should be | saved from our | enemies : and from the | hands of | all that | hate us ;

5 To perform the mercy promised to our forefathers,ᵛ and to remember His | holy | Covenant :

6 To perform the oath which He sware to our forefather | Abraham that | He would | give us ;

7 That we being delivered out of the hand of our enemies,ᵛ might serve | Him without | fear :

8 In holiness and righteousness before Him | all the | days of our | life.

9 And thou, child, shalt be called the | Prophet of the | Highest : for thou shalt go before the face of the | Lord to pre- | pare His | ways ;

10 To give knowledge of salvation | unto His | people : for the re- | mission | of their | sins,

11 Through the tender | mercy of our | God : whereby the day-spring from on | high hath | visited | us ;

12 To give light to them that sit in darkness,ᵛ and in the | shadow of | death : and to guide our feet | into the | way of | peace.

GLORIA.

6 JUBILATE DEO

Psalm 100.

G. J. Elvey.

A

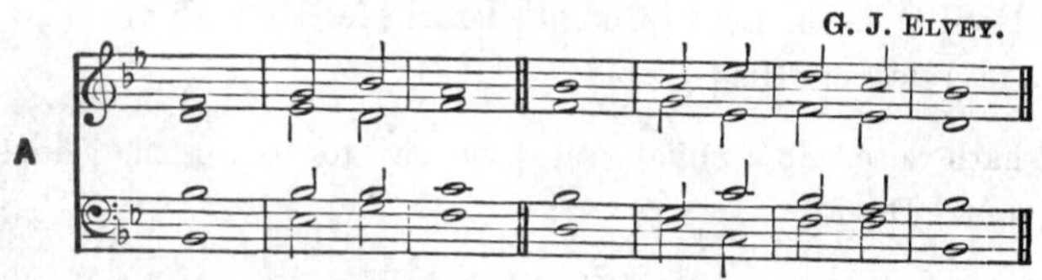

J. Battishill.

B

G. M. Garrett.

C

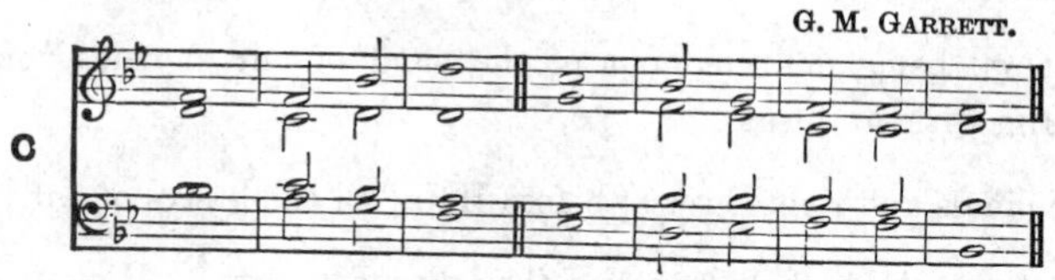

R. Woodward.

D

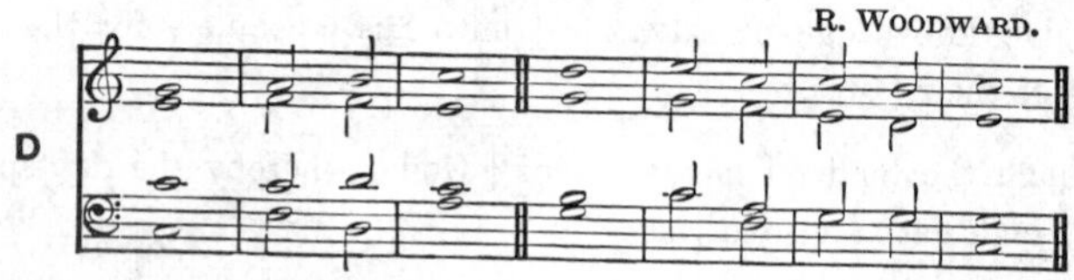

G. J. Elvey.

E

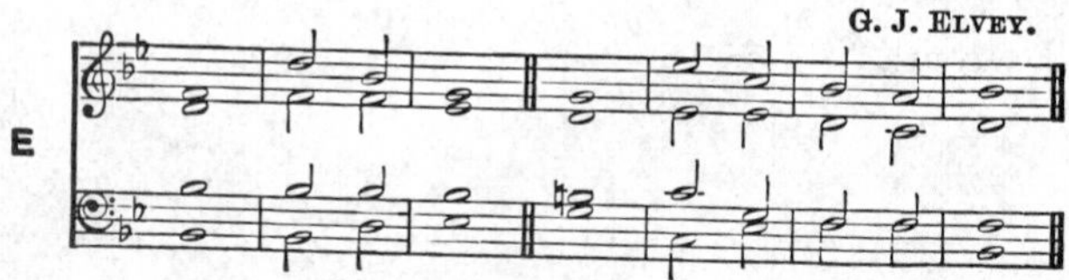

1 O BE joyful in the | Lord, all ye | lands : serve the Lord with gladness,ᵛ and come before His | presence | with a | song.

2 Be ye sure that the | Lord He is | God : it is He that hath made us, and not we ourselves ;ᵛ we are His | people, and the | sheep of His | pasture.

3 O go your way into His gates with thanksgiving,ᵛ and into His | courts with | praise : be thankful unto | Him, and speak | good of His | name.

4 For the Lord is gracious,ᵛ His mercy is | ever- | lasting : and His truth endureth from gener- | ation to | gener- | ation.

GLORIA.

7 MAGNIFICAT

LUKE 1. 46—55.

A J. ROBINSON.

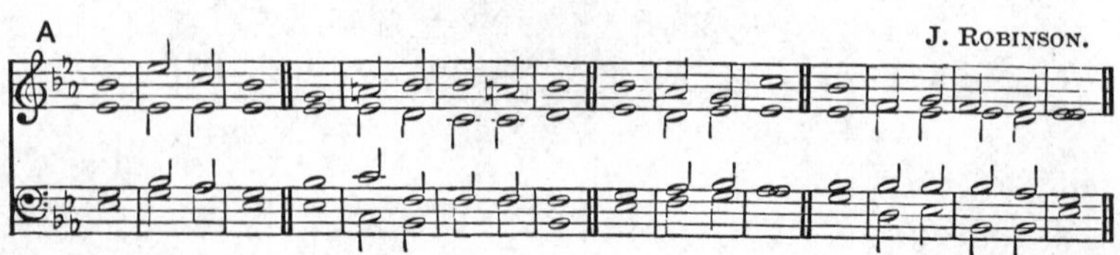

B S. WESLEY.

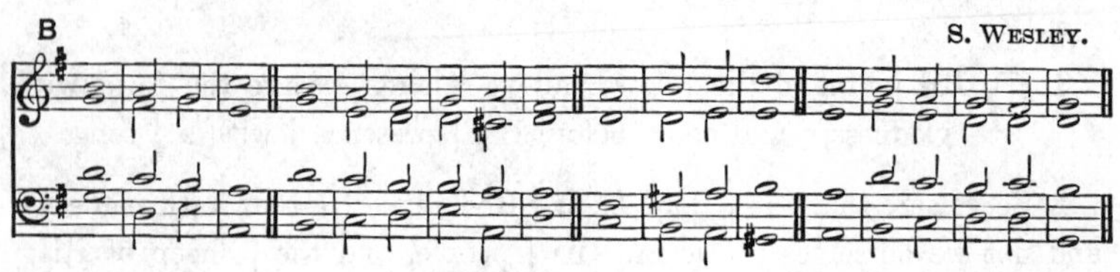

C G. COOPER.

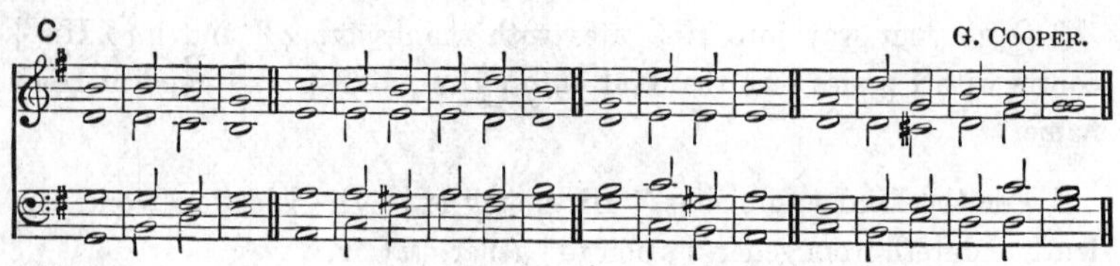

D T. A. WALMISLEY.

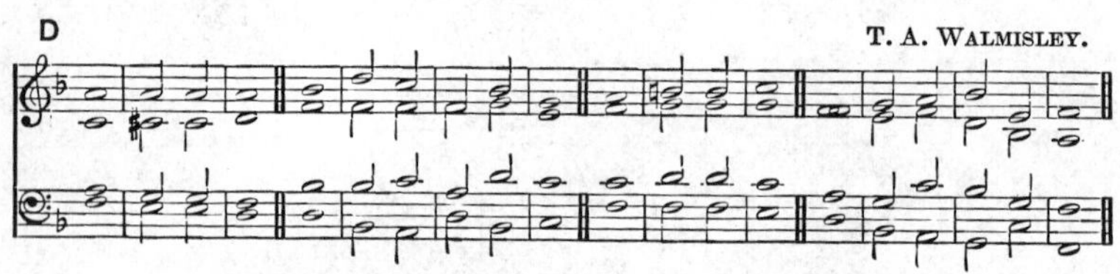

E W. WOLSTENHOLME.

1 MY soul doth | magnify the | Lord : and my spirit hath re- | joiced in | God my | Saviour.

2 For | He hath re- | garded : the | lowliness | of His | hand-maiden.

3 For be- | hold, from | henceforth : all gener- | ations shall | call me | blessèd.

4 For He that is mighty hath | magnified | me : and | holy | is His | name.

5 And His mercy is on | them that | fear Him : through- | out all | gener- | ations.

6 He hath showed | strength with His | arm : He hath scattered the proud in the imagin- | ation | of their | hearts.

7 He hath put down the mighty | from their | seat : and hath ex- | alted the | humble and | meek.

8 He hath filled the | hungry with | good things : and the rich He | hath sent | empty a- | way.

9 He re- | membering His | mercy : hath | holpen His | servant | Israel.

10 As He promised | to our | forefathers : Abraham | and his | seed, for | ever.

GLORIA.

8 CANTATE DOMINO

PSALM 98.

E. G. MONK.

A

G. J. ELVEY.

B

J. JONES.

C

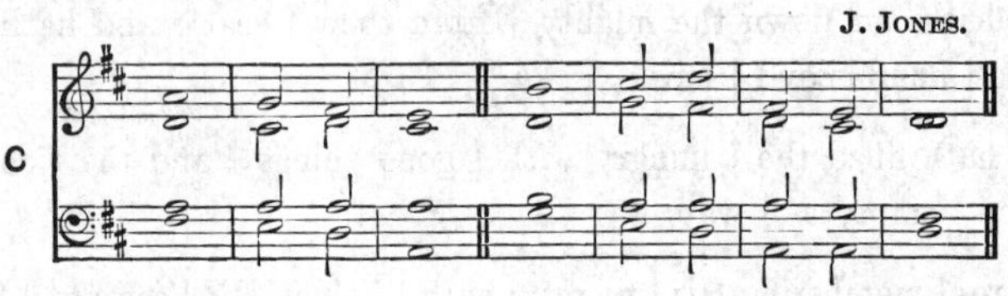

J. STAINER.

D

1 O SING unto the | Lord a new | song : for | He hath done | marvellous | things.

2 With His own right hand, and with His | holy | arm : hath He | gotten Him- | self the | victory.

3 The Lord declared | His sal- | vation : His righteousness hath He openly | showed in the | sight of the | heathen.

4 He hath remembered His mercy and truth toward the | house of | Israel : and all the ends of the world have | seen the sal- | vation of our | God.

5 Show yourselves joyful unto the Lord, all ye lands,ᵛ sing, re- | joice, and give | thanks.

6 Praise the Lord upon the harp :ᵛ sing to the | harp with a | psalm of | thanksgiving.

7 With trumpets | also and | shawms : O show yourselves joyful be- | fore the | Lord the | King.

8 Let the sea make a noise, and all that | therein | is : the round world, and | they that | dwell there- | in.

9 Let the floods | clap their | hands : and let the hills be joyful to- | gether be- | fore the | Lord.

For He cometh to | judge the | earth :

10 With righteousness shall He judge the | world and the | people with | equity.

GLORIA.

9 DEUS MISEREATUR

PSALM 67.

J. NARES.

A

J. BARNBY.

B

By permission of Novello and Company, Limited.

W. LEE.

C

P. HAYES.

D

Parisian Tone.

E

1 GOD be merciful unto | us, and | bless us : and show us the light of His countenance,ᵛ and be | merciful | unto | us.

2 That Thy way may be | known upon | earth : Thy saving | health a- | mong all | nations.

3 Let the people praise | Thee, O | God : yea, let | all the | people | praise Thee.

4 O let the nations re- | joice and be | glad : for Thou shalt judge the folk righteously,ᵛ and | govern the | nations upon | earth.

5 Let the people praise | Thee, O | God : yea, let | all the | people | praise Thee.

6 Then shall the earth bring | forth her | increase : and God, even our own | God, shall | give us His | blessing.

7 God | shall | bless us : and all the | ends of the | world shall | fear Him.

GLORIA.

10 NUNC DIMITTIS

LUKE 2. 29—32.

G. J. ELVEY.

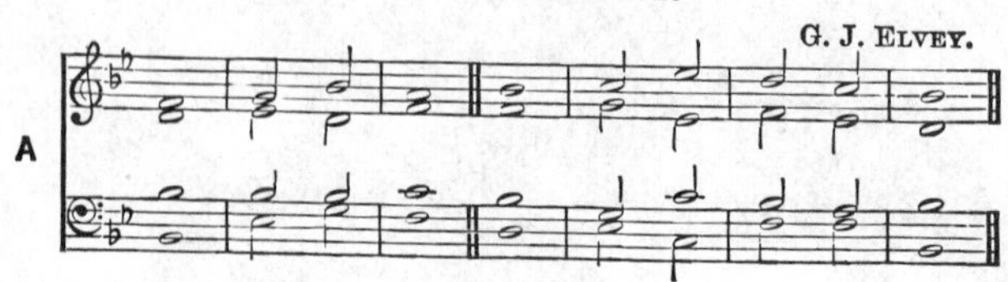

W. TURNER.

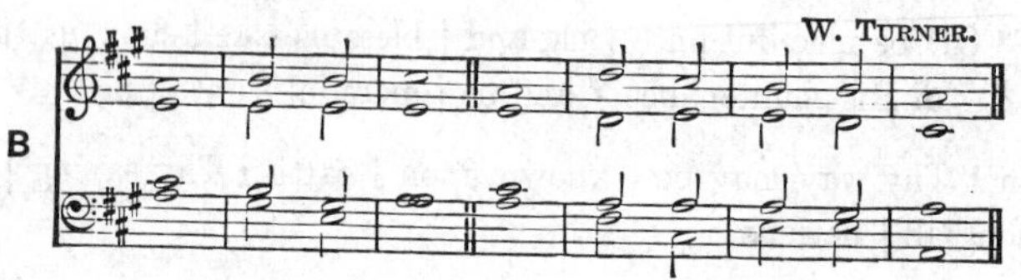

G. A. MACFARREN.

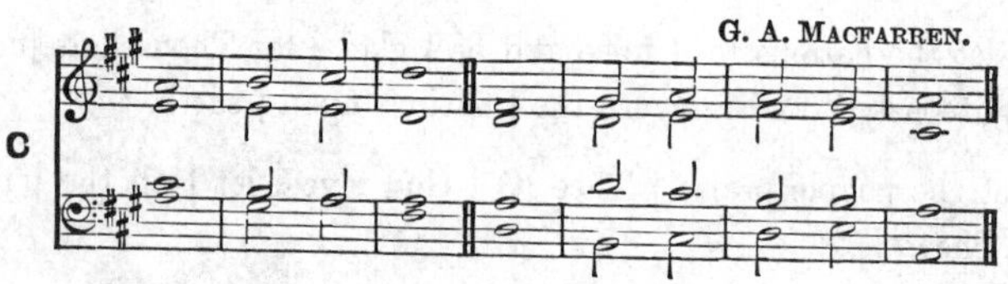

E. G. MONK.

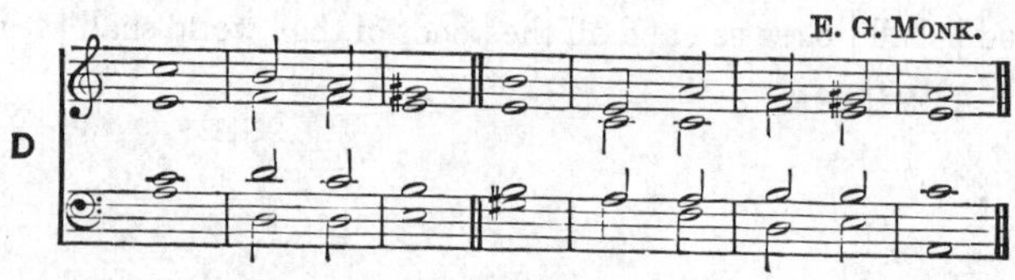

W. CROFT.

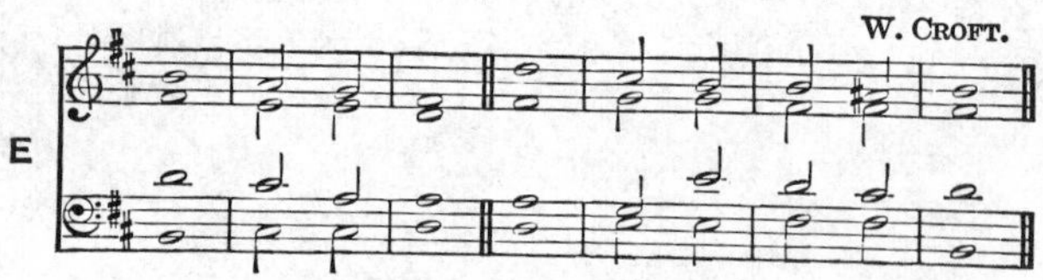

G. F. BROCKLESS.

1 LORD, now lettest Thou Thy servant de- | part in | peace : ac- | cording | to Thy | word.

2 For mine eyes have | seen Thy sal- | vation :

3 Which Thou hast prepared be- | fore the | face of all | people ;

4 To be a light to | lighten the | Gentiles : and to be the | glory of Thy | people | Israel.

GLORIA.

11 SALVATOR MUNDI

1 O SAVIOUR of the world, the Son, Lord Jesus : Stir up Thy strength and help us, we humbly beseech Thee.

2 By Thy Cross and precious blood Thou hast redeemed us : Save us and help us, we humbly beseech Thee.

3 Thou didst save Thy disciples when ready to perish : Hear us and save us, we humbly beseech Thee.

4 Let the pitifulness of Thy great mercy : Loose us from our sins, we humbly beseech Thee.

5 Make it appear that Thou art our Saviour and mighty Deliverer : O save us, that we may praise Thee, we humbly beseech Thee.

6 Draw near, according to Thy promise from the throne of Thy glory : Look down and hear our crying, we humbly beseech Thee.

7 Come again, and dwell with us, O Lord Christ Jesus : Abide with us forever, we humbly beseech Thee.

8 And when Thou shalt appear with power and great glory : May we be made like unto Thee in Thy glorious kingdom.

9 Thanks be to Thee, O Lord : Hallelujah.

AMEN.

12 SURSUM CORDA

1 LIFT up your hearts : We lift them up unto the Lord.

2 Let us give thanks unto the Lord our God : It is meet and right so to do.

3 It is very meet, right and our bounden duty : That we should at all times and in all places give thanks unto Thee, O Lord.

4 Holy Father : Almighty, Everlasting God.

5 Therefore with angels and archangels : And with all the company of heaven,

6 We laud and magnify Thy glorious name : evermore praising Thee and saying,

7 Holy, holy, holy : Lord God of hosts.

8 Heaven and earth are full of Thy gloıy : glory be to Thee O Lord most high.

AMEN.

13 GLORIA IN EXCELSIS

1 GLORY be to God on high : And in earth peace, goodwill towards men.

2 We praise Thee, we bless Thee, we worship Thee : We glorify Thee, we give thanks to Thee for Thy great glory,

3 O Lord God, heavenly King : God the Father Almighty.

4 O Lord, the only begotten Son, Jesus Christ : O Lord God, Lamb of God, Son of the Father, that takest away the sins of the world, have mercy upon us.

5 Thou that takest away the sins of the world : have mercy upon us.

6 Thou that takest away the sins of the world, receive our prayer : Thou that sittest at the right hand of God the Father, have mercy upon us.

7 For Thou only art holy : Thou only art the Lord.

8 Thou only, O Christ, with the Holy Ghost, art most high : In the glory of the Father.

AMEN.

14 AGNUS DEI

1 O LAMB of God, that takest away the sins of the world : Have mercy upon us.

2 O Lamb of God, that takest away the sins of the world : Have mercy upon us.

3 O Lamb of God, that takest away the sins of the world : Grant us Thy peace.

15

PSALM 1.

1 BLESSED is the man that walketh not in the counsel of the ungodly,ᵛ nor standeth in the | way of | sinners : nor | sitteth in the | seat of the | scornful.

2 But his delight is in the | law of the | Lord : and in His law doth he | meditate | day and | night.

3 And he shall be like a tree planted by the rivers of water,ᵛ that bringeth forth his | fruit in his | season : his leaf also shall not wither ;ᵛ and whatso- | ever he | doeth shall | prosper.

4 The un- | godly are | not so : but are like the | chaff which the | wind driveth a- | way.

5 Therefore the ungodly shall not | stand in the | judgement : nor sinners in the | congregation | of the | righteous.

6 For the Lord knoweth the | way of the | righteous : but the | way of the un- | godly shall | perish.

GLORIA.

16

PSALM 2. 1—8, 10—12.

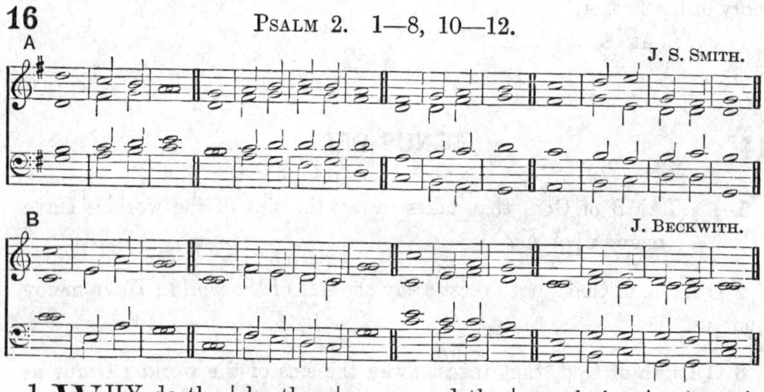

1 WHY do the | heathen | rage : and the | people im- | agine a | vain thing ?

2 The kings of the earth set themselves,ᵛ and the rulers take | counsel to- | gether : against the Lord, and a- | gainst His An- | ointed | saying,

3 Let us break their | bands a- | sunder : and | cast a- | way their | cords from us.

4 He that sitteth in the | heavens shall | laugh : the Lord shall | have them | in de- | rision.
5 Then shall He speak unto them | in His | wrath : and vex them | in His | sore dis- | pleasure.
6 Yet have I | set my | King : upon my | holy | hill of | Zion.
7 I will declare the decree,ᵛ the Lord hath | said unto | me : Thou art my Son,ᵛ this | day have | I be- | gotten thee.
8 Ask of Me, and I shall give thee the heathen for | thine in- | heritance : and the uttermost parts of the | earth for | thy pos- | session.
9 Be wise now therefore, O ye kings,ᵛ be instructed, ye | judges of the | earth :
10 Serve the Lord with | fear and re- | joice with | trembling.
11 Kiss the Son, lest He be angry,ᵛ and ye perish from the way,ᵛ when His wrath is kindled | but a | little : Blessed are all they that | put their | trust in | Him.

Gloria.

17 Psalm 5. 1—5, 7, 8, 11, 12.

1 GIVE ear to my | words, O | Lord : con- | sider my | medi- | tation.
2 Hearken unto the voice of my cry, my | King, and my | God : for | unto Thee | will I | pray.
3 My voice shalt Thou hear in the | morning, O | Lord : in the morning will I direct my prayer unto | Thee, and | will look | up.
4 For Thou art not a God that hath | pleasure in | wickedness : neither shall | evil | dwell with | Thee.
5 The foolish shall not | stand in Thy | sight : Thou | hatest all | workers of in- | iquity.
6 But as for me, I will come into Thy house in the multitude | of Thy | mercy : and in Thy fear will I worship | toward Thy | holy | temple.
7 Lead me, O Lord, in Thy righteousness be- | cause of mine | enemies : make Thy way | straight be- | fore my | face.
8 Let all those that put their trust in | Thee re- | joice : let them ever shout for joy, because Thou defendest them :ᵛ let them also that love Thy | name be | joyful in | Thee.
9 For Thou, Lord, wilt | bless the | righteous : with favour wilt Thou | compass him | as with a | shield.

Gloria.

18

PSALM 8.

1 O LORD our Lord, how excellent is Thy | name in all the | earth : who hast set Thy | glory a- | bove the | heavens.
2 Out of the mouth of babes and sucklings hast Thou ordained strength be- | cause of thine | enemies : that Thou mightest still the | enemy | and the a- | venger.
3 When I consider Thy heavens,ᵛ the | work of Thy | fingers : the moon and the | stars, which | Thou hast or- | dained ;
4 What is man, that Thou art | mindful of | him : and the son of man, | that Thou | visitest | him ?
5 For Thou hast made him a little lower | than the | angels : and hast crowned | him with | glory and | honour.
6 Thou madest him to have dominion over the | works of Thy | hands : Thou hast put | all things | under his | feet.
7 All | sheep and | oxen : yea, | and the | beasts of the | field ;
8 The fowl of the air, and the | fish of the | sea : and whatsoever passeth | through the | paths of the | seas.
9 O | Lord our | Lord : how excellent is Thy | name in | all the | earth !

GLORIA.

19

PSALM 15.

1 LORD, who shall a- | bide in Thy | tabernacle : who shall | dwell in Thy | holy | hill ?
2 He that walketh uprightly, and | worketh | righteousness : and | speaketh the | truth in his | heart.
3 He that backbiteth not with his tongue,ᵛ nor doeth | evil to his | neighbour : nor taketh up a re- | proach a- | gainst his | neighbour.
4 In whose eyes a vile person is contemned ;ᵛ but he honoureth them that | fear the | Lord : He that sweareth to his own | hurt, and | changeth | not.
5 He that putteth not out his money to usury,ᵛ nor taketh reward a- | gainst the | innocent : He that doeth these | things shall | never be | moved.

GLORIA.

20 PSALM 16.

1 PRESERVE | me, O | God : for in | Thee do I | put my | trust.
2 O my soul, thou hast said unto the Lord, | Thou art my | Lord : my goodness ex- | tendeth | not to | Thee ;
3 But to the saints that are | in the | earth : and to the excellent, in | whom is | all my de- | light.
4 Their sorrows shall be multiplied that hasten after an- | other god : their drink offerings of blood will I not offer,ᵛ nor take up their | names in- | to my | lips.
5 The Lord is the portion of mine inheritance and of my cup,ᵛ Thou main- | tainest my | lot :
6 The lines are fallen unto me in pleasant places,ᵛ yea, I | have a | goodly | heritage.
7 I will bless the Lord, who hath | given me | counsel : my reins also in- | struct me | in the | night seasons.
8 I have set the Lord | always be- | fore me : because He is at my right hand, | I shall | not be | moved.
9 Therefore my heart is glad, and my | glory re- | joiceth : my flesh | also shall | rest in | hope.
10 For Thou wilt not leave my | soul in | hell : neither wilt Thou suffer Thine | Holy One to | see cor- | ruption.
11 Thou wilt show me the | path of | life : in Thy presence is fullness of joy ;ᵛ at Thy right hand there are | pleasures for | ever- | more.

GLORIA.

21 PSALM 18. 1—19.

1 I WILL love Thee, O | Lord, my | strength :
2 The Lord is my rock, and my | fortress, and | my de- | liverer.
My God, my strength, in | whom I will | trust : my buckler, and the
horn of my sal- | vation and | my high | tower.

3 I will call upon the Lord, who is worthy | to be | praised : so shall | I be | saved from mine | enemies.

4 The sorrows of death | compassed | me : and the floods of ungodly | men made | me a- | fraid.

5 The sorrows of hell | compassed me a- | bout : the snares of | death pre- | vented | me.

6 In my distress I called upon the Lord, and cried | unto my | God : He heard my voice out of His temple,ᵛ and my cry came before Him, | even | into His | ears.

7 Then the earth | shook and | trembled : the foundations also of the hills moved and were | shaken, be- | cause He was | wroth.

8 There went up a smoke | out of His | nostrils : and fire out of His mouth devoured : | coals were | kindled | by it.

9 He bowed the heavens | also, and came | down : and | darkness was | under His | feet.

10 And He rode upon a cherub, | and did | fly : yea, He did | fly upon the | wings of the | wind.

11 He made darkness His | secret | place : His pavilion round about Him were dark waters | and thick | clouds of the | skies.

12 At the brightness that was before Him His | thick clouds | passed : hail- | stones and | coals of | fire.

13 The Lord also thundered in the heavens,ᵛ and the Highest | gave His | voice : hail- | stones and | coals of | fire.

14 Yea, He sent out His | arrows, and | scattered them : and He shot out | lightnings, | and dis- | comfited them.

15 Then the channels of waters were seen,ᵛ and the foundations of the world were discovered at Thy re- | buke, O | Lord : at the | blast of the | breath of Thy | nostrils.

16 He sent from a- | bove, He | took me : He drew me | out of | many | waters.

17 He delivered me from my strong enemy, and from | them which | hated me : for | they were too | strong for | me.

18 They prevented me in the day of my calamity,ᵛ but the | Lord was my | stay.

19 He brought me forth also into a large place,ᵛ He delivered me, be- | cause He de- | lighted in | me.

GLORIA.

22 PSALM 18. 25—32, 35.

1 WITH the merciful Thou wilt | show Thyself | merciful : with an upright man | Thou wilt | show Thyself | upright ;

2 With the pure Thou wilt | show Thyself | pure : and with the froward | Thou wilt | show Thyself | froward.

3 For Thou wilt save the afflicted people : ᵛ but wilt bring | down high | looks.

4 For Thou wilt light my candle ;ᵛ the Lord my | God will en- | lighten my | darkness.

5 For by Thee I have | run through a | troop : and by my God have | I leaped | over a | wall.

6 As for God, His way is perfect ;ᵛ the word of the | Lord is | tried : He is a buckler to all | those that | trust in | Him.

7 For who is | God save the | Lord : or | who is a | rock save our | God ?

8 It is God that girdeth | me with | strength : and | maketh | my way | perfect.

9 Thou hast also given me the | shield of Thy sal- | vation : and Thy right hand hath holden me up,ᵛ and Thy | gentleness hath | made me | great.

GLORIA.

23 PSALM 19.

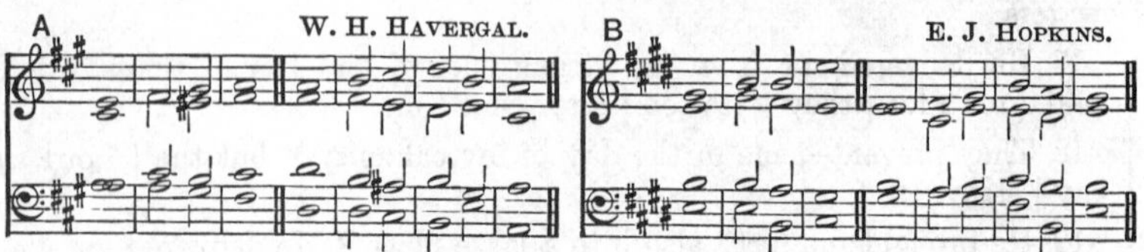

1 THE heavens declare the | glory of | God : and the firmament | showeth His | handy- | work.

2 Day unto day | uttereth | speech : and | night unto | night showeth | knowledge.

3 There is no speech nor language where their | voice is not | heard :

4 Their line is gone out through all the earth,ᵛ and their | words to the | end of the | world.

In them hath He set a tabernacle | for the | sun :

5 Which is as a bridegroom coming out of his chamber,ᵛ and rejoiceth as a | strong man to | run a | race.

6 His going forth is from the end of the heaven, and his circuit | unto the | ends of it : and there is nothing | hid from the | heat there- | of.

7 The law of the Lord is perfect, con- | verting the | soul : the testimony of the Lord is sure, | making | wise the | simple.

8 The statutes of the Lord are right, re- | joicing the | heart : the commandment of the Lord is | pure, en- | lightening the | eyes.

9 The fear of the Lord is clean, en- | during for | ever : the judgements of the Lord are true and | righteous | alto- | gether.

10 More to be desired are they than gold,ᵛ yea, than | much fine | gold : sweeter also than | honey | and the | honeycomb.

11 Moreover by them is Thy | servant | warned : and in keeping of them | there is | great re- | ward.

12 Who can under- | stand his | errors : cleanse Thou | me from | secret | faults.

13 Keep back Thy servant also from presumptuous sins ;ᵛ let them not have do- | minion | over me : then shall I be upright,ᵛ and I shall be innocent | from the | great trans- | gression.

14 Let the words of my mouth, and the meditation of my heart,ᵛ be acceptable | in Thy | sight : O Lord, my | strength, and | my re- | deemer.

GLORIA.

24 PSALM 20. 1—7.

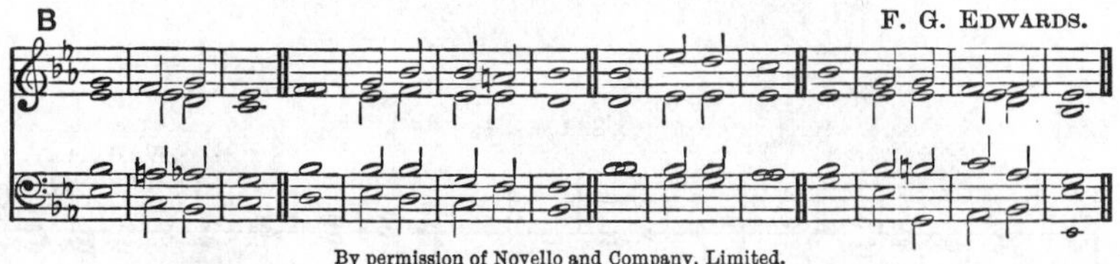

By permission of Novello and Company, Limited.

1 THE Lord hear thee in the | day of | trouble : the name of the | God of | Jacob de- | fend thee ;

2 Send thee | help from the | sanctuary : and | strengthen thee | out of | Zion ;

[3 Remember all thy offerings,˅ and ac- | cept thy burnt | sacrifice ;
4 Grant thee according to thine own | heart and ful- | fil all thy | counsel.

5 We will rejoice in Thy salvation,˅ and in the name of our God we will | set up our | banners : the Lord ful- | fil all | thy pe- | titions.

6 Now know I that the Lord | saveth His a- | nointed : He will hear him from His holy heaven with the saving | strength of | His right | hand.

7 Some trust in chariots, and | some in | horses : but we will remember the | name of the | Lord our | God.

GLORIA.

25 PSALM 23.

[1 THE Lord is my shepherd I | shall not | want :
2 He maketh me to lie down in green pastures :˅ He leadeth | me be- | side the still | waters.

3 He re- | storeth my | soul : He leadeth me in the paths of | righteousness | for His | name's sake.

4 Yea, though I walk through the valley of the shadow of death,˅ I will | fear no | evil : for Thou art with me :˅ Thy rod and Thy | staff they | comfort | me.

5 Thou preparest a table before me in the presence | of mine | enemies : Thou anointest my head with | oil ; my | cup runneth | over.

6 Surely goodness and mercy shall follow me all the | days of my | life : and I will dwell in the | house of the | Lord for | ever.

GLORIA.

26 PSALM 24.

1 THE earth is the Lord's, and the | fullness there- | of : the world, and | they that | dwell there- | in.

2 For He hath founded it up- | on the | seas : and established | it up- | on the | floods.

3 Who shall ascend into the | hill of the | Lord : or who shall | stand in His | holy | place ?

4 He that hath clean hands | and a pure | heart : who hath not lifted up his soul unto | vanity, nor | sworn de- | ceitfully.

5 He shall receive the blessing | from the | Lord : and righteousness from the | God of | his sal- | vation.

6 This is the generation of | them that | seek Him : that | seek Thy | face, O | Jacob.

7 Lift up your heads, O ye gates ;ᵛ and be ye lift up, ye ever- | lasting | doors : and the King of | glory | shall come | in.

8 Who is this | King of | glory ? : The Lord strong and | mighty, the Lord | mighty in | battle.

9 Lift up your heads, O ye gates ;ᵛ even lift them up, ye ever- | lasting | doors : and the King of | glory | shall come | in.

10 Who is this | King of | glory ? : The Lord of hosts, | He is the | King of | glory.

GLORIA.

27 PSALM 27.

J. TURLE.

E. F. RIMBAULT.

1 THE Lord is my light and my salvation | whom shall I | fear? : the Lord is the strength of my life,ᵛ of | whom shall I | be a- | fraid?

2 Though an host should encamp against me, my | heart shall not | fear : though war should rise against me, in | this will | I be | confident.

3 One thing have I desired of the Lord, that will | I seek | after : that I may dwell in the house of the Lord all the days of my life,ᵛ to behold the beauty of the Lord, | and to in- | quire in His | temple.

4 For in the time of trouble He shall hide me in | His pa- | vilion : in the secret of His tabernacle shall He hide me ;ᵛ He shall set me | up up- | on a | rock.

5 And now shall mine head be lifted up above mine enemies | round a- | bout me : therefore will I offer in His tabernacle sacrifices of joy ;ᵛ I will sing, yea, I will sing | praises | unto the | Lord.

6 Hear, O Lord, when I | cry with my | voice : have mercy | also up- | on me, and | answer me.

7 When Thou saidst, | Seek ye My | face : my heart said unto Thee, Thy | face, Lord, | will I | seek.

8 Hide not Thy face far from me ;ᵛ put not Thy servant a- | way in | anger : Thou hast been my help ;ᵛ leave me not, neither forsake me, O | God of | my sal- | vation.

9 When my father and my | mother for- | sake me : then the | Lord will | take me | up.

10 Teach me Thy | way, O | Lord : and lead me in a | plain path, be- | cause of mine | enemies.

11 Deliver me not over unto the | will of mine | enemies : for false witnesses are risen up against me, and | such as | breathe out | cruelty.

12 I had fainted,ᵛ unless I had believed to see the goodness of the Lord in the | land of the | living.

13 Wait on the Lord,ᵛ be of good courage, and He shall strengthen thine heart :ᵛ | wait, I | say, on the | Lord.

GLORIA.

28 PSALM 30.

A S. WESLEY.

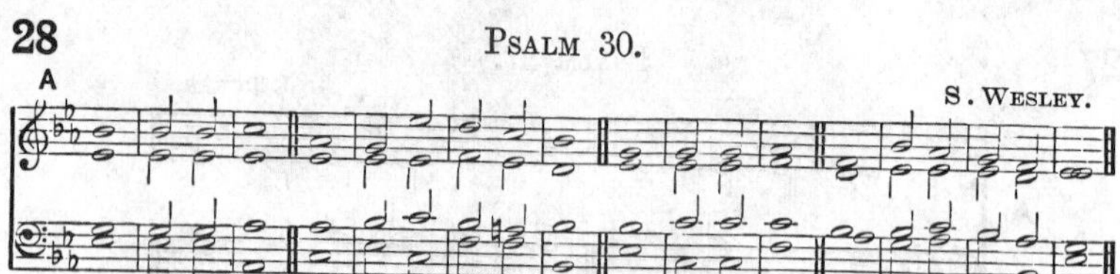

B T. ATTWOOD.

1 I WILL extol Thee, O Lord ;ᵛ for Thou hast | lifted me | up : and hast not made my | foes to re- | joice over | me.
2 O Lord my God, I | cried unto | Thee : and | Thou hast |
healèd | me.
3 O Lord, Thou hast brought up my | soul from the | grave : Thou
hast kept me alive, that I should | not go | down to the | pit.
4 Sing unto the Lord, O ye | saints of | His : and give thanks at the
re- | membrance | of His | holiness.
5 For His anger endureth but a moment ;ᵛ in His | favour is | life :
weeping may endure for a night, but | joy cometh | in the | morning.
[6 And in my prosperity I said I shall | never be | moved :
7 Lord, by Thy favour Thou hast made my mountain to stand strong :ᵛ
Thou didst hide Thy | face, and | I was | troubled.]
8 I cried to | Thee, O | Lord : and unto the Lord | I made | suppli- |
cation.
9 What profit is there in my blood, when I go | down to the | pit :
Shall the dust praise Thee ? | Shall it de- | clare Thy | truth ?
[10 Hear, O Lord, and have mercy upon me :ᵛ Lord, be | Thou my |
helper.
11 Thou hast turned for me my | mourning | into | dancing :]
12 Thou hast put | off my | sackcloth : and | girded | me with | gladness;
13 To the | end that my | glory : may sing praise to | Thee and | not
be | silent :
14 O | Lord my | God : I will give | thanks unto | Thee for | ever.

GLORIA.

29 PSALM 34.

A T. A WALMISLEY.

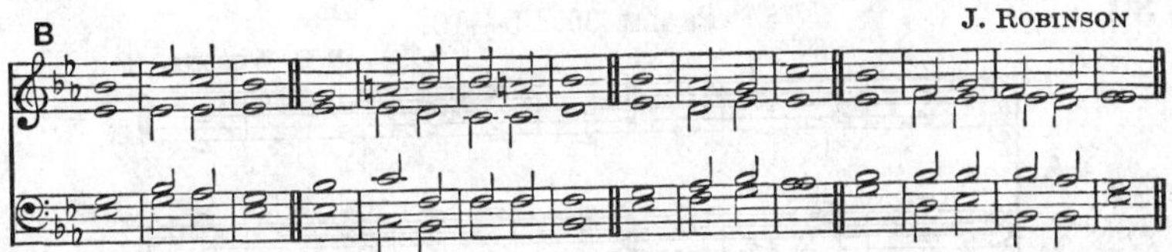

1 I WILL bless the | Lord at | all times : His praise shall con- | tinually be | in my | mouth.
2 My soul shall make her | boast in the | Lord : the humble shall | hear thereof, | and be | glad.
3 O magnify the | Lord with | me : and let us ex- | alt His | name to- | gether.
4 I sought the | Lord, and He | heard me : and de- | livered me from | all my | fears.
5 They looked unto | Him, and were | lightened : and their | faces were | not a- | shamed.
6 This poor man cried, | and the Lord | heard him : and saved him | out of | all his | troubles.
7 The angel | of the | Lord : encampeth round about them that | fear Him, | and de- | livereth them.
8 O taste and see that the | Lord is | good : blessed is the | man that | trusteth in | Him.
9 O fear the Lord, | ye His | saints : for there is no | want to | them that | fear Him.
10 The young lions do lack, and | suffer | hunger : but they that seek the Lord | shall not want | any good | thing.
11 Come, ye children, hearken | unto | me : I will | teach you the | fear of the | Lord.
12 What man is he that de- | sireth | life : and loveth many | days that | he may see | good ?
13 Keep thy | tongue from | evil : and thy | lips from | speaking | guile.
14 Depart from evil, | and do | good : seek | peace, | and pur- | sue it.
15 The eyes of the Lord are up- | on the | righteous : and His ears are | open | unto their | cry.
16 The face of the Lord is against | them that do | evil : to cut off the re- | membrance of | them from the | earth.
17 The righteous cry, | and the Lord | heareth : and delivereth them | out of | all their | troubles.
18 The Lord is nigh unto them that are of a | broken | heart : and saveth such as | be of a | contrite | spirit.
19 Many are the afflictions | of the | righteous : but the Lord de- | livereth him | out of them | all.
20 He keepeth | all his | bones : not | one of | them is | broken.
21 Evil shall | slay the | wicked : and they that hate the | righteous | shall be | desolate.
22 The Lord redeemeth the | soul of His | servants : and none of them that | trust in Him | shall be | desolate.

GLORIA.

30

PSALM 36. 5—10.

1 THY mercy, O Lord, is | in the | heavens : and Thy faithfulness | reacheth | unto the | clouds.
2 Thy righteousness is | like the great | mountains ; Thy judgements are a great deep :ᵛ O Lord, Thou pre- | servest | man and | beast.
3 How excellent is Thy loving- | kindness, O | God ! : therefore the children of men put their trust under the | shadow | of Thy | wings.
4 They shall be abundantly satisfied with the fatness | of Thy | house : and Thou shalt make them drink of the | river | of Thy | pleasures.
5 For with Thee is the | fountain of | life : in Thy | light shall | we see | light.
6 O continue Thy loving-kindness unto | them that | know Thee : and Thy righteousness | to the | upright in | heart.

GLORIA.

31

PSALM 40. 1—11.

1 I WAITED patiently | for the | Lord : and He inclined unto | me, and | heard my | cry.
2 He brought me up also out of an horrible pit, out of the | miry | clay : and set my feet upon a | rock, and es- | tablished my | goings.
3 And He hath put a new song in my mouth, even praise | unto our | God : many shall see it, and | fear, and shall | trust in the | Lord.
4 Blessèd is that man that maketh the | Lord his | trust : and respecteth not the proud, nor such as | turn a- | side to | lies.

5 Many, O Lord my God, are Thy wonderful works which Thou hast done,ᵛ and Thy thoughts which | are to | us-ward : they cannot be reckoned up in order unto Thee :ᵛ if I would declare and speak of them, they are | more than | can be | numbered.

6 Sacrifice and offering Thou didst not desire ;ᵛ mine | ears hast Thou | opened : burnt-offering and sin-offering | hast Thou | not re- | quired.

7 Then said I, | Lo, I | come : in the volume of the | book it is | written of | me,

8 I delight to do Thy will, | O my | God : yea, Thy | law is with- | in my | heart.

9 I have preached righteousness in the | great congre- | gation : lo, I have not refrained my | lips, O | Lord, thou | knowest.

10 I have not hid Thy righteousness within my heart ;ᵛ I have declared Thy faithfulness and | Thy sal- | vation : I have not concealed Thy loving-kindness and Thy | truth from the | great congre- | gation.

11 Withhold not Thou Thy tender mercies from | me, O | Lord : let Thy loving-kindness and Thy | truth con- | tinually pre- | serve me.

GLORIA.

32 PSALM 42. 1—5, 7—11 ; 43 : 3—5.

F. WALKER.

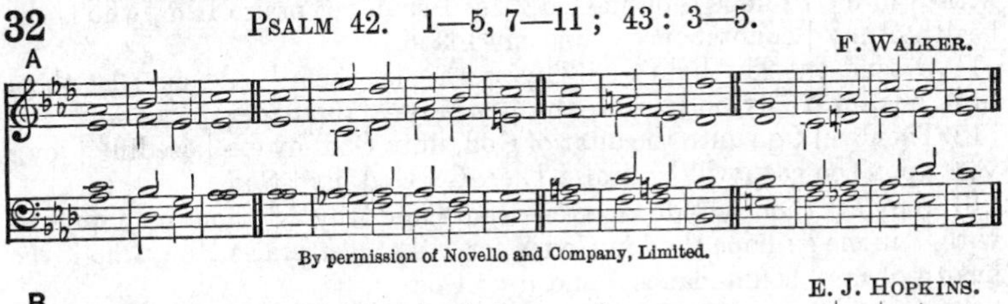

By permission of Novello and Company, Limited.

E. J. HOPKINS.

1 AS the hart panteth | after the | water brooks : so panteth my | soul after | Thee, O | God.

2 My soul thirsteth for God, for the | living | God : when shall I | come and ap- | pear before | God ?

3 My tears have been my meat | day and | night : while they continually | say unto me, | Where is thy | God ?

4 When I remember these things, I pour out my | soul in | me : for I had gone with the multitude, I went with | them to the | house of | God.

With the voice of | joy and | praise : with a | multi- | tude that kept | holy-day.

5 Why art thou cast down, O my soulᵛ and why art thou dis- | quieted | in me ? : hope thou in God,ᵛ for I shall yet praise Him for the | help of His | counten- | ance.

6 Deep calleth unto deep at the | noise of Thy | water-spouts : all Thy waves and Thy | billows | are gone | over me.

7 Yet the Lord will command His loving-kindness | in the | day-time : and in the night His song shall be with me,ᵛ and my prayer | unto the | God of my | life.

A F. WALKER.

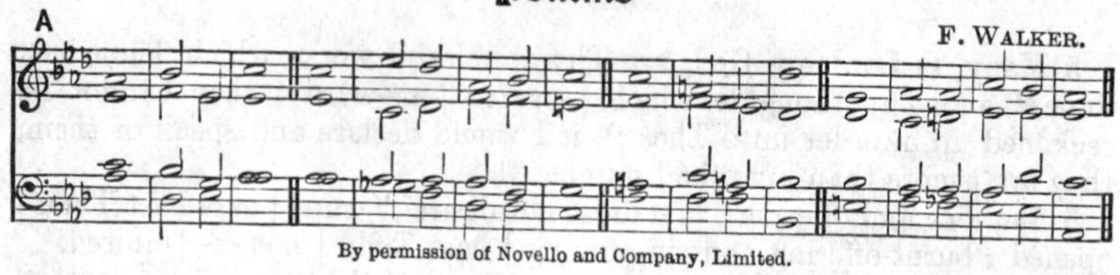

By permission of Novello and Company, Limited.

B E. J. HOPKINS.

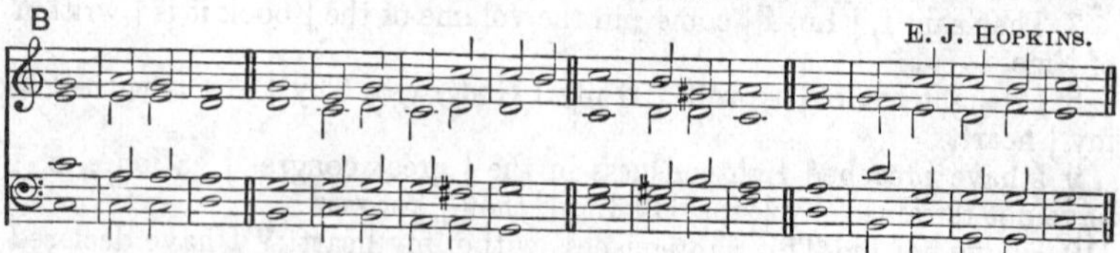

8 I will say unto God my rock,∨ Why hast | Thou for- | gotten me : why go I mourning because of the op- | pression | of the | enemy ?
9 As with a sword in my bones, mine | enemies re- | proach me : while they say daily | unto me, | Where is thy | God ?
10 Why art thou cast down, O my soul∨ and why art thou dis- | quieted with- | in me ? : hope thou in God,∨ for I shall yet praise Him, who is the health of my | countenance, | and my | God.
11 O send out Thy light and Thy truth | let them | lead me : let them bring me unto Thy holy | hill, and | to Thy | tabernacles.
12 Then will I go unto the altar of God, unto God my ex- | ceeding | joy : yea, upon the harp will I | praise Thee, O | God my | God.
13 Why art thou cast down, O my soul∨ and why art thou dis- | quieted with- | in me ? : hope thou in God,∨ for I shall yet praise Him, who is the health of my | countenance, | and my | God.

GLORIA.

33 PSALM 46.

G. A. MACFARREN.

J. BATTISHILL.

1 GOD is our | refuge and | strength : a very | present | help in | trouble.
2 Therefore will not we fear, though the | earth be re- | moved : and though the mountains be carried | into the | midst of the | sea ;
3 Though the waters thereof | roar and be | troubled : though the mountains | shake with the | swelling there- | of.
4 There is a river, the streams whereof shall make glad the | city of | God : the holy place of the | tabernacles | of the most | High.

5 God is in the midst of her ;ᵛ she shall | not be | moved : God shall | help her, and | that right | early.
6 The heathen raged, the | kingdoms were | moved : He | uttered His | voice, the earth | melted.
7 The Lord of | hosts is | with us : the God of | Jacob | is our | refuge.
8 Come, behold the | works of the | Lord : what desolations | He hath | made in the | earth.
9 He maketh wars to cease unto the | end of the | earth : He breaketh the bow, and cutteth the spear in sunder ;ᵛ He burneth the | chariot | in the | fire.
10 Be still, and know that | I am | God : I will be exalted among the heathen,ᵛ I will be ex- | alted | in the | earth.
11 The Lord of | hosts is | with us : the God of | Jacob | is our | refuge.

GLORIA.

34 PSALM 48. 1—3, 8—14.

J. H. MAUNDER.

A

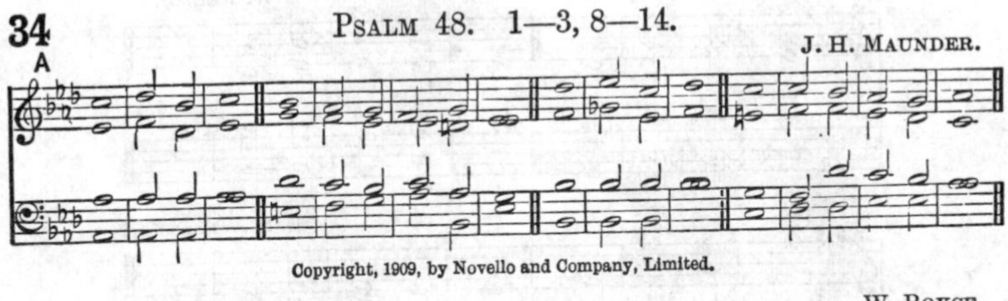

W. BOYCE.

B

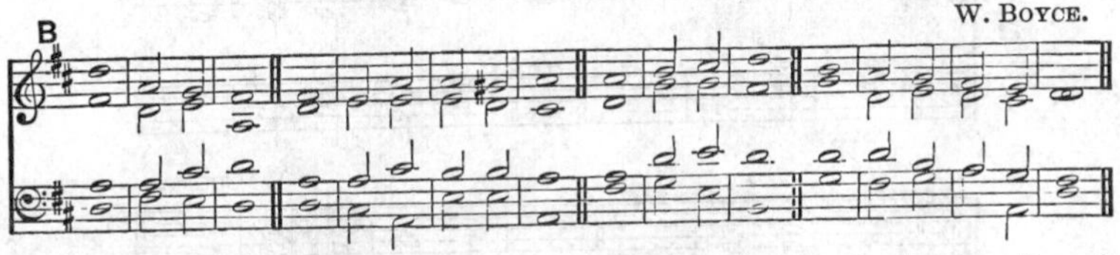

1 GREAT is the Lord, and greatly | to be | praised : in the city of our God, in the | mountain | of His | holiness.
2 Beautiful for situation, the joy of the whole earth, | is mount | Zion : on the sides of the north, the | city | of the great | King.
[3 God is known in her palaces | for a | refuge :
4 As we have heard, so have we seen in the | city of the | Lord of | hosts.]
5 In the | city of our | God : God will es- | tablish | it for | ever.
6 We have thought of Thy | loving- | kindness : O | God in the | midst of Thy | temple.
7 According to Thy name, O God, so is Thy praise unto the | ends of the | earth : Thy right | hand is | full of | righteousness.
8 Let mount | Zion re- | joice : let the daughters of Judah be | glad be- | cause of Thy | judgements.
9 Walk about Zion, and go | round a- | bout her : tell the towers thereof. | Mark ye | well her | bulwarks :
10 Con- | sider her | palaces : that ye may tell it to the | gener- | ation | following.
11 For this God is our God for | ever and | ever : He will be our guide | even | unto | death.

GLORIA.

35

PSALM 51. 1—4, 9—17.

1 HAVE mercy upon me, O God, according to Thy | loving- | kindness : according unto the multitude of Thy tender mercies | blot out | my trans- | gressions.

2 Wash me throughly from | mine in- | iquity : and | cleanse me | from my | sin.

3 For I acknowledge | my trans- | gressions : and my | sin is | ever be- | fore me.

4 Against Thee,ᵛ Thee only, have I sinned, and done this | evil in Thy | sight : that Thou mightest be justified when Thou | speakest, and be | clear when Thou | judgest.

5 Hide Thy | face from my | sins : and | blot out all | mine in- | iquities.

6 Create in me a clean | heart, O | God : and re- | new a right | spirit with- | in me.

7 Cast me not a- | way from Thy | presence : and take not Thy | holy | spirit | from me.

8 Restore unto me the joy of | Thy sal- | vation : and up- | hold me with | Thy free | spirit.

9 Then will I teach trans- | gressors Thy | ways : and sinners shall be con- | verted | unto | Thee.
10 Deliver me from blood-guiltiness, O God,ᵛ Thou God of | my sal- | vation : and my tongue shall | sing a- | loud of Thy | righteousness.
11 O Lord, open | Thou my | lips : and my | mouth shall show | forth Thy | praise.
12 For Thou desirest not sacrifice | else would I | give it : Thou de- | lightest | not in burnt- | offering.
13 The sacrifices of God are a | broken | spirit : a broken and a contrite heart, O | God, Thou wilt | not des- | pise.

GLORIA.

36

PSALM 62.

1 TRULY my soul | waiteth upon | God : from Him | cometh | my sal- | vation.
2 He only is my rock and | my sal- | vation : He is my defence ;ᵛ I shall | not be | greatly | moved.
3 How long will ye imagine mischief a- | gainst a | man : ye shall be slain all of you ;ᵛ as a bowing wall shall ye be, and | as a | tottering | fence.
4 They only consult to cast him down from his excellency ;ᵛ they de- | light in | lies : they | bless with their | mouth, but they curse | inwardly.
5 My soul, wait thou | only upon | God : for my expect- | ation | is from | Him.
6 He only is my rock and | my sal- | vation : He is my defence | I shall | not be | moved.
7 In God is my salvation | and my | glory : the rock of my strength, and my | refuge, | is in | God.
8 Trust in | Him at | all times : ye people, pour out your heart before Him : | God is a | refuge | for us.
9 Surely men of low degree are vanity, and men of high degree | are a | lie : to be laid in the balance, they are alto- | gether | lighter than | vanity.
10 Trust not in oppression, and become not | vain in | robbery : if riches increase, | set not your | heart up- | on them.
11 God hath spoken once ; | twice have I | heard this : that power be- | longeth | unto | God.
12 Also unto Thee, O Lord, be- | longeth | mercy : for Thou renderest to every man ac- | cording | to his | work.

GLORIA.

37

PSALM 63. 1—8.

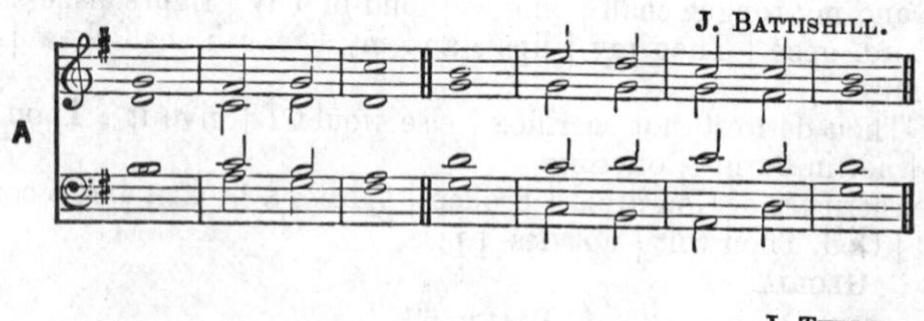

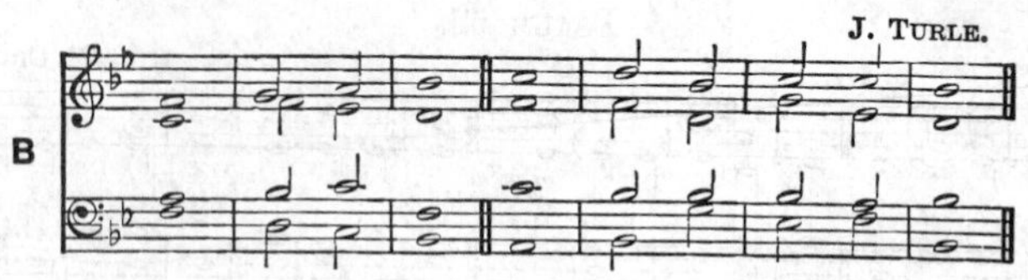

1 O GOD, Thou art my God ;ᵛ early | will I | seek Thee : my soul thirsteth for Thee,ᵛ my flesh longeth for Thee in a dry and thirsty land, | where no | water | is ;

2 To see Thy | power and Thy | glory : so as I have | seen Thee | in the | sanctuary.

3 Because Thy loving-kindness is better than life my | lips shall | praise Thee.

4 Thus will I bless Thee while I live :ᵛ I will | lift up my | hands in Thy | name.

5 My soul shall be satisfied as with | marrow and | fatness : and my mouth shall | praise Thee with | joyful | lips :

6 When I remember Thee up- | on my | bed : and medi- | tate on Thee | in the night | watches.

7 Because Thou hast | been my | help : therefore in the shadow of Thy | wings will | I re- | joice.

8 My soul followeth hard | after | Thee : Thy right | hand up- | holdeth | me.

GLORIA.

38

Psalm 65.

1 PRAISE waiteth for Thee, O | God, in | Sion: and unto | Thee shall the | vow be per- | formed.

2 O Thou that | hearest | prayer : unto | Thee shall | all flesh | come.

3 Iniquities pre- | vail a- | gainst me : as for our transgressions | Thou shalt | purge them a- | way.

4 Blessed is the man whom Thou choosest, and causest to approach unto Thee,V that he may | dwell in Thy | courts : we shall be satisfied with the goodness of Thy house, | even of Thy | holy | temple.

5 By terrible things in righteousness wilt Thou answer us,V O God of | our sal- | vation : who art the confidence of all the ends of the earth,V and of them that are afar | off up- | on the | sea :

6 Which by His strength setteth fast the mountains being | girded with | power :

7 Which stilleth the noise of the seas,V the noise of their | waves and the | tumult of the | people.

8 They also that dwell in the uttermost parts are a- | fraid at Thy | tokens : Thou makest the outgoings of the morning and | evening | to re- | joice.

9 Thou visitest the earth, and waterest it :V Thou greatly enrichest it with the river of God, which is | full of | water : Thou preparest them corn, when Thou hast | so pro- | vided | for it.

10 Thou waterest the ridges thereof abundantly :V Thou settlest the | furrows there- | of : Thou makest it soft with showers :V Thou | blessest the | springing there- | of.

11 Thou crownest the year with Thy goodness,V and Thy | paths drop | fatness.

12 They drop upon the pastures of the wilderness,V and the little hills re- | joice on | every | side.

13 The pastures are clothed with flocks,V the valleys also are covered | over with | corn : they shout for | joy, they | also | sing.

GLORIA.

39

PSALM 66. 1, 2, 16—20.

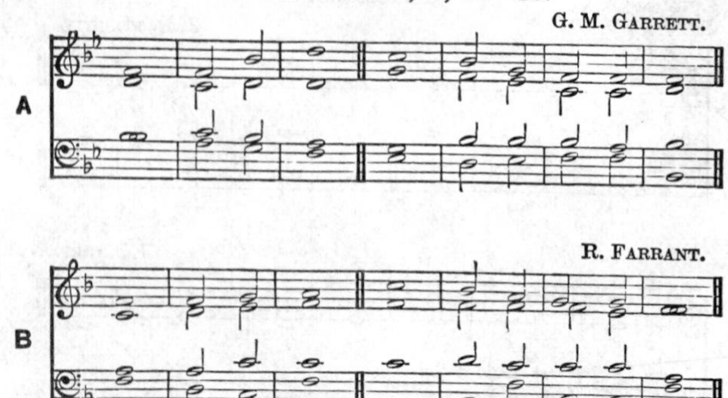

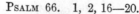

1 MAKE a joyful noise unto God, | all ye | lands :
2 Sing forth the honour of His name | make His praise |
glori- | ous.
3 Come and hear, all | ye that fear | God : and I will declare | what He
hath | done for my | soul.
4 I cried unto Him with my mouth,ᵛ and He was ex- | tolled with
my | tongue.
5 If I regard iniquity in my | heart the | Lord will not | hear me.
6 But verily God hath heard me :ᵛ He hath attended to the | voice
of my | prayer.
7 Blessed be God, which hath not turned away my | prayer nor His |
mercy | from me.

GLORIA.

40

PSALM 72. 1—19.

1 GIVE the king Thy judgements, O God :ᵛ and Thy righteousness | unto the king's | son.

2 He shall judge Thy people with righteousness | and Thy | poor with | judgement.

3 The mountains shall bring | peace to the | people : and the | little | hills, by | righteousness.

4 He shall judge the poor of the people,ᵛ he shall save the children | of the | needy : and shall | break in | pieces the op- | pressor.

5 They shall fear Thee as long as the sun and | moon en- | dure : through- | out all | gener- | ations.

6 He shall come down like rain up- | on the mown | grass : as | showers that | water the | earth.

7 In his days shall the | righteous | flourish : and abundance of peace so | long as the | moon en- | dureth.

8 He shall have dominion also from | sea to | sea : and from the river | unto the | ends of the | earth.

9 They that dwell in the wilderness shall | bow be- | fore him : and his | enemies shall | lick the | dust.

10 The kings of Tarshish and of the isles | shall bring | presents : the kings of Sheba and | Seba shall | offer | gifts.

11 Yea, all kings shall fall down before him,ᵛ all | nations shall | serve him.

12 For he shall deliver the needy when he crieth,ᵛ the poor also, and | him that | hath no | helper.

13 He shall spare the | poor and | needy : and shall | save the | souls of the | needy.

14 He shall redeem their soul from de- | ceit and | violence : and precious shall their | blood be | in his | sight.

15 And he shall live, and to him shall be given of the | gold of | Sheba : prayer also shall be made for him continually ;ᵛ and | daily shall | he be | praised.

16 There shall be an handful of corn in the earth upon the top of the mountains,ᵛ the fruit thereof shall | shake like | Lebanon : and they of the city shall | flourish like | grass of the | earth.

17 His name shall en- | dure for | ever : his name shall be con- | tinued as | long as the | sun :

And men shall be | blessèd in | him : all | nations shall | call him | blessèd.

18 Blessèd be the Lord God, the | God of | Israel : who only | doeth | wondrous | things.

19 And blessèd be His glorious | name for | ever : and let the whole earth be filled with His glory ; | Amen, and | A- | men.

Gloria.

41

PSALM 73. 1—6, 13—26, 28.

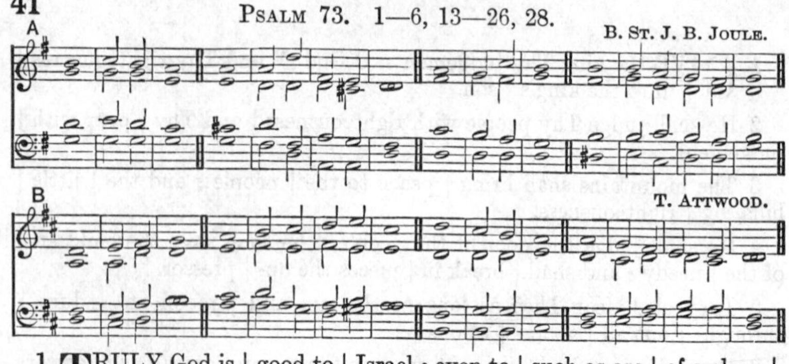

1 TRULY God is | good to | Israel : even to | such as are | of a clean | heart.

2 But as for me, my feet were | almost | gone : my | steps had | well-nigh | slipped.

3 For I was envious | at the | foolish : when I saw the pros- | perity | of the | wicked.

[4 For there are no bands in their death :ᵛ but their | strength is | firm.

5 They are not in trouble as other men,ᵛ neither are they | plagued like | other | men.]

6 Therefore pride compasseth them about | as a | chain : violence | covereth them | as a | garment.

7 Verily I have cleansed my | heart in | vain : and | washed my | hands in | innocency.

8 For all the day long have | I been | plagued : and | chastened | every | morning.

9 If I say, | I will speak | thus : behold, I should offend against the gener- | ation | of Thy | children.

10 When I | thought to | know this : it | was too | painful for | me ;

11 Until I went into the sanctu- | ary of | God : then | understood | I their | end.

12 Surely Thou didst set them in | slippery | places : Thou castedst them | down in- | to des- | truction.

13 How are they brought into desolation, | as in a | moment ! : they are | utterly con- | sumed with | terrors.

14 As a dream | when one | awaketh : so, O Lord, when Thou awakest, | Thou shalt des- | pise their | image.

15 Thus my | heart was | grieved : and | I was pricked | in my | reins.

16 So foolish was | I, and | ignorant : I was | as a | beast be- | fore Thee.

17 Nevertheless I am con- | tinually | with Thee : Thou hast | holden me | by my right | hand.

18 Thou shalt guide me | with Thy | counsel : and | afterward re- | ceive me to | glory.

19 Whom have I in | heaven but | Thee ? : and there is none upon earth that | I de- | sire be- | side Thee.

20 My | flesh and my heart | faileth : but God is the strength of my | heart, and my | portion for | ever.

21 But it is good for me to draw | near to | God : I have put my trust in the Lord God, that | I may de- | clare all Thy | works.

GLORIA.

42

PSALM 77.

D. PURCELL.

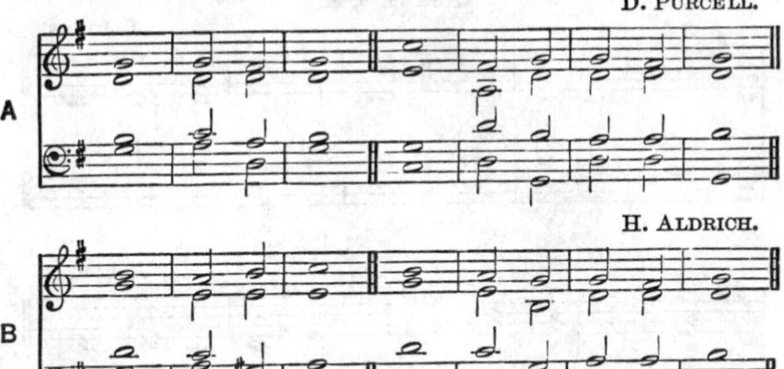

H. ALDRICH.

1 I CRIED unto God with my voice,ᵛ even unto | God with my |
voice ; and | He gave | ear unto | me.
2 In the day of my trouble I | sought the | Lord : my sore ran in the
night, and ceased not,ᵛ my | soul re- | fused to be | comforted.
3 I remembered | God, and was | troubled : I complained, and my |
spirit was | over- | whelmed.
4 Thou | holdest mine eyes | waking : I am so troubled | that I | cannot |
speak.
5 I have considered the | days of | old : the | years of | ancient | times.
6 I call to remembrance my song in the night,ᵛ I commune with |
mine own | heart : and my | spirit made | diligent | search.
7 Will the Lord cast | off for | ever ? : and | will He be | favourable
no | more ?
8 Is His mercy clean | gone for | ever ? : doth His promise | fail for |
ever- | more ?
9 Hath God forgotten | to be | gracious ? : hath He in anger | shut up
His | tender | mercies ?
10 And I said, This is | my in- | firmity : but I will remember the years
of the | right hand | of the most | High.
11 I will remember the | works of the | Lord : surely I will re- | member
Thy | wonders of | old.
[12 I will meditate also of all Thy work and | talk of Thy | doings.
13 Thy way, O God, is in the sanctuary,ᵛ who is so | great a | God as
our | God ?]
14 Thou art the God that | doest | wonders : Thou hast declared Thy |
strength a- | mong the | people.
15 Thou hast with Thine arm re- | deemed Thy | people : the | sons of |
Jacob and | Joseph.
16 The waters saw Thee, O God, the waters saw Thee | they were |
afraid : the | depths | also were | troubled.
17 The clouds poured out water,ᵛ the skies | sent out a | sound : Thine
arrows | also | went a- | broad.
18 The voice of Thy thunder was | in the | heaven : the lightnings
lightened the | world the earth | trembled and | shook.
19 Thy way is in the sea, and Thy | path in the great | waters : and Thy |
footsteps | are not | known.
20 Thou leddest Thy people | like a | flock : by the | hand of | Moses
and | Aaron. GLORIA.

43 PSALM 84.

[1 HOW amiable are Thy tabernacles O | Lord of | hosts !
2 My soul longeth, yea, even fainteth for the courts of the
Lord :ᵛ my heart and my flesh crieth | out for the | living | God.]
3 Yea, the sparrow hath found an house, and the swallow a nest for
herself,ᵛ where she may | lay her | young : even Thine altars, O Lord of |
hosts, my | King, and my | God.
4 Blessèd are they that | dwell in Thy | house : they | will be still |
praising | Thee.
5 Blessèd is the man whose | strength is in | Thee : in whose | heart
are the | ways of | them.
6 Who passing through the valley of Baca | make it a | well : the |
rain also | filleth the | pools.
7 They go from | strength to | strength : every one of them in | Zion
ap- | peareth before | God.
8 O Lord God of hosts, | hear my | prayer : give | ear, O | God of |
Jacob.
9 Behold, O | God our | shield : and look upon the | face of | Thine
a- | nointed.
10 For a day in Thy courts is better | than a | thousand : I had rather
be a door-keeper in the house of my God, than to | dwell in the | tents of |
wickedness.
11 For the Lord God is a sun and shield ;ᵛ the Lord will give | grace
and | glory : no good thing will He withhold from | them that | walk up- |
rightly.
12 O | Lord of | hosts : blessèd is the | man that | trusteth in | Thee.

GLORIA.

44 PSALM 86. 1—16.

B J. T. Harris.

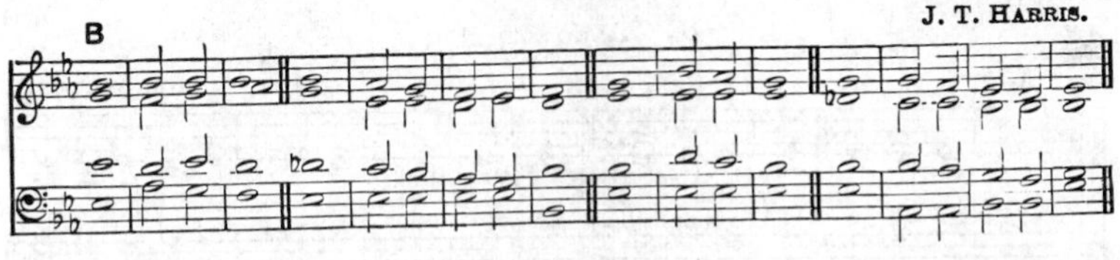

C J. Turle, from H. Purcell.

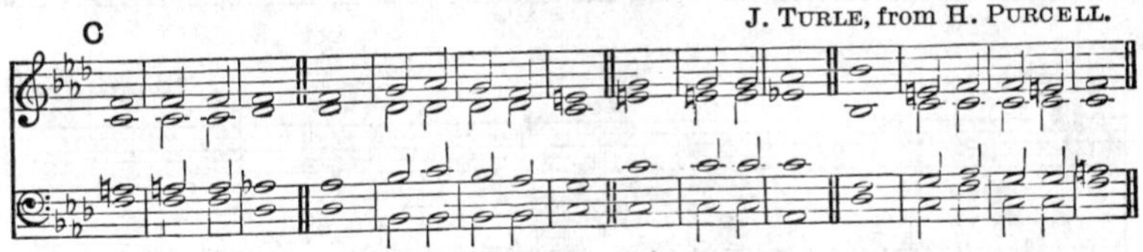

1 BOW down Thine | ear, O | Lord : hear me for | I am | poor and | needy.

2 Preserve my soul, for | I am | holy : O Thou my God, save Thy | servant that | trusteth in | Thee.

3 Be merciful unto | me, O | Lord : for | I cry | unto Thee | daily.

4 Rejoice the | soul of Thy | servant : for unto Thee, O Lord, do | I lift | up my | soul.

5 For Thou, Lord, art good, and ready | to for- | give : and plenteous in mercy unto all | them that | call up- | on Thee.

6 Give ear, O Lord, | unto my | prayer : and attend to the | voice of my | supplic- | ations.

7 In the day of my trouble I will | call upon | Thee : for | Thou wilt | answer | me.

8 Among the gods there is none like unto | Thee, O | Lord : neither are there any | works like | unto Thy | works.

9 All nations whom Thou hast made shall come and worship before | Thee, O | Lord : and shall | glori- | fy Thy | name.

10 For | Thou art | great : and doest wondrous things : | Thou art | God a- | lone.

11 Teach me Thy way, O Lord ;ᵛ I will | walk in Thy | truth : unite my | heart to | fear Thy | name.

12 I will praise Thee, O Lord my God, with | all my | heart : and I will glorify Thy | name for | ever- | more.

13 For great is Thy | mercy to- | ward me : and Thou hast delivered my soul | from the | lowest | hell.

14 O God, the proud are risen against me,ᵛ and the assemblies of violent men have sought | after my | soul : and | have not | set Thee be- | fore them.

15 But Thou, O Lord, art a God | full of com- | passion : and gracious, longsuffering, and | plenteous in | mercy and | truth.

16 O turn unto me, and have | mercy up- | on me : give Thy strength unto Thy servant, and | save the | son of Thine | handmaid.

Gloria.

45 Psalm 89. 1—18.

1 I WILL sing of the mercies of the | Lord for | ever : with my mouth will I make known Thy | faithfulness to | all gener- | ations.

2 For I have said, Mercy shall be | built up for | ever : Thy faithfulness shalt Thou establish | in the | very | heavens.

3 I have made a covenant | with my | chosen : I have | sworn unto | David my | servant,

4 Thy seed will I es- | tablish for | ever : and build up thy | throne to | all gener- | ations.

5 And the heavens shall praise Thy | wonders, O | Lord : Thy faithfulness also in the | congregation | of the | saints.

6 For who in the heaven can be compared | unto the | Lord : who among the sons of the mighty can be | likened | unto the | Lord ?

7 God is greatly to be feared in the assembly | of the | saints : and to be had in reverence of all | them that | are a- | bout Him.

8 O Lord God of hosts, who is a strong Lord | like unto | Thee : or to Thy | faithfulness | round a- | bout Thee ?

9 Thou rulest the raging | of the | sea : when the waves thereof a- | rise, Thou | stillest | them.

10 Thou hast broken Rahab in pieces, as | one that is | slain ; Thou hast scattered Thine | enemies with | Thy strong | arm.

11 The heavens are Thine, the earth | also is | Thine : as for the world and the fullness thereof, | Thou hast | founded | them.

12 The north and the south | Thou hast cre- | ated them : Tabor and Hermon | shall re- | joice in Thy | name.

13 Thou hast a | mighty | arm : strong is Thy hand, and | high is | Thy right | hand.

14 Justice and judgement are the habitation | of Thy | throne : mercy and truth shall | go be- | fore Thy | face.

15 Blessèd is the people that know the | joyful | sound : they shall walk, O | Lord, in the | light of Thy | countenance.

16 In Thy name shall they re- | joice all the | day : and in Thy righteousness | shall they | be ex- | alted.

17 For Thou art the glory | of their | strength : and in Thy favour our | horn shall | be ex- | alted.

18 For the Lord is | our de- | fence ; and the Holy One of | Israel | is our | King.

GLORIA.

46 PSALM 90.

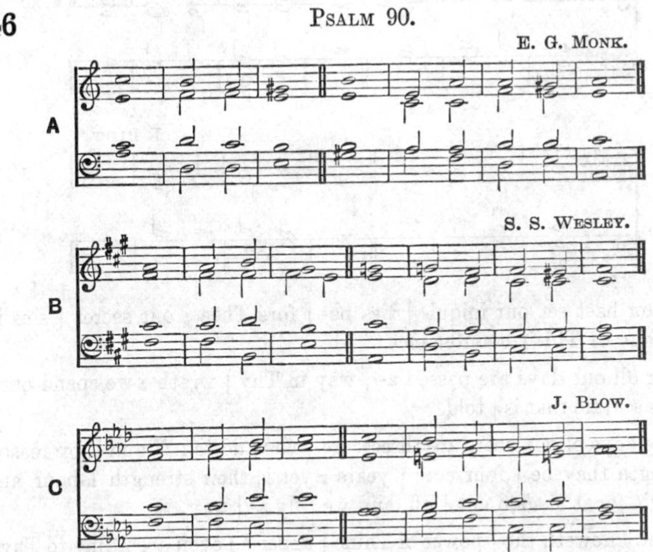

1 LORD, Thou hast | been our | dwelling-place : in | all | gener- | ations.

2 Before the mountains were brought forth, or ever Thou hadst formed the | earth and the | world : even from everlasting to ever- | lasting, | Thou art | God.

3 Thou turnest | man to de- | struction : and sayest, Re- | turn, ye | children of | men.

4 For a thousand years in Thy sight are but as yesterday | when it is | past : and | as a | watch in the | night.

5 Thou carriest them away as with a flood ;ᵛ they | are as a | sleep : in the morning they are like | grass which | groweth | up.

6 In the morning it flourisheth, and | groweth | up : in the evening | it is cut | down, and | withereth.

7 For we are consumed | by Thine | anger : and | by Thy | wrath are we | troubled.

8 Thou hast set our iniqui- | ties be- | fore Thee : our secret | sins in the | light of Thy | countenance.

9 For all our days are passed a- | way in Thy | wrath : we spend our | years as a | tale that is | told.

10 The days of our years are threescore years and ten ;V and if by reason of strength they be | fourscore | years : yet is their strength labour and sorrow ;V for it is soon cut | off, and we | fly a- | way.

11 Who knoweth the | power of Thine | anger ? : even according to Thy | fear, so | is Thy | wrath.

12 So teach us to | number our | days : that we may ap- | ply our | hearts unto | wisdom.

13 Return, O | Lord, how | long ? : and let it re- | pent Thee con- | cerning Thy | servants.

14 O satisfy us early | with Thy | mercy : that we may re- | joice and be | glad all our | days.

15 Make us glad according to the days wherein | Thou hast af- | flicted us : and the | years wherein | we have seen | evil.

16 Let Thy work appear | unto Thy | servants : and Thy | glory | unto their | children.

17 And let the beauty of the Lord our | God be up- | on us : and establish Thou the work of our hands upon us ;V yea, the work of our | hands es- | tablish Thou | it.

Gloria.

47 PSALM 91. 1—6, 9—16.

1 HE that dwelleth in the secret place | of the most | High : shall abide under the | shadow of | the Al- | mighty.

2 I will say of the Lord, He is my refuge | and my | fortress : my | God in | Him will I | trust.

3 Surely He shall deliver thee from the | snare of the | fowler : and | from the | noisome | pestilence.

4 He shall cover thee with His feathers, and under His | wings shalt thou | trust : His truth shall | be thy | shield and | buckler.

5 Thou shalt not be afraid for the | terror by | night : nor for the | arrow that | flieth by | day ;

6 Nor for the pestilence that | walketh in | darkness : nor for the des- | truction that | wasteth at | noonday.

7 Because thou hast made the Lord, which | is my | refuge : even the most | High, thy | habit- | ation ;

8 There shall no | evil be- | fall thee : neither shall any | plague come | nigh thy | dwelling.

9 For He shall give His angels charge | over | thee : to | keep thee in | all thy | ways.

10 They shall bear thee | up in their | hands : lest thou dash thy | foot a- | gainst a | stone.

11 Thou shalt tread upon the | lion and | adder : the young lion and the dragon shalt thou | trample | under | feet.

12 Because he hath set his love upon Me,ᵛ therefore will | I de- | liver him : I will set him on high, be- | cause he hath | known My | name.

13 He shall call upon Me, and | I will | answer him : I will be with him in trouble ;ᵛ I will de- | liver him, and | honour | him.

14 With long life will I | satisfy | him : and | show him | My sal- | vation.

GLORIA.

48

Psalm 92. 1—8, 12—15.

1 It is a good thing to give thanks | unto the | Lord : and to sing
praises | unto Thy | name, O most | High :
2 To show forth Thy loving-kindness | in the | morning : and Thy |
faithfulness | every | night,
3 Upon an instrument of ten strings, and up- | on the | psaltery : upon
the | harp with a | solemn | sound.
4 For Thou, Lord, hast made me glad | through Thy | work : I will |
triumph in the | works of Thy | hands.
5 O Lord, how | great are Thy | works ! : and Thy | thoughts are |
very | deep.
6 A brutish man | knoweth | not : neither | doth a fool | understand | this.
7 When the wicked spring as the grass, and when all the workers of
in- | iquity do | flourish : it is that they shall | be des- | troyed for | ever :
8 But | Thou | Lord : art most | high for | ever- | more.
9 The righteous shall flourish | like the | palm-tree : he shall | grow like
a | cedar in | Lebanon.
10 Those that be planted in the | house of the | Lord : shall | flourish in
the | courts of our | God.
11 They shall still bring forth | fruit in old | age : they | shall be | fat
and | flourishing ;
12 To show that the | Lord is | upright : He is my rock, and there is no
un- | righteous- | ness in | Him. Gloria.

49

Psalm 93.

1 THE Lord reigneth, He is clothed with majesty ;ᵛ the Lord is clothed with strength, wherewith He hath | girded Him- | self : the world also is established, | that it | cannot be | moved.
2 Thy throne is es- | tablished of | old : Thou | art from | ever- | lasting.
3 The floods have lifted up, O Lord, the floods have lifted | up their | voice : the | floods lift | up their | waves.
4 The Lord on high is mightier than the noise of | many | waters : yea, than the | mighty | waves of the | sea.
5 Thy testimonies are | very | sure : holiness becometh Thine | house, O | Lord, for | ever.

GLORIA.

50 PSALM 97.

1 THE Lord reigneth ;ᵛ let the | earth re- | joice : let the multitude of | isles be | glad there- | of.
2 Clouds and darkness are | round about | Him : righteousness and judgement are the habi- | tation | of His | throne.
3 A fire goeth before Him,ᵛ and burneth up His enemies | round a- | bout.
4 His lightnings enlightened the | world : the earth | saw, and | trembled.
5 The hills melted like wax at the | presence of the | Lord : at the | presence of the | Lord of the whole | earth.
6 The heavens de- | clare His | righteousness : and all the | people | see His | glory.
7 Confounded be all they that serve | graven | images : that boast themselves of idols : | worship Him, | all ye | gods.
8 Zion | heard, and was | glad : and the daughters of Judah rejoiced be- | cause of Thy | judgements, O | Lord.
9 For Thou, Lord, art high above | all the | earth : Thou art exalted | far a- | bove all | gods.
10 Ye that love the Lord, hate evil ;ᵛ He preserveth the | souls of His | saints : He delivereth them | out of the | hand of the | wicked.
11 Light is | sown for the | righteous : and gladness | for the | upright in | heart.
12 Rejoice in the | Lord, ye | righteous : and give thanks at the re- | membrance | of His | holiness.

GLORIA.

51 Psalm 103.

1 BLESS the Lord, | O my | soul : and all that is within me, | bless His | holy | name.
2 Bless the Lord, | O my | soul : and for- | get not | all His | benefits :
3 Who forgiveth | all thine in- | iquities : who | healeth | all thy dis- | eases ;
4 Who redeemeth thy | life from des- | truction : who crowneth thee with loving- | kindness and | tender | mercies ;
5 Who satisfieth thy | mouth with good | things : so that thy | youth is re- | newed like the | eagle's.
6 The Lord executeth righteous- | ness and | judgement : for | all that | are op- | pressed.
7 He made known His | ways unto | Moses : His acts | unto the | children of | Israel.
8 The Lord is | merciful and | gracious : slow to | anger, and | plenteous in | mercy.
9 He will not | always | chide : neither will He | keep His | anger for | ever.
10 He hath not dealt with us | after our | sins : nor rewarded us ac- | cording to | our in- | iquities.
11 For as the heaven is high a- | bove the | earth : so great is His | mercy toward | them that | fear Him.

12 As far as the east is | from the | west : so far hath He re- | moved our trans- | gressions | from us.
13 Like as a father | pitieth his | children : so the Lord | pitieth | them that | fear Him.
14 For He | knoweth our | frame : He re- | membereth that | we are | dust.
15 As for man, his | days are as | grass : as a | flower of the | field, so he | flourisheth.
16 For the wind passeth over it, and | it is | gone : and the place there- | of shall | know it no | more.
17 But the mercy of the Lord is from everlasting to everlasting upon | them that | fear Him : and His righteousness | unto | children's | children;
18 To such as | keep His | covenant : and to those that remember | His com- | mandments to | do them.
19 The Lord hath prepared His | throne in the | heavens : and His kingdom | ruleth | over | all.
20 Bless the Lord, ye His angels, that ex- | cel in | strength : that do His commandments, hearkening | unto the | voice of His | word.
21 Bless ye the Lord, all | ye His | hosts : ye ministers of | His, that | do His | pleasure :
22 Bless the Lord, all His works in all places of | His do- | minion : bless the | Lord, | O my | soul.

GLORIA.

52 PSALM 104. 1—4, 24, 31—35.

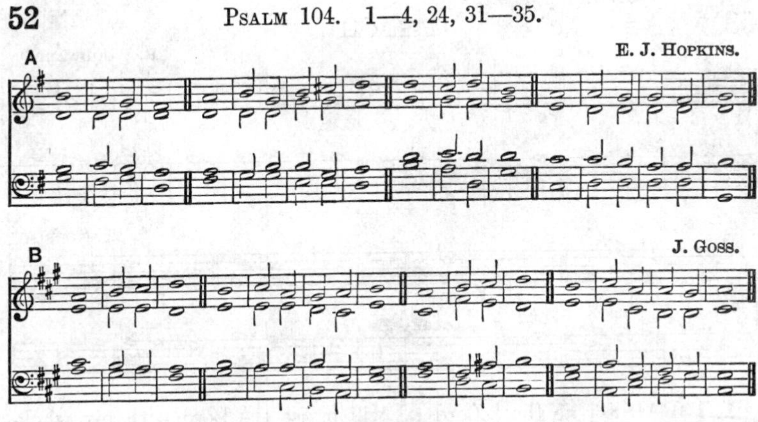

1 BLESS the Lord, | O my | soul : O Lord my God, Thou art very great ;ᵛ Thou art | clothed with | honour and | majesty.
2 Who coverest Thyself with light as | with a | garment : who stretchest out the | heavens | like a | curtain :
3 Who layeth the beams of His chambers | in the | waters : who maketh the clouds His chariot :ᵛ who walketh up- | on the | wings of the | wind :
4 Who maketh His | angels | spirits : His | ministers a | flaming | fire :

5 O Lord, how manifold | are Thy | works ! : in wisdom hast Thou made them all,ᵛ the | earth is | full of Thy | riches.

6 The glory of the Lord shall en- | dure for | ever : the | Lord shall re- | joice in His | works.

7 He looketh on the | earth, and it | trembleth : He | toucheth the hills, | and they | smoke.

8 I will sing unto the Lord as | long as I | live : I will sing praise to my God | while I | have my | being.

9 My meditation of Him | shall be | sweet : I | will be | glad in the | Lord.

10 Let the sinners be consumed out of the earth, and let the wicked | be no | more : Bless thou the Lord, O my | soul, Praise | ye the | Lord.

GLORIA.

53 PSALM 111.

1 PRAISE | ye the | Lord : I will praise the Lord with my whole heart,ᵛ in the assembly of the upright, and | in the | congre- | gation.

2 The works of the | Lord are | great : sought out of all | them that have | pleasure there- | in.

3 His work is | honourable and | glorious : and His | righteousness en- | dureth for | ever.

4 He hath made His wonderful works to | be re- | membered : the Lord is | gracious and | full of com- | passion.

5 He hath given meat unto | them that | fear Him : He will ever be | mindful | of His | covenant.
6 He hath showed His people the | power of His | works : that He may give them the | heritage | of the | heathen.
7 The works of His hands are | verity and | judgement : all | His com- | mandments are | sure.
8 They stand fast for | ever and | ever : and are | done in | truth and up- | rightness.
9 He sent redemption | unto His | people : He hath commanded His covenant for ever ;ᐯ holy and | reverend | is His | name.
10 The fear of the Lord is the be- | ginning of | wisdom : a good understanding have all they that do His commandments ;ᐯ His | praise en- | dureth for | ever.

Gloria.

54 Psalm 112.

T. Attwood.

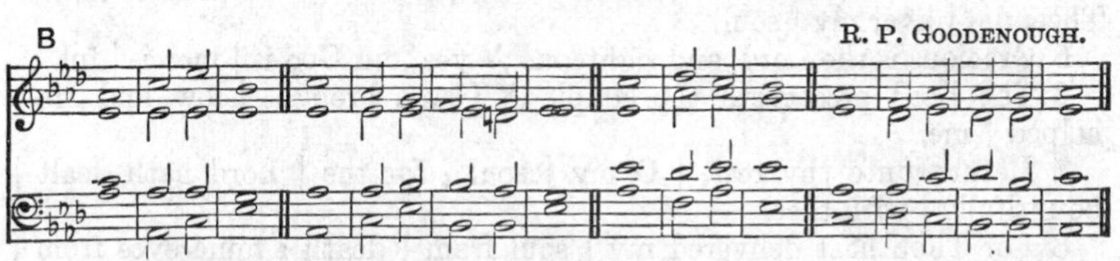

1 PRAISE | ye the | Lord : Blessèd is the man that feareth the Lord,ᐯ that delighteth | greatly in | His com- | mandments.
2 His seed shall be | mighty upon | earth : the generation of the | upright | shall be | blessèd.
3 Wealth and riches shall | be in his | house : and his | righteousness en- | dureth for | ever.
4 Unto the upright there ariseth | light in the | darkness : he is gracious, and | full of com- | passion, and | righteous.
5 A good man showeth | favour, and | lendeth : he will | guide his affairs with dis- | cretion.
6 Surely he shall not be | moved for | ever : the righteous shall be in | ever- | lasting re- | membrance.
7 He shall not be afraid of | evil | tidings : his heart is fixed, | trusting | in the | Lord.
8 His heart is established, he shall | not be a- | fraid : until he see his de- | sire up- | on his | enemies.
9 He hath dispersed, he hath given to the poor ;ᐯ his righteousness en- | dureth for | ever : his horn shall | be ex- | alted with | honour.
10 The wicked shall see it, and be grieved ;ᐯ he shall gnash with his teeth, and | melt a- | way : the de- | sire of the | wicked shall | perish.

Gloria.

55

PSALM 116.

1 I | LOVE the | Lord : because He hath heard my | voice and my | suppli- | cations.
2 Because He hath inclined His | ear unto | me : therefore will I call upon | Him as | long as I | live.
3 The sorrows of death | compassed | me : and the pains of hell gat hold upon me : | I found | trouble and | sorrow.
4 Then called I upon the | name of the | Lord : O Lord, I be- | seech Thee, de- | liver my | soul.
5 Gracious is the Lord, and righteous ;ᵛ yea, our God is | merci- | ful.
6 The Lord preserveth the simple :ᵛ I was brought | low, and He | helpèd | me.
7 Return unto thy rest, | O my | soul : for the | Lord hath dealt | bountifully | with thee.
8 For Thou hast delivered my | soul from | death : mine eyes from | tears, and my | feet from | falling.
9 I will walk before the Lord in the | land of the | living.
10 I believed, | therefore | have I | spoken :
I was | greatly af- | flicted.
11 I said in my | haste All | men are | liars.
12 What shall I render | unto the | Lord : for | all His | benefits | toward me ?
13 I will take the | cup of sal- | vation : and | call upon the | name of the | Lord.
14 I will pay my vows unto the Lord,ᵛ now in the presence of | all His | people.
15 Precious in the sight of the | Lord is the | death of His | saints.
16 O Lord, truly | I am Thy | servant : I am Thy servant, and the son of Thine handmaid : | Thou hast | loosed my | bonds.
17 I will offer to Thee the sacri- | fice of | thanksgiving : and will | call upon the | name of the | Lord.
18 I will pay my vows | unto the | Lord : now in the | presence of | all His | people,
19 In the | courts of the | Lord's house : in the midst of thee, O Jer- | usalem. | Praise ye the | Lord.

GLORIA.

56 Psalm 118. 14—26, 28, 29.

S. S. Wesley.

1 THE Lord is my | strength and | song : and | is become | my sal- | vation.

2 The voice of rejoicing and salvation is in the tabernacles | of the | righteous : the right | hand of the | Lord doeth | valiantly.

3 The right hand of the | Lord is ex- | alted : the right | hand of the | Lord doeth | valiantly.

4 I shall not | die, but | live : and de- | clare the | works of the | Lord.

5 The Lord hath | chastened me | sore : but He hath not given me | over | unto | death.

6 Open to me the | gates of | righteousness : I will go into them, and | I will | praise the | Lord :

7 This | gate of the | Lord : into | which the | righteous shall | enter.

8 I will praise Thee for | Thou hast | heard me : and | art become | my sal- | vation.

9 The stone which the | builders re- | fused : is become the | head-stone | of the | corner.

10 This | is the Lord's | doing : it is | marvellous | in our | eyes.

11 This is the day which the | Lord hath | made : we will re- | joice and be | glad in | it.

12 Save now, I be- | seech Thee, O | Lord : O Lord, I be- | seech Thee, | send now pros- | perity.

13 Blessèd be he that cometh in the | name of the | Lord : we have blessed you | out of the | house of the | Lord.

14 Thou art my God, and | I will | praise Thee : Thou art my | God, I | will ex- | alt Thee.

15 O give thanks unto the Lord, for | He is | good : for His | mercy en- | dureth for | ever.

Gloria.

57 PSALM 121.

A

J. CAMIDGE.

B

A. H. MANN.

1 I WILL lift up mine eyes unto the hills,ᵛ from whence | cometh my | help.

2 My help cometh from the | Lord which made | heaven and | earth.

3 He will not suffer thy | foot to be | moved : He that | keepeth thee | will not | slumber.

4 Behold, He that | keepeth | Israel : shall | neither | slumber nor | sleep.

5 The | Lord is thy | keeper : the Lord is thy | shade upon | thy right | hand.

6 The sun shall not smite thee by day nor the | moon by | night.

7 The Lord shall preserve thee from all evil | He shall pre- | serve thy | soul.

8 The Lord shall preserve thy going out and thy | coming | in : from this time forth, and | even for | ever- | more.

GLORIA.

58 PSALM 122.

J. FOSTER.

A

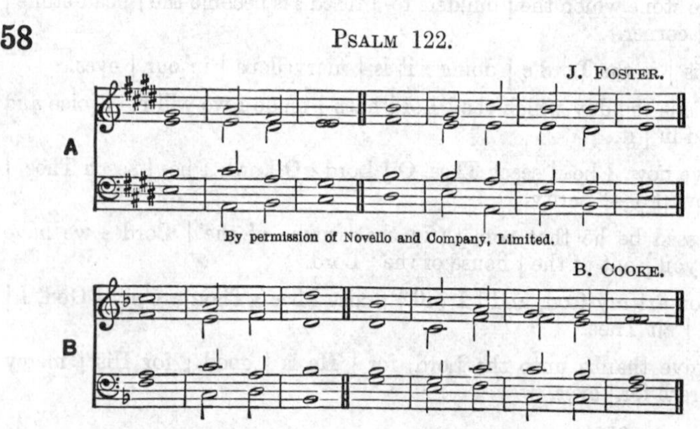

By permission of Novello and Company, Limited.

B. COOKE.

B

1 I WAS glad when they | said unto | me, : Let us go | into the | house of the | Lord.

2 Our feet shall stand with- | in thy | gates, : O | Jer- | usal- | em.

3 Jerusalem is builded | as a | city : that | is com- | pact to- | gether :

4 Whither the tribes go up, the tribes of the Lord,ᵛ unto the | testimony of | Israel, : to give thanks | unto the | name of the | Lord.

5 For there are set | thrones of | judgement, : the | thrones of the | house of | David.

6 Pray for the peace of Jerusalem ;ᵛ they shall | prosper that | love thee.

7 Peace be within thy walls, and pros- | perity with- | in thy | palaces.

8 For my brethren and companions' sakes,ᵛ I will now say, | Peace be with- | in thee :

9 Because of the house of the Lord our | God I will | seek thy | good.

GLORIA.

59 PSALM 130.

1 OUT | of the | depths : have I | cried unto | Thee, O | Lord.

2 Lord, | hear my | voice : Let Thine ears be attentive to the | voice of my | suppli- | cations.

3 If Thou, Lord, shouldest mark iniquities, O | Lord, who shall | stand ?

4 But there is forgiveness with | Thee, that Thou | mayest be | feared.

5 I wait for the Lord, my | soul doth | wait, : and | in His | word do I | hope.

6 My soul waiteth for the Lord more than they that | watch for the | morning : I say, more than | they that | watch for the | morning.

7 Let Israel | hope in the | Lord : for with the Lord there is mercy, and with | Him is | plenteous re- | demption.

8 And He | shall redeem | Israel : from | all his in- | iqui- | ties.

GLORIA.

60 PSALM 139. 1—12, 17, 18, 23, 24.

1 O LORD, Thou hast | searched me, and | known me.
2 Thou knowest my down-sitting and mine up-rising,ᵛ Thou under- | standest my | thought afar | off.
3 Thou compassest my path and my | lying | down, : and art ac- | quainted with | all my | ways.
4 For there is not a | word in my | tongue, : but, lo, O Lord, Thou | knowest it | alto- | gether.
5 Thou hast beset me be- | hind and be- | fore : and | laid Thine | hand up- | on me.
6 Such knowledge is too | wonderful | for me : it is high, I | cannot at- | tain unto | it.
7 Whither shall I | go from Thy | spirit : or | whither shall I | flee from Thy | presence ?
8 If I ascend up into | heaven, Thou art | there : if I make my bed in | hell, behold, | Thou art | there.
9 If I take the | wings of the | morning, : and dwell in the | uttermost | parts of the | sea ;
10 Even there shall | Thy hand | lead me : and | Thy right | hand shall | hold me.
11 If I say, Surely the | darkness shall | cover me : even the | night shall be | light about | me.
12 Yea, the darkness hideth | not from | Thee : but the night | shineth | as the | day.
The darkness | and the | light : are | both a- | like to | Thee.
13 How precious also are Thy thoughts unto | me, O | God ! : how | great is the | sum of | them !
14 If I should count them, they are more in | number than the | sand : when I awake, | I am | still with | Thee.
15 Search me, O God, and | know my | heart : try | me, and | know my | thoughts :
16 And see if there be any wicked | way in | me, : and | lead me in the | way ever- | lasting.

GLORIA.

61 PSALM 145.

From LUTHER.
C

J. TURLE.
D

1 I WILL extol Thee, my God, O King,˅ and I will bless Thy name
for | ever and | ever.
2 Every day will I bless Thee,˅ and I will praise Thy | name for | ever
and | ever.
3 Great is the Lord, and greatly | to be | praisèd : and His | greatness |
is un- | searchable.
4 One generation shall praise Thy | works to an- | other : and shall
de- | clare Thy | mighty | acts.
5 I will speak of the glorious honour | of Thy | majesty : and | of Thy |
wondrous | works.
6 And men shall speak of the might of Thy | terrible | acts : and | I will
de- | clare Thy | greatness.
7 They shall abundantly utter the memory of | Thy great | goodness :
and shall | sing of Thy | righteous- | ness.
8 The Lord is gracious, and | full of com- | passion : slow to | anger, |
and of great | mercy.
9 The Lord is | good to | all : and His tender mercies are | over | all
His | works.
10 All Thy works shall | praise Thee, O | Lord : and Thy | saints shall |
bless | Thee.
11 They shall speak of the glory | of Thy | kingdom : and | talk | of Thy |
power ;

12 To make known to the sons of men His | mighty | acts : and the glorious | majesty | of His | kingdom.

13 Thy kingdom is an ever- | lasting | kingdom : and Thy dominion endureth through- | out all | gener- | ations.

14 The Lord upholdeth | all that | fall, : and raiseth up | all those | that be bowed | down.

15 The eyes of all | wait upon | Thee : and Thou givest | them their | meat in due | season.

16 Thou | openest Thine | hand : and satisfiest the desire of | every | living | thing.

17 The Lord is righteous in | all His | ways : and | holy in | all His | works.

18 The Lord is nigh unto all them that | call upon | Him : to all that | call upon | Him in | truth.

19 He will fulfil the desire of | them that | fear Him : He also will | hear their | cry, and will | save them.

20 The Lord preserveth all | them that | love Him : but all the | wicked will | He des- | troy.

21 My mouth shall speak the | praise of the | Lord : and let all flesh bless His holy | name for | ever and | ever.

GLORIA.

62 Psalm 146.

1 PRAISE | ye the | Lord : Praise the | Lord, | O my | soul.
2 While I live will I | praise the | Lord : I will sing praises unto
my God while | I have | any | being.
3 Put not your trust in princes, nor in the | son of | man : in | whom
there | is no | help.
4 His breath goeth forth, he returneth | to his | earth : in that very |
day his | thoughts | perish.
5 Happy is he that hath the God of Jacob | for his | help : whose hope
is | in the | Lord his | God :
6 Which made heaven and earth, the sea, and all that | therein | is :
which | keepeth | truth for | ever :
7 Which executeth judgement | for the op- | pressed : which | giveth |
food to the | hungry.
The Lord looseth the prisoners :
8 The Lord openeth the | eyes of the | blind : the Lord raiseth | them
that | are bowed | down.
The Lord | loveth the | righteous :
9 The | Lord pre- | serveth the | strangers.
He relieveth the | fatherless and | widow : but the way of the wicked
He | turneth | upside | down.
10 The Lord shall | reign for | ever : even thy God, O Zion, unto all
gener- | ations. | Praise ye the | Lord.

Gloria.

63

Psalm 148.

A

W. Marsh.

B

W. H. Havergal.

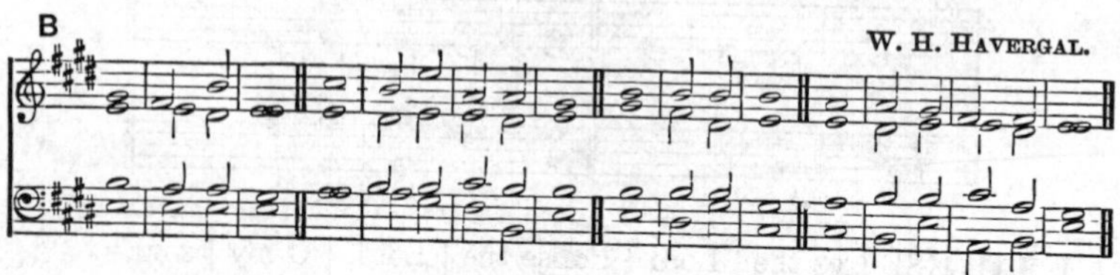

1 PRAISE | ye the | Lord : Praise ye the Lord from the heavens | praise Him | in the | heights.

2 Praise ye Him, all His angels ;ᵛ praise ye Him, | all His | hosts.

3 Praise ye Him, sun and moon ;ᵛ praise Him, | all ye | stars of | light.

4 Praise Him, ye | heavens of | heavens : and ye waters that | be a- | bove the | heavens.

5 Let them praise the | name of the | Lord : for He commanded, | and they | were cre- | ated.

6 He hath also stablished them for | ever and | ever : He hath made a de- | cree which | shall not | pass.

7 Praise the Lord from the earth, ye | dragons, and all | deeps.

8 Fire, and hail, snow, and vapours ;ᵛ stormy | wind ful- | filling His | word.

9 Mountains and all hills ;ᵛ fruitful | trees, and all | cedars.

10 Beasts, and all cattle ;ᵛ creeping | things, and | flying | fowl.

11 Kings of the earth, and all people ;ᵛ princes, and all | judges of the | earth :

12 Both young men, and | maidens, old | men and | children :

13 Let them praise the | name of the | Lord : for His name alone is excellent ;ᵛ His glory is a- | bove the | earth and | heaven.

14 He also exalteth the horn of His people,ᵛ the praise of | all His | saints : even of the children of Israel,ᵛ a people near | unto Him. | Praise ye the | Lord.

Gloria.

64 PSALM 150.

P. HUMFREY.

1 PRAISE | ye the | Lord. : Praise God in His sanctuary,ᵛ praise Him in the | firmament | of His | power.

2 Praise Him for His | mighty | acts : praise Him according | to His | excellent | greatness.

3 Praise Him with the | sound of the | trumpet : praise Him | with the | psaltery and | harp.

4 Praise Him with the | timbrel and | dance : praise Him with stringed | instru- | ments and | organs.

5 Praise Him up- | on the loud | cymbals : praise Him up- | on the high | sounding | cymbals.

6 Let every thing | that hath | breath : praise the | Lord. Praise | ye the | Lord.

GLORIA.

65

NUMBERS 6, 24—26.

1 THE Lord | bless thee, and | keep thee :
2 The Lord make His face shine upon thee,v and be | gracious |
unto | thee :

3 The Lord lift up His | countenance up- | on thee : and | give | thee |
peace.

66

JOB 28. 12—28.

1 BUT where shall | wisdom be | found ? : and where is the | place
of | under- | standing ?

2 Man knoweth not the | price there- | of : neither is it | found in the |
land of the | living.

3 The depth saith, It is | not in | me : and the sea saith, | It is | not
with | me.

4 It cannot be | gotten for | gold : neither shall silver be | weighed for
the | price there- | of.

5 It cannot be valued with the | gold of | Ophir, : with the precious |
onyx, | or the | sapphire.

6 The gold and the | crystal cannot | equal it : and the exchange of it
shall not be for | jewels | of fine | gold.

7 No mention shall be made of coral | or of | pearls : for the price of |
wisdom | is above | rubies.

8 The topaz of Ethiopia | shall not | equal it : neither shall it be |
valued | with pure | gold.

9 Whence then | cometh | wisdom ? : and where is the | place of |
under- | standing ?

10 Seeing it is hid from the | eyes of all | living : and kept | close from
the | fowls of the | air.

11 De- | struction and death | say : We have heard the | fame thereof |
with our | ears.

12 God understandeth the | way there- | of : and He | knoweth the |
place there- | of.

13 For He looketh to the | ends of the | earth : and | seeth | under the
whole | heaven ;

14 To make the | weight for the | winds : and He | weigheth the | waters
by | measure.

15 When He made a de- | cree for the | rain : and a way for the | light-
ning | of the | thunder.

16 Then did He | see it, and de- | clare it : He prepared it, | yea, and |
searched it | out.

17 And unto man He said,v Behold, the fear of the Lord, | that is |
wisdom : and to depart from | evil is | under- | standing.

67 Isaiah 12.

1 AND in that day thou shalt say, O Lord, | I will | praise Thee : though Thou wast angry with me,ᵛ Thine anger is turned
away, | and Thou | comfortedst | me.
2 Behold, God is my salvation ;ᵛ I will trust, and | not be a- | fraid :
for the Lord Jehovah is my strength and my song ;ᵛ He | also is be- |
come my sal- | vation.
3 Therefore with joy shall ye draw water out of the | wells of sal- |
vation : And | in that | day shall ye | say,
4 Praise the Lord, call upon His name,ᵛ declare His doings a- | mong
the | people : make mention | that His | name is ex- | alted.
5 Sing unto the Lord ;ᵛ for He hath done | excellent | things : this is |
known in | all the | earth.
6 Cry out and shout, thou in- | habitant of | Zion : for great is the Holy
One of Israel | in the | midst of | thee.

68 Isaiah 25. 1, 8, 9; 26, 2—4.

1 O LORD, | Thou art my | God : I will exalt Thee, | I will | praise Thy | name.
2 For Thou hast done | wonderful | things : Thy counsels of old are |
faithful- | ness and | truth.
3 He will swallow up | death in | victory : and the Lord God will wipe
away | tears from | off all | faces ;
4 And the rebuke of His people shall He take away from off | all the |
earth : for the | Lord hath | spoken | it.
5 And it shall be said in that day, Lo, | this is our | God : we have
waited for | Him, and | He will | save us :
6 This is the Lord,ᵛ we have | waited for | Him : we will be glad and
re- | joice in | His sal- | vation.
7 Open | ye the | gates : that the righteous nation which keepeth the |
truth may | enter | in.
8 Thou wilt keep him in perfect peace, whose mind is | stayed on |
Thee : be- | cause he | trusteth in | Thee.
9 Trust ye in the | Lord for | ever : for in the Lord Jehovah is | ever- |
lasting | strength.

69 Isaiah 35.

1 THE wilderness and the solitary place shall be | glad for | them : and the desert shall rejoice, and | blossom | as the | rose.
2 It shall | blossom a- | bundantly : and rejoice | even with | joy and |
singing.
3 The glory of Lebanon shall be given unto it,ᵛ the excellency of |
Carmel and | Sharon : they shall see the glory of the Lord,ᵛ and
the | excellency | of our | God.

4 Strengthen | ye the weak | hands : and con- | firm the | feeble | knees.

5 Say to them that are of a fearful | heart, Be strong | fear not : behold, your God will come with vengeance,∨ even God with a recompense, | He will | come and | save you.

6 Then the eyes of the blind shall be opened :∨ and the ears of the | deaf shall be un- | stopped.

7 Then shall the lame man leap as an | hart and the | tongue of the dumb | sing.

8 For in the wilderness shall waters break out, and | streams in the | desert.

9 And the parched ground shall become a pool :∨ and the | thirsty land | springs of | water.

10 In the habitation of dragons | where each | lay : shall be | grass with | reeds and | rushes.

11 And an highway shall be there, and a way,∨ and it shall be called The | way of | holiness : the un- | clean shall | not pass | over it.

12 But it shall | be for | those : the wayfaring men, though | fools, shall not | err there- | in.

13 No lion | shall be | there : nor any ravenous beast shall go up there- | on, it shall | not be found | there.

14 But the redeemed shall walk there.∨

15 And the ransomed of the | Lord shall re- | turn : and come to Zion with songs and everlasting | joy up- | on their | heads.

16 They shall obtain | joy and | gladness : and sorrow and | sighing shall | flee a- | way.

70 — Isaiah 52. 7—10.

1 HOW beautiful upon the mountains are the feet of him that | bringeth good | tidings, : that publisheth peace, that | bringeth good | tidings of | good.

2 That | publisheth sal- | vation : that saith unto | Zion, | Thy God | reigneth !

3 Thy watchmen shall | lift up the | voice : with the voice to- | gether | shall they | sing :

4 For they shall see | eye to | eye : when the | Lord shall | bring again | Zion.

5 Break | forth into | joy : sing together ye waste | places | of Jer- | usalem.

6 For the Lord hath | comforted His | people : He | hath re- | deemed Jer- | usalem.

7 The Lord hath made bare His | holy | arm : in the | eyes of | all the | nations :

8 And all the ends of the | earth shall | see : the sal- | vation | of our | God.

71 ISAIAH 60. 1—11, 18—20.

1 ARISE, shine ; for thy | light is | come : and the glory of the |
Lord is | risen up- | on thee.
2 For, behold, the darkness shall | cover the | earth : and | gross |
darkness the | people.
3 But the Lord shall a- | rise up- | on thee : and His glory | shall be |
seen up- | on thee.
4 And the Gentiles shall | come to thy | light : and kings to the | bright-
ness | of thy | rising.
5 Lift up thine eyes round a- | bout, and | see : all they gather themselves
to- | gether, they | come to | thee.
6 Thy sons shall | come from | far : and thy daughters | shall be |
nursed at thy | side.
7 Then thou shalt see, and | flow to- | gether : and thine heart shall |
fear, and | be en- | larged.
8 Because the abundance of the sea shall be converted | unto | thee :
the forces of the | Gentiles shall | come unto | thee.
9 The multitude of camels shall | cover | thee : the dromedaries of
Midian and Ephah, | all they from | Sheba shall | come.
10 They shall bring | gold and | incense : and they shall shew forth the |
praises | of the | Lord.
11 All the flocks of Kedar shall be gathered together | unto | thee : the
rams of Nebaioth shall | minister | unto | thee.
12 They shall come up with acceptance | on mine | altar : and I will |
glorify the | house of my | glory.
13 Who are these that | fly as a | cloud : and | as the | doves to their |
windows ?
14 Surely the isles shall | wait for | me : and the ships of Tarshish first
to bring thy sons from far,˅ their silver | and their | gold with | them.
15 Unto the name of the Lord thy God, and to the Holy | One of | Israel :
because | He hath | glorified | thee.
16 And the sons of strangers shall | build up thy | walls : and their kings
shall | minister | unto | thee.
17 For in my | wrath I | smote thee : but in my favour have | I had |
mercy on | thee.
18 Therefore thy gates shall be | open con- | tinually : they shall | not be
shut | day nor | night.
19 That men may bring unto thee the forces | of the | Gentiles : and |
that their | kings may be | brought.
20 Violence shall no more be heard in thy land,˅ wasting nor destruction
with- | in thy | borders.,
21 But thou shalt call thy walls Sal- | vation | and thy gates | Praise.
22 The sun shall be no more thy | light by | day : neither for brightness
shall the | moon give | light unto | thee :

23 But the Lord shall be unto thee an everlasting light, and thy | God
thy | glory.
24 Thy sun shall no more go down ;v neither shall thy | moon with- |
draw it- | self :
25 For the Lord shall be thine ever- | lasting | light : and the days of
thy | mourning | shall be | ended.

72 1 Cor. 5. 7—8 ; Rom. 6. 9—11 ; 1 Cor. 15. 20—22, 57.

1 CHRIST our passover is | sacrificed | for us : therefore | let us |
keep the | feast ;
2 Not with the old leaven,v nor with the leaven of | malice and |
wickedness : but with the unleavened bread of sin- | ceri- | ty and | truth.
3 Christ being raised from the dead | dieth no | more : death hath no
more do- | minion | over | Him.
4 For in that He died, He died | unto sin | once : but in that He liveth,
He | liveth | unto | God.
5 Likewise reckon ye also yourselves to be dead indeed | unto | sin :
but alive unto God through | Jesus | Christ our | Lord.
6 Christ is risen | from the | dead : and become the | firstfruits of |
them that | slept.
7 For since by | man came | death : by man came also the resur- |
rection | of the | dead.
8 For as in | Adam all | die : even so in Christ shall | all be | made |
alive.
9 But | thanks be to | God : which giveth us the victory through | our
Lord | Jesus | Christ.

73 Ecclesiasticus 44. 1—15.

1 LET us now praise | famous | men : and our | fathers | that
be- | gat us.
2 The Lord hath wrought great | glory by | them : through His great |
power | from the be- | ginning.
3 Such as did bear | rule in their | kingdoms : men renowned for their
power ;v giving counsel by their understanding, | and de- | claring |
prophecies :
4 Leaders of the people by their counsels,v and by their knowledge of
learning | meet for the | people : wise and | eloquent | in their in- | struc-
tions.
5 Such as found out | musical | tunes : and re- | cited | verses in | writing.
6 Rich men | furnished with a- | bility : living peaceably | in their |
habi- | tations :

7 All these were honoured in their | gener- | ations : and were the |
glory | of their | times.

8 There be of them, that have left a | name be- | hind them : that their |
praises might | be re- | ported.

9 And some there be, which | have no me- | morial : who are perished,
as though | they had | never | been :

10 And are become as though they had | never been | born : and their |
children | after | them.

11 But these were | merciful | men : whose righteousness | hath not |
been for- | gotten.

12 With their seed shall continually remain a | good in- | heritance :
and their children | are with- | in the | covenant.

13 Their seed | standeth | fast : and their | children | for their | sakes.

14 Their seed shall | remain for | ever : and their glory shall | not be |
blotted | out.

15 Their bodies are | buried in | peace : but their name | liveth for |
ever- | more.

16 The people will | tell of their | wisdom : and the congre- | gation will |
shew forth their | praise.

74 WISDOM 3. 1—9.

1 BUT the souls of the righteous are in the | hand of | God : and |
there shall no | torment | touch them.

2 In the sight of the unwise they | seemed to | die : and their de- |
parture is | taken for | misery.

3 And their going from us to be utter destruction ;ᵛ but | they are in |
peace.

4 For though they be punished in the sight of men,ᵛ yet is their | hope
full of | immor- | tality.

5 And having been a little chastised,ᵛ they shall be | greatly re- |
warded : for God proved them, and found them | worthy | for Him- | self.

6 As gold in the furnace | hath He | tried them : and re- | ceived them |
as a burnt | offering.

7 And in the time of their visitation | they shall | shine : and run to
and fro like | sparks a- | mong the | stubble.

8 They shall judge the nations, and have dominion | over the | people :
and their | Lord shall | reign for | ever.

9 They that put their trust in Him shall under- | stand the | truth :
and such as be faithful in love | shall a- | bide with | Him :

10 For grace and mercy is | to His | saints : and He hath | care for |
His e- | lect.

GOD spake these words, and said; I am the Lord thy God: Thou shalt have none other gods but Me.

Lord, have mercy upon us, and incline our hearts to keep this law.

Thou shalt not make to thyself any graven image, nor the likeness of any thing that is in heaven above, or in the earth beneath, or in the water under the earth. Thou shalt not bow down to them, nor worship them: for I the Lord thy God am a jealous God, and visit the sins of the fathers upon the children unto the third and fourth generation of them that hate Me, and show mercy unto thousands in them that love Me and keep My commandments.

Lord, have mercy upon us, and incline our hearts to keep this law.

Thou shalt not take the name of the Lord thy God in vain: for the Lord will not hold him guiltless that taketh His name in vain.

Lord, have mercy upon us, and incline our hearts to keep this law.

Remember that thou keep holy the Sabbath-day. Six days shalt thou labour, and do all that thou hast to do; but the seventh day is the Sabbath of the Lord thy God. In it thou shalt do no manner of work, thou, and thy son, and thy daughter, thy man-servant, and thy maid-servant, thy cattle, and the stranger that is within thy gates. For in six days the Lord made heaven and earth, the sea, and all that in them is, and rested the seventh day: wherefore the Lord blessèd the seventh day, and hallowed it.

Lord, have mercy upon us, and incline our hearts to keep this law.

Honour thy father and thy mother; that thy days may be long in the land which the Lord thy God giveth thee.

Lord, have mercy upon us, and incline our hearts to keep this law.

Thou shalt do no murder.

Lord, have mercy upon us, and incline our hearts to keep this law.

Thou shalt not commit adultery.

Lord, have mercy upon us, and incline our hearts to keep this law.

Thou shalt not steal.

Lord, have mercy upon us, and incline our hearts to keep this law.

Thou shalt not bear false witness against thy neighbour.

Lord, have mercy upon us, and incline our hearts to keep this law.

Thou shalt not covet thy neighbour's house, thou shalt not covet thy neighbour's wife, nor his servant, nor his maid, nor his ox, nor his ass, nor any thing that is his.

Lord, have mercy upon us, and write all these Thy laws in our hearts, we beseech Thee.

The Commandments of the Lord Jesus

St. Matthew 22; St. Mark 12; St. John 13.

JESUS said: The first of all the commandments is: The Lord our God is one Lord: and thou shalt love the Lord thy God with all thy heart, and with all thy soul, and with all thy mind, and with all thy strength. This is the first and great commandment.

Lord, have mercy upon us, and incline our hearts to keep this law.

And the second is like unto it, namely this: Thou shalt love thy neighbour as thyself.

Lord, have mercy upon us, and incline our hearts to keep this law.

A new commandment I give unto you, That ye love one another; as I have loved you, that ye also love one another.

Lord, have mercy upon us, and write all these Thy laws in our hearts, we beseech Thee.

Responses to the Commandments

No. 1

After the 1st, 3rd, 5th, 7th and 9th.
Andante.
J. F. Bridge.
p
Lord, have mercy up - on . . us, and in-cline our hearts to keep this law.
p
After the 2nd, 4th, 6th and 8th.
Unison.
Lord, have mer-cy up - on us, and in-cline our hearts to keep this law.
p

After the 10th.

By permission of Novello and Company, Limited.

After the 1st, 3rd, 5th, 7th and 9th. J. F. BRIDGE.

Responses to the Commandments

After the 2nd, 4th, 6th and 8th.
Unison.
p
Lord, have mer - cy up - on us, and in -
- cline our hearts to keep this law.
After the 10th.
p
Lord, have mer - cy up - on us, and write all these Thy
laws . . in our hearts, we be - seech . . . . Thee.
pp
rall.

Responses to the Commandments

No. 3

After the 1st, 3rd, 5th, 7th and 9th.
J. Merbecke.
Har. by J. Stainer.
cresc.
Lord, have mer - cy up- on us, and incline our hearts to keep this law.
After the 2nd, 4th, 6th and 8th.
Unison.
Lord, have mer - cy up - on us,
cresc.
and in - cline our hearts to keep this law.
After the 10th.
Slow.
Lord, have mer - cy up - on us, and write all these Thy laws in our hearts, we be-seech Thee.

By permission of Novello and Company, Limited.

Responses to the Commandments

No. 4
J. Stainer.
mp
cresc.
dim.
Lord, have mer-cy up-on us, and in-cline our hearts to
keep this law.
After the 10th.
Lord, have mer-cy up-on us, and
write all these Thy laws in our hearts, we be-seech Thee.
Slow.
pp
Copyright, 1899, by Novello and Company, Limited.
No. 5
After the 1st, 2nd, 3rd, 7th, 8th and 9th.
B. Agutter.
Lord, have mercy up-on .. us, and incline our hearts to keep this law.
After the 4th, 5th and 6th.
mf
Lord, have mercy up-on . . us, and incline our hearts to keep this law.

Responses to the Commandments

After the 10th.
Lord, have mer - cy up - on . . us, and write all these Thy
rall.
laws in our hearts, we be - seech . . Thee.
rall.
By permission. From Service in A♭ major. (Messrs. Paxton & Co., Ltd.)
No. 6
E. H. Thorne.
sostenuto.
p
cresc.
dim.
Lord, have mer - cy up - on . . us, and in - cline our hearts to
p
cresc.
dim.
After the 10th.
p
p
cresc.
keep this law. Lord, have mer - cy up - on . . us, and
p
p
cresc.
Lento.
pp
write all these Thy laws in our hearts, we be - seech Thee.
pp
By permission of Novello and Company, Limited.

The Beatitudes

77

BLESSÈD are the poor in spirit : for theirs is the Kingdom of Heaven.
Grant us this grace, we beseech Thee, O Lord.

Blessèd are they that mourn : for they shall be comforted.
Grant us this grace, we beseech Thee, O Lord.

Blessèd are the meek : for they shall inherit the earth.
Grant us this grace, we beseech Thee, O Lord.

Blessèd are they which do hunger and thirst after righteousness : for they shall be filled.
Grant us this grace, we beseech Thee, O Lord.

Blessèd are the merciful : for they shall obtain mercy.
Grant us this grace, we beseech Thee, O Lord.

Blessèd are the pure in heart : for they shall see God.
Grant us this grace, we beseech Thee, O Lord.

Blessèd are the peacemakers : for they shall be called the children of God.
Grant us this grace, we beseech Thee, O Lord.

Blessèd are they which are persecuted for righteousness' sake : for theirs is the Kingdom of Heaven.
Write these words in our hearts, we beseech Thee, O Lord.

No. 1

From Ancient Sources.

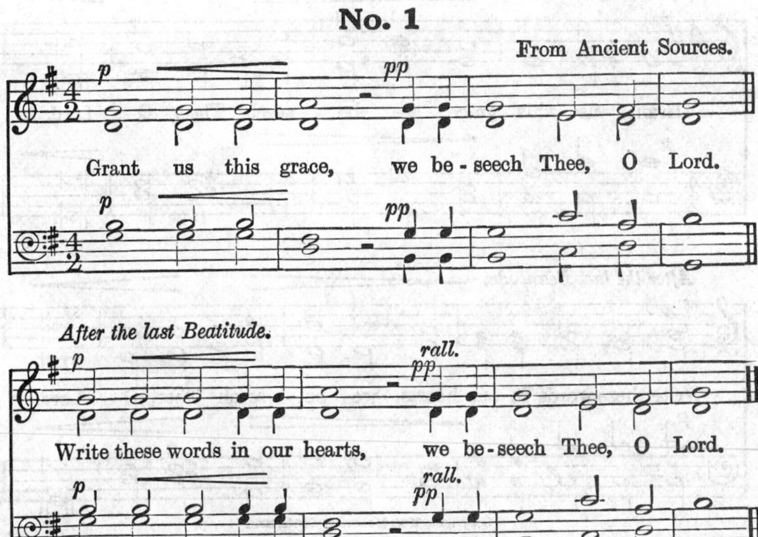
p
pp
Grant us this grace, we be - seech Thee, O Lord.
After the last Beatitude.
rall.
Write these words in our hearts, we be - seech Thee, O Lord.

The Beatitudes

No. 2

Adapted from Tallis' Litany.

p
pp
Grant us this grace, we be-seech Thee, O Lord. . .
p
pp
After the last Beatitude.
p
rall.
pp
Write these words in our hearts, we be-seech Thee, O Lord . . .
p
rall.
pp

No. 3

Adapted from Tallis' Litany.

p
Grant us this grace, we be - seech Thee, O Lord.
p
After the last Beatitude.
p
Write these words in our hearts, we be - seech Thee, O Lord.
p

These may be sung alternately, or a single setting only taken.

The Lord's Prayer

78

OUR Father, which art in heaven, Hallowed be Thy Name, Thy kingdom come, Thy will be done, in earth as it is in heaven. Give us this day our daily bread; And forgive us our trespasses, As we forgive them that trespass against us; And lead us not into temptation, But deliver us from evil. For Thine is the kingdom, the power and the glory, For ever and ever, Amen.

I

INDEX OF ANCIENT HYMNS, CANTICLES, PSALMS, AND PASSAGES OF SCRIPTURE

PSALMS

PASSAGES OF SCRIPTURE AND PASSAGES WITH RESPONSES

SINGLE CHANTS

DOUBLE CHANTS

QUADRUPLE CHANT

II

INDEX OF TUNES

ALPHABETICALLY ARRANGED

The numbers in (—) indicate a hymn at which the tune is referred to by cross reference.

III

METRICAL INDEX OF TUNES

The numbers in (—) indicate a hymn at which the tune is referred to by cross reference.

C.M. and refrain

D.C.M.

L.M.

L.M. and Hallelujahs

L.M. and refrain

D.L.M.

IV

COMPOSERS, ARRANGERS, AND SOURCES OF TUNES

** Denotes an arrangement by the person named.*

When the Composer's dates are unknown the year of the first appearance of the tune is given.

V
INDEX OF AUTHORS, TRANSLATORS, AND SOURCES OF HYMNS

** Denotes a translation by the person named*

VI

HYMNS WITH TUNES AND METRES

Hymns marked * are suitable for Young People.
Numbers with v. in front refer to the Section of Verses.

FIRST LINE	NO.	TUNE	METRE
A charge to keep I have	578	Cambridge	S.M.
*A gladsome hymn of praise we sing	971	The Blessed Name	8.7.8.7. (Iambic) and refrain
A little child may know	853	Newland ..	S.M.
A safe stronghold our God is still ..	494	Ein' feste Burg ..	8.7.8.7.6 6.6 6.7.
A spark of that ethereal fire ..	v.45	Worsley, No. 270 ..	8 8.8 8.8 8.
A virgin most pure, as the prophets do tell	128	A virgin most pure	11 11.11 11. and refrain
Abide among us with Thy grace ..	698	Abbey ..	C.M.
Abide with me ; fast falls the eventide	948	Eventide	10 10.10 10.
Above the clear blue sky	834	Children's Voices ..	6.6.6.6.4.4 4.4.
According to Thy gracious word ..	763	Abbey ..	C.M.
Across the sky the shades of night	961	The Golden Chain	8.7.8.7.8 8.7.
Ah, holy Jesu, how hast Thou offended	177	Herzliebster Jesu	11 11.11 5.
Ah ! Lord, with trembling I confess	480	Babylon's Streams	L.M.
Ah ! whither should I go	364	Wirksworth ..	S.M.
All as God wills, who wisely heeds ..	629	St. Austin	C.M.
*All creatures of our God and King	28	St. Francis (Lasst uns erfreuen) ..	8 8.8 8. and refrain
All glory, laud, and honour	84	St. Theodulph ..	7.6.7.6.D.
All glory to God in the sky	902	St. Cyprian	8.8.8.8.D.
*All hail the power of Jesu's name ..	91	Miles Lane	C.M.
*All my heart this night rejoices ..	121	Bonn	8.6.6.D.
All my hope on God is founded ..	70	Meine Hoffnung ..	8.7.8.7.3 3 7.
*All people that on earth do dwell	2	Old 100th	L.M.
All praise to Him who dwells in bliss	934	Epworth	C.M.
All praise to our redeeming Lord ..	745	Lucius	C.M.
All thanks be to God..	262	Derbe	5 5.5 11.D.
All thanks to the Lamb	747	St. Ignatius ..	5.5.5.5.6.5.6.5.
All things are possible to him ..	548	Holy Faith ..	8.8.8.8.8 8.
All things bright and beautiful ..	851	All things bright and beautiful (Keats) (i) Royal Oak (ii) ..	7.6.7.6. and refrain
*All things praise Thee, Lord most high	29	Te laudant omnia..	7 7.7 7.7 7.
All things which live below the sky	852	Rodmell	C.M.
All ye that pass by	188	Darlington	5 5 11.D.
Almighty Father, who dost give ..	907	Vermont	L.M.
And are we yet alive	709	Falcon Street ..	S.M.
And art Thou come with us to dwell	259	St. Sepulchre ..	L.M.
And can I yet delay	v.22	Shirland, No. 341 ..	S.M.
And can it be that I should gain ..	371	Sagina (i) .. Lansdown (ii) ..	8.8.8.8.8 8.
And did those feet in ancient time	v. 1	Sannox, No. 887 ..	D.L.M.
And didst Thou love the race that loved not Thee	149	Artavia	10.10.10.6.
And let our bodies part	807	Doncaster (Bethlehem) (i) Canada (ii)	S.M.
And now, O Father, mindful of the love	759	Unde et memores ..	10 10.10 10.10 10.
And will this sovereign King ..	v. 3	Millennium, No. 114	6.6.6.6.8 8.
*Angel voices, ever singing	668	Eide (i) .. Angel Voices (ii) ..	8.5.8.5.8 4.3.
*Angels from the realms of glory ..	119	Woodford Green (i) Iris (ii) ..	8.7.8.7.4.7.
Angels holy, High and lowly ..	27	Lytham St. Annes (i) Seraphim (ii) ..	4 4.7.8 8.7
*Another year is dawning	954	Another Year (i) Cherry Tree Carol (ii)	7.6.7.6.
Arise, my soul, arise	368	St. Swithin ..	6.6.6.6.8 8.
*Arm of the Lord, awake, awake ..	486	Justification ..	L.M.
Around the throne of God in heaven	656	Glory	8.6.8.6. and refrain
Art thou weary, art thou languid ..	320	Stephanos	8.5.8.3.

FIRST LINE	NO.	TUNE	METRE
As helpless as a child who clings ..	508	Christmas Carol ..	D.C.M.
As pants the hart for cooling streams	455	Martyrdom ..	C.M.
*As with gladness men of old ..	132	Orient	7 7.7 7.7 7.
*At even, ere the sun was set ..	689	Angelus	L.M.
At the Cross! At the Cross ..	v.13		Irregular
At the Cross, her station keeping ..	185	Stabat Mater ..	8 8.7.D.
At Thy feet, O Christ, we lay ..	933	St. John	7 7.7 7.7 7.
Author of faith, eternal Word ..	362	Mainzer	L.M.
Author of life divine	764	Wesley	6.6.6.6.8 8.
*Awake, awake to love and work ..	588	Sheltered Dale ..	8.6.8.6.8.6.
*Awake, glad soul, awake, awake ..	214	Belgrave	C.M.
*Awake, my soul, and with the sun	931	Morning Hymn ..	L.M.
Awake, our souls! Away, our fears	418	Samson	L.M.
Away in a manger, no crib for a bed	860	Away in a Manger	11 11.11 11.
Away, my needless fears	510	Clifton	S.M.
Away with gloom, away with doubt	231	Blairgowrie.. ..	8.8.8.6.4.6.
Away with our fears, Our troubles..	278	Ardwick	5 5.5 11.
Away with our fears! The glad ..	874	Builth	5 6.9.6 6.9.
Away with our sorrow and fear ..	648	Hymn of Eve (Uxbridge)	8.8.8.8.D.
Be it according to Thy word ..	v.39	Bedford, No. 155 ..	C.M.
*Be it my only wisdom here	576	Grosvenor	8 8.6.D.
Be known to us in breaking bread ..	766	Belmont	C.M.
*Be Thou my Vision, O Lord of my heart	632	Slane	Irregular
Be with us, gracious Lord, to-day ..	983	Winchester New ..	L.M.
Before Jehovah's awful throne ..	3	Old 100th	L.M.
Before Thy throne, O God, we kneel	884	Strasburg	8 8.8 8.8 8.
Begin, my soul, some heavenly theme	72	St. Magnus	C.M.
Begone, unbelief; my Saviour is near	511	Spetisbury	10 10.11 11.
*Behold a little Child	164	Shebbear College ..	6.6.6.6.8 8.
Behold! a Stranger at the door ..	332	Entreaty	L.M.
Behold Me standing at the door ..	331	Behold Me standing	L.M. and refrain
Behold the Lamb of God, who bears	312	New 113th	8.8.8.8.8 8.
Behold, the mountain of the Lord ..	904	Glasgow	C.M.
Behold the Saviour of mankind ..	193	Burford	C.M.
Behold the servant of the Lord ..	572	Mozart	8.8.8.8.8 8.
Behold us, Lord, a little space ..	949	St. Bernard ..	C.M.
Being of beings, God of love ..	383	Tottenham ..	C.M.
Believe not those who say	591	St. Thomas.. ..	S.M.
Belovèd, let us love	444	Frogmore	6.4.6.4.
*Beneath the Cross of Jesus	197	Beneath the Cross of Jesus	7.6.8.6.8.6.8.6.
Blessèd are the pure in heart ..	571	Tichfield	7 7.7 7.D.
Blessèd assurance, Jesus is mine ..	422	Blessèd assurance	Irregular
Blessèd Jesus, here we stand ..	752	St. Mark	7.8.7.8.8 8.
Blest are the humble souls that see	697	Abney	L.M.
Blest are the pure in heart	950	Egham	S.M.
Blest be the dear uniting love ..	712	Tiverton	C.M.
Bread of heaven, on Thee I feed ..	769	Spanish Chant ..	7 7.7 7.7 7.
Bread of the world, in mercy broken	756	Rendez à Dieu ..	9.8.9.8.D.
Break, day of God, O break.. ..	253	Burton (i) .. .. Arncliffe (ii) ..	6.6.6.6.8 8.
Break Thou the bread of life ..	309	Bethsaida	6.4.6.4.D.
Breathe on me, Breath of God ..	300	St. Beuno	S.M.
Brethren in Christ, and well beloved	710	Otterbourne ..	L.M.
Brief life is here our portion ..	652	Ewing (i) .. .. St. Alphege (ii) ..	7.6.7.6.D. 7.6.7.6.
*Brightest and best of the sons of the morning	122	Spean (i) .. .. Epiphany Hymn (ii)	11.10.11.10.
Brightly beams our Father's mercy ..	582	Let the lower lights	8.7.8.7. and refrain
*Brightly gleams our banner ..	617	Armageddon ..	6.5.6.5.D. and refrain
Build us in one body up	v.43	Tichfield, No. 571 ..	7 7.7 7.D.
By Christ redeemed, in Christ restored	773	Memoria (i).. .. Willenhall (ii) ..	8 8 8.4.
By the holy hills surrounded ..	704	Sleepers, wake ..	8.9.8.D. 6 6.4.4 4 8.
Captain of Israel's host, and Guide..	608	Marienlyst	8.8.8.8.8 8.
Children of Jerusalem	837	Infant Praise ..	7 7.7 7. and refrain
*Children of the heavenly King ..	696	Trull (i) Melling (ii)	7 7.7 7.
Christ, above all glory seated ..	225	Dulcina	8.7.8.7.
*Christ for the world, we sing ..	805	Doxford (i) .. .. Edinburgh (ii) ..	6 6.4.6 6 6.4.

FIRST LINE	NO.	TUNE	METRE
Christ, from whom all blessings flow	720	Vienna	7 7.7 7.
Christ is our corner-stone	702	Harewood	6.6.6.6.8.8.
*Christ is risen! Hallelujah!	206	Morgenlied	8.7.8.7.D. and refrain
Christ is the foundation	981	Goshen	6.5.6.5.D.
Christ Jesus lay in death's strong bands	210	Christ lag in Todesbanden	8.7.8.7.7.8.7.4.
Christ, of all my hopes the ground	89	Lübeck	7.7.7.7.
Christ the Lord is risen again	207	Würtemberg	7 7.7 7.4.
*Christ the Lord is risen to-day	204	Easter Morn	7 7.7 7. and Hallelujahs
Christ, who knows all His sheep	639	Cambridge	6 6.6.5.6.5.
Christ, whose glory fills the skies	924	Heathlands	7.7.7.7.7 7.
*Christian, seek not yet repose	491	Camberwell	7.7.7.3.
*Christians, awake, salute the happy morn	120	Yorkshire	10 10.10 10.10 10.
*City of God, how broad and far	703	Richmond (i) Bristol (ii)	C.M.
Come, all whoe'er have set	606	Warsaw	6.6.6.6.8 8.
Come, and let us sweetly join	748	Hart's	7 7.7 7.
Come, divine Interpreter	306	Spanish Chant	7.7.7.7.7 7.
Come down, O Love Divine	273	Down Ampney	6 6.11.D.
Come, holy celestial Dove	294	Sion	8.8.8.8.D.
Come, Holy Ghost, all-quickening fire, Come, and in me	299	Arne's	8.8.8.8.8 8.
Come, Holy Ghost, all-quickening fire, Come, and my	553	Tarsus	8 8.8.D.
Come, Holy Ghost, our hearts inspire	305	Richmond	C.M.
Come, Holy Ghost, our souls inspire	779	Veni Creator	L.M.
Come, Holy Ghost, Thine influence shed	767	Hampstead	C.M.
Come, Holy Spirit, heavenly Dove	292	Manchester	C.M.
Come in, O come! The door stands open now	472	Battle	10 10.10 10.
*Come, let us all unite and sing	22	Better World	8.3.8.3.8 8 8.3.
Come, let us anew	956	Derbe	5 5.5 11.
*Come, let us join our cheerful songs	85	Nativity	C.M.
Come, let us join our friends above	824	St. Matthew	D.C.M.
Come let us sing of a wonderful love	314	Wonderful Love (i)	10.4.10.7.4 10.
Come, let us to the Lord our God	342	Byzantium	C.M.
Come, let us use the grace divine	749	Dundee (French)	C.M.
Come let us, who in Christ believe	333	Attercliffe	C.M.
Come, let us with our Lord arise	661	Plymouth Dock	8 8.8 8.8 8.
*Come, my soul, thou must be waking	929	Meine Armuth	8 4.7.D.
Come, my soul, thy suit prepare	540	Christ Chapel	7 7.7 7.
Come, O come, in pious lays	20	Te Deum laudamus	7 7.7 7.D.
Come, O my God, the promise seal	559	Ballerma	C.M.
Come, O Thou all-victorious Lord	347	York	C.M.
Come, O Thou Traveller unknown	339	Wrestling Jacob	8.8.8.8.8 8.
Come, O Thou Traveller unknown [Abbreviated version]	340	David's Harp	8.8.8.8.8 8.
Come on, my partners in distress	487	Praise	8 8.6.D.
Come, Saviour, Jesus, from above	546	Wareham	L.M.
Come, sinners, to the gospel feast	323	Fulda	L.M.
Come, Thou everlasting Spirit	765	Sicilian Mariners	8.7.8.7.
Come, Thou Fount of every blessing	417	Normandy	8.7.8.7.D.
Come, Thou long-expected Jesus	242	Stuttgart	8.7.8.7.
Come to our poor nature's night	297	Angelus	7 7 7.5.
Come unto Me, ye weary	328	Come unto Me	7.6.7.6.D.
Come, ye sinners, poor and wretched	324	Bryn Calfaria	8.7.8.7.4.7.
Come, ye thankful people, come	962	St. George's, Windsor	7 7.7 7.D.
*Come, ye that love the Lord	410	Ridge (i) Ascension (ii)	D.S.M.
Commit thou all thy griefs	507	Franconia (i) Song 20 (ii)	S.M.
Conquering Prince and Lord of glory	227	Salzburg	8.7.8.7.7 7.7 7.
Cradled in a manger, meanly	127	Òran na Prasaich (*The Song of the Manger*) (i) St. Winifred (ii)	8.7.8.7.D.
Creator Spirit; by whose aid	293	Attwood	8 8.8 8.8 8.
*Crown Him with many crowns	271	Diademata	D.S.M.
Day after day I sought the Lord	367	Lincoln	C.M.
*Day by day we magnify Thee	867	Slingsby	8.7.8.7.
Day of wrath! O day of mourning	646	Dies Iræ	8 8 8.
Dear Lord and Father of mankind	669	Georgia	8.6.8 8.6.

FIRST LINE	NO.	TUNE	METRE
Dear Master, in whose life I see ..	163	Gillingham ..	L.M.
Deepen the wound Thy hands have made	556	Bangor	C.M.
Deepen the wound Thy hands have made	v.34	Dundee (French), No. 749 ..	C.M.
Depth of mercy! can there be ..	358	Redhead No. 47 ..	7 7.7 7.
*Dismiss me not Thy service, Lord ..	580	Spohr	8.6.8.6.8.6.
Disposer Supreme, and Judge of the earth	788	St. Merryn	10.10.11.11.
Drawn to the Cross which Thou hast blessed	345	Isleworth	8 8 8.6.
Earth below is teeming	966	Princethorpe ..	6.5.6.5.D.
Earth, rejoice, our Lord is King ..	246	Ephraim ..	7 7.7 7.
Earth, with all thy thousand voices	61	Exultation	8.7.8.7.D.
Entered the holy place above ..	232	Adam	8.8.8.8.8 8.
Ere God had built the mountains ..	60	Pearsall	7.6.7.6.D.
Ere I sleep, for every favour ..	947	Evensong	8.3 3.6.
Eternal beam of light divine ..	496	Invitation	L.M.
Eternal depth of love divine ..	63	Ossett	L.M.
Eternal Father, strong to save ..	917	Melita	8 8.8 8.8 8.
*Eternal Light! Eternal Light ..	544	Newcastle (i) .. Royal Fort (ii) ..	8.6.8 8.6.
Eternal Power! whose high abode..	6	Saul (Fertile Plains)	L.M.
Eternal Ruler of the ceaseless round	892	Song 1 ..	10.10.10.10.10 10.
Eternal Son, eternal Love	794	St. Pancras ..	L.M.
Eternal Sun of Righteousness ..	378	Dublin	C.M.
Fainting soul, be bold, be strong ..	479	Hotham	7.7.7.7.D.
Faith, mighty faith, the promise sees	v.24	Tottenham, No. 383	C.M.
Faith of our fathers, living still ..	402	Faith of our fathers	8.8.8.8. and refrain
Far off we need not rove	440	Fulneck	6 6.7.7.7.7.
Far round the world Thy children sing their song	798	Parting	10.10.10.10.
Father Divine, I come to Thee ..	935	Motherland	L.M.
Father, I dare believe	564	Ripon	S.M.
*Father, I know that all my life ..	602	Arabia (i) .. .. Lebanon (ii) ..	8.6.8.6.8.6.
Father, if justly still we claim ..	284	Illsley	L.M.
Father, in high heaven dwelling ..	938	Evening Hymn ..	8 8.7.D.
Father, in whom we live	39	Fairfield	D.S.M.
Father, lead me day by day ..	849	Supplication ..	7 7.7 7.
*Father, let me dedicate	957	Dedication	7.5.7.5.D.
*Father, let Thy kingdom come ..	810	Da Christus geboren war	7.7.7.7.
Father of all, in whom alone ..	304	Tallis' Ordinal ..	C.M.
Father of all, to Thee	740	Bevan	6.6.6.6.8 8.
Father of all! whose powerful voice	47	Eisenach	L.M.
Father of everlasting grace	730	Stamford	8 8.8.D.
Father of heaven, whose love profound	38	Rivaulx	L.M.
Father of Jesus Christ, my Lord ..	561	Solomon	C.M.
Father of men, in whom are one ..	982	Exeter	8 8 8.D.
Father of mercies, in Thy word ..	302	Tiltey Abbey ..	C.M.
Father, Son, and Holy Ghost ..	574	Wellspring	7.7.7.7.7 7.
Father, who art alone	915	Ings	6.6.6.6.8 8.
Father, who on man dost shower ..	894	Quem pastores laudavere	8 8 8.7.
Father, whose everlasting love ..	75	Melcombe	L.M.
Fierce raged the tempest o'er the deep	167	St. Aëlred	8 8 8.3.
*Fight the good fight with all thy might	490	Shepton-Beauchamp	L.M.
*Fill Thou my life, O Lord my God	604	St. Fulbert (i) .. Beatitudo (ii) ..	C.M.
*Fling out the banner! Let it float ..	817	Pentecost	L.M.
For all the saints who from their labours rest	832	Sine nomine (i) .. For all the saints (ii)	10 10 10.4.
For ever here my rest shall be ..	456	Martyrdom ..	C.M.
For ever with the Lord	658	Nearer Home ..	D.S.M.
For souls redeemed, for sins forgiven	v.11	Almsgiving, No. 969	8 8 8.4.
*For the beauty of the earth ..	35	Noricum	7.7.7.7.7 7.
*For the might of Thine arm we bless Thee	715	Mountain Christians	Irregular
For those we love within the veil ..	657	Meyer (Es ist kein Tag)	8.8.8.4.

FIRST LINE	NO.	TUNE	METRE
For you and for me	v.16	Harwich, No. 66	5 5 11.D.
Forget them not, O Christ, who stand	789	Fritwell	8 8.
Forth in Thy name, O Lord, I go	590	Antwerp	L.M.
*Forth rode the knights of old	819	Jericho Tune	D.S.M.
Forty days and forty nights	165	Heinlein	7.7.7.7.
*Forward! be our watchword	619	Forward! be our watchword	6.5. (12 lines)
Friend of the home, as when in Galilee	753	Ffigysbren	10 10.10 10.
*From all that dwell below the skies	4	St. Francis (Lasst uns erfreuen)	8 8.8 8. and Hallelujahs
From every stormy wind that blows	535	Pavia	L.M.
From glory to glory advancing	30	Sheen	14 14.14 15.
*From Greenland's icy mountains	801	Missionary	7.6.7.6.D.
*From north and south and east and west	266	Meyer (Es ist kein Tag)	8 8 8.4.
*From the eastern mountains	133	Kirkbraddan (i) Foundation (ii)	6.5.6.5.D.
From Thee all skill and science flow	921	Land of Rest	D.C.M.
From trials unexempted	476	Greenland	7.6.7.6.D.
Gentle Jesus, meek and mild	842	Innocents (i) Gentle Jesus (ii)	7 7.7 7.
Give heed, my heart, lift up thine eyes	126	Vom Himmel hoch (Erfurt)	L.M.
Give me the enlarged desire	v.31	Jeshurun, No. 68	7.6.7.6.7.7.7.6.
Give me the faith which can remove	390	Mount Sion	8.8.8.8.8 8.
Give me the wings of faith to rise	831	Mylon	C.M.
Give to the winds thy fears. Part 2	507	Franconia (i) Song 20 (ii)	S.M.
Glad was my heart to hear	680	Falcon Street	S.M.
*Glorious things of thee are spoken	706	Lux Eoi	8.7.8.7.D.
Glory be to God on high	134	Hatfield	7.6.7.6.7.7.7.6.
*Glory to Thee, my God, this night	943	Tallis' Canon	L.M.
Go, labour on; spend, and be spent	589	Grenoble	L.M.
Go not, my soul, in search of Him	281	Walsall	C.M.
Go to dark Gethsemane	194	Llyfnant	7.7.7.7.7 7.
*God be in my head	405	God be in my head	Irregular
God be with you till we meet again	914	Randolph	9.8 8.9.
*God bless our native land	880	Moscow	6 6.4.6 6 6.4.
God from on high hath heard	140	St. Cecilia	6.6.6.6.
God has given us a Book full of stories	857	The story of Jesus	Irregular
God is a name my soul adores	41	Breslau	L.M.
God is ascended up on high	220	God is ascended	L.M. and Alleluias
God is gone up on high	219	Dudley	6.6.6.6.8 8.
*God is love: His mercy brightens	53	Sussex (i) Unser Herrscher (ii)	8.7.8.7.
God is the refuge of His saints	705	Lasus	L.M.
*God is with us, God is with us	252	Pilgrim brothers	8.7.8.7.D.
*God is working His purpose out	812	Medak (i) Purpose (ii)	Irregular
God loved the world of sinners lost	337	Wondrous Love	C.M. and refrain
God make my life a little light	845	Capel	C.M.
God moves in a mysterious way	503	Irish	C.M.
God my Father, loving me	840	Peacefield	7 7.7 7.
God of all power, and truth, and grace	562	Ombersley	L.M.
God of all-redeeming grace	566	Benevento	7.7.7.7.D.
God of almighty love	595	Carlisle	S.M.
God of mercy, God of grace	681	Dix	7 7.7 7.7 7.
God of my life, through all my days	429	God of my life (i) Heaton Norris (ii)	L.M.
God of my salvation, hear	365	Faith	7.6.7.6.7.8.7.6.
God of our fathers, known of old	889	Lest we forget	8.8.8.8.8 8.
God of our fathers, unto Thee	887	Sannox	D.L.M. and refrain
God of pity, God of grace	682	Huddersfield (i) Capetown (ii)	7 7 7.5.
God of the living, in whose eyes	974	God of the living	8 8.8 8.8 8.
God of unexampled grace	191	Pelham	7.6.7.6.7.7.7.6.
God reveals His presence	31	Compton	6.6 8.D.3 3.6 6.
God save our gracious Queen	879	National Anthem	6 6.4.6 6 6.4.
God the All-terrible! King, who ordainest	901	Russia	11.10.11.9.
God the Father, be Thou near	952	Palestine	7.7.7.7.
God's trumpet wakes the slumbering world	401	Nativity	C.M.
Good Christian men, rejoice	143	In dulci jubilo	Irregular
Good Thou art, and good Thou dost	59	Elevation	7.6.7.6.7.8.7.6.

FIRST LINE	NO.	TUNE	METRE
*Gracious Spirit, dwell with me	291	Cassel	7 7.7 7.7 7.
Gracious Spirit, Holy Ghost	290	Charity	7 7 7.5.
Grant me my sins to feel	v.19	Cambridge, No. 234	S.M.
Granted is the Saviour's prayer	277	Buckland	7 7.7 7.
Great God, indulge my humble claim	389	Warrington	L.M.
Great God of wonders ! all Thy ways	356	Sovereignty	8.8.8.8.8 8.
Great is our redeeming Lord	699	Josiah	7.6.7.6.7.7.7.6.
Great is the Lord our God	676	St. George	S.M.
*Guide me, O Thou great Jehovah	615	Cwm Rhondda (i) Oriel (ii)	8.7.8.7.4.7.
Hail, gladdening Light, of His pure glory poured	937	Sebaste	Irregular
Hail ! holy, holy, holy Lord	37	Dunfermline	C.M.
Hail the day that sees Him rise	221	Ascension	7 7.7 7. and Alleluias
Hail, Thou once despisèd Jesus	228	Austria	8.7.8.7.D.
*Hail to the Lord's Anointed	245	Lancashire (i) Herrnhut (ii)	7.6.7.6.D.
*Happy are they, they that love God	419	Binchester	C.M.
Happy the heart where graces reign	442	Lynton	C.M.
Happy the man that finds the grace	360	Blockley	L.M.
Happy the souls to Jesus joined	818	St. Leonard	C.M.
Hark ! hark, my soul ! Angelic songs are swelling	651	La Suissesse (i) Pilgrims (ii)	11.10.11.10. and refrain
Hark, how the watchmen cry	481	Victory	D.S.M.
Hark, my soul ! it is the Lord	432	St. Bees	7 7.7 7.
*Hark the glad sound ! the Saviour comes	82	Bristol	C.M.
Hark ! the gospel news is sounding	315	St. Raphael	8.7.8.7.4.7.
*Hark ! the herald-angels sing	117	Berlin	7 7.7 7.D. and refrain
*Hark ! The song of jubilee	829	Thanksgiving	7 7.7 7.D.
Hark ! The sound of holy voices	830	Deerhurst	8.7.8.7.D.
Hark, 'tis the watchman's cry	482	Clarion	6.4.6.4.6 7 6.4.
Hark what a sound, and too divine for hearing	254	Highwood	11.10.11.10.
He dies ! the Friend of Sinners dies	195	Merthyr Tydfil	D.L.M.
He that is down needs fear no fall	514	Assurance (i) Dovedale (St. Hugh) (ii)	C.M.
He wants not friends that hath Thy love	714	O Jesu mi dulcissime	L.M.
Head of Thy church triumphant	411	Dying Stephen (i) Deliverance (ii)	7.7.4 4.7.D.
Head of Thy Church, whose Spirit fills	814	Doversdale	L.M.
Heal us, Immanuel ; hear our prayer	155	Bedford	C.M.
Hear Thou my prayer, O Lord	543	Egypt	S.M.
Hear us, O Lord, from heaven, Thy dwelling-place	970	Peel Castle	10.10 10.10.
Heavenly Father, Thou hast brought us	614	Salvator	8.7.8.7.D.
Help us to help each other, Lord	717	Lunenburg	C.M.
Here, Lord, we offer Thee all that is fairest	972	Springfield	11.10.11.10.
Here, O my Lord, I see Thee face to face	772	St. Agnes	10.10.10.10.
High in the heavens, eternal God	48	Berkshire	L.M.
Hills of the North, rejoice	815	Little Cornard	6.6.6.6.8 8.
Holy, and true, and righteous Lord	570	Uffingham	L.M.
Holy Father, in Thy mercy	916	St. Helen's	8.5.8.3.
Holy Ghost, my Comforter	287	Stabat Mater	7 7 7.
Holy, holy, holy, Lord God Almighty	36	Nicæa	11 12.12 10.
Holy Lamb, who Thee confess	598	Syria	7 7.7 7.D.
*Holy Spirit, hear us	286	North Coates	6.5.6.5.
Holy Spirit pity me	296	Heinlein	7 7.7 7.
Holy Spirit, truth Divine	288	Christus	7 7.7 7.
Hosanna, loud hosanna	836	Ellacombe	7.6.7.6.D.
How beauteous are their feet	778	Day of Praise	S.M.
How blessèd, from the bonds of sin	583	Beulah	D.C.M.
*How blest is life if lived for Thee	404	David's Harp	L.M.
How can a sinner know	377	St. Michael	S.M.
How do Thy mercies close me round	877	Saxby	L.M.
How happy are they	407	Hungerford	5 6.9.6 6.9.
How happy every child of grace	627	Spes celestis	D.C.M.
How pleasant, how divinely fair	711	Nicomachus	L.M.
How shall a sinner find	203	Shaftesbury	6 6.7.7.7.7.
How shall I sing that majesty	78	Soll's sein	D.C.M.
How shall I thank Thee for the grace	v.38	Monmouth, No. 428	8 8.8 8.8 8.
How sweet the name of Jesus sounds	99	St. Peter	C.M.
Hushed was the evening hymn	848	Samuel	6.6.6.6.8 8.

FIRST LINE	NO.	TUNE	METRE
I am not skilled to understand ..	381	Keston	8 8 8.7. Iambic
I am not worthy, holy Lord ..	758	Leicester	C.M.
*I am so glad that our Father in heaven	421	I am so glad ..	10 10.10 10. and refrain
*I am Thine, O Lord; I have heard Thy voice	746	Draw me nearer ..	10.7.10.7. and refrain
*I am trusting Thee, Lord Jesus ..	521	Eastergate (i) Trust (ii)	8.5.8.3.
*I bind unto myself to-day	392	St. Patrick ..	Irregular
I bless the Christ of God	112	Narenza	S.M.
I bow in silence at Thy feet ..	687	Erskine	8 8 8.6.
I bring my sins to Thee	520	Carinthia	6.6.6.6.8 8.
I cannot tell why He, whom angels worship	809	Londonderry Air ..	Irregular
I could not do without Thee ..	522	Magdalena	7.6.7.6.D.
I dared not hope that Thou wouldst deign to come	623	Nachtlied	10 10.10 10.10 10.
*I give my heart to Thee	393	Ich halte treulich still	D.S.M.
I have no help but Thine (Part 2) ..	772	St. Agnes	10.10.10.10.
I hear Thy welcome voice	351	Calvary	S.M. and refrain
*I heard the voice of Jesus say ..	154	Kingsfold (i) .. Vox Dilecti (ii) ..	D.C.M.
I hoped that with the brave and strong	592	Cripplegate.. ..	D.C.M.
*I hunger and I thirst..	462	Ibstone	6.6.6.6.
I know that my Redeemer lives, And ever	565	Crediton	C.M.
I know that my Redeemer lives, What joy	235	Torquay	L.M.
I lift my heart to Thee	451	Sursum corda ..	6.4.6.4.10 10.
I love to hear the story	856	Angels' Story ..	7.6.7.6.D.
I love to think, though I am young	855	Newbury	C.M.
I met the good Shepherd	174	St. Wilfrid	6.5.6.5.D.
*I need Thee every hour	475	I need Thee ..	6.4.6.4. and refrain
I sing the almighty power of God ..	46	St. Saviour ..	C.M.
I thank Thee, uncreated Sun ..	v. 9	St. Chrysostom (Barnby), No. 755	8.8.8.8.8 8.
'I the good fight have fought' ..	492	Holy Rood ..	S.M.
I think, when I read that sweet story of old	865	Athens	Irregular
I to the hills will lift mine eyes	625	Dundee (French) ..	C.M.
I vow to thee, my country	900	Thaxted	Irregular
I want a principle within	626	Albano	C.M.
I want the Spirit of power within ..	280	Lusatia	8.8.8.8.8 8.
I will accept His offer now ..	v.26	Farrant, No. 539 ..	C.M.
I will not let Thee go, Thou help in time of need	523	Tenax	12.4 4.10.6 6.10.6.
I will sing the wondrous story ..	380	Hyfrydol	8.7.8.7. and refrain
I would commune with Thee, my God	454	St. Frances ..	C.M.
I wrestle not now, but trample on sin	v.41	Hanover, No. 8 ..	10 10.11 11.
I'll praise my Maker while I've breath	428	Monmouth	8 8.8.D.
*I'm not ashamed to own my Lord ..	485	Azmon	C.M.
Immortal, invisible, God only wise ..	34	St. Denio	11 11.11 11.
Immortal Love, for ever full ..	102	Stracathro	C.M.
In age and feebleness extreme ..	v.47	Marylebone, A. T... No. 32	8 8.8 8.8 8.
In all my vast concerns with Thee	57	Wiltshire	C.M.
*In full and glad surrender	567	St. Victor	7.6.7.6.
In heavenly love abiding	528	Penlan	7.6.7.6.D.
In loving-kindness Jesus came ..	336	He lifted me ..	8 8 8.6. and refrain
In memory of the Saviour's love ..	762	Arnold's	C.M.
In our dear Lord's garden	843	Castle Eden ..	6.5.6.5.
In our work and in our play ..	871	Ashburton ..	7 7.7 7. and refrain
In the bleak mid-winter	137	Cranham	Irregular
In the Cross of Christ I glory ..	183	Love Divine ..	8.7.8.7.
In the Name of Jesus	249	Evelyns	6.5.6.5.D.
Infinite God, to Thee we raise ..	33	Strasburg	8 8.8 8.8 8.
It came upon the midnight clear ..	130	Noel	D.C.M.
*It fell upon a summer day	166	Childhood	8.8.8.6.
It is a thing most wonderful ..	854	Herongate	L.M.

FIRST LINE	NO.	TUNE	METRE
It passeth knowledge, that dear love of Thine	436	It passeth knowledge	10 10.10 10.4.
*I've found a Friend; O such a Friend	423	Constance	8.7.8.7.D. Iambic
Jerusalem, my happy home, Name ever	650	Jerusalem	C.M.
Jerusalem, my happy home, When shall	655	Bocking (i) .. .. Diana (ii)	C.M.
Jerusalem the golden (Part 2) ..	652	Ewing (i) .. St. Alphege (ii) ..	7.6.7.6.D.
Jesus, all-atoning Lamb	552	Keine Schönheit hat die Welt	7 7.7 7.
Jesus be endless praise to Thee (Part 2)	370	Confidence	L.M.
*Jesus calls us! O'er the tumult ..	157	St. Catherine ..	8.7.8.7.
*Jesus Christ is risen to-day ..	205	Llanfair	7.7.7 7. and Hallelujahs
Jesus comes with all His grace ..	87	Orientis partibus (i) Savannah (Herrnhut) (ii)	7.7.7 7.
Jesus, Friend of little children	841	Westridge (i) .. Derwent (ii) ..	8.5.8.3.
Jesus hath died and hath risen again	374	Jesus saves me now	10.7.10.5. and refrain
Jesus hath died that I might live ..	560	Devizes	C.M.
Jesus, high in glory	838	Glenfinlas	6.5.6.5.
Jesus, I fain would find	385	Tytherton	S.M.
Jesus, I will trust Thee	171	Jesus, I will trust Thee (Reliance)	11 11.11 11. and refrain
Jesus, if still the same Thou art ..	349	Carey's	8.8.8.8.8 8.
Jesus, if we aright confess	785	Old 44th	D.C.M.
Jesus, in whom the weary find ..	357	Marienbourn ..	8.8.8.8.8 8.
Jesus, keep me near the Cross ..	199	Near the Cross ..	7.6.7.6. and refrain
Jesus, let all Thy lovers shine ..	603	Attercliffe	C.M.
Jesus lives! thy terrors now ..	216	St. Albinus ..	7.8.7.8.4.
Jesus, Lord of life and glory ..	724	Jordan	8.7.8.7.4.7.
*Jesu, Lover of my soul	110	Hollingside ..	7.7.7.7.D.
Jesus, meek and gentle	734	St. Constantine ..	6.5.6.5.
Jesus, mighty to renew	v.20	Benevento, No. 876	7 7.7 7.D.
Jesu, my Lord, my God, my All ..	438	St. Chrysostom (Barnby) ..	8 8.8 8.8 8.
Jesus, my Saviour, Brother, Friend	478	Angels' Song ..	L.M.
Jesus, my strength, my hope ..	542	Leominster ..	D.S.M.
Jesu, my Truth, my Way	635	Potsdam	S.M.
Jesu, priceless treasure	518	Jesu, meine Freude	6 6.5.6 6.5.7.8 6.
Jesus! Redeemer, Saviour, Lord	366	Epworth	C.M.
*Jesus shall reign where'er the sun ..	272	Truro	L.M.
*Jesus, stand among us	684	Caswall	6.5.6.5.
*Jesus, still lead on	624	Spire	5 5.8.8.5 5.
*Jesus, Sun and Shield art Thou ..	95	Coldrey	7.6.7.6.7 7.
Jesus, Sun of Righteousness ..	733	Lux Prima ..	7.7.7.7.7 3.
Jesus, tender Shepherd, hear me ..	844	Evening Prayer ..	8.7.8.7.
Jesus, the all-restoring Word ..	464	Coleshill	C.M.
Jesus, the Conqueror, reigns ..	243	Ishmael	D.S.M.
Jesus, the First and Last	105	St. Olave	6 6.6 6.6 6.
Jesus, the gift divine I know ..	605	Colchester ..	8.8.8.8.8 8.
Jesus the good Shepherd is ..	621	Bread of Heaven ..	7.7.7.7.7 7.
Jesus! the name high over all ..	92	Lydia	C.M.
Jesus, the sinner's Friend, to Thee ..	344	Dorchester	L.M.
Jesu! The very thought is sweet ..	106	Pavia	L.M.
*Jesu, the very thought of Thee ..	108	Kilmarnock ..	C.M.
Jesu, the word bestow	248	St. George ..	S.M.
*Jesus, these eyes have never seen ..	111	Southwell ..	C.M.
*Jesu, Thou Joy of loving hearts ..	109	Wareham	L.M.
Jesus, Thou soul of all our joys ..	670	Grosvenor	8 8.6.D.
Jesus, Thou sovereign Lord of all ..	534	St. Werbergh ..	8.8.8.8.8 8.
Jesu, Thy blood and righteousness	370	Confidence	L.M.
Jesu, Thy boundless love to me ..	430	Giessen	8.8.8.8.8 8.
Jesus, Thy far-extended fame ..	153	Antwerp	L.M.
Jesus, Thy wandering sheep behold	791	Elim (Hesperus) ..	L.M.
Jesu, to Thee our hearts we lift ..	737	Cheshunt College ..	8.8.8.8.8 8.
Jesus, to Thee we fly	233	Irene	6 6.7.7.7.7.
Jesus, to Thy table led	770	Tyholland	7 7 7.
Jesus, united by Thy grace	721	St. David	C.M.

HYMNS WITH TUNES AND METRES

FIRST LINE	NO.	TUNE	METRE
Jesus, we look to Thee	718	Reuben	S.M.
Jesus, we on the word depend ..	275	Newhaven (Luton)	L.M.
Jesus, we thus obey	761	St. Augustine ..	S.M.
Jesus, where'er Thy people meet ..	675	Redhead No. 4 ..	L.M.
Jesus, who lived above the sky ..	146	Philippine	L.M.
Jesus, with Thy Church abide ..	727	Agapé	7 7 7.6.
Join all the glorious names	96	Southampton ..	6.6.6.6.8 8.
Join, all ye ransomed sons of grace	960	Winchester Old ..	C.M.
Judge eternal, throned in splendour	883	Rhuddlan	8.7.8.7.8.7.
*Just as I am, Thine own to be ..	394	Just as I am (i) .. Howcroft (ii) ..	8 8 8.6.
Just as I am, without one plea ..	353	Misericordia (i) .. Gainsworth (ii) ..	8 8 8.6.
*King of glory, King of peace ..	23	Gwalchmai ..	7.4.7.4.D.
King of the City Splendid	891	Urbis Rex	7.6.7.6.7.4.
Lamb of God, I look to Thee (Part 2)	842	Innocents (i) .. Peacefield (ii) ..	7 7.7 7.
Lamb of God, whose dying love ..	181	Atonement	7.6.7.6.7.8.7.6.
Land of our Birth, we pledge to thee	899	Land of our Birth..	L.M.
*Lead, kindly Light, amid the encircling gloom	612	Sandon	10.4.10.4.10 10.
*Lead us, heavenly Father, lead us ..	611	Mannheim	8.7.8.7.8.7.
Lead us, O Father, in the paths of peace	613	All Souls	10.10.10.10.
Leader of faithful souls, and Guide..	610	Mount Beacon ..	8.8.8.8.8.8.
Leave God to order all thy ways ..	504	Bremen	8.8.8.8.8.8.
*Let all the world in every corner sing	5	Dallas (i) .. .. Luckington (ii) ..	10 4.6 6.6 6.10 4.
Let earth and heaven agree ..	114	Millennium.. ..	6.6.6.6.8 8.
Let earth and heaven combine ..	142	Adoration	6.6.6.6.8 8.
Let earth's wide circle round ..	v. 6	Laudes Domini, No. 113	6 6.6.D.
Let everlasting glories crown ..	532	St. Gregory ..	L.M.
Let Him to whom we now belong ..	382	Byzantium	C.M.
*Let the song go round the earth ..	806	Heaven	7.5.7.5.7 7.
Let us join—'tis God commands ..	713	Love-Feast	7 7.7 7.D.
*Let us with a gladsome mind ..	18	Ever faithful ..	7 7.7 7.
*Life and light and joy are found ..	416	Charterhouse ..	7.7.7.7.7 7.
*Life of ages, richly poured ..	908	Brandenburg ..	7.7.7.7.
Lift up your heads, ye gates of brass	265	Bromsgrove ..	C.M.
Lift up your heads, ye mighty gates	890	Marazion	8 8.8 8.8 8.6 6.
Lift up your hearts to things above	722	Chimes	C.M.
Lift up your hearts ! We lift ..	686	Birmingham (i) Woodlands (ii) ..	10 10.10 10.
Light of light, enlighten me ..	663	Lüneburg	7.8.7.8.7 7.
Light of the lonely pilgrim's heart ..	268	Nox præcessit ..	C.M.
Light of the world, faint were our weary feet	636	Barton	10.4.10.4.10 10.
Light of the world, Thy beams I bless	531	Hull	8 8.6.D.
Light of those whose dreary dwelling	261	Saltash	8.7.8.7.D.
Lo, God is here ! Let us adore ..	683	Vater Unser (Old 112th) ..	8.8.8.8.8 8.
Lo ! He comes with clouds descending	264	Helmsley	8.7.8.7.4.7.
Long did I toil, and knew no earthly rest	458	Song 1	10.10.10.10.10 10.
Look from Thy sphere of endless day	790	Fulda	L.M.
Look, ye saints ! The sight is glorious	226	Triumph	8.7.8.7.4.7.
Looking upward every day	850	Excelsior	7.6.7.6.
*Lord and Saviour, true and kind ..	868	Boyce (Sharon)	7 7.7 7.
Lord, as to Thy dear Cross we flee	512	Wigtown	C.M.
*Lord, behold us with Thy blessing (Part 1)	870	Pilgrimage (i) .. Tonbridge School (ii)	8.7.8.7.4.7.
Lord Christ, when first Thou cam'st to men	906	Elberfeld	8.7.8.7.8 8.7.
*Lord, dismiss us with Thy blessing (Part 2)	870	Pilgrimage (i) .. Tonbridge School (ii)	8.7.8.7.4.7.
Lord, dismiss us with Thy blessing, Fill	693	Dismissal	8.7.8.7.4.7.
Lord God, by whom all change is wrought	55	Kingston	8 8.6.D.
Lord God the Holy Ghost	298	Bowden	S.M.
Lord, grant us, like the watching five	786	Lothian	8 8.6.D.
Lord, her watch Thy Church is keeping	267	Alleluia	8.7.8.7.D.

FIRST LINE	NO.	TUNE	METRE
Lord, I believe a rest remains ..	563	Redhead No. 66 ..	C.M.
Lord, I hear of showers of blessing	321	Even me (i) .. Even me (ii)	8.7.8.7. and refrain
Lord, I was blind! I could not see	373	A Babe is born (i) Ely (ii)	L.M.
Lord, if at Thy command ..	792	Mount Ephraim ..	S.M.
*Lord, in the fullness of my might ..	396	Skelmorlie	C.M.
Lord, in the strength of grace ..	594	St. Michael ..	S.M.
Lord, in this Thy mercy's day ..	725	St. Philip	7 7 7.
Lord, it belongs not to my care ..	647	Cheshire	C.M.
Lord! it is good for us to be ..	168	Stanley	D.L.M.
Lord Jesus Christ, our Lord most dear	755	St. Chrysostom (Barnby) ..	8 8.8 8.8 8.
Lord Jesus, in the days of old ..	941	Companion ..	8.8.8.8.8 8.
Lord Jesus, think on me ..	239	Southwell	S.M.
Lord, my time is in Thy hand ..	v.30	Leamington, No. 465	7.6.7.6.7.7.7.6.
Lord of all being, throned afar ..	32	Maryton	L.M.
Lord of Life and King of Glory ..	397	Calvary	8.7.8.7.8.7.
*Lord of our life, and God of our salvation	729	Cloisters ..	11 11 11.5.
Lord of the harvest, hear	787	Avon	S.M.
Lord of the living harvest	793	Herrnhut ..	7.6.7.6.D.
*Lord of the worlds above ..	678	Darwall's 148th ..	6.6.6.6.4.4 4.4.
*Lord, speak to me, that I may speak	781	Galilee	L.M.
Lord, teach us how to pray aright ..	539	Farrant	C.M.
*Lord, that I may learn of Thee ..	549	Simplicity	7 7 7 7.
Lord, Thou hast been our dwelling-place	694	Dettingen	8.7.8.7.8 8.7.
Lord, Thy ransomed Church is waking	796	Contemplation ..	8.7.8.7.D.
*Lord, Thy word abideth ..	308	Ravenshaw.. ..	6 6 6 6.
Lord, we believe to us and ours ..	274	Winchester New ..	L.M.
Lord, when we have not any light ..	846	This endris nyght ..	C.M.
Lord, while for all mankind we pray	881	Lincoln	C.M.
*Love came down at Christmas ..	138	Hermitage	6.7.6.7.
Love divine, all loves excelling ..	431	Love Divine (i) Bithynia (ii) ..	8.7.8.7.D.
Love is the key of life and death ..	435	Lovest thou Me ..	8.8.8.4.
Love of love, and Light of light ..	493	Ratisbon (Jesu, meine Zuversicht) ..	7.8.7.8.7 7.
Loved with everlasting love ..	443	Loughborough College	7.7.7.7.D.
*Low in the grave He lay	211	Christ arose ..	6.5.6.4. and refrain
*Make me a captive, Lord	596	Llanllyfni	D.S.M.
Make our earthly souls a field ..	v.42	Elevation, No. 59 ..	7.6.7.6.7.8.7.6.
Man of Sorrows! What a name ..	176	Gethsemane ..	7 7 7.8.
*Master, speak! Thy servant heareth	780	St. Leonard (i) Ottawa (ii)	8.7.8.7.7 7.
Meet and right it is to sing	17	Amsterdam ..	7.6.7.6.7.7.7.6.
Mine eyes have seen the glory ..	260	Vision (i) .. Battle Hymn (ii) ..	Irregular
Morning comes with light all-cheering	928	Gounod	8.7.8.7.7 7.
*My faith looks up to Thee ..	238	Harlan	6 6.4.6 6 6.4.
My Father, for another night ..	926	St. Timothy ..	C.M.
My God, how wonderful Thou art ..	73	Westminster ..	C.M.
My God, I am Thine	406	Harwich	5 5 11.D.
My God! I know, I feel Thee mine	387	Warwick	C.M.
My God, I love Thee—not because..	446	Culross	C.M.
My God, I thank Thee, who hast made	524	Wentworth ..	8.4.8.4.8.4.
*My God, is any hour so sweet ..	536	Memoria (i).. Southport (ii) ..	8.8.8.4.
*My God, my King	425	Springtide Hour ..	4 4.6.D.
My God, the spring of all my joys ..	408	St. Bernard ..	C.M.
My heart and voice I raise ..	115	Ascalon	6 6.8.D.
My heart is fixed, eternal God ..	403	Christ for me ..	8.3.8.3.8 8 8.3.
My heart is full of Christ, and longs	270	Worsley	8.8.8.8.8 8.
My heart is resting, O my God ..	473	Nettleham	Irregular
*My Jesus, I love Thee, I know Thou art mine	437	My Jesus, I love Thee	11 11.11 11.
My Saviour! how shall I proclaim..	388	Angels' Song ..	L.M.
My Saviour, Thou Thy love to me ..	169	Sidmouth	8.8.8.8.8 8.
My song is love unknown	144	Love unknown ..	6.6.6.6.4.4 4.4.
My soul don't delay	v.21	Harwich, No. 406 ..	5 5 11.D.
My soul, praise the Lord	45	Old 104th	5.5.5.5.6.5.6.5.
My soul, repeat His praise ..	54	Selma	S.M.
My soul, there is a country	466	Pastor	7.6.7.6.
My soul, through my Redeemer's care	384	Angels' Song ..	L.M.
My spirit longs for Thee	467	Psalm 32	6.6.6.6.
My spirit on Thy care	506	In Memoriam ..	S.M.

FIRST LINE	NO.	TUNE	METRE
Nearer, my God, to Thee	468	Horbury (i).. .. Nearer to Thee (ii) .. Nearer, my God, to Thee (iii).. ..	6.4.6.4.6 6.4.
Never further than Thy Cross ..	198	Cross	7.7.7.7.
No, not despairingly	354	St. Werburgh ..	6.4.6.4.6 6.4.
None is like Jeshurun's God ..	68	Jeshurun	7.6.7.6.7.7.7.6.
None other Lamb, none other Name	94	All Hallows ..	8.10.10.4.
Not all the blood of beasts	234	Cambridge	S.M.
Not for our sins alone	743	Frilford	6.6.6.6.6.6.
Not what these hands have done	81	St. Bride	S.M.
Now all the woods are sleeping ..	946	Innsbrück	7 7.6.7 7.8.
Now I have found the ground wherein	375	Madrid (i) .. .. Anchor (ii)	8.8.8.8.8 8.
Now let me gain perfection's height	v.36	Eden, No. 449 ..	L.M.
Now let us see Thy beauty, Lord ..	450	Edgware ..	C.M.
*Now praise we great and famous men	896	Brynhyfryd ..	8.7.8.7.
*Now thank we all our God	10	Nun danket ..	6.7.6.7.6.6.6.6.
*Now the day is over	944	Eudoxia	6.5.6.5.
Now the labourer's task is o'er ..	976	Requiescat ..	7.7.7.7.8 8.
Now the year is crowned with blessing	967	Morgenlied ..	8.7.8.7.D. and refrain
O bless the Lord, my soul	424	Mount Ephraim ..	S.M.
O blessèd life! the heart at rest ..	529	Redhead No. 4 ..	L.M.
O Bread to pilgrims given	768	Passion Chorale ..	7.6.7.6.D.
O breath of God, breathe on us now	285	Calm	L.M.
O brother man, fold to thy heart thy brother	911	Intercessor ..	11.10.11.10.
O Christ, our God, who with Thine own hast been	731	Cœna Domini	10 10.
O Church of God, arise	795	Kingsland	6.6.6.6.
*O come, all ye faithful	118	Adeste fideles ..	Irregular
O come and dwell in me	554	Huddersfield ..	S.M.
O come and mourn with me awhile	187	St. Cross	L.M.
O come, let us adore Him	v. 7	Adeste fideles, No. 118	Irregular
O come, little children, I pray ye come all	861	Temple Fortune ..	11 11.11 11.
O come, O come, Immanuel.. ..	257	Veni Immanuel (Ephratah) ..	8 8.8 8. and refrain
O come, ye sinners, to your Lord ..	325	Elim (Hesperus) ..	L.M.
*O day of rest and gladness	659	Munich	7.6.7.6.D.
O disclose Thy lovely face	545	Arfon	7.7.7.7.7 7.
O Father, all creating	776	Day of Rest ..	7.6.7.6.D.
O filial Deity	97	Eccles	6 6.7.7.7.7.
O for a closer walk with God ..	461	Cheshire	C.M.
O for a heart to praise my God ..	550	Abridge	C.M.
O for a thousand tongues to sing ..	1	Richmond (i) .. Lydia (ii)	C.M.
O for this love let rocks and hills ..	v. 8	St. Bernard, No. 949	C.M.
O gladsome light, O grace	936	Brindley	6 6.7.D.
O God, how often hath Thine ear ..	750	Eaton	8.8.8.8.8 8.
O God, my God, my all Thou art ..	471	Berkshire	L.M.
O God, my strength and fortitude ..	24	Palatine	C.M.
O God of all grace	66	Harwich	5 5 11.D.
O God of Bethel, by whose hand ..	607	Tallis' Ordinal ..	C.M.
O God of God, in whom combine ..	65	Tarsus	8 8.8.D.
O God, of good the unfathomed sea	67	Dresden	8 8.8.D.
O God, of good the unfathomed sea	v. 4	Dresden, No. 67 ..	8 8.8.D.
O God of love, O King of peace ..	903	Erhalt' uns, Herr ..	L.M.
O God of Love, to Thee we bow ..	774	Saffron Walden ..	8 8 8.6.
O God of mercy, God of might ..	728	Amor Dei	8 8 8.6.
O God of our forefathers, hear ..	723	Vater Unser (Old 112th)	8.8.8.8.8 8.
*O God our Father, who dost make us one	688	Morecambe ..	10 10.10 10.
O God, our help in ages past ..	878	St. Anne	C.M.
O God, the Rock of Ages	958	Heber	7.6.7.6.D.
O God, Thou bottomless abyss ..	42	Vom Himmel hoch (Erfurt)	L.M.
O God, to whom the faithful dead ..	826	St. Justin	8 8.6.D.
O God, what offering shall I give ..	573	Pater omnium ..	8.8.8.8.8 8.
O grant us light, that we may know	630	Alstone	L.M.
*O happy band of pilgrims	618	Knecht	7.6.7.6.
*O happy day that fixed my choice	744	Happy day.. ..	L.M. and refrain

FIRST LINE	NO.	TUNE	METRE
O happy home where Thou art loved the dearest	875	Strength and Stay	11.10.11.10.
O heavenly King, look down from above	7	Houghton	10 10.11 11.
O Holy Spirit, God	279	Drumcondra ..	S.M.
O how blest the hour, Lord Jesus ..	664	St. Oswald	8.7.8.7.
*O Jesus Christ, grow Thou in me ..	463	Westminster New	C.M.
O Jesus, full of truth and grace ..	346	Valete	8.8.8.8.8 8.
*O Jesus, I have promised	526	Norwick (i).. .. Wolvercote (ii) ..	7.6.7.6.D.
O Jesus, King most wonderful ..	107	Bishopthorpe ..	C.M.
O Jesus, my hope	200	Old German ..	5 5 12.D.
*O Jesus, Thou art standing	330	Llangloffan ..	7.6.7.6.D.
O Jesus, we are well and strong ..	847	Solothurn	L.M.
O King of kings, O Lord of hosts ..	888	Rex regum ..	D.C.M.
O King of mercy, from Thy throne on high	633	St. Cyril	10 10
O Light, from age to age the same	980	St. Francis Xavier	C.M.
O little town of Bethlehem	125	Bethlehem	8.6.8.6.7.6.8.6.
*O Lord and Master of us all.. ..	103	St. Hugh	C.M.
O Lord, enlarge our scanty thought	449	Eden	L.M.
O Lord, how happy should we be ..	551	Plymouth	8 8.6.D.
*O Lord of every lovely thing ..	587	Nicolaus (Lobt Gott)	8.6.8 8.6.
*O Lord of heaven and earth and sea	969	Almsgiving ..	8 8 8.4.
O Lord of life, Thy quickening voice	930	Dorking	C.M.
O Lord, who by Thy presence hast made light	953	Toulon	10.10.10.10.
O Love divine, how sweet Thou art	434	Allgütiger, mein Preisgesang	8 8.6.D.
O Love divine, that stooped to share	918	St. Petrox	L.M.
O Love divine! what hast Thou done	186	God of the living ..	8.8.8.8.8 8.
O Love Divine! whose constant beam	674	Boston	L.M.
O Love, how deep, how broad, how high	62	O amor quam exstaticus ..	L.M.
*O Love of God, how strong and true	52	Martham	L.M.
O Love that wilt not let me go	448	St. Margaret ..	8 8.8 8.6.
O Love, who formedst me to wear ..	447	Aldersgate Street ..	8.8.8.8.8 8.
*O loving Lord, who art for ever seeking	577	Zu meinem Herrn ..	11.10.11.10.
*O Master, let me walk with Thee ..	600	Kettering ..	D.L.M.
O my Saviour, hear me	453	O my Saviour, hear me ..	6.5.6.5.7 7.6.5.
O perfect life of love	190	Fons Amoris ..	S.M.
O perfect Love, all human thought transcending	777	O perfect Love ..	11.10.11.10.
O sacred Head once wounded ..	202	Passion Chorale ..	7.6.7.6.D.
O safe to the Rock that is higher than I	499	Shelter	11 11.11 11. and refrain
O Saviour, bless us ere we go ..	692	St. Matthias ..	8.8.8.8.8 8.
O Saviour, I have nought to plead	439	Saffron Walden ..	8.8.8.6.
O Son of Man, our hero strong and tender	241	Welwyn	11.10.11.10.
O splendour of God's glory bright ..	932	St. Venantius (i) Deventer (ii) ..	L.M.
O that each in the day	v.48	Derbe, No. 956 ..	5 5 5.11.
O that the perfect grace were given	v.33	Arnold's, No. 736 ..	C.M.
O that the world might taste and see	v.10	Nativity, No. 85 ..	C.M.
O the bitter shame and sorrow ..	170	All of Thee ..	8.7.8.8.7.
O Thou before whose presence ..	922	Komm, Seele ..	7.6.7.6.D.
*O Thou not made with hands ..	707	Old 120th ..	6.6.6.6.6 6.
O Thou to whose all-searching sight	505	Psalm 8 (Whitehall)	L.M.
O Thou who camest from above ..	386	Wilton	L.M.
O Thou, whom once they flocked to hear	156	St. Luke	L.M.
O Thou whose hand hath brought us	984	Jubilate	7.6.7.6.D.
*O timely happy, timely wise ..	927	Melcombe	L.M.
*O what shall I do my Saviour to praise	420	St. Merryn	10 10.11 11.
*O Word of God incarnate	303	Bentley (i) .. Nyland (ii)	7.6.7.6.D.
O word of pity, for our pardon pleading	240	L'Omnipotent ..	11.10.11.10.
*O worship the King	8	Hanover	5.5.5.5.6.5.6.5.
O worship the Lord in the beauty of holiness	9	Woodhouse Grove (i) Sanctissimus (ii) ..	12.10.12.10.
O ye who taste that love is sweet ..	893	Delhi	8 8 8.

FIRST LINE	NO.	TUNE	METRE
Object of my first desire	90	Theodora	7.7.7.7.
O'er the harvest reaped or lost	593	Retirement	7.8.7.8.7 7.7 7.
Of the Father's love begotten	83	Corde natus	8.7.8.7.8.7.7.
Oft I in my heart have said	530	Barnabas	7.6.7.6.7.7.7.6.
Oft in danger, oft in woe	488	University College	7 7.7 7.
Omnipotent Lord, my Saviour and King	502	Laudate Dominum	10 10.11 11.
Omnipotent Redeemer	251	Worship	7.7.4 4.7.D.
Omnipresent God, whose aid	876	Benevento	7.7.7.7.D.
On all the earth Thy Spirit shower	301	Simeon	L.M.
On wings of living light	209	Gratitude	6.6.6.6.8 8.
Once again, dear Lord, we pray	797	Staples	7 7.7 7.
Once in royal David's city	859	Irby	8.7.8.7.7 7.
Once to every man and nation	898	Adrian	8.7.8.7.D.
*One there is above all others	100	All Saints	8.7.8.7.7 7.
One who is all unfit to count	159	Fingal	C.M.
*Onward! Christian soldiers	822	St. Gertrude	6.5.6.5.D. and refrain
Open, Lord, my inward ear	465	Leamington	7.6.7.6.7.7.7.6.
Oppressed with sin and woe	352	St. Bride	S.M.
*Our blest Redeemer, ere He breathed	283	St. Cuthbert	8.6.8.4.
Our day of praise is done	690	Franconia	S.M.
Our Father, by whose servants	979	Meirionydd	7.6.7.6.D.
Our Father, hear our longing prayer	739	Aberdeen	C.M.
Our life is hid with Christ in God	823	St. Lawrence	C.M.
Our Lord is risen from the dead	222	Hermann	L.M. and Hallelujahs
Out of the depths I cry to Thee	359	St. Martin	8.6.8.6.8 8.7.
Pass me not, O gentle Saviour	335	Pass me not	8.5.8.5. and refrain
Peace, doubting heart! my God's I am	500	Leicester	8.8.8.8.8 8.
Peace, perfect peace, in this dark world of sin	501	Song 46 (i) Pax tecum (ii)	10 10.
Pleasant are Thy courts above	679	Maidstone	7 7.7 7.D.
Plenteous He is in truth and grace	v.14	Grosvenor, No. 576	8 8.6.D.
Plunged in a gulf of dark despair	179	Oldbury	C.M.
Praise, Lord, for Thee in Zion waits	695	Mainzer	L.M.
*Praise, my soul, the King of heaven	12	Praise, my soul (i) Regent Square (ii)	8.7.8.7.4.7.
*Praise, O praise our God and King	19	Monkland	7 7.7 7.
Praise the Lord who reigns above	14	Russell Place	7.6.7.6.7.7.7.6.
Praise the Lord! Ye heavens, adore Him	13	Laus Deo	8.7.8.7.
*Praise to our God, who with love never swerving	869	Bede	11.10.11.10.
Praise to the Holiest in the height	74	Gerontius	C.M.
Praise to the living God	15	Leoni	6.6.8.4.D.
Praise to the Lord, the Almighty	64	Lobe den Herren	14 14.4 7.8.
*Praise ye the Lord! 'Tis good to raise	79	Justification	L.M.
Pray, without ceasing pray	541	Bonar	D.S.M.
Prayer is the soul's sincere desire	533	Nox præcessit	C.M.
*Raise the psalm: let earth adoring	16	Austria	8.7.8.7.D.
Rejoice and be glad! the Redeemer hath come	230	Rejoice and be glad	Irregular
Rejoice for a brother deceased	973	David	8.8.8.8.D.
Rejoice, O land, in God thy might	882	Gonfalon Royal	L.M.
Rejoice, the Lord is King	247	Gopsal	6.6.6.6.8 8.
Rejoice to-day with one accord	885	Gloria in Excelsis	8.7.8.7.6 6.6 6.7.
Remember all the people	864	Holmbridge	7.6.7.6.D.
Remember, Lord, my sins no more	v.29	St. Cross, No. 187	L.M.
Rescue the perishing, care for the dying	338	Rescue	11.10.11.10. and refrain
Rest of the weary	101	Theodora	5.4.5.4.D.
Revive Thy work, O Lord	738	Revive Thy work, O Lord	S.M. and refrain
Riches unsearchable	441	Dominica	S.M.
Ride on, ride on in majesty	192	St. Drostane	L.M.
Ring out, wild bells, to the wild sky	905	Grenoble	L.M.
Rise up, O men of God	585	Watchman	S.M.
Rock of Ages, cleft for me	498	Redhead No. 76	7 7.7 7.7 7.
Round the Lord in glory seated	25	Würzburg	8.7.8.7.D.

FIRST LINE	NO.	TUNES	METRE
Safe home, safe home in port ..	977	Safe Home	6.6.6.6.8 8.
Salvation ! O the joyful sound ..	250	Ashley	C.M. and refrain
Saviour, again to Thy dear name we raise..	691	Ellers (i) .. .. Adoro Te (ii) ..	10 10.10 10.
Saviour, and can it be	760	Devotion	6 6.7.7.7.7.
*Saviour, blessèd Saviour	672	Norfolk Park ..	6.5.6.5.D.
Saviour from sin, I wait to prove ..	558	St. Catherine ..	8.8.8.8.8 8.
Saviour, like a Shepherd lead us ..	609	Lewes	8.7.8.7.4.7.
Saviour, Prince of Israel's race ..	348	Christopher ..	7.7.7.7.7 7.
Saviour, quicken many nations ..	800	Bethany	8.7.8.7.D.
*Saviour, Thy dying love	579	Something for Thee	6.4.6.4.6 6 6.4.
Saviour, we know Thou art ..	269	St. Godric	6.6.6.6.8 8.
Saviour, when in dust to Thee ..	726	Aberystwyth ..	7 7.7 7.D.
*Saviour, while my heart is tender ..	395	Shipston	8.7.8.7.
Scatter the last remains of sin ..	v.35	Sawley, A.T. No. 9	C.M.
See, amid the winter's snow.. ..	124	Oxford	7 7.7 7. and refrain
See how great a flame aspires ..	263	St. George's, Windsor	7.7.7.7.D.
See Israel's gentle Shepherd stand ..	751	Dublin	C.M.
See, Jesu, Thy disciples see	719	Bishopthorpe ..	C.M.
See the Conqueror mounts in triumph	223	Rex gloriæ	8.7.8.7.D.
*Servant of all, to toil for man ..	575	St. James ..	C.M.
Shall I, for fear of feeble man ..	783	Birstal	L.M.
Shepherd divine, our wants relieve	736	Arnold's	C.M.
Shine Thou upon us, Lord	782	Supplication ..	6.6.6.6.D.
Show me the way, O Lord	622	Cords of love ..	6.4.6.4.10 10.
Simply trusting every day	517	Trusting Jesus ..	7 7.7 7. and refrain
Since the Son hath made me free ..	568	Crowland	7 7.7 7.7 7.
Sing Alleluia forth in duteous praise	671	Alleluia perenne ..	10 10.7.
Sing praise to God who reigns above	415	Mit Freuden zart ..	8.7.8.7.8 8.7.
Sing to the great Jehovah's praise ..	959	Northrop	C.M.
Sing we the King who is coming to reign	116	Sing we the King (i) Glory Song (ii) ..	10 10.10 10. and refrain
Sinners Jesus will receive	322	Christ receiveth ..	7.7.7.7. and refrain
Sinners, obey the gospel word ..	326	Liverpool .. .. (Newmarket) ..	L.M.
Sinners, turn ; why will ye die ..	327	Anima Christi ..	7 7.7 7.D.
Soldiers of Christ, arise	484	From strength to strength	D.S.M.
Sometimes a light surprises	527	Petition	7.6.7.6.D.
Son of God, if Thy free grace ..	477	Gersau	7.6.7.6.7.8.7.6.
Souls of men, why will ye scatter ..	318	Cross of Jesus (i) Omni die (ii) ..	8.7.8.7.
*Sow in the morn thy seed	599	Swabia	S.M.
Speed Thy servants, Saviour, speed them	808	St. Thomas ..	8.7.8.7.4.7.
Spirit blest, who art adored ..	295	Joseph	7 7 7.6.
Spirit divine, attend our prayers ..	289	St. Agnes	C.M.
Spirit of faith, come down ..	363	Ich halte treulich still	D.S.M.
Spirit of wisdom, turn our eyes ..	282	Pembroke	8 8.6.D.
Spread, O spread, thou mighty word	804	Dent Dale	7 7.7 7.
Spread the table of the Lord ..	757	Culbach	7.7.7.7.
Stand, soldier of the Cross ..	754	Kerry	S.M.
Stand up and bless the Lord ..	685	Doncaster (Bethlehem) ..	S.M.
*Stand up, stand up for Jesus ..	821	Morning Light ..	7.6.7.6.D.
*Standing at the portal	955	Fylde	6.5.6.5.D. and refrain
Stay, Master, stay upon this heavenly hill	586	Unde et memores ..	10 10.10 10.10 10.
Stay, Thou insulted Spirit, stay ..	v.23	Melcombe, No. 927	L.M.
Still, still with Thee, when purple morning breaketh	474	Alverstoke	11.10.11.10.
Still the night, holy the night ..	123	Stille Nacht ..	Irregular
Still with Thee, O my God	470	Selma	S.M.
Strong Son of God, immortal Love..	86	Song 5	L.M.
Stupendous height of heavenly love	135	Dura	8.8.8.8.8.8.
*Summer suns are glowing	673	Ruth	6.5.6.5.D.
*Sun of my soul, Thou Saviour dear	942	Hursley (i) .. .. Abends (ii)	L.M.
Sunset and evening star	640	Crossing the Bar ..	Irregular
Surrounded by a host of foes ..	483	Defiance	8.8.8.8.8 8.

FIRST LINE	NO.	TUNE	METRE
Sweet is the memory of Thy grace	56	St. Stephen ..	C.M.
Sweet is the sunlight after rain	662	Woolmer's	L.M.
Sweet is the work, my God, my King	665	Eignbrook	L.M.
Sweet place : sweet place alone ..	653	Christchurch ..	6.6.6.6.8.8.
Sweetly the holy hymn	732	Southport	S.M.
Take my life, and let it be	400	Consecration ..	7 7.7 7.
Take my poor heart, and let it be ..	v.27	Job, A.T. 14 ..	L.M.
Talk with us, Lord, Thyself reveal	460	Tiverton	C.M.
Teach me, my God and King ..	597	Sandys	S.M.
*Tell me the old, old story	161	Tell me	7.6.7.6.D. and refrain
Tell me the stories of Jesus	858	Stories of Jesus ..	8.4.8.4.5.4.5.4.
Ten thousand times ten thousand ..	828	Alford	7.6.8.6.D.
That day of wrath, that dreadful day	645	Llef	L.M.
That mighty faith on me bestow ..	v.25	Irish, No. 503 ..	C.M.
That mystic Word of Thine, O sovereign Lord	469	Song 24	10.10.10.10.
*The Church's one foundation ..	701	Aurelia	7.6.7.6.D.
The day is past and over	951	St. Anatolius (i) ..	
		St. Anatolius (ii) ..	7.6.7.6.8 8.
The day of resurrection !	208	Ellacombe	7.6.7.6.D.
*The day Thou gavest, Lord, is ended	667	Radford (i)	
		St. Clement (ii) ..	
		Les commandemens de Dieu (iii) ..	9.8.9.8.
The fields are all white	799	Colvend	5.6.6.5.9.
*The first Nowell the angel did say ..	131	The first Nowell ..	Irregular
The foe behind, the deep before ..	218	The foe behind ..	Irregular
The Galilean fishers toil	509	St. Leonard's ..	D.C.M.
*The glory of the spring how sweet ..	409	Sharon	C.M.
The God of Abraham praise.. ..	21	Leoni	6.6.8.4.D.
*The God of love my Shepherd is ..	51	St. Columba ..	C.M.
The God of love, to earth He came	372	Arlington	C.M.
The God who reigns on high (Part 3)	21	Leoni	6.6.8.4.D.
The golden gates are lifted up ..	224	London New ..	C.M.
The head that once was crowned with thorns	244	St. Magnus	C.M.
The heavens declare Thy glory, Lord	802	New Sabbath ..	L.M.
The homeland ! The homeland ..	654	Homeland	Irregular
*The King of love my Shepherd is ..	76	Hardwicke (i) ..	
		Dominus regit me (ii)	8.7.8.7. (Iambic)
*The Lord's my Shepherd, I'll not want	50	Kilmarnock ..	C.M.
The Lord Jehovah reigns ..	58	Adoration	6.6.6.6.8 8.
The Lord my righteousness I praise	v. 5	Confidence, No. 370	L.M.
The Lord will come, and not be slow	813	Gräfenberg ..	C.M.
*The Maker of the sun and moon ..	136	Newbury	C.M.
The night is come, wherein at last we rest	945	The Blessed Rest ..	10 10.10 4.
The people that in darkness lay ..	379	Nunhead	L.M.
The race that long in darkness pined	139	Dunfermline ..	C.M.
The radiant morn hath passed away	940	St. Gabriel	8.8.8.4.
The royal banners forward go ..	184	Vexilla Regis (i)	
		Breslau (ii) ..	L.M.
The saints of God, their conflict past	825	Rest..	8 8.8 8.8 8.
The sands of time are sinking ..	637	Rutherford ..	7.6.7.6.7.6.7.5.
The shepherds had an angel.. ..	863	Christina	Irregular
*The Son of God goes forth to war ..	816	Fight of Faith ..	D.C.M.
The spacious firmament on high	44	Firmament ..	D.L.M.
The Spirit breathes upon the word	307	St. James ..	C.M.
*The spring again is here	965	Sandys	S.M.
The star of morn has risen	925	Moseley	6.6.8.4.
The strife is o'er, the battle done ..	215	Victory	8 8 8.4.
The sun is sinking fast	939	St. Columba ..	6.4.6.6.
The thing my God doth hate ..	547	Aynhoe	S.M.
The voice that breathed o'er Eden	775	St. Alphege ..	7.6.7.6.
Thee, Jesus, full of truth and grace	519	Abridge	C.M.
Thee, Jesus, Thee, the sinner's Friend	369	Purleigh	8 8.6.D.
Thee will I love, my strength, my tower	445	New 113th.. ..	8.8.8.8.8 8.
Thee will I praise with all my heart	80	Dresden	8 8.8.D.
Their names are names of kings ..	827	Frogmore	6.4.6.4.
Then let us attend	v.46	Derbe, No. 262 ..	5 5.5 11.D.
There for me the Saviour stands ..	v.17	Christus, No. 288 ..	7 7.7 7.
*There is a book, who runs may read	43	St. Flavian ..	C.M.
There is a fountain filled with blood	201	Martyrdom.. ..	C.M.
There's a Friend for little children	839	In Memoriam ..	8.6.7.6.7.6.7.6.
There is a green hill far away ..	180	Horsley	C.M.

FIRST LINE	NO.	TUNE	METRE
There is a land of pure delight ..	649	Beulah	C.M.
*There's a light upon the mountains	256	There's a light upon the mountains ..	15 15.15 15.
There is no sorrow, Lord, too light	237	Windsor	C.M.
There were ninety and nine that safely lay	334	Good Shepherd (i) The ninety and nine (ii)	Irregular
These things shall be : a loftier race	910	Arizona	L.M.
They who tread the path of labour	601	Everton	8.7.8.7.D.
Thine arm, O Lord, in days of old ..	919	St. Matthew ..	D.C.M.
Thine be the glory, risen, conquering Son	213	Maccabæus ..	10 11.11 11. and refrain
Thine for ever! God of love ..	569	Newington	7 7.7 7.
This blessèd word be mine	v.49	Franconia, No. 507	S.M.
This is the day of light	660	Dulwich College ..	S.M.
This, this is the God we adore ..	69	Celeste	8.8.8.8.
Thou art coming, O my Saviour ..	258	Beverley	8.7.8 8.7.7.7.7.7.
Thou art my God, and Thee I praise	v. 2	Stamford, No. 730..	8 8.8.D.
Thou art my life; if Thou but turn away	162	Löwenstern ..	10 10 10.
Thou art the Way : to Thee alone	160	Redhead No. 66 ..	C.M.
Thou canst o'ercome this heart of mine	v.18	Sawley, A.T. No. 9	C.M.
*Thou didst leave Thy throne ..	150	Margaret	Irregular
Thou God of truth and love.. ..	716	St. Godric	6.6.6.6.8 8.
Thou gracious God, whose mercy lends	873	Wendell	L.M.
Thou great mysterious God unknown	376	Traveller	8 8.6.D.
Thou great Redeemer, dying Lamb	104	Hensbury	C.M.
Thou hidden love of God, whose height	433	Aldersgate Street ..	8.8.8.8.8 8.
Thou hidden Source of calm repose	98	Warwick Gardens	8.8.8.8.8.8.
Thou Jesu, Thou my breast inspire..	584	Old 113th	8 8.8.8 8.8.D.
Thou Judge of quick and dead ..	644	Dynbych	D.S.M.
Thou say'st : Take up thy cross ..	158	Submission ..	S.M.
Thou Shepherd of Israel, and mine	457	Arabia	8.8.8.8.D.
Thou to whom the sick and dying ..	920	Evensong	8.7.8.7.7 7.
Thou whose almighty word	803	Malvern	6 6.4.6 6 6.4.
Though nature's strength decay (Part 2)	21	Leoni	6.6.8.4.D.
Throned upon the awful Tree ..	189	Nicht so traurig ..	7 7.7 7.7 7.
Through all the changing scenes of life	427	Wiltshire	C.M.
*Through the love of God our Saviour	525	Ar hyd y nos ..	8.4.8.4.8 8.8.4.
Through the night of doubt and sorrow	616	Ebenezer (i) .. Marching (ii) ..	8.7.8.7.D. 8.7.8.7.
Thy ceaseless, unexhausted love ..	49	University	C.M.
Thy faithfulness, Lord, each moment we find	311	Montgomery ..	10 10.11 11.
Thy kingdom come, O God	811	St. Cecilia	6.6.6.6.
Thy kingdom come—on bended knee	742	Blackburn	C.M.
*Thy life was given for me	391	Baca	6.6.6.6.6 6.
Thy way, not mine, O Lord ..	515	Moab	6.6.6.6.D.
Tired with the greatness of my way	v.15	Pembroke, No. 282	8 8.6.D.
'Tis done! Thou dost this moment save	v.40	Attercliffe, No. 603	C.M.
*'Tis not to ask for gifts alone ..	537	Reverence	8 8.8 8.4.
To God be the glory	313	To God be the glory	11 11.11 11. and refrain
To God, the only Wise	638	St. Augustine ..	S.M.
To the haven of Thy breast ..	459	St. Dorothea ..	7.6.7.6.7.8.7.6.
To the hills I lift mine eyes ..	497	St. Hilary	7.6.7.6.7.7.7.6.
To the Name of our salvation ..	93	Grafton	8.7.8.7.8.7.
To Thee, O Lord, our hearts we raise	964	Golden Sheaves (i) Bishopgarth (ii) ..	8.7.8.7.D. (Iambic)
To Thee our God we fly	886	Gratitude	6.6.6.6.8 8.
To us a child of royal birth	141	Berkshire	L.M.
Touched by the loadstone of Thy love	v.44	Abridge, No. 550 ..	C.M.
Turn back, O man, forswear thy foolish ways	912	Old 124th	10 10.10 10.10.
Victim divine, Thy grace we claim	771	Euphony	8.8.8.8.8 8.
*Wake, awake, for night is flying ..	255	Sleepers, wake ..	8 9.8.D.6 6.4.8 8.
Walk in the light : so shalt thou know	631	Tiltey Abbey ..	C.M.

FIRST LINE	NO.	TUNE	METRE
*We bless Thee, Lord, for all this common life	872	Chilton Foliat ...	10 10.10 10.
We come unto our fathers' God ..	71	Luther	8.7.8.7.8 8.7.
We give immortal praise	40	Croft's 136th ...	6.6.6.6.8 8.
*We give Thee but Thine own ..	923	Windermere ...	S.M.
We have heard a joyful sound ..	316	Jesus saves ...	7.3.7.3.7.7.7.3.
We have not known Thee as we ought	741	Credo ...	8.8.8.8.8 8.
We know, by faith we surely know	88	St. Asaph	D.C.M.
We love the place, O God	677	Quam dilecta ...	6.6.6.6.
*We love Thy Kingdom, Lord ..	708	St. Giles	S.M.
We plough the fields, and scatter ..	963	Wir pflügen.. ...	7.6.7.6.D. and refrain
We rose to-day with anthems sweet	666	Norwood	L.M.
*We saw Thee not when Thou didst come	148	Credo	8.8.8.8.8 8.
*We sing the praise of Him who died	196	Church Triumphant	L.M.
*We thank Thee, Lord, for this fair earth	414	Holly	L.M.
Weary of earth and laden with my sin	355	Dalkeith	10 10.10 10.
Weary souls that wander wide ..	319	Wellspring	7.7.7.7.7 7.
Weep not for Him who onward bears	175	St. Mary	C.M.
Welcome, happy morning! Age to age shall say	212	Salve, festa dies	11 11.11 11. and refrain
*What a Friend we have in Jesus ..	538	What a Friend ..	8.7.8.7.D.
What are these arrayed in white ..	833	Benevento	7.7.7.7.D.
What grace, O Lord, and beauty shone	145	Clinton	C.M.
What is our calling's glorious hope	557	Stafford	C.M.
*What means this eager, anxious throng	152	Nazareth	8 8.8 8.8 9.
What service shall we render thee ..	897	Forest Green ...	D.C.M.
What shall I do my God to love, My loving	77	Jerusalem	C.M.
What shall I do my God to love, My Saviour	452	Stella	8.8.8.8.8 8.
What shall I do to keep	v.28	Vigil, A.T. No. 4 ..	S.M.
What shall I render to my God ..	399	Morna	C.M.
What shall we offer our good Lord..	784	Duke Street ..	L.M.
When all Thy mercies, O my God ..	413	Harington	C.M.
When God is mine, and I am His ..	v.37	Farrant, No. 539 ..	C.M.
When God of old came down from heaven	276	Winchester Old ..	C.M.
When, His salvation bringing ..	835	Tours	7.6.7.6.D.
*When I survey the wondrous Cross..	182	Rockingham ..	L.M.
When Jesus makes my heart His home	v.32	Belmont, No. 766 ..	C.M.
*When morning gilds the skies ..	113	Laudes Domini ..	6 6.6.D.
When mothers of Salem	866	Salem	Irregular
When my love to Christ grows weak	178	Simplicity	7 7.7 7.
When, my Saviour, shall I be ..	555	Pleyel	7 7.7 7.
When on my day of life the night is falling	642	Gifford	11.10.11.6.
When our heads are bowed with woe	978	Redhead No. 47 ..	7 7.7 7.
When quiet in my house I sit ..	310	Companion ..	8.8.8.8.8 8.
When shall Thy love constrain ..	341	Shirland	S.M.
When the day of toil is done ..	975	Irene	7 7 7.5.
*When the Lord of Love was here ..	147	Salvator	7 7.5.D.
When the weary, seeking rest ..	735	Intercession ..	7.5.7.5.7.5.7.5.8 8.
When this passing world is done ..	643	Pressburg ..	7 7.7 7.7 7.
When Thy soldiers take their swords	398	Nutbourne	7 7.7 7.7 7.
When we walk with the Lord ..	516	Trust and obey ..	6 6.9.D. and refrain
When wilt Thou save the people ..	909	Commonwealth ..	7.6.7.6.8 8 8.5.
Where cross the crowded ways of life	895	St. Bartholomew ..	L.M.
Where shall my wondering soul begin	361	Old 23rd	8.8.8.8.8 8.
Wherewith, O God, shall I draw near	343	Jena	L.M.
While ebbing nature grieves ..	641	Annue Christe ..	6.6.6.6.D.
*While shepherds watched their flocks by night	129	Winchester Old ..	C.M.
Who fathoms the eternal thought ..	513	Green Hill	C.M.
Who in the Lord confide	700	Ishmael	D.S.M.
*Who is He, in yonder stall	151	Who is He? ..	7 7. and refrain
*Who is on the Lord's side	820	Hermas	6.5. (12 lines)
Who on earth can conceive	v.50	Hungerford, No. 407	5 6.9.6 6.9.
*Who puts his trust	495	Walton	4 4.7. (12 lines)
*Who would true valour see	620	Monks Gate ..	6.5.6.5.6 6 6.5.
Whosoever heareth! Shout, shout the sound	317	Whosoever will ...	10 11 11.7. and refrain

FIRST LINE	NO.	TUNE	METRE
*Will your anchor hold in the storms of life	634	Will your anchor hold	Irregular and refrain
Wise men, seeking Jesus	862	Worship	6.5.6.5.
With broken heart and contrite sigh	350	Plaistow	L.M.
With gladness we worship, rejoice as we sing	11	Datchet	11 11.11 11.
With glorious clouds encompassed round	172	Manchester ..	C.M.
With joy we meditate the grace ..	236	Oldham Street ..	C.M.
With the sweet word of peace ..	913	Verbum pacis ..	6.6.8.4.
Workman of God! O lose not heart	489	Grainger ..	C.M.
Worship, and thanks, and blessing	412	Dying Stephen (i) Deliverance (ii) ..	7.7.4 4.7.D.
Would Jesus have the sinner die ..	173	Euphony	8.8.8.8.8 8.
Ye faithful souls who Jesus know ..	229	Festus	L.M.
Ye holy angels bright	26	Croft's 136th ..	6.6.6.6.4.4.4.4.
Ye humble souls that seek the Lord	217	Wetherby	C.M.
Ye mountains and vales, in praises abound	v.12	Old 104th, No. 45 ..	10 10.11 11.
Ye neighbours and friends of Jesus draw near	329	Old 104th	10 10.11 11.
Ye servants of God	426	Laudate Dominum	5.5.5.5.6.5.6.5.
Ye servants of the Lord	581	St. Ethelwald ..	S.M.
Ye that do your Master's will ..	628	Truro	7 7.7 7.7 7.
*Yes, God is good—in earth and sky	968	Daniel (i) Williams (ii) ..	L.M.
Yield to me now; for I am weak (Part 2)	339	Wrestling Jacob ..	8.8.8.8.8 8.

VII

FIRST LINE OF HYMNS FOR LITTLE CHILDREN AND VERSE SECTION

HYMNS

VERSES

Doxology

L.M.
French Psalter,
1551.
Praise God, from whom all blessings flow ; Praise
Him, all crea - tures here be - low ;
Praise Him a - bove, ye heav'n-ly host ; Praise
Fa - ther, Son, and Ho - ly Ghost. A-men.